# SAFETY LEADERSHIP and Professional Development

Edited By
Richard Olawoyin and Darryl C. Hill

Park Ridge, Illinois

American Society of Safety Professionals, 520 N. Northwest Highway, Park Ridge, IL 60068


Managing Editor: Rick Blanchette, ASSP
Editor: Adept Content Solutions
Text design and composition: Adept Content Solutions
Cover design: Robert Ayers, Publication Design, Inc.

Print ISBN: 978-0-939874-18-7
E-book ISBN: 978-0-939874-19-4

Printed in the United States of America

27 26 25 24 23 22 21 20 19 18 1 2 3 4 5 6 7 8

Library of Congress Cataloging-in-Publication Data

Names: Olawoyin, Richard, editor. | Hill, Darryl C., editor.
Title: Safety leadership and professional development / edited by Richard Olawoyin and Darryl C. Hill.
Description: Park Ridge, IL : American Society of Safety Professionals, 2018. | Includes bibliographic references and index.
Identifiers: LCCN 2018010864 (print) | LCCN 2018013517 (ebook) | ISBN 9780939874194 (ebook) | ISBN 9780939874187 (hardcover : alk. paper)
Subjects: LCSH: Industrial safety. | Executive coaching.
Classification: LCC T55 (ebook) | LCC T55 .S21533 2018 (print) | DDC 658.3/82--dc23
LC record available at https://lccn.loc.gov/2018010864

# CONTENTS

**Section 3: Professional Development**



**Section 4: Technical Contents**



**Section 5: Culture**

# FOREWORD

## Kathy A. Seabrook

Occupational safety and health (OSH) professionals are leaders, and we are leading in a time of great change. Mergers and acquisitions, continual technology innovations, and technological advancements are the norm, and OSH professionals find themselves taking on new roles in sustainability, product stewardship, risk management, and security. At the end of the day, professional success will be a measure of our ability to learn and adapt to these changes, along with meeting and exceeding the expectations of our internal and external organizational stakeholders.

The business world is changing as evidenced by the growing influences of sustainability and human capital management on the expectations of OSH performance. Materiality disclosure expectations by investors, customers, and other external stakeholders are driving our boards of directors, CEOs, and C-suites to ask us about occupational health and safety and environmental risk within the organizations they lead. Are you ready for those questions? What influence do you currently have in your organization? How well do you leverage OSH in organizational decision-making? Do you know your organization's significant OSH risks? Are you proactively communicating these risks to the decision-makers in your organization? What change are you driving? Are you leading or following? These are the right questions for OSH professionals in our changing times. Are you ready with the answers when your business leaders start asking these questions?

Now more than ever, OSH safety professionals have line of sight to the boardroom where we have influence organization-wide. Leadership means seeking out and seizing opportunity. Leaders see how the dots connect at the strategic business level and today, opportunity abounds. Leaders are futurists, anticipate change, and are out in front of opportunity because they know opportunity always leads to organizational change. And they have leadership courage in the face of that change.

Work for OSH professionals at this level is not for the faint-hearted. The keys to success lay in operating as equal business partners, understanding people and our role as an agent of change and coach, harnessing technology and facilitating organizational learning through failure, such as OSH incidents.

Dr. Darryl C. Hill and Dr. Richard Olawoyin have assembled some of the brightest minds and thought leaders in OSH today. They bring their insights and perspectives to this book on everything from ethics and leadership to organizational change, influential relationship, harnessing technology, and big data. This book is a timely read for every OSH professional, no matter where you are on your career journey.

Learn from the thought leaders in this book; use it as a roadmap on your career journey. Figure out the answer to the bigger questions: What is trending in your industry sector. What is keeping your CEO up at night? Who are your organization's internal and external stakeholders? Who are the early adopters and influencers you can leverage to drive OSH change initiatives in your organization? Leaders with OSH expertise need to focus on these types of big-picture, business-aligned questions to ensure safe and healthy workplaces with minimal impacts to our communities and environment.

The collection of great minds and thought leaders in this book will no doubt assist you in leading environmental, safety, and health within your organization. It is a thought-provoking read, calibrating you for leadership success in all you do.

Kathy A. Seabrook, CSP, CFIOSH, EurOHSM
OSH Professional and Futurist

# PREFACE

## Richard Olawoyin and Darryl C. Hill

*Safety Leadership and Professional Development* provides a comprehensive roadmap that defines the safety profession and promotes leadership and professional developments for undergraduate, graduate, and post-graduate students; certification trainees; higher education; and occupational safety and health (OSH) professionals in disciplines specific to OSH, sciences, engineering, and related areas. The book delivers evidence-based learning on required career skills development, theories of leadership, and how to make relational connection between the skills and the theories in an increasingly challenging workplace environment. Students and OSH professionals are provided leading practices and practical solutions to strengthen their understanding and approach in key OSH areas.

The structure of the book supports building self-competencies through professional development based upon topics very relevant to the profession. The topics are divided into five sections: ethics, leadership and management, certifications and accreditation, professional development, technical contents, and culture. Each chapter includes learning outcomes and questions to encourage readers to engage in critical thinking and analysis of key OSH topics. Students and OSH professionals may reflect on their learning and experience in comparison to industry experts and professors in the OSH profession.

The chapter authors are considered the "thought leaders" in the profession and are representatives from the private sector, higher education, certification and accreditation organizations, and professional organizations. The contributors have substantial and varied experiences. The authors' credentials include professional engineers, certified safety professionals, and other accredited certifications. Several contributors are current or past presidents / vice presidents of corporations, ASSP/BCSP board members, ASSP/BCSP past-presidents, ASSP Fellows, and ABET commission members and academic program evaluators.

An additional feature of the book is the contents alignment with the Board of Certified Safety Professionals (BCSP) blueprint. These contents are useful to individuals preparing for the certification examinations and developing competencies. Competencies and an overall understanding for book key concepts and principles are developed with case studies, contributor insight, and key point callouts. This approach, combined with the chapter authors' backgrounds, make the book unique and valuable for the OSH profession.

The editors are excited to add this publication to the body of knowledge. The book, a double-blind, peer-reviewed publication, is a comprehensive resource that will assist OSH stakeholders to meet the challenges during the twenty-first century. Chapter authors and technical reviewers have worked tirelessly to provide their insight, knowledge, and comments to produce a leading publication that will advance the

OSH profession and be an everyday resource for the students and OSH professional, which can also be used for job training and preparation through institutional career services, seminars, webinars, workshops, and professional development conferences. It is our goal that the readers will view the book as a valuable resource in their career progression and in our pursuit to *protect people, property, and the environment.*

Richard Olawoyin, PhD, CSP, CEP
and Darryl Hill, PhD, CSP
Editors

# CONTRIBUTORS

## Richard Olawoyin and Darryl C. Hill


### Editors

Richard Olawoyin PhD, CEP, CSP
Oakland University
Rochester, Michigan, USA

Darryl C. Hill, PhD, CSP
FirstGroup of America
Cincinnati, Ohio, USA

### Chapter Authors

Mary Asher, GSP
Fiat Chrysler Automobiles
Holly, Michigan, USA

Mark R. Bennett , AIC
Risk Innovation Group
Millersville, Pennsylvania, USA

Brian Benson, MS
University of Central Missouri
Warrensburg, Missouri, USA

Jeanette Black, EdD, SPHR, SHRM-SCP
University of Wisconsin-Stout
Menomonie, Wisconsin, USA

James G. Borchardt, CPE, CSP
Construction Ergonomics LLC
Bettendorf, Iowa, USA

Erin E. Bowen , PhD
Robertson Safety Institute, Embry-Riddle Aeronautical University
Prescott, Arizona, USA

Sang D. Choi, PhD, CSP, CPE
University of Wisconsin–Whitewater
Whitewater, Wisconsin, USA

Erika Cleary, GSP
Eaton Corporation
Troy, Michigan, USA

Patrick Frazee, CSP
Oakland University
Rochester, Michigan, USA

Thomas Fuller, ScD, CIH, CSP, MSPH, MBA
Illinois State University
Normal, Illinois, USA

Hailey Fulton
Limbach
Pontiac, Michigan, USA

Jeremy M. Gernand, PhD, CRE, CSP
Pennsylvania State University—University Park
University Park, Pennsylvania, USA

Alice L. Greife, CIH, PhD, FAIHA
University of Central Missouri
Warrensburg, Missouri, USA

Don Groover, CIH(ret), CSP
Senior Vice President, Dekra Insight
Oxnard, California, USA

Joel M. Haight, PhD, PE
Swanson School of Engineering
University of Pittsburgh
Pittsburgh, Pennsylvania, USA

Carl W. Heinlein, CSP, ARM, CRIS
American Contractors Insurance Group
Wexford, Pennsylvania, USA

Stephanie Helgerman, MS, CSP
Granville, Ohio, USA

Mary Hoffman-Pancake, PMP
The Ohio State University
Columbus, Ohio, USA

Christopher Janicak, PhD, CSP, CEA, ARM
Indiana University of Pennsylvania
Indiana, Pennsylvania, USA

Jessica Jannaman, MSSM
DURA Automotive Systems, LLC
Auburn Hills, Michigan, USA

Paulette Lantuh, CSP
Kodak Alaris Inc.
Rochester, New York, USA

Todd William Loushine , PhD, PE, CSP, CIH
University of Wisconsin–Whitewater
Whitewater, Wisconsin, USA

Cheri Marcham, PhD, CIH, CSP, CHMM, FAIHA
Embry-Riddle Aeronautical University
Daytona Beach, Florida, USA

Thomas J. Martin, CIH, CSP
Ramboll Environ, Inc.
Ann Arbor, Michigan, USA

Aaron R. Munoz , AAS
ARM Safety
Dearborn, Michigan, USA

Shoji Nakayama, CSP, PhD
Purdue University Northwest
Hammond, Indiana, USA

Jack Ogutu, PhD, CSP
Millersville University
Millersville, Pennsylvania, USA

Oladapo Okareh PhD
University of Ibdan College of Medicine
Ibadan, Nigeria

Jim Ramsay, PhD, MA, CSP
University of New Hampshire
Manchester, New Hampshire, USA

Tom Reeves
Engaged Change Solutions
Columbus, Ohio, USA

Amanda Reid, Esq.
ABET
Baltimore, Maryland, USA

Kathy A. Seabrook, CSP, CFIOSH, EurOSHM
Global Solutions, Inc.
Mendham, New Jersey, USA

Kevin Slates, EdD, MPA, CSP
Indiana University School of Public Health
Bloomington, Indiana, USA

James D. Smith, MS, CSP
Arthur J. Gallagher & Co.
Boca Raton, Florida, USA

Steve Smith CSP (Rtd)
Lake Orion, Michigan, USA

Elbert Sorrell EdD, CSP
University of Wisconsin-Stout
Menomonie, Wisconsin, USA

Garrett Stricker, CSP
SRG Global
Troy, Michigan, USA

Geena Tacconelli, GSP
Sachse Construction
Detroit, Michigan, USA

Treasa M. Turnbeaugh, PhD, MBA, CSP, ASP, CET, CAE, IOM
Board of Certified Safety Professionals
Indianapolis, Indiana, USA

Tania Van der Stap, BBus, AssocDip HS
Align Risk Management
Perth, Western Australia, Australia

John N. Zey, CIH, EdD, FAIHA
University of Central Missouri
Warrensburg, Missouri, USA

# REVIEWERS

The editors and publisher are grateful for the support from the technical reviewers. Without their contributions, insight, and advice, this book would not have been possible.

Dennis Andrew
Mary Asher
Tom W. Barnett
David W. Bird
Morgan Bliss
Kimberly A. Bucek
Eileen Bullen
Brett Carruthers
Jason Dean
Kathi Dobson
Paul Esposito
Mohamad Syazli Bin Fathi
David Fender
David Ferguson
Hamid Fonooni
Chris Grieshaber
Juan D. Gutierrez
Kahlilah Guyah
Brenden Heidrich
Carl Heinlein
Darryl C. Hill
Bernard Himmelsbach
Steve Hughes
Kodunthirapully Jayaraman
Mohamed Khalaf
Robert Kirkby
Ethan Laubach
Courtney D. Lewis
Bruce Lyon
Bryan Lyons
Steve McConnell
Nick Miedema
Scott Myles
James S. Nelson
Kasarachi Nnadede
Rhonda O'Keefe
Richard Olawoyin
Samuel Oyewole
Jeffrey Pollard
Sathyanarayanan Rajendran
Matt Romer
Erick H.-Saia
Ricky Sanders
Donald Schmid
Josh Sitz
Diondria Smith
Michelle Southward
Leslie Stockel
Liz Thornhill
Robert Van Til
Marlene Vazquez
Florine W. Vincik
Pamela Walaski
Bob Weltzer
Rebecca Zaror

SECTION 1

# ETHICS, LEADERSHIP, AND MANAGEMENT

CHAPTER 1

# ETHICAL DECISION-MAKING AND MORAL DISTRESS IN EHS PRACTICE

Richard Olawoyin

## Learning Objectives

1. Define ethics and professionalism and the role of EHS professionals in relation to moral virtues
2. Discuss the crucial attributes of effective and solution-driven leadership
3. Explain the integral role of personal responsibility with professionalism and leadership
4. Articulate the role of a leader in influencing behavioral safety standards
5. Identify and describe the contributing factors to moral distress and strategies appropriate for resolution

## Key Terms

**Ethics, behavior, circle of influence, moral distress, professionalism**

## Abstract

Environmental health and safety (EHS) education will provide valuable skills that may be transferred into professional careers. Recently there has been increased interest in and focus on EHS educators emphasizing the intrinsic importance of the social dimensions of developing professional identity by many different means, including professionalization, standards, rules, and codes of conduct established by the profession, as well as character development and appropriate practice of virtues. These virtues include honesty, empathy, and leadership courage. These traits are usually not highlighted in the curriculum of EHS education. This chapter aims to provide insight into the concepts of professionalism in EHS. Promotion of ethics and incorporating socially acceptable norms and character development are crucial for professionalism. The end result should be a dynamic, situated, and enduring professional identity. This concept can be effective when reflective practice is embraced to promote unwavering ethics and an integral professional EHS identity that will nurture professional growth all through the individual's career.

## Introduction to Ethics and Professionalism

Professionals in the EHS discipline have leadership responsibilities that require strategic thinking, ethics, and professionalism. The precise definition of ethics is difficult to develop due to the varying perceptions of people about what is considered to be right or wrong. The term *ethics* was ultimately derived from the Greek word *ethos*. Ethos represents principles, decision-making frameworks, and habits that systematically define the concept of right and wrong conduct. Ethics denotes logical standards of right and wrong that suggest acceptable human conduct, usually in relation to rights, responsibilities, societal welfare, benefits, justice, or certain reasonable qualities that uphold the right cause.

Ethics set standards that define sensible obligations to desist from wrongful behaviors. These include workplace dishonesty, harassment, assault, fraud, intentional malice, wasting resources, defamation, aggression, and hostility. Ethical standards also consist of personal virtues, such as decency, empathy, honesty, and reliability. Additionally, ethical standards involve various rights. These include the right to life, privacy, liberty, and freedom from injury/damage. These ethical standards are satisfactory because they are sustained by reliable and justifiable intentions. Proper workplace ethics are essential for organizations to succeed; these are dependent on individual character and are the foundation of moral qualities. An employee may commit the ethical "sin of omission" and may be aware that an action is wrong. The employee may still commit the act because it ends in a personal gain. Organizations want employees who possess ethics intrinsically. However, ethics can be taught in the workplace. The culture of an organization should have safety and ethics at the center. An organization must stress the importance of being active in the area of business ethics (Afford 2010).

The culture of an organization should have safety and ethics at the center.

**Figure 1.1**
Professional ethical dynamics

EHS professionals must endeavor to make decisions based on what is right and must conduct work-related tasks ethically, following a professional routine and demonstrating excellent character. Excellent character is when someone behaves properly even when no one is watching. Figure 1.1 illustrates the ethical decision-making dynamic that professionals may potentially experience.

EHS professionals are constantly making decisions, and as figure 1.1 illustrates, the ethical decision-making processes are affected by different factors that may involve motivations, culture, beliefs, expectations, learned professional experiences, and education. Professionals use these factors for ethical decision-making; however, they make adjustments based on prevailing situations (Walker and Breitsameter 2015).

Professionalism is the conduct, intentions, or virtues that distinguish or symbolize the profession or an EHS professional. It indicates the quality of expertise or service provided. Professionalism consists of a set of character traits, such as competency, trustworthiness, compassion, respect for others, and professional and social responsibility. Organizations are aware that their professional reputation can make the difference between business success and failure. This is why organizations strive to retain their most professional employees. Professionalism centers on success and influence, possessing the reputation for distinction, and having the quality of excellence. Being a professional who always conducts business by high professional standards can create excellent opportunities both in personal circumstances and at the workplace.

There has been increased interest in professional employee-centered safety and care in many disciplines, including in EHS. These organizations and agencies include the National Safety Council (NSC), the American Society of Safety Professionals (ASSP), the American Industrial Hygiene Association (AIHA), and the National Institute of Occupational Safety and Health (NIOSH). These organizations have made advances to educate professionals on ethics and professionalism. Professionalism is a proficiency that is not readily measured and consequently must be characterized by more qualitative methods. There is no single certified, consistent tool that can measure professionalism, so teaching professionalism can therefore be challenging (Veloski et al. 2005). In an effort to teach and evaluate ethics and professionalism in the EHS curriculum, educational degree programs are beginning to consider and integrate multiple methods into the curriculum (Hochberg et al. 2010; Hendee et al. 2012), such as dedicated lectures, seminars/webinars, demonstrations, role-modeling, and multiple-source formative feedback from peer interactions and mentoring. To help reinforce the lessons, small group sessions and professional development events should be utilized.

Organizations have the obligation to support teaching ethics and professionalism through a variety of methods. These can include established curricula processes, structures, traditions, and routines ensuring that ethical practices are promoted and validated as important across the organization. The development of personal responsibility through a "hidden curriculum" in college education and training programs for building professional integrity and values is highly important (Blasco 2012). Such moral instruction may be implicitly embedded in learning experiences.

> Professionalism centers on success and influence, possessing the reputation for distinction, and having the quality of excellence.

The aim of these learning experiences is to enhance the effectiveness of transferring reflective learning (RL) to evidence-based reflective practice (RP). Reflective learning is the process of thinking about situations and processes with the goal of acquiring acknowledge. Individuals are encouraged to engage in critical and reflective thinking about their professional interactions. RL also serves as a strategy for future learning in practice. However, RP is a process by which an individual analyzes an issue, experience, or action to be taken, with the expected outcome being to promote self-responsiveness and professional competency (Epstein and Hundert 2002). The assumption is that reflecting on personal actions and engaging in analytical thinking can help improve individual performance and enhance professional growth by providing improved personal comprehension and strategies for prospective learning (Bethune and Brown 2007). Routine engagement in RPs can benefit professional development by enhancing theoretical knowledge, improving professional practice behavior, understanding the employee-employer relationship, and enhancing communication and other technical skills.

> Individuals are encouraged to engage in critical and reflective thinking about their professional interactions.

Ethics and professionalism are integral to the overall success of EHS professionals. Key components of workplace ethics for professionals must include being a trusted leader, taking responsibility for the good of everyone, and acting on the best available information to make good judgments (Pressman 2006). There are conflicts where ethical decision-making processes can be used to reach a resolution. These include identifying areas of conflict, identifying other resources, providing support and understanding, and moving toward a resolution. The goal is a third way forward, something besides two extremes. Ethics and professionalism applied to conflicts are not always about picking an extreme but bringing those involved to a central view so everyone can move forward and progress can be made.

## Personal Ethics and Professionalism

Employees' personal ethics and behavioral conduct are sets of principles and values that guide their day-to-day interactions and sense of right and wrong. Personal ethics differ between all individuals, and many factors influence ethical values and codes. These factors include, but are not limited to, colleagues, internship supervisors, professional codes of ethics, family, friends, and religious and moral influences. Contented and confident employees with high moral values are most productive, so it is crucial to establish code of ethics and professionalism in the workplace for employees to learn from and implement.

Contented and confident employees with high moral values are most productive, so it is crucial to establish code of ethics and professionalism in the workplace for employees to learn from and implement.

Valentine (2015) conducted a study to measure the impact of implementing corporate ethical values (CEVs) on workplace behavior at a sales company. The study determined that the unique nature of the work environment for sales professionals often results in little management oversight of employee behavior, which may lead to misbehavior and a poor work ethic. The results of the study showed that the development and implementation of CEVs can mitigate concerns about unethical conduct and that ethical values are positively related to job satisfaction and negatively related to workplace bullying (Kung et al. 2015). It can be inferred that any type of workplace would benefit from CEVs. People with good personal ethics are often also considered to be most professional.

Ethics and professionalism applied to conflicts are not always about picking an extreme but bringing those involved to a central view so everyone can move forward and progress can be made.

### Putting moral values into practice

What can professional or managerial leaders do regularly and proactively to inspire ethical behavior in the workplace? A few strategic practices discussed can help professional leaders navigate their establishments ethically. It is necessary to close all existing gaps between knowing what to do and taking the specific required actions. If the right things to be done are known, they must be done (ASSE 2005). It is unethical for professionals to be aware of misconduct or wrongdoing and not report it. Some reasons for ethical indiscretions in the business environment were articulated in the book *There Is No Such Thing as Business Ethics* (Maxwell 2003). It was explained that some people justify these actions with relativism. Relativism is a philosophical position that suggests that there is no absolute truth; instead, there are the truths that a specific culture or individual believes in. Though this theory of value judgments supports diverse and intricate actions that are done by those that agree with the concept, the main point is that the right things are often left undone. Even with the knowledge of what is right, people may still choose to do the opposite.

Relativism is a philosophical position that suggests that there is no absolute truth in existence except the truths that a specific culture or individual believes in.

Operating in a company of people with the relativist point of view may be dangerous to an individual's long-term integrity as a credible leader. Hence, it is important for professionals in leadership positions to remain meticulous and measured. This is especially true when they are deciding on their organizational partners, collaborators, and employees. Managerial professionals consider personal values just as much as skillsets when building a team or selecting individuals for certain tasks within an organization. In the bestselling business book *Good to Great*, Collins (2001) highlights how sustainable and continuing success is contingent on the ability to proactively select the right people for any kind of operation. People-selection skills must be prioritized, and most importantly, selecting the right people with similar moral values in an organization is crucial to developing an ethical environment and ensuring the continued overall success of any establishment.

The question now is must every viewpoint and value held by people be completely known before their selection into an organization? After the selection process is completed, there is a need to provide an environment that will encourage the new workers to socialize and learn about the values inherent in an organization. As professionals with managerial roles, it is important to stay engaged with the workforce. By staying engaged with the new personnel, managers can promote the organization's values during orientation and training. Both new and current employees will find messages promoting ethical behavior influential on their judgments since they come from the managerial leaders. More importantly, the promotion of ethical behavior will be more powerful when the values are affirmed through the consistent actions of everyone within the organization.

To ensure that these values are properly entrenched in organizational practice, there must be proper follow-up and accountability. Established processes, structures, and procedures will build behavioral integrity and facilitate the connection of assurances with actions, which will also serve as reminders of pledged commitments. If behaviors are driven by values, the alignment or integration of words and actions enables the advancement of ethical workplace safety that is sustainable. The overall practice of ethical behavior in an organization can be positively influenced by managerial leaders through equitable resource allocation. Leaders are often responsible for managing major resources such as human resources, data and information, finances, capital assets, and time. Appropriately allocating these important resources through equitable processes will eliminate doubt and the possibility that workers might see the system as unfair or partial. This is important to the overall ethical culture in an organization. If proper ethical behaviors based on strong values for justice and impartiality are practiced by managerial leaders, there will be organization-wide acceptance and practice of ethical conducts.

If behaviors are driven by values, the alignment or integration of words and actions enables the advancement of ethical workplace safety that is sustainable.

## Codes of ethical conduct: The behavioral safety standards

Professionals and managerial leaders ideally possess internalized morals that are sustained by established organizational ethical behavioral principles in the form of written "codes of conduct." Ethical behavioral safety standards typically integrate explicit guidelines for conduct within particular functional place of work. An example of this may be the development and outline of specific criteria to be followed for reporting accidents, harassment, fraud, and travel expense reimbursements in an organization. How can things be better? According to *The Power of Idealistic-Realism: How Great Leaders Inspire and Transform* (Conant 2012), things can be made better by striving for higher ground to make a difference for oneself and others. This higher ground can be set by adhering to ethical codes of conduct, which may be grouped under the three different categories shown in table 1.1.

When professionals and managerial leaders have the responsibility of engaging employees and ensuring that these codes of behavioral conduct are followed, they could be involved in circumstances in which they may be required to take "reasonable actions" for

**Table 1.1** Categories of ethical codes of conduct

| Category | Ethical Code of Conduct | Description |
|---|---|---|
| 1 | Inspirational-Idealistic | Specific themes are laid out in this category that are not anchored to specific situations or behaviors.<br>Examples: "Be truthful and equitable," "Be honest at all times," "Make prudent decisions on all matters," etc. |
| 2 | Regulatory | Prescriptions of what professionals (or the profession as a whole) can or cannot do and what they should aspire for. Consequences that follow noncompliance will be sanctions. Regulatory codes are intended to serve as a jurisprudential tool when disputes occur. |
| 3 | Educational/ Learning Centered | For each specific application, laid-out principles that guide behavioral responses and effective decision making in the eventual circumstances. This procedure is harmonious with developing and learning organizational culture. |

the implementation of these ethical practices. This process is a learning opportunity for professionals, which will serve to improve learning experiences and enhance ethical decision-making skills. Ethical codes of conduct can direct employees' behavior to ensure that they do the right thing. This can be done by providing guidance/reminders or using prompts or written instructions. These principles and codes trigger employees' internalized values, leading to increased strength through firm but objective administration of consequences.

## The Progress Formulation for Ethical Behavior

OSOU (n. d.) theorizes that integrating moral values, engagement, and behavioral criteria, can yield a useful formula. This formula can promote the prospect of organizational ethical behavior.

$$IEB = MV + BC + CA \dots \dots \quad \text{(Eq.1.1)}$$

Where *IEB* is improved ethical behavior, *MV* = moral value, *BC* = behavioral criteria and codes, and *CA* = coordinated action. This equation can be applied any time an employee enters the workforce to gauge ethical progress as time goes on. Improved ethical behavior can be observed through moral values, behavioral criteria, coordinated action, and time. Improved ethical behavior should be a goal for every employee. Improved ethics and ethical behavior will benefit the organization by promoting positive qualities in employees. Leadership skills will be developed, and employees will be motivated to behave ethically. As EHS professionals, it is essential to be accustomed to adopting the necessary moral values and integrating them with coordinated leadership engagement in the workplace. Examples of this engagement include impartial resource allocation, proper selection of employees, and new employee training and orientation. The training sessions will benefit employees by properly teaching and implementing ethical behaviors. The criteria for ethical behavioral conduct can be supplemented as applicable. Application of the IEB formula can positively influence the global display of organizational ethical conduct and motivate its implementation into professional leadership practice. The benefits of adapting this formula organization-wide are enormous. Adapting this formula for the entire organization will ensure that everyone, from upper management to an entry-level employee, practices proper ethical behavior. This formula can be taught though seminars and memos. Reinforcement should be included in the seminars so the behaviors stay ethical and positive. All stakeholders deserve to be treated decently; a culture tolerating immoral behavior has the potential of promoting detrimental and illicit activities in the organization. Organizational ethical conduct should be the socially responsible practice accepted in the society.

All stakeholders deserve to be treated decently; a culture tolerating immoral behavior has the potential of promoting detrimental and illicit activities in the organization.

## Ethical Conflicts and Moral Distress: Causal Factors and Effects

Ethical conflicts are ubiquitous in today's professional practice. Many organizations are trying to achieve more with fewer resources, and EHS professionals are seeing technological advances and emerging challenges that could increase fatalities and injuries, both of which could cause moral distress as a consequence of moral conflict. These conflicts ensue when one is unable to take what one considers to be the correct action.

Moral distress—the physical, emotional, and psychological response to the feeling of being constrained from executing ethically appropriate action or responding to ethically challenging situations (Fourie 2015)—may have severe consequences for EHS professionals and the organizations they serve as they struggle to preserve moral integrity through perplexing situations. The concept was first introduced in 1993 (Musto and Schreiber 2012).

Moral distress can also be described as the experience of suffering due to circumstances in which people feel morally liable and have decided on the appropriate action to take ethically, but because of real or perceived constraints, the actions cannot be executed; therefore the individuals are led to believe that they are committing a moral offense by their inaction. The experience can be described as initial (such as frustration, anxiety, apprehension, and anger) or reactive distress (such as ineffectiveness, self-deprecation, low self-confidence, and culpability). Moral distress is an important predictor of employee burnout (Epstein and Delgado 2010; Rushton et al. 2015).

Individuals should be professionally proficient in analyzing situations and using their best judgments to make proper choices by considering all conceivable solutions before making ethical decisions.

Once the decisions are made, there must also be available reasons for the steps taken. Figure 1.2 shows an integrated conceptual framework from which ethical decisions can be made. Experimental studies show strong relationships between moral distress and low employee morale (Gaudine and Beaton 2002) and issues with worker turnover and retention (Corley et al. 2001). Using a numerical scale to investigate the effects of moral distress among healthcare workers, researchers observed that 50 percent of the people sampled have contemplated leaving their jobs and the

Figure 1.2
Integrated ethical decision-making framework

profession completely, while 15 percent of them left a previous position for the same reason (Pauly et al. 2009). Management staff also experience moral distress from priority-setting issues involving appropriately allocating resources (Mitton et al. 2010). In some instances, a management staff member or team may be charged with selling an organizational decision or direction that they do not share or believe in, or in other cases, managers are unable to ethically fulfill their obligations to peers, colleagues, or staff. Being forced to violate strongly held ethical and moral values may accentuate the experience or feeling of moral distress.

## Strategies for Addressing Moral Distress

Moral distress is a pertinent managerial notion that is not exclusive to line staff or regular employees. It is evident that moral distress coming out of ethical dilemmas plays a crucial role in creating deleterious organizational and individual consequences, such as emotional and physical effects on personnel. Hence, useful strategies for tackling the problem include identifying the situations, conditions, or circumstances that may potentially lead to moral distress, considering the adverse effects that may ensue, and envisaging possible individual and organizational reactions to both ethical dilemmas and moral distress.

Additionally, pragmatic managers should respond to moral distress with honor and validation, acknowledging the underlining issues. This may involve creating opportunities for thoughtful discussion on ethical concerns and collaborative engagements with sharing of stories among personnel. This could have a positive therapeutic effect and help mitigate the issues.

For organizations endeavoring to improve outcomes, it is essential to implement strategies that would address ethical issues and have a process in place to effectively reduce employees' exposure to situations with prevalent ethical conflicts. In doing so, the rates of employee turnover and work burnout will be minimized.Some of the organizational strategies may include:

1. Support for a professional code of ethics. Professional organizations have frameworks that guide professional conducts. Encouraging professionals to familiarize themselves with the codes and put them into practical daily use will serve the good purpose of eliminating ethical conflicts and moral distress. This can be achieved if the organizations incorporate an appropriate professional code of ethics as behavioral attributes in the job descriptions and review the demonstration of these behaviors during the annual performance evaluations.
2. Continuous training and education. Ethical standards may not be native to everyone on every issue, especially in very complex situations. Ethical training with case study examples explaining the application of theoretical ethics to real-world problems should be included in training for new employees and in all other educational and job training programs. Education provides professionals with the tools they need to make informed decisions. When ethical dilemmas are encountered in professional practice, the professional should swiftly reflect on the ethical categories and work toward resolving the prevailing issues with certainty for success.
3. Encourage open dialogue. Ethical issues are complex, and individuals respond to situations differently based on their personal experiences and values. Therefore, promoting a professional practice environment that strongly supports employees to raise ethical questions and concerns, no matter how complicated the situation may be, it will empower the individuals and others in the organization to tackle similar issues whenever they are in the position to make ethical decisions. This empowerment is also guaranteed to minimize the pervasiveness of moral distress across the organization.
4. Shared experience of pain and suffering. When individuals from a variety of disciplines are brought together to work, the team members' closeness and collaborative exchange of experiences could prove beneficial in addressing moral distress.

5. Proximal ethics mentor. Ethical conflict resolution can be quite difficult, since as humans, we have diverse ideas on how to do the right thing, which creates complications. It is helpful for organizations to have unit-based ethical mentors (or ethicists) whom the professionals can confide in and who in turn can provide valuable counsel that will help the individual refocus and reflect on the best choices to make in different situations, thereby preventing moral distress or advanced ethical dilemmas. Observing situations from alternative perspectives can reassure employees and bolster their confidence about the decisions to be made. Professionals encumbered by intense ethical issues, conceivably situations related to their personal lives to past ethical dilemmas, may be supported by attending individual sessions with a certified counselor from an employee-assistance program (EAP) or similar programs.

It is helpful for organizations to have unit-based ethical mentors (or ethicists) who the professionals can confide in and who in turn can provide valuable counsel.

There are resources available to employees to facilitate quick recovery from moral distress of any kind. It is important that all issues should be promptly identified and addressed in real time. Debriefing affected employees on the issues is an essential first step and useful mechanism in the recovery process. If the condition is serious, the EHS professional should consider referring the employee to a program for further assistance. "Organizational Prozac" is an effective method that the workplace community can adopt to help a distressed worker. "Organizational Prozac" is a program in which leaders, managers, and society as a whole are dependent on an artificial positivity. Although this method can be positive for a distressed worker, it can create misunderstandings and can leave organizations ill-prepared to deal with unexpected events and setbacks (Collinson 2012).

Other ethical decision-making strategies that can mitigate the occurrence of moral distress include:

**Team Building**: The value of teamwork cannot be overstated because teamwork improves communication (detecting distress early), creates a trusting environment between workers and their management/leaders, increases motivation among all employees, and improves productivity, which in turn will increase the profitability of the organization. Professional leaders should engage in collaborative work with transparency, vigilance, and positive attitudes to foster the attitude of "caring for one another." Ethical values essential to collaborative engagement are trust, accountability, respect, fairness, compassion, courage, and impartiality (Watcher and Bird 2011). Being able to work as part of a team increases one's ethical behavior and professionalism. A vital aspect of workplace ethics is working well with others, including peers, supervisors, and customers. Not all employees will always get along or like each other, but it is crucial that they be able to set aside personal differences to reach a larger goal (Amico n. d.). In these instances, those who can put aside their differences to work as a team capture moral integrity.

When putting a team together, a leader must stress the importance of collaborating efficiently on tasks, working toward the team's development, and meeting the goal of the organization. Mentoring and skills-building play an important role in collaborative team efforts, as well as adequate education. Communication within a team should involve affirming positive behaviors and encouraging members to overcome undesirable moral behaviors. A team must also be flexible and creative. Building up team members' confidence and creating a safe environment that encourages fellow employees to talk freely will produce trust, safety, and assurance, and ultimately resolve situations of inherent distress. EHS professional leaders and teams must think outside of the box at times to

When putting a team together, a leader must stress the importance of collaborating efficiently on tasks, working toward the team's development, and meeting the goal of the organization.

ensure optimal results in welfare and safety performance, as well minimize distresses. Without great leadership, none of the aforementioned teamwork can happen effectively.

Teamwork can help the EHS professional become more successful. Safety is not a one-person job but requires the entire organization to work together. A company (teammates) must agree that safety is as important as job completion and should work together to prevent workplace accidents. When the organization actively cares about health and safety, the EHS professional is more successful in getting employees to comply with safety policies and procedures. EHS professionals cannot keep employees safe by themselves; everyone within the organization has to work together.

EHS professionals and their teams must think outside of the box at times to ensure optimal results in welfare and safety performance, as well as minimize distresses. Without great leadership, none of the aforementioned teamwork can happen effectively. EHS professional leaders must take active steps founded on ethical conduct in order to lead and successfully be an integral part of an organization. The EHS professional leader should assist management and employees with building effective safety skills and intervening and helping when there is distress. In addition, EHS professionals must assist in identifying and evaluating high-risk hazards in the workplace, monitoring issues that may result in moral distress and developing creative solutions, and providing effective interventions for employees.

**Effective Organization:** An organization must be willing to offer assistance to the affected employees. To resolve moral distress before it results in moral disempowerment, organizations should support workers "resilience and effectiveness in working constructively with moral distress" (Carse 2013). There must be continuous inspiration and cooperation, and the entire organization must be energizing. There should be opportunities for breaks and places of sanctuary within the workplace. There should be real-time interventions, such as one-on-one meetings, safe huddles, and rituals of letting go. The management team and the EHS professional leaders must be effective (through training) at addressing distress, which could also include developing a healing team as part of the emergency preparedness program. Working with management to find and eliminate ethical stressors is one of the most impactful ways to reduce moral distress (Trautmann 2015). Other opportunities for organizations to be proactive at eliminating workplace distress include appropriately allocating local resources (including resources for conflict resolution), designating leadership responsibility appropriate for overseeing employees' "welfare, wellness, ethical conducts" and adequate provision of guidance, counselling and training to the employees periodically.

The management team and the EHS professional leaders must be effective (through training) at addressing distress, which could also include developing a healing team as part of the emergency preparedness program.

EHS professional leaders must take active steps founded on ethical conduct in order to lead and successfully be an integral part of an organization.

**Community Resources:** It is crucial to reach out to the community and utilize community resources as necessary. Trust must be built with workers, consumers, and the community. The EHS professional leader could institutionalize a system of reaching out to employees and providing an avenue for employees to seek assistance. This could be done by establishing a compliance hotline, providing a suggestion box, or setting up a message board via paper or the Internet. They must also help in preparing employees for changes and unforeseen problems within the establishment, creating solutions, and taking suggestions to improve the workplace. Knowing the employees and recognizing any differences in actions or behaviors will go a long way in detecting moral distress early and will ensure that the intervention is effective. A leader should have effective coping mechanisms available to all employees, educate employees on suicide awareness, and ensure that employees know of the available community resources, such as crisis lines or centers, therapists, or grief counseling through hospice care. Employees should be rewarded and recognized for safe practices and encouraged in times of distress. Perhaps an incentive program or an appreciation board could be established within the workplace to increase morale. Community programs may be developed for the employees, such as "back-to-school backpacks," after-school or summer programs for disadvantaged youth, internship programs, career preparation fairs, ice cream socials, and so forth to strengthen community ties and ties within the organization. Positive messaging and actions must be implemented to demonstrate to the community that the organization cares about the safety and health of its employees and the surrounding environment and community. Positive messages and incentive programs can motivate ethical behavior. Companies sometimes expect ethical behavior, but if they want to promote this as a prominent behavior, then they need to provide encouragement through community resources. Providing rewards for ethical behavior can encourage other employees to strive to do the same. The more you reward employees for sound ethical decisions, the more likely others will follow suit (Belcher n. d.).

> Employees should be rewarded and recognized for safe practices and encouraged in times of distress. Positive message and incentive programs can motivate ethical behavior.

**Leadership Responsibility:** Leaders with ethical influence are role models. Leaders set and uphold the standards for the workplace. In many cases, an ethical leader can convey positive results while reducing negative results (Treviño et al. n. d.). EHS professional leaders must establish a sustainable safe culture that will boost morale and reduce the incidence of moral distress. Leaders should also lead by demonstrating positive and ethical behaviors that will influence employees to maintain safety-based behaviors at all times. Leaders must possess integrity, which will be reflected through their interactions with employees and management, reactions to crises, and methods of implementation for policies and procedures (Institute of Medicine 2000). Leadership responsibility for EHS professional leaders involves taking bold steps to create solutions and monitor progress to foster safety practices and morale in the workplace. To do this, strategies need to be developed and implemented and also evaluated for effectiveness. Keeping the lines of communication open between the leader and other employees is important to guard against moral distress.

> Leadership responsibility for EHS professional leaders involves taking bold steps to create solutions and monitor progress to foster safety practices and morale in the workplace.

## Conclusion

Incorporating ethical instruction as a part of the students' learning experience will help students and young professionals to develop in-built strength to act ethically beyond stakeholder's expectations and to have a global perspective on moral practices that will not consider monetary incentives and personal interests before people's best interests. These best practices will develop leaders with integrity, foster leadership values (such as accountability, transparency, and moral sensitivity), and promote sustainability. Ethics and professionalism go hand in hand and are crucial values and qualities required in the EHS profession. Other qualities that are desirable are listed in table 1.2. The existence of moral dilemmas may also lead to moral distress and other distresses in the workplace, and they must be addressed to guarantee a workplace free from hazards. This chapter discusses the importance of ethics and professionalism to EHS professional leaders. A variety of strategies and resources will be used to address distress in an ethical way and create solutions to issues within the workplace.

**Table 1.2** Desirable leadership attributes for EHS professionals

| Critical Attributes | Extremely Important Attributes | Significant Attributes |
|---|---|---|
| 1. Empowering, supporting, motivating, trusting<br>2. Practical visionary, long-term viewpoint<br>3. Cooperating, sharing, team playing and team building<br>4. Renewing, learning, growing, educating<br>5. Self-assured and competent | 1. Inclusive communicator<br>2. Having culture and values, serving as a role model<br>3. Being productive, efficient, determined<br>4. Facilitator<br>5. Principled integrator<br>6. Decision-maker | 1. Being communicative<br>2. Demonstrating time-management and prioritization skills<br>3. Being action oriented<br>4. Making contribution, commitment, legacy<br>5. Being innovative and imaginative |

It is imperative for EHS professionals to recognize the signs and symptoms of distress early, so they can take proper steps to address the issue and thus keep the workplace safe (Lester 2010). It is in the best interest of the employer and managerial professional leaders to avoid creating a negative environment or immoral situations. If these stressors do occur, recognizing and intervening as well as improving the work environment are important steps to take before any injuries or illnesses occur.

Great leaders start off as great followers, and they look for the good in employees and situations. Psychosocial and scientific studies have presented increasing evidence that what you consistently think about is what you eventually become. Therefore, for leaders, the most significant strategy for success is to visualize specific moral goals and constantly work toward achieving each and every one of them. Leaders are not exempt from a fear of failing, which may result in procrastination that keeps them from doing what is necessary to achieve their goals. To be a moral, professional, and goal-oriented leader, a person must take action on ethical practice immediately in all aspects of life. Setbacks may be encountered; however, the key to success is a person's reaction to disappointing situations and setbacks. Being fiercely persistent is the key. Being a leader also provides a variety of opportunities to learn. To surpass all moral expectations as a leader, it is vital to collaborate and partner with other successful people whose abilities, skills, and resources may be required to achieve goals. Learning from ethical and experienced people would undoubtedly improve the leader's skills. The people in the individual's immediate surroundings with extraordinary skills will propel the individual to a preferred and desired leadership position. The EHS profession is a people profession. Exuding moral virtues at the workplace requires that as a leader, the development of genuine and sincere interest in others should be demonstrated using the excellent people skills needed to become an effective leader. This is done by acknowledging employees, recommending them for promotion when appropriate, empowering them to be their best, and building their self-esteem. Personal appreciation from leaders to employees is far more effective and the most motivating incentive for employees. Finally, EHS professionals should be enthusiastic in everything they do, and lead by example by showing integrity. It is ideal to practice all of these regularly and train others to do same, and the resulting legacy as a leader will be exemplary.

## Questions

1. Name the different factors that may affect ethical decision-making.

2. The process of thinking about situations and processes with the goal of acquiring acknowledge is known as ______________________________
3. Improved ethical behavior (IEB) can be observed through a combination of what factors?
4. List six organizational strategies for mitigating the occurrence of moral distress.
5. Ethics set standards that sanction sensible obligations to desist from wrongful behavior. Name five examples of wrongful behaviors.

## References

Afford, B. (2010). "Managing Workplace Ethics Can Generate Competitive Advantage." *Journal of Business and Economics Research* 8(1): 87

American Society of Safety Engineers (ASSE). (2005). *Management and the Responsibilities of the Safety Professional*|. http://www.asse.org/professionalaffairs/action/management-and-the-responsibilities-of-the-safety-professional/.

Amico, S. (n. d.). "Workplace Ethics and Behavior." Accessed September 22, 2015. http://smallbusiness.chron.com/workplace-ethics-behavior-5239.html.

Babbel, S. (2012). "Compassion Fatigue: Bodily Symptoms of Empathy." *Psychology Today*. Accessed September 22, 2016. https://www.psychologytoday.com/blog/somatic-psychology/201207/compassion-fatigue.

Belcher, L. (n. d.). "Ways to Promote Ethical Conduct." Accessed September 22, 2015. http://smallbusiness.chron.com/ways-promote-ethical-conduct-24132.html.

Bethune, C., and J. B. Brown. (2007). "Residents' Use of Case-based Reflection Exercises." *Canadian Family Physician* 53: 471–76.

Blasco, M. (2012). "Aligning the Hidden Curriculum of Management Education with PRME." *Journal of Management Education* 36(3): 364–88. Accessed September 22, 2015. http://dx.doi.org/10.1177/1052562911420213.

Carse, A. (2013). "Moral Distress and Moral Disempowerment." *Narrative Inquiry in Bioethics* 3(2): 147–51.Collins, J. (2001). *Good to Great: Why Some Companies Make the Leap . . . and Others Don't.* New York: Free Press.

Corley, M. C., R. K. Elswick, M. Gorman, and T. Clor. (2001). "Development and Evaluation of Moral Distress Scale." *Journal of Advanced Nursing* 33(2): 250–56.

Epstein, E. G., and S. Delgado. (2010). "Understanding and Addressing Moral Distress" *Online Journal of Issues in Nursing* 15(3): 1B.Fourie, C. (2015). "Moral Distress and Moral Conflict in Clinical Ethics." *Bioethics* 29(2): 91–97.

Epstein, R. M., and E. M. Hundert. (2002). "Defining and Assessing Professional Competence. *Journal of the American Medical Association* 287: 226–35.

Gaudine, A., and M. Beaton. (2002). "Employed to Go against One's Values: Nurse Managers' Accounts of Ethical Conflict with Their Organization." *Canadian Journal of Nursing Research* 34(2): 17–34.

Hamric, A. B. (2012). "Empirical Research on Moral Distress: Issues, Challenges, and Opportunities." *HEC Forum* 24(1): 39–49.

Hendee W, J. L. Bosma, L. B. Bresolin, L. Berlin, R. N. Bryan, and R. B. Gunderman. (2012). "Web Modules on Professionalism and Ethics." *Journal of the American College of Radiology* 9(3):170–73.

Hochberg, M.S., A. Kalet, S. Zabar, E. Kachur, C. Gillespie, and R. S. Berman. (2010). "Can Professionalism Be Taught? Encouraging Evidence. *American Journal of Surgery* 199: 86–93.

Institute of Medicine (US). (2000). *Safe Work in the 21st Century: Education and Training Needs for the Next Decade's Occupational Safety and Health Personnel.* Washington, DC: The National Academies Press.

Johnson, A. (2012). "Safety Ethics." Accessed September 22, 2015. http://www.safetyandhealthmagazine.com/articles/safety-ethics-2.

Khadka, S. (2015, May 28). "Professionalism in Clinical Pharmacy Practice." Accessed June 6, 2017. https://www.slideshare.net/srkhere/professionalism-in-clinical-pharmacy-practice-48713020.

Kung, J. W., P. J. Slanetz, G. C. Huang, and R. L. Eisenberg. (2015) "Reflective Practice: Assessing Its Effectiveness to Teach Professionalism in a Radiology Residency." *Academic Radiology* 22(10): 1280–86.

Lester, N. (2010). "Compassion Fatigue." *Mental Health Practice* 14: 11.

Levi, B. H., N. J. Thomas, M. J. Green, C. A. Rentmeester, and G. D. Ceneviva. (2004). "Jading in the Pediatric Intensive Care Unit: Implications for Healthcare Providers of Medically Complex Children." *Pediatric Critical Care Medicine* 5(3):275–77.

Manchester Metropolitan University (MMU). (2004). "Departmental Health and Safety Inspections." Accessed September 22, 2015. www.mmu.ac.uk/humanresources/health/manual/pdf/departmental-inspections.pdf.

Maxwell, J. (2003). *There's No Such Thing as Business Ethics.* Boston: Warner Books, Inc.

Mitton, C., S. Peacock, J. Storch, N. Smith, and E. Cornelissen. (2011). "Moral Distress among Health System Managers: Exploratory Research in Two British Columbia Health Authorities." *Health Care Analysis* 19(2): 107–21.

Musto, L. and R. S. Schreiber. (2012). "Doing the Best I Can Do: Moral Distress in Adolescent Mental Health Nursing." *Issues in Mental Health Nursing* 33(3): 137–44.

National Child Traumatic Stress Network (n. d.). "Secondary Traumatic Stress." Accessed September 22, 2015. http://www.nctsn.org/resources/topics/secondary-traumatic-stress.

O'Connor, T. (2013). "Implications of Moral Distress." *Kai Tiaki: Nursing New Zealand* 19(10): 3.

Olawoyin, R. (2015). "Ethics and Professionalism." Oakland University. Accessed September 22, 2015. OSH 245.

Odisha State Open University (OSOU). (n. d.). "Business Ethics: An Overview." Accessed September 22, 2015. http://osou.ac.in/eresources/DED-07-BLOCK-03.pdf.

Pauly, B., C. Varcoe, J. Storch, and L. Newton. (2009). "Registered Nurses' Perceptions of Moral Distress and Ethical Climate." *Nursing Ethics* 16(5): 561–73.

Pressman, A. (2006). "Do the Right Thing." In *Professional Practice 101: Business Strategies and Case Studies in Architecture* (2nd ed.) 57. Hoboken, NJ: Wiley.

Rushton, C. H., J. Batcheller, K. Schroeder, and P. Donohue. (2015). "Burnout and Resilience among Nurses Practicing in High-Intensity Settings." *American Journal of Critical Care* 24(5): 412–20.

Trautmann, J. (2015). "Moral Distress: Recognition, Diagnosis, and Treatment." *Journal of Infusion Nursing* 38(4): 285–89.

Treviño, L., D. Mayer, and N. Epley. (n. d.). "Leadership." Accessed September 21, 2015. http://ethicalsystems.org/content/leadership.

Valentine, S., G. Fleischman, and L. Godkin. (2015). "Rogues in the Ranks of Selling Organizations: Using Corporate Ethics to Manage Workplace Bullying and Job satisfaction. *Journal of Personal Selling & Sales Management* 35(2): 143–63.

Veloski, J. J., S. K. Fields, J. R. Boex, and L. L. Blank. (2005) "Measuring Professionalism: A Review of Studies with Instruments Reported in the Literature between 1982 and 2002." *Academic Medicine* 80(4): 366–70.

Wachter, J. K., and A. J. Bird. (2011). "Ethical Considerations for Data Collection, Analysis, and Interpretation." In *Applied Quantitative Methods for Occupational Safety and Health*, 67–89. San Diego: University Readers.

Walker, A., and C. Breitsameter. 2015. "Ethical Decision-Making in Hospice Care." *Nursing Ethics* 22(3): 321–30.

Zavotsky, K. E., and G. K. Chan. (2016). "Exploring the Relationship among Moral Distress, Coping, and the Practice Environment in Emergency Department Nurses." *Advanced Emergency Nursing Journal* 38(2): 133–46.

# CHAPTER 2

# TRANSPARENT LEADERSHIP

Tom Martin

## Learning Objectives

After studying this chapter, the reader will be able to:

1. Apply self- and situational awareness towards leadership development
2. Internalize moral perspectives through self-regulatory processes
3. Recognize the value of transparency and transformation as a leader
4. Execute appropriate judgement and promote workplace safety climate

## Key Terms

Leadership, safety climate, culture, transformation, values

## Abstract

Transparency, as used in science, engineering, business, the humanities, and other social contexts implies openness, communication, and accountability. Transparency is operating in such a way that it is easy for others to see what actions are performed (University of California, Berkeley n. d.).By inference then, "transparent leadership" means that leaders are open, available for communication from a variety of organizational pathways and sources, and perceived as accountable for their actions.

## Introduction: What Is Transparent Leadership?

*Transparent leadership* is somewhat of a buzzword these days. Partly, this is due to transformations that continue to occur in the business world following the Enron scandal and the regulatory requirements that were created in the United States to ensure candidness in risk communications within corporations. This also may be due to an increased awareness of the benefits of transparent leadership as an organizational philosophy.

In the context of the practice of workplace safety and health, transparent leadership plays a vital role in creating and sustaining an organizational safety climate that has safety as a core value. There is value in examining this statement in more detail. In doing so, we gain a better understanding of how leaders can impact safety.

> Safety culture is a reflection of the organization's values, norms, expectations, etc., whereas safety climate consists of the organization's perceptions of safety as measured by tools such as safety perception surveys.

Often, the terms *safety climate* (which is based on perceptions) and *safety culture* are used interchangeably to describe or explain the less tangible reasons for safety outcomes. However, there are distinct differences between the two. Safety culture is a reflection of the organization's values, norms, expectations, etc., whereas safety climate consists of the organization's perceptions of safety as measured by tools such as safety perception surveys. Safety climate should be thought of as a leading indicator of safety culture and is measurable. A good example of a safety perception survey is the National Safety Council's (NSC) "Safety Barometer" (National Safety Council 2017).The correlating relationships between leadership practices, safety climate (as measured by employee perception surveys), and safety outcomes (which are often measured by observed safety behaviors and injury rates) have previously been established (Zohar 2002; Guildenmund 2000; Hoffman and Morgeson 1998). How leader transparency might then impact safety outcomes is largely based on how leaders are perceived as being open, available, and accountable for decisions that affect workplace safety.

Leaders frequently make decisions that affect employee safety perceptions and ultimately safety-related outcomes. This becomes more apparent when common organizational decisions are examined in the broader context of safety. Some common examples might include work shift and overtime decisions, equipment changes, the assignment of personnel to certain jobs with higher levels of safety risks, and other decisions that affect working conditions. Often leaders do not view these decisions initially as having anything to do with safety per se but as ones are necessary for the efficient and necessary operation of the organization.

The perception of leaders as transparent is important. Roughly half of all managers don't trust their leaders (Hurley 2006). While decision-making falls within the purview (and accountability) of management, the transparency with which decisions are communicated will affect employee perceptions and attitudes in many aspects of the work environment, including safety.

## Comparison to Transformational Leadership

A concept that is similar to transparent leadership is transformational leadership as introduced by James MacGregor Burns (Cherry 2017). This concept was later expanded by Bernard M. Bass into what is today referred to as Bass transformational leadership theory. This theory contains most of the components that also describe transparent leadership:

1. Intellectual Stimulation—The leader creates an environment in which "thinking outside the box" is not only encouraged but is embedded in the organizational culture. The status quo is regularly challenged, and new ways of looking at old problems are normalized. A good example for the safety profession is Fred Manuele.
2. Individualized Consideration—Transformational leadership in a hierarchical organization requires that ideas are safe to express and explore. Leaders actively express (and demonstrate) this safety through thoughtful moderation during discussions and provide active encouragement to the expression and exploration of ideas.
3. Inspirational Motivation—Transformational leaders create a contagious excitement that readily transfers to others. They create a connection between people and focus it on an idea or goal.
4. Idealized Influence—Transformational leaders are sustainable role models. The way employees work together and treat each other is (in large part) a reflection of the organizational leadership. Transformational leaders have an outsized role in creating and sustaining a culture of trust and respect.

The importance of transparent (and transformational) leadership as a vital part of workplace safety is well understood. The Occupational Safety and Health Administration (OSHA) identifies management commitment and worker involvement as two of the key elements of an effective safety and health management system. The other elements are hazard prevention and control, worksite analysis, and training (OSHA 2017). Both management commitment and worker involvement contain elements of transparent leadership.

To understand transparent leadership better, one should examine its workplace impacts at the individual, site, and governance (corporate) levels.

## Individual Level Transparent Leadership (Worker/Employee)

Safety professionals may be surprised to read about leadership at the hourly worker level of the organization, but they really should not be. Frequently the most powerful influencers of safety climate are other employees. Wise organizations will harness the informal leadership networks that exist at many sites to further safety objectives. Anyone and everyone can be a safety leader/influencer, often with the simplest of acts, as the following examples show:

Wise organizations will harness the informal leadership networks that exist at many sites to further safety objectives.

- Reminding others who have forgotten to wear their PPE to put it on
- Consistently using the handrail when on stairs
- Looking both ways when crossing an aisle shared with powered industrial trucks (PITs)
- Observing new employees and informing or reminding them of site hazards and safe work practices

Such actions by supervisors are usually thought of as part of their corporate responsibilities, which is true. However, when these same actions come from peers, they communicate somewhat differently. When initiated by peers, they help establish safety norms and values in the workplace. Done well, this type of transparent leadership can convey a culture of care, ownership, and concern for safety that is sometimes difficult to achieve in any other way. This will have a positive impact on safety climate.

Transparent leadership can also come from other employee-level sources. Skilled trade organizations, union shops, certain departments (e.g., maintenance), etc. can be sources of a type of cultural-level transparent leadership in which safety norms that have been established over years are ingrained into these organizations. This can often be seen in certain high-risk trades; the author has seen this occur in the electrical, ironworker, and emergency responder trades. In these, a family- or team-like environment is created, where everyone is expected to watch out for everyone else's safety in addition to their own. When this works well, it gives the organization a team-like feel that helps facilitate the discussions of safety concerns.

In a similar vein, "200% Safety Accountability" programs, which try to create the same type of family-like environment, have sprung up at many companies in recent years. They operate under the premise that "I'm accountable for my own safety and accountable for yours as well," or using a more Biblical reference, "I am my brother's (and sister's) keeper." To work well, there needs to be an explicit understanding that any safety feedback you (as a team member) receive is being given in the spirit of care and concern for your well-being and that you would expect the same from the person you are giving safety feedback to if the situation were reversed. While the accountability is more of a social compact than a true accountability for someone else's safety, the effect on safety climate is tangible when these programs are working well.

To work well, there needs to be an explicit understanding that any safety feedback you (as a team member) receive is being given in the spirit of care and concern for your well-being, and that you would expect the same from the person you are giving safety feedback to, if the situation was reversed.

## Site-Level Transparent Leadership (First-Level Supervision and Site Management)

Many of today's workplaces consist of central governance organizations, with one or more site locations in which service, manufacturing, or other value-added activities take place. In these types of site-level organizations, the site leader and day-to-day supervisory leaders play an important role in how employees perceive the safety climate: that is, the value, perceptions, and beliefs placed on safety in an organization. The author has witnessed that the first-level supervisor generally has closer and more frequent contact with the employees he or she supervises than anyone else in the organization does, save perhaps the employee's coworkers. Transparency by the first-level supervisor in general is critical in shaping safety climate from the perspective of the employee if for no other reason than their personal familiarity with the supervisor versus higher level management. Also, at this level supervision tends to be more operational, that is,

Transparency by the first-level supervisor in general is critical in shaping safety climate from the perspective of the employees, if for no other reason than their personal familiarity with the supervisor v. higher-level management.

focused on the specific activities and performance of the individual employee (Hoffman and Morgeson 1999). The opportunities to align the individual employee's safe work behaviors with broader organizational goals are greater at this level of supervision.

In organizations where transparent leadership has broken down at the first-level supervisor, value conflicts between perceived organizational priorities for safety and productivity may result in risk-taking behaviors. An employee might choose not to lock out the hazardous energies of an item of equipment because executing the proper energy control procedure would result in a longer period of downtime. He or she may feel that risks have been overstated in training and procedures when supervisors are not perceived as advocating for safety (or visibly practicing safety protocols). While it is fortunately rare to have a

While it is fortunately rare to have a supervisor advocate against an established safety procedure or rule, in the absence of transparency and advocacy employees may feel that safety is not a priority.

supervisor advocate against an established safety procedure or rule, in the absence of transparency and advocacy employees may feel that safety is not a priority. It is important to remember that not every employee will come into a workplace with the same level of risk understanding and tolerance; it is up to the employer to ensure that safety practices and risk management do not conflict (or give the perception of conflict) with expectations of productivity. The first-level supervisor is critical in this regard.

These types of conflicts (production versus safety) can often be identified as causal or contributing factors in investigations of accidents or incidents and should always be given appropriate consideration in understanding the role human factors can play. Such investigations should always seek to understand what was going on in an employee's mind that led up to the event and try to understand if conflicting value communications may be a contributing factor. This is easier said than done, of course. Understanding these value conflicts and resolving them will help prevent future accidents and incidents.

For the safety professional seeking to positively influence the safety climate through transparent leadership at the first-level of supervision, some of the tools and techniques listed may prove to be of value:

- Crafting (and coaching) consistent value messaging for first-level supervision on safety policies, guidelines, and site-specific safety information
- Supporting supervisors in the personal (small group and one-on-one) dissemination of this information through coaching and role-playing

- Creating storylines, which are safety value communications delivered in a story format (versus a rote explanation of a safety policy). Storylines can be delivered in a format such as (1) "this adverse event happened to me or someone I know," (2) "this is how it could have been prevented," and (3) "this is how I would feel if something like this happened here (or to you)." Note that the third part is the most important from a transparent leadership perspective.

Supervisors might say, "I don't have any of these types of stories." Safety professionals should be able to find suitable stories from your company site, other companies' sites, the news, OSHA, U.S. Chemical Safety Board website, etc. The points to stress are more about the safety value communications and less about the specific content of the storyline, although the story line should be at least relatable to site employees, lest they miss the broader points of the message.

To help support open dialog between managers, executive leaders, and hourly employees, an energy company created and disseminated a laminated card with five questions for supervisors and leaders to ask themselves each day:

- What did I do *today* to improve safety at this site?
- What did I do *today* to communicate my personal safety values to my employees?
- Did I have a positive personal communication with each of my employees *today*?
- Am I "leading with safety" *today*?
- Did all of my employees get a quality prejob briefing *today*?

The purpose of this recital was to reinforce transparent leadership by making this a daily habit. By the way, this daily recital was also shared with hourly employees, who were asked to support the supervisors by initiating the positive personal communications. This was often done tongue-in-cheek ("Hey, boss, where is my positive safety communication today?"), but the safety climate reasons that spawned the recital were not forgotten. The author has witnessed on many occasions that humor can be an icebreaker in starting a more open dialog about safety values.

The key point to remember is to be transparent (as previously defined) when implementing these types (or any type) of messaging intended to influence safety climate through transparent leadership. This is not necessarily something that comes naturally to everyone; in fact, a few "old-school" managers might consider it a weakness while in a supervisory capacity (which is not true, of course). The use of role playing and active listening techniques can help those leaders for whom this does not come more naturally.[9] The next level of the organizational hierarchy (site management) is considered to be more tactically focused on the general means and methods of achieving the site's production and profitability goals. At this level, transparent leadership can also have a significant effect on safety for the average employee.

The key point to remember is to be transparent (as previously defined) when implementing these types (or any type) of messaging intended to influence safety climate through transparent leadership.

The site manager, or his or her organizational equivalent, is the visible day-to-day representative of the broader (corporate) organization. The site manager's words and actions have a strong influence on the actions of the site's hourly and salaried workforce; this is necessary, as the site manager's main role is to achieve a desired output (e.g., services, materials, etc.) using the site's resources. The difference here is that the site manager's primary tool for achieving these outputs is the site management team, not (typically) directing workers individually. Andriessen (1978) concluded that while supervisors are a decisive factor in the safety behavior of the workforce, it is management that set the supervisor's goals, objectives, and priorities. Thus, higher-level management can have a greater degree of influence on workers' safety behavior than supervisors. He argues that even if direct supervision does not place a high priority on safety, workers may still work safely when higher management stresses safety.

This helps illustrate the strong influence that site leaders can have on safety. Transparent leadership at this level may create sustainable safety values, even without optimal first level supervision support. Intuitively, however, merely "talking the talk" will not sustain a favorable site safety climate for very long. As mentioned earlier in the definition of transparent leadership, the need for both first-level managers and site leaders to be accountable for safety is needed.

## Transparent Leadership (Executive Management)

In researching this chapter, the unfortunate truth is that the number of articles and news stories that detail the failure of executive management in safety leadership far outnumber the success stories. The conviction of former Massey Energy CEO Don Blankenship in relation to the deaths of twenty-nine miners killed at work in West Virginia is a critical reminder of the important role that most senior executives in a business play in safety governance and safety leadership. Kirstin Ferguson identifies four specific components of safety leadership relevant to the most senior leaders of an organization, the CEO or president and their teams and the board. These components include vision, personal commitment, decision-making, and transparency (Ferguson 2016).

The conviction of former Massey Energy CEO Don Blankenship in relation to the deaths of twenty-nine miners killed at work in West Virginia is a critical reminder of the important role that most senior executives in a business play in safety governance and safety leadership.

With regard to transparency, Ferguson writes,

> The final area of safety leadership focuses on the need for senior executives and board m embers to ensure open, transparent communications regarding safety performance to encourage a culture of continuous improvement. Transparency in this context includes being open to scrutiny of safety performance through monitoring and communicating the effectiveness of safety initiatives. Senior leaders demonstrate transparency through formal and informal communications, which celebrate safety successes, as well as openly communicating safety challenges as they emerge. In a practical sense, this may involve ensuring a consistent and comparable range of lagging and leading indicators are reported and disclosed to stakeholders, developing open communications with other companies to develop best practices in safety and including team safety performance within an executive remuneration system. (Ferguson 2016)

From a high-level perspective, senior executives operate at the strategic level where the focus is on the operation of the company as a whole. Organizational metrics allow senior executives to keep their fingers on the pulse of the company, and while safety is (unfortunately) notoriously difficult to measure, it is being measured, usually through lagging indicators such as incident/injury rates.

Senior leaders need to consider the need to occasionally bypass the usual flow of safety information from bottom to top, and see/hear for themselves what employees at every level are experiencing in the way of safety climate. In certain continuous improvement models/systems, this type of activity is sometimes called a "go and see." Opportunities for safety value messaging along the lines of transparent leadership are potential outcomes from go and see activities.

To facilitate communications between leaders and employees, the same energy company that created the laminated "Five Daily Questions for Supervisors/ Leaders to Ask Themselves" card also created a card for senior leaders on "go and see" activities. This card was titled "Ten Sample High-Value Safety Communications" and was intended for senior leaders to use in creating dialog around safety with hourly employees:

Ten Sample High-Value Safety Communications

- Where do you think the next injury will be at this site?
- When was your last safety meeting? What did you talk about?

- What was the last near miss event that was discussed?
- What did you discuss at your prejob briefing today?
- What is the most important safety rule here? Why?
- What are the top three opportunities for improving safety here?
- How would you rate safety at this site on a scale of 1 to 5, with 5 being the best? What would it take to be a "5" in safety at this site?
- If someone sees someone else at this site doing something unsafe, do you think that they would feel comfortable saying something to them about it?
- How often do your leader(s) talk to you about their personal safety values/commitments?
- What does "safety as a core value" mean to you personally?

These are powerful substantive questions, and they require more than a simple yes or no. The responses to these questions can create dialog, provide the opportunity to communicate values, and give the senior leader a deeper understanding of the safety climate at the site. For the employee, in addition to conveying information, the process of asking for and listening to replies can create trust in the senior leader.

## Conclusions

Transparent leadership is a powerful positive means of both communication and governance. Personal experience, however, has taught that many companies tend to overestimate their implementation of transparent leadership. It is not likely to be the natural condition of a company's management styles and systems, and it generally will not happen unless senior leaders make it an organizational value. It takes considerable effort, skill, practice, and commitment to make it happen throughout the organization.

For you as a safety professional, understanding the dynamics of transparent leadership can help you understand a key influencer of organizational safety climate. Being able to support your organization's safety climate with transparent leadership concepts will provide a better understanding of issues at all levels. And perhaps most importantly, practicing transparent leadership yourself will help you gain the trust and confidence of the people you work for and serve, which is always a good thing.

## Questions

1. What does the author mean by "transparency"?
2. What are the differences between "safety culture" and "safety climate"?
3. What characteristic(s) of transparent leadership does the Occupational Safety and Health Administration (OSHA) define as key elements of an effective safety and health management system?
4. What potential behavior(s) may occur when there is a breakdown in transparent leadership by the first-level supervisor?
5. What four specific components of safety leadership are relevant to the most senior leaders of an organization?

## References

Andriessen, J. (1978). "Safe Behavior and Safety Motivation." *Journal of Occupational Accidents* 1(4): 363–76.

Cherry, Kendra. (2017). "What Is Transformational Leadership?" https://www.verywell.com/what-is-transformational-leadership-2795313.

Ferguson, Kirstin. (2016). "Safety Governance Inside the Boardroom: The Role of Senior Executives and Board Directors in Safety Leadership." *EHS Today*. http://ehstoday.com/safety-leadership/safety-governance-inside-boardroom-role-senior-executives-and-board-directors-safe?page=1.

Flin, R., and S. Yule. (2004). "Leadership for Safety: Industrial Experience." *Quality and Safety in Health Care 13* (Suppl. 2): ii45–ii51. Guildenmund, F. W. (2002). "The Nature of Safety Culture: A Review of Theory and Research." *Safety Science* 34: 215–57.

Hoffmann, D. A., and F. P. Morgeson. (1999). "Safety-Related Behavior as a Social Exchange: The Role of Perceived Organizational Support and Leader-Member Exchange." *Journal of Applied Psychology* 84: 286–96.

Hurley, R. F. (2006, September). "The Decision to Trust." *Harvard Business Review*. https://hbr.org/2006/09/the-decision-to-trust.National Safety Council. 2017. "Safety Barometer." (Survey tool.) http://www.nsc.org/Measure/Pages/safety-management-employee-perception-surveys.aspx.

Positive Psychology Program. (2016). "Active Listening: The Art of Empathetic Conversation." https://positivepsychologyprogram.com/active-listening.

U.S. Occupational Safety and Health Administration (OSHA). (2016). *Recommended Practice for Safety and Health Programs*. Publication No. 3885. www.osha.gov/shpguidelines.

University of California, Berkeley. (n. d.) "Communicating with Transparency and Integrity." Accessed July 23, 2017. http://sa.berkeley.edu/sites/default/files/images/communicatingwithtransparency.pdf.

Zohar, D. (2002). "The Effects of Leadership Dimensions, Safety Climate, and Assigned Priorities on Minor Injuries in Work Groups." *Journal of Organizational Behavior* 23: 75–79.

CHAPTER 3

# EMPLOYEE-CENTERED SAFETY CULTURES: INDIVIDUAL AND CORPORATE SOCIAL RESPONSIBILITY

Elbert Sorrell and Jeanette Black

## Learning Objectives

After studying this chapter, the reader will be able to:

1. Discuss the definitions and relationship between organizational culture and climate
2. Evaluate the relationship between safety climate, safety culture, and organizational culture
3. Articulate an understanding of the constructs associated with injury-free work environments
4. Summarize the components of a psychologically healthy workplace
5. Present the benefits of implementing a people-centered safety culture
6. Recognize the need for true leadership and corporate social responsibility

## Key Terms

**Organizational culture, safety culture, people-centered safety culture, psychologically healthy workplaces, leadership, corporate social responsibility**


## Abstract

A review of literature surrounding the profession of occupational safety and health suggests numerous changes have shaped the means, methods, and processes adopted by safety professionals to address the prevailing issues associated with workplace injuries and illnesses. These changing safety paradigms represent shifts in the thinking, processes, and actions that safety professionals use to minimize hazards and risks, as well as the negative consequences associated with them. It has become increasingly clear through empirical observations that safety professionals and the leadership of organizations have recognized that they must increase their efforts to improve the physical conditions of the workplace. To this end, safety and health professionals find themselves constantly implementing technology-based engineering controls coupled with related administrative controls to address a particular problem. Even with these controls in place, injuries and illnesses continue to represent a significant constraint on organizations, hindering their ability to truly maximize operational efficiency and effectiveness. Consequently, profitability is also compromised by employee injuries and illnesses and the escalating cost of workers' compensation, health plan benefit usage, and related disability benefit plans. This chapter seeks to inform and present the effects and impacts of designing and implementing a people-centered approach to safety cultures in organizations.

## Introduction

As the discipline of safety continues to mature and as a profession as opposed to an occupation, the psychosocial aspect of safety has been being presented as a paradigm shift. These psychosocial aspects are directly related to employees' work environment and oftentimes under the direct influence of the leadership of the organization. Some of the most significant considerations associated with psychosocial aspects of work are linked to the physical and mental demands of the job, one's ability to govern himself within a work environment, and the necessary social support enabling workers to contribute to individual well-being within the context of a people-centered work environment.

Some of the most significant considerations associated with psychosocial aspects of work are linked to the physical and mental demands of the job.

Geller (2011) provides a summary of the prevailing paradigm linked to this movement. He suggests that historically the focus of accident prevention has been associated with what safety professionals recognize as the three e-words:

1. Engineering—Design the safest equipment, environmental settings, or protective devices
2. Education—Educate people regarding the use of engineering interventions
3. Enforcement—Use discipline to enforce compliance with recommended work-safety practices.

Geller (2011) continues to argue that this safety-related paradigm has had some significant impact on how safety professionals attempt to manage the safety process and makes the argument that this process also has contributed to a decrease in work-related injuries and illnesses. While he argues that improvements have been made, he recognizes that there is still a tremendous amount of work that must be accomplished. Geller advocates that safety professionals in general and organizational leaders specifically should add three new e-words into leadership: empowerment, empathy, and emotion. Geller suggests that incorporating empowerment, empathy, and emotion into leadership consciousness would allow organization safety performance to rise above its current plateau and make strides toward an injury-free work culture. There is a need to take into consideration human dynamics of injury prevention, and this could be accomplished by improving the safety culture within an organization (Geller 2011).

## Organizational Culture

There are many definitions and perspectives about organizational culture (table 3.1). Organizations can be viewed as dynamic interactive components that possess a sense of energy from the interactions between individuals and the commonality of shared values (Schein 2010). Organizational culture, when it is rooted in shared values and a deep sense of purpose that people find meaningful, serves as a powerful framework and filter for making decisions at all levels within an organization. Culture provides the unwritten rules of the workplace. These rules are those expected behaviors, such as codes of conduct and dress codes that provide structure within the organization.

Organizational culture, when it is rooted in shared values and a deep sense of purpose that people find meaningful, serves as a powerful framework and filter for making decisions at all levels within an organization.

**Table 3.1** Definitions of organizational culture

| Author | Definition |
|---|---|
| Kroeber and Kluckhohn (1952) | Transmitted patterns of values, ideas, and other symbolic systems that shape the behavior of an organization. |
| Hofstede (1980) | "The collective programming of the mind that distinguishes the members of the organization from another. This included shared beliefs, values and practices that distinguished one organization to another." |
| Swartz and Jordon (1980) | Patterns of beliefs and expectations shared by members that produce norms shaping behavior. |
| Ouchi (1981) | Set of symbols, ceremonies, and myths that communicated the underlying values and beliefs of the organization to its employees. |
| Martin and Siehl (1983) | Glue that holds together an organization through shared patterns of meaning. Three component systems: context or core values, forms/processes of communication (e.g., jargon), and strategies to reinforce content (e.g., rewards, training programs). |
| Uttal (1983) | Shared values (what is important) and beliefs (how things work) that interact with organization's structures and control systems to produce behavioral norms (the way we do things around here). |
| Adler (1986) | Refers to something shared by all or almost all members of some social groups, something that the older members of the group try to pass on to the younger members, and something that shapes organizational behavior or structure. |
| Denison (1990) | Refers to the underlying values, beliefs, and principals that serve as a foundation for an organization's management system as well as the set of management practices and behaviors that both exemplify and reinforce those basic principles. |
| Schein (1992, 2004, 2010) | A pattern of shared basic assumptions learned by a group as it evolved its problems of external adaptation and internal integration, which has worked well enough to be considered valid and therefore to be taught to new members as the correct way to perceive, think, and feel in relation to those problems. |
| Trompenaars (1993) | The way in which people solve problems. It is a shared system of meanings. It dictates what we pay attention to, how we act, and what we value. |

*Continued*

**Table 3.1** Definitions of organizational culture *(continued)*

| Author | Definition |
|---|---|
| Goffee (1996) | Is an outcome of how people relate to one another. |
| Schneider (1997) | Shared patterns of behavior and the meaning of that behavior. |
| Cameron and Quinn (1999) | What is valued, the dominate leadership styles, the language of success that makes an organization unique. |
| Sullivan (2001) | Refers to the total lifestyle of a people, including all the values, ideas, knowledge, behaviors, and material objects that they share. |
| Wood (2001) | The systems of shared beliefs and values that develop within an organization or within its subunits that guide the behaviors of its members. |
| Wiesner (2002) | A way of looking at organizations by their shared values and behavior. |
| Thomas and Tung (2003) | Refers to evolving set of shared beliefs, values, attitudes, and logical processes that provide cognitive maps for people within a given societal group to perceive, think, reason, act, react, and interact. |
| Anthon (2004) | The set of values, beliefs, and understandings shared by an organization's employees and its rank among an organization's most powerful component. |
| Taylor (2004) | Refers to what is created from the messages that are received about how people are expected to behave in the organization. |
| Wagner (2005) | An informal, shared way of perceiving life and membership in the organization that binds members together and influences what they think about themselves and their work. |
| Hofstede and Hofstede (2005) | The unwritten book with rules of the social game. |

Adapted from *Culture, Leadership, and Organizations: The GLOBE Study of 62 Societies*, by R. J. House, P. J. Hanges, M. Javidan, P. W. Dorfman, and V. Gupta, 2004, Thousand Oaks, CA: Sage (as cited in Abu-Jarad, I. Y., Yusof, N., and Nikbin, D. (2010), "A Review Paper on Organizational Culture and Organizational Performance," *International Journal of Business and Social Science* 1(3): 35.) Copyright 2004 by Sage. Adapted with permission.

Organizational culture can appear transparent or even nonexistent to those embedded in the culture. This general acceptance of the culture reflects the deeply held beliefs and behavior norms of the group, which is frequently referred to as the organization's soul or organizational glue—what holds its disparate pieces (the employees) together. Only when someone new joins the group do the unspoken expectations surface for practices or decision-making processes—how things are done (Schein 2010). Culture manifests in various ways because employees bring different interests, experiences, responsibilities, and values with them into the organization (Martin 2005), and culture is interpreted, evaluated, and enacted on the basis of each unique employee's views. Practices within the culture indicate what is perceived as right or wrong, good or bad, and define that culture (Gehman and Trevino 2013).

## Safety Culture as a Subset of Organizational Culture

The functional significance of developing a positive organizational culture indicates that it could be used as a means to encourage the mind-set and direction of an organization. Organizational commitment to embrace this prevailing philosophy could become the basis of bridging organizational behavior with strategic management interests. On the other-hand, safety culture is more difficult to define in absolute terms. Safety cultures, like organizational culture, are reflected in an organization's shared values and beliefs.

> Safety culture refers to the extent to which participants throughout an organization value safety and take individual and group responsibility to make informed decisions about work-related activities and functions.

Still, some published definitions of safety culture use similar descriptions to provide a basic understanding of the concept. Pizzi, Goldfarb, and Nash (2001) suggest that an exact definition of safety culture does not exist. That is, safety culture refers to the extent to which participants throughout an organization value safety and take individual and group responsibility to make informed decisions about work-related activities and functions that have organizational/safety-related implications. Furthermore, there appear to be recurring themes in the literature defining safety culture, and these themes share a number of consistent descriptions.

Specifically, Pizzi et al. (2001) note several attributes that organizations with positive safety cultures possess, including:

1. Involved and engaged upper management
2. Acknowledgment of high-risk work-related activities
3. High levels of organizational trust that result in blame-free work environments where individuals are encouraged to report accidents and near-misses
4. Collaboration across the ranks to seek work process improvements and solutions
5. Willingness to provide the necessary resources to support safety

Similar approaches to and explanations about safety culture have been advocated by several renowned safety professionals, including Manuele (1993), Geller (1996), Petersen (2003), and Krause (2005). These authors and practitioners have made significant contributions to the body of knowledge defining safety culture and are conceptually in agreement with the statements made above.

Cooper (2000) attempts to expand upon the expressed themes of safety cultures. He explains why the development of a safety culture is critical in business and industry. The author implies that if organizational leaders are serious about improving organizational excellence, they must embrace leadership initiatives that can make a significant positive impact with regard to the identification, elimination, and prevention of workplace safety and health hazards and risks. Cooper (2000) makes the point that accident causation models recognize that there is a causal relationship between psychological, situational, and behavioral factors.

Research by Reason (as cited by Cooper 2000) argues that there is a reciprocal relationship between organizational characteristics identified within high- versus low-accident facilities. The conclusion suggests that if there is a relationship between organizational systems, modes of organizational behavior, and the workers' psychological attributes, it is reasonable to assume that there is an accident causation chain at all levels of the organization. Cooper (2000) concludes this argument by suggesting that it is the leadership that drives organizational factors and that leadership and their focus on employees as the greatest organizational assets must be addressed to improve systemic workplace safety initiatives and issues.

People spend a significant portion of their lives at work, and changes in the work environment can have profound influence on their health, well-being, and performance. Fostering a work culture that is mindful of the importance of work–life balance, employee growth and development, health and safety, and employee engagement can be the key to achieving sustainable employee well-being and organizational performance (Grawitch, Gottschalk, and Munz 2006). Designing the workplace to promote employee well-being and safety must be aligned with a high-performing, caring workplace culture (Kalliath and Kalliath 2012).

Fostering a work culture that is mindful of the importance of work-life balance, employee growth and development and health and safety, and employee engagement can be the key to achieving sustainable employee well-being and organizational performance.

People are willing to actively care in special ways for their family members. The result is maximum trust, sense of belonging, and actively caring behaviors that enhance for safety and health of family members. To the extent these guidelines are followed among members of a corporate family, an actively caring culture will help to develop trust and belongingness among people and result in the implementation and demonstration of safety behaviors among all family members—at home and at work. Building a sense of community or belongingness among coworkers will improve organizational safety. Safety improvement requires interpersonal observation and feedback for a people-centered safety culture to occur; people must adopt a collective win/win perspective instead of the individualistic win/lose orientation common in many work settings. A sense of belongingness and interdependency leads to interpersonal trust and caring—essential features of an actively caring organizational culture (Geller 2003).

Safety improvement requires interpersonal observation and feedback for a people-centered safety culture to occur; people must adopt a collective win/win perspective.

People-first safety environments focus on creating quality work environments, which can boost productivity and the bottom line. Safety culture reflects attitudes, beliefs, perceptions, and values that employees at all levels share with a deep sense of purpose and meaning (Manuele 2015; Schein 2010). Safety cultures serve as a powerful framework and filter for making decisions at all organizational levels (Manuele 2015). However, a strong belief in people—employees—shapes a people-centered safety culture, which is crucial for leaders to understand and embrace. To achieve an injury-free workplace, attention must be focused in three areas: (1) the environment (including tools, equipment, and climate) of the work setting; (2) the person (including employee knowledge, attitudes, beliefs, and personalities); and (3) behavior, including safe and at-risk work practices as well as interpersonal conversations (Geller 2003). Employers must address each of these areas daily as part of their efforts to remove environmental hazards, decrease at-risk behaviors, increase safe behaviors, and provide more user-friendly or ergonomically sound workstations.

A people-centered approach to organizational safety culture leads to sustained high-level performance and profits over an extended period of time

The people-centered approach to organizational safety culture leads to sustained high-level performance and profits over an extended period of time. Flexible, innovative, adaptive, and safety focused, these organizations are quick to adapt to changing market dynamics by leveraging the talent of their employees through ideas and brainstorming, and they assist and support employee success through the integration of technology (Cardador and Rupp 2011). A people-centered safety cultures are founded on the ideas that all people are important, a strong belief in people shapes the organizational culture, happy people working together perform more safely and at higher levels, and all people benefit as a result (Black and La Venture 2015, p. 9).

## All People Are Important

An organization's safety culture, which is a subset of its overall culture, results from decisions made at the senior management level that result in acceptable or unacceptable operational risk levels (Manuele 2015). Outcomes of those decisions could be positive or negative. The view that all people are important provides the foundation for creating an exciting, supportive, dynamic, and innovative work environment. It also supports substantial growth and profits. To accomplish this, organizational leaders, middle management, and frontline supervisors must shift their focus from numbers and results to the organization's greatest asset—employees. When the corporate environment is designed to focus on its people through safety, it builds trust and leverages the talent within the organization, which can be used to develop performance measures and business success factors that are reflective of the employee culture.

When the corporate environment is designed to focus on its people through safety, it builds trust and leverages the talent within the organization, which can be used to develop performance measures and business success factors that are reflective of the employee culture.

Lawler (as cited in Weymes 2005) lists six characteristics that can be used to describe high performance in people-centered organizations, with a focus on individual involvement and effective leadership as the basis for control:

1. Organizational cultures can be the ultimate competitive advantage.
2. Involvement can be the most effective source of control.
3. All employees add significant value.
4. Lateral processes are the key to organizational efficiencies.
5. Organizations should be designed around people, products, and customers.
6. Efficient leadership focused on employees rather than profits as key to effective organizational leadership and business success through the development of an effective safety culture.

As a result, workers feel that they get to do what they do best every day, that their opinions count, that their coworkers share their commitment to quality, and that they feel a personal connection between their work and the company's mission. The impact of the people-centered safety culture is substantial and synergistic (Geller 2008; Weymes 2005).

The organizational dilemma can be simply stated: Companies must create an environment where trust, creativity, and innovation flourish while meeting the performance criteria specified by the stakeholders. Applying this philosophy to organizational design ensures that the nature of the organization is shaped by the people in the organization. The starting point for designing, developing, and transforming an organization lies in the understanding of the people in the organization and the relationships between these individuals and external stakeholders (Weymes 2005). Developing the vision and goals, creating a focus on the customer, and developing systems and processes are not to be ignored. Health and safety professionals act as agents of change, both in respect to the technology of the company and the design of its workplaces, and in the organization of the company health and safety management system (Manuele 2015). The starting point lies in the nature of the relationship among people (Sagiv, Schwartz, and Arieli 2011).

Health and safety professionals act as agents of change, both in respect to the technology of the company and the design of its workplaces.

Many organizational and safety leaders are conditioned to avoid failure. Geller (2008) relates this conditioned state to anxiety and suggests there is research to support claims that avoiding failure is good for safety. "People who have constant anxiety about the possibility of a workplace injury are going to do everything they can to put themselves in control of preventing injuries, and so put their safety-focused anxiety on hold" (p. 136). Unfortunately, the traditional accountability approach to safety is failure focused, which affects another a-word—attitude. More specifically, the typical organization focuses on injury rate statistics that are negative and not diagnostic. Moreover, when workers are held accountable for safety-related behaviors, it is usually about the occurrence of at-risk behavior or lack of certain safe behaviors. This is failure–avoidance accountability, impacting attitude in undesirable directions (Geller 2008). This leads to an organizational culture focused on the metrics, rules, and regulations; inevitably systems and processes tend to be developed to ensure staff conformance to those rules. Such quantitative targets usually dictate behavior. Rules and regulations control behavior, stifle creativity, and build an environment based on mistrust, self-interest and ambition, deceit, and complaints. But the organization that creates an environment that allows employees freedom may generate new and innovative approaches, foster harmonious working relationships, and build trust and integrity (Weymes 2005).

Rules and regulations control behavior, stifle creativity, and build an environment based on mistrust, self-interest and ambition, deceit, and complaints.

Therefore, an organization's performance depends on the nature of the relationships formed by individuals within that organization. Employees are rational individuals who are seeking self-actualization (achieving one's purpose in life), happiness, and wisdom. Research suggests leaders are more self-directed and optimistic when they put more focus on achieving proactive success rather on avoiding reactive failure (Covington 1972; Covington and Omelich 1979). Effective leaders enrich their work culture and help workers become self-directed, self-accountable, and self-motivated. Peterson (2001) advocates an integration of the humanistic and behavioristic approaches to understanding and helping people in the context of organizational safety. This becomes the foundation of people-centered approach to building a safety culture (Geller 2005).

Effective leaders enrich their work culture and help workers become self-directed, self-accountable, and self-motivated.

The success and synergy of the people-centered approach to safety is the foundational belief that all people—employees, customers, suppliers, and community members—are important. This belief in people and the accompanying values of treating each person and task with dignity, trust, and respect serve as both the bedrock foundation for business decisions and a springboard for performance, growth, and innovation. Thus, all people benefit in the challenges, risk, and success of the organization, resulting in increased employee engagement and commitment to an injury-free safety culture.

### A Strong Belief in People Shapes an Organizational Safety Culture

People-centered cultures view employees as a long-term investment, a source of competitive advantage that must be supported and protected.

Organizational and safety leaders increase organizational success by

- asking people what they do for safety;
- giving priority to proactive process numbers that reflect achievement rather than focusing on reactive injury reports which suggest failure;
- recognizing individuals and work teams for their safety related accomplishments; and
- promoting a safety scorecard that holds people accountable for completed process activities related to injury prevention (Geller 2008).

Thus, by focusing on the people of the organization, both the company and the employees win. Their organizational cultures are centered and dependent on people. As a result, firms with healthy people-centered safety cultures are constantly changing and adapting to new ideas, people, resources, technology, challenges, and opportunities (Geller 2008; Sagiv et al. 2011).

> People-centered cultures view employees as a long-term investment, a source of competitive advantage that must be supported and protected.

### Happy People Working Together Perform at Higher Levels

In today's fast-paced business environment, the quality of working relationships and trust generated by unwavering business integrity is emerging as a key competitive and strategic advantage. Sagiv et al. (2011) showed that people-focused cultures, coupled with effective leadership, help managers respond more rapidly to customer needs and changes in the business environment. Because leadership and frontline managers care deeply about their people, they tend to listen more intently to what the company's various stakeholders have to say (Sagiv et al. 2011). Geller (2008) states the best safety leaders are enthusiastic and passionate, and show respect and appreciation for the people they lead. Such adaptive organizations consistently and substantially outperform companies with more traditional corporate cultures on four major measures: revenue, workforce expansion, stock price, and net income.

### All People Benefit as a Result

To have impact on long-term economic performance, a people-first safety culture must be embedded in the day-to-day operations of the company. When leaders at all levels truly believe that all people are important and support that belief with their actions, amazing things can happen. There is a strong correlation between a belief in people, working together, and long-term profit, growth, and a safe work environment for all employees (Manuele 2015).

> There is a strong correlation between a belief in people, working together, and long-term profit, growth, and a safe work environment.

## Seven Key Elements to Sustain People-Centered Safety Cultures

Research by Black and LaVenture (2015), Kendall and Bodinson (2010), and Krueger (1994) suggest that people-centered cultures share the following key elements:

- leveraging people-first core values;
- leadership that walks the talk;
- open communication;
- high levels of trust;
- aligned operations and work environments focused on HR and talent development practices;
- change responsiveness; and
- organizational resiliency (as cited in Black and LaVenture 2015, p.16).

These elements are incorporated into the fabric of the organization and are built on the aspirations, talents, and dreams of the employees and constantly interact with and shape each other (Kendall and Bodinson 2010). Organizations that promote such values as openness, trust, initiative, teamwork and collaboration, the humane treatment of workers, creativity, quality, empowerment, and delegation obtain better results (Becker, Huslid, and Ulrich 2001; Huang and Dastmalchian 2006).

Health and safety professionals must operate with the seven key elements in addition to a business framework. These professionals must understand business management, business ethics, analysis and analytical tools for analysis, finance, budgeting, cash flow, and executive decision-making (Manuele 2015). Imagine an organizational safety framework that tracks environmental hazards removed, near-hit reports submitted and reviewed, safety audits completed, interpersonal observation and feedback sessions conducted, safety suggestions received and implemented, and safe versus at-risk behaviors observed per work team (Manuele 2015). Such accountability systems put people in control of an achievement-oriented approach to injury prevention. Such practices not only increase success-seeking behaviors focused on safety but also helps to change accountability to focus on employee engagement while creating an organizational culture and climate that is empowered (Geller 2008, p. 33). In addition, imagine employee safety meetings, asking participants to state publicly what they have done for safety. Work teams would not be ranked according to reactive injury records but recognized for actions taken to prevent personal injury. Furthermore, imagine performance appraisals that include a checklist of safety accomplishments rather than total recordable injury rate (Geller and Wiegand 2005). This cultivates an achievement orientation and moves safety seekers toward promotion of a people-centered safety culture.

## Organizational Values

Organizational values are a company's foundation for governance. The more ambiguous and uncertain the environment is, the more unstable and less enduring are the organizational values to the employees, which creates distrust in the organization (Adler 2001; Schein 2010). Specific value practices are only as strong and durable as the social network and fabric within a culture. Such networks can be a source of resiliency or fragility, depending on the organizational environment (Gehman and Trevino 2013).

Values are general standards or principles that are considered desirable, such as loyalty, helpfulness, fairness, predictability, reliability, honesty, responsibility, integrity, competence, consistency, and openness (Hultman 2005; Olson and Zanna 1993; Rokeach 1973). Typically, employees incorporate organizational values into their own value systems and prioritize them in terms of their relative importance as guiding principles (Rokeach 1973). The employees' value systems guide their behavior and interpretation of experience by furnishing criteria that can be used to evaluate and understand events and actions in the surrounding work environment. A value system determines which behaviors, events, situations, or people are desirable within organizations (Jones and George 1998). Values vary not only by content but also by function or purpose. The visible dimension of culture is reflected in the espoused values, philosophy, and mission of the organization, whereas the invisible dimension lies in the unspoken set of values that guide employees' actions and perceptions in the organization (Martins and Meyer 2012; McDermott and O'Dell 2001). Fostering a work culture that is mindful of the importance of work-life balance, employee growth and development, health and safety, and employee engagement can be the key to achieving sustainable employee well-being and organizational performance (Grawitch et al. 2006).

The employees' value systems guide their behavior and interpretation of experience by furnishing criteria that can be used to evaluate and understand events and actions in the surrounding work environment.

## Organizational Climate

Organizational climate, which is defined as "a set of measurable properties of the work environment, perceived directly or indirectly by the people who live and work in this environment and assumed to influence their motivation and behavior" (Litwin and Stringer 1968, p. 1), is important in organizational development primarily because providing a good workplace for employees is a key consideration for modern organizations. Value systems are the foundation of an organization's climate, and a safe work environment entails a strong value system that has been put into action (Manuele 2015; Momeni 2009).

### The Effects of Organizational Climate on the Organization's Performance

Organizational climate can explain the behavior of people in the workplace. Kaczka and Kirk (1968) found that it affected workplace performance. In their study, an employee-centered climate was associated with higher performance—lower unit cost and higher profits.

In fact, the relationship between climate and employee well-being (e.g., satisfaction and stress levels) has been widely studied. These studies link climate factors—leadership, communication openness, participative management, and conflict resolution—with employee satisfaction and, inversely, with dissatisfaction and stress levels (Schneider 1985). Stressful organizational climates are characterized by limited employee participation in decision-making, the use of punishment and negative feedback as motivation, conflict avoidance, confrontation in place of problem solving, and negative relationships between the group and its leaders. Socially supportive climates benefit employee mental health, leading to lower rates of anxiety and depression (Repetti 1987), fewer sick days and workers' compensation cases, and less turnover. Research shows that shared perceptions of undesirable organizational features are connected to low morale and instances of psychogenic illness (Colligan, Pennebaker, and Murphy 1982).

In a people-centered safety organization, employees do not need an outside accountability system to motivate them to follow safety relevant procedures.

The following are a few examples of the characteristics of people-centered organizational safety cultures that have real impact on the bottom-line:

- decreased turnover
- decreased workers' compensation claims
- outperforming competitors and realizing bottom-line impacts from their human capital functions
- intentional cultural design for bringing out the best in people and thereby producing organizational capability that delivers sustainable business results
- a sustained organizational environment that leads to the personal development of its employees and profit
- the continuous, positive development of people's strengths and character, which, in turn, continuously improves the employees' quality, productivity, and service in these organizations (Saylor Foundation 2015; Kalliath and Kalliath, 2012).

In a people-centered safety organization, employees do not need an outside accountability system to motivate them to follow relevant safety procedures. Rather these employees hold themselves accountable to perform work practices safely. They are committed to safety and health protocols when working with their coworkers and at home in their own backyards, when no one else is there to hold them accountable (Geller and Wiegand 2005).

Great workplaces start with management creating quality relationships. As van Marrewijk (2004) found, great workplaces are measured by the quality of the following three interconnected relationships:

1. the relationship between employees and management;
2. the relationship between employees and their jobs or organizations; and
3. the relationships between employees and other employees (p. 8).

Effective leaders reward behaviors consistent with their vision and thereby motivate the successive occurrences of relevant discretionary behavior. Employees are more likely to help others when they have relatively high levels of self-esteem, self-efficacy, personal control, optimism, and a sense of belongingness, all of which increases actively caring behavior toward employees, thus facilitating a people-focused safety culture (Geller and Wiegand 2005).

A psychologically healthy workplace (PHW) fosters employee health and well-being while enhancing organizational performance and productivity.

## Psychologically Healthy Workplaces

According to the American Psychological Association's Center for Organizational Excellence (APA COE 2015), a psychologically healthy workplace (PHW) fosters employee health and well-being while enhancing organizational performance and productivity. Psychologically healthy work practices can be grouped into the five categories found in table 3.2.

Psychological health is an issue that challenges all organizations, irrespective of the company's size or industry. As a result, the ability for organizations to maximize employee performance is contingent on the organization's leadership capacity and willingness to address issues related to the employees' health. The focus in the past has been on physical health alone, but today conversations must be expanded to also cover psychological health and well-being, including

**Table 3.2** Psychologically healthy workplaces

| Work Practice | Characteristics |
|---|---|
| Employee involvement | • Self-managed work teams<br>• Employee committees or task forces<br>• Continuous improvement teams<br>• Participative decision-making<br>• Employee suggestion forums, such as a suggestion box and monthly meetings |
| Work–life balance | • Flexible work arrangements, such as flextime and telecommuting<br>• Assistance with childcare<br>• Eldercare benefits<br>• Resources to help employees manage personal financial issues<br>• Availability of benefits for family members and domestic partners<br>• Flexible leave options beyond those required by the Family and Medical Leave Act |
| Employee growth and development | • Continuing education courses<br>• Tuition reimbursement<br>• Career development or counseling services<br>• Skills training provided in-house or through outside training centers<br>• Opportunities for promotion and internal career advancement<br>• Coaching, mentoring, and leadership development programs |
| Health and safety | • Training and safeguards that address workplace safety and security issues<br>• Efforts to help employees develop a healthy lifestyle, such as stress management, weight loss, and smoking cessation programs<br>• Adequate health insurance, including mental health coverage<br>• Health screenings<br>• Access to health/fitness/recreation facilities<br>• Resources to help employees address life problems, e.g., grief counseling, alcohol abuse programs, Employee Assistance Programs (EAPs), and referrals for mental health services |
| Employee recognition | • Fair monetary compensation<br>• Competitive benefits packages<br>• Acknowledgment of contributions and milestones<br>• Performance-based bonuses and pay increases<br>• Employee awards<br>• Recognition ceremonies |

Adapted from *Resources for Employers*, by the American Psychological Association (APA), Center for Organizational Excellence, 2015, Washington, DC: APA. Copyright 2015 by APA. Adapted with permission.

considerations for the individual, the family, and the community.

The concept of PHW developed as a result of linking several different but related disciplines in order to better understand the relationship between employee well-being and organizational performance. The combined disciplines of medicine, occupational health psychology, epidemiology, health promotion, and positive psychology have influenced this emerging discipline (Day and Randell 2014). The premise of PHW focuses on the development of employees' health and well-being as a precursor to the development of sustainable and socially responsible work environments.

## Defining Psychologically Healthy Workplaces

An examination of the literature defining the concept of PHW revealed several definitions. While several definitions were offered, many of their themes were similar. For example, Cooper and Cartwright (as cited in Day and Randell 2014) defined PHW as an organization characterized by its ability to stay financial solvent and at the same time be physically and psychologically healthy, which results in a healthy and satisfying work environment and organizational culture. Likewise, Grawitch, Gottschalk, and Munz (as cited in Day and Randell 2014) defined PHW by highlighting the importance of the development of positive employee outcomes and positive organizational outcomes to ensure continued organizational and operational effectiveness. A definition that appears to be most relevant as it relates to occupational safety and health was offered by Grawitch, Ledford, Ballard, and Barber (as cited by Day and Randell 2014).

Day and Randell (2014) suggest that PHW is an organizational commitment that incorporate practices, programs, and polices directed at preventing potential negative consequences in the form of negative well-being including workplace injuries and illnesses. This definition captures all of the above stated definitions and is in line with the title of this chapter. A similar and relevant definition is given by Cooper (as cited in Day and Randell, 2014). These authors state the following: "PHW are workplaces that are dedicated to promoting and supporting the physical and psychological health and well-being of their employees while simultaneously incorporating solid business practices, to remain as an efficient and productive business entity and having a positive impact on their clients and community."

## Communication and Employee Involvement in Psychologically Healthy Workplaces

The concept of communication is a critical element in ensuring that employees have a clear understanding of their expectations and are provided with the necessary resources to accomplish the various tasks associated with their job functions. The website published by American Psychological Association (APA 2016) clearly summarizes the role of communication and its importance to building PHW.

> Communication is a critical element in ensuring that employees have a clear understanding of their expectations.

Communication is the paramount mechanism for developing and making known various organizations' objectives and targets determined to assist in building the health of the organization. Communication in PHW primarily should enlighten and empower employees at all levels. The information communicated should flow freely throughout the organization. The flow of information could be both formal and informal. It should include bottom-up communication, top-down communication, and horizontal communication. According to the American Psychological Association (APA 2016), communication strategies that can be used to improve workplace systems could include:

- Providing opportunities for employees to provide feedback to management
- Making goals and actions committed to by the organization clear
- Determining employee needs and resources needs, enabling them to perform their job duties efficiently and effectively

- Communicating information about the outcomes of various workplace practices

According to Grawitch, Ballard, Ledford, and Barber (2009), employee involvement plays a critical role in the creation and sustainability of PHW. They discuss types of employee engagement and indicate that employee involvement needs to be associated with both simple practices such as open-door polices, suggestion forms, and employee surveys and high levels of engagement, such as self-managed work teams, high-involvement systems, and sometimes employee ownership. Based on this information it can be inferred that employees who have work environments with high involvement and engagement are more likely to take individual responsibility, which is an outcome of PHW.

Furthermore, Gibson, Porath, Benson and Lawler (as stated in Grawitch et al. 2009) have confirmed that organizations that have practices promoting high levels of employee involvement show a positive relationship between them and organizational performance and effectiveness, including high employee morale. Other studies that concur with these findings (positive organizational performance) are cited in the research studies by Vandenberg, Richardson, and Rogers; and Freeman and Rogers (as cited in Grawitch, Gottschalk and Munz 2006). The results of these studies highlight the importance of employee engagement in PHW.

## Significance of People-Centered Safety Cultures as PHWs

According to the APA (as cited by Chen and Li 2009) occupation health and safety (OHS) is a major pillar of a healthy workplace. In a PHW, workers are empowered to exercise their knowledge, skills, and abilities to obtain OHS mandates. There are known individual factors that have a direct relationship to promoting the employees' ability to perform their work tasks in a safe manner. Campbell, McCloy, Oppler, and Sager (as cited by Chen and Li 2009) suggest that the key factors include declarative knowledge, procedural knowledge and skills, and motivation.

Knowledge is the effective transfer of relevant safety information about task requirements and equipment operations. Procedural knowledge and skill are related to how to perform a job in a safe manner. These factors are combined with adequate training and recognition and consequently workers in PHW have the intrinsic motivation to carry out their job function in a safe manner.

### Communication and Employee Involvement in Psychologically Healthy Workplaces

Communication is a critical element in ensuring that employees have a clear understanding of their expectations and are provided with the necessary resources to accomplish the various tasks associated with their job functions. The website published by the APA (2016) clearly summarizes the role of communication and its importance in building psychosocially healthy workplaces. Communication coupled with understanding is the bedrock of the five PHW practices listed above. Communication is paramount for developing and making known the various objectives and targets of the organization that assist in building its health. The primary purpose of communication in PHW should be to enlighten and empower employees at all levels.

Communication is paramount for developing and making known the various objectives and targets of the organization that assist in building its health.

Geller (2011) makes the case that safety performance has improved over the years. Furthermore, a review of various accident statistics also highlights that improvements in safety performance have been made. While it cannot be argued that improvements have been made, the fact of the matter is that opportunities for improvements continue to exist. Since the passage of the Occupational Safety and Health Act (OSHA) of 1970, there have been countless measures implemented to improve workplace safety. There is an abundance of literature related to safety that supports this claim. For example, the US Bureau of

> While there has been improvement in workplace safety statistics, there is still convincing evidence that if safety in the workplace is to continue to improve, it must be driven by organizational leadership.

Labor Statistics (BLS) recently published an Economic News Release (October 2015) indicating that 3.0 million nonfatal workplace injuries and illnesses were reported by private industry employers in 2014, for a rate of 3.2 cases per 100 full-time workers. Of these injuries and illnesses, 1.5 million cases reported in 2014 involved days away from work, job transfer or restrictions (DART cases). DART cases occurred at a rate of 1.7 cases per 100 full-time workers, which is identical to the same measure in 2013.

For the past several years OSHA provides statistical data highlighting accomplishments resulting from federal governmental intervention. Specifically, OSHA reports a 50-percent decrease in work-related fatalities and a decrease in occupational injuries by 40 percent over several years. These statistics verify that the advent of OSHA has made a positive impact on workplace safety. The National Safety Council (NSC) also reports significant improvement in overall safety performance of business and industry. However, the NSC as well as OSHA recognize that while there has been improvement in workplace safety statistics, there is still convincing evidence that if safety in the workplace is to continue to improve, it must be driven by organizational leadership that is committed to improving the organization's safety culture.

An examination of the evolution of the safety movement documents the processes and strategies implemented to improve workplace safety. Safety has evolved from the concept of injury prevention to risk control management. Emphasis has broadened from engineering to management. Safety specialists have advanced from "inspectors" to "managers/directors," and benefits have come from a management approach that integrates safety, health, and environmental affairs into the existing management systems. In order to integrate safety into existing management systems, safety professionals must expand their knowledge and skillset beyond safety and health. This broader perspective requires knowledge in the areas of operations management and organizational development/culture as well as competence in the many technical areas related to safety and health. Authors such as Krause (2005), Manuele (1993), McKinnon (2007), and Bird and Davies (1996) all advance the idea of system/strategic thinking. The primary significance associated with improving the safety process requires leadership to improve the culture and climate of an organization, which leads to sustained improvement in all facets of the business, including safety.

With the many changes and paradigm shifts related to safety, no one can dispute there have been many positive outcomes surrounding the safety movement. These positive outcomes can be attributed to increased safety and health regulatory expectations, NIOSH sponsored research, and the enhanced knowledge of safety professionals adopting intervention strategies that go beyond regulatory compliance. These combined efforts have contributed to the protection of workers from safety and health hazards in an ever-changing work environment.

> US businesses spent in excess of $60 billion to compensate injured workers for disabling, nonfatal workplace injuries in 2016.

There are many opportunities and challenges surrounding workplace safety and health. In a study conducted by Liberty Mutual (2016), the insurance company created a workplace safety index. This safety index identifies the leading causes and direct cost of workplace accidents. The insurer suggests the ten leading causes of workplace injuries and illness account for 86 percent of the total estimated workers' compensation direct costs nationwide. According to NIOSH (2015), workplace hazards continue to inflict a tremendous toll on the nation in terms of human and economic cost. NIOSH also recognizes efforts to improve workplace safety will largely depend on collaborative efforts and actions of employers, employees, NIOSH partners, state and local governments, industry, labor, academia, and community organizations.

This information reported by NIOSH and Liberty Mutual supports the claim made by Geller (2005) related to the need for organizational leaders to incorporate the concepts of empowerment, empathy, and emotion into the work environment in an attempt to improve the safety culture within their organizations.

In addition to the social costs, workplace injuries and illnesses have a major impact on an employer's bottom line. The Liberty Mutual Workplace safety index (2016) indicates that US businesses spent in excess of $60 billion to compensate injured workers for disabling, nonfatal workplace injuries. This is an estimated cost of more than a billion dollars a week. There are also indirect costs associated with workplace injuries; these include costs associated with training replacement employees, accident investigations and implementation of corrective measures, lost productivity, repairs of damaged equipment and property, and lower employee morale and absenteeism.

In addition, the Occupational Safety and Health Administration has recently adjusted the penalty structure. Penalties for violations classified as serious, other-than-serious, and failure to abate have been increased from $7,000 to $12,471, and for willful and repeated violations, the penalties have increased from $70,000 to $124,709. The direct costs associated with workplace accidents and the cost of OSHA noncompliance fines create a critical productivity oversight and have a direct impact on an organization's profitability. These costs essentially represent a sunk cost: payments are made, and nothing is gained in return. With the cost of workers' compensation at an all-time high and OSHA noncompliance fines increasing, the time is ripe for organizational leaders to embrace building strong, resilient, and sustainable organizational cultures that will ultimately contribute to a safe, healthy, and productive workforce.

## Leadership That Walks the Talk

Traditionally, leaders are viewed as the head of the organization, but more recent literature is now describing the concept of leadership throughout the organization. Inspirational leaders are those in the organization who can inspire the others around them to exceed their personal best. Such leaders are tenacious, committed, and driven by a passion and sense of personal responsibility, not rules and regulations. They are open to new ideas, always pushing the envelope, yet watching and observing. They are people catalysts, coaching and guiding, benevolent yet demanding, and revered for their knowledge. They are problem solvers and constant communicators, fun loving and friendly. In the area of personal integrity, values pertaining to honesty and fairness are mentioned in every study. Kouzes and Posner (1995) found that honesty was ranked first among the characteristics of admired leaders, followed by being forward looking (setting a vision) and having the ability to inspire (motivating people to follow the vision).

Specific leadership principles and strategies are needed to empower a workforce to become self-accountable for injury prevention and actively care for the safety and health of employees. Organizational leaders of people-centered safety cultures demonstrate the following traits:

1. A strong commitment from the CEO and all levels of leadership to being a great place to work by supporting an employee-first strategy, manifesting the belief that employees are indispensable to the success of the business
2. Active communication platforms between employees and leadership, leveraging a two-way system of communication of information aligned with high levels of trust that allow all aspects (positive and negative) of any issue(s) to be presented without retribution
3. A lack of titles, labels, and status distinctions to create a workplace that is a work environment where all employees are valued
4. A work environment where employees are empowered and as a result take pride in their jobs, their team, and their organization (Black and La Venture 2015, p. 51)

It is important to distinguish between managers who hold people accountable and leaders who inspire people to be responsible or self-accountable (Geller 1999). While managers are assigned their supervisory position, leaders earn their role through interpersonal interaction. Geller (2008) demonstrated that leaders who use a people-centered approach to safety bring out the best in employees by showing them intrinsic consequences of meaningful work. Such leaders inspire employees to be accountable by

1. demonstrating humility;
2. acknowledging the contributions of others;
3. accepting personal responsibility for failure;
4. promoting a learning culture;
5. demonstrating optimistic success-seeking strategies over pessimistic failure-avoiding tactics;
6. making rigorous and discriminating decisions that impact the business positively with employees at the center, rather than ruthless and indiscriminate personal decisions; and
7. encouraging self-motivation (p. 29).

While managers are assigned their supervisory position, leaders earn their role through interpersonal interaction.

## Transparency and Open Communication

Top companies open the books—literally—for all their people, providing transparency and sharing financial and organizational performance information on a regular basis throughout the organization. People-centered safety cultures practice full transparency—sharing profit and loss data, productivity statistics, safety and health statistics, cash-flow challenges, stock values, investment strategies, and other financial information with all their people. They want everyone to understand what it takes to run the business and how much it costs. In addition, they equip employees with the information and tools they'll need to cut costs and increase productivity.

Communication is vital for organizational success. Open communication becomes the heart of the organization through the members' forging relationships with key constituents, developing trust, and circulating critical data, ideas, challenges, and solutions. Open communication means much more than extolling management's sanitized version of reality in newsletters, slogans, and videos; it means telling the truth about the business by giving all people access to the financial information and data the organization is using for decision-making and forecasting.

Open communication is an important theme for creating a safety culture and learning culture. For a people-centered safety culture, it is important that leaders, managers, and supervisors practice open communication (Hofmann and Stetzer 1998; Kath, Marks, and Ranney 2010). Employees must be able to discuss issues cooperatively with managers and peers without fear of retaliation. Any issues raised by personnel have to be communicated openly to other colleagues across the site (Gibbons, von Thaden, and Wiegmann 2006). Similarly, a people-centered safety culture requires transparency through open dialogue operationalized through multiple channels of communication. Safety cultures are reinforced by communication processes and systems that capture and share and evolve relevant knowledge across the organization (Littlejohn, Lukic, and Margaryan 2014).

Open communication becomes the heart of the organization through the members' forging relationships with key constituents, developing trust, and circulating critical data, ideas, challenges, and solutions.

Multiple open channels of communication should be in place to allow for effective and multidirectional information flow. Effective systems should be implemented to capture and share relevant knowledge across the company (Littlejohn et al. 2014). Work group meetings, customer contacts, training seminars, quarterly plant meetings, meetings with shift representatives or liaisons, and other face-to-face sessions all represent key two-way channels of communication. Managing, learning from, and acting on the knowledge and wisdom generated by this ongoing exchange can make organizational communication a bottom-line business result. The more people know, the better they will perform. Communication keeps employees from reinventing processes and procedures and facilitates organizational learning. To achieve results, open communication requires ongoing systems and processes designed to provide and capture reliable information on a real-time basis. When communication is kept in the open, problems and issues can be identified early and addressed quickly, thereby saving time and money.

Open communication requires strong leadership and a deep level of commitment among all managers, supervisors, and corporate executives. Walking the talk on the production floor, as well as in the corporate handbook, is essential. Leadership is practicing respect for people. Being a good communicator means being a good listener. Good leaders listen first, using active listening skills and a genuine desire to know how things are working (Black and La Venture 2015; Geller and Wiegand 2005). Leaders need to pay close attention to symbolic communication as well. Simple acts—emptying garbage or sweeping the sidewalk, for example—communicate volumes about respect for people and the tasks they perform. Open communication builds relationships with employees.

## Trust above All Else

Trust is defined as the willingness to be vulnerable to the actions of another (De Dreu, Koole, and Steinel 2000). Trust is essential to collaboration, building connections, and helping develop healthy relationships in the workplace. Trust affects our perceptions, assumptions, attitudes, behaviors, cooperation, and overall performance in an organization.

Trust is the product of relationships and connections between individuals, between top management and entry-level employees, between organizations and stakeholders, and between organizations and government. A culture of trust in an organization focused on safety begins with trust among top leadership, which facilitates strategy implementation. If the leadership team members trust each other, they can more easily build trust with their employees and gather the necessary buy-in to move the organization in the right direction (Bazerman, Curhan, Moore, and Valley 2000).

People (employees) are disposed toward fairness, a necessary condition for trust and trustworthiness. This tendency toward trust and reciprocity is balanced by a willingness to punish those who fail to act fairly, even at a cost to themselves. Cultural variations are very likely and condition the degree to which people are willing to trust others (Fichman 2003). With unconditional trust—in which shared values create a common bond—a different scenario occurs. People begin to feel that they are not merely coworkers or business acquaintances but colleagues, friends, or team members. In other words, although the presence of conditional trust allows a group to work toward a common goal, the existence of unconditional trust can fundamentally change the quality of the relationship and can convert a group into a team.

Conversely, when there is a lack of aligned core values or investment in the employee relationship, people are less likely to cooperate. There is no assurance of shared values that would orient the parties to the future, and as such relationships are less likely to be positive (Jones and George 1998). If individuals do not trust and respect each other, passion may not exist throughout the organization, and employees may feel some pride for their employer, but the organization will not be a family. The working environment is unlikely to be harmonious.

Unconditional trust also promotes seven kinds of social processes that can lead to the development of synergistic team relationships in an organizational setting. In turn, these can lead to superior performance. These organizational structures incorporate

- broad role definitions;
- communal relationships;
- high levels of confidence in others;
- help-seeking behavior;
- the free exchange of knowledge and information;
- a subjugation of personal needs and ego for the greater common good; and
- high levels of involvement (Jones and George 1998).

Companies need to provide high-quality, affordable products and services at competitive prices. People-centered safety cultures build trust and interdependence. Employees know what is going on and they see the important role that they play for the total success of the organization. Safety, health, and environmental training and standards of performance must be maintained and available to all employees. High levels of integrity are required. Managers and supervisors must have the courage and commitment to go into their organizations talking with, listening to, and developing safety improvements by listening to their employees and leveraging a people-centered approach to safety (Knowles 2015).

## Finding—and Keeping—the Right Employees

Winning companies place a premium on recruiting, hiring, and training highly talented people. Hires that are not an organizational fit are costly, so people-centered organizations want to get it right the first time. Organizations should seek to recruit and select individuals who have superior attitudes, values, competencies, motivation and commitment to work safely on their jobs. People-centered safety organizational cultures embrace recruitment and hiring practices that identify candidates that demonstrate the ability to work safely. The more rigorous and comprehensive recruitment and selection practices are, the greater the opportunity to create a safe working environment. New employees must know how to prevent injuries in the workplace. Organizations with a people-centered approach to safety mentor and train employees effectively (Leffakis and Schoff 2012).

Hytter (2007) demonstrated that workplace factors such as rewards, leadership style, career opportunities, training and development of skills, physical working conditions, and work–life balance have an indirect influence on retention. Several other factors also influence employee engagement and retention: the existence of challenging and meaningful work, opportunities for advancement, empowerment, responsibility, managerial integrity and quality, and new opportunities or challenges (Birt, Wallis, and Winternitz 2004). Walker (2001) also identified seven factors that encouraged retention, which were identified as

1. compensation and appreciation of the work performed;
2. the provision of challenging work;
3. opportunities to learn;
4. positive relationships with colleagues;
5. recognition of capabilities and performance contributions;
6. a good work–life balance; and
7. good communication within the organization.

## High-Performance Organizations (HPOs) Exercise the Right Human Resources (HR) Practices

Whether an organization is high performing depends on the mental models of its HR team. The mental models that HR professionals form may affect their effectiveness at work, the workplace experiences of their employees, the strategies and practices of their firms, and the professionalism of HR as a strategic partner in the organization (Labedz and Lee 2011). Pfeffer (2005) suggests that diagnosing and changing mental models held within organizations may be the most important task facing HR.

Changing mental models through critical self-reflection on behavior may help HR and leadership build relationships with employees, promote a healthy organizational culture, and avoid costly turnover. HPOs are committed to providing stable work environments for their employees, with equal opportunity for learning, personal growth, and development. They implement this by building relationships and treating their employees with respect and a caring attitude. The leaders and HR professionals of an HPO understand the importance of cultivating healthy environments and developing relationships with their employees, connecting with them, and connecting people to what is important in their own lives (Hassan 2007).

## Communities of Work

Communities of work tend to behave as flexible networks of people in which the organizational identity provides the glue. Individuals are socialized by and identify with these communities of work. People belonging to a community of work permanently face a complex balancing act across four dimensions:

1. Organizational values shape the community of work, connect necessary talents to the organization, and provide the groundwork for a specific identity.
2. Organizational values also lay the foundation for the organization to function as a societal actor. Organizations that are in a quest to embed corporate social responsibility in their strategy should make these values explicit to all stakeholders.
3. Organizational values provide the basis for the continuous creation of social capital inside and outside the organization.
4. Organizational values guide the behavior of employees in their interaction with stakeholders, inside and outside the organization (Metcalf and Benn 2012).

A satisfying work environment is created through supporting the employees on several fronts: competitive compensation, learning opportunities for career advancement, effective communication, and support of a psychologically healthy environment. An organizational culture aligned with these and other factors will result in happier employees who will work harder for the company and who will stay with the organization longer. Making the workplace pleasant for both employees and managers can help in employee retention and satisfaction, and this can lead to increased productivity, better communication, and improved profitability. Employees who enjoy their workplace are more open to embracing the corporate culture. They may also be more willing to share it and the company's goals with their colleagues and with customers.

## Aligned Operations and Work Environments Focus on Human Resources and Talent Development Practices

In people-centered safety cultures, the corporate structure and design, facilities and architecture, and behind-the-scenes services such as research and development, marketing, accounting, finance, and HR are carefully aligned to support people, relationships, and the process of working together (Osborne and Cowen 2002).

Making the workplace pleasant for both employees and managers can help in employee retention and satisfaction, and this can lead to increased productivity, better communication, and improved profitability.

HR plays a vital role in incorporating a value component into practices such as employee selection, appraisal, training and development, compensation, and reward systems (Hassan 2007). Investing in the human and social capital of employees is critical for today's organizations (Luthans, Vogelgesang, and Lester 2006). According to Denison (1990), organizations achieve greater effectiveness to the extent that their consistency in translating core values is developed within their HR policies and practices. Enhancing the employability of their employees fosters engagement from those employees, and organizations realize the added benefit of increased commitment and ownership from them as well (Luthans et al. 2006). Successful organizations employ innovative talent development practices to retain and support their employees (Zairi 1998).

Companies serious about obtaining profits by supporting their people will expend the effort needed to ensure that they recruit the right people in the first place. First, the organization needs to have a large applicant pool from which to select. Second, the organization needs to be clear about the most critical skills and attributes of the ideal candidate. Third, the skills and abilities sought must be carefully considered and should be consistent with the particular job requirements and the organization's approach to its market. Fourth, organizations should screen primarily for important attributes that are difficult to change through training and should emphasize the qualities that differentiate the candidates.

After they are hired, employees need strong reward systems and motivators to perform at their full ability and to develop a sense of ownership of the organization. Supervisors and managers must consider the importance of collaboration and sharing best practices when designing reward systems (Martins and Meyer 2012). Compensation and incentive plans, for example, are tied to department and organizational performance as well as to individual achievement. Therefore, a real source of competitive advantage is an organization's ability to create conditions that allow its members to experience unconditional trust (Jones and George 1998). Sustained profitable growth requires alignment between the goals and objectives of the employee value proposition and the total rewards strategy of the business. It also requires a culture that attracts and retains talented employees with the skills that the organization needs (Towers Watson 2014a; Towers Watson 2014b). People-process cultures manage the organization's intellectual and social capital—as well as its ability to listen and respond to customers and employees—as critical factors in developing effective asset and process HR development strategies. These strategies are focused on workforce development practices and smart business strategies that get results.

People-process cultures manage the organization's intellectual and social capital—as well as its ability to listen and respond to customers and employees—as critical factors in developing effective asset and process HR development strategies.

Organizational support requires the organizational culture to encourage new opportunities. It necessitates cooperation between departments to allow those employees who share a passion to embrace it (Martins and Meyer 2012). In people-centered safety cultures, the traditional corporate command and control barriers of hierarchy, rank, and status are replaced by processes and work environments that encourage, recognize, and reward teamwork, flexibility, and innovation (Geller and Wiegand 2005).

## Meaningful Work

Many employees today want to work for an organization that embraces and engages them as a whole person—work that gives the employees a sense of purpose and leaders who provide them with a clear purpose. Specifically, employees want to make decisions and perform work that is meaningful and psychologically rewarding and that helps fulfill their emotional and social needs (Sisodia et al. 2014). People are often not fully engaged at work, because they don't get to make meaningful decisions (Bakke 2013). This dissatisfaction is not uncommon; trust in others' ability to make meaningful decisions is rare (Bakke 2013, p. 203). The employees of HPOs know their work has inherent value and will positively affect the lives of others. This is demonstrated through HPO systems that are structured to reward employees for making positive contributions to their organization and to the broader community and for being responsible global citizens. These employees gain deep satisfaction from their work.

Business strategies and tactics combine with people skills to make innovation possible.

In people-centered safety cultures, the emphasis is on people, teamwork, and creativity, which offer rich opportunities for any organization. Business strategies and tactics combine with people skills to make innovation possible. People-first companies engage in continuous improvement and rigorous preventive maintenance and safety programs on a continuous cycle. Giving people the best tools available to get the job done places a premium on those people and on their performance.

## Change Responsiveness

Organizational leaders at all levels must communicate, educate, and reinforce the how, why, and what a people-focused safety culture looks like in terms of everyday work behaviors (Eaton and Kilby 2015). Leaders of people-centered safety culture organizations are astutely aware of this and leverage the "people first" and "together we achieve more" and "all people benefit" core values in daily operations as well as in long-term operational strategy.

Leaders inspire and motivate employees by clearly articulating a promising and compelling vision for the future. Empowerment is also an incentive system to reward employee performance (Charran 2005; Geller 2005; Gratton, Hope-Hailey, Stiles, and Truss 1999). By empowering employees, leaders can create a perception among employees that they are being taken seriously, listened to, and valued as members of the organization.

Leaders inspire and motivate employees by clearly articulating a promising and compelling vision for the future.

A willingness to serve people's real needs helps promote their development. This includes respect, conflict resolution, and paying attention to their legitimate interests, but also, a real appreciation for others, and acting with a sense of service and cooperation. (Men and Stacks 2013; Tidor and Morar 2013).

Employees are the voices who represent organizations and are the formal and informal "brand" of the organization and its leadership. Favorable employee perception of the organization helps build and protect organizational reputation. In today's ever-changing economic environment, employees are viewed as credible sources by external stakeholders (Men 2011; White, Vanc, and Stafford 2010; Grunig and Grunig 2002; Gotsi and Wilson 2001). The role of leadership communication in creating reputation should be emphasized, but maintaining such organizational reputation is based on the overall evaluation of a company based on an employee's experience in the company over time. Good reputation

Leaders can create a perception among employees that they are being taken seriously, listened to, and valued as members of the organization.

in the eyes of employees reinforces employee commitment to the values, beliefs, mission, and objectives of the company,, thereby impacting organizational performance and effectiveness. With the advent of today's social medial landscape, the employee's role as a communication asset should not be underemphasized (Men and Stacks 2013). Employees are increasingly empowered to communicate with others and initiate dialogues within the social and public domain. How the employees perceive the organization determines what they say publicly, and their opinions consequently become the basis of organizational perception. In summary, what employees say about the organization and their commitment to safety culture is perceived to be more credible and authentic than messages from senior management or the communications team within the organization (Manuele 2015; Kim and Rhee 2011).

## Organizational Resiliency

Organizational resiliency is the capacity of an organization to respond to and even prosper from negative circumstances (Luthans et al. 2006, p. 30). Many corporate leaders have used today's fast-paced business environment and the need to stay nimble as justification for massive layoffs, a heavy use of temporary or contract workers, skyrocketing executive compensation, and the elimination of employment security. Organizational resiliency is important to these leaders for continuous improvement and success in today's marketplace while avoiding measures such as massive layoffs. The ability of leaders to convey the message of hope to employees during the process of change results in significant organizational resiliency and the capacity for change in organizations (Manuele 2015; Geller 2005).

People-based core values help build cultural systems focused on safety that allow an organization to adapt to, facilitate, and create change, which makes these cultures and organizations more resilient (Norman, Luthans, and Luthans. 2005). A high-performance people-centered safety culture is able to galvanize its customers, suppliers, employees, and other key stakeholders to reduce threats and to better capitalize on opportunities.

The ability of leaders to convey the message of hope in the change process to employees results in a significant organizational resiliency and capacity for change in organizations

"Achieving competitive success through people involves fundamentally altering how we think about the workforce and the employment relationship," Pfeffer (1998) wrote. "It means achieving success by working *with* people, not by replacing them or limiting the scope of activities. It entails seeing the workforce as a source of strategic advantage, not just as a cost to be minimized or avoided" (p. 16).

Alignment, motivation, organization, and control can help an organization's performance, but only if the resulting actions fit an intelligent business strategy for the specific environment in which the firm operates.

Alignment, motivation, organization, and control can help an organization's performance, but only if the resulting actions fit an intelligent business strategy for the specific environment in which the firm operates. In a people-process culture, managing the organization's intellectual capital—its shared knowledge and its ability to listen and respond to its customers and its people—is a critical factor in developing effective work groups and smart business strategies.

The size of the organization can have a significant impact on how it reacts to change. Smaller organizations are frequently able to incorporate strategic management principles over the short term because of simple organizational structures that enable flexibility, facilitate communication, and reduce reactions to change (Flavel and Williams 1996). Conversely, larger organizations require detailed plans to communicate the goals of the larger organization to its employees. This can lead to a lack of flexibility and speed, as well as reduced responsiveness to the external environment (Connell 2001).

People-first safety cultures invest heavily in their people and in organizational learning by providing extensive, ongoing communication and rich opportunities for technical training, professional development, education, career planning, and growth (Black and La Venture 2015; Manuele 2015). Keeping individual business units small also facilitates agility in the people process. This is done for two strategic reasons: (1) to maintain the people-first culture and sense of community and (2) to develop highly focused business units with unique capabilities to serve a variety of mainstream and niche markets. The adaptive nature of people-centered safety culture organizations consistently and substantially outperforms more traditional corporate cultures in the areas of employee engagement, safety and health, revenue, workforce development, stock price, and net income.

Keeping individual business units small also facilitates agility in the people process.

## Responsible Global Citizenship

HPOs consist of globally responsible citizens who think critically and act wisely to advance the common good by responding to a wide range of stakeholders. Indeed, employees and organizations may start out by focusing on serving their own interests but evolve over time to serve purposes that transcend mere survival and self-interest. HPOs lead the way in corporate social responsibility. The stakeholders of these organizations adopt new corporate social responsibility values, apply new leadership styles, learn new skills, design more effective decision-making methods, and structure their organization accordingly (van Marrewijk 2004).

Van Marrewijk (2004) found that to enhance organizational performance, corporations need to focus on their social dimensions. This means that they need to strive to align both the individual and the collective interests of their employees and that the employees need to match their values, personal drivers, capacities, and ambitions with those of the workplace environment. "The alignment of personal and collective interests has become essential to contemporary business. No longer can companies treat their employees as resources, as numbers, as costs, but as human beings" (van Marrewijk 2004, p. 136). Employees should not be thought of as assets or liabilities, but rather as human beings who have social needs.

Global corporations take leadership in ensuring that proper safety standards are followed and enforced by all stakeholders. Moreover, change processes for values, patterns of thought, and beliefs that center on people are encouraged to foster a safety culture. Such leadership entails bringing all stakeholders to elaborating both a strategy and an action plan to diminish risk and increase focus on the greatest asset of the organization, the employees (Lorenzo, Esqueda, and Larson 2010).

## Organizational Ethics and Moral Fitness

Cultures that do not espouse a people-oriented focus to safety tend to be obsessed with short-term gains as opposed to long-term success. They hire and retain slash-and-burn leaders that view people as operating costs to be eliminated or restructured or as easily replaceable commodities. Status, ego, ingrained management behaviors, shareholder pressure, ethical lapses, greed, resistance to change, fear, control, poor processes, and system alignment all play a role in this leadership style (Giberson, Resick, Dickson, Mitchelson, Randall, and Clark 2009).

> There is inherent dignity associated with labor.

The application of a people-centered approach to safety is grounded in ethics approach and reciprocity that has important implications for safety professionals that have the following implications (Kapp and Parboteeah, as cited in Wachter 2011):

1. Employees have a right to just and equitable treatment; safety professionals have a responsibility to ensure that the right to employment does not endanger workers' physical welfare or jeopardize their moral integrity for all employees.
2. There is inherent dignity associated with labor, and employees are humans deserving dignity and are not merely means of production; thus, employers and employees should treat all people with consideration.
3. There is a moral imperative for safety professionals to care for others; safety professionals are required to remove hardships, regardless of the cost (p. 52).

Organizational cultures can also be classified as either ethical or unethical, which can be described through the company's policies, procedures, operating principles, and training (Schein 2010). For example, an artifact of an ethical culture may be a formal code of ethics or a business code of conduct that is based on conducting business honestly. Companies that invest in instilling ethical principles in their organizational culture demonstrate a strong commitment to their organizational values, empowerment, and trust. Ethics provides standards in an organizational culture and the framework for decision-making (Schein 2010). When organizations adopt an ethics-based approach, safety truly becomes a corporate value and cannot be constrained by or reduced to factors such as compliance, cost-benefit determinations, risk analyses, metrics, human error, or human behavior. In addition, organizations that use an ethics-based approach to safety management exhibit certain admirable characteristics (Tidwell 2000). For example, safety is valued and openly discussed; a set of obligations is shared by employer and employees, including duty of care owed to the employee, duty of mutual loyalty and

> Companies that invest in instilling ethical principles in their organizational culture demonstrate a strong commitment to their organizational values, empowerment, and trust.

respect, right of the employee to be informed of risk and right of the employee to refuse work where risk is unacceptable; and a formal code of ethical conduct is established by management, where everyone is held accountable for behavior against those ethical standards (Wachter 2011).

However, the top leaders must model ethical behavior and must show high levels of trust and respect to their fellow members of the culture. Training provides the mechanism for employees to internalize the company's ethics into their daily roles. Along with the trust and respect factors, strong organizational cultures with high ethical standards provide external confidential reporting mechanisms for addressing ethical violations (Giberson et al. 2009).

Training provides the mechanism for employees to internalize the company's ethics into their daily roles.

Employees at all levels need to develop a greater degree of ethical and moral fitness. The recognition of the common dignity and rights of every person implies an essential equality. Although each person is different, he or she is someone unique, unrepeatable, and different from all other people. Recognizing these essential qualities of equality, dignity, uniqueness, and diversity is central to a people-process culture.

Another characteristic of every human being is sociability, the capacity to associate and participate in social life. Most people recognize the capacity for the personal growth of human beings, including different aspects such as physical, logical, aesthetic, and moral growth. This shared belief in the dignity of every person and the capacity for personal growth, especially through the acquisition of virtues, is a basic feature of people-process cultures.

Caring for people and a sense of service generates loyalty.

To achieve a people-centered safety culture, it makes sense to include the management of business toward the common good as one of the features for an organizational humanizing culture instead of the management of business exclusively for profits, power, or any other particular interest if those are contrary to the common good. Caring for people and a sense of service generates loyalty. To summarize, recognition and respect for people and their human rights, care, service, and management toward the common good must include shared beliefs and values in a people-process culture. Management must demonstrate genuine care for their employees. Respecting people and their human rights also means integrity, with a steadfast attitude of trustfulness, keeping promises and fulfilling contacts, fairness, and organizational justice. In other words, people assist, support, and compete with one another through care and service (Grisez and Shaw 1998, p. 54).

## Corporate Social Responsibility and Sustainability

Russell, Haigh, and Griffiths (2007) determined that there are four distinct understandings of sustainability in organizations. Managers described sustainability in terms of

1. a corporation working toward long-term economic performance;
2. a corporation working toward positive outcomes for the natural environment;
3. a corporation that supports employees and social outcomes; or
4. a corporation with a holistic approach to conducting business within a community.

Doing business is no longer only making profits; organizations also have to behave in a socially responsible way. This responsibility includes not only environmental concerns, such as minimizing the organization's carbon footprint, but also must be expanded to include social system issues and international economic issues that must be highly integrated into the organization (Metcalf and Benn,2012). This quest for new and expanding responsibilities—often called *corporate social responsibility*—implies taking into account issues beyond the conventional scope of a business.

Corporate social responsibility refers to a growing appeal for organizations to take a broader social responsibility into account, behaving accordingly in an accountable manner, thus behaving as good corporate citizens (Schoemaker, Nijhog, and Jonker 2006). Roome (1992) further suggested that organizational change should be embraced and that an ethical approach to work should be developed among all employees for organizational sustainability. In this way, employees become the sustainability champions for the company and the community. This is a characteristic of people-process organizations. The main focus of corporate social responsibility is defining the corporate identity, making the company more transparent, trying to develop a system of accounting for one's actions (Driscoll and Hoffman 2000). Such linkage is a powerful mediator for successful implementation of sustainability or may even be an expression of it (Metcalf and Benn 2012).

The main focus of corporate social responsibility is defining the corporate identity, making the company more transparent, trying to develop a system of accounting for one's actions

The benefits of a people-centered approach to safety culture include (Górny 2014)

- comfortable working conditions that contribute to the good health of employees;
- adherence to occupation safety rules ensuring that employees are properly treated;
- unrestricted access to various forms of employment;
- protection against adverse consequences of the organization's activities (p. 49).

The sustainable people-process organization can be described as one that reflects the definition of the sustainable organization as those organizations that build on natural capital, enhance human and societal welfare, and contribute to appropriate economic and technological development (Russell and McIntosh 2011). These companies are innovative and people focused. Sustainability principles are embedded across the organization and within every aspect of the organizational culture. This is the manner in which people-process culture leaders conduct business through the adoption of long-term perspectives that support their employees, business, and communities.

The responsible organization can be seen as an organization trying to develop itself as an open system, based on its values and combining market orientation and social responsibility in an indivisible yet distinctive way. Determining which corporate social responsibility activities companies should carry out and which demands and expectations of the society should be taken into account is paramount. Accordingly, an organization is responsible to multiple stakeholders.

Corporate social responsibility includes the economic, legal, ethical, and philanthropic responsibilities of an organization derived from the claims of its various stakeholders (Lis 2012). Sustainability programs can provide a vehicle for engaging current and new employees (Boudreau and Ramstad 2005; Montiel 2008).

Companies with a people-centered approach to safety demonstrate value respect for people integrated with informational transparency. The organization's commitment is enhanced because there is a strong belief and acceptance of the values and goals of the organization, a willingness to undertake substantial efforts (by the leadership) on behalf of the organization, a strong desire to stay in the organization, and a commitment to the beliefs of the organization (Ortega-Parra and Sastre-Castillo 2013). These people-centered safety cultures display the following seven core values:

1. customer focused
2. results oriented
3. innovative
4. respectful of people
5. transparent
6. ethical
7. socially responsible

To ensure that a socially responsible approach effectively influences the development of a safety culture, an organization must identify the links and issues associated with the methods and scope of decision-making, such as:

- enterprise type, size, and the nature of the business;
- the place of business, including, in particular, the social, environmental and economic profiles of the geographic areas in which a company pursues its business activities;
- the profile of the labor force/employees carrying out work;
- the organization's mission, vision, core values, and codes of conduct;
- areas of interest for internal and external stakeholders; and
- decision-making structures in place in the organization and the nature of its decision-making processes (Górny 2014, p. 50).

A central consideration of company whose working conditions are satisfactory in organizational and technical terms is related to the following:

- tangible working conditions, that is, material factors (basic machinery and equipment, supplementary equipment, working facilities), physical factors (lighting, temperature, noise, mechanical vibrations, radiation), chemical, organic and biological factors (fumes, gases and aerosols)
- work organization covering the division of labor, work schedules and rules governing work performance
- economic and social aspects of the performance of work (Gorny 2014, p. 51).

A reference to social responsibility criteria also allows organizations to find alignment between these issues and safety culture improvements. Some of the crucial features of social responsibility linked to safety culture include (Gasięski and Piskalski 2004 as cited in Górny 2014):

- maintaining a good relationship between employees and management, respecting industry rules and regulations,
- ensuring good relations in the workplace,
- properly compensating employees for overtime,
- ensuring appropriate working conditions (including occupational safety),
- maintaining a proper relationship with local communities, and
- caring for the natural environment and recognizing its influence on working conditions (p. 52)

The goal of monitoring actions associated with social responsibility is to show all concerned that such actions are conducted as intended. Keeping continuous track of changes in the environment and changing expectations is intended to help identify new opportunities in the realm of social responsibility and to ensure the organization benefits in all aspects of its activities.

## Succession Planning and Leader Development

Organizational leadership influences employees' attitudes and behavior through empowering them. Employee empowerment refers to the process or state that can be characterized as competency or "skill" and the ability to make decisions and act accordingly (Men and Stacks 2013). Empowerment has been found to facilitate and embed the relationship between leadership and employee attitudes, specifically, job satisfaction and affective commitment to the organization (Men and Stacks 2013).

Knowing how people develop certainly helps organizations in designing their succession system and leadership development pipeline (Dai, Tang, and De Meuse 2011). By identifying the crucial leadership competencies for different positions at varying levels and matching these competencies with the right developmental experiences, organizations can reduce the time needed to prepare an individual for various leadership roles and positions, because there is little or no effort wasted on learning already-known skills. However, organizations are facing increasingly challenges in developing the full range of leadership competencies through traditional career ladder of experiences. Developmental job assignments do not have to be formal and hierarchical and can be accomplished without moving people into new jobs but instead by using lateral assignments. The direct implication of this finding is that organizations should develop their leaders early, leveraging the daily operations of the business (Dai et al. 2011). Organizations therefore should focus their leadership development efforts on the accurate early assessment and identification of potential leadership talent and start the development process early, assigning the right experiences to develop the right competencies at the right time (Dai et al. 2011).

Organizations therefore should focus their leadership development efforts on early assessment and identification of leadership talent potential accurately, start the development early, and assign the right experiences to develop the right competencies at the right time.

A safety culture matters. Not only does culture reside within individuals, but it is also the hidden force that drives most of our behavior both inside and outside organizations (Schein 2004). The essence of culture is not what is visible on the surface. It is the shared ways groups of people understand and interpret the world. Perry (2001) suggests that the more dynamic and turbulent the economy, the higher the potential for innovation, which provides a means for organizations with a people-process culture to survive and remain competitive. Innovation provides a means for their competitiveness, survival, and growth. Dyer (1998) found successful firms utilized a more professional culture that focused on individuals. Zahra, Hayton, and Salvato (2004) noted that innovative products, processes, tactics, and strategies were developed and brought to market more quickly by utilizing the

Innovation provides a means for competitiveness, survival, and growth.

collective knowledge of employees. The authors determined that building relationships with external sources and suppliers also provided information, knowledge, and advice, which were critical for innovation and continuous organizational learning. Creativity and innovation can be developed, sustained, and enhanced through formal and informal mechanisms such as training and education (Zahra et al. 2004).

Such knowledge generation can spark innovation and be cultivated in the following ways:

- reinforcing trust between coworkers
- improving communication between staff through office and building design
- practicing job rotation to facilitate communication through knowledge sharing and transfer
- creating a strong relationship between employees and leadership, decreasing hierarchical lines of communication and practicing open-door policies
- providing sufficient information systems
- providing effective rewards to reinforce knowledge
- increasing the level of employee participation in decision-making
- developing relationships with universities, technical colleges, and industry-based institutes to facilitate learning and increase social capital (Al-Alawi, Al-Marzooqi, and Mohammed 2007; Laforet 2013)

In today's global marketplace, it is essential to work effectively with others. When leaders are asked about challenges in the workplace, relationship issues with employees tend to be the concern most often noted (Brotheridge and Long 2007). The ability to derive value from human differences is a core skill for twenty-first-century leaders. Today's more global and diverse workforce requires a leader's awareness of cultural nuances, and as a result, requires flexible leadership focused on leveraging collaboration among and coaching of employees. All of these tasks require leaders to balance their own strong identities with the daily effort to understand that people (employees) are different from themselves. The concepts, testimony, and research presented in this chapter illustrate that when organizations emphasize an approach that combines a people-process culture with social responsibility, there is a host of benefits, including more productive and satisfied employees, stronger ties to the community, and greater corporate visibility (McWilliams and Siegel 2001).

## Review Questions

1. Provide an explanation of the organizational benefits when EHS professionals move beyond the traditional accident prevention methods involving engineering/technology based and administrative controls.
2. Explain the key elements of a people-centered safety culture as a subset of organizational culture and how this approach impacts organizational performance.
3. Explain the role of leadership principles and strategies and the significance of accountability in people-centered safety cultures.
4. Review the work practices and characteristics of psychologically healthy workplace and provide an argument that support this concept as an integral component of an organization's core values.
5. Explain the role organizational ethics and moral fitness play in people-centered-safety cultures and how such factors promote employee safe work practices.
6. Define the critical aspects of corporate social responsibility and elaborate how they are linked to sustainable people-centered safety cultures in organizations.

## References


Adler, P. S. (2001) "Market, Hierarchy, and Trust: The Knowledge Economy and the Future of Capitalism." *Organizational Science* 12(2): *215–34*.

Al-Alawi, A. I., N. Y. Al-Marzooqi, and Y. F. Mohammed. (2007). "Organizational Culture and Knowledge Sharing: Critical Success Factors." *Journal of Knowledge Management* 11(2): *22–42*.

American Psychological Association Center for Organizational Excellence (APA COE). (2015). "Resources for Employers." Washington, DC: APA.

American Psychological Association. (n. d. a). APA Center for Organizational Excellence: "The Role of Communication." Accessed September 1, 2016. http://www.apaexcellence.org/resources/creatingahealthyworkplace/theroleofcommunication/.

American Psychological Association. (n. d. b). APA Center for Organizational Excellence: "Employee Involvement." Accessed September 1, 2016. http://www.apaexcellence.org/resources/creatingahealthyworkplace/employeeinvolvement/.

American Psychological Association. (n. d. c). APA Center for Organizational Excellence: "Health and Safety." Accessed September 1, 2016. http://www.apaexcellence.org/resources/creatingahealthyworkplace/healthandsafety/.

Bakke, D. (2013). *The Decision Maker.* Seattle, WA: Pear Press.

*Bazerman, M. H.,* J. R. Curhan, D. A. Moore, and K. L. Valley. (2000). "Negotiation." *Annual Review of Psychology* 51: 279–314.

Becker, B. E., M. A. Huslid, and D. Ulrich. (2001). *The HR Scorecard. Boston*: Harvard Business School Press.

Bird, F., and R. J. Davies. (1996). *Safety and the Bottom Line. Loganville, GA.: Institute Publishing.*Birt, M., T. Wallis, and G. Winternitz. (2004). "Talent Retention in a Changing Workplace: An Investigation of Variables Considered Important to South African Talent." *South African Journal of Business Management* 35(2): 25–31.

Black, J., and K. La Venture. (2015). *The Human Factor to Profitability: Building a People-Centered Culture for Long-Term Success.* Austin, TX: River Grove Books.

Boudreau, J. W., and P. M. Ramstad. (2005). "Talent Ship, Talent Segmentation, and Sustainability: A New HR Decision Science Paradigm for a New Strategy Definition." *Human Resource Management* 44: 129–136.

Brotheridge, C. M., and S. Long. (2007). "The Real-world Challenges of Managers: Implications for Management Education." *Journal of Management Development* 26(9): 832–42.

Cardador, M. T., and D. E. Rupp. (2011). "Organizational Culture, Multiple Needs and the Meaningfulness of Work." In N. Ashkanasy, C. Wilderom, and M. Peterson (eds.), *The Handbook of Organizational Culture and Climate* (2nd ed.), 158–80. Los Angeles, CA: Sage.

Charran, R. (2005). "Ending the CEO succession crisis." *Harvard Business Review* 83(2): 72–81).

Chen, P. Y., and Y. Li. (2014). "Occupational Health and Safety." In A. Day, K. Kelloway E., and J. Hurrell (eds.), *Workplace Well-Being: How to Build Psychologically Healthy Workplaces*, 75–88. Hoboken, NJ: Wiley-Blackwell.

Colligan, M., J. W. Pennebaker, and L. R. Murphy. (1982). *Mass Psychogenic Illness: A Social Psychological Analysis.* Hillsdale, NJ: Erlbaum.

Connell, J. (2001). "Influence of Firm Size on Organizational Culture and Employee Morale." *Journal of Management Research* 1(4): *220*–32.

Cooper, M. D. (2000). "Towards a Model of Safety Culture." *Safety Science* 36(2): 111–36. http://doi.org/10.1016/S0925-7535(00)00035-7.

Covington, M. V., and C. L. Omelich. (1979). "It's Best to Be Able and Virtuous Too: Student and Teacher Evaluative Responses to Successful Effort." *Journal of Educational Psychology* 71: 688–700.

Covington, M. V. (1992). *Making the Grade. A Self-Worth Perspective on Motivation and School Reform.* Cambridge: Cambridge University Press.

Dai, G., K. Y. Tang, and K. P. De Meuse. (2011). "Leadership Competencies across Organizational Levels: A Test of the Pipeline Model." *Journal of Management Development* 30(4): 366–80.

Day, A., and K. D. Randell. (2014). "Definition and Components of a Psychologically Healthy Workplace." In A. Day, K. Kelloway, and J. Hurrell (eds.), *Workplace Well-Being: How to Build Psychologically Healthy Workplaces*, 10–26. Hoboken, NJ: Wiley-Blackwell.

De Dreu, C. K. W., S. L. Koole, and W. Steinel. (2000). "Unfixing the Fixed Pie: A Motivated Information-processing Approach to Interactive Negotiation." *Journal of Personality and Social Psychology* 79: 975–87.

Denison, D. R. (1990). *Corporate Culture and Organizational Effectiveness.* New York: Wiley.

*Driscoll, D. M.*, and W. M. Hoffman. (2000). *Ethics Matters. How to Implement Values-Driven Management.* Waltham, MA: Bentley College.

*Dyer, W. G.* Jr. (1998). "Culture and Continuity in Family Firms." *Family Business Review* 1(1): 37–50.

Eaton, D., and G. Kilby. (2015). "Does Your Organizational Culture Support Your Business Strategy?" *Journal for Quality and Participation* 37(4): 4–7.

Fichman, M. (2003). "Straining towards Trust: Some Constraints on Study Trust in Organizations." *Journal of Organizational Behavior* 24(2): 133–57.

Flavel, R. W., and J. Williams. (1996). *Strategic Management: A Practical Approach.* Sydney: Prentice Hall.

*Gehman, J.*, and L. K. Trevino. (2013). "Values Work: A Process Study of the Emergence and Performance of Organizational Values Practices." *Academy of Management Journal* 6(1): 84–112.

Geller, E. S. (2011). "People-powered Safety: Paradigm Shifts for an Actively Caring Work Culture." *Safety 2011 Professional Development Conference Proceedings.* Chicago: American Society of Safety Engineers.

Geller, E. S. (2008). "People-based Leadership: Enriching a Work Culture for World Class Safety." *Professional Safety* 53(3): 29–36.

Geller, E.S. (2005). *People-based Safety: The Source.* Virginia Beach, VA: Coastal Training and Technology Corporation.

Geller, E. S. (2003). "People-based Safety: The Psychology of Actively Caring." *Professional Safety,* 33–43.

Geller, E. S. (1999). "Sustaining Participation in a Safety Improvement Process: Ten Relevant Principles from Behavioral Science." *Professional Safety* 44(9): 24–29.

Geller, E. S. (1996). *The Psychology of Safety: How to Improve Behaviors and Attitudes on the Job.* Radnor, PA: Chilton Book.

Geller, E. S., and D. M. Wiegand. (2005). "People-based Safety: Exploring the Role of Personality in Injury Prevention." *Professional Safety*, 28–37.

Gibbons, A. M., T. L. von Thaden, and D. A. Wiegmann. (2006). "Development and Initial Validation of a Survey for Assessing Safety Culture within Commercial Flight Operations." *International Journal of Aviation Psychology* 16(2): 215–38.

Giberson, T. R., C. J. Resick, M. W. Dickson, J. K. Mitchelson, K. R. Randall, and M. A. Clark. (2009). "Leadership and Organizational Culture: Linking CEO Characteristics to Cultural Values." *Journal of Business Psychology* 24: 123–37.

Górny, A. (2014). "Influence of Corporate Social Responsibility (CSR) on Safety Culture." *Management* 18(1): 43–57.

Gotsi, M., and A. M. Wilson. (2001). "Corporate Reputation: Seeking a Definition." *Corporate Communications: An International Journal* 6(1): 24–30.

Gratton, L., V. Hope-Hailey, P. Stiles, and C. Truss (1999). "Linking Individual Performance to Business Strategy: The People Process Model." *Human Resource Management* 38(1): 17–31.

Grawitch, M. J., M. Gottschalk, and D. C. Munz. (2006). "The Path to a Healthy Workplace: A Critical Review Linking Healthy Workplace Practices, Employee Well-being, and Organizational Improvements." *Consulting Psychology Journal: Practice and Research* 58(3): 129–47.

Grawitch, M. J., G. E. Ledford, D. W. Ballard, and L. K. Barber. (2009). "Leading the Healthy Workforce: The Integral Role of Employee Involvement." *Consulting Psychology Journal: Practice and Research* 61(2): 122–35.

Grisez, G., and R. Shaw. (1998). *Beyond the New Morality: The Responsibility of Freedom.* Notre Dame, IN: University of Notre Dame Press.

*Grunig, J. E.,* and L. A. Grunig. (2002). "Implications of the IABC Excellence Study for PR educatIon." *Journal of Communication Management* 7(1): 34–42.

Hassan, A. (2007). "Human Resource Development and Organizational Values." *Journal of European Industrial Training* 31(6): 435–48.

Hofmann, D.A., and A. Stetzer. (1998) "The Role of Safety Climate and Communication in Accident Interpretation: Implications for Learning from Negative Events." *Academy of Management Journal* 41(6): 644–57.

Huang, H. J., and A. Dastmalchian. (2006). "Implications of Trust and Distrust for Organizations: Role of Customer Orientation in a Four-nation Study." *Personnel Review* 35(4): 361–71.

Hultman, K. (2005). "Evaluating Organizational Values." *Organization Development Journal* 23(4): 32–44.

Hytter, A. (2007). "Retention Strategies in France and Sweden." *The Irish Journal of Management* 28(1): 59–79.

Jones, G. R., and J. M. George. (1998). "The Experience and Evolution of Trust: Implications for Cooperation and Teamwork." *Academy of Management Review* 23(3): 531–46.

Kaczka, E., and R. Kirk. (1968). "Managerial Climate, Work Groups and Organizational Performance." *Administrative Science Quarterly* 12: 252–71.

Kalliath, T., and P. Kalliath. (2012). "Changing Work Environments and Employee Wellbeing: An Introduction. *International Journal of Manpower* 33(7): 729–37.

Kath, L. M., K. M. Marks, and J. Ranney. (2010) "Safety Climate Dimensions, Leader–Member Exchange, and Organizational Support as Predictors of Upward Safety Communication in a Sample of Rail Industry Workers." *Safety Science* 48(5): 643–50.

Kendall, K., and G. Bodinson. (2010). "The Power of People in Achieving Performance Excellence." *The Journal for Quality and Participation* 33(2): 10–14.

Kim, J.-N., and Y. Rhee. (2011). "Strategic Thinking about Employee Communication Behavior (ECB) in Public Relations: Testing the Models of Megaphoning and Scouting Effects in Korea." *Journal of Public Relations Research 23*(3): 243–68.

Knowles, R. N. (2015). "Partner-centered Safety: A New Approach to Achieving Sustainable, Safety Excellence." *EHS Today.* http://ezproxy.lib.uwstout.edu/login?url=http://search.proquest.com/docview/1673315520?accountid=9255.

Kouzes, J. M., and B. Z. Posner. (1995). *The Leadership Challenge: How to Keep Getting Extraordinary Things Done in Organizations.* San Francisco: Jossey-Bass.

Krause, T. R. (2005). *Leading with Safety.* Hoboken, NJ: Wiley-Interscience.

Krueger, C. (1994). *The People Process Culture Handbook.* Phillips Plastics Corporation.

*Labedz, C. S.,* and J. Lee. (2011). "The Mental Models of HR Professionals as Strategic Partners." *Journal of Management & Organization* 17(1): 56–76.

Laforet, S. (2013). "Innovation Characteristics of Young and Old Family-owned Businesses." *Journal of Small Business and Enterprise Development* 20(1): 204–24.

Leffakis, Z. M., and R. Schoff. (2012). "Stop Doing Things Dangerously." *Industrial Engineer* 44(6): 48–53.

Liberty Mutual Research Institute for Safety. (2016). *2016 Liberty Mutual Workplace Safety Index.* http://www.libertymutualgroup.com/researchinstitute.

Lis, B. (2012). "The Relevance of Corporate Social Responsibility for a Sustainable Human Resource Management: An Analysis of Organizational Attractiveness as a Determinant in Employees' Selection of a (Potential) Employer." *Management Revenue* 23(3): 279–95.

Littlejohn, A., D. Lukic, and A. Margaryan. (2014). "Comparing Safety Culture and Learning Culture." *Risk Management* 16(4): 272–93.

Litwin, G. H., and R. A. Stringer. (1968). *Motivation and Organizational Climate.* Boston: Division of Research, Graduate School of Business Administration, Harvard University.

Lorenzo, O., P. Esqueda, and J. Larson. (2010). "Safety and Ethics in the Global Workplace: Asymmetries in Culture and Infrastructure." *Journal of Business Ethics* 92(1): 87–106.

Luthans, F., G. R. Vogelgesang, and P. B. Lester. (2006). "Developing the Psychological Capital of Resiliency." *Human Resource Development Review* 5(1): 25–43.

Manuele, F. A. (2015). "Culture Change Agent." *Professional Safety* 60(12): 38–44.

Manuele, F. A. (1993). *On the Practice of Safety.* New York: Van Nostrand Reinhold.

Martin, J. (2005). "Organizational Culture." In N. Nicholson, P. G. Audia, and M. M. Pillutla (eds.), *The Blackwell Encyclopedia of Management (2nd ed., Vol. 11),* 272–278. Malden, MA: Blackwell.

Martins, E. C., and H. W. J. Meyer. (2012). "Organizational and Behavioral Factors that Influence Knowledge Retention." *Journal of Knowledge Management* 16(1): 77–96.

Mathis, T. L., and S. M. Galloway. (2013). *STEPS to Safety Culture Excellence.* Hoboken, NJ: John Wiley & Sons.

McDermott, R., and C. O'Dell. (2001). "Overcoming Cultural Barriers to Sharing Knowledge." *Journal of Knowledge Management* 5(1): 76–85.

McKinnon, R. C. (2007). *Changing Safety's Paradigms.* Lanham, MD.: Government Institutes.

McWilliams, A., and D. Siegel. (2001). "Corporate Social Responsibility: A Theory of the Firm Perspective." *Academy of Management Review* 26(1): 117–27.

Men, L. R. (2011). "Exploring the Impact of Employee Empowerment on Organization-Employee Relationship." *Public Relations Review* 37(4): 435–37.

Men, L. R., and D. W. Stacks. (2013). "The Impact of Leadership Style and Employee Empowerment on Perceived Organizational Reputation." *Journal of Communication Management* 17(2): 171–92.

Metcalf, L., and S. Benn. (2012). "Leadership for Sustainability: An Evaluation of Leadership Ability." *Journal of Business Ethics* 112(3): 369–84.

Momeni, N. (2009). "The Relation between Managers' Emotional Intelligence and the Organizational Climate They Create." *Public Personnel Management* 38(2): 35–48.

Montiel, I. (2008). "Corporate Social Responsibility and Corporate Sustainability." *Organization & Environment* 21: 245–69.

National Institute for Occupational Safety and Health. (2015). *NIOSH Fact Sheet.* https://www.cdc.gov/niosh/docs/2013-140/pdfs/2013-140.pdf

Norman, S., B. Luthans, and K. Luthans. (2005). "The Proposed Contagion Effect of Hopeful Leaders on the Resiliency of Employees and Organizations." *Journal of Leadership & Organisational Studies* 12(2): 55–64.

Occupational Safety and Health Administration. (2016). "OSHA Penalties Adjusted as of August 2016." https://www.osha.gov/penalties/.

Olson, J. M., and M. P. Zanna. (1993). "Attitudes and Attitudes Change." *Annual Review of Psychology* 44: 117–54.

Ortega-Parra, A., and M. A. Sastre-Castillo. (2013). "Impact of Perceived Corporate Culture on Organizational Commitment." *Management Decision* 51(5): 1071–83.

Osborne, R. L., and S. S. Cowen. (2002). "High Performance Companies: The Distinguishing Profile." *Management Decision* 40(3): 227–31.

Perry, P. M. (2001). "Holding Your Top Talent." *Research Technology Management* 44(3): 26–30.

Peterson, D. (2001). *Authentic Involvement.* Itasca, IL: National Safety Council.

Petersen, D. (2003). *Techniques of Safety Management: A System Approach.* Des Plaines, IL: American Society of Safety Engineers.

Pfeffer, J. (1998). *The Human Equation: Building Profits by Putting People First.* Boston: Harvard Business School Press.

Pfeffer, J. (2005). "Changing Mental Models: HR's Most Important Task." *Human Resource Management* 44(2): 123–28.

Pizzi, L. T., N. I. Goldfarb, and D. B. Nash. (2001). "Promoting a Culture of Safety." *Making Health Care Safer: A Critical Analysis of Patient Safety Practices*, 447.

Repetti, R. L. (1987). "Individual and Common Components of the Social Environment at Work and Psychological Well-being." *Journal of Personality and Social Psychology* 52(4): 710–720.

Rokeach, M. (1973). *The Nature of Human Values.* New York: The Free Press.

Roome, N. (1992). "Developing Environmental Management Systems." *Business Strategy and the Environment* 1(1): 11–24.

Russell, S. V., N. Haigh, and A. Griffiths. (2007). "Understanding Corporate Sustainability: Recognizing the Impact of Different Governance Systems." In. S. Benn and D. Dunphy (eds.), *Corporate Governance and Sustainability*, 36–56). Abington, MA: Routledge.

Russell, S. V., and M. McIntosh. (2011). "Changing Organizational Culture for Sustainability." In N. Ashkanasy, C. Wilderom, and M. Peterson (eds.), *The Handbook of Organizational Culture and Climate (2nd ed.)*, 393–411). Los Angeles: Sage.

Sagiv, L., S. H. Schwartz, and S. Arieli. (2011). "Personal Values, National Culture, and Organizations." In N. Ashkanasy, C. Wilderom, and M. Peterson (eds.), *The Handbook of Organizational Culture and Climate (2nd ed.)*, 515–37). Los Angeles: Sage.

Saylor Foundation. (2015). *Organizational Behavior.* Washington, DC: Saylor Foundation. http://www.saylor.org/site/textbooks/Organizational%20Behavior.pdf.

Schein, E. [H.] (2010). *Organizational Culture and Leadership* (4th ed.). San Francisco: Jossey-Bass.

Schein, E. [H.] (2004). *Organizational Culture and Leadership (3rd ed.).* San Francisco: Jossey-Bass.

Schneider, B. (1985). "Organizational Behavior." *Annual Review of Psychology* 36(1): 573–611.

Schoemaker, M., A. Nijhof, and J. Jonker. (2006). "Human Value Management: The Influence of the Contemporary

Developments of Corporate Social Responsibility and Social Capital on HRM." *Management Revue* 17(4): 448–65.

Sisodia, R., D. Wolfe, and J. Sheth. (2014). *Firms of Endearment: How World-Class Companies Profit from Passion and Purpose.* Upper Saddle River, NJ: Pearson Education.

Tidor, A., and L. Morar. (2013). "Changing Organizational Culture for Enterprise Performance." *Economic and Social Development Conference Proceedings, 2nd International Scientific Conference,* 1361–68.

Tidwell, A. (2000). "Ethics, Safety and Managers." *Business and Professional Ethics Journal* 19: 161–80.

Towers Watson. (2014a). "2014 Talent Management and Rewards Study: Making the Most of the Employment Deal." New York: Towers Watson.

Towers Watson. (2014b). "The Targeted Employee Value Proposition: Drive Higher Performance through Key Talent and Differentiated Rewards." New York: Towers Watson.

U.S. Department of Labor, Bureau of Labor Statistics. (2015). *National Census of Fatal Occupational Injuries in 2014 (preliminary results).* http://www.bls.gov/news.release/pdf/cfoi.pdf.

Van Marrewijk, M. (2004). "The Social Dimension of Organizations: Recent Experiences with Great Places to Work Assessment Practices." *Journal of Business Ethics* 55(2): 135–46.

Wachter, J. K. (2011). "Ethics: The Absurd yet Preferred Approach to Safety Management." *Professional Safety* 56(6): 50–57.

Walker, J. W. (2001). "Zero Defections?" *Human Resource Planning* 24(1): 6–8.

Weymes, E. (2005). "Organizations which Make a Difference: A Philosophical Argument for the 'People Focused Organization.'" *Corporate Governance* 5(2): 142–58.

White, C., A. Vanc, and G. Stafford. (2010). "Internal Communication, Information Satisfaction, and Sense of Community: The Effect of Personal Influence" *Journal of Public Relations Research* 22(1): 65–84.

Zahra, S. A., J. C. Hayton, and C. Salvato. (2004). "Entrepreneurship in Family vs. Non-family Firms: A Resource-based Analysis of the Effect of Organizational Culture." *Entrepreneurship Theory and Practice* 28(4): 363–81.

Zairi, M. (1998). "Managing Human Resources in Healthcare: Learning from World Class Practices. Part 1." *Health Manpower Management* 24(2): 48–57.

CHAPTER 4

# LEADING TO SUSTAINABLE SUCCESS

Patrick Frazee

## Learning Objectives

After studying this chapter, the reader will be able to:

1. Recognize the impact of workplace culture
2. Identify a strong EHS culture in a company
3. Assess the importance of building relationships
4. Identify the desired role for an EHS professional within an organization
5. Identify a sound practical approach to making recommendations

## Key Terms

**Change, graduates, relationships, organization, policies, procedures**

## Abstract

Environmental health and safety (EHS) is a profession that has a mission to help and protect people and the environment. When EHS graduates begin their professional careers (i.e., the first job), it is not uncommon for them to want to "change the world." This is not only a good thing but something to encourage. Accidents still happen where workers are still getting hurt; the environment still needs to be protected, and there is still much room for improvement. The challenge is to be able to actually make improvements. Change is always easier said than done. Regardless of which profession we are talking about, change is never easy. There often seems to be a built-in resistance to change. Change usually means costs in terms of both money and time—especially up front. To be effective in making changes, one needs to be a good salesperson. One has to show how the change will positively affect others and the organization where he or she works. It is easy to enter a situation or a new job and see lots of things that are wrong and then tell everyone what is wrong and make recommendations or suggestions to fix the problems. However, to fix any problem, one must first understand what the real problem is, not just the surface issues. This chapter is intended to provide EHS professionals with skills to become effective agents for change and effective leaders in the EHS profession. Recent EHS graduates arrive at their new jobs filled with fresh ideas and lots of energy and enthusiasm. They arrive with a fresh set of eyes and are on the lookout for ways to improve the current program and establish themselves as professionals. In addition, they hope to have that satisfaction that comes from knowing that they have helped others. In short, they want to make a difference. However, before they jump into the swamp with both feet, it is important to create a well-thought-out plan that ensures success, both for the short term as well as the long term.

It is important to keep in mind that someone other than the EHS professional has the authority, the power, and the will to make changes. This means that when the newly hired EHS person wants something done, it will probably cost money, and because the EHS professional is not the plant manager or the CEO or the person in charge, he or she will have to rely on someone else to approve the recommendations and to make sure they are implemented and maintained.

## Introduction: Organizational Structure

Understanding the organizational structure is an important first step at the start of a new job. Whether this is a person's first job or a new job with a different company or organization does not matter. It is important for either situation and for many reasons. First, by understanding the organizational structure one can see how he or she fits into it and how others that one must work with also fit into the overall scheme of things. Understanding reporting relationships will help one understand how things work in the company. A good place to start is the structure at the location where one is working on a daily basis. But it is also important to look at the structure of the corporation as a whole. This will help in seeing the organizational structure and who is responsible for the different processes and activities in the organization. Why is this important? By understanding the organizational structure, one can identify whom to go to when something needs to get done, especially if the need is immediate. It will also give one an idea of how safety, health, and the environment fit into the organization's goals and objectives. Finding the organizational structure is usually easier today because organizational charts are available electronically. As one studies the organization's structure and hierarchy, one also should identify various goals, policies, missions, and objectives. These too will help show how EHS fits into this organization. It would be very helpful to identify those departments or teams that have responsibilities in the area of EHS, including their staff sizes. One very important aspect is finding out the responsibilities of immediate supervisors as well as his or her supervisor. This will help in understanding who the competitors are for the organization's limited time, dollars, and other resources.

## Culture

Next, understanding the culture in an organization is extremely important. This includes the culture in the organization both locally and at the corporate level. One of the easiest to understand definitions of culture is this: culture is the way things really are or how they really work in the organization. Many organizations have several stated goals and objectives and may say that those for safety, health, and the environment are the most important. Many companies may claim that safety is number one. However, in reality, safety's actual position may be number three, four, five, or even lower. Thus, by understanding the culture one can find out in reality where and how EHS fits in to an organization's priorities and the grand scheme of things. How can one find out the real value EHS has in an organization? It does not come from reading the policies and procedures but rather from talking to people and by observing how people react to certain situations.

> Culture is the way things really are or how they really work in an organization.

Speed limit enforcement is a good illustration of culture (see figure 4.1). In Michigan and many other states in the United States of America, the posted speed limit for many interstate expressways is 70 miles per hour. However, based on numerous informal surveys of Michigan drivers of all ages performed by the author, the actual speed limit is somewhere between 75 to 78 miles per hour. What this means is that before a policeman stops a driver, the vehicle speed has to exceed 75 miles per hour even though the posted limit is 70 miles per hour. In other states, it may be a little different. The real speed limit there may be 72 or 73 miles per hour. That is the culture for that state, and the suggestion is that drivers from that state know what the real speed limit is. Many college football fans are familiar with the long-time, very intense rivalry between the University of Michigan Wolverines and the Ohio State University Buckeyes. Can one imagine a Michigan driver crossing the state line into the neighboring state of Ohio for the first time? If that driver is not careful, he or she may find out the hard way what the real speed limit is in Ohio for someone who has a Michigan license plate. The same is true in an organization. The people working there know how things really work and whether the organization is really serious about the safety of its employees.

Figure 4.1
The "real" speed limit is a matter of local culture.

Now we will look at a simple example that is closer to home. Consider following this suggested scenario. Start with you entering an area where safety glasses and hearing protection are required. Make sure you are as inconspicuous as possible so that no one knows you are there. Just look around and see who is wearing safety glasses and hearing protection. Are people putting on their glasses when they see you coming or when they see the safety person coming? What happens when a member of management, such as the supervisor, comes into the area? Are workers putting on their hearing protection when they see someone approaching their work area? Or is everyone already wearing their hearing protection and safety glasses, including supervisors, engineers, and the plant manager? It may take a while to discover the real culture at a facility and probably a longer time to discover it at the corporate level, but be persistent and keep talking to others and observing people in your organization both locally and at higher levels. These activities are beneficial in learning how things really work in an organization. It does not take very long to find out by observation and conversations what the real culture is like in an organization. The more one engages in these types of activities, the more one will understand about the culture and the way things really are when it comes to EHS. Knowing the culture and the organization is very valuable when trying to make changes and improvements in the existing EHS programs and processes. It is important that one knows how EHS fits in with the priorities of an organization. This knowledge will help in determining how easy or difficult it will be to make changes.

Tom Brady was the manufacturing manager for the General Motors automotive metal stamping division. Plant managers at twelve large stamping plants reported to Tom. During a plant tour, Tom noticed that one stamping press operator was not wearing the proper gloves for protection from sheet metal lacerations. Tom walked up to the press, personally shut it off, and informed the supervisor that he could not turn the press back on until the operator had the appropriate personal protective equipment. This was a dramatic event because normally a person in Tom's position would give an order to a subordinate if he or she observed something that needed to be fixed. In the case, Tom took direct action. News of this incident spread like wildfire among the other stamping plants. The incident illustrates two important points. First, the culture at that plant prior to Tom's visit was one that considered productivity more important than safety. Even though safety was stated to be the number one priority and personal protective equipment (PPE) was required at that press, the real priority was productivity. The second point is that a member of top management initiated a change in the culture by his actions. He sent a strong message to the management at the plant and all the other plants under his control that safety is more important than productivity. What this organization learned that day was that although productivity is essential to a viable business, it is not acceptable to achieve success in productivity at the expense of safety. If production goals cannot be met safely, production will stop until the goals can be met safely.

It is not uncommon for a company to use several different measures to determine whether it is performing well and meeting its goals and objectives. This is another critical area for determining where EHS ranks in an organization. These key performance measures normally include cost, quality, productivity, and customer satisfaction. The EHS professional should look at where and how safety, health, and environmental issues are being measured. Is performance related to EHS issues considered one of the top measures? The key measurements may be displayed in a conference room or be the topic of discussion at regular meetings. It is relatively easy to find out if health, safety, and the environment are included in any posted performance measures. What if the EHS professional were to observe the postings in the plant manager's conference room? Are there any charts on the wall showing EHS data such as injury rates? Is there similar information in other areas of the organization, such as at the department level? It is also important to observe whether safety measures are openly and visibly displayed for anyone to see versus being kept in a notebook or on a computer system. Visibly displaying EHS performance all the way down to the plant level is a good indication that EHS has a high priority in this organization. Figure 4.2 shows an example of a chart that contains several key business performance measures. Note that a safety performance indicator is shown as the first measure. If a chart similar to this was displayed throughout an organization and was specific for a department or area, what message would it send about the importance of worker safety? What conclusions might one draw if one saw performance measures visibly displayed throughout an organization and EHS was not included in any of them? Measuring EHS performance and displaying it clearly is an indication of how important EHS is to the organization and its leaders.

The OSH professional should look at where and how where safety, health, and environmental issues are being measured. Is performance related to EHS issues considered one of the top measures?

Status of Key Performance Measures – Acme Widget Co.
YTD through June 2016

| Measure | Target | Actual | Status |
|---|---|---|---|
| Injury/Illness rate | 1.0 | 0.8 | |
| Cost per unit | $25 | $23 | |
| Quality (defects per 1000) | 0.5 | 0.7 | * |
| Satisfied Customers score | 95 | 89 | |
| Sales (units per month x 1000) | 7 | 7.5 | |

* Corrective action plan required

Figure 4.2
Status of key performance measures.

What about meeting agendas? Where is the topic of EHS placed in a management meeting? Normally, top management at a local organization will meet regularly—at least weekly—to discuss the key performance measures. Is EHS included in any of those meetings? What happens when there is a work-related injury? Who is notified of the injury, and when are they notified. What happens after the injury notification? Who investigates the incident? Who writes the report? Who receives a copy of the report? What action is taken after the investigation is completed? As one answers these questions, it becomes clearer and clearer how EHS ranks in an organization's priority list, and one will get a better and better picture of the safety culture in the organization and company.

There are a number of highly successful companies in the United States, such as Alcoa and DuPont, where top management requires that a report for every injury recorded on the Occupational Safety and Health Administration (OSHA) log be sent to the CEO's office. Many companies require the plant manager or someone of similar stature or title to report in person to the CEO about any serious injuries or incidents that occur at his or her plant. It is clear that these companies that have truly placed EHS as one of their top priorities are not only successful financially but are considered benchmark companies in the area of EHS.

There are many examples that show how management commitment can affect a company's overall performance in safety and health. One example is General Motors (GM), one of the world's largest automobile manufacturers. In the early 1990s, Paul O'Neill (72nd US secretary of treasury and previously CEO of Alcoa) joined the board of directors of General Motors (Frame 1994). Paul began asking questions about the company's safety performance and record. When he found out that injury and illness rates in GM were more or less average, he initiated a project within the company to improve its safety performance. Under the direction of Jack Smith (GM CEO at that time) and Harry Pearce (executive vice president), GM began a cultural change journey that engaged management at every level of the organization in the corporation's safety and health process (Simon and Frazee 2005). This top management commitment is still evident today under the leadership of Mary Barra, the current GM CEO. The results have been highly commendable. Since the mid-1990s, GM's injury/illness rates have decreased by over 95 percent (Barra 2016).

## Relationships

Another essential part of being a leader is developing relationships. No matter what one does, one will develop relationships with other people in an organization on a daily basis. Some may be better than others. But it is important to understand that each of us individually has a key role in determining how those relationships will turn out. We all need to recognize that in this field we will inevitably be working with people all the time. This means we will be working with people at all levels of the organization—people with different backgrounds and responsibilities and with different personal goals. After all, is it not people whom we are trying to help and protect? So we might as well make an effort to understand what motivates others' actions and how to communicate with them effectively. If we have an idea and the idea is worthwhile, we have to convince others of that. We have to get them on our side. If we do, we have a much better chance of seeing our idea become reality. We first have to communicate that idea to others in a way that convinces them that the idea makes sense and has some benefit. In the area of EHS, the benefit seems to be obvious. No one wants to be hurt or have their health jeopardized. What if an EHS professional has an idea that will improve the safety program or procedure at his or her organization and ultimately result in fewer injuries? The idea makes sense to the EHS professional, but now he or she has to make sure that it also makes sense also to his or her management, his or her peers, and the workers. If it does not make sense to any of these, chances are good that it is not going to work and will not be implemented. Having the idea make sense depends on how well the EHS professional communicates to others and how open others are to receiving the message.

The most important factor in successful communication and developing good relationships is trust. If there is little or no trust between two persons, there cannot be much of a relationship. If someone trusts you, there is a very good chance that they will listen when you talk with them. If they do not trust you, no matter how eloquent you are or how many facts you throw at them, in many cases it is unlikely that they will hear a word being said. One of the best ways to establish trust in a relationship is to be true to your word and always be honest; in other words, "walk the talk." Abraham Lincoln once said, "Honesty is the best policy." People can quickly see whether a person is sincere by what he or she does more than by what he or she says. The other important aspect of developing trust in this area of EHS is sending the "I care" message. What this means is that in all that an EHS professional says and does, he or she must demonstrate genuine care about the person he or she is speaking with as well as others. Here is an example to illustrate this idea.

> The most important factor in successful communication and developing good relationships is trust.

Let's say that you, the reader, are an EHS professional. You are observing employees working in an aerial platform. One of the workers has a harness on but is not tied off. You know that this situation not only violates both company policy and OSHA regulations but also poses a risk of a fall resulting in a serious injury. When the worker sees you, he attaches his lanyard to an anchor point. You wait for the platform to be lowered to ground level and begin speaking to the worker who had not tied off. What will you say to him? Will you discipline him? Should he be sent home without pay? What if you asked him about his family or loved ones? What if you told him you were concerned about his safety and didn't want him to get hurt? What approach do you think would be most appropriate to send the "I care" message? What approach do you think would be most effective in getting the employee to think about his own safety? If you let him know that you care about him and his safety, chances are good that you may have not only prevented a future injury but also gained a friend and ally in the safety arena. Next time you see him and talk with him, it is much more likely that he will be willing to listen to you. Getting workers to think about safety and to act safely when no one is looking is a significant achievement. Many workers throughout GM and Delphi have expressed the following thought when it comes to others telling them how to do their job: "Unless I sense that you care about me, I don't care what you are saying to me." It is not possible to overemphasize the importance of talking to workers on a daily basis to find out what's really going on in the organization. Workers need to view the EHS professional as someone who genuinely cares about their health and safety and is their ally, friend, and helper. If they trust the EHS professional, they will listen to him or her, but more importantly, they will talk to him or her. They will let the EHS professional know what is really going on at the worker level. They will tell him or her about their issues and concerns and about near miss incidents and conditions that could result in serious injury. These are gifts can be used to prevent future injuries. If one listens to them and their concerns and helps them make their jobs easier and safer, they will in turn make the EHS professional's job easier.

A very important aspect of developing relationships with the workers is understanding why workers perform unsafe acts. It is safe to say that no worker comes to his or her job on a daily basis intending to get hurt. If an EHS professional walks around his or her organization and watches workers, he or she will most likely observe unsafe acts regularly. It is easy to walk up to an employee and advise them that they just did something that was unsafe, but it is more important to find out why. Usually, there are lots of reasons why workers perform unsafe acts. A sample list of those reasons gathered from workers is shown below:

- Time pressure due to the production schedule or management
- "I arrived at the job but didn't have the right tools (parts), so I improvised."
- "The process or machine design prevents me from doing the job according to the safe procedure."
- "It's too difficult to do it the right way."
- "It takes too long to do it the right way."
- "I wasn't thinking"; "I was thinking about some personal problems."
- "This machine is constantly breaking, and it takes too long to lock it out."
- A faulty or incomplete work procedure
- "We've always done it this way."
- "This is the way the other workers taught me."
- "When I get this job done, I can go on break."
- "I know what I'm doing. I've done this job a hundred times before."

If one has a good working relationship with the employees, they will tell him or her about why they do a job a certain way. Often the EHS professional will find out that there is a deeper cause that when addressed or fixed will eliminate the need or desire to perform that unsafe act. The result can be the prevention of an injury.

If one has a good working relationship with the employees, they will tell him or her about why they do a job a certain way.

In many organizations workers are represented by a union. Establishing a good working relationship with union representatives can be extremely beneficial in getting changes made to improve the program. The concept of improved worker health and safety is a win-win situation for the EHS professional, the company, the union, and the workers. It is important to recognize that union representatives are elected, and that means that sometimes politics are involved in a situation.

Relationships with other management organizations are also important. There are many companies or departments in those companies that view EHS as a burden, a thorn in the side. The EHS professional will usually be interacting with departments such as engineering, purchasing, maintenance, shipping and receiving, and others. Each department has a specific function with goals and objectives. If the plant manager sends the message that EHS is one of the top priorities, then it should also be one of the top priorities for the individual departments in an organization. These departments are the ones who will get things done at a local organization. Establishing and maintaining a good working relationship with each of them is critical for getting changes implemented. If one identifies a new high-tech safety feature for forklifts, he or she needs to get the approval from the purchasing department and the shipping and receiving department in order to get it installed in the forklifts. The shipping and receiving department owns and operates the plant's forklifts, and they have to be convinced that the new device is not going to slow down the flow of materials. They also have to make sure that the new device is reliable so that the forklifts are not in for maintenance all the time. Purchasing has to make sure they can find the device at the proper quantity and quality and price. Developing good working relationships with the personnel in these departments will make the entire process of procuring and implementing an idea much easier.

## Roles and Responsibilities

Once the EHS professional understands the organization, knows its culture, and has established good working relationships, he or she has tremendous opportunities to lead and bring about changes and improvements in the EHS program and procedures in order to create a safer and healthier environment. As previously mentioned, a key requirement for a strong EHS culture is having top management at the local and corporate level take responsibility for EHS. When that happens, the EHS job is much easier, and the role of the EHS professional is much clearer. The ideal role for an EHS professional is that of a consultant and advisor. If an organization puts the EHS professional in the role of policeman or makes him or her responsible for preventing injuries, that will be a difficult job. If the organization blames the EHS professional whenever there is an injury, it might be worthwhile to consider a different job or organization.

Chances are very good that the supervisor of the EHS professional has more responsibilities than the EHS professional does. Many of these responsibilities may be in areas other than EHS. Because of their training and skills, EHS professionals are looked at as experts when an EHS issue arises. The EHS professional has unique knowledge and skills that are needed for the protection of workers and the environment. Top management in most companies will acknowledge that their workers are their most valuable assets. The EHS professional should be the person who provides those responsible for the health and safety of their workers and the environment with solid professional guidance, direction, and information. In many cases, those in positions of authority—including the plant manager, vice president, and CEO—do not understand EHS well enough to develop appropriate EHS policies and procedures. That is why they hired an

The ideal role for an OSH professional is that of a consultant and advisor.

EHS professional. However, if they are willing to enforce the policies and procedures the EHS professional provides, they will need some help from him or her. For example, if EHS is going to be a top priority at a location, everyone must understand that. This starts at the top with the plant manager. He or she must be able to send that message on a continual basis to all the members of the organization. He or she needs to ask the right questions and expect certain performance. Often plant managers and those in upper management are very comfortable talking about issues such as cost, quality, efficiency, and other business parameters, but they are very uncomfortable talking about EHS issues. This is where the EHS professional can help by coaching them. This may sound difficult because they are usually pressed for time, but it can be easily done and will pay big dividends. It does not have to be a long, drawn-out teaching session. For example, what if the EHS professional developed a set of simple laminated cards with some EHS questions on them? He or she could give those to the top leadership in his or her local organization and encourage them to pose these questions to their subordinates. They are just questions related to a few key EHS areas with no specific answers. Several examples of such questions are:

- When was the last time you discussed a safety issue with your employees? What was the issue?
- When was the last time you were personally involved with an accident investigation? Tell me about it.
- What is the most difficult obstacle you face in your effort to reduce injuries in your area?
- Which job or activity in your area has the most injuries?

As can be seen, the management person asking the questions does not need to know the answers. However, just by asking the questions, management conveys to the person being asked the message that EHS is important and that the boss cares about the health and safety of the workers and the environment. This approach gives leadership confidence and makes them comfortable with talking to subordinates and workers about safety and health. It gets them visibly involved in the EHS process and sends the message that EHS is a priority. As time goes on, leadership will become more and more knowledgeable about EHS issues and will need less and less coaching.

The role of chief EHS consultant in an organization requires some effort on the part of the EHS professional to maintain that status. Learning is a lifelong project. EHS professionals must stay up-to-date on information about the profession. This goes far beyond being up-to-date with OSHA regulations. It means keeping up with the articles published in scientific journals and other publications (such as American National Standards Institute [ANSI] standards), attending professional conferences, serving on technical committees, and networking with other EHS colleagues.

## Policies and Procedures

It is up to the EHS professional to develop the right policies, procedures, and methods for a safe and healthy environment. It is the responsibility of others to ensure that those policies, procedures, and methods are properly implemented and maintained on a daily basis. For example, the EHS professional may develop a lockout procedure for a specific type of operation, but others are responsible for ensuring that that procedure is being followed on a daily basis. The EHS professional may also be responsible for monitoring the various aspects of the program and reporting the results to various levels of the organization. Frequently it takes someone in the field with proper knowledge to determine whether the established EHS procedures are being followed or properly implemented.

Another important area in leadership is identifying priorities. It is not uncommon for EHS professionals to be overwhelmed by their responsibilities. Many of them will say, “I work ten to twelve hours per day and never seem to get caught up. There are many days when I just get further and further behind.” To be a successful leader in the EHS field, it is very important to be able to prioritize problems and issues. Certainly supervisors of EHS professionals and their superiors will help establish a list of priorities. But remember that their lists may be different than that of the EHS professional. This is where people skills and relationships will be tested. Also remember that labor unions and workers also have a list of priorities. The EHS professional may find himself or herself caught in the middle of a tug-of-war regarding what should get done first. This is a challenge that nearly all EHS professionals face. The best advice is to stay focused on the health, safety, and well-being of the workers and the environment. Try to stay out of the politics of a situation whenever possible. Implementation of a practice or procedure that will eliminate or minimize serious hazards such as a fall or lockout is certainly a higher priority than making sure all the aisles have fresh yellow paint.

> To be a successful leader in the EHS field, it is very important to be able to prioritize problems and issues.

As the EHS professional goes through his or her daily activities and observes workers, he or she may come across situations that pose an imminent danger. It is highly recommended that one does whatever is necessary to either eliminate the hazard or remove workers from the hazard. A few years ago, an industrial hygienist from the corporate office for a large corporation was performing various evaluations at a local iron foundry to evaluate various industrial hygiene programs at that facility. One of the evaluations involved measuring carbon monoxide levels at different locations in the cupola where scrap steel is turned into molten iron. When he measured well over one thousand parts of carbon monoxide per million parts of air by volume (ppm) in an overhead area where there were several workers, he immediately approached the workers and advised them to leave the area. The level that has been identified as immediately dangerous to life or health by the U.S. National Institute of Occupational Safety and Health is 1,200 ppm. However, the workers had never seen this gentleman before and were skeptical about the warning because they had to finish their job. The corporate professional then immediately went to the plant manager's office and told him that unless he removed those workers from that area there would there most likely be at least one fatality within the hour. The plant manager immediately responded and ordered the supervisors to ensure the workers vacated the area. This quick action most likely saved the life of at least one worker. So when confronted with an imminent danger, do not hesitate to take whatever action is necessary to save a life or prevent an injury.

## Making Sound Recommendations: The Butler

When one sees something that needs improvement or something that may be noncompliant, the natural tendency is to fix it right away. In the EHS area there is often a tendency to "play it safe" when it comes to the health and safety of the workers. This means that if we have any doubt about a situation or if we do not have all the facts, we may make recommendations that go well beyond what is needed for worker safety. These recommendations may be not only unnecessary but also detrimental to both the organization as well as the EHS professional personally. Earlier we talked about relationships and how important they are. If other departments or areas of the organization view safety as a burden and do not see the value of one's suggestions or recommendations, it may be more difficult to get things done, and they may view the EHS professional as a hindrance to the organization's goals and objectives. How many interlocks are needed on a gate that is the access point to an area of operation hazard? Clearly, fourteen interlocks would be overkill. To illustrate the need for appropriate recommendations, consider the following example titled "The Butler" (see figure 4.3).

In a conversation with a university instructor of an EHS program, the following assignment was given each time a particular EHS course was taught. Every semester students were asked to perform a job safety analysis for several different simple jobs. The purpose was to identify any hazards associated with a job and develop corresponding safety procedures and methods to perform that job safely. For this particular job, a butler was required to dust a chandelier in the foyer of a private home. Invariably, 75 to 80 percent of the students came up with the following recommendations to address what they perceived were the hazards.

The procedure for the butler is as follows:

- Inspect the ladder to make sure it is not damaged or defective.
- Place the ladder on a level surface to ensure it is stable.
- Lock or secure the entrance door to ensure no one enters while butler is on the ladder.
- Wear hard hat to prevent head injury.
- Wear safety glasses to prevent dust from getting into eyes.
- Wear respirator to prevent inhalation of dust.
- Wear shoes with nonslip soles to prevent slipping while on ladder.
- Lockout electrical circuit in basement to prevent anyone from turning on the chandelier when dusting
- Wear utility belt to hold duster to maintain three-point contact while climbing ladder

Figure 4.3
The Butler, fully prepared to tackle his job.

Even though this example seems a bit ridiculous, it does offer insight into how many young EHS professional approach problems. Even though the butler is safe, there may be some who draw the conclusion that we have gone way overboard when it comes to the recommendations. It is important that we keep the worker's safety in mind as well as the goals of the organization. At the same time, we should look at our recommendations from the standpoint of the worker. In this case, how likely is it that the butler is going to wear all of these devices that we have recommended? Sometimes there is a fine line that we have to walk in balancing practicality and the beat. Also keep in mind that there will be a time when one's recommendations are viewed as overkill when in reality they are not. Thus, there may be circumstances where one will be pressured to ease up on his or her recommendations at the expense of worker safety. It will take courage to stand for what is right and what will protect workers.

> A leader is never satisfied with the status quo but is always looking for ways to improve and become better personally, for the organization, and for the worker.

## Summary

A true EHS professional possesses the skills, knowledge, and desire to help and protect workers and the environment. He or she also has the potential to be a leader in this field.

However, becoming an effective leader requires some additional skills, a lot of effort, and an ability to work with people. The effective leader knows his or her organization and how it functions. This leader becomes familiar with the people at every level of the organization—from the top to the hourly workers. The leader learns about and understands others' goals, objectives, and motivations. One needs to develop and maintain good relationships with people at every level based on establishing trust and sending the "I care" message. The EHS leader will need to be an expert consultant in the field. He or she will be the go-to person for any EHS issue. This requires that leader to stay abreast of the latest developments and technology in the profession. He or she will need to use his or her knowledge and skills to develop effective and efficient policies and procedures. He or she will need to coach those in authority who have the responsibility to implement ideas and recommendations. Lastly, he or she must make sure any recommendations are sound ones that not only protect the employees in their organization but also make sense and are doable.

One final thought is this: a leader is never satisfied with the status quo but is always looking for ways to improve and become better personally, for the organization, and for the worker. A leader is looking for ways to take the EHS program from good to great. The goal is to be the best!

## Questions

1. Why is understanding the organizational structure so important for getting things accomplished?
2. What are some things that one can do to understand the safety culture in an organization?
3. Why are relationships so important for leaders?
4. What is the ideal role in an organization for an EHS professional?
5. Why is the setting of priorities so important for leaders?

## References

Barra, M. (June 2016). Personal communication.

Frame, P. (1994). "GM Board Termed Deficient." *Automotive News* (May 16).Simon, S. I., and P. R. Frazee. (2005). "Building a Better Safety Vehicle." *Professional Safety* (January): 36–44.

Personal conversations with workers represented by the Canadian Automobile Workers and United Automobile, Aerospace and Agricultural Implement Workers of America over a period from 1995 through 2008.

CHAPTER 5

# GLOBAL TOPICS IN OCCUPATIONAL SAFETY AND HEALTH

Thomas Fuller

## Learning Objectives

After studying this chapter, the reader will be able to:

1. Describe the extent of global workplace injuries and illnesses
2. Characterize the economic consequences of global workplace injuries and illnesses
3. List the major international governmental organizations with roles in occupational safety and health
4. List the major international nongovernmental and professional organizations with roles in occupational safety and health

## Key Terms

**Global, international, international standards, professional organizations, occupational safety, occupational health**

## Abstract

The globalization of business and industry has led to an increased interest in international aspects and issues of occupational safety and health management. International regulations and guidelines of practice now exist that place a legal and ethical burden on OSH professionals to navigate through a sea of change to be sure they are following the accepted standards of practice at their particular workplaces. Whether their organization or company has workers traveling internationally, manufactures or sells products abroad, or hires immigrants or migrants, the OSH professional has an ethical duty to help management provide safe working conditions for all employees.

## Introduction

In the past, just knowing and understanding how occupational safety and health worked in our own countries was good enough. But in recent years, the globalization of business enterprise has expanded at a pace and to an extent that few working in the field can avoid the interaction with OSH objectives and regulations of other nations. This now raises the need to be able to clearly understand how OSH is practiced and regulated in other countries, and it presents explicit challenges regarding how to integrate the practices in one country with those of others.

The OSH professional should also be aware of cultural differences between countries that may affect how organizations and workers regard and implement safety systems. OSH professionals must consider new communication methods and sensitive cultural issues (i.e., females in the workplace, attire, and other social norms). The organizations discussed in this chapter can be considered an introduction and a starting point for information on many of the important aspects of practicing occupational safety in a foreign environment.

## Growth and Globalization

In the past 50 years, the world population has more than doubled. In 1950 the world life expectancy was 48 years. In 2015 the world life expectancy was 71.4 years (Our World in Data 2017). Developing countries are brimming with young workers seeking jobs. More developed countries have responded by moving labor-intensive activities overseas where the workforce is abundant but not highly skilled and therefore less expensive. As a result, rates of occupational accidents have shifted toward the less developed countries (Hämäläinen 2009).

Globalized companies in developed countries have also moved their hazardous operations overseas to take advantage of not only cheap labor but also lax environmental and occupational safety regulations (Goldstein, Helmer, and Fingerhut 2001). Advanced technological countries and corporations sell their obsolete industrial processes and equipment (and even banned chemicals) to less developed countries. With them go the inherent hazards (Stellman 1998).

Governments are glad to turn a blind eye for the sake of jobs and tax revenues at the expense of the environment and general public health and wellbeing (Brown 2002). "Local bureaucrats are notoriously corrupt and often strike deals to overlook environmental and safety violations" (MacSheoin 2009). Examples abound, such as the Bhopal gas tragedy in 1984 and the Rana Plaza building collapse in Bangladesh in 2013, where lax safety, zoning, and building standards led to exasperating public and occupational losses (Castleman 2016). Despite a public outcry for better transparency of the activities of corporations in developed nations, the tangled web of associations and agreements between companies and a variety of suppliers and contractors operating abroad is often difficult to unwind. A handful of corporate social responsibility watchdog groups attempt to uncover the worst cases, but often even the best corporations have a difficult time ensuring that their suppliers and contractors follow internationally accepted environmental and safety codes.

A comprehensive review article by MacSheoin concluded that despite new regulations since the Bhopal disaster in India and the United States, international agreements and policy responses have not succeeded in reducing the overall number of ongoing chemical release incidents; indeed, severe and devastating accidents could still occur in both low- and high-income countries (MacSheoin 2009). Neither plant process safety, chemical control, nor emergency response programs have been fully developed to the point where massive loss of life would be prevented.

In some countries, the governments themselves are the bad actors. The World Health Organization (WHO) has recommended that special attention be paid to the elimination of asbestos-related diseases, and the EWG Action fund reports that asbestos has been banned in 55 countries (EWG Action Fund 2017). The worldwide death toll from cancer and mesothelioma due to occupational exposures to asbestos is estimated at 107,000 annually. But numerous countries around the world, including Brazil, China, and Russia, are still mining, using, and selling asbestos. Global consumption of asbestos exceeds 2 million tons annually, with 90 percent used in building materials, of which 85 percent is consumed in Asia (Castleman 2016).

As modern economies of developed countries moved from a post-Fordist productivity model of heavy industrial manufacturing toward a service-oriented business model, the health and safety hazards in society were diminished (Van Stolk, Staesky, and Kim 2012). But as a result, heavy manufacturing operations and jobs moved to developing countries and

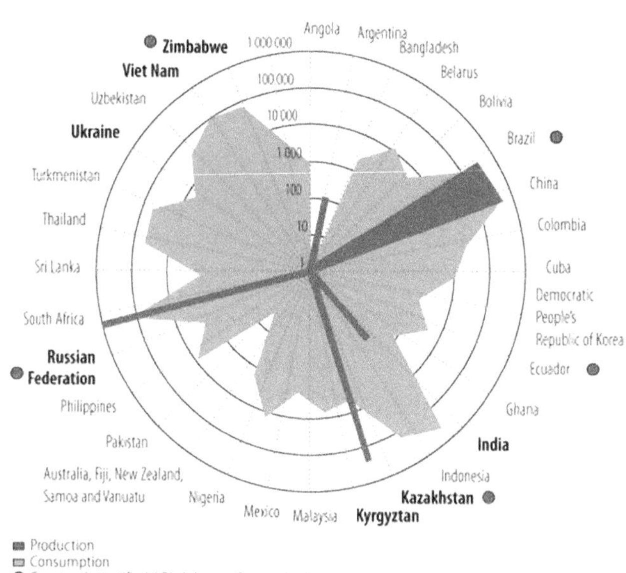


Figure 5.1
Asbestos producers and consumers in 35 countries, 2011 (from Ogunseitan 2015).

with them the inherent risks. Work in these countries is shifting from the countryside and agriculture toward more populated areas for work in construction, production, mining, and transport. New workers with little training, experience, or education are exposed to complex and dangerous industrial processes, toxic chemicals, and physical hazards.

At the seventh meeting of the World Health Organization Collaborating Centers for Occupational Health in 2006, a declaration on workers' health specified that all workers of the world deserved safe and healthful working conditions (World Health Organization 2006). With the rapid expansion of global markets, there have been numerous technical improvements in working conditions; however, many do not trickle down—or over—to developing countries. Corporate and national competitiveness has led to unsafe conditions and practices and weak legislation on and enforcement of workplace health and safety. Growing inequities between countries, industries, and social groups present ethical and moral dilemmas to governments and companies operating internationally. Even social factors that have nothing to do with the workplace directly, such as nutritional levels or public health, can impact the health and safety of employees in the workplace.

> Case:
> You are the health and safety manager at a mining jobsite in Kenya. Your workforce is composed of local men and women who are extremely malnourished and underweight. As a result, none of the respirators that have been shipped to you from the corporate headquarters in New York fit the workers properly, and most of the workers do not pass the qualitative fitness test. There is pressure by the site manager to continue working because the operation is very expensive and time sensitive. What action would you take to both protect the workforce and get the job done?

This case shows that health and safety answers are not always easy. The ethical answer is to only allow the workers to work when adequate protection is available. Limiting these workers, however, may negatively impact their wages and ability to support their families. It highlights the need to plan for a variety of possible contingencies that might arise when working and managing projects abroad.

Tackling the obstacles to equal levels of occupational safety and health on a global scale will take new initiatives and require the will of companies, governments, and working professionals. Communication and networking will be important tools for the expansion of technological advances and education to developing countries. Health and safety research will also need to cross borders in order to more fully understand occupational hazards and the need for controls in developing countries.

## Global Numbers of Injuries and Illnesses

The total cases of fatal work-related disease (WRD) in 2002 were approximately 2 million. The International Labour Organisation (ILO) estimates that 2.3 million people die each year from work-related accidents or diseases, or 6,300 workers each day (International Labour Organization). The most common fatalities caused by work include cancer (25%), circulatory diseases (21%), and communicable diseases (28%). These causes combined account for 90 percent of all fatal WRD (Hämäläinen, Saarela, and Takala 2011). In 1998, there were 264 million nonfatal and 350,000 fatal occupational accidents globally (Hämäläinen, Takala, and Saarela 2006).

In his investigation, Takala discovered that there were 2.3 million occupationally attributable deaths per year. The largest killers in this study were work-related cancer (32%), circulatory diseases (23%), communicable diseases (17%), and accidents (18%). Workplace controls have reduced exposures to toxic agents and carcinogens in developed countries in recent years; however, the shift of technology to developing countries has led to an increase in the numbers of both work-related diseases and accidents (Takala et al. 2014).

One of the global problems with comparing injuries and illnesses across borders is that each country has its own recording and reporting scheme, and the methods are not always comparable between countries (Takala et al. 2014). Therefore it is very difficult to make accurate comparisons between countries without complicated analyses that include numerous assumptions and hypothetical data. In addition, different or inadequate methods used to measure exposure lead to further inaccuracies. Many worker health directories do not include information on such illnesses as respiratory diseases, infectious agents, cancer, or heart disease. As a result, the global burden of occupational injury and illness is grossly underestimated, with the majority of the shortfall due to inaccurate estimates of work-related diseases (Driscoll et al. 2005).

The European Union Directorate General of Employment and Social Affairs defines an accident at work as "a discrete occurrence in the course of work which leads to physical or mental harm." This includes cases of acute poisoning and willful acts of other persons, as well as accidents occurring during work but off the company's premises, even those caused by third parties. It excludes deliberately self-inflicted injuries, accidents on the way to and from work (commuting accidents), accidents having only a medical origin, and occupational diseases. The phrase "in the course of work" means while engaged in an occupational activity or during the time spent at work. This includes cases of road traffic accidents in the course of work (European Communities 2001).

In 2007, the percentage of European Union (EU) accidents that resulted in more than 3 days of absence from work was 3.2 percent for men and 2.1 percent for women. The overall occurrence of accidents at work in 2007 was 3.2 percent (Eurostat 2009). The most common work-related health problems in the EU were reported as musculoskeletal disorders (60%), followed by stress, depression, and anxiety (14%) (Eurostat 2009). In a review study of workplace injuries and illnesses conducted by Weevers (Weevers et al. 2005), the most common causes of work absences in developed countries studied were musculoskeletal disorders (39%), respiratory disorders (29%), and psychological disorders (13%) (Weevers et al. 2005).

In a report published in 2009 the global occupational fatality rate was 15.2 per 100,000 workers (Hämäläinen 2009). Fatality rate comparisons by continent from the same study are shown in table 5.1.

**Table 5.1** Fatality rate by continent in 2001 (created from Hämäläinen 2009)

| Continent | Fatalities per 100,000 |
|---|---|
| Africa | 18.6 |
| North America | 13.7 |
| Asia | 13.9 |
| Europe | 6.9 |
| Australia | 9.3 |
| World Average | 15.2 |

In developing countries, communicable diseases are a significant source of work-related disease. Agriculture is a major contributor to infectious disease in workers, along with healthcare and food production (Hämäläinen, Saarela, and Takala 2011).

In an extensive report on worldwide occupational risks, Nelson reported that occupational diseases and injuries accounted for 24 million years of healthy life lost and 1.5 percent of all mortality. The leading occupational cause of death was chronic obstructive pulmonary disease (COPD) at 37 percent. The leading cause of years of healthy life lost was unintentional injuries (44%) followed by occupational hearing loss (18%) (Nelson et al. 2005).

Work-related health problems and diseases as defined by the EU are "illnesses, disabilities, and physical or psychic health problems, apart from accidental injuries, that were caused or made worse by work" (European Communities 2001). In 2007, 8.6 percent of workers in the EU were reported to have a work-related health problem. Bone, joint or, muscle problems affecting the back were the leading causes.

In the United States, the Bureau of Labor Statistics (BLS) has been collecting data on workers' injuries, illnesses, and fatalities for over 130 years. With the creation of the Occupational Safety and Health Act of 1970, employers were required to collect and report specific information about the effectiveness of their health and safety programs, and a complex scheme of data collection and reporting was implemented, with the input being fed to the BLS for statistical analysis and publication. This data allowed the BLS to collect useful information about the numbers and types of injuries, what types of jobs and industries were the most hazardous, where the most effective improvements could be made in the activities of workplaces, and where to create future regulations (Bureau of Labor Statistics 2015).

Fatality rates for agricultural workers are higher than all other industries (Centers for Disease Prevention and Control). This work presents a variety of chemical, biological, and mechanical hazards. Farmers work long hours in adverse conditions of weather and terrain and with dangerous and heavy equipment. They often work alone, far from medical responders. This is true for farmers in any country.

In India, the leading causes of farm injury were from hand tools (64.7%) and farm machinery (29.1%) (Das 2014). In the United States, where farming is more mechanized, tractor overturns were the leading cause of death (Centers for Disease Control and Prevention).

As industrialization and urbanization increase in developing countries, there is evidence that work-related health effects also increase and that even those occurrences are underreported (Hämäläinen, Saarela, and Takala 2009). In addition, work-related diseases associated with chemical exposures are likely to increase in the next decades, but many of the health effects and illnesses associated with these exposures go unidentified. Risks from occupational cancer in developing countries are expected to rise, and exposures to cancer-causing chemicals and agents should be monitored closely (Purdue et al. 2015). In addition, as competitiveness increases in global markets, it puts added pressure on companies to increase process and production rates, leading to musculoskeletal stressors and resultant injuries that also need to be identified and controlled.

## Global Costs Associated with Accidents and Incidents

Economic losses are not only felt by companies and countries, but individuals and families suffer large financial consequences too. An occupational injury to one working member of a family can reduce income dramatically and place additional burdens on other family members to pick up the slack in terms of working hours, completing household duties, and taking care of children. In the United States, low-income families with little savings can be forced into poverty when one worker suffers workplace injuries that lead to medical bills and lost wages. For single-parent families, an injury that requires extensive time away from work and reduction in wages can be devastating. As a result, many workers continue to

**Table 5.2** European Union costs of workplace injury and illness (created from European Agency for Safety and Health at Work 2015)

| Country | % of GNP |
|---|---|
| Austria | 1.4 |
| Belgium | 2.3 |
| Denmark | 2.7 |
| Finland | 3.8 |
| France | 0.6 |
| Ireland | 0.4 |
| Italy | 3.2 |
| Luxembourg | 2.5 |
| Netherlands | 2.6 |
| Spain | 3.0 |
| Sweden | 4.0 |
| United Kingdom | 1.1 |

work while injured, not only for the income but due to fears about losing their job, losing the potential for advancement/seniority, and other related reasons (Boden 2005).

The direct cost of disabling workplace injuries in the United States amounted to over 53 billion USD, representing 71 percent of the total compensation cost burden in 2008 (Liberty Mutual Research Institute for Safety 2011). The global economic burden of workplace accidents and workplace-related illnesses is estimated at 4 percent of global gross domestic product (GDP) each year (International Labour Organization). Table 5.2 presents a breakdown of costs of injury and illness attributable to work in terms of gross national product (GNP) for countries in the European Union.

Although young workers have higher rates of work injuries, older workers are more likely to die from a workplace injury. Older workers have higher rates of falls and fractures, whereas younger workers are more likely to suffer from injuries due to contact with mechanical devices or moving parts of equipment (Fan, McLeod, and Koehoorn 2012). Physical jobs account for a large proportion of workplace injuries in any age group. These demographics become important in analyzing the public health and workplace safety implications as work shifts and moves cross-culturally. More advanced societies tend to have older workforces; however, developing countries tend to have a significantly larger proportion of younger workers. These factors need to be considered and accommodated for in appropriate OSH management systems and possibly even facility design, work design, or the selection of personal protective equipment.

There is growing evidence that however underreported work-related injuries from accidents are, much less is known or documented about chronic exposure to chemicals and associated health effects. Inaccurate exposure assessment methodologies, little toxicological data or understanding, and few epidemiological studies due to the long latency periods of many diseases make it difficult to truly understand the hazards workers are faced with today, especially in underdeveloped countries (Hämäläinen, Saarela, and Takala 2009).

## Intergovernmental Occupational Safety and Health Organizations and Regulating Bodies

As countries become more interdependent globally, there are greater incentives for mutual agreements regarding the identification and control of risks. This is overtly true and visible for environmental hazards, where the failure of one country to maintain adequate control over releases can have monumental adverse effects in neighboring and even distant countries, such as a meltdown of nuclear materials or a release of toxic chemicals. But this has also become increasingly true for occupational hazards as worker populations have become more aware and affluent. Both workers and their employers have come to realize the value of a life and good health in the workforce. Other stakeholders, such as business investors, also understand that the sustainability of organizations, and even the financial and political stability of nations, are linked to a safe and healthy workforce (Kirchsteiger 2005).

Countries have learned to work together to exchange information in shared capacities for the benefit of all governments, organizations, and workers. By collecting and transparently sharing objective data and information between agreement states or institutions, common interests, goals, and objectives can be attained for the benefit of all. Decisions can be made collectively in guidance documents and treaties for assessing risks and setting priorities for appropriate controls. Balances can be struck within decision-making processes to reduce uncertainty and take a precautionary approach to potential hazards. In order to achieve the goals of international agreements, a large number of organizations have been created over the past several decades. Some of these are described in the following sections.

## European Union

The Treaty on the Functioning of the European Union gives the EU authority to create agencies that then write directives that are laws that each member country must transpose into national laws within set deadlines. EU Council Regulation (EC) No. 2062/94 established a European Agency for Safety and Health at Work in 1994 (European Agency for Safety and Health at Work 1994). EU-OSHA is allocated funds by the EU's budgetary authority, which is made up of the European Parliament (directly elected MEPs) and the Council of the European Union (representatives of the twenty-eight member state governments.

The goal of the agency is to encourage improvements in working conditions for the health and safety of workers under existing treaty conditions through support of successive action programs (European Agency for Safety and Health at Work 1994). Some of the main goals of the regulation are to

- collect and disseminate technical, scientific, and economic information in member states to the broader community to set priority development;
- perform occupational safety and health research and disseminate results;
- promote cooperation and exchange of information between member states;
- organize conferences and seminars for the exchange of expert information;
- collect and disseminate information on OSH to developing countries;
- support safety and health in small- to medium-sized companies; and
- contribute to the development of community action programs that relate to worker safety.

The EU European Framework Directive on Safety and Health at Work (Directive 89/391 EEC) adopted in 1989 was a substantial milestone in improving safety and health at work. It allows for the creation of detailed directives that guarantee minimum safety and health requirements throughout Europe that all member governments must adhere to for worker safety. Member states are free to adopt stricter rules for the protection of workers when transposing EU directives into national law. Therefore, legislative requirements in the field of safety and health at work can vary across EU member states (European Agency for Safety and Health at Work 2016a).

EU guidelines are nonbinding documents that aim to facilitate the implementation of European directives. Different types of guidelines include recommendations from various other organizations, such as the EU, EU social partner agreements, and others (European Agency for Safety and Health at Work 2016b).

## World Health Organization

The World Health Organization considers itself the world guardian of public health. The WHO has offices in more than 150 countries where they work with governments and other partners with the goal of

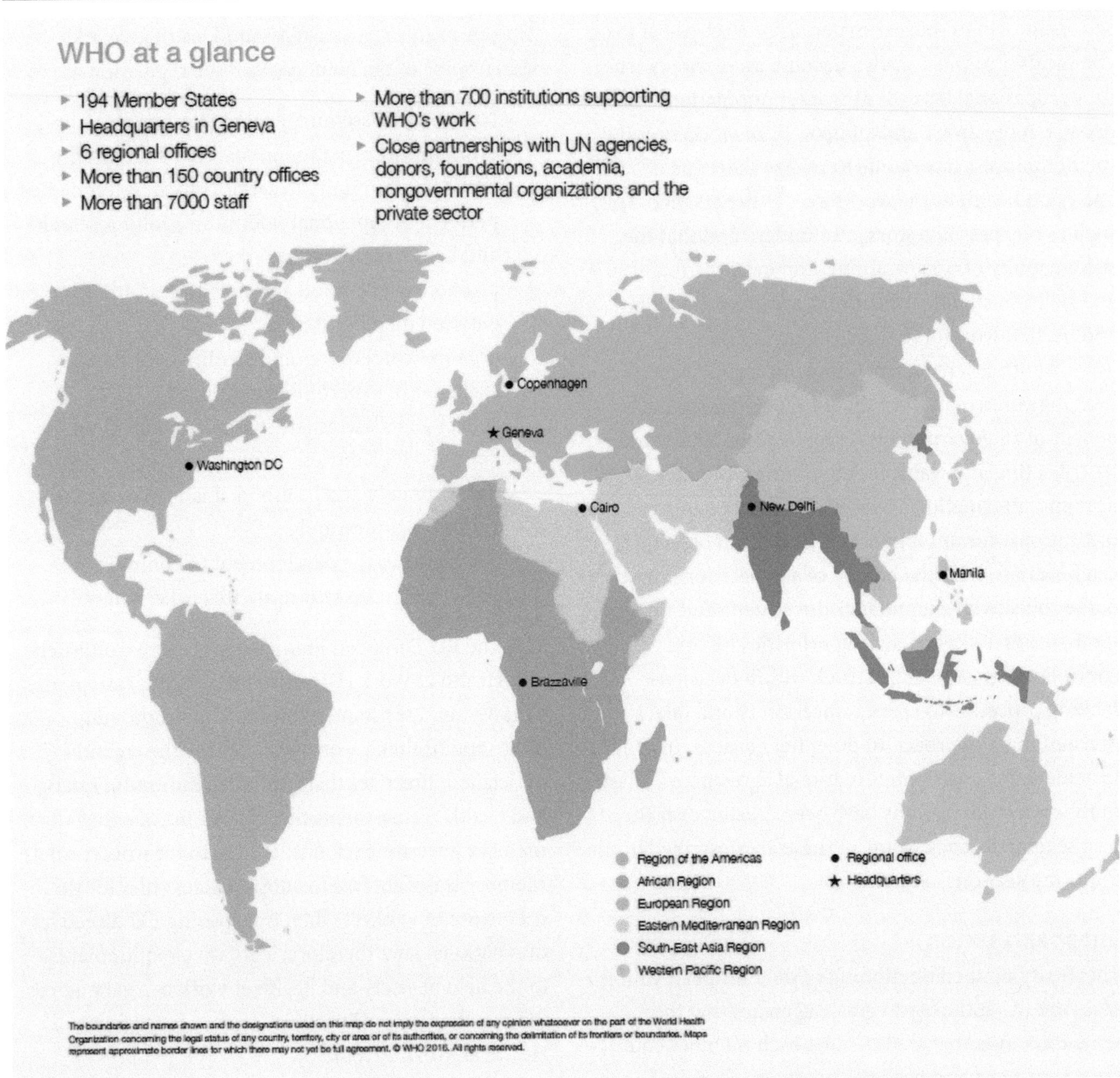


Figure 5.2
WHO regional offices

providing the highest possible standards of health in society (World Health Organization 2016).

The WHO works to build consensus with member states on a variety of occupational safety and health topics. A number of publications are available online regarding workplace safety and disease, including psychosocial hazards, infectious diseases, and general working conditions (World Health Organization 2007).

## International Labour Organization (ILO)

The International Labour Organization (ILO) was founded in 1919 as a means to bring 187 member countries together to set labor standards, develop policies, and promote fair and decent work for all people. The tripartite governance structure represents governments, workers, and employers (with a 2:1:1 ratio). In 1946 the organization became the first specialized agency of the United Nations. To date, the ILO has created nearly 200 conventions within a complex system of labor standards that can be ratified by member states. These ratifications are a form of treaty or agreement between the member states to "follow the rules" and promulgate and enforce regulations covering the conventions within their own national regulations and laws (International Labour Organization).

The ILO conventions cover a broad spectrum of topics. Some of the conventions specifically involve worker safety and health, as well as working conditions. There are 8 fundamental conventions, which 91.7 percent of the member states have ratified (International Labour Organization 2014).

ILO conventions for occupational safety and health are provided in section 12 (International Labour Organization 2014). In addition to conventions, the ILO publishes related recommendations that support them and clarify how an organization would go about meeting their intent. There are several general provisions for occupational safety and health in section 12.1, which are followed by conventions and recommendations for more specific risks, such as protection from radiation, asbestos, and chemicals. Section 12.3 covers the mining, agriculture, and construction industries in detail. Safety and health sections also appear in entirely different convention sections too. For example, conventions on seafaring include sections on marine worker safety (International Labour Organization 2018).

## International Standards Organization

The International Standards Organization (ISO) is a non-profit network of international standards-developing bodies. The organization was formed in 1946 and since then has created nearly 2,000 standards on almost all aspects of technology and manufacturing. Standards are created by the consensus of 162 countries and 3,368 different technical bodies. Many ISO standards are pertinent to environmental health and safety (International Standards Organization).

ISO 18001 is based on British standard BS OHSAS and sets minimum requirements for occupational health and safety. This document is expected to be replaced by 45001, which was approved in January 2018. ISO 45001 is a consensus guideline that is intended to help organizations manage workplace risks and improve the performance of their occupational safety and health management systems. By implementing the standard, organizations can systematically evaluate workplace conditions and processes to determine where improvements may be needed to reduce the exposure of workers to hazardous materials or working conditions. The goal of this standard is also to reduce the overall cost of incidents, likelihood of regulatory noncompliance, and insurance premiums associated with accidents.

The ISO 14001 standard is specifically written to address certain areas of environmental management. It provides useful templates and guidelines for companies and organizations to measure and control their environmental impacts and to meet applicable regulatory standards. Companies can use the standard and possible certification to demonstrate commitment to environmentally safe practices to stakeholders and the general public.

Risk management frameworks are provided in ISO 31001. The standard describes methods of risk identification and reduction. It also addresses health and safety concerns within the overall system. ISO 31001 is supported by ISO 31010 on risk assessment techniques.

The ISO/IEC Guide 51—Safety Risk Assessment document specifically addresses health and safety risks. This guide provides recommendations for risk reduction in the combination of people, property, and the environment.

## International Agency for Research on Cancer (IARC)

The International Agency for Research on Cancer is a specialized research branch of the WHO with the goal of promoting international collaboration on cancer research. The agency brings data and information from countries around the world together to evaluate via an interdisciplinary process using epidemiology, laboratory sciences, and biostatistics to identify the causes of cancer. With this important information in hand, the IARC can help prioritize medical research directions and preventive measures in order to reduce the global burden of disease from cancer (International Agency for Research on Cancer 2016).

### International Commission on Radiation Protection (ICRP)

The International Commission on Radiological Protection was created in 1928 as a global organization to develop radiation protection standards, guidelines, and regulations. The main goal is to help prevent cancer and other diseases caused by exposure to ionizing radiation and radioactive materials (International Commission on Radiological Protection).

## Nongovernmental International Professional Organizations

In the past several years a variety of nongovernmental international professional organizations have formed to improve communications between professionals practicing in different countries. These groups have other goals in addition, including developing standards of practice, conducting research, and providing training and support to safety and health practitioners in developing countries. Some of these organizations are described in the following sections.

### International Occupational Hygiene Association (IOHA)

The International Occupational Hygiene Association is a global community of occupational hygienists and professionals who are dedicated to the discipline and application of the inherent principles used to protect workers from hazards and to reduce injury and illness (International Occupational Hygiene Association). Activities include the development of comprehensive health and safety training materials and holding international conferences to support the exchange of information and ideas. With over 13,000 chartered safety and health practitioners, IOHA has more certified professionals than any other organization (International Occupational Hygiene Association).

### Workplace Health Without Borders (WHWB)

Workplace Health Without Borders is a not-for-profit organization founded in 2011 to address occupational health and safety issues in the developing world. The goal of WHWB is to engage volunteers with expertise in exposure and risk assessment, hazard control, and other technical areas of occupational hygiene to donate time to support projects for underserved worker populations around the world. The focus of the organization is on research, infrastructure development, and training that will improve worker health in low-income and low-opportunity countries and regions (Workplace Health Without Borders).

### Institute of Occupational Safety and Health (IOSH)

The Institute of Occupational Safety and Health was registered in 1962 as a charity with the goal of improving health and safety at work and to support the development of safety professionals working in the field. With over 44,000 members, this is the world's largest health and safety professional membership organization (Institute of Occupational Safety and Health 2015, 2018).

### International Commission on Occupational Health (ICOH)

The International Commission on Occupational Health is an international nongovernmental professional society founded in 1906 to promote occupational health and safety. The organization provides a broad platform for the dissemination of scientific information through coordination of conferences around the world and a variety of technical reports and other publications. There are 2,000 professional members in 93 countries (International Commission on Occupational Health).

The ICOH is recognized by the United Nations as a nongovernmental organization (NGO), has close working relationships with ILO, WHO, and UNEP, and has thirty-seven scientific committees. Its official languages are English and French.

### International Network of Safety and Health Professional Organisations (INSHPO)

The International Network of Safety and Health Professional Organisations is a forum for international collaboration among professional organizations with the goal of improving safety and health at work (International Network of Safety and Health Practitioner Organisations).[47] The INSHPO conducts meetings to share information and publishes OSH-related materials online as a means to spread awareness of workplace health and safety issues and controls. This organization is not-for-profit, and board members serve without compensation. Current projects include development and dissemination of core competencies for OSH professions, designation of moral codes of conduct, and educational equivalency comparisons.

### European Network of Safety and Health Professional Organisations (ENSHPO)

The European Network of Safety and Health Professional Organisations was established in 2001 to bring together health and safety professional organizations from across Europe. The main objectives of ENSHPO are to act as a forum where practitioners can exchange information, experiences, and good practices on a wide variety of pertinent topics and to develop a European-wide recognition of OSH practitioner qualifications and training (ENSHPO).

### Occupational Hygiene Training Association (OHTA)

The Occupational Hygiene Training Association is a not-for-profit organization created to promote better standards in occupational hygiene practice globally. Training programs and materials are developed and then made freely available online for use by students or trainers. OHTA is supported by several national occupational hygiene associations and IOHA.

OHTA has also created an international qualifications framework for students that have taken courses and passed associated examinations demonstrating competency in course topics. Many of these courses are taught around the world in developing countries by professionals on a voluntary basis as a means to encourage OSH in low-income areas. Other companies teach the OHTA courses for a profit to students looking to expand their qualifications and credentials. These courses often work as stepping-stones for professionals who eventually enter formal OSH educational programs and receive university degrees (Occupational Health Training Association).

## Reflection

As global economies and business enterprises become increasingly intertwined, there is an expanding need for occupational safety and health professionals to be aware of global health and safety impacts and costs. There is a need to understand and be aware of international regulations, organizations, and resources. The thorough understanding of codes of practice in only one country is no longer adequate, and professionals need to be able to navigate operations and health and safety management across international borders with employees in several different countries and cultures at the same time.

## Questions

1. Why is it important for a practicing occupational safety and health professional to be aware of the global topics and issues in workplace safety and health?
2. What is one of the problems in comparing the levels of workplace safety and health between different countries?
3. Who should care about the economic costs of global workplace injuries and illnesses?
4. What is the rationale for the development of European Union directives for worker health and safety?
5. What organizations are involved in the operations and activities of the International Labour Organization?

## References

Boden, L. (2005). "Running on Empty: Families, Time, and Workplace Injuries." *American Journal of Public Health* 95(11): 1894–97.

Brown, G. (2002). "The Global Threats to Workers' Health and Safety on the Job." *Social Justice* 29(3): 12–25.

Bureau of Labor Statistics. (2015). "The Quest for Meaningful and Accurate Occupational Health and Safety Statistics." *Monthly Labor Review* (December): 1–19.

Castleman, B. (2016). "The Export of Hazardous Industries in 2015." *Environmental Health* 15:8.

Centers for Disease Prevention and Control. "Agricultural Safety." Accessed June 16, 2016. https://www.cdc.gov/niosh/topics/aginjury/.

Das, B. (2014). "Agricultural Work-related Injuries among the Farmers of West Bengal, India." *International Journal of Injury Control and Safety Promotion* 21(3): 2051–15.

Das, B. (2014). "Agricultural work related injuries among the farmers of West Bengal, India." *International Journal of Injury Control and Safety Promotion* 21(3), 205–15.

Driscoll, T., J. Takala, K. Steenland, C. Corvalan, and M. Fingerhut. (2005). "Review of Estimates of the Global Burden of Injury and Illness Due to Occupational Exposures,." *American Journal of Industrial Medicine* 48: 491–502.

ENSHPO. "About ENSHPO." Accessed July 1, 2016. http://www.enshpo.eu/userfiles/2015_09_22%20%20About%20ENSHPO%20.pdf.

European Agency for Safety and Health at Work. (2016a). "European Directives on Safety and Health at Work." Accessed June 17, 2016. https://osha.europa.eu/en/safety-and-health-legislation/european-directives.

European Agency for Safety and Health at Work. (2016b). "European Guidelines." Accessed June 17, 2016. https://osha.europa.eu/en/safety-and-health-legislation/european-guidelines.

European Agency for Safety and Health at Work. (2015). "Economic Impact of Occupational Safety and Health in the Member States of the European Union" (September). https://osha.europa.eu/en/node/7106/file_view. Accessed June 28, 2016.

European Agency for Safety and Health at Work. (1994). "European Union Council Regulation (EC) No. 2062/94, 8 July, 1994." *Official Journal of the European Union* L. 216 (August 20).

European Communities. (2001). *European Statistics on Accidents at Work (ESAW) Methodology—2001 Edition.* Luxembourg: Office for Official Publications of the European Communities.

Eurostat. (2009). "8.6% of Workers in the EU Experienced Work-related Health Problems." *Statistics in Focus* 63 (2009): 12. Accessed July 1, 2016. http://ec.europa.eu/eurostat/documents/3433488/5283817/KS-SF-09-063-EN.PDF/10b62d3b-e4dd-403f-b337-af6ffd3de8de.

EWG Action Fund. (2017). Accessed May 11, 2017. http://www.asbestosnation.org/facts/asbestos-bans-around-the-world/.

Fan, J., C. McLeod, and M. Koehoorn. (2012). "Descriptive Epidemiology of Serious Work-Related Injuries in British Columbia, Canada." *PLoS* ONE 7(6).

Goldstein, G., R. Helmer, and M. Fingerhut. (2001). "Mobilizing to Protect Worker's Health: The WHO Global Strategy on Occupational Health and Safety." *African Newsletter on Occupational Health and Safety* 11: 56–60.

Hämäläinen, P. (2009). "The Effect of Globalization on Occupational Accidents." *Safety Science* 47: 733–42.

Hämäläinen, P., K. Saarela, and J. Takala. (2011). "Global Estimates of Fatal Work-related Diseases by Region and Disease Group." *International Journal of Occupational and Environmental Health* 17(1): 49–56.

Hämäläinen$_b$, J., K. Saarela, and P. Takala. (2009). "Global Trend According to Estimated Number of Occupational Accidents and Fatal Work-related diseAses at Region and Country Level." *Journal of Safety Research* 40: 125–39.

Hämäläinen, P., J. Takala, and K. Saarela. (2006). "Global Estimates of Occupational Accidents." *Safety Science* 44: 137–56.

Institute of Occupational Safety and Health. (2018). "About Membership." Accessed June 13, 2016. http://www.iosh.co.uk/Membership/About-membership.aspx.

Institute of Occupational Safety and Health. (2015). "Annual Report 2015." Accessed June 21, 2016. https://www.iosh.co.uk/~/media/Documents/About%20us/Annual%20report%202015/POL3016%20-%20Annual%20Report%202015%20011015%20WEB.pdf?la=en.

International Agency for Research on Cancer. (2016). "IARC A Unique Agency—Cancer Research for Cancer Prevention." Accessed June 22, 2016. http://www.iarc.fr/en/about/iarc-brochure-web.pdf.

International Commission on Occupational Health. "About ICOH." Accessed June 29, 2016. http://www.icohweb.org/site/about-icoh.asp.

International Commission on Radiological Protection. Accessed June 22, 2016. http://www.icrp.org/index.asp.

International Labour Organization. (2018). "List of Instruments by Subject and Status." Accessed June 23, 2016. http://www.ilo.org/dyn/normlex/en/f?p=1000:12030:0::NO.

International Labour Organization. (2014). *Rules of the Game—A Brief Introduction to International Labour*

*Standards.* http://www.ilo.org/wcmsp5/groups/public/---ed_norm/---normes/documents/publication/wcms_318141.pdf.

International Labour Organization. "Safety and Health at Work." http://www.ilo.org/global/topics/safety-and-health-at-work/lang--en/index.htm. Accessed June 16, 2016.
International Network of Safety and Health Practitioner Organisations. "Homepage." Accessed July 1, 2016. http://www.inshpo.org.

International Occupational Hygiene Association. Accessed June 21, 2016. http://ioha.net.

International Standards Organization. Accessed June 23, 2016. http://www.iso.org/iso/home.html.

Kirchsteiger, C. (2005). "Review of Industrial Safety Management by International Agreements and Institutions." *Journal of Risk Research* 8(1): 31–51.

Liberty Mutual Research Institute for Safety 2010. (2011). *Liberty Mutual Workplace Safety Index.* Hopkinton, MA: Liberty Mutual.

MacSheoin, T. (2009). "Waiting for Another Bhopal." *Global Social Policy* 9(2): 408–03.

Nelson, D., M. Concha-Barrientos, T. Driscoll, K. Steenland, F. Fingerhut, L. Punnett, A. Pruss-Ustun, J. Leigh, and C. Corvalan. (2005). "The Global Burden of Selected Occupational Diseases and Injury Risks: Methodology and Summary." *American Journal of Industrial Medicine.* 48: 400–418.

Occupational Health Training Association. "The Occupational Health Training Association." Accessed June 30, 2016. http://www.ohlearning.com/about-ohta/purpose-and-principles.aspx.

Purdue, M., S. Hutchings, L. Rushton, and D. Silverman. (2015). "The Proportion of Cancer Attributable to Occupational Exposures." *Annals of Epidemiology* 25: 188–92.

Stellman, J. (1998). "The ILO Encyclopedia of Occupational Health and Safety: A Multidisciplinary Challenge." *International Labour Review* 137(3): 410–18.

Takala, J., P. Hämäläinen, K. Saarela, L. Yun, K. Manickam, T. Jin, P. Heng, C. Tjong, L. Kheng, S. Lim, and G. Lin. (2014). "Global Estimates of the Burden of Injury and Illness at Work in 2012." *Journal of Occupational and Environmental Hygiene* 11(5): 326–37.

Van Stolk, C., E. Staesky, and C. Kim. (2012). *Management of Occupational Safety and Health—An Analysis of the Findings of the European Survey of Enterprises on New and Emerging Risks (ENSER)*, edited by W. Cockburn. Bilbao, Spain: European Agency for Safety and Health at Work.

Weevers, H., A. van der Beek, J. Anema, W. van der, and W. van Mechelen. (2005). "Work-related Diseases in General Practice: A Systematic Review." *Family Practice* 14: 1–8.

Workplace Health Without Boarders. "Homepage." Accessed July 1, 2016. http://www.whwb.org/home/.

World Health Organization. (2016). "The Global Guardian of Public Health." http://www.who.int/about/what-we-do/global-guardian-of-public-health.pdf?ua=1.

World Health Organization. (2014). "Asbestos: Elimination of Asbestos-related Diseases." Fact Sheet No. 343 (July). Accessed June 14, 2016. http://www.who.int/mediacentre/factsheets/fs343/en/.

World Health Organization. (2007). "Healthy Workplaces: A WHO Global Model for Action." Accessed June 23, 2016. http://www.who.int/occupational_health/healthy_workplaces/en/.

World Health Organization. (2006). "Declaration on Workers Health." Approved at the Seventh Meeting of the WHO Collaborating Centres for Occupational Health, Stresa, Italy, June 8–9, 2006.

CHAPTER 6

# PREPARING EHS STUDENTS AND YOUNG PROFESSIONALS FOR ETHICAL ISSUES

John N. Zey, Shoji Nakayama, Alice L. Greife, and Brian Benson

## Learning Objectives

After studying this chapter, the reader will be able to:

1. Discuss the history of ethics, including some of the early ethical guidelines
2. Discuss the primary issues in dealing with ethical situations in the EHS profession
3. Apply concepts learned in this chapter to help navigate through ethical dilemmas
4. Prepare a basic lecture on ethics in EHS

## Key Terms

**Ethics, ethical codes, ethical dilemmas, EHS leadership, EHS students, EHS young professionals**


## Abstract

Ethics is a topic that environmental health and safety (EHS) students and professionals encounter on a regular basis. Although ethics is often taught and discussed by both students and professionals, some may not realize how murky ethical issues can be. The simple question, "Is this an unethical issue?" is not as easily answered as some might assume. In this chapter, the authors provide students and young EHS professionals with some perspectives on the early ethical codes, some of the primary ethical concepts, some confounding issues that ethics often involves, and tips for navigating ethical dilemmas they may face.


## Introduction

What is ethics? We often hear this word *ethics* in our daily lives. Most of us probably think we know what it means, but have you ever stopped and considered the outcome before you take an action? Do you always follow what you think you should be doing? Is this "common sense"? Regardless of your answers to these questions, we often see and hear negative consequences due to an individual's bad ethical decisions. In our discipline of environmental health and safety, these negative consequences can lead to an injury, a death, or an environmental catastrophe. It is therefore very important for both EHS students and young professionals to be aware of the significance of ethics in the EHS discipline and know how they may be able to navigate through ethical dilemmas should they ever face such situations in the future.

We all have faced a situation where we had to make an ethical decision. Undoubtedly, we have faced such situations numerous times, but if you are currently attending college or even just graduated from an academic institution, you may not think of the variety of ethical decisions you have already made in life. You have made many choices. Most of these did not fall into the category of ethical dilemmas, but some certainly did. Some simple examples of ethical dilemmas are situations like these:

- You had a chance to cheat on a test or to borrow a friend's homework and simply copy the answers.
- You could spend six hours over two nights writing a ten-page paper for Friday's class or go to the ballgame tonight and just buy the paper online instead.
- You ordered meal number 1 at a fast-food drive-through restaurants, which costs $5.00, because that's all you could afford, but they gave you meal number 5 instead, which costs $7.00. Should you tell them that?

These are some examples of the many ethical dilemmas in daily our lives. Some of the ethical dilemmas that students encounter in college will continue to occur in their professional careers. No one can escape from these often murky and certainly unpleasant situations.

> It is very important for both EHS students and young professionals to be aware of the significance of ethics in the EHS discipline and know how they may be able to navigate through ethical dilemmas should they ever face such situations in the future.

This chapter was written to inform current EHS students and young EHS professionals about the importance of ethics in our discipline and to provide some tips to help them make decisions when they face ethical dilemmas.

## Ethics Defined

Ethics is a branch of philosophy focused on the study of values and morality. The word *ethics* is derived from the Greek work ethikos ("of or for morals"). Ancient philosophers were concerned with the functioning society as a whole and the individual's role in it (Krause 2007). Furthermore, the Merriam-Webster Dictionary defines ethics as "the discipline dealing with what is good and bad and with moral duty and obligation" (Merriam-Webster Dictionary, n. d.).

Ethical concern is not something new. Formalized ethical standards have been around for over 3,700 years. Ethics in environmental health and safety is an outgrowth of basic ethics that began hundreds of years ago. Many ancient religious texts have versions of the Golden Rule: "in everything do to others as you would have them do to you" (Oxford Biblical Studies Online, n. d.). Other examples of early codes of proper conduct for humans include the Egyptian *Book of the Dead and* the Code of Hammurabi. They are among the first written guidelines on how people should act and are also considered to be among the first ethical codes. This idea is supported by publications from other professions, including management, construction, fire safety, and the health professions (Saatci 2014; Hamarneh 1993; ASCE Code of Ethics; National Fire Protection Association, n. d.). The following quote from the American Society of Civil Engineers summarizes the sources of current ethics: "The codification of ethics has taken many forms: from the Ten Commandments, to the Doctrine of Socrates, to the *Nicomachean Ethics*, to the Code of Hammurabi, to the American Constitution, to the Golden Rule, to the ASCE Code of Ethics. The ASCE Code of Ethics is tailored to the professional civil engineer" (ASCE Code of Ethics).

## Ethical Expectations among Professional Organizations

Many professional organizations identify ethical expectations among professionals under their "code of conduct" section, which is intended to help a young professional gain a better understanding of professional ethics and provide resources to help solve professional ethical dilemmas. Some of those organizations relevant to our discipline include the American Society of Safety Professionals (ASSP), the American Board of Industrial Hygiene (ABIH), the Board of Certified Safety Professionals (BCSP), and the American Industrial Hygiene Association (AIHA), to name a few. Let's take a look at some of their expectations. Of the four, the ethical code of the BCSP and the ABIH are enforceable to those professionals who hold their credentials through these two entities. Both organizations provide a set of standards and responsibilities in their codes of ethics (ABIH 2007; BCSP 2016). We have provided the specific set of standards for each organization below.

## The Standards and Responsibilities for the American Board of Industrial Hygiene (ABIH 2007)

I. Responsibilities to ABIH, the profession and the public.
   A. Certificant and candidate compliance with all organizational rules, policies and legal requirements.
      1. Comply with laws, regulations, policies and ethical standards governing professional practice of industrial hygiene and related activities.
      2. Provide accurate and truthful representations concerning all certification and recertification information.
      3. Maintain the security of ABIH examination information and materials, including the prevention of unauthorized disclosures of test information.
      4. Cooperate with ABIH concerning ethics matters and the collection of information related to an ethics matter.
      5. Report apparent violations of the ethics code by certificants and candidates upon a reasonable and clear factual basis.
      6. Refrain from public behavior that is clearly in violation of professional, ethical or legal standards.

II. Responsibilities to clients, employers, employees and the public.
   A. Education, experience, competency and performance of professional services.
      1. Deliver competent services with objective and independent professional judgment in decision making.
      2. Recognize the limitations of one's professional ability and provide services only when qualified. The certificant/candidate is responsible for determining the limits of his/her own professional abilities based on education, knowledge, skills, practice experience and other relevant considerations.
      3. Make a reasonable effort to provide appropriate professional referrals when unable to provide competent professional assistance.
      4. Maintain and respect the confidentiality of sensitive information obtained in the course of professional activities unless: the information is reasonably understood to pertain to unlawful activity; a court or governmental agency lawfully directs the release of the information; the client or the employer expressly authorizes the release of specific information; or, the failure to release such information would likely result in death or serious physical harm to employees and/or the public.
      5. Properly use professional credentials, and provide truthful and accurate representations concerning education, experience, competency and the performance of services.
      6. Provide truthful and accurate representations to the public in advertising, public statements or representations, and in the preparation of estimates concerning costs, services and expected results.
      7. Recognize and respect the intellectual property rights of others and act in an accurate, truthful and complete manner, including activities related to professional work and research.

   8. Affix or authorize the use of one's ABIH seal, stamp or signature only when the document is prepared by the certificant/candidate or someone under his/her direction and control.

B. Conflict of interest and appearance of impropriety.
   1. Disclose to clients or employers significant circumstances that could be construed as a conflict of interest or an appearance of impropriety.
   2. Avoid conduct that could cause a conflict of interest with a client, employer, employee or the public.
   3. Assure that a conflict of interest does not compromise legitimate interests of a client, employer, employee or the public and does not influence or interfere with professional judgments.
   4. Refrain from offering or accepting significant payments, gifts or other forms of compensation or benefits in order to secure work or that are intended to influence professional judgment.

C. Public health and safety.
   1. Follow appropriate health and safety procedures, in the course of performing professional duties, to protect clients, employers, employees and the public from conditions where injury and damage are reasonably foreseeable.

## The Standards for the Board of Certified Safety Professionals' Code of Ethics (BCSP 2016)

1. Hold paramount the safety and health of people, the protection of the environment and protection of property in the performance of professional duties and exercise their obligation to advise employers, clients, employees, the public, and appropriate authorities of danger and unacceptable risks to people, the environment, or property.
2. Be honest, fair, and impartial; act with responsibility and integrity. Adhere to high standards of ethical conduct with balanced care for the interests of the public, employers, clients, employees, colleagues and the profession. Avoid all conduct or practice that is likely to discredit the profession or deceive the public.
3. Issue public statements only in an objective and truthful manner and only when founded upon knowledge of the facts and competence in the subject matter.
4. Undertake assignments only when qualified by education or experience in the specific technical fields involved. Accept responsibility for their continued professional development by acquiring and maintaining competence through continuing education, experience, professional training and keeping current on relevant legal issues.
5. Avoid deceptive acts that falsify or misrepresent their academic or professional qualifications. Not misrepresent or exaggerate their degree of responsibility in or for the subject matter of prior assignments. Presentations incident to the solicitation of employment shall not misrepresent pertinent facts concerning employers, employees, associates, or past accomplishments with the intent and purpose of enhancing their qualifications and their work.
6. Conduct their professional relations by the highest standards of integrity and avoid compromise of their professional judgment by conflicts of interest. When becoming aware of professional misconduct by a BCSP certificant, take steps to bring that misconduct to the attention of the Board of Certified Safety Professionals.
7. Act in a manner free of bias with regard to religion, ethnicity, gender, age, national origin, sexual orientation, or disability.
8. Seek opportunities to be of constructive service in civic affairs and work for the advancement of the safety, health and wellbeing of their community and their profession by sharing their knowledge and skills.

From the codes of ethics for two organizations that grant professional certification, it can be seen that codes of ethics are expectations and thus are an integral part of becoming successful EHS professionals.

## Ethics within the EHS Profession

### Are EHS Ethics Black and White?

The issue of whether ethics is black and white or consist of shades of gray has been discussed by professionals in many disciplines (Wade 2005; Bruhn 2009; Birch et al. 2000; Johnson 2012). Ashley Johnson, in an article in the National Safety Council's *Safety+Health* journal, lists comments from several safety professions concerning this issue (Johnson 2012).

There is often a divide among safety professionals whether ethical issues are simply black and white or if there are gray areas where ethical decisions are tougher to make. In other words, some professionals believe that ethical decisions are almost always black and white. They claim that some safety professionals have created a gray area in order to accommodate management or the company's needs instead of standing up for what they believe is right or wrong and making the right ethical decision. In such situations, the safety professionals must make a compromise in order to survive and stay employed within their organization (Johnson 2012).

Working in the EHS professions often involves ethical issues. Common values or ethical codes of conduct among EHS professionals include protection of people, property, and the environment. In addition, EHS professionals must implement established guidelines and policies to protect those three components. When EHS professionals make a decision, it must be fair, honest, and consistent. This is important because ethical codes are designed for fair treatment and to be fair, decisions must be consistent (Johnson 2012).

Working in the EHS professions often involves ethical issues. Common values or ethical codes of conduct among EHS professionals include protection of people, property, and the environment.

An additional ethical question that EHS professionals must answer is whether something is legal or illegal. If something is illegal, it is often unethical. But does it mean something is ethical if it is legal? This is something EHS professionals will need to decide based on the internal guidelines they have. These ethical decisions are not simply black or white; they are often clouded in shades of gray (Wade 2005; Bruhn 2009; Birch et al. 2000; Johnson 2012).

### Ethics Can Be Muddled

The meaning of ethics is different from one individual to another due to one's social culture, homeland, and upbringing. What one person thinks is ethical may be totally unethical to another. Most organizations have annual ethics training that is mandatory for all employees. This training is often used to satisfy corporate requirements and may actually teach the participant very little. Leemann (2010), in fact, believes that ethics cannot be taught due to the extreme diversity from one individual to another. Perhaps the key is that individuals need to have a solid foundation from their home environment.

Some safety professionals may never encounter a clear unethical safety or health issues in their careers (Leemann 2010). However, almost all will encounter situations where they see things that they view as inappropriate and are unsure of what action, if any, they should take. They may even find themselves in companies that have ethically collapsed.

Jennings (2007) offers safety professionals several warning or tell-tale signs that a company has ethically collapsed. According to Jennings, the warning signs of ethical collapse include pressure to maintain numbers, fear and silence, young guns and a bigger-than-life CEO, a weak board of directors, conflicts overlooked or unaddressed, innovation like no other company, and goodness in some areas atoning for evil in others (Jennings 2007).

Each of us has our own ethical compass or code of ethics we live by based on our personal and professional beliefs and experiences. Violating our individual code of ethics can create a difficult personal situation. Perhaps the most difficult situation arises when our friends, family members, or colleagues act in a manner that you find questionable. How would you make a decision in such instances? Would you make your decision based on your code of ethics, or would you ignore it because of your close relationship with the person who appears to be acting unethically?

## Research Findings of Ethics in EHS

In order to combat such compromises, Jan Wachter (2011), an associate professor in the Department of Safety Sciences at Indiana University of Pennsylvania, advocates following an ethics-based safety management approach. He proposes we move away from the traditional safety-management approach based on compliance and loss control to ethics-based safety management programs. Following an ethics-based system allows ethical decisions to be incorporated into the work process, creating multiple opportunities to consider the most ethical actions to take. Senior management must be on board in order to incorporate an ethics-based safety system into the work process and practices. Ideally, they must move away from simple compliance, cost-benefit analyses, and risk reduction to simply doing what is right. Organizational change begins with management truly valuing employees and safety culture.

According to Kapp and Parboteeah (2008), "Organizational climate symbolizes what an organization truly values and is revealed through the shared perceptions of employees as to the kinds of behaviors that are encouraged, supported and rewarded within an organization." The ethical climate includes personal safety ethics of individuals and the ethics included in the safety culture of the organization. The ethical climate incorporates the organization's shared perceptions about what behaviors are considered right or wrong. The three types of ethical climates seen in organizations include (a) utilitarian or benevolent, (b) principled, and (c) egoist. Utilitarian or benevolent climates revolve around doing the most good for the most people. Principled climates support fundamental truths, such as doing the right thing or obeying the law. Egoist climates promote self-interest (Kapp and Parboteeah 2008).

Research conducted by Kapp and Parboteeah (2008) found that the utilitarian climate was associated with fewer injuries but not with stronger motivation to improve safety. Workers in principled climates showed more motivation to comply with rules, while the egoist climate had neither positive nor negative associations with injuries and safety motivation. The research concluded that there is no ideal climate within organizations. The best action to take is not to try to change the ethical climate but to figure out what the climate is and then connect with and adapt to it.

Kapp (2012) also identified that personal ethics plays an important role in safety performance. He found that first-line supervisors who had a strong commitment to personal safety could positively influence their subordinates, even in an organization with a negative ethical climate. He also found the opposite—that first-line supervisors who had poor safety ethics could negatively influence subordinates even though the organizational climate as a whole was positive.

The goal of EHS professionals is to do their best with what they are given. EHS professionals are most comfortable when organizational ethics match with their personal ethics. Often this is not the case. Organizational policy will not always match with what the EHS professional believes to be right or wrong. They must be change agents in the organization, sometimes working in places where safety commitment is lacking. It can be uncomfortable at times, but safety professionals must stick with their ethical values and make the case for safety (Kapp 2012).

Many experienced EHS professionals probably have learned that ethical dilemmas are much more common than the novice EHS professional may realize. Furthermore, not all members belonging to of a professional society, who are supposed to follow ethical standards, always follow the rules and guidelines established by their societies. According to Lack, about 15 percent of a group will not follow the rules. His

EHS professionals are most comfortable when organizational ethics match with their personal ethics. Often this is not the case.

comments were based on research conducted by experts in ethics (Lack 2001). In a study Burgess and Mullen conducted in England in 2002, they found that 77 percent of a group of industrial hygienists reported witnessing acts of potential ethical misconduct. The majority of the industrial hygienists surveyed worked for the government, the military, or industry (Burgess and Mullen 2002). Based on the above information, it should not be surprising that EHS professionals will not always conform to commonly accepted behaviors in the organization.

## Using a Safety Program as an Approach to Build an Ethical Organization

Krause (2007) states that a safety program can be the starting point for building an ethical organization. Ethics ties closely with a corporate social responsibility. Corporate social responsibility includes employees, customers, shareholders, and the community at large. The company must decide how to fulfill its obligations to employees, customers, shareholders, and the community while ensuring long-term sustainability. Many safety leaders believe that a safe workplace lays the foundation for organizational excellence and integrity in strategic, financial, and operational performance.

Below, you will find those five ethical principles of safety leaders (left column) and five key cultural factors predictive of desired ethical and safety outcomes often seen in a principle-driven culture (right column) as identified by Krause (2007).

A safety program led by men and women with strong ethical principles can enhance and create an

**Table 6.1** Ethical principles and cultural factors affecting safety

| Ethical principles of safety leaders | Cultural factors predictive of desired ethical and safety outcomes |
|---|---|
| 1. **Value for human life**—The belief that preservation and protection of human life supersedes other goods.<br>2. **Integrity**—The commitment to telling the truth and keeping promises, plus applying the best of one's abilities, promotes worker loyalty and commitment.<br>3. **Justice**—A strong sense of fair dealing with employees establishes trust between leaders and their reports.<br>4. **The good of the many**—A belief that excellence stems from a concern for the achievement of the common good, as opposed to what is good just for the individual person or company.<br>5. **Excellence**—The belief that whatever degree of safety or integrity we have achieved, we always have the opportunity to improve. | 1. **Procedural justice**—If leaders seem to be making decisions in fair ways, workers assume they can follow instructions without fear of mistreatment.<br>2. **Open and candid upward communications**—In an environment where supervisors and other leaders respond well to communications from lower down in the organization, even to bad news, ethical issues are more likely to surface before they become a crisis.<br>3. **Inclination of workers to approach peers on sensitive issues**—A leader can foster a culture where it is acceptable and expected that employees approach each other about difficult issues surrounding safety, ethics, and other critical areas.<br>4. **Perceived organizational support for espoused values**—When employees see their leaders demonstrate a commitment to stated values, they are more likely to respond in kind.<br>5. **Management credibility**—Employees who see their managers as credible are more likely to take personal responsibility for their performance and support new initiatives. |

organizational culture with similar ideals. The safety program can be, and often is, the starting point for building an ethical organization.

## The Signs and Strategies for Coping with Unethical Practices

Many EHS professionals follow ethical leadership practices. Often, the reason many of them entered the profession is to help others do what is ethical in and of itself. Problems arise when senior leadership or those above the EHS manager practice unethical behavior for economic gain. Senior leadership often creates unrealistic goals or deadlines, pressuring those under them to get the job done. While it is understandable that the company needs to get the project done to become competitive in this global marketplace, such pressure e could negatively impact the organization. It often conflicts with safety and health practices, causing them to be cut back in order to fulfill the senior leadership's demands. Leemann (2012) describes these practices as "twisted leadership safety ethics." Leemann lists the leading indicators of unethical leaders, which include

1. leads with a bad safety attitude;
2. lies to his safety professionals, followers, and peers;
3. takes advantage of his safety professionals and followers;
4. takes personal credit for the safety group's accomplishments;
5. uses politics to gain power in an amoral manner;
6. does not focus on the common safety good of the organization;
7. does not support his safety professionals or his followers;
8. displays a "double-tongued" safety behavior or talks the talk;
9. sacrifices his safety professionals and followers for personal gain; and
10. fails to model the safety way for his followers.

Nielsen (1989) provides twelve strategies individuals can choose from when dealing with unethical behavior in an organization. His twelve strategies are as follows:

1. Secretly blow the whistle within the organization
2. Quietly blow the whistle, informing a responsible higher-level manager
3. Secretly threatening the offender with blowing the whistle
4. Secretly threatening a responsible manager with blowing the whistle outside the organization
5. Publicly threatening a responsible manager with blowing the whistle
6. Sabotage the implementation of the unethical behavior
7. Quietly refraining from implementing an unethical order or policy
8. Publicly blowing the whistle within the organization
9. Conscientiously objecting to an unethical policy or refusing to implement the policy
10. Indicating uncertainty about or refusing to support a cover-up in the event the individual and/or organization gets caught
11. Secretly blowing the whistle outside the organization
12. Publicly blowing the whistle outside the organization (Nielsen, 1989)

## Ethical Leadership

### Core Leadership Principles

Information from the homepage of Southeastern University (n. d.) provides a nice discussion of five core principles of leadership. The five core principles of ethical leadership can be traced back to the days of Aristotle. These principles span all industries and provide a foundation for the development of an ethics-based leadership style. Those core principles are:

1. Ethical leaders respect others.
2. Ethical leaders serve others.
3. Ethical leaders are just.
4. Ethical leaders are honest.
5. Ethical leaders build community. (Southeastern University n. d.)

### Ethical Leadership in the Military

Gary L. Winn discusses the trove of excellent research in leadership available from the United States military. He makes the point that most academic programs do not utilize the research conducted by the military. As pointed out in his article, the military has been training leaders for over two hundred years. A basic goal shared by both the military and EHS professionals concerns protecting people, property, and business efficacies for their organization (Winn 2014). The following quote is from his article: "While military institutions take four years to instill values-based leadership, they do so to produce leaders who put peoples' safety, health, and welfare before every decision each day and expect the same of their subordinates" (Winn 2014). Since EHS professionals should be leaders in an organization, the above concepts should considered.

> A basic goal shared by both the military and EHS professionals concerns protecting people, property, and business efficacies for their organization.

## Examples of Questionable Behavior

If you are currently enrolled in a college class or have recently graduated from a college, you will undoubtedly face situations such as those presented above and will need to take appropriate action. You will probably be among the group of EHS professionals who drive the safety profession for the next thirty to forty years. As a result, the authors would like to share some important and helpful guidelines that may help future EHS professionals in such encounters.

This section provides several cases dealing with a variety of questionable behaviors by both students and professionals that the authors have experienced or learned of from other sources. While these are not clear ethical dilemmas, they do raise some serious issues for the participants. Some of these are likely to be faced by EHS professionals. Some of these are things that have occurred, while others are examples of things that could occur. In all cases, there can be differences in how individuals view the issue.

### Cases/Scenarios

The first group of examples comes from the authors' experience teaching over a twenty-one-year time period.

Students involved in academic dishonesty. The methods vary and include:

- Cheat notes scribbled on a body part or item of clothing. A colleague in another department observed one student wearing a baseball cap who appeared to be praying. The student had written answers on the underside of the bill of his cap.
- While taking a test, one student looks at another student's test.
- A student uses a cell phone to access the course website for answers.
- A student shares answers on homework with another student.
- A student uses graded homework from a previous semester that the student obtained from a friend.
- Students ask other students to sign their names on the signature sheet so they can sleep in.

The next few examples involve EHS professionals who may be interacting with EHS students:

- Students who are performing an internship do a project at the request of their supervisor. They produce a product, but their supervisor presents it as his or her own without giving the student any credit. The authors tell students who report this occurrence to be very careful with how they respond. In a perfect world that should not happen, but it does. The student is an unknown to most of the company personnel, so the company leadership may take the word of their employee over that of the student intern.
- An EHS professional states disparaging comments about an organization or program based on hearsay. In other words, they know very little about the subject but repeat what they heard from other EHS professionals and do so in a public

setting. This has happened to the authors on some occasions. In these instances, the person making the public statements was repeating what they heard from other people. Students, do not—we repeat, do not—say disparaging remarks in a public setting about issues on which you have no first-hand knowledge.

Do not, we repeat, do not say disparaging remarks, in a public setting, about issues on which you have no first-hand knowledge

- EHS professionals who work for a government agency take a government car home against the rules to save themselves time the next morning.
- Government employees on government business trips check into a more expensive hotel, get the receipt, then check out and stay at a cheaper hotel and keep the difference.
- Company representatives offer money to government inspectors to "modify" sampling results so they can "meet" the standard.
- An acquaintance who is a certified industrial hygienist (CIH) tells one of the authors that he knows of another CIH who is doing unethical activities and asks the author (who does not have first-hand knowledge of the activities) to report the second CIH to ABIH.
- Canned program. Companies sell training programs, but the EHS professionals who work for the company know that the program doesn't fit every company that buys the program.
- In a blind review of a grant application, unnamed reviewers made the following paraphrased statement: "This faculty cannot be expected to teach research skills as they have limited research experience." This statement concerned a faculty with two members who retired from a government research entity, and both had worked on multiple research studies. One faculty member had supervised other researchers in this government entity.
- From another blind review comes the following statement, once again paraphrased. The authors report a certification success rate of about 50 percent. This is low for an EHS academic program. Our response to that was "low based on what?" At that time, very few EHS programs were reporting alumni success in obtaining certification. This claim was baseless, but due to the blind review, there was little that could be done to counter the claim.
- Finally, we offer one additional example from the author's experience. This incident involved government supervisors who enforced their agency's rule prohibiting government employees providing food for guests taking training courses or participating in government meetings, yet they readily provided food when the supervisor's superiors attended meetings.

For each of the scenarios presented above, the authors ask the reader to consider whether the actions of the EHS professional were ethical. The authors' answer is "it depends." We have provided some suggestions as to what the person observing, hearing, or experiencing can do to rectify some of the issues.

Reading the case studies in Wachter's AIHA guide (2014) to ethics will give you a better appreciation of the types of issues that can arise when you leave college and enter the fascinating world of an EHS professional. We have described the ethical aspects as sometimes murky. It is the authors' belief that you will find often it so. We trust you will be able to navigate the ins and outs of the EHS profession's ethical environment. Our advice to our students—and all other students—is to research the professional standards and codes of ethics for your profession. Take as many courses and workshops on ethics as you can. If possible, take an ethics course in college. Interact with EHS professionals to find out how they function. The authors have helped present ethics lectures at EHS workshops and full-day professional development conferences (PDCs). If you really want to learn more about ethics, volunteer to teach it. Experts in adult learning suggest that teaching is the best way to learn and retain information.

Following are selected cases from the AIHA Ethics publication. The authors only present the initial description and encourage the reader to obtain and read the complete case study from Wachter's publication (2014).

- An industrial hygienist realizes his company may have received a major contract due to his familial connection with the client.
- A safety manager is directed by the corporate office not to record an injury (but to pay out worker's compensation cost for it) so that safety performance measures and subsequent bonuses are achieved.
- An industrial hygienist believes a homeowner has a significant exposure risk but cannot disclose confidential data to her.
- A human resources (HR) manager is feeling pressure to reduce the rigor of safety training and the time allocated to it.
- A product safety specialist keeps getting fired for pointing out his employers' lack of regulatory compliance.
- A safety coordinator offers a training class that he is not certified to teach.
- A junior industrial hygienist is unsure about confessing to a mathematical error and reissuing a sampling and analysis report.
- An EHS directory bypasses normal recruitment procedures and hires a former coworker with minimum qualifications as the associate EHS director.

Our advice to our students—and all other students—is to research the professional standards and codes of ethics for your profession. Take as many courses and workshops on ethics as you can. If possible, take an ethics course in college. Interact with EHS professionals to find out how they function.

## Reflection and Suggestions

The information presented in this chapter is not meant to answer all questions that may arise concerning ethical issues in the environmental health and safety discipline. The purpose of this chapter is to provide readers an awareness of the ethical dilemmas they may face in the EHS profession. The authors trust that readers will benefit from the information and recommendations provided in this chapter to aid their decisions should they face an ethical situation. Fortunately, there are numerous publications on the topic of ethics in environmental health and safety that can be used as references. As stated previously, different people often view a situation in differing ways. Not everyone considers an event to have the same meaning. No one should consider the examples discussed in this chapter as concrete evidence of wrong-doing. Unless there is a prohibition against some action, and in addition those responsible for maintaining the standards are willing to intercede, no one is likely to be held accountable. In addition, EHS professionals must be willing to take a stand against unprofessional actions. Humans are not machines who will always do what is expected.

Different people often view a situation in differing ways. Not everyone considers an event to have the same meaning.

The authors encourage students and recent graduates to take the issue of ethics seriously and immerse themselves in ethics literature. The time devoted to this endeavor will be worth the benefits. The authors offer the following advice:

- Learn the rules of the organization or society you are a member of so you are not caught unaware.
- Do your work as if you would have to defend it in a court. Many EHS practitioners will do just that. Even if you never end up in court defending your professional work, you will be better able to withstand challenges to previous work you have done. Just because you are honest and try to be ethical in your work, that does not mean you will not be challenged.
- As discussed by Manuele (2014), upper management sets the culture for an organization. Be selective in choosing the organization you work for. Interviews for employment should be a two-

way street. Assess how passionate the organization is about ethical behavior. If you find you made a mistake and determine that changing the culture is unlikely, start looking for a new place to work.
- Continue to immerse yourself in activities that focus on ethics, such as reading and participating in professional society meetings at both the local and national level.
- Maintain a network of trusted colleagues that you can depend on for advice and counsel.
- Never let money be the overriding factor in the company and job you select for your employment.

In this chapter, the authors have provided students and young EHS professionals some perspectives on the early ethical codes, some of the primary ethical concepts, some confounding issues that ethics often involves, and tips for navigating ethical dilemmas they may face. The authors hope the above information is helpful for students and newly graduated EHS professionals as they progress through their EHS careers.

## Questions

1. What is the definition of ethics?
2. Explain why many ethics experts view religion as one of the foundational underpinnings for ethics.
3. Explain why potential unethical behavior is often not a definitive "yes or no" as far as an individual's actions are concerned.
4. List the six recommendations (advice) on ethical issues provided by the authors.
5. If an action is legal, is it also always ethical?

## References

American Board of Industrial Hygiene (ABIH). (2007). Code of Ethics. Accessed May 19, 2017. http://www.abih.org/sites/default/files/downloads/ABIHCodeofEthics.pdf.

Birch, M., D. Elliot, and M. Trankel. (2000). "Black and White and Shades of Gray: A Portrait of the Ethical Professor." *Ethics and Behavior*. Accessed May 22, 2017. http://www.tandfonline.com/ doi/abs/10.1207/s15327019eb09035?journalCode=hebh20. Published online 8 Jan 2010.

Board of Certified Safety Professionals (BCSP). (2016). Code of Ethics. Accessed May 20, 2017. http://www.bcsp.org/Portals/0/Assets/DocumentLibrary/BCSPcodeofethics.pdf.

Bruhn, J. G. (2009). "The Functionality of Gray Area Ethics in Organization." *Journal of Business Ethics*. Accessed May 22, 2017. shttp://link.springer.com/article/10.1007%2Fs10551-008-9994-7?LI=true.

Burgess, G. L., and D. Mullen. (2002). "Observations of Ethical Misconduct among Industrial Hygienists in England." *AIHA Journal* 63: 151–54.

Hamarneh, S. K. (1993). "Practical Ethics in the Health Professions. Part I—The Hammurabi and Hippocratic Codes." *PubMed* 36(1): 11–24. Accessed May 21, 2017. https://www.ncbi.nlm.nih. gov/pubmed/11652804.

Jennings M. M. (2007). "Seven Signs of Ethical Collapse." Markkula Center for Applied Ethics. Santa Clara University. Accessed May 22, 2017. https://www.scu.edu/ethics/focus-areas/business-ethics/resources/seven-signs-of-ethical-collapse/.

Johnson, A. (2012). "Safety Ethics: Black and White? Or Shades of Gray?" *Safety+Health*. Accessed May 22, 2017. http://www.safetyandhealthmagazine.com/articles/safety-ethics-2.

Kapp E. A. (2012). "The Influence of Supervisor Leadership Practices and Perceived Group Safety Climate on Employee Safety Performance." *Safety Science* 50(4): 1119–24.

Kapp E. A., and K. P. Parboteeah. (2008). "Ethical Climate and Safety Performance." *Professional Safety* 53(7): 28–31.

Krause, T. R. (2007). "The Ethics of Safety." *Occupational Hazards* 69(6): 28.

Lack, R. (2001). *Safety, Health and Asset Protection: Management Essentials*. Boca Raton, FL: Lewis Publishers.

Leemann, J. E. (2010). "Systems Thinking: Twisted Leadership Safety Ethics." *Industrial Safety and Hygiene News (ISHN)* 44(6): 18.

Leemann, J. E. (2012). "Ethics Are Easily Muddled." *ISHN* 46(9): 20, 22.

Manuele, F. A. (2014). *Advanced Safety Management: Focusing on Z10 and Serious Injury Prevention* (2nd ed.). Hoboken, NJ: John Wiley & Sons, Inc.

*Merriam-Webster Dictionary* (n. d.). Accessed May 20, 2017. https://www.merriam-webster.com/dictionary/ethic.

National Fire Protection Association (n. d.). "Codes and Standards for the Built Environment." In Chapter 3: NFPA. https://www.nfpa.org/-/media/Files/Forms-and-premiums/Fire-Protection-Handbook/codesfph.ashx-

?la=en&hash=314C9254F5053A13AD23332C65A01F8F-D21EC28E.

Nielsen, R. P. (1989). "Changing Unethical Organizational Behavior." *The Academy of Management Executive* 3(2): 123.

Oxford Biblical Studies Online (n. d.). "Golden Rule." Accessed May 20, 2017. http://www.oxfordbiblicalstudies.com/article/opr/t94/e775.

Saatci, E. Y. (2014). "Management through the Lenses of Ancient People." *International Journal of Social Science and Humanity* 4(5). Accessed May 20, 2017. http://www.ijssh.org/papers/377-C00021.pdf.

Southeastern University. (n. d.). "Five Principles of Ethical Leadership." Accessed May 19, 2017. http:// homepages.se.edu/cvonbergen/files/2012/12/Principles-of-Ethical-Leadership 1.pdf.

The American Society of Civil Engineers (2011). The ASCE Code of Ethics Principles, Study, And Application. Accessed May 21, 2017. http://www.asce.org/uploadedFiles/About_ASCE/Ethics/Content_Pieces /ASCE-Code-Of-Ethics-2012-FINAL-HIGH.pdf.

Wachter, J. K. (2011). "Ethics: The Absurd yet Preferred Approach to Safety Management." *Professional Safety* 56(6): 50.

Wachter, J. (2014). "Ethics for the Safety and Health Professional: Approaches and Case Studies." Falls Church, VA: American Industrial Hygiene Association.

Wade, D. T. (2005). "Ethics, Audit, and Research: All Shades of Grey." *British Medical Journal*; London 330.7489: 468.

Winn, G. L. (2014). "Safety Leadership Insights from Military Research." *Professional Safety* 59(1): 32–38.

CHAPTER 7

# QUALITIES AND BEST PRACTICES OF EHS LEADERS

Paulette Lantuh

## Learning Objectives

After studying this chapter, the reader will be able to:

1. Identify two best practices of EHS leaders
2. Explain why strong partnerships between EHS leaders and business leaders are necessary for success
3. Explain the significance of risk management as a fundamental technical competency
4. Identify practical actions to organize the technical work and gain in-depth knowledge of the business' EHS issues
5. Identify a process and resources to develop a professional competency development plan
6. Explain challenges and problem solving approaches identified by exceptional EHS leaders

## Key Terms

**Best practices, EHS leaders, general industry, professional development, business value, risk management, technical competency, personal effectiveness**

## Abstract

Environmental, health, and safety (EHS) professionals play a crucial role in enabling enterprises to operate in the global marketplace. The responsibilities of EHS professionals are extensive and comprehensive, including striving to achieve a workplace that maintains the safety and health of employees and to ensure compliant operations and products, all while protecting the environment, company assets, and reputation. Successful EHS initiatives contribute to business value and profitability. These outcomes are best achieved when EHS professionals demonstrate competence through strong technical and leadership skills and partner with business leaders to align EHS initiatives with the goals and objectives of the enterprise.

The best practices in this chapter provide guidance for EHS professionals who desire to be recognized as EHS leaders. EHS leaders who consistently deliver positive EHS results are often sought after for positions of greater responsibility and complexity, leading to enriching career opportunities, advancement, and personal satisfaction from achieving business objectives and protecting people and the environment.

The continual development of technical competence and alignment of EHS with the business are presented as significant, impactful best practices of EHS leaders based on literature and empirical evidence. Definitions of terms, foundational principles, a roadmap of practical activities to organize the work, and recommendations from exceptional EHS leaders are provided to explain the best practices.

## Introduction

In all industries, leaders share best practices on successful approaches that create positive outcomes. For those implementing best practices, it is beneficial to learn from and apply others' experiences to drive results such as improved performance, productivity, and competitive advantage. In highly dynamic global markets, today's EHS professionals are called upon to protect people, facilities, and the environment and reduce risk, as well as create value and profitability for the business. This chapter provides EHS best practices based on literature and empirical evidence to help EHS professionals develop and demonstrate strong technical, leadership, and business skills that advance and mature EHS, business, and operating outcomes.

> EHS leaders with consistent, positive track records are sought after for positions of greater responsibility and complexity, leading to enriching career opportunities, advancement, and personal satisfaction.

The chapter begins with a definition of terms, followed by explanation of the best practices from three perspectives:

1. Foundational principles on the relationship between business leaders and EHS leaders and the significance of risk management as a fundamental EHS competency
2. Roadmap of practical activities to organize and prioritize the work, gain in-depth knowledge of the business, and develop a plan to continuously develop and strengthen competency
3. Insights and recommendations from exceptional EHS leaders

## Definition of Terms

In this chapter, the terms *occupational health and safety (OHS) professional*, *environmental, health, and safety (EHS) professional*, and *EHS leader* are used.

The basis for the role of the occupational health and safety professional is the *OHS Professional Capability Framework* published by the International Network of Safety and Health Practitioner Organisations.

The *OHS Professional Capability Framework* outlines seven dimensions to describe the areas of activity of the OHS professional:

1. systems management approach
2. organizational OHS culture
3. OHS risk management processes
4. measurement and evaluation of OHS performance
5. knowledge management
6. communication, engagement, and influence
7. professional and ethical practice (INSHPO 2015)

Many OHS professionals working in general industry for enterprises that operate facilities and sell products or services have integrated responsibilities that also include environmental scope. The same agents and exposures that are managed from a health and safety perspective are also managed from an environmental perspective. In addition, several dimensions outlined by the *OHS Professional Capability Framework*, such as management systems, risk management, and performance management, are often implemented as integrated EHS systems. By extension, the term *EHS* is used to represent the broadest application of occupational environmental, health, and safety responsibilities.

The term *EHS leaders* is used to describe career EHS professionals who are champions of and advocates for healthy workers, safe workplaces, and well-managed environmental impacts. EHS leaders maintain high standards for ethics and performance, influence management, engage people, drive results, and meet or exceed the expectations of stakeholders by making significant contributions that protect people, the environment, and the business.

## Two Foundational Principles

The following two principles—the relationship between EHS leaders and business leaders and risk management as a fundamental technical competency—are essential to EHS leadership because the principles establish optimal relationships with decision makers and provide structure to guide the technical work.

### Relationship between Business Leaders and EHS Leaders

The literature contains many ideas on best practices and successful leadership approaches. There is strong agreement in the belief that leadership and involvement of top management are essential to success.

The European Agency for Safety and Health at Work studied the literature and case studies from sixteen countries in the European Union. The analysis concluded that OHS improvements will be made only with a prevention culture driven by the organization's leaders and that leadership and management factors have the most impact on whether OHS measures succeed or fail (EU-OSHA 2012).

> Top management leadership and involvement are imperative to EHS success. EHS cannot be performed as an isolated function; EHS must be integrated with the business for overall success.

The National Institute for Occupational Safety and Health published guidance for establishing effective worker health programs. Best and promising practices include the need for a human-centered organizational culture, engagement of supervisors and managers at all levels, and demonstrated leadership in words and actions (NIOSH 2008).

The International Standard ISO 14001 Environmental Management Systems (2015) indicates that the success factors of an environmental management system are dependent on commitment from all levels and functions of the organization, led by top management. Top management can effectively address its risks and opportunities by integrating environmental management into the organization's business process, strategic direction, and decision-making, aligning them with other business priorities and incorporating environmental governance into its overall management system (ISO 2015).

The International Network of Safety and Health Practitioner Organization created a business-value pyramid that conceptualizes the relationship between OHS professionals and business value. At the base of the pyramid, the body of knowledge is represented as the foundation of professional practice. Qualifications, experience, professional certification, roles and tasks, and personal attributes lead to business value, with the potential to deliver business value dependent on actual support for OHS and the OHS professional (INSHPO 2014).

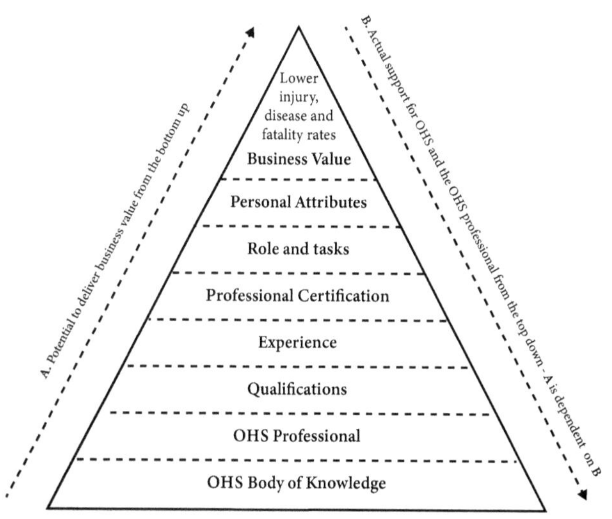


Figure 7.1
Conceptualizing the relationship between the occupational health and safety profession and business value (the value pyramid)

These examples clearly demonstrate the importance of management ownership and involvement. Business leaders are ultimately responsible for business performance, including EHS performance and culture. EHS leaders leverage their technical knowledge to educate, coach, influence, enable, and support the business in the achievement of its initiatives. Although some might consider a supportive role a diminished one, perhaps even suggesting an inability to make decisions, solve problems, or implement solutions, a partnership between business leaders and EHS leaders is a position of strength. When EHS leaders' technical expertise is combined with knowledge of the business's operations, products, and services, it creates solutions that add value to the business. A perfect textbook solution won't be considered successful if it is not supported by the business, and without a receptive partner, the best technical advice is useless. EHS leaders who effectively engage business leaders through strong partnerships and integration with business strategies at all levels of the organization enable EHS solutions that protect people and the environment and also benefit the bottom line.

## Significance of Risk Management as a Fundamental Technical Competency

Risk management is a fundamental technical competency applicable across the broad spectrum of practice. EHS leaders use risk management concepts daily, formally and informally, to evaluate the significance of issues and communicate recommendations and action plans. Risk provides a common language for communicating with decision makers, especially when explaining the significance of hazards or justifying why or why not to spend money. Risk-based management systems ensure that an organization systematically addresses the most important issues. EHS leaders who demonstrate proficiency with a variety of risk-assessment methodologies and comprehensively apply risk-management principles to their work are equipped to address complex challenges already at hand as well as new challenges introduced by change.

> Risk management is the most fundamental and valuable competency for EHS leaders.

American Society of Safety Professionals president Tom Cecich (2016–2017) speaks about the importance of risk management:

> Complying with regulations is how organizations obey the law. Identifying, assessing, mitigating, managing and communicating workplace risk is how organizations gain competitive advantage or achieve mission success. There is another compelling reason to focus on workplace risk: Senior management understands the concept of managing risk, whether it is operational risk, financial risk, reputational risk, market risk or a similar business concern. When we communicate in terms of workplace risk, we clearly define for management the need to act and plainly describe the potential consequences of inaction. We deliver the greatest value to our organizations and clients when we use our technical knowledge to identify and assess risks, then apply our business skills to develop and communicate effective solutions. By doing so, we protect workers and ultimately contribute directly to our organizations' success. (ASSE 2016)

A case study demonstrates the power of risk management to create quantifiable business value. John Piampiano, MS, CSP, has over 25 years of EHS experience working with large, multinational manufacturing companies and is a thought leader on risk assessment through his participation on ANSI standard writing and technical report subcommittees: B11.TR3-2000 (Risk Assessment and Risk Reduction—A Guideline to Estimate, Evaluate and Reduce Risks Associated with Machine Tools); B11.0-2015 (Safety of Machinery; General Requirements and Risk Assessment); and B11.19-2010 (Performance Requirements for Safeguarding). In his current role as a senior technology manager for a Fortune 100 company, Piampiano manages a risk-based enterprise-wide strategy and program to prioritize and evaluate projects for funding. Piampiano overcame the challenge of variable and subjective scores from different users by applying a customized risk assessment methodology that quantifies severity scores of various injuries (e.g., burns, lacerations, fractures, electric shock, falls) based on medical and anthropometric data and standardizes probability scores by linking the likelihood of their occurrence to the reliability and effectiveness of controls. For example, behavior-based administrative controls (e.g., personal protective equipment) have low reliability and effectiveness and therefore a high likelihood of occurrence. Secondary engineering controls (e.g., a fixed barrier guard with an interlock) have high reliability and effectiveness and a very low likelihood of occurrence. This risk-assessment program has been institutionalized throughout his company worldwide. The many benefits include

- consistent analysis and understanding of hazards and associated risks
- identification of all viable options to reduce residual risk
- consistent risk-based decision making criteria and risk tolerance (acceptance) thresholds throughout the company
- foundation for informed risk-based decisions within senior leadership teams
- common language for senior leaders to employ when framing risk-based messages
- sustainable process for leveraging corporate resources (staff, capital, senior leader focus areas)
- management accountability and responsibility for decisions
- employee engagement at multiple levels of the organization
- prioritization of current and future work based on a robust model
- streamlined, efficient, and cost-effective process for continuously and systematically reducing risk

In this case study, risk assessment was applied to machinery and machinery safeguards and extended to other hazards and exposures, such as burns, lacerations, fractures, electric shock, and falls. In reality, the basic risk assessment process (i.e., the identification of hazard or exposure, severity, probability, controls, and estimation of potential for harm) is consistently applied to managing most hazards and exposures that EHS professionals encounter in the workplace. Examples include assessments of exposure to chemicals, noise, and radiation; ergonomic evaluations of force, posture, and repetition; and industry-specific applications (e.g., hazard and operability studies and fault tree analysis) in the chemical, oil, and gas industries.

This case study also highlights a standard approach to developing technical competency:

- Learn the science and engineering principles, theory, and methodology associated with the subject.
- Benchmark best practices and approaches used in industry.
- Customize their application to the needs of the employer, continuously refining and improving the approach based on lessons learned and needs.
- Standardize use, educate stakeholders, and integrate the practice into the business process.
- Involve business leaders and senior management for leadership and support.
- Provide ongoing oversight and stewardship.

## Practical Activities to Organize the Work, Align with the Business, and Strengthen Competency

This section contains a list of practical activities to organize the work, gain in-depth knowledge of the business's EHS issues, and develop a plan to continuously develop and strengthen competency.

A typical day for an EHS professional often includes routine EHS activities such as inspections, management of change reviews, compliance requirements, scorecard updates, training, meetings, and tours. Unplanned events such as a regulatory agency visits, permit exceedance, medical emergencies, or product recall may occur. Fulfilling job responsibilities, targeting business needs and risks, providing meaningful technical advice, and effectively engaging with stakeholders may be challenging. It is logical for an EHS professional to ask *what are the top priorities, how should the work be organized, and what actions will be the most impactful?*

The following activities will help the EHS professional identify business issues, priorities, and risks; establish credibility within the organization; and identify impactful actions.

1. **Develop key relationships, tour the operations, and make customer visits to become familiar with products and services.** Obtain input on EHS concerns, business challenges, and risks. Become familiar with the flow of chemicals, materials, and equipment from the point of entry to use, storage, distribution, and end-of-life.
2. **Establish routine updates with senior leaders and supervisors.** Senior leaders are often interested in strategy, policy, performance, and significant issues that can significantly impact personnel, product, and the community. Supervisors are often interested in issues that directly affect their people's safety, well-being, productivity, and cost. Product managers are interested in issues that impact markets, suppliers, customers, competitors, and supply chain.
3. **Learn what is currently being done to comply with regulations and manage risk.** Initially this step involves talking to people within the business and reviewing information, but over time, it will evolve to verifying the accuracy and appropriateness of the information and systems.
4. **Establish a process to track emerging issues and regulatory changes.** Sources of information include subscriptions to government newsletters, paid subscriptions to services that monitor regulations and trends, and participation in industry-specific organizations and trade associations.
5. **Learn the business strategies for investments, growth, and management of unprofitable or non-strategic parts of the business.** Work with business leaders to analyze EHS aspects and initiatives to support the business strategy, such as expansion or closure of facilities, new technology developments, addition or removal of product line, acquisition of new businesses, changes in go-to-market models, and changes in supplier or product sourcing.

Integration of EHS into the business's operations, products, and services is critical to enabling success and delivering positive results in terms of profitability, productivity, competitive advantage, brand image, and reputation.

Sustainability is becoming a business practice driven by the investment community. Sustainable business practices can make the business and brand better and more profitable. Safety and health initiatives, particularly as part of a broad sustainability effort, can positively affect an organization's brand and long-term viability. Successful EHS professionals who understand sustainability principles and can communicate with senior management using the language of business about how sustainability affects their

**Table 7.1** Key relationships

| Operational Focus | Product Focus |
|---|---|
| • Operations and maintenance supervisors<br>• Facility manager<br>• Team leaders and employees on all shifts<br>• Contacts from related EHS disciplines (e.g., industrial hygienist, ergonomist, environmental engineer, occupational medical professionals)<br>• Human resources manager | • Product development engineers<br>• Product managers<br>• Sales, service, marketing managers<br>• Liaisons with key customers |
| • Warehousing managers<br>• Purchasing managers<br>• Legal staff | |

Table 7.2 Information related to status of EHS compliance and risk

<table>
<tr><th>Operational Focus</th><th>Product Focus</th></tr>
<tr><td colspan="2">• EHS policy<br>• Management system document or EHS manual<br>• Management system certifications (e.g., ISO 14001, OHSAS 18001, ISO 9001)<br>• Environmental aspects and impacts<br>• Risk assessments<br>• Master requirements document, including regulatory applicability and training<br>• Leading and lagging performance measures<br>• Schedule of due dates for compliance requirements (e.g. inspections, reports, permits)<br>• Corrective action logs<br>• Audit and inspection reports</td></tr>
<tr><td>• Hazards, exposures, and controls<br>• Safe work instructions for employees<br>• Training programs<br>• Injury logs, near-miss reports<br>• Emergency procedures<br>• Chemical list<br>• Repetitive maintenance tasks for safety critical components such as sprinklers, alarms, safety interlocks, monitoring equipment<br>• Waste disposal profiles, sewer and emission permits</td><td>• Customer- and country-specific requirements<br>• Supplier expectations<br>• Supplier compliance and conformance documents<br>• Specifications for products, parts, and packaging<br>• Product declarations of environmental aspects and attributes of products (e.g., TSCA, REACH, RoHS declarations of conformity)<br>• Product life cycle assessments<br>• Product safety testing reports<br>• Voluntary sustainability commitments (e.g., EPEAT or ENERGYSTAR™ ecolabels)<br>• Product end-of-life management</td></tr>
</table>

organizations will only become more relevant to their organizations and their sustainability strategy. EHS professionals who align their organization's safety and health initiatives with existing sustainability strategies can create value for their company's overall workplace safety and health objectives (Hill and Seabrook 2013).

6. **Establish a personal development plan.** Continual improvement of knowledge, skills, and abilities is necessary to remain relevant, demonstrate credibility and value, and meet the challenges of the profession. The EHS field is broad, and the global workplace is always changing. The body of knowledge develops, technology evolves, and personal aspirations and career goals change. Each professional should create and manage a personal development plan that is a continuous improvement cycle of needs assessment, self-assessment, and capability development in the areas of technical expertise, personal effectiveness, and functional expertise specific to the employer's business and EHS issues.

   Technical expertise is the foundation of EHS leadership and includes proficiency with the body of knowledge, education, and certification. Certainly, outstanding and accomplished EHS leaders without degrees or certification effectively lead within their scope and situation. However,

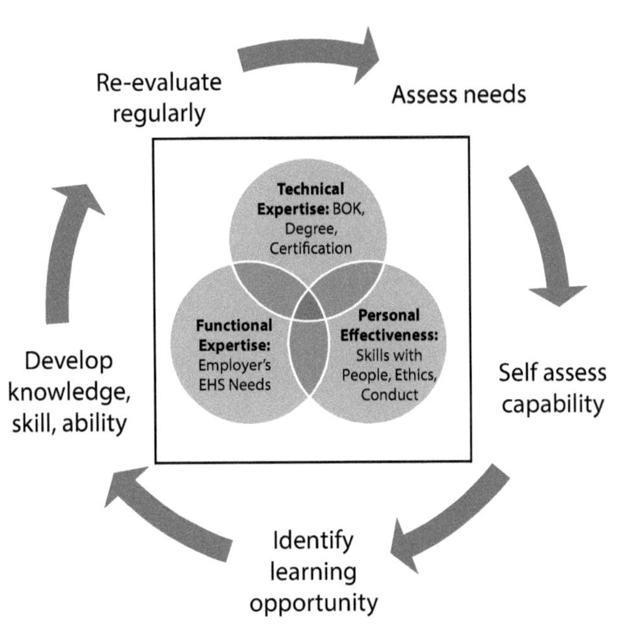


Figure 7.2
Personal development cycle

degrees and certification are best practices because of the systematic, comprehensive preparation and broad exposure to the requisite knowledge and skills applicable to the broad spectrum of practice.

Strong communication skills enable EHS leaders to execute their technical EHS work positively, respectfully, and effectively. Leadership requires personal effectiveness skills, such as creating a high-performing team capable of diverse thought, empowering others, achieving consensus, and resolving conflict. Leaders strive to continually improve their personal effectiveness skills through training, practice, self-reflection, and feedback. Many companies invest in development of personal effectiveness skills and offer leadership-development training. Company training promotes engagement with other employees, strengthens networks and relationships, and provides insight into company culture and core values. Group experiential training for natural work teams strengthens working relationships and develops leadership competencies broadly within the organization. This training often includes a mentor or sponsor for the trainee to obtain ongoing support and collaboration.

Changes such as updated regulations and standards, new job assignments, new business initiatives, new technology, and so on trigger reevaluation of applicability and needs. Learning opportunities take many forms depending on complexity of the learning objective. An effective plan balances multiple types of learning

**Table 7.3** Examples of EHS initiatives that align with business initiatives

| Operational Focus | Product Focus |
|---|---|
| • Third-party certification of facilities (e.g., ISO 14001, OHSAS 18001)<br>• Reduction of emissions<br>• Reduction of hazardous waste<br>• Reduction of water usage<br>• Reduction of energy usage<br>• Reduction of greenhouse gas emissions<br>• Reduction of carbon footprint<br>• Reduction of workplace injury rate<br>• Increased recycling<br>• Increased landfill free waste | • Improved energy efficiency based on life cycle assessments<br>• Reduction in packaging materials or component weights<br>• Elimination of restricted materials<br>• Attainment of voluntary eco labels and sustainability initiatives<br>• Improved processes with first-, second-, and third-tier suppliers<br>• Increased take-back and recycling programs<br>• Reduction of carbon footprint and greenhouse gas emissions |

opportunities such as training, conferences, formal mentoring programs, membership in and service to professional societies, participation in industry associations, and on-the-job learning experiences.

Actively manage your personal development plan to remain relevant, demonstrate credibility and value, and meet the challenges of the profession.

Ideally, the professional development plan is reviewed regularly with supervisors to incorporate input and ensure support. It is the EHS leader's responsibility to actively manage his or her development plan in conjunction with the supervisor. It is helpful to ask about the company's investment in competency development and, if not

**Table 7.4** Resources for competency development

| Resources |
|---|
| **Body of Knowledge**<br>• OHS Professional Capability Framework: A Global Framework for Practice, Roles, Knowledge and Skills. http://www.inshpo.org/docs/INSHPO_2015-OHS_Professional_Capability_Framework.pdf<br>• Certified Safety Professional Blueprints and Study Sources. http://www.bcsp.org/CSP |
| **EHS Degree from Accredited Program**<br>• ABET Accredited Program Search. http://main.abet.org/aps/Accreditedprogramsearch.aspx<br>• BCSP Qualified Academic Programs. http://www.bcsp.org/Portals/0/Assets/DocumentLibrary/BCSP_GSP_QAP_List.pdf |
| **Certification**<br>• Certified Safety Professional. http://www.bcsp.org/CSP<br>• Safety Certifications at a Glance. http://www.bcsp.org/Certifications/Safety-Certifications-at-a-Glance<br>• American Board of Industrial Hygiene. "Become Certified." http://www.abih.org/become-certified<br>• Institute of Hazardous Materials Managers. CHMM. http://www.ihmm.org/certificants/chmm |
| **Professional Society, Networks, Peer Groups, Training**<br>• American Society of Safety Professionals. Practice Specialties and Common Interest Groups. http://www.assp.org/membership/communities<br>• American Society of Safety Professionals. Professional Development and Events http://www.assp.org/education<br>• American Society of Safety Professionals. Professional Safety Journal and archives http://www.assp.org/publications/professional-safety/archives<br>• American Society of Safety Professionals. Business of Safety Resource Center http://www.asse.org<br>• American Society of Safety Professionals. Risk Assessment Institute http://assp.org/advocacy/risk-assessment-institute |
| **Mentorship Program**<br>• American Society of Safety Professionals.Mentoring Program. http://assp.com/membership/communities |

*Continued*

**Table 7.4** Resources for competency development *(continued)*

| Industry Associations and Industry Specific Standards |
|---|
| • National Fire Protection Association. http://www.nfpa.org/<br>• American Petroleum Institute. http://www.api.org/. (see Products and Services. Standards)<br>• Semiconductor Industry Association. http://www.semiconductors.org/issues/environment/environment_safety_health/ (see Policy Priorities. Environment, Safety & Health) |
| **Personal Effectiveness Skills** |
| • Myers-Briggs Personality Inventory. http://www.myersbriggs.org/my-mbti-personality-type/mbti-basics/<br>• LPI ®: Leadership Practices Inventory®. http://www.leadershipchallenge.com/Leaders-Section-Assessments.aspx<br>• DiSC Dimensions of Behavior. https://www.discprofile.com/what-is-disc/overview/<br>• True Colors Personality Assessment. https://truecolorsintl.com/ |
| **On-the-Job Learning (examples)** |
| • Visit manufacturer of machine guards and safety interlocks<br>• Practice and obtain feedback on skills such as consensus building and conflict resolution<br>• Benchmark with similar companies on greenhouse gas emissions |

well supported, allocate time and funds to pursue educational opportunties independently.

Table 7.4 identifies resources for competency development.

## Best Practices from Exceptional EHS Leaders

Sage advice and lessons learned from experience enhance scholastic education. Two distinguished and well-respected industry EHS leaders were interviewed to obtain their ideas on best practices for early career EHS professionals.

The first leader was selected because of her ability to consistently bring out the best in people, inspire people to take action, transform situations wrought with significant challenges and adversity, and achieve remarkable results. Debra Schoch, MS, CIH, "had the privilege to lead" over 150 EHS professionals in her 30-year career in multiple senior EHS manager and director roles at Eastman Kodak Company.

Schoch explained that EHS professionals need certain skills beyond technical skills. They need to be good communicators and listeners, flexible in their thinking, quick on their feet to find creative ways to solve problems, and able to focus on priorities that lead clients in the right direction. Schoch identified these best practices for EHS professionals: (1) establish strong relationships with business leaders, (2) directly involve leaders in setting goals and selecting annual performance metrics, (3) recognize outstanding EHS performance by leaders, and (4) involve the team in recognizing and solving problems.

Schoch also shared successful problem-solving approaches for answering difficult questions, handling the discovery of a significant problem, and navigating emotionally charged issues. The advice for answering difficult questions such as "we've been doing this for years, what is the likelihood of an inspection?" is to articulate the reasons why action is necessary beyond compliance with a legal requirement and to explain how the action will benefit the company, environment, people in the organization, and the bottom line. A successful approach for discovery of a significant problem is to talk to the line leader before the situation is documented. Spend time together to diagnose the problem and agree on actions. Document the actions already in progress, work together to resolve issues, follow up, and keep track of progress. Finally, for emotional issues such as allegations of widespread indoor air quality problems or a cancer cluster, recognize that a third-party expert will be needed to provide an objective perspective and help to rebuild employee trust. In these situations, the EHS professional needs to explain to line leaders that this is how these situations are best handled and then assist in facilitating meetings with employees. Schoch advises EHS professionals to always to take the high road, adhere to the profession's code of ethics, and escalate if asked to compromise.

A second leader was invited to contribute to because of his leadership example during a period of dramatic business disruption. Despite significant challenges, this leader consistently delivered positive results to shareholders and left a legacy that is a world-class benchmark of EHS excellence. Dave Kiser, PhD, senior EHS executive, directed EHS and sustainability functions worldwide for the Eastman Kodak Company and International Paper. Kiser has provided direct leadership to hundreds of EHS leaders globally.

Kiser advises young EHS professionals to build a strong technical foundation through formal education, experience, and certification; invest in development of professional competencies; and continue to learn and stay educated. He emphasized the importance of learning business concepts in addition to EHS concepts and staying abreast of the business developments and strategies of the company. This will help establish credibility with business leaders and will lead to overall greater personal satisfaction and effectiveness.

In Kiser's experience, qualities of agile learners (Mitchinson and Morris 2014) and emotional intelligence (Goleman 2016) are predictive of high-performing leaders. Effective communication and values-based behaviors are essential. Values are fundamental to an organization, and EHS leaders should examine how company and personal values impact the execution of their work. Effective communication enables EHS leaders to engage, motivate, and empower others. It is helpful for individuals to understand their own personality type and communication tendencies and be able to recognize and adapt to others' communication styles.

In order to manage risk and protect the business, EHS leaders must become knowledgeable of the business environment and the organization's business strategies. Business success requires a partnership; EHS cannot carry it all. Business leaders must view EHS as their responsibility—own it, lead it, and be responsible for outcomes—EHS professionals should not feel threatened when a line leader takes charge. Conversely, if a leader does not take charge, the EHS professional must tactfully ensure that the leader accepts this responsibility. Involving a disengaged leader takes time and patience, relationship building, and establishment of common ground, such as employees and contractors having a fundamental right to expect injury-free workplace or customers to expect compliant products free of defects that create unintended consequences. "Looking sideways" for an influential or natural leader to act as a champion often is successful. It is important to EHS professionals to recognize the need to be flexible and make compromises. EHS leaders must be able to sort out true regulatory obligations from desirable actions and determine the right level of control without overcontrolling and wasting resources. Overly conservative interpretations of regulations can also lead to inefficient use of resources and extra cost. Risk management is critical to efficient prioritization and allocation of resources throughout the enterprise.

> EHS leaders effectively utilize the tools and organize EHS activities to drive results that increase business value and profitability.

## Expected Results

This chapter has explored best practices that create an environment for EHS professionals to become successful EHS leaders. Strong competence and close alignment with the business enable EHS leaders to implement impactful initiatives that increase business value and profitability, protect people and the environment, and provide career advancement opportunities. A few examples of impactful EHS initiatives include:

- cost avoidance from fewer injuries and illnesses
- conservation of natural resources
- minimal fines and penalties during unplanned audits and inspections
- selection as partner or supplier of choice due to strong EHS management systems and sustainability practices
- new products commercialized without EHS-related delays, recalls, and product liability

There are many more examples of impactful EHS initiatives. EHS is a noble profession with daily opportunities to help people, protect the environment, use technology to solve problems, and position employers for profitability and success. EHS leaders have unlimited possibilities to use their creativity to develop innovative solutions, expand the knowledge of EHS within the business and the profession, and motivate and inspire others to improve on today's best practices. The future is bright and promises an interesting journey for those who are committed to becoming the respected EHS leaders and experts of tomorrow.

## Questions

1. Explain why risk management can be considered the most fundamental technical competency.
2. Identify four actions to enable an EHS professional to develop an in-depth knowledge of the business.
3. What are three necessary areas of EHS competency development?
4. The first step to developing a personal competency roadmap is to perform a capability self-assessment against the body of knowledge for the profession. Identify two resources that may be used for an initial self-assessment.
5. Explain the importance of continual development of personal effectiveness skills.

## References


American Society of Safety Engineers (ASSE). (2016). "It's All about Risk—President's Blog." Accessed August 14, 2016. http://www.asse.org/its-all-about-risk/.

European Agency for Safety and Health at Work (EU-OSHA). (2012). *Leadership and Occupational Safety and Health (OHS): An Expert Analysis.* Accessed August 14, 2016. https://osha.europa.eu/en/publications/literature_reviews/leadership-and-occupational-safety-and-health-osh-an-expert-analysis/view.

Goleman, D. (2016). "About Daniel Goleman." Accessed August 14, 2016. http://www.danielgoleman.info/biography/.

Hill, D. C., and K. A. Seabrook. (2013). "Safety and Sustainability Understanding the Business Value." *Professional Safety Journal* 58(6): 81–92.

International Network of Safety and Health Practitioner Organisations (INSHPO). (2014). *The Value Proposition for the Occupational Health and Safety Professional: Literature Review.* Accessed May 24, 2017. http://www.inshpo.org/docs/INSHPO_OSH_prof_lit_review_online_0914.pdf.

International Network of Safety and Health Practitioner Organisations (INSHPO). (2015). *OHS Professional Capability Framework: A Global Framework for Practice, Roles, Knowledge and Skills.* Accessed August 14, 2016. http://www.inshpo.org/docs/INSHPO_2015-OHS_Professional_Capability_Framework.pdf.

International Standard Organization (ISO). (2015). ISO 14001 *Environmental Management Systems—Requirements with Guidance for Use.* ISO 14001:2015 (E) (in press).

Mitchinson, A., and R. Morris. (2014). "Learning about Learning Agility." Center for Creative Leadership. Accessed August 14, 2016. http://insights.ccl.org/wp-content/uploads/2015/04/LearningAgility.pdf#_ga=1.4792698.876882752.1471136071.

National Institute for Occupational Safety and Health Initiative (NIOSH). (2008). "Essential Elements of Effective Workplace Programs and Policies for Improving Worker Health and Wellbeing." Accessed August 14, 2016. http://www.cdc.gov/niosh/TWH/essentials.html.

CHAPTER 8

# HEALTH AND SAFETY MANAGEMENT SYSTEMS: MEASUREMENT OF EFFECTIVENESS

Joel M. Haight

## Learning Objectives

After studying this chapter, the reader will be able to:

1. Utilize regulatory standards as a guide to apply policies, procedures, standards, and occupational safety and health principles
2. Recognize best practices, origin of the standards, and the process for policy application
3. Evaluate HSMS and determine appropriate hazard controls following the hierarchy of controls and analyze effective safety and health management systems and task-oriented training

## Key Terms

**ANSI/ASSE/AIHA Z10, BS OHSAS 18002:2008, ISO 14001, ISO 45001, strategic element, lagging indicator**

## Abstract

In this chapter, the idea of leadership in the health and safety field is covered. While a leadership is not always necessarily intertwined with a management system, it is proposed here that a health and safety management system (HSMS) is used by safety leaders as they manage the safety and health activities in their operations. HSMSs have become a popular way to manage an organization's efforts to protect their workers. The International Standards Organization is moving forward in their development of a health and safety management system (ISO-45001 Occupational Health and Safety) and so far has recently approved the international standard in draft form. OSHA and MSHA propose regulations on the subject; ANSI/AIHA/ASSE Z10–2012 Occupational Health and Safety Management Systems, BS OHSAS18001 Occupational Health and Safety Management System, and many of the National Mining Association's member companies are currently beginning the implementation of *CORE Safety*, a mining version of the health and safety management system that the other organizations are developing and implementing.

## Introduction

There are earlier management system-like processes that have been implemented over the years, such as OSHA's Process Safety Management of Highly Hazardous Chemicals (PSM) standard and the American Chemistry Council's Responsible Care process. These systems are quite mature as they are twenty-four and more than twenty-eight years old respectively. But what is the difference between an HSMS versus how health and safety has traditionally been managed for years? Those who have been in the safety field for twenty or more years will recognize the more traditional "safety program" approach to injury prevention. It is an interesting question to ponder as to why so many now perceive management systems to be a better way to manage the health and safety business. Have historical injury prevention goals not been achieved through the traditional approach? What makes us think that a new, more systems-based approach will help us to prevent more injuries and other loss-related incidents?

Maybe the more systematic approach makes us feel more organized. Maybe the increasingly active discussion and marketing activities of management systems in the safety business have gotten this updated approach in front of more people. Are management systems being taught more in the universities that traditionally train safety people? This author believes that it is never good to rush headlong into the use of any new approach to protecting people until one understands what the approach really involves, what resources will be necessary to develop and implement it properly, and what the potential unintended consequences may be. How will we measure the effectiveness of the HSMS after we do begin to implement it? That is a critical aspect of any new approach, and it is one that has not been adequately addressed in the research literature yet.

With so many questions to answer, let us begin the discussion first by sorting out what an occupational health and safety management system is and what the differences and similarities may be between each of the systems discussed above (Haight et al. 2013).

It is critical to establish that the content and the mix of those content elements within the management system are appropriate and that their implementation will be effective. Although Responsible Care has been around since 1988 and the OSHA PSM standard since 1992 (an earlier standard from the American Petroleum Institute RP750 Process Hazards Analysis from 1990 also addressed this systems-based approach), empirical evidence of the effectiveness of this systems-based approach has not yet been adequately established by the research community. Since this health and safety management systems approach is relatively new, there has not been adequate system performance history for us to prove that they (the HSMSs) accomplish our health and safety objectives or that if they do, to what extent (in this case health and safety objectives means preventing industrial injuries). It is given that "to prove" means to statistically determine that any changes in injury rates are due to the effect of one or more element of the HSMS. So, why are the regulatory agencies, consensus organizations, and industry associations so actively supporting the HSMS way of doing business? Since we have not yet adequately proven a one best way to measure HSMS effectiveness, why are there so many different HSMSs being promoted?

In 2013, Haight et al. proposed that the answers to these questions can be determined through comparative analysis and review of the published scientific literature, as well as the results of theoretical and empirical HSMS research conducted by several researchers working in this area. In these studies, we are able to find empirical evidence that explains the differences and similarities in content of various HSMS models and discuss the benefits and costs associated with their implementation. These authors (Haight et al. 2013) also find studies that support the idea that effectiveness in injury prevention is predominately attributable to implementation of a health and safety management system. It is expected that our readers, after reading this chapter, will better understand what HSMSs are, how they are expected to work, and what the differences and similarities between various proposed HSMSs are. If you have made the decision to implement an HSMS, you should determine if it is right for you and—if the systems-based approach is right—which system is best. It should be expected that

It should be expected that one understands which or how many of their current intervention activities can be part of a management system and how they can integrate those activities into their HSMS, should they choose to adopt one.

one understands which or how many of their current intervention activities can be part of a management system and how they can integrate those activities into their HSMS should they choose to adopt one. With the right tools, in general, you would want to be prepared to develop and implement an HSMS that you determine is right. The "right tools" will be discussed in more detail later in the chapter.

But first, what is a health and safety management system, anyway? There are many definitions in play, but in general an HSMS would or should have the same attributes as any management system. A system can be considered to be a grouping of interrelated and often interdependent components that are brought together in an industrial environment meant to help generate or achieve a common objective or perform a common function (Haight et al. 2013). Common attributes of a system that show up most often in the literature are *interrelatedness* or *interdependence* in system components with and between each other. The literature also often notes a common objective. An example of a natural system is a respiratory system, which is made up of the trachea, the bronchioles, the lungs, the alveolar ducts, and so forth. These components all work together to oxygenate the blood and remove carbon dioxide. An example in the manufacturing world might be an electric power supply system that includes the power supply, wiring, circuit protection, switches, and outlets. As noted in Haight et al. (2013), Elsayed and Boucher (1994, 1) one can define a production system as "a collection of components such as material, labor, capital and knowledge that goes into the manufacture of a product. How this collection of components is put together in any specific situation defines the particular system." Another definition of a system proposed by Eisner (2002, 3) is "any process that converts inputs to outputs."

A management system can be considered an administrative version of the natural and manufactured systems described above. Therefore, we will settle on a definition of a management system here as a structure and set of processes, procedures, policies, or actions that are implemented within an organization to achieve a defined objective or perform a common function in an efficient and structured way (Haight et al. 2013). An example of a manmade management system might be a purchasing or procurement system used by an organization to manage its supplies, raw materials, finished inventory, spare parts, and so on. This system may integrate people, software, and processes, which work interdependently to identify, record, and track suppliers, raw material and parts availability, inventory/stock levels, and so forth. It might include an ordering component, a warehouse stocking component, a quality-control component for material received, and a pricing component. All components work together to ensure that the organization's purchasing and inventory management goals are met. Another specific example of a management system might be a personnel management system bringing together people and processes to recruit, hire, and retain people so that the best talent is brought together and maintained to help ensure that the organization can achieve its business goals.

However, we are currently more interested in the analysis of an even more specified system: an occupational health and safety management system. The American National Standards Institute (ANSI) ANSI/ASSE/AIHA Z10 standard titled "Occupational Health and Safety Management System" defines "a set of interrelated elements that establish or support occupational health and safety policy and objectives, and mechanisms to achieve those objectives in order to improve occupational health and safety (ANSI/ASSE/AIHA Z10–2010). The British Standard (BS OHSAS

18001:2007) and its guidelines for implementation (BS OHSAS 18002:2008 Occupation Health and Safety Assessment Series for health and safety management systems) define an HSMS as "part of an organization's management system used to develop and implement its OH&S (occupational health and safety) policy and

> The ISO 45001 standard will become the system of choice around the world as it has both the input and the support from around the world. No other system has such extensive and diverse input.

manage its OH&S risks." There are also three notes associated with the definition, and they read, (1) "A management system is a set of interrelated elements used to establish a policy and objectives and to achieve those objectives," (2) "A management system includes organizational structure, planning activities (including, for example, risk assessment and the setting of objectives), responsibilities, practices, procedures, processes and resources," and (3) "Adopted from International Standards Organization (ISO), ISO 14001: 2004" (Haight et al. 2013). More importantly, since the writing of Haight et al. (2013), ISO 45001 has been approved and published. This author expects that this ISO standard will become the system of choice around the world, as it has both the input and the support from around the world. No other system has such extensive and diverse input. The components that make up ISO 45001 are also very similar to all of the other systems included in this discussion.

## Management Systems Comparison

There is great similarity between the fundamental definition of a system, the extended idea of a management system, and definitions of an even further extended HSMS. The key similarities are element interrelatedness, interdependence between system elements, and a common objective in system performance. Because health and safety (H&S) risks are generated by complex physical, cognitive, and behavioral phenomena that can originate in both the natural and the manmade world, acceptable mitigation of this risk can also be complex. Response necessarily involves the proactive implementation of a management system that can address such complexities, and therefore, it is proposed that this is the reason HSMSs have gotten so much recent attention.

There are many different HSMSs available, and there is much overlap between them. An HSMS is basically a performance standard; hence specific implementation is up to each implementer. Given this, it would not matter which system an organization chooses to implement. There are many to choose from nonetheless, and while some of the titles of each specific system element may be slightly different, they all address roughly the same elements. Elements such as employee participation, leadership, hazard identification and risk assessment, accountability and authority, emergency preparedness, organizational culture, and so on make up the structure of all of the systems in existence—including the ISO standard ISO 45001.

In general, all of the HSMS offerings have a similar purpose: they are all performance based, and they all provide the framework for establishing standards and guidelines achieving an organization's health and safety objectives. Any differences between the management systems that do exist probably would not be recognizable as differences until implementation begins. At this point, each organization, through its creative implementation strategies and actual intervention activity, will undoubtedly look different from company to company. However, the robust structure of an HSMS helps to ensure that the awareness effect and implementation effect are in play to help guide people to a more cautious and calculated set of behavior patterns. For example, while most of the systems have in their structure an employee participation element, the way each individual organization chooses to engage employees may be completely different. One organization may use employees in an advisory role and only to offer input to safety and health policy. Another organization may involve employees in a more hands-on way and allow employees to make decisions on intervention priorities, to conduct risk analyses, and to develop safe operating procedures (Haight et al. 2013).

The differences may result from slightly different goals or timelines; they could be due to differences in leadership or its commitment. Organizational culture can be a major force in dictating how and when implementation occurs. It is proposed that there is a culture effect even though only the NMA CORE Safety system includes an explicit element related to the organizational culture as it relates to safety and its influence on the organization. However, according to Burns et al. (2006), and Choudhry et al. (2007), the importance of an organizational culture that is conducive to safety is considered to be important because of the generalized trust and value congruence between organizations and their employees. It may be useful to present a list of both strategic- and tactical-level HSMS elements so that one can see structure and the depth of coverage that they all seem to possess. See table 8.1 to note the strategic level element list. Then see table 8.2 to note the extensive tactical intervention activity list to get a feel for an even greater depth of coverage that the HSMS structure provides.

In deciding between systems to implement, one can rest easy knowing that because the structure of each system is so similar, you almost cannot go wrong. There may be limitations, however, due to your particular industry. For example, NMA CORE targets the mining industry, Responsible Care targets the chemical manufacturing industry, and OSHA PSM is a requirement for the process industries. Implementation of Z10–2010 or BS OHSAS 18001:2007 is less restricted when considering specific industries, and ISO 45001 will also be less restrictive when it takes effect (Haight et al. 2013, 2014).

A significant challenge will be development and implementation of specific HSMS interventions. Many traditional H&S program elements and intervention activities can fit management system expectations, but a question is raised as to whether implementation of a particular element under the traditional health and safety management program banner would have the same effect. The question must be asked because it is not clear that the traditional safety and health program enjoys the same benefits of management support, employee ownership and participation, organizational culture conduciveness, or the same level of organization and structure as an HSMS with a defined, singular purpose or goal. However, by the same token, it has not even yet been adequately proven that the HSMS in fact achieves health and safety goals, either.

**Table 8.1** Strategic level elements of HSMS across several available systems

| HSMS Strategic Elements |
|---|
| Policy |
| Planning |
| Management Leadership |
| Resources, Roles, and Responsibilities |
| Leadership Development |
| Accountability and Authority |
| Assessment and Prioritization Objectives |
| Allocation of Resources |
| Hierarchy of Controls |
| Definition of Legal Requirements |
| Implementation Plans |

An organization should, in its effort to establish an HSMS, work to make use of any element already being implemented, even though it may be part of a more traditional approach. That provides a sense of certainty, but while there is comfort in the known, implementing a new management system requires change. There will necessarily have to be curtailing of some elements and

**Table 8.2** Tactical level HSMS elements across several available systems

| HSMS Elements |
|---|
| Hazard Identification, Risk Assessment, and Controls |
| Employee Participation |
| Management of Change |
| Education and Training |
| Incident Investigation |
| Audits |
| Contractor Safety |
| Emergency Preparedness |
| Management Review |
| Document Control |
| Monitoring and Measurement |
| Nonconformity and Corrective Actions |
| Work Procedures and Permits |
| Operating Procedures |
| Feedback and Planning Process |
| Design Review |
| Cultural Enhancement |
| Communication Process |
| Occupational Health |
| Behavior Optimization |
| Mechanical Integrity |

starting of completely new elements. Table 8.3 shows a listing of some examples of common traditional H&S management program activities that may be considered for HSMS adoption. It may ease the process of HSMS implementation when the only thing that is needed is to add structure and tracking to existing processes. Foundation building may also be required if leadership support and commitment, employee ownership, and a conducive organizational culture are not yet in place (Haight et al. 2001a).

While getting started may be easier because of what an organization is already doing, it is by no means an easy process. A significant difference in how an HSMS is implemented from one organization to another may have little to do with the specific program elements or intervention activities and more to do with how they are implemented and with the leadership in charge of their implementation. HSMS implementation is more than just starting a new audit process or a new risk-assessment process. An organization must have an organizational culture that supports both implementation of an HSMS and its long-term maintenance (Johnson 1973).

## HSMS versus H&S Traditional Program Differences

HSMS emphasizes system-wide record keeping, document control, and integrated inter-element tracking of nonconformance, whereas the traditional approach does not necessarily involve these foundational activities. It is an important difference that qualifies HSMS as a systems-based approach. An example of this is when all procedures across the organization's operations are produced with the same format and same quality. This provides a familiarity that contributes to system-wide successful use of the procedures. Another systems-based example is when all nonconformance records are kept in the same tracking system; no matter if their source is incident investigations, compliance audits, preventive maintenance findings, and so on, they are addressed using the same risk-ranking process. This allows for sound, consistent, and cost-effective risk-reduction

**Table 8.3** Traditional health and safety processes and where they might fit in the new HSMS structure (adapted from Haight et al. 2013)

| New HSMS Elements | Hazard Analysis | Incident Investigation | Training and Development | Emergency Response | S&H Audits | Safety Meetings | Contractor Safety |
|---|---|---|---|---|---|---|---|
| Hazard Identification, Risk Assessment, and Controls | X | X | | X | | | |
| Employee Participation | X | X | X | X | X | X | X |
| Management of Change | X | | X | X | | | |
| Education and Training | | | X | | | X | |
| Incident Investigation | X | X | | | | | |
| Audits | | | | | X | | |
| Contractor Safety | X | | | | | | X |
| Emergency Preparedness | | X | | X | X | | |
| Management Review | X | X | X | X | X | X | X |
| Document Control | X | X | X | X | X | X | X |
| Monitoring and Measurement | X | X | X | X | X | X | X |

*Continued*

**Table 8.3** Traditional health and safety processes and where they might fit in the new HSMS structure (adapted from Haight et al. 2013) *(continued)*

| | | | | | | | |
|---|---|---|---|---|---|---|---|
| Nonconformity and Corrective Actions | X | X | | | X | | X |
| Work Procedures and Permits | | | X | | X | | |
| Operating Procedures | | | X | | | | |
| Feedback and Planning Process | X | X | X | X | X | X | X |
| Design Review | X | X | | | | | |
| Cultural Enhancement | | | | | X | X | |
| Communication Process | X | X | X | X | X | X | X |
| Mechanical Integrity | X | | | | X | | |

implementation. Document control across all system elements also ensures consistent updating that is reflected in equipment drawings and specifications, inspection records, operating procedures, risk-assessment results, and nonconformance documentation. Although these important activities may or may not have been a part of traditional safety programs, it is likely they were not previously integrated within the management structure.

Another important difference between the two approaches is the structure of an HSMS over a virtually unstructured traditional program. The definition of responsibilities and accountabilities, inter-element interdependence, non-conformance tracking, system-wide management reviews and risk assessments, resource allocation, and investment decisions produce a much stronger potential to guarantee successful implementation and the subsequent realization of incident and injury objectives.

An important difference between the traditional program approach and that of the management systems identified in this chapter is that they all operate using a general Deming Plan-Do-Check-Act (PDCA) cycle. The first step in PDCA being to plan, it is easy to recognize that there is much to do before any physical activity takes place in the form of an intervention (Deming 2000; Deming and Edwards 1982). In the planning process, an organization would first have to develop the policy and set performance objectives as well as get employee and management buy-in and employee ownership. Several of the HSMSs support elements target this planning stage, and this is one of the first places in the cycle where differences between safety and health programs and HSMSs emerge, as traditional safety and health programs do not necessarily have a built-in planning provision.

> An important difference between the traditional program approach and that of the management systems as identified in this chapter is that they all operate using a general Deming Plan-Do-Check-Act cycle.

It is during the "do" part of the PDCA cycle that intervention activity implementation happens. This is, for example, the safety and health training, inspections, preventive maintenance inspections, safety meetings, awareness campaigns, behavioral safety observations, risk analyses, work permit system implementation, and so forth. How these are built and how they are implemented is critical. While some of the same physical and sometimes cognitive and behavioral activities happen, the differences in the "who" and the "how" of the activities may be stark. Under the traditional safety program banner, these activities may have been implemented individually, by different people, each with their own objectives. Implementation of the same activities within the framework of an organized system ensures a unified objective and complementary (as opposed to competitive) functions. Here it is planned for the elements to complement, interact with, or depend on the proper implementation of each other. Within a system, the intervention activities are implemented such that their implementation and maintenance can be optimized in terms of quality and amount of effort with the goal of optimizing the overall system's objective of reducing the number and severity of injuries and illnesses.

While one would see similar activities in a traditional safety program approach, the HSMS has built into its structure elements to address the "check" and "act" phases of the PDCA cycle as well. It is proposed that this structure then helps to ensure or at least improve the probability of success. A management review and proactive and reactive checking (e.g., audits, inspections, and investigations) elements contribute to the "check" step. The "act" step would be covered by elements related to corrective action. The entire structure and the continuous loop–continuous improvement nature of HSMS—or any management system for that matter—also help to increase the likelihood of success.

While effectiveness measurement of HSMS will be addressed in more detail in the next section, it is proposed here that using a system-based approach to implement H&S interventions allows more effective measurement opportunity, which also yields advantages over the traditional program approach. In sum, the authors claim that the fundamental principles of a systems approach provide three significant benefits over and above a traditional safety program approach: The systems approach brings the attributes of *oneness of purpose* and *interdependence between system elements*, and it creates a structure and a level of *organization* that we were unable to achieve with traditional safety program efforts. With these improvements we are able to benefit from a substantial increase in measurement accuracy and the ability to establish accountability, both of which increase the likelihood of organizational safety performance success. They also provide an opportunity to optimize the whole system such that efficiency can be improved by the big-picture implementation and quest to minimize incidents and injuries while concurrently minimizing resources and maximizing quality of implementation (Haight et al. 2001b; Iyer et al. 2004).

## Management System: Intervention Effectiveness Measurement

Quantitative measurement of H&S program effectiveness is difficult, and as such, the safety community has been discussing, arguing, and challenging the concept and the methods for years. Health and safety programs have the intended goal of preventing injuries and illnesses, but how could we possibly know if an injury or illness has been prevented? We are not able to count things that don't happen. If one less injury has occurred by the end of this year than by the end of last year, how do we know whether it was due to natural variability or even just by luck or chance or that the health and safety program implementation was responsible for the reduction? For many years, safety professionals have developed and used various methods to measure the effectiveness of their efforts that use the end-of-year incident rates to compare to last year's incident rate or an average rate over some period of time. Many members of the safety community have recognized that this process leads only to the classic yo-yo effect on the incident rates as more resources are allocated to injury prevention when the rate is high and fewer resources are allocated when the rate is low (Haight et al. 2013 and 2014). It may not be adequately thorough to use only "lagging indicators," which are indicators of events that have already happened and used to manage future efforts. In other words, these measures *lag* behind the opportunity to implement effective prevention interventions.

Unfortunately, the use of lagging indicators has naturally led to a movement toward using measures referred to as "leading indicators" alone. Leading indicators reference the quality of certain H&S interventions' implementation (Toellner 2001; Haight and Thomas 2003; Manuele 2009; Wachter 2012). Leading indicators are held up by many in the H&S community as being an improved way to measure effectiveness because they are proactive. This has merit as leading indicators allow adjustments to be made before an injury happens. However, this approach has not yet been proven to be valid for accurate measures of performance. No one can say for sure that any change in injury or incident rates is due to anything being done as part of the HSMS. Using either leading or lagging indicators proves nothing about the effectiveness in safety performance. It provides only a by-chance, "feel-good sense of reason"–based (as coined by Shakioye and Haight 2009) comfort level about the program or the HSMS.

To effectively use these leading and lagging indicators, one has to determine the mathematical relationship between them. The up-to-date research and its accompanying published literature does not yet adequately address the interactive effects between performance variables and the cause-and-effect relationships between leading and lagging indicators. There were a number of studies done over the last eighteen years that have gotten us closer to understanding this interactive effect; however, we are not quite ready to generalize that work across all industries without using individual organizational data to validate the mathematical models. Several studies by Haight and his research teams (Haight et al. 2001a, 2001b, 2003; Iyer et al. 2004,, 2005; Shakioye and Haight 2009; and Oyewole et al. 2010), have shown validated quantitative models, but because of high variability, the certainty with which they are able to explain the variation with the model is about 65–70 percent. More work like this is needed. Salas and Hallowell (2016) have taken a slightly different approach than Haight and his teams, but the concept of mathematically explaining the effect of leading indicators and their effect on incidents has clearly been validated.

The measurement difficulty as evidenced in the systems-based approach that is not fully appreciated within the traditional approach is that industry in general has an expectation to measure intervention quality, and that hasn't been done adequately yet. HSMS success may be best described as being measurable through the use of arcane or esoteric characteristics; that is, they are difficult to nearly impossible to quantitatively measure. The systems-approach requirements or drivers that are seen as being most guilty are leadership and management commitment, employee ownership, and an organizational culture that is conducive to successful and positive implementation of an HSMS. How would one measure something indicating conduciveness to successful implementation of an HSMS?

HSMS success may be best described as being measurable through the use of arcane or esoteric characteristics; that is, they are difficult to nearly impossible to quantitatively measure.

According to Haight et al. (2013), there was supposedly a sign hanging on the office door of Albert Einstein at Princeton that read, "Not everything that counts can be counted, and not everything that can be counted counts." This probably means that he must have agreed with this very philosophy that defines the difficulty with measuring the effectiveness of HSMS. Presented with this problem, many researchers have worked with or have developed nonquantitative techniques that can be used to assess the effectiveness or the contribution of the more arcane elements of an HSMS. Various quality indices and surveys that can measure the level or presence of these drivers have been used and have been accepted. Another example may be that the OSHA's Safety and Health Program Management Guidelines (Federal Registrar 54: 3904–16); several programmatic, procedural, and behavioral examples of observable ways that organizations can demonstrate management commitment and employee participation are presented (Haight et al. 2014). There are experienced professionals that can offer their opinion on whether high levels of these elements are present; however, sometimes it is not easy or even possible to define or present a number that represents a conducive organizational culture, a committed leader, or an employee who feels ownership over aspects of HSMS. What is required here is to measure, or describe qualitatively, existing levels of the defining characteristics of leadership, ownership, and organizational culture, showing some measure or index of their levels that will allow comparison of those levels to system outputs over time and to compare those levels to the experience of other organizations (similar and dissimilar) to establish baseline measures. At that point, continuous measurement of those values over time can yield some sense of improvement or some sense that improvement is not happening. A question of certainty of results, however, remains with all of these approaches.

Another benefit that an HSMS provides to the measurement problem is the fact that it promotes the opportunity for a risk-based approach to implementation. One would expect that when changes to the injury-prevention strategy or implementation tactics occur, the organizational risk would change. This doesn't require high sample numbers in order to get statistically significant results. One needs only to evaluate the changes in the input to the HSMS and evaluate the impact on the resulting output risk level. When an organization is able to define its baseline operating risk and then establish a level of risk that it is willing and able to tolerate, it has its basis to compare against different levels of quantity and quality of implementation across the whole system on an instantaneous and longitudinal basis. While risk itself is not a straightforward, mathematically quantitative measure, its indexing quality does provide a means to perform relative ranking of intervention options or levels or quality of implementation of interventions with a consistent measure. It is semi-quantitative at best, but because of its consistency quality, it provides a means and a measure to make decisions around the levels associated with investment, amount and quality of effort, adequacy of the performance, and guidance as to the overall direction the system should take.

There are quantitative aspects of an HSMS that do, however, provide an opportunity for true intervention effectiveness measurement. Research has been scratching at the surface of statistically significant measures of HSMS performance for the last sixteen years. Haight et al. (2001a, b), Haight and Thomas (2003), and Iyer et al. (2004, 2005) determined that to truly measure H&S intervention effectiveness, one has to establish the mathematical relationship between the leading (input) indicators and lagging (output) indicators. With this representative mathematical relationship, there is a chance that we can start to explain any variation in injury rates that we experience in our organizations. This not only addresses the direct effects of each individual intervention, it also provides measurement of the interactive effects between performance variables. Haight et al. (2001a) were the first to establish that determining this mathematical relationship was possible, but there has been much work since then as other researchers have determined how to better use this mathematical relationship. As with any input/output model, the resulting function provides an opportunity to mathematically explain a real system as it operates.

However, care should be taken in developing models because all mathematical models contain some error. They provide their usefulness as decision-making tools, provided uncertainty is minimized to the point that any residual error can be accepted or at least taken into account. In general, in research, one would attempt to minimize uncertainty by increasing the number of samples; however, the level of uncertainty in the results may not be improved solely by collecting additional data if the variation in the system is great. That is also a problem that has plagued this effectiveness-measurement research. The level of certainty can refer to the amount of variation in the output variable that one is able to explain through the experimentation and subsequent modeling. If the incident rate, for example, does not respond to a change in the amount or quality of implementation of one or more of the HSMS element interventions, the lack of variation in the output may not be able to be explained with acceptable certainty by the variation in the input variables. With any human-based system, uncertainty in the results will undoubtedly be higher than when analyzing a system driven by the more predictable natural and physical laws. However, without data collection, experimentation, analysis, and modeling, the level of certainty around any decision made about the performance of the system is zero. The results of the more recent research in this area of HSMSs have shown that the level of uncertainty has been reduced to roughly 30 percent (Al-Mutairi and Haight 2009; Shakioye and Haight 2009; Oyewole et al. 2010).

The research of Shakioye et al. (2009) and Oyewole et al. (2010) have yielded some interesting results. Shakioye et al. (2009) showed, through extensive operations research methodology, that the incident rates predicted by his mathematical model representing the effectiveness of the health and safety system were predictable. This is shown in figure 8.1.

Oyewole et al. (2010) took the earlier operations research methodology work a step further by using surface-response methodologies. He also treated the interactive effects between intervention activities

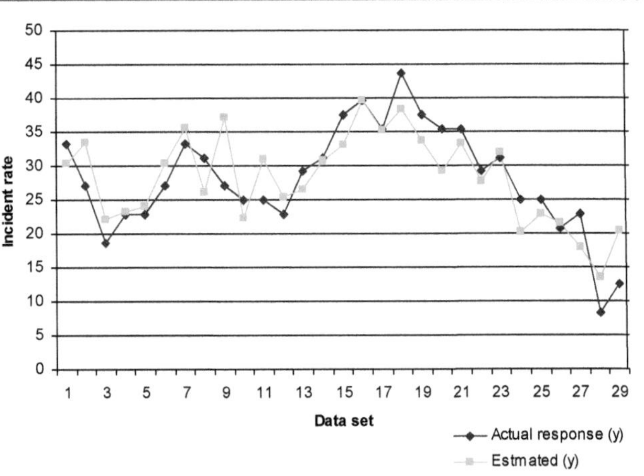


Figure 8.1
Actual weekly incident rates versus model-generated estimation of the incident rates. (Adapted from Shakioye and Haight 2009)

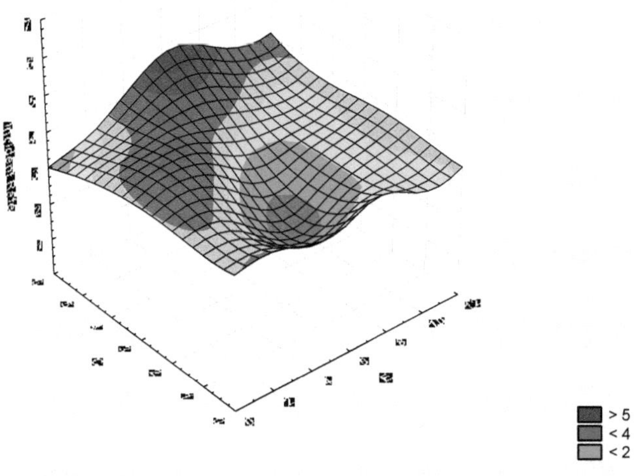


Figure 8.2
Response surface plot of incident rate versus HSMS variables C and E. (Adapted from Oyewole et al. 2010)

more thoroughly than the previous researchers. The limitation here is in the difficulty of making a five-dimensional model a three-dimensional model so that it could be shown graphically. From figures 8.2 and 8.3, we can see from the 3D surface that the incident rate responds to the interactive effect of two variables from the HSMS being studied. We can then

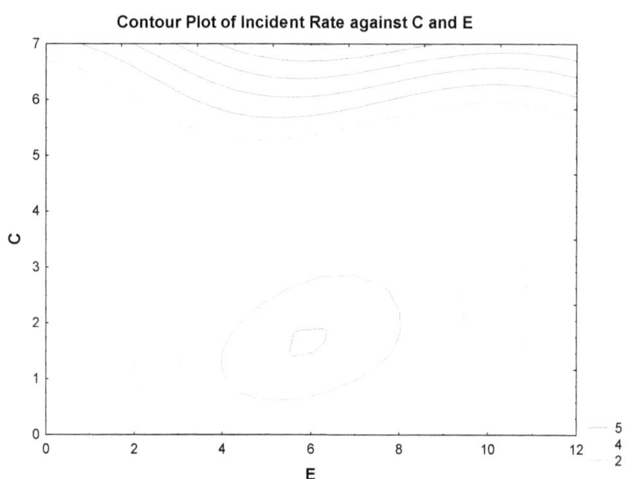


Figure 8.3
Contour plot of incident rate versus HSMS variables C and E. (Adapted from Oyewole et al. 2010)

take this information and make adjustments to the implementation of variables C and E of this particular HSMS so that we can attempt to minimize the incident rate. The same model information is presented in two ways to allow better visualization of the model results. From figure 8.3, one can discern that the minimized incident rate is achieved at the indexed value of the implementation quality or quantity of the two subject variables to be at approximately level 2.5 for variable C and level 6 for variable E.

This information should not be construed as *the* answer to the safety problem but only as an answer that suggests certain adjustments that can be made to HSMS implementation and only with roughly 70-percent certainty. It is encouraging work and, as is, can be a tremendous benefit to those charged with successful implementation of an HSMS. However, much more work needs to be done. The key takeaway here is that it appears to be possible to measure HSMS implementation effectiveness, at least with the current proven levels of certainty around 68–70 percent.

## Interpretations and Conclusions

Health and Safety Management Systems are becoming more and more popular. There appears to be significant regulatory and consensus organizations and industry group support for this movement. There are differences in how they are implemented and the expectations from them and the traditional style H&S program. The main differences appear to be that HSMS provides structure, "integratedness," and oneness of purpose that are not provided in the traditional programmed approach. There are difficulties, however, in that the success of HSMS depends upon strong leadership or management support, active employee participation, and a conducive organizational culture, which are not easy to create and are very difficult to measure and maintain.

It appears through comparative analysis that an organization can rely on many of the intervention activities that make up their existing health and safety program that can possibly go a long way toward forming the foundation for HSMS implementation should that organization determine that they want to go in that direction. For those that choose to implement HSMS, there appears to be a great number of resources available to assist, depending upon the industry in which the organization resides or which consensus organization to which the organization belongs.

It may be some time before it is possible to truly determine the effectiveness of HSMS or even that HSMS is better than the traditional approach. However, there seems to be much energy around implementation of HSMS, and sometimes that energy alone can contribute to an overall improvement. One thing remains clear, though, and that is that the main objective of any safety and health approach is to prevent people from getting injured. As such, the effort to do that is worth it until we can determine its effectiveness for certain.

## Questions

1. Please define a system, as presented in the book.
2. Please define a management system.
3. Please define an occupational safety and health management system.
4. When measuring health and safety management systems using leading and lagging indicators, it is best to do what?

5. What is the name and number of an important standard that is planned for publication in 2018 that will significantly influence the development of occupational safety and health management systems in industry world-wide?

## References


Al-Mutairi, A, and J. M. Haight, J.M. (2009). "Forecasting Incident Rates through Artificial Intelligence." *Professional Safety* 54(9): 40–48.

American National Standard for Occupational Health and Safety Management. (2010). *ANSI Z10-2010.* American National Standards Institute, Inc. Fairfax, VA: American Industrial Hygiene Association.

Burns, C., K. Mearns, and P. McGeorge, P. (2006). "Explicit and Implicit Trust within Safety Culture." *Risk Analysis* 26(5): 1139–50.

Choudhry, R. M., D. Fang, and S. Mohamed. (2007). "The Nature of Safety Culture: A Survey of the State-of-the-Art." *Safety Science* 45(10): 993–1012.

Deming, W. E., and D. W. Edwards. (1982). *Quality, Productivity, and Competitive Position* 183. Cambridge, MA: Massachusetts Institute of Technology, Center for Advanced Engineering Study.

Deming, W. E. (2000). *Out of the Crisis.* Cambridge, MA: MIT Press.

Eisner, H. (2002). *Essentials of Project and Systems Engineering Management* (2nd ed.). New York: John Wiley and Sons, Inc.

Elsayed, E. A., and T. O. Boucher. (1994). *Analysis and Control of Production Systems* (2nd ed.) Prentice Hall International Series in Industrial and Systems Engineering, W. J. Fabrycky and J. H. Mize (eds.). Upper Saddle River, NJ: J. W. Wiley and Sons, Inc.

Haight, J. M., P. L. Yorio, K. A. Rost, and D. R. Willmer. (2014). "Health and Safety Management Systems—a Comparative Analysis of Content and Impact." *Professional Safety* 59(5): 44–51.

Haight, J. M., P. L. Yorio, and D. R. Willmer. (2013). "Health and Safety Management Systems—A Comparative Analysis of Content and Impact.," *Proceedings of the American Society of Safety Engineers Professional Development Conference.* Las Vegas.

Haight, J. M., and R. E. Thomas. (2003). "Intervention Effectiveness Research—A Review of the Literature on 'Leading Indicators.'" *Chemical Health and Safety—American Chemical Society—Division of Chemical Health and Safety* 10(2): 21–25.

Haight, J. M., R. E. Thomas, L. A. Smith, R. L. Bulfin, and B. L. Hopkins. (2001a). "Evaluating the Effectiveness of Loss Prevention Interventions: Developing the Mathematical Relationship between Interventions and Incident Rates for the Design of a Loss Prevention System (Phase 1)." *Professional Safety* 46(5): 38–44.

Haight, J. M., R. E. Thomas, L. A. Smith, R. L. Bulfin, and B. L. Hopkins. (2001b). "An Analysis of the Effectiveness of Loss Prevention Interventions: Design, Optimization, and Verification of the Loss Prevention System and Analysis Model (Phase 2)." *Professional Safety* 46(6): 33–37.

Iyer, P. S., J. M. Haight, E. del Castillo, B. W. Tink, and P. W. Hawkins. (2005). "A Research Model—Forecasting Incident Rates from Optimized Safety Program Intervention Strategies." *Journal of Safety Research* 36(4): 341–51.

Iyer, P. S., J. M. Haight, E. del Castillo, B. W. Tink, and P. W. Hawkins. (2004). "Intervention Effectiveness Research: Understanding and Optimizing Industrial Safety Programs Using Leading Indicators." *Chemical Health and Safety—American Chemical Society—Division of Chemical Health and Safety* 11(2): 9–19.

Johnson, W. G. (1973). *Management Oversight and Risk Tree-MORT* (No. DOE/ID/01375-T1; SAN-821-2). Scoville, ID: Aerojet Nuclear Co.

Manuele, F. A. (2001). "Leading and Lagging Indicators: Do They Add Value to the Practice of Safety?" *Professional Safety* 54(12): 42–47.

Occupational Health and Safety Management Systems. (2008). Guidelines for Implementation of OHSAS 18001: OHSAS: 2007, 18002:2008, BSI British Standards. London: BSI Group Headquarters.

Occupational Health and Safety Management Systems. (2007). OHSAS 18001:2007, BSI British Standards. London: BSI Group Headquarters.

Oyewole, S. A. (2009). "The Implementation of Statistical and Forecasting Techniques in the Assessment of Safety Intervention Effectiveness and Optimization." PhD dissertation. State College, PA: Pennsylvania State University.

Oyewole, S. A., J. M. Haight, A. Freivalds, D. Cannon, and L. Rothrock. (2010). "Statistical Evaluation of Safety Intervention Effectiveness and Optimization of Resource Allocation." *Journal of Loss Prevention in the Process Industries* 23(5): 585–93.

Shakioye, S. O., and J. M. Haight. (2009). "Modeling Using Dynamic Variables—An Approach for the Design of Loss Prevention Programs." *Safety Sciences* 48: 46–53.

Salas, R., and M. Hallowell. (2016). "Predictive Validity of Safety Leading Indicators: Empirical Assessment of the Oil and Gas Sector." *Journal of Construction Engineering and Management* 142(10).

Toellner, J. (2001). "Identifying and Measuring Leading Indicators." *Professional Safety* 46(9): 2–47

Wachter, J. K. (2012). "Trailing Safety Indicators, Enhancing Their Value through Statistics." *Professional Safety* 57(4): 48–53.

SECTION 2

# THE PROFESSION: CERTIFICATIONS AND ACCREDITATION

CHAPTER 9

# FRAMING THE OCCUPATIONAL SAFETY AND HEALTH PROFESSION: A BRIEF HISTORY AND ROADMAP FOR THE FUTURE

Jim Ramsay

## Learning Objectives

After studying this chapter, the reader will be able to:

1. Provide a glimpse into the history and development of the occupational safety and health (OSH) function in both society and the workplace by appreciating select milestones
2. Articulate the characteristics of a mature profession
3. Provide a roadmap or set of steps that OSH must follow to finalize its development into a mature profession

## Key Terms

**Safety, profession, educational standards, curriculum, roadmap**

## Abstract

What makes a job an occupation? What does it take for an occupation to be considered a profession? To the practitioner or the casual observer, these may sound like odd or even irrelevant questions. However, it turns out that they are quite central to an occupation's growth and maturation lifecycle. For example, for one to refer to oneself as a "professional," there needs to be a recognized profession in which one practices and to which one belongs. Herein lies the challenge. Who's to say that a given occupation is or is not a profession or that a given practitioner is or is not a professional? Simply put, a profession requires one to achieve specific education and training, while an occupation is what one does to earn a living. However, there is literature around how occupations evolve into professions and known characteristics that all mature professions share. Interestingly, and as may already be clear, while all professions start as occupations, not all occupations mature into professions.

## A Brief History of the Safety Profession

As the name *safety* implies, the discipline of occupational safety and health (OSH) was born out of disaster, or more precisely out of a series of disasters. As early as the late 1880s, "muckrakers" pushed for social reform of unsafe working conditions. Literary efforts such as Upton Sinclair's *The Jungle* (1906) and the "Pittsburg Survey" of 1908 (Kellogg 1908) highlighted the death and disability consequences of unsafe working conditions. These and other efforts produced landmark reforms in federal legislation such as the Food and Drug Act of 1906 and the Meat Inspection Act of 1906. In addition to legislative reform, professional safety societies began to form following worksite disasters. For example, the American Society of Safety Professionals (ASSP) was born in 1911 following the tragic fire at the Triangle Shirtwaist Factory in New York City that killed sixty-two people (ASSE 2017). ASSP (initially called the United Association of Casualty Inspectors and recently renamed from the American Society of Safety Engineers) was the first official safety-oriented professional society.

ASSP was the first official safety-oriented professional society.

Interestingly, the Triangle fire tragedy occurred as a direct result of an inadequate number of skilled or educated safety personnel on staff who could identify and control risks. In addition to an inadequate safety workforce, there were no safety standards or laws, regulations, or rules designed to keep workers safe and healthy. Further, there were no regulatory bodies, whose function it would be to optimize worker health and safety, at the state or federal level. Last, there were no professional societies available to join or professional credentials to pursue or academic educational degrees designed to study and understand workplace risk. Consequently, organizations had no constraints on their processes, and workers had no idea how to respond to or prepare for emergencies. Hence, obvious safety risks went unmitigated as they were no one's professional responsibility. Over time, even entirely preventable risks went unrecognized and unchallenged. Disaster, death, and disability were all too often thought of as part of one's job and no one's direct responsibility to prevent.

Disaster, death, and disability were all too often thought of as part of one's job and no one's direct responsibility to prevent.

Seemingly out of the muckraking movement, from major disasters like the Triangle disaster arose the beginnings of the safety movement, both organizationally and legislatively. For example, just two years after the formation of ASSP, the National Safety Council (NSC) began in 1913. Years later, in 1953 President Eisenhower awarded the NSC a congressional charter to work on safety prevention (OHSonline 2017). In 1915, the US Department of Labor was established by the Organic Act and issued the first set of safety regulations (USDoL 2017). The Federal Compensation Act of 1916 provided benefits for the first time to workers who were injured or contracted illnesses in the workplace as part of their jobs. In addition, this act established the Office of Workers' Compensation Programs (USDoL 2017). World War I served to introduce several more modern safety concepts, such as personal protective equipment in the form of gas masks used to resist gas attacks.

Following the war, several new ideas emerged that impacted safety of work life. These ideas included incident reporting and analysis by the NSC in 1921 (NSC 2017), traffic laws in 1924, emergency eye-wash showers in 1928, the formation of the Bureau of Labor Standards and enactment of the Walsh-Healy Act (aka the Public Contracts Act) of 1936 that established minimum wages, and finally health and safe standards for contracts in excess of $10,000 (USDoL 2017). It would be another 35 years until the ultimate legislative reform would occur with the passage of the Occupational Safety and Health Act (USDoL

2017). This act created not only the Occupational Safety and Health Administration (OSHA) under the administration of the Department of Labor as an enforcement body, but also the National Institute of Occupational Safety and Health (NIOSH) as part of the Public Health Service to serve as the research body that creates the science behind the standards (USDoL 2017).

The main goal of OSHA is twofold: to protect workers and the employer from preventable safety and health risks.

The next major legislative development in the maturation of the safety profession was the Occupational Safety and Health Act of 1971 (OSHA 2017). The main goal of OSHA is twofold: to protect workers *and* the employer from preventable safety and health risks. The OSHA website succinctly states the mission of OSHA.

In 1970, the United States Congress and President Richard Nixon created the Occupational Safety and Health Administration (OSHA), a national public health agency dedicated to the basic proposition that no worker should have to choose between their life and their job (All about OSHA 2016 ).

Under the administration of the US Department of Labor, OSHA was created by the Occupational Safety and Health Act "to assure safe and healthful conditions for working men and women by setting and enforcing standards and providing training, outreach, education and compliance assistance. Under the OSHA law, employers are responsible for providing a safe and healthful workplace for their workers" (All about OSHA 2016, 4).

While OSHA's job is mainly enforcement of mandates, rules, standards, best practices, and regulations, it is not their job to devise the science behind the rules, standards, and regulations. This job falls to the National Institute of Occupational Safety and Health (NIOSH). The OSH Act of 1970 "established NIOSH as a research agency focused on the study of worker safety and health, and empowering employers and workers to create safe and healthy workplaces." NIOSH is part of the US Centers for Disease Control and Prevention in the US Department of Health and Human Services. It has the mandate to assure "every man and woman in the Nation safe and healthful working conditions and to preserve our human resources." NIOSH has more than 1,300 employees from a diverse set of fields, including epidemiology, medicine, nursing, industrial hygiene, safety, psychology, chemistry, statistics, economics, and many branches of engineering" (NIOSH 2017). NIOSH funds, contracts, and conducts basic and applied research to better understand the safety and health risks of employees in all employment settings. In addition, NIOSH researches how to design the most effective safety and health standards, protective technologies, and work practices. NIOSH also works through its Board of Scientific Counselors and with the National Academy of Sciences to ensure that its science and its findings are of the highest scientific rigor and quality.

NIOSH researches how to design the most effective safety and health standards, protective technologies, and work practices.

Following the OSH Act and beginning in the mid-to-late 1970s, occupational safety and health began to grow as a profession and subsequently as an academic discipline. As standards were added (e.g., control of hazardous energy, blood-borne pathogens, hazard communication, etc.), skills and knowledge specific to OHS practitioners started to become integrated into business and environmental operations.

In addition to the development of a legislative basis for worker and workplace safety and health, also critical to the development of a profession is an academic infrastructure of bona fide and legitimate degree programs. Toward this end, it took several more years for higher education to eventually devise and create academic degree programs in OSH that focused on developing a capable and adequate workforce. As another step in the evolution of the OSH profession, the first standards-setting body and professional certification in OHS became available in

1969 when the Board of Certified Safety Professionals (BCSP) began and created its signature professional certification: the Certified Safety Professional (CSP) (BCSP 2017). Until the advent of the CSP, there were no bona fide metrics against which to determine professional requirements for OSH practitioners. The discipline had been unregulated and unstructured. It was unregulated in the sense that anyone could claim to be a safety professional with or without an education and with or without a professional credential. It was unstructured in the sense that it was impossible to identify standardized approaches to identify and mitigate workplace life and health risks.

Until the advent of the CSP, there were no bona fide metrics against which to determine professional requirements for OSH practitioners. The discipline had been unregulated and unstructured.

One result of a lack of professional certification was that academic programs had virtually no guidance as to what to teach. Consequently, OSH degree programs were graduating "safety professionals" who varied widely in both competence and capability. Complicating matters was a lack of a consensus concerning academic education standards. Thus, the OSH discipline was not supported by professional practice guidelines, an established certification market, or guidance as to a model OSH curriculum or standards. As a result, the OSH "profession" had no defensible professional identity, no practice boundaries, and virtually no accountability. From the practice to the classroom, *safety* was essentially anything anyone said it was.

One result of a lack of professional certification was that academic programs had virtually no guidance as to what to teach. Consequently, OSH degree programs were graduating "safety professionals" who varied widely in both competence and capability.

To better understand how the worksite function called "safety" might continue to evolve into a profession, the next section will explore the nature of what defines a profession. A discussion on how current research efforts have specifically defined the OSH discipline follows. Finally, the chapter will conclude with a proposed set of steps OSH should pursue to finalize its maturation as a profession.

## What Is a Profession?[1]

During this somewhat slow but progressive evolution, the safety profession was maturing, growing, and professionalizing. But how does one distinguish between an occupation and a profession? All professions seem to mature through a lifecycle. That is, new discovery, knowledge (e.g., quantum mechanics), or newly codified sets of operating procedures based on new technology (e.g., medical technicians or insurance claims adjusters) can each act as an impetus for the formation of a new profession. Professions, then, begin to develop and grow and finally mature. Eventually, professions either persist or fade away over time. To understand what a profession may or may not be or how it becomes recognized as a sovereign discipline, we will investigate the characteristics that mature disciplines or professions demonstrate. The *American Heritage Dictionary* (online) defines a profession as "(a) an occupation or career; (b) An occupation, such as law, medicine, or engineering, that requires considerable training and specialized study; or (c) The body of qualified persons in an occupation or field" (*American Heritage Dictionary* 2017). Indeed, Paul Starr states, "Quite aside from specialized knowledge, professionals possess an advantage in judgment" (Starr 1984, 5). Further, one can observe across several more mature disciplines (e.g., engineering, medicine, law, nursing) that specialized knowledge or skill is required in the execution of the duties in the profession. A more detailed discussion of the common characteristics shared by all professions is discussed next.

1 Please see Ferguson and Ramsay 2010 for a more complete treatment of how professions form.

All professions seem to mature through a life cycle ... new discovery, knowledge (e.g., quantum mechanics) or newly codified sets of operating procedures based on new technology (e.g., medical technicians or insurance claims adjusters) can each act as an impetus for the formation of a new profession.

## Common Characteristics of a Profession

Dean (1995) suggests characteristics that are consistent with established professions, including a service orientation and a code of professional ethics, a specialized body of knowledge, a distinct educational tract that derives from the specialized body of knowledge and associated educational credentials, continuous learning and professional development, and a social or collegial dimension. As per Ferguson and Ramsay (2010), the following five characteristics are sustainably established for a discipline to be considered a profession.

**Characteristics of a profession:** service orientation and a code of professional ethics, a specialized body of knowledge, a distinct educational tract which derives from the specialized body of knowledge and associated educational credentials, continuous learning and professional development, and a social or collegial dimension.

### Characteristic 1: A Service Orientation and a Code of Professional Conduct

Most recognized professions provide a valuable service to society and operate with little or no self-interest. The code maintains a professional orientation and a service mentality and specifies practice within the guidelines of an ethical code. The code is often written and states what is and is not acceptable behavior. Professional codes of conduct become the guiding set of behavioral standards used by the professionals in ethically difficult situations and helps maintain the service orientation of the profession. The ASSP Code of Professional Conduct for Safety Professionals is (ASSE 2012):

**Commitment to professionalism:** treat others with respect, maintain the confidentiality of information acquired through professional practice, avoid situations that create actual, potential, or perceived conflicts between personal and professional interests, and so forth.

- Serve the public, employees, employers, clients, the Society, and the profession with fidelity, honesty, and impartiality.
- In all professional relationships, treat others with respect, civility, and without discrimination.
- Abstain from behavior that will unjustly cause harm to the reputation of the Society, its members, and the profession.
- Continually improve professional knowledge, skills, competencies, and awareness of relevant new developments through training, education, networking, and work experiences.
- Consider qualifications before undertaking any professional activity and perform only those services that may be handled competently.
- Make informed decisions in the performance of professional duties that adhere to all relevant laws, regulations, and recognized standards of practice.
- Inform all appropriate parties when professional judgment indicates that there is an unacceptable level of risk of injury, illness, property damage, or environmental harm.
- Maintain the confidentiality of information acquired through professional practice that is designated or generally recognized as nonpublic, confidential, or privileged.
- Accurately represent professional qualifications including education, credentials, designations, affiliations, titles, and work experience.
- Avoid situations that create actual, potential, or perceived conflicts between personal and professional interests, and if a potential conflict of interest arises, disclose all applicable facts to potentially affected parties.

### Characteristic 2: Specialized (Discipline-Specific) Body of Knowledge

As mentioned in the definition, a profession is built upon specialized knowledge and skills. Professionals develop special skills and knowledge through education and training in order to serve clients effectively. Such a distinct and specific body of knowledge is the core of the identity (definition) of all professions. It is critical for the profession to clearly define this core knowledge and skills. This concept will be further developed in the next section.

### Characteristic 3: Academic Qualifications/Education

The third characteristic of a recognized profession is an extensive and competency-based education. In addition, a representational professional association nurtures the defining education standards by providing a means to build, maintain, and expand the education standards and ethics over time. Educators transmit knowledge, skills, values and professional behavior to their students across the curriculum. As theory and knowledge evolves over time, standards are revised and distributed. The prestige and status of the profession and its knowledge base are enhanced through a set of competency-based educational standards that are adopted uniformly across the academic programs of the discipline. Most often, specialized accreditation is the preferred vehicle to accomplish this, but more on this later.

Mature professions such as medicine or law share common characteristics. One such characteristic is an internship or some other culminating, off-campus experience that allows the student to experience professional life outside the comfort of the classroom. Such experiences allow students to apply the specialized body of knowledge and skills in a real-world setting under the supervision of more experienced professionals.

Educators transmit knowledge, skills, values, and professional behavior to their students across the curriculum. The prestige and status of the profession and its knowledge base are enhanced through a set of competency-based educational standards that are adopted uniformly across the academic programs of the discipline.

### Characteristic 4: Established Continuous Professional Education/ Lifelong Learning Structures

After basic academic preparation is completed, professionals continue to learn and renew core skills and knowledge through continuing education. Continuing education occurs through several avenues such as classes, seminars, additional formal education and the study of professional literature, or professional certifications. Professionalism assumes that education is a continuous process across one's career. In addition, professions themselves grow and mature over time as research addresses challenges faced by practitioners and as those solutions to those challenges become integrated in academic degree programs. Professionals contribute to this maturation process through their own study, practice, and research, all made available to the community of practitioners through publications, presentations, standards development, and other communications.

Emerging professionals become members of a common group or community through identification with the values, practices, educational background, and personal identity of the profession.

### Characteristic 5: Socialization/Collegiality

Professional socialization involves the building of a group identity, a collegial consciousness. Often such is initiated through the education process, which provides a means to socialize emerging professionals. Emerging professionals become members of a common group or community through identification with the values, practices, educational background, and personal identity of the profession. Further, the profession may also develop licensure, certification, or other forms of membership validation that confirm the professional identity of its members and that indicate a qualification

OSH has not achieved occupational closure through licensure or other credentialing. In combination, the demarcation between the qualified and the unqualified would be relatively straightforward.

to practice. Specifically, licensure often exists on a state-by-state basis. Licensure is said to produce "occupation closure" (Ferguson and Ramsay 2010) by confirming or validating membership through enforcing laws and by restricting illegal practice by nonmembers of the profession. A good example of licensure that creates closure is the professional engineers (PE) credential for engineers (Dean 1995).

## Origins of a Profession's Identity

Considering the earlier distinction between an occupation and a profession, how does an occupation become recognized as a profession? This recognition is sometimes referred to as *professionalization*, and it is a social process that involves at least the following three steps:

1. Establishment of a metric (or set of metrics) that can discern the "qualified" from the "unqualified" to practice.
2. Development of a sustainable and representative professional body or association to oversee the adherence of its members to a professional code of ethics, separate from that of a professional credential, facilitating professional networking, management, and advancement of education standards and the creation and distribution of the discipline's body of knowledge through peer-reviewed scientific methods.
3. Establishment of a consensus set of professional educational qualifications, which is usually managed and promoted by the professional association and a recognized accrediting organization. Critical to this step is that the education standards be outcomes based (i.e., are professional competencies) that are developed through research, supported by best practices, and approved by consensus and widely (if not uniformly) adopted by all higher education programs in the discipline.

There are two core characteristics of mature professions that OSH lacks. The first is its failure to motivate accreditation of all OSH academic programs. Second, OSH has not achieved occupational closure through licensure or other credentialing. In combination, the demarcation between the qualified and the unqualified would be relatively straightforward. Were all OSH degree programs to require a minimum set of education standards (i.e., accreditation), and were OSH able to achieve closure, the profession would become closed to entry from outsiders, amateurs, and the unqualified. Also, practitioners would share a common language and competence. In contrast, mature professions are easily characterized by a more uniform distribution of professional credentials (or licensure, certification, etc.) among practitioners. In addition, the fact that all educational programs in mature professions are accredited means that members of a mature profession share a consensus set of knowledge, skills, and abilities required in practice.

> To frame the operating boundaries of any discipline, it is most logical to use student learning outcomes as opposed to more arbitrary criteria, such as job descriptions and job titles.

Ultimately, the education component is the key to all mature disciplines. The next section more deeply explores the role education has in the development of any profession.

## The Necessary Role of Education in Framing a Profession[2]

Academic qualifications provided in an educational setting are a common characteristic of recognized and mature professions. Formal education conveys specialized knowledge, skills, and abilities through course work and other educational experiences, such as internships and capstones. To frame the operating boundaries of any discipline, it is most logical to use student learning outcomes as opposed to more arbitrary criteria, such as job descriptions and job

2 A specific treatment of how a new set of education standards were derived for the OSH discipline can be found in Ramsay and Hartz 2017.

titles. Consequently, the knowledge, skills, and abilities/behaviors (KSAs) students are expected to be able to demonstrate at graduation become the basis for professional definition. Once vetted as credible and comprehensive indicators of the profession, KSAs (aka competencies) become the basis of outcomes-based accreditation typically conducted by organizations who are themselves accredited to conduct such quality assurance reviews of academic programs.

Accreditation may engender "thoughts of elitism, undue barriers to entry and exclusion to some, excess expense and effort to others, and still to others, may indicate a measure of sanctification, somewhat like the 'United States Department of Agriculture approved beef' stamp of approval for high quality programs."

As most academics likely know, accreditation is oft cited as a *quality control* measure in higher education. However, the general term *accreditation* is very broad indeed and includes many types and levels of application. Consequently "accreditation" suggests different things to different people. For example, Ramsay (2013, 20)[3] states that accreditation may engender "thoughts of elitism, undue barriers to entry and exclusion to some, excess expense and effort to others, and still to others, may indicate a measure of sanctification, somewhat like the 'United States Department of Agriculture approved beef' stamp of approval for high quality programs." Keep in mind that accreditation itself cannot guarantee occupational closure. Rather, program-level accreditation is focused on demonstrating evidence of their students meet minimal performance outcomes and on evidence of the processes they use to sustain continuous quality improvement. Hence, a systematic and performance-based structure such as outcomes-based accreditation can assure students, faculty, programs, constituents, and institutions that KSAs required by their chosen profession have indeed been taught. As the author states:

> This efficiency has its roots in free market economics. It can be argued that accreditation allows for more efficient information exchanges between the suppliers of education (academic programs, faculty) and the consumers of education (the private and public sector entities that hire graduates) and students (those who acquire education). In addition, accreditation enables market efficiency in at least two ways. First, programs can be more efficient because accreditation lessens the likelihood of a program developing courses or concentrations not of interest to education's consumers. Second, consumers can act more efficiently since they absorb graduates who progress through a continuous improvement process is substantiated by a third party. Third, academic providers adhering to the process of outcomes-based education can more completely engage in continuous quality improvement by virtue of the assessment and reporting requirements inherent in accreditation which in turn keep the faculty appropriately credentialed, and the outcomes current, and relevant. (Ramsay 2013, 20)

Programs can be more efficient because accreditation lessens the likelihood of a program developing courses or concentrations not of interest to education's consumers. Academic providers adhering to the process of outcomes-based education can more completely engage in continuous quality improvement.

Accreditation standards in disciplines such as law, nursing, and medicine require academic programs to demonstrate and measure (i.e., assess) how the standards central to the practice or body of knowledge of their discipline are achieved. For example, the Liaison

3 A more thorough treatment of the value of accreditation as a vehicle for establishing and disseminating education standards can be found in Ramsay, Sorrell, and Hartz 2014.

Committee on Medical Education (LCME) publishes standards for medical school accreditation, which include medical ethics, critical thinking, inter-professional collaborative skills, and so forth (LCME 2014). In turn, accreditation requires medical schools to create self-studies that describe how each required standard is accomplished to ascertain the degree to which these outcomes are being obtained by students. Logically, the presence of well-established occupational closure in medicine (like in engineering, nursing, and law) ensures that all medical schools teach and accomplish the same minimal set of education standards and that practitioners all have licenses. As a result, the medical field, licensing boards, employers, and the public can all depend on each medical graduate to have approximately the same introductory set of knowledge, skills, and abilities. And without proper licensure, one may not legally consider oneself a physician. However, in OSH, the lack of occupational closure and high job placement rates combine to create a very non-uniform adoption of accreditation standards across OSH programs nationwide. Indeed, by a simple count, the vast minority (likely less than 20%) of OSH programs (i.e., either graduate or undergraduate degree programs in regionally accredited institutions of higher education, including EHS programs, not including IH programs) counted by ASSP are ABET accredited. Further complicating a wider dissemination of standards across OSH programs has been how OSH standards have been developed over time. For example, although the Education Standards Committee (ESC) of the ASSP sets accreditation standards, these standards have traditionally not been the consensus product of a national effort involving subject matter experts, policy experts, academics, and practitioners. Without a consensus set of recognized education standards, and without a licensure infrastructure, occupational closure cannot occur in OSH. And without closure, one cannot frame the OSH discipline as a profession.

Without a consensus set of recognized education standards, and without a licensure infrastructure, occupational closure cannot occur in OSH. And without closure, one cannot frame the OSH discipline as a profession.

## Competencies, Capabilities and Learning Outcomes

Competencies and capabilities are typically the components of employee job descriptions and the basis of performance appraisals. Learning outcomes tend to be the knowledge, skills, and behaviors that compose an academic curriculum. Learning outcomes, including established areas of research and practice, define the body of knowledge of the occupational safety and health profession. In addition, they can be organized into themes or categories called *knowledge domains*. In this sense competencies are directly related to learning outcomes.

Competence can be thought of as the ability to execute/complete a task skillfully, correctly, and professionally, while capability is the ability to apply theoretical knowledge that underpins practice in occupations and the industry-specific knowledge and skills that transcend a specific workplace and the tacit knowledge of the workplace.

According to the International Network for Safety and Health Practitioners (INSHPO 2015), competence can be thought of as the ability to execute/complete a task skillfully, correctly, and professionally. In contrast, capability can be thought of as the ability to apply theoretical knowledge that underpins practice in occupations and the industry-specific knowledge and skills that transcend a specific workplace and the tacit knowledge of the workplace. In OSH, there are at least two categories of competencies: *technical* and *adaptive*, which work together to create one's professional capability. Competencies derived from the literature and from best academic practices are considered technical, while adaptive competencies are more focused on the "softer skills" of day-to-day professional life. Adaptive competencies include things such as leadership, communication, relationship building, trust, partnering, collaboration, and learning (Heifetz 1994).

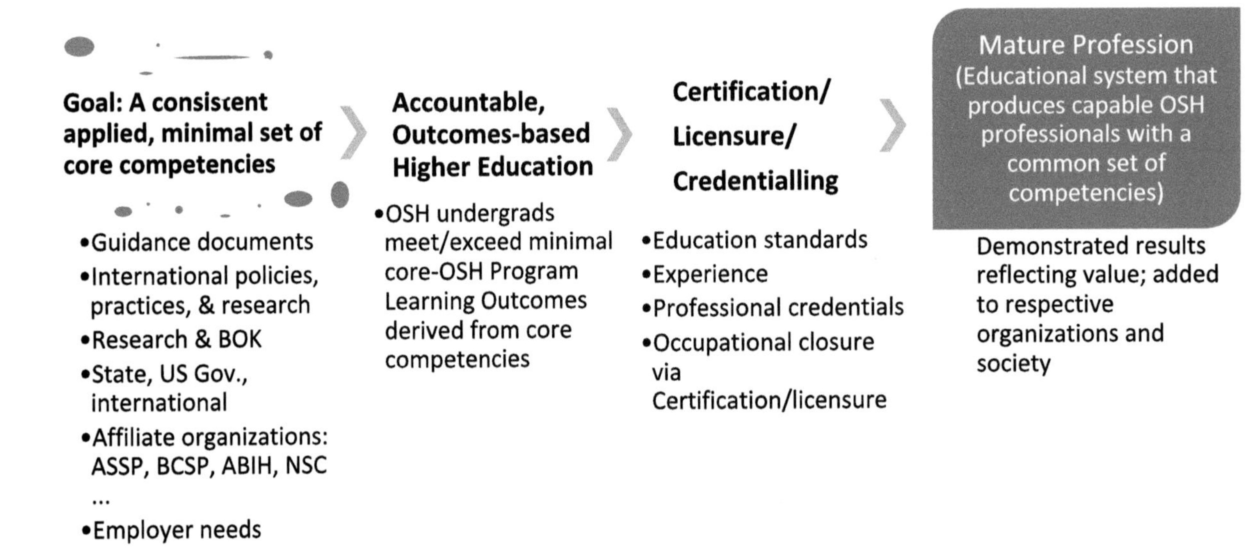

**Goal: A consistent applied, minimal set of core competencies**

- Guidance documents
- International policies, practices, & research
- Research & BOK
- State, US Gov., international
- Affiliate organizations: ASSP, BCSP, ABIH, NSC ...
- Employer needs

**Accountable, Outcomes-based Higher Education**

- OSH undergrads meet/exceed minimal core-OSH Program Learning Outcomes derived from core competencies

**Certification/ Licensure/ Credentialling**

- Education standards
- Experience
- Professional credentials
- Occupational closure via Certification/licensure

**Mature Profession** (Educational system that produces capable OSH professionals with a common set of competencies)

Demonstrated results reflecting value; added to respective organizations and society

Figure 9.1
Learning outcomes/competencies and their connection to occupational closure.

Figure 9.1 (Ramsay and Hartz 2017) organizes the notions of learning outcomes/competencies and occupational closure.

## Creating Education Standards: The Core of How to Frame OSH as a Profession[4]

As has been noted above, mature disciplines frame their operating boundaries by education standard that are developed by consensus through their respective professional associations. This is normally accomplished by using best practices, the published literature, needs of prevailing policy and regulatory environments, and the professional opinion of subject matter experts (SMEs). It would be most logical for OSH to emulate this process as it attempts to frame itself as a sovereign discipline and as it matures into a profession. As specified in the standard operating guidelines of the committee, defining minimal education standards for the OSH profession is a primary goal of the ASSP ESC. As the acknowledged global leader in academic program accreditation, ASSP works with ABET, Inc. to accredit OSH programs. As an ABET member society, ASSP supports several ASSP members who serve ABET in a variety of roles, including on the ABET board of directors, board of delegates, and the Applied Sciences Commission (one of four ABET commissions and the one from which all OSH programs are accredited). In addition, ASSP supports ABET program accreditation by selecting and training program evaluators and assists dozens of programs seeking ABET accreditation.

As the acknowledged global leader in academic program accreditation, ASSP works with ABET, Inc. to accredit OSH programs. ASSP also supports ABET program accreditation by selecting and training program evaluators and assists dozens of programs seeking ABET accreditation.

Within ASSP, professionalizing OSH has been underway for over fifty years. The concept of using SMEs and workshops to devise OSH education standards has been consistent with prevailing strategy by ASSP leadership. As expressly stated by ASSP presidents and as stated in the ASSP strategic plan, demarking the road for OSH professionalization has

4 Adapted from Ramsay and Hartz 2017

a long history. In his April 2015 President's Message, Michael Belcher noted the ASSE executive board reorganization and four strategic goals: (1) enhance member communities recognizing their important role, (2) assure quality and pertinent opportunities for professional development, (3) serve the profession by facilitating OSH consensus standards, and (4) build the value of the profession, including "do everything possible to advance professionalism and ensure that only competent professionals perform OSH duties" (ASSE 2016). In their 2010 *Professional Safety Journal* article, Ferguson and Ramsay (2010) noted the success of the OSH profession will be dependent upon differentiating member capabilities by assuring minimal OSH educational standards, defining competent experience, passing appropriate credentialing exams, meeting certification continuance requirements, and ultimately achieving occupational closure.

> The OSH profession will be dependent upon differentiating member capabilities by assuring minimal OSH educational standards, defining competent experience, passing appropriate credentialing exams, meeting certification continuance requirements and ultimately achieving occupational closure.

Utilizing methods from Hartz (2014), Ramsay and Hartz facilitated two national workshops that included members from the ASSP Education Standards Committee and several subject matter experts from a variety of industries. The main goal of the SMEs was to codify and establish a set of knowledge domains that describe the OSH discipline and subsequently produce a minimum set of student learning outcomes (or competencies) within each knowledge domain. Hartz (2014) defined "experts" or SMEs as those professionals who have in the last five years, singularly or in combination, (1) serve(d) on an advisory committee of an ABET-ASAC accredited program; (2) published peer-reviewed OSH literature; (3) serve(d) on a National OSH Committee or research task force; (4) serve(d) as a terminal degreed associate or full professor faculty member, holding a current and germane board certification; (5) work(ed) full time as an OSH practitioner at a facility or job site with demonstrated OSH performance excellence, verified by a third party; or (6) hired and managed bachelors of science OSH program graduates at a facility or job site with demonstrated OSH performance excellence, verified by a third party (Hartz 2014). Functionally, the first workshop was focused on producing a consensus set of knowledge domains that would in turn be used to characterize and define the OSH discipline. The second workshop focused on developing a consensus set of learning outcomes (aka competencies) within each domain. Ultimately, a set of knowledge domains and competencies within each domain would compose an OSH model curriculum from which accreditation standards can be derived.

The first workshop, in April 2015, produced seven knowledge domains that were more deeply refined to include identifiable student learning outcomes (SLOs) in the second workshop that took place in January 2016. Knowledge domains and SLOs were not intended to be exhaustive but, instead, representative. A consensus set of SLOs from a national sample of SMEs means that a representative group of SMEs have agreed that these are the best, most important SLOs to teach undergraduates in each knowledge domain. This is critical to establishing legitimacy of the intellectual core of a profession. Table 9.1 represents the knowledge domains and student learning outcomes that were the collective product of both workshops and post hoc consensus by the ASSP ESC.

Organizing the results of both workshops as a model curriculum accomplished three important goals for the OSH discipline. First, as in other mature disciplines, the methods used to obtain the knowledge domains and competencies were a critical component to the aspiration of the subsequent set of accreditation standards achieving widespread credibility and

**Table 9.1** The OSH model curriculum (Ramsay and Hartz 2017)
The final set of knowledge domains and competencies within each domain

1. **Evidenced Based.** The OHS professional of the future will utilize research and evidence to drive problem-solving and integrate value-added practical solutions into organizational goals.
   a. Discern, collect, analyze, and interpret relevant data to reduce the risk profile of an organization
   b. Conduct a thorough literature review utilizing peer-reviewed scientific literature to develop practical solutions for identified problems
   c. Integrate financial justifications into the development of policies, procedures, and systems that align with organizational strategic plans
   d. Develop and track both leading and lagging indicators to measure OSH program effectiveness and demonstrate continuous improvement
   e. Apply knowledge of working requirements and best practices to prepare, review, and revise OSH policy
   f. Develop a computer program to help analyze complex processes
   g. Develop and present training at worker and management levels

2. **Communication.** The OSH professional will interact effectively with stakeholders, colleagues, and employees, fostering mutual respect and shared decision-making to enhance worker health and safety.
   a. Apply interpersonal communication skills to effectively influence audience
   b. Demonstrate effective written communication skills
   c. Demonstrate the development and delivery of effective training by employing various media
   d. Apply facilitation, team building, and problem-solving skills
   e. Interpret and disseminate relevant safety, health, and environmental (SH&E) information to inform target audience

3. **Risk Management.*** The OSH professional of the future will participate in and contribute to the process of conserving assets and earning powers of an organization by minimizing the effects of loss.
   a. Generate controls based on risk assessment using the hierarchy of controls model
   b. Analyze the financial and nonfinancial benefits of controls
   c. Demonstrate ability to communicate the financial and nonfinancial benefits of controls
   d. Relate to concepts of risk transfer and corporate and social responsibility
   e. Define risk terminology
   f. Provide examples of risk-assessment techniques
   g. Facilitate operational risk assessments to provide decision-makers risk-based information
   h. Incorporate risk assessment and prevention through design (PtD) concepts in the design and redesign phases of systems, products, and services

*Continued*

**Table 9.1** The OSH model curriculum (Ramsay and Hartz 2017)
The final set of knowledge domains and competencies within each domain *(continued)*

| |
|---|
| 4. **Business.** The OSH professional will be able to develop, articulate, and execute a business case for protecting the company's internal and external assets, stakeholders, and the community.<br>a. Analyze and calculate return on investment to be able to plan, articulate, market, and sell SH&E initiatives to executive management<br>b. Demonstrate the ability to align the business case with the safety goals of the organization (case studies and teaching notes)<br>c. Understand, interpret, and translate financial performance ratios and their impact on SH&E initiatives<br>d. Identify the issues and problems that impact the business and be able to articulate the problem, identify the merits in addressing the problem on economic, societal, and social responsible basis, and being able to collect data and analyze to inform<br>e. Ability to determine tangible and intangible return on investment in presenting the business case to protect the business, people, and environment<br>f. Understand the relationships and business impact on worksite health and safety and human resources benefit programs, and through that, role identification, collaboration, and relationship building<br>g. Build and apply financial business budgeting process for SH&E operation<br>h. Explain to management how the business case impacts the community<br>i. Demonstrate servant leadership to achieve measurable business and people-focused results |
| 5. **Leadership.** The ability to influence the behavior of individuals, systems, and work groups in a way that will facilitate the achievement of shared goals.<br>a. Demonstrate the ability to lead multidisciplinary teams<br>b. Build relationships with all stakeholders<br>c. Analyze human behavior, team dynamics, and individual performance to prevent occupational injury<br>d. Support all stakeholders to manage risk<br>e. Conceive ways to add value<br>f. Demonstrate problem-solving skills<br>g. Explain the importance of leadership in a risk-management context<br>h. Provide leadership in the organization's SH&E management system |

*Continued*

**Table 9.1** The OSH model curriculum (Ramsay and Hartz 2017)
The final set of knowledge domains and competencies within each domain *(continued)*

6. **Informatics.** The collection, classification, storage, retrieval, and dissemination of recorded knowledge to help make informed and data driven decisions about occupational health and safety threats and hazards.
   a. Demonstrate proficiency and use of software and equipment needed to identify occupational hazards and risk
   b. Analyze data to support risk-reduction decision-making
   c. Ability to utilize contemporary computer skills to gather applicable data and present relevant metrics to influence decision-making
   d. Apply consensus standards and regulatory resources to mitigate risk
   e. Demonstrate knowledge of various SH&E management systems
   f. Ability to effectively use contemporary instrumentation and technology to effectively gather pertinent data
   g. Access, interpret, and apply applicable standards to subject operations
   h. Demonstrate application of risk-based principles to prioritize between competing operational needs
   i. Understand how to implement SH&E audit and inspection testing systems
   j. Understand and apply risk assessment methodology to support decision-making
   k. Demonstrate knowledge of basic engineering skills (e.g., reading CAD/CAM drawings)

7. **Professionalism.** Includes accountability to establish workplace programs and worker safety/health advocacy practices in a moral, legal, ethical, and socially responsible manner.
   a. Recognize and accept their level of competence and need for assistance
   b. Demonstrate legal, moral, and sustainability principles through their actions
   c. Identify legal and regulatory obligations in their work environment
   d. Explain the difference between compromise and professional obligations
   e. Address gaps between policy and practice

* The risk-management section leveraged existing theory and practices as exemplified by the following standards: ISO 31000/ANSI/ASSP Z690.2 (ISO 31000 2015), *Risk Management*, ANSI/ASSP Z590.3 *Prevention through Design* (ANSI/ASSP Z590.3-2011), Z10-2012 *Occupational Health and Safety Management Systems* (ANSI/ASSP Z10-2012).

adoption by academic programs. Second, ultimately, widespread adoption of such education standards paves the way for occupational closure and the ultimate demarcation of OSH as a sovereign profession. Third, organizing the discipline around knowledge domains and competencies allows for a formal and professional identity for the OSH discipline. This is indeed akin to how several other mature disciplines have defined themselves. That is, standards provide a professional identity that is concise; based on science, best practices, and policy; and supported by the consensus opinion of a robust set of SMEs, including student competencies that will in turn structure OSH education nationwide.

## Tying It All Together

A defining characteristic of all mature disciplines and professions seems to be a common core of educational standards, which they use to define who they are and who they are not. As occupations mature over time and eventually become professions, they tend to develop professional certifications, education standards that are adopted by all academic degree programs.

Such education standards then become the basis for recognized accreditation. Mature disciplines also have professional associations, peer-reviewed journals and a body of knowledge, continuing professional education, conferences that share and disseminate scholarship, and best practices. Such disciplines develop mechanisms that filter who is and who is not eligible to practice in the profession—that is, they have occupational closure. Currently, OSH seems to be well along the trajectory of professionalization, exhibiting many of the characteristics of other, more mature professions listed above. However, as has been pointed out, OSH still lacks several key characteristics of mature professions, such as occupational closure. There are likely several, albeit somewhat anecdotal, reasons for this. First, both licensure and accreditation can be expensive and labor intensive, and both seemingly appear unnecessary in markets eager to employ graduates or in markets seemingly uninterested in identifying bona fide practitioners from the unqualified. Widespread and uniform adoption of accreditation can also be difficult if the education standards appear irrelevant or unhelpful or fail to represent current research, policy, or best practices. By leveraging the collective wisdom of a national panel of SMEs to produce a consensus set of knowledge domains and competencies, this article presented a partial solution to the professionalization trajectory for OSH. What remains to professionalize OSH is a mechanism for occupational closure, such as state-based licensure and a complete adoption of education standards using recognized accreditation in all OSH academic degree programs.

Mature disciplines also have professional associations, peer-reviewed journals and a body of knowledge, continuing professional education, conferences that share and disseminate scholarship, and best practices.

## Roadmap to Professionalization

The OSH profession has tremendous opportunities to shape its own future and meet the many emergent challenges OSH professionals will face. Finally, it seems logical to claim that the OSH "profession" has reached a time in its history when it should be able to define what it is, what it is not, and who should and should not be able to practice. Such a definition would be based upon a body of knowledge that in turn represents the consensus opinion of practitioners and scholars and is based in research, best practice, and policy and regulatory needs. It is time for the OSH discipline to achieve closure and become a mature profession. Therefore, to advance the OSH profession and achieve occupational closure and subsequent professional sovereignty, Ramsay and Hartz (2017) recommend the following:

It seems logical to claim that the OSH "profession" has reached a time in its history when it should be able to define what it is and what it is not, and who should be able to practice and who should not.

1. Establish a widespread and uniform adoption of a common set of education standards as presented in this article for college and university programs producing OSH job seekers. This can best be achieved through recognized program level accreditation through, for example, ABET, Inc. Recognized program-level accreditation should be the gold standard by which program quality is considered.
2. Until perfect uniformity of accreditation (such as the case for programs in engineering, medicine, dietetics, nursing, law, etc.) is achieved, an alternative system of academic accountability should be constructed and implemented nationwide. For those programs not pursuing accreditation, ASSP should create a structure and process that transparently characterizes the degree to which the non-accredited program complies with its model curriculum and competencies. Although the process may vary somewhat, the process would be somewhat like criteria used in the program-level accreditation process.
3. All practitioners should be professionally certified using certifications that themselves are accredited (i.e., BCSP as accredited by CHEA) and which

require an educational background from an accredited academic program. Professional certifications and education standards should stay sustainably coupled.

4. Practitioners, board examiners, academics, and policymakers should form a mechanism whereby education standards and continuing education and professional certifications communicate and work in concert to achieve long-term sustainable professional competence.
5. Achieve occupational closure. That is, there should be barriers to entry for participating OSH professionals. This will require steps 1–4 above to be achieved first. Following achieving steps 1–4, a national system of registration or licensure should be developed. In addition, employers and the federal government will need to be included in the development of common understanding of terms and requirements used in job descriptions.
6. A code of professional ethics needs to be uniformly adopted by all practitioners. This can be achieved through the professional certification process or the licensure/registration process.

## Questions

1. What are the primary characteristics all mature disciplines seem to share?
2. Would you characterize occupational safety and health as a profession, a discipline, or a trade? Explain your answer.
3. What role(s) do both institutional and specialized (i.e., program-level) accreditation play in the making of a true profession?
4. Describe the role(s) risk management seems to play in both the practice and in the proposed new set of OSH standards. How might you revise your characterization of OSH from question 2 above in terms of risk management?
5. What can you contribute to the "roadmap to professionalization" as described above?

## References

All about OSHA. (2016). OSHA publication 3302–11R, 2016.

ANSI/ASSP Z10-2012. (2012). *Occupational Health and Safety Management Systems.* Park Ridge, IL: American Society of Safety Engineers.

ANSI/ASSP Z590.3-2011. (2011). *Prevention through Design: Guidelines for Addressing Occupational Hazards and Risks in Design and Redesign Process.* Park Ridge, IL: American Society of Safety Engineers.

ASSE. (2017). "History of the Safety Profession." Accessed January 2017. http://www.asse.org/about/history/.

ASSE. (2016). "Strategic Outlook." Accessed January 2017. http://www.asse.org/our-strategic-outlook/ December 2016.

ASSE. (2012). "Code of Professional Conduct." Accessed February 2018. http://www.asse.org/about/sog-section-652/

BCSP (2017). "About the Board of Certified Safety Professionals." Accessed January 2017. http://www.bcsp.org/About.

Dean, J. (1995). "What Makes a Profession." *Fund Raising Management* (November).

Ferguson, L., and J. Ramsay. (2010). "The Role of Education and Certification in Occupational Safety Becoming a Profession." *Professional Safety* (October).

Hartz, W. E. (2014). "21st-Century US Safety Professional Educational Standards: Establishing Minimum Baccalaureate Graduate Learning Outcomes for Emerging Occupational Health and Safety Professionals." *Antioch* 465. Cambridge MA: Harvard University Press.

Heifetz, R. A. (1994). *Leadership without Easy Answers.* Cambridge, MA: Belknap Press of Harvard University Press.

INSHPO (International Network of Safety and Health Practitioner Organizations). (2015). "The OHS Professional Capability Framework: A Global Framework for Practice." Accessed December 2016. http://www.inshpo.org/docs/INSHPO_2015-OHS_Professional_Capability_Framework.pdf.

ISO 31000 (2015). "ISO 31000: A Practical Guide for SMEs." Accessed June 2017. https://www.iso.org/files/live/sites/isoorg/files/archive/pdf/en/iso_31000_for_smes.pdf.

Kellogg, P. (1908). "The Pittsburg Survey in Six Volumes." Accessed January 2017. https://archive.org/stream/pittsburghsurvey05kelluoft/pittsburghsurvey05kelluoft_djvu.txt.

Liaison Committee on Medical Education (LCME). (2016). "Functions and Structure of a Medical School." Accessed December 2016. https://members.aamc.org/eweb/upload/LCME%20Standards%20May%202012.pdf.

Occupational Safety and Health Administration (OSHA). (2017). "The OSH Act of 1970." Accessed January 2017. https://www.osha.gov/laws-regs/oshact/toc.

OHSonline. (2017). "History of the Safety Profession." Accessed January 2017. https://ohsonline.com/Articles/2007/01/01/Safety-Timeline.aspx?Page=2.

Ramsay, J. (2013). "The Case to Accredit Homeland Security: Why Outcomes-based Accreditation Makes Sense." *Journal of Homeland Security Education* 2.

Ramsay, J., and W. Hartz. (2017). "A Competency-Based Model Curriculum for Occupational Safety and Health: Results from Two National ASSE Education Standards Workshops." *Professional Safety* (March).

Ramsay, J., E. Sorrell, and W Hartz. (2015). "Outcomes Based Accreditation: Advancing the OSH Profession." *Professional Safety* (February).

Sinclair, U. (1906) *The Jungle*. Toronto: Grosset Publications.

Starr, P. (1984) *The Social Transformation of American Medicine*. New York: Basic Books.

US Department of Labor (DoL). (2017). "An Act to Establish the Department of Agriculture." Accessed January 2017. https://www.nal.usda.gov/act-establish-department-agriculture/.

CHAPTER 10

# ABET ACCREDITATION: THE CULTURE OF PROFESSIONAL QUALITY ASSURANCE

Amanda Reid

## Learning Objectives

After studying this chapter, the reader will be able to:

1. Discuss the accreditation process for institutional programs
2. Recognize the proof of professional competency through accreditation
3. Evaluate outcomes-based assessment and the peer review model of accreditation

## Key Terms

**Accreditation, assessment, programs, continuous improvement, ABET, safety, engineering**

## Abstract

In the United States, higher education accreditation is a peer-review process that assures the quality of the postsecondary education students receive. It does so by determining if educational programs meet defined standards of quality. Once achieved, accreditation is not permanent; it is renewed periodically to ensure that the quality and continual improvement efforts of the educational program are maintained.

## Introduction

Academic accreditation in the United States is voluntary, decentralized, and carried out by nongovernmental, nonprofit organizations. The process of academic accreditation typically culminates in an external quality review by a team of professional experts from academia and industry.

The term accreditation differs from certification and licensure in that it refers to the assessment of academic programs or educational institutions, while the latter terms are used to recognize individuals' accomplishments or credentials.

> Accreditation refers to assessment of academic programs or educational institutions.

There are two main types of accreditation in the United States: one is institutional, and the other is specialized, or program, accreditation. Institutional accreditation is carried out by regional or national accrediting bodies, which accredit entire institutions. Institutional accreditation in this country is tied as well to the ability of educational institutions to qualify their students to obtain student loans.

Specialized, or program, accreditation, on the other hand, is directed at programs within an institution and is not generally tied to qualification of an institution for student loan monies. The driver for specialized accreditation is different from the institutional accreditation as it arose in large part out of assuring competence of those obtaining degrees leading to professional practice. That mission of assuring that educational programs prepare their graduates for that professional practice is what drives the Accreditation Board for Engineering and Technology (ABET) and led the American Society of Safety Professionals (ASSP) to embrace accreditation as a path to defining and ensuring competencies in safety professionals.

Founded in 1911, ASSP is the world's oldest professional safety society. ASSP is a global association of safety professionals, representing more than 37,000 members worldwide.

ASSP is a member society of ABET and holds curricular responsibility for safety and similarly named programs being accredited by ABET, as well as sharing curricular responsibility for environmental health and safety (EHS) programs with the American Industrial Hygiene Association (AIHA). ASSP therefore is responsible for developing program criteria that safety programs applying for accreditation must meet, along with the ABET general criteria. ASSP also provides the safety professionals who actually carry out the peer review of the programs.

As a specialized accreditor, ABET accredits programs in applied and natural science (including mathematics), computing, engineering, and engineering technology at the associate's, bachelor's, and master's degree levels. For those programs to be eligible for ABET accreditation, the institution in which they are housed must already have verifiable governmental, national, or regional recognition to confer degrees.

ABET defines an educational program as an integrated, organized experience that culminates in the awarding of a degree. The program must have educational objectives for the program, student outcomes, a curriculum, faculty, and facilities.

ABET's processes are highly respected for their outcomes-based approach, nonprescriptive nature, and responsiveness to industry. ABET is also one of very few accreditors in the United States to have achieved ISO 9001 certification of its accreditation processes.

An educational program is an integrated, organized experience that culminates in the awarding of a degree.

Currently, ABET accredits more than 3,800 programs at 770 colleges and universities in thirty-one countries through its four commissions. Safety program accreditation falls under the Applied and Natural Science Accreditation Commission.

## Relationship of Accreditation to Proof of Professional Competency

A century ago, anyone could work as an engineer without proof of competency. In order to protect public health, safety, and welfare, the first engineering licensure law was enacted in 1907 in Wyoming. Now every state regulates the practice of engineering to ensure public safety. They do so by granting only professional engineers (PEs) the authority to sign and seal engineering plans and offer their services to the public. State licensing boards typically approve engineering programs accredited by the Accreditation Board for Engineering and Technology, Inc. (ABET), and the Canadian Accreditation Board (CAD) but may approve others as having equal standing. State board approval of an engineering educational program is often based on ABET accreditation (National Society of Professional Engineers 2018).

ABET (originally Engineers' Council for Professional Development, ECPD) was created in 1932 by five engineering professional societies and the National Council of State Boards of Engineering Examiners. From the beginning, accreditation of engineering programs was directed at ensuring that professional standards were set for the competencies needed by an engineer to practice and build the profession.

ASSP was to follow a similar path in developing the safety profession, using a combination of certification and accreditation to do so.

In addition to engineering programs, ABET accredits engineering technology, applied science (originally denominated engineering-related), and computing programs. In 2015 ABET began a pilot to add accreditation of natural science programs, including chemistry, physics, biology, environmental science, geology, and mathematics. This expansion has moved ABET solidly into STEM (science, technology, engineering, and mathematics) accreditation as a whole. The Applied and Natural Science Accreditation Commission (ANSAC), where accreditation of the safety, industrial hygiene, EHS, and health physics programs are located, has so far within natural science accredited programs in chemistry, geology, biotechnology, mathematics, pharmacobiology, and petroleum sciences. This year ANSAC is on track to approve accreditation of programs in actuarial science, biology, and nursing sciences, with more requests for accreditation visits in the coming year.

Graduates from many of the safety and industrial hygiene–related disciplines become professionals in fields that provide certification through independent certification bodies, such as eligibility for the Certified Safety Professional (CSP), Certified Industrial Hygienist (CIH), Certified Health Physicist (CHP), or Certified Construction Manager (CCM).

As accreditation and certification have always gone hand in hand for ABET, safety program accreditation was a natural match, combining accreditation to define what a graduate needs to know to be a safety professional with certification of professionals.

## Partnership with the American Society of Safety Professionals (ASSP)

ASSP (formerly the American Society of Safety Engineers, ASSE) recognized that occupational safety and health (OSH), as a newer profession, had not developed a solid identity the way that law, engineering, or medicine, for example, had. The lack of such clearly defined identity made it easy for those not qualified in OSH to fill positions. Experienced safety professionals recognized that their professional stature suffered when employers and customers dealt with those holding themselves out as OSH "professionals" who did not have the qualifications, skills, or experience needed to offer competent advice on safety and health matters.

In the early 1960s, ASSP embarked on an ambitious program to further define the safety profession by determining what a student needed to know upon graduation to become a safety professional. Their work in defining the body of knowledge and competencies needed was done together with the creation of the certified safety professional (CSP) certification, followed by accreditation of safety programs.

ASSP defines safety professionals and their functions as follows:

### Scope of a Safety Professional

To perform their professional functions, safety professionals must have education, training, and experience in a common body of knowledge. Safety professionals need to have a fundamental knowledge of physics, chemistry, biology, physiology, statistics, mathematics, computer science, engineering mechanics, industrial processes, business, communication, and psychology. Professional safety studies include industrial hygiene and toxicology, design of engineering hazard controls, fire protection, ergonomics, system and process safety, safety and health program management, incident investigation and analysis, product safety, construction safety, education and training methods, measurement of safety performance, human behavior, environmental safety and health, and safety, health, and environmental laws, regulations, and standards. Many safety professionals have backgrounds or advanced study in other disciplines, such as management and business administration, engineering, education, physical and social sciences, and other fields. Others have advanced study in safety. This extends their expertise beyond the basics of the safety profession.

### Functions of a Safety Professional

In addition to its efforts to define the body of safety knowledge and competencies, ASSE has identified the following four areas as those relating to the protection of people, property and the environment are:

1. Anticipate, identify, and evaluate hazardous conditions and practices.
2. Develop hazard control designs, methods, procedures, and programs.
3. Implement, administer, and advise others on hazard control programs.
4. Measure, audit, and evaluate the effectiveness of hazard control programs. (ASSE 2017)

More recently, ASSP has utilized the work they had done to define the profession in the United States to reach out for a global definition. ASSP joined with the Canadian Society of Safety Engineers (CSSE) and the Institution of Occupational Safety and Health (IOSH) in the United Kingdom to create the International Network of Safety & Health Practitioner Organizations (INSHPO) in 2001. INSHPO has since grown to include fourteen member organizations in eleven countries.

## Certification and Accreditation

Certification is a designation earned by a person who shows qualification (usually knowledge, experience, and skills) to perform a job or task. Certifying bodies have their own requirements for what one must achieve to become certified. For example, the Board of Certified Safety Professionals has eligibility requirements that include an academic component (either a bachelor's degree or higher in any field from an accredited institution or an associate degree in safety, health, or environment from an accredited institution) and four years of professional safety experience in order to sit for the examination. Until the end of 1997, applicants could substitute work experience for a bachelor's degree. Beginning in 1998, education became a requirement.

Certification is a designation earned by a person who shows qualification (usually knowledge, experience, and skills) to perform a job or task.

Roger Brauer, PhD, PE, CSP, who was the executive director of the Board of Certified Safety Professionals (BCSP) from 1995 to 2010, described the early years of developing certification of safety professionals and accreditation of programs. In 1963 the ASSP Professional Development Project outlined the scope and functions of professional safety and began the process of developing a curriculum for a Bachelor of Science degree.

ASSP then formed an *ad hoc* committee in 1967, whose work led to the creation of the Board of Certified Safety Professionals (BCSP). That body became a not-for-profit corporation in 1969. The sponsoring organizations included:

- American Society of Safety Engineers (ASSE), 1974 (now ASSP)
- American Industrial Hygiene Association (AIHA), 1974
- System Safety Society (SSS), 1977 (now the International System Safety Society)
- Society of Fire Protection Engineers (SFPE), 1984
- National Safety Council (NSC), 1994
- Institute of Industrial Engineers (IIE), 1994
- National Fire Protection Association (NFPA), 2007
- National Environmental, Health and Safety Training Association (NESHTA), 2011

In developing the examination materials, BCSP initially relied on a National Institute of Occupational Safety and Health (NIOSH) study. However, in the early 1990s, BCSP issued surveys to practitioners and conducted job analyses, ultimately completing its own study of professional safety practice. This study was used to craft the CSP exams but also validated the definition of safety practice and assisted in formulating academic curricula for safety degrees. OSHA 3071, Job Hazard Analysis, states,

> When is it appropriate to hire a professional to conduct a job hazard analysis? If your employees are involved in many different or complex processes, you need professional help conducting your job hazard analyses. Sources of help include your insurance company, the local fire department, and private consultants with safety and health expertise. In addition, OSHA offers assistance through its regional and area offices and consultation services.

ASSE described their move to initiate certification and accreditation in their publication "The First 75 Years: 1911–1986" as follows:

> [Accreditation was] part of a two-fold plan to professionalize the rapidly expanding safety profession. The plan contained two objectives: certifying safety practitioners and accrediting degree programs in various safety specialties. ASSE achieved the certification objective first, in large part because it was less complex. Accreditation, however, proved to be a much tougher challenge.
>
> In January 1973, ASSE announced its intention to accredit nonengineering degrees in safety. Society members felt an accepted set of safety criteria for college safety programs was a way to combat the "uncertain quality" that could result otherwise.
>
> The Society President at the time, B. Gawain Bonner . . . noted that since OSHA had created wider employer interest in hiring safety professionals, more colleges and universities were responding with programs to train people to fill the "expanding opportunities in the field." He emphasized that "notable disparities" existed in the "quality and content" of the various available programs. See also, "Our Pursuit of Professionalism."
>
> With the assistance of a special task force, Dr. Grimaldi developed an "Accreditation Guidelines" document in 1975, and by 1978 the Society formed an Accreditation Council. . . . Its goal was ambitious: to establish ASSE as the recognized accrediting agency for nonengineering college and university curricula in safety and health. . . .
>
> In 1983 ASSE accredited the undergraduate safety sciences course at Indiana University of Pennsylvania . . . [followed by accreditation of] three degree programs at the University of Southern California. (ASSE n. d.)

Dr. Paul Specht, chair of the ASSP Academic Accreditation Council (AAC) from 1983 to 1985 and 1998 to 2003, recalled the early efforts to create a meaningful accreditation process through ASSP. When it became apparent that the accreditation process could be better managed by a professional accreditation organization, the Society worked to merge ASSP's accreditation with ABET's because ABET's purpose, goals, and philosophy were very similar to ASSP's.

> As Chair of the ASSE AAC, I presented a curriculum position paper to BCSP and ABET representatives at a meeting in Atlanta, Ga. on Oct. 11, 1983. It took us until 1991 to actually sign a memorandum of understanding between ASSE and ABET. ASSE did its last accreditation visits in 1992–93 and then turned over the accreditation to ABET. During that period, I shepherded the Occupational Safety and Hygiene Management program at Millersville University through ASSE accreditation. We have had a program in safety and later in environmental, health and safety accredited by ABET ever since. Like a number of those of us who were involved in the early stages of developing safety accreditation (Drs. Roger Brauer, William Tarrants, James Oppold and Charlie McGlothlin), I became an ABET commissioner, taking out accreditation teams to visit the programs. I later became the chair of the commission and when my term on what is now ANSAC was completed, I agreed

to represent ASSE on the ABET Board of Directors. (Specht, 2018)

Clearly, ASSP saw the creation of OSHA and its transactions with employers, encouraging the hiring of safety professionals as an impetus to define the safety professional and set standards, much as the safety engineers had experienced through their long history of accreditation (by ABET) and dealings with licensure standards (Allen 2006).

> ASSP saw the creation of OSHA was an impetus to define the safety professional and set standards.

Dr. Brauer said that the Board of Certified Safety Professionals contributed a great deal to shaping the program criteria for safety programs and encouraging programs to seek ABET accreditation through recognizing the role of accreditation in preparing graduates to sit for the BCSP examinations. Dr. Brauer served on ASSP's accrediting body before becoming chair of the activity for several years. He was one of the members of the team that visited the first program to be accredited at Indiana University of Pennsylvania. At the time, accreditation was a work in progress, with that visit underscoring the need to differentiate between accrediting a program at the baccalaureate level and one at the master's level. It also prompted the ASSP Academic Accreditation Council to publish three guides for bachelor's and master's safety degrees and for safety engineering bachelor's degrees. The latter was accepted by ABET's Engineering Accreditation Commission.

When ASSP joined forces with ABET, ASSP took curricular responsibility for safety and similarly named programs using the ASSP/BCSP Curriculum Standards for Baccalaureate Degrees in Safety as the basis for the program criteria ASSP proposed and ABET adopted for accrediting safety programs. As part of the agreement, ABET grandfathered the accreditation of the existing seven bachelor's degree programs and four master's degree safety programs that ASSP had accredited. Most of those programs have maintained ABET accreditation ever since.

ASSP made clear that one of the drivers for joining ABET was the fact that ABET enjoyed recognition by the Council on Postsecondary Accreditation (COPA), the national body that recognized both regional and specialized accreditors. Later COPA was succeeded by the current Council on Higher Education Accreditation (CHEA), which similarly recognizes ABET.

Dr. Lon Ferguson, former chair of the Department of Safety Sciences at Indiana University of Pennsylvania, recalls that when his program was preparing for the transition from being accredited by ASSP to being accredited by ABET, they had to make curricular changes in the program to add more math and science, the requirements for which were more rigorous under the ABET criteria.

Years later, in 2003, ASSP and AIHA collaborated to create joint criteria for accrediting EHS programs. Bret Clausen, Lon Ferguson and Tom Bresnahan of ASSP met in Chicago to discuss the program criteria. The two societies collaborate on EHS visits, with one program evaluator coming from ASSP and one from AIHA. To make changes to the EHS program criteria, both societies must come to an agreement. Recently, some of the ABET-accredited safety programs have transformed their curricula to become EHS programs, at which point the "new" EHS programs must be reviewed under the EHS program criteria.

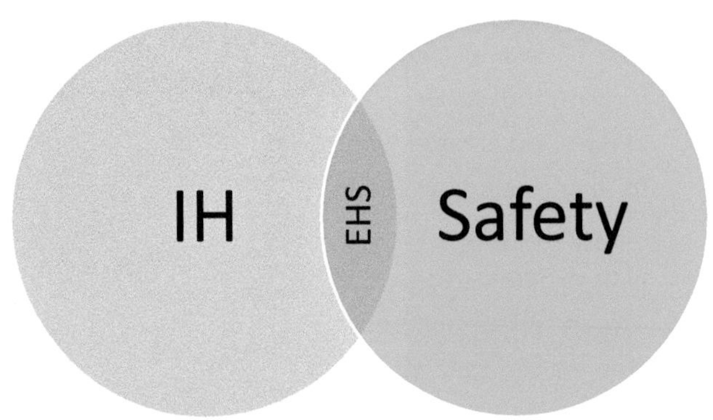


Figure 10.1
Safety and industrial hygiene combined curricular components to form the environmental, health, and safety program criteria

## Outcomes-Based Assessment and ASSP's View of It

In the 1990s there was a shift in the emphasis in higher education from assessing teaching methodology to assessing student learning as a way of measuring educational quality (Hirsch and Weber 1999). That required assessing the performance of graduates (Related Accreditation Commission Annual Report 2000–2001). In the late 1990s, ABET embraced the shift away from prescriptive methods of evaluating programs to adopting a new accreditation model, known as EC2000 (referring to curriculum for engineering programs in the year 2000), requiring outcomes-based assessment. ANSAC (then known as the Related Accreditation Commission, RAC) followed suit with an outcomes-based assessment version of its criteria. The RAC adopted both general and program level outcomes-based criteria in 1999, which were approved by the ABET Board in October 2000 after a year of comment and review. The RAC conducted its first outcomes-based accreditation pilot visit in 2000–2001, allowing a two-year transition period for programs undergoing reaccreditation to elect whether to be reviewed under the previous criteria or the new outcomes-based criteria. Beginning in 2004–2005, all the commission's general reviews were conducted according to the new criteria (Article Four of ABET Constitution).

ABET's move to outcomes-based assessment resulted in significant changes in criteria, processes, and procedures, emphasizing "what the students learn" more than "what the students are taught." The outcomes-based criteria also require that the programs assess the ongoing consistency of the educational objectives with the institutional mission and the program's constituents' needs. As a result, programs must interact closely with the industries and other employers hiring their graduates as part of their review.

Under outcomes-based assessment, institutions and programs define the mission of the institution and the program and then tailor the educational objectives for the program to meet the needs of the program's constituencies and stakeholders. The outcomes are aimed at preparing the graduate for professional practice. It is up to the program to demonstrate how the criteria are being met and that they are actively engaged in continually improving their student outcomes. To do so requires the programs to involve their constituencies, with emphasis on advisory committees formalizing the process of engagement. ABET has been refining its process on an ongoing basis since it embraced outcomes-based assessment, involving its Academic Advisory Council and its Industrial Advisory Council in the process. The model allows programs and institutions to define their own constituencies and stakeholders and tailor their programs accordingly, rather than taking a one-size-fits-all approach.

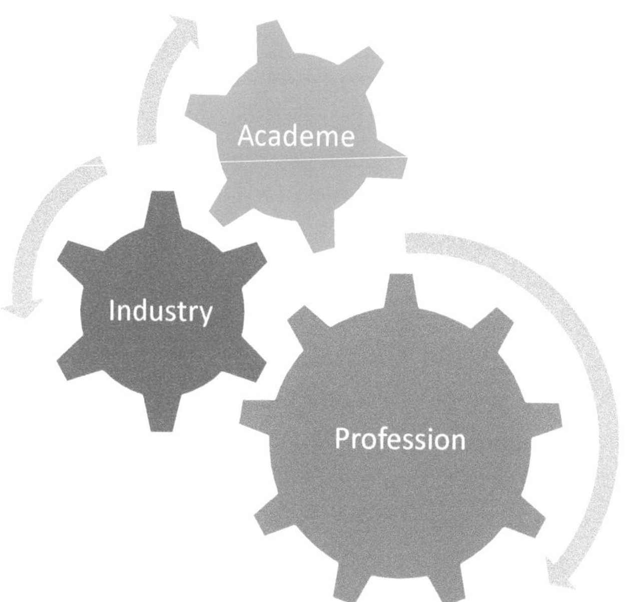


Figure 10.2
ABET accreditation involves academe, industry, and the profession

In 2002 ABET commissioned a three-and-a-half–year study of the impact of the change to outcomes-based assessment in engineering programs. The study, conducted Lisa R. Lattuca, Patrick T. Terenzini, and J. Fredricks Volkwein of the Center for the Study of Higher Education at Pennsylvania State University, titled "Engineering Change: A Study of the Impact of EC2000," found that:

> According to program chairs and faculty members, engineering program curricula changed considerably following

> implementation of the EC2000 criteria. Although few programs reduced their emphasis on the foundational topics in mathematics, basic science, and engineering science, both program chairs and faculty members report increased emphasis on nearly all of the professional skills and knowledge sets associated with EC2000 . . . Three-quarters or more of the chairs report moderate or significant increases in their program's emphasis on communication, teamwork, use of modern engineering tools, technical writing, lifelong learning, and engineering design.
>
> Similarly, more than half of the faculty respondents report a moderate to significant increase in their emphasis on the use of modern engineering tools, teamwork, and engineering design in a course they taught regularly. EC2000's focus on professional skills might also be expected to lead to changes in teaching methods as faculty members seek to provide students with opportunities to learn and practice their teamwork, design, and communication skills. Consistent with that expectation, half to two-thirds of the faculty report that they have increased their use of active learning methods, such as group work, design projects, case studies, and application exercises, in a course they teach regularly . . . faculty members believe ABET has had a statistically significant and independent influence on all measures of curricular or instructional change, and program chairs see a significant and independent ABET influence in two of three curricular areas.

ANSAC has seen similar trends developing in applied and natural science program accreditation, including the ABET model being a draw for new disciplines, such as construction management and now natural science programs. ABET, at the prompting of ABET's Academic Advisory Committee, is now in national dialogue with its constituencies regarding revisions to the student outcomes required under General Criterion 3. The Engineering Accreditation Commission has posted their approved changes on the ABET website for implementation in 2019–20. ANSAC's Criteria Committee has posted their proposed changes on the ABET website for review and comment. ANSAC's General Criterion 3 student outcomes provide the baseline of what the program must demonstrate their students have learned by the time of graduation. The current ANSAC version of the General Criterion 3 includes:

> Baccalaureate degree programs must demonstrate that graduates have:
>
> (a) an ability to apply knowledge of mathematics, science, and applied sciences
> (b) an ability to design and conduct experiments, as well as to analyze and interpret data
> (c) an ability to formulate or design a system, process, or program to meet desired needs
> (d) an ability to function on multidisciplinary teams
> (e) an ability to identify and solve applied science problems
> (f) an understanding of professional and ethical responsibility
> (g) an ability to communicate effectively
> (h) the broad education necessary to understand the impact of solutions in a global and societal context
> (i) a recognition of the need for and an ability to engage in life-long learning
> (j) a knowledge of contemporary issues
> (k) an ability to use the techniques, skills, and modern scientific and technical tools necessary for professional practice.

Additionally, ANSAC's Criterion 5: Curriculum states that:

> The curriculum must include:
>
> a. a combination of college-level mathematics and basic sciences (some with experimental experience) appropriate to the discipline
> b. applied science topics appropriate to the program

c. a general education component that complements the technical content of the curriculum and is consistent with the program and institution objectives.

Students in baccalaureate degree programs must also be prepared for applied science practice through a curriculum culminating in comprehensive projects or experiences based on the cumulative knowledge and skills acquired in earlier course work.

The above curriculum requirements define subject areas appropriate for programs to be accredited under the ANSAC General Criterion 5 but do not prescribe specific courses. See the ABET website (www.abet.org) for the proposed changes to Criterion 3 and Criterion 5.

When ABET first started moving to outcomes-based assessment, ASSP was a strong proponent of the change, seeing the less prescriptive, more process-oriented approach as being more consistent with what safety programs needed to develop and grow. ASSP commissioners led the call for the then Related Engineering Commission (RAC) to follow the Engineering Accreditation Commission's lead and move to outcomes-based assessment, which the RAC did the following year. Commissioners from ASSP, especially James Oppold, spearheaded the efforts to change the name of the commission from engineering related to applied science, thus forming the Applied Science Accreditation Commission (now the Applied and Natural Science Accreditation Commission).

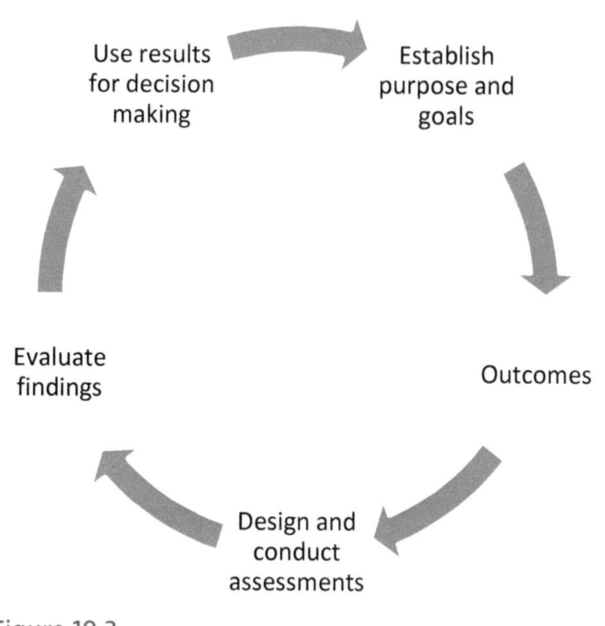


Figure 10.3
Continuous improvement process

By embracing outcomes-based assessment, ABET developed an ongoing process to improve quality of students' educational experience using a systematic process that is documented and repeatable. It allows the program to assess its performance against criteria and to take actions to improve the program. Accreditation is a part of continuous quality improvement (CQI).

## Peer Review Model of Accreditation

The ABET model of outcomes-based assessment provides a consistent process of accreditation across all its commissions. ABET relies on its member societies for subject matter expertise. Not only do the societies provide the program criteria specific to the needs of their discipline, but they also provide the program evaluators to conduct the visits.

In order to recruit safety professionals to conduct the visits, ASSP had to develop a process for identifying qualified safety professionals to become ABET safety program evaluators. Initially ASSP did so through the ASSP Academic Accreditation Council and Educational Standards Committee. Later, ASSP invited ABET staff members to preside over an exhibit booth at ASSP's annual meeting. There ABET staff and ABET commissioners and program evaluators provided by ASSP engage with ASSP members at the exhibition hall, encouraging them to sign up to become program evaluators. ABET later developed a workshop on accreditation to present at the ASSP annual meeting.

Once ASSP approves candidates to become program evaluators, ABET puts these candidates through a rigorous training process. The training involves online training modules, taking twenty to twenty-five hours to complete, and requires written work and the completion of three end-of-module proficiency assessments, with a mentor assigned by the society to assist. Once the online training is complete, PEV Candidates (PEVCs) attend face-to-face training at the ABET Learning Center in Baltimore. This is a one-and-a-half–day experiential workshop that simulates an onsite visit. The training ensures a consistency of understanding and preparation among the new program evaluators, which is later augmented with additional yearly online training.

The competencies required for a program evaluator can be found in Table 10.1.

Each of the societies with curricular responsibility in a commission is also responsible for nominating commissioners to serve on the commission. ABET commissioners' primary role is to serve as team chairs on the visits and on the interim reports. The team chair is responsible for the leadership and process on a site visit, while the program evaluators act as the subject matter specialists.

For team chairs, the threshold for eligibility includes having served as a program evaluator on at least three accreditation visits. The leadership of each commission is drawn from the commission itself. ABET seeks a balance of evaluators and commissioners drawn from both academia and industry.

As part of ABET's assessment process, team chairs submit evaluations of the program evaluators on their teams, and program evaluators submit evaluations of the team chairs. Additionally, ABET requests that the program leadership for programs being evaluated also submit an evaluation of the team. These evaluations are assessed and taken into consideration for remediation where needed and advancement where warranted, as well as defining other problems with the process to be improved.

**Table 10.1** ABET competency model for program evaluators (from ABET n.d.)

| |
|---|
| Program evaluators should meet the following minimum qualifications:<br>• Demonstrated interest in improving education.<br>• Current member (or willing to join) one of ABET's technical and professional societies. |
| For computing professionals, membership in *ACM* or *IEEE/CS* fulfills this requirement.<br>• Formal education and degree appropriate to the field.<br>• Experience with accreditation processes and / or quality improvement processes.<br>• Proficiency using word processing programs, spreadsheets, and PDF files.<br>• Be willing to take the required program evaluator training courses.<br>• Meet any additional society-specific requirements. |
| Experienced program evaluators interested in going on on-site reviews outside of the United States must meet these additional qualifications:<br>• Service as a program evaluator on at least four on-site reviews in the US.<br>• Consistent record of meeting program evaluator performance expectations.<br>• Service as a program evaluator or team chair on at least one ABET on-site review in the last two years. |
| **ABET Program Evaluator Competency Model** |
| Successful program evaluators exhibit the knowledge, skills, and attitudes listed below in the ABET Program Evaluator Competency Model and are evaluated against these competencies after each assigned program evaluation. |

*Continued*

**Table 10.1** ABET competency model for program evaluators (from ABET n.d.) *(continued)*

| |
|---|
| **Technically Current**<br>• Demonstrates required technical credentials for the position<br>• Engaged in lifelong learning and current in their field<br>• Able to apply technical knowledge to ascertain the level of conformance to program accreditation requirements<br>• Remains current in accreditation procedures and requirements |
| **Effective at Communicating**<br>• Easily conducts face-to-face interviews<br>• Writes clearly and succinctly<br>• Presents focused, concise oral briefings<br>• Interviews personnel to understand program operations<br>• Writes succinct, criterion-centered statements of program strengths and weaknesses<br>• Develops succinct findings for exit interview<br>• Keeps team chair informed prior to and during the visit |
| **Interpersonally Skilled**<br>• Friendly and sets others at ease<br>• Listens and places input into context<br>• Remains open-minded and avoids personal bias<br>• Forthright, doesn't hold back what needs to be said<br>• Adept at pointing out strengths and weaknesses in nonconfrontational manner<br>• Interviews and readily obtains input from faculty, administration, industry advisors, and students<br>• Evaluates program against criteria within the context of the institution<br>• Evaluates and constructively conveys program strengths and weaknesses |
| **Team-Oriented**<br>• Readily accepts input from team members<br>• Works with team members to reach consensus<br>• Values team success over personal success<br>• Compares program findings with those of other visitation team members to improve consistency<br>• Looks for and listens to common issues across programs<br>• Assists other team members as needed during the visit |
| **Professional**<br>• Conveys professional appearance and demeanor<br>• Is committed to contributing and adding value to the evaluation process<br>• Considered a person with high integrity and ethical standards<br>• Represents ABET and responsible technical society as a practicing professional<br>• Willing to make observations to stimulate innovation and further the program's efforts toward continuous improvement<br>• Shows professional respect for institution faculty and staff<br>• Upholds ABET code of conduct at all times |

*Continued*

**Table 10.1** ABET competency model for program evaluators (from ABET n.d.) *(continued)*

| **Organized** |
|---|
| • Is focused on meeting deadlines<br>• Focuses on critical issues and avoids minutia<br>• Displays take-charge initiative<br>• Takes responsibility and works under minimum supervision<br>• Formulates preliminary program strengths and weakness assessment based upon review of materials supplied prior to the visit<br>• Focuses on critical findings, effectively cites supportive observations, relates to appropriate criteria and suggests possible avenues to resolution<br>• Submits high quality documentation to team chair on time<br>• Makes difficult recommendations when appropriate |

## How ABET Ensures That the Competencies Necessary Are Reflected in the Accreditation Process

ABET is a federation of thirty-five member societies. A society petitioning to become a member of ABET must demonstrate in their application that they have the following characteristics:

1. active engagement in the dissemination of technical knowledge;
2. demonstrated interest and capability in the accreditation process;
3. substantial membership of employed graduates in the discipline;
4. an organizational structure that has an educational component; and
5. evidence the society speaks for the technical community it represents. (ABET Constitution, Article IV.B.)

Applicants for admission as a member society of ABET must additionally demonstrate they would have responsibility for a discipline within applied or natural science, computing, engineering, engineering technology, or other such disciplines as may be appropriate at the post-secondary level. The membership application must be ratified by two-thirds of the ABET member societies (2016 Criteria for Accrediting Applied and Natural Science Programs).

Once a society becomes an ABET member and is granted lead society status toward a particular discipline, the society can then develop program criteria tailored to ensuring the programs are teaching the competencies necessary for a graduate in that discipline to acquire. For example, a safety program applying for ABET accreditation must demonstrate that it meets not only the ANSAC general criteria but also that program graduates possess the necessary knowledge and skills to competently and ethically implement and practice applicable scientific, technical and regulatory domains of the safety, health, and environmental profession. In addition, the program must demonstrate that graduates can apply college algebra, statistics, chemistry, physics, and human physiology/biology as they pertain to the practice of the safety, health, and environmental discipline.

The ABET/ANSAC Safety Program Criteria currently require that graduates be able to:

1. anticipate, recognize, evaluate, and develop control strategies for hazardous conditions and work practices;
2. demonstrate the application of business and risk management concepts;
3. demonstrate an understanding of the fundamental aspects of safety, industrial hygiene, environmental science, fire science, hazardous materials, emergency management, ergonomics, and/or human factors;
4. design and evaluate safety, health, and/or environmental programs;

5. apply adult learning theory to safety training methodology;
6. identify and apply applicable standards, regulations, and codes;
7. conduct accident investigations and analyses;
8. apply principles of safety and health in a non-academic setting through an intern, cooperative, or supervised experience.

Programs at the master's level must include meeting the criteria for baccalaureate level applied science programs, with the following additions: one year of study beyond the baccalaureate level and a project or research activity resulting in a report that demonstrates both mastery of the subject matter and a high level of oral and written communication skills.

There are separate program criteria for environmental, health, and safety programs, for industrial hygiene programs, and for health physics programs.

## ASSP Initiative to Expand the Number of Accredited Safety Programs

ASSP's Educational Standards Committee is responsible for designing and monitoring programs that will increase the pursuit of higher education in the field of occupational safety and health. To do so they seek out innovative ways to expand terminal degree programs in safety, cultivate opportunities for safety-related research, and work to advance progressive, realistic, and comprehensive safety postsecondary education accreditation efforts. The committee also selects site evaluators, conducts training programs for accreditation visit teams, and provides assistance to colleges and universities pursuing ABET accreditation.

In 2011, the Educational Standards Committee undertook a study to determine what portion of the universities with OSH and related programs in the United States were candidates for ABET accreditation or on the path toward it. ASSP identified 129 safety-related degree programs to survey. In analyzing the curriculum of the universe of OSH programs and related programs, ASSP found as a general observation that the main difference between the total weighted scores of accredited and unaccredited programs tended to be weaknesses in the number of recommended courses offered. They used that information to devise an approach to unaccredited programs in terms of helping them find the capacity to pursue accreditation.

From the surveys and assessments, ASSP selected thirty-three programs that appeared to be potential candidates for accreditation. Since the process of work with these programs began, four new safety programs have been accredited, and others have indicated that they are preparing to apply in the near future.

ASSP's approach to encouraging more safety programs to apply for accreditation also included a

**Table 10.2** ABET-accredited programs in safety, environmental health and safety, and fire protection

| Institution | Degree Programs | Accreditation Dates |
|---|---|---|
| Central Washington University | Safety and Hygiene Management (BS) | 2015–present |
| East Carolina University | Occupational Safety (MS) | 2013–present |
| Fairmont State University (WV) | Occupational Safety (BS) | 2006–present |
| Illinois State University | Safety (BS) | 2013–present |
| Indiana State University | Safety Management (BS) | 2014–present |

*Continued*

**Table 10.2** ABET-accredited programs in safety, environmental health and safety, and fire protection *(continued)*

| | | |
|---|---|---|
| Indiana University of Pennsylvania | Safety, Health and Environmental Applied Sciences (BS) | 2013–present |
| Marshall University (WV) | Safety Technology (BS) | 1993–present |
| Millersville University of Pennsylvania | Occupational Safety & Environmental Health (BS) | 1993–present |
| Montana Tech of the University of Montana | Occupational Safety and Health (BS) | 2011–present |
| Murray State University (KY) | Occupational Safety and Health (BS and MS) | 1988–present |
| Oakland University (MI) | Occupational Safety and Health (BS) | 2003–present |
| Oklahoma State University | Fire Protection and Safety Technology (BS) | 1977–present |
| Southeastern Louisiana University | Occupational Safety, Health, and Environment (BS) | 2008–present |
| The University of Findlay (OH) | Environmental Safety and Occupational Health Management (BS) | 2006–present |
| Trinidad State Junior College (CO) | Occupational Safety and Health Technology (AAS) | 2000–present |
| University of Central Missouri | Occupational Safety and Health (BS) | 1991–1995, 1999–present |
| University of Houston—Clear Lake (TX) | Environmental Science—Safety (BS) | 2007–present |
| University of Houston—Downtown (TX) | Fire Protection Engineering Technology (BSET) | 2006–present |
| University of Maryland | Fire Protection Engineering (BS) | 1976–present |
| University of Wisconsin-Whitewater | Occupational Safety (BS) | 2013–present |
| West Virginia University | Safety Management (MS) | 1993–present |

framework for reducing the costs of accreditation visits through conducting partially virtual visits, where only the team chair would travel to the campus and the program evaluators would conduct their review remotely. Hamid Fonooni, then professor at East Carolina University, spearheaded putting together the plan, which was adopted as a pilot by ANSAC for the 2013–14 accreditation cycle.

Through the pilot, the institutions post the display materials online (i.e., typically textbooks, assignments, exams, and examples of student work in a range of quality). Provision for access to such online materials must be made available during the team chair's onsite visit. The interviews with faculty, staff, and students are done through videoconferencing. Cameras are used to accompany faculty and the team chair on examination of laboratories. The program evaluators participate remotely in conferences and the exit interview. So far ANSAC has conducted seven such visits and is on track to conduct four more in the next accreditation cycle. The partially virtual visit currently saves the program a minimum of the fee for an evaluator involved in the visit. Only programs seeking reaccreditation qualify currently for the partially virtual pilot. The early consensus from ANSAC leadership is that the partially virtual visit option is here to stay.

The ASSP Foundation's James A. Oppold Fund has also been instrumental in encouraging accreditation of new safety programs by providing substantial funding to institutions for the initial ANSAC site visit and some funding for reaccreditation visits.

## Conclusion

ABET's unique federated organizational model allows it to take strength from the diversity of organizations involved in its mission, while the outcomes-based assessment model, coupled with the ownership of the societies holding curricular responsibility for the particular programs involved, has made ABET an enduring approach to quality assurance and accreditation. ASSP's partnership with ABET, to achieve the ends of defining and recognizing the safety profession, has provided a positive example of a structure that can endure beyond just engineering and serve the needs of disciplines within the STEM family of programs.

## Questions

1. What is the difference between accreditation and certification?
2. What does "peer review" mean in the context of accreditation?
3. What is the relationship between outcomes-based accreditation and engaging stakeholders?
4. How does ASSP interact with ABET to ensure the competencies of the safety profession are covered?
5. What was ASSP's two-fold plan to professionalize the safety profession?

## References

ABET. n.d. ABET Program Evaluator Competency Model. Accessed March 31, 2018. http://www.abet.org/competency-model-for-program-evaluators/.

Allen, M. J. (2006). *Assessing General Education Programs.* San Francisco: Jossey-Bass.

ASSE. (n.d.). "The First 75 Years: 1911–1986." American Society of Safety Engineers.

ASSE. (2017). "Scope and Functions." American Society of Safety Engineers. Accessed November 17. https://www.asse.org/about/scope-and-functions/.

Hirsch, W. Z., and L. E. Weber. (1999). *Challenges Facing Higher Education at the Millennium.* Phoenix, AZ: Oryz Press.

National Society of Professional Engineers. (2018). "Licensure FAQS." https://www.nspe.org/resources/licensure/resources/licensure-faqs#licensure%20requirements.

Specht, P. (2018). Personal communication (February 15).

CHAPTER 11

# THE POWER OF CERTIFICATIONS IN EHS PROFESSIONAL PRACTICE

Cheryl Marcham, Treasa Turnbeaugh, and Carl Heinlein

## Learning Objectives

After studying this chapter, the reader will be able to:

1. Describe reasons why EHS professionals should become certified
2. Explain the difference in a certification and a certificate program
3. Describe the examination development process
4. Explain the importance of accreditation as it pertains to certification

## Key Terms

**Accredited certification body, Angoff Method, blueprint, certificant, certificate, certification, code of ethics, competencies, cut score, distractor, item, item writing, job task analysis, minimally qualified candidate, psychometry, reliability, role delineation, validation survey, validity**

## Abstract

Certification by an accredited certification body is the ultimate sign of professionalism for those in the environmental health and safety (EHS) field. This chapter will address reasons why EHS practitioners become certified. It will also address the technical side of certification to provide a full appreciation of the power of accredited certifications.

## Introduction

The need for EHS practitioners covering the fields of environmental health, environmental science, occupational and industrial safety, and occupational and industrial hygiene has and will continue to grow significantly. The US Bureau of Labor Statistics (BLS) (2015) reports that in 2014, environmental scientists, environmental science and protection technicians, occupational health and safety (OHS) specialists, and occupational safety and health technicians—all subsets of EHS practitioners—held about 216,200 jobs, with the number of new jobs in those fields expected to increase by 17,800 in the year 2024 (see table 11.1).

**Table 11.1** EHS jobs and job outlook as of 2014

| Job Title | Number of Jobs | Number of New Jobs Expected through 2024 | Job Outlook (% Change) |
|---|---|---|---|
| Environmental Scientists | 94,600 | 10,200 | 11% (faster than average) |
| Environmental Science and Protection Technicians | 36,200 | 3,400 | 9% (faster than average) |
| Occupational Health and Safety Specialists | 70,300 | 2,800 | 4% |
| Occupational Health and Safety Technicians | 15,100 | 1,400 | 9% (faster than average) |
| Total | 216,200 | 17,800 | |

Source: Bureau of Labor Statistics, *Occupational Outlook Handbook*, 2015.

Similarly, in 2011, the National Institute for Occupational Safety and Health (NIOSH) commissioned a study titled "National Assessment of the Occupational Safety and Health Workforce." The survey of those practicing in the occupational safety and health fields showed that there were over 48,000 OHS professionals in the US workforce across the 9 disciplines of interest to this study with the composition primarily safety professionals (59%) followed by industrial hygienists (15%). The other major disciplines represented in the survey data were occupational health nursing (9%) and occupational medicine (3%) (McAdams et al. 2011). This survey indicated that for at least the OHS subset of EHS Practitioners:

1. Employers expect to hire over 25,000 OHS professionals over the next 5 years, needing to fill an average of just over 5,000 positions per year. While many of these positions will be filled by new graduates of OHS training programs, many are also likely to be filled by OHS professionals currently in the workforce or by professionals who do not have OHS training.
2. Safety professionals represent about 73 percent of the OHS professionals employers expect to hire over the next 5 years.
3. Industrial hygienists represent about 9.5 percent of the OHS professionals employers expect to hire over the next 5 years.
4. In 2011, OHS programs graduated about 2,845 new OHS professionals at the bachelor's degree level and higher and over the next 5 years are expected to graduate just under 13,000 OHS professionals (far under the expected need of 25,000 OHS professionals). (McAdams et al. 2011)

Clearly EHS is a solid choice of profession, and there is a demand for more graduates than are being produced by the universities. This means that those who have graduated in other fields or those with no experience may also be entering the EHS workforce. In fact, a 2017 survey by the National Safety Council revealed that because of the shortage of qualified OHS professionals, 65 percent of OHS professionals believe that employers will fill safety and health positions from within the organization, even if the employee has little or no safety experience.

One way for an employer to differentiate whom to hire for the position is by hiring candidates who present quality credentials in the field of EHS. In the NIOSH assessment of the OHS workforce (McAdams et al. 2011), 51 percent of employers expressed an expectation that they would require all or some of the safety professionals they will hire to hold a professional certification. For industrial hygiene positions, 70 percent of employers indicated that they would require all or some of those hired to hold a professional certification (McAdams et al. 2011). This means that to be competitive in the workforce, the true EHS professional should consider seeking out and attaining these credentials.

One way for an employer to differentiate whom to hire for the position is by hiring candidates who present quality credentials in the field of EHS.

## Certification versus Certificate

It is important to understand that certification and certificate programs are different processes meeting different needs. Certification is defined by the Institute for Credentialing Excellence (ICE) as a

> voluntary process by which a non-governmental entity grants a time-limited recognition and use of a credential to an individual after verifying that he or she has met predetermined and standardized criteria. It is the vehicle that a profession or occupation uses to differentiate among its members, using standards, sometimes developed through a consensus-driven process, based on existing legal and psychometric requirements. (Knapp et al. 2006)

Certification is a process by which a professional is evaluated against a psychometrically established industry standard of required knowledge and skills. Psychometry is the field of study concerned with the theory and techniques of psychological measurement, which includes measurement of knowledge, abilities, attitudes, and personality traits. Following the psychometric process ensures that the evaluation is objective, practical, fair, reliable, and valid (Marcham et al. 2018). The successful candidate is awarded the use of a certification designation for a given time period during which the certificant (holder of the certification) is held accountable for continuing professional development and complying with a defined code of ethics (Wright et al. 2015). Examples of EHS certifications are the Certified Safety Professional (CSP), Certified Industrial Hygienist (CIH), and Certified Hazardous Materials Manager (CHMM).

In contrast, a certificate program generally results from an educational process (a class or series of classes with a specific focus) and is an end result (no continuing professional development is required to maintain the certificate), and assessment tools are typically not set through a psychometric standard–setting process but instead are established by the program instructor to measure knowledge of listed program outcomes (Knapp et al. 2006). ICE also refers to the assessment scope of a certification program typically being broad versus a certificate program, which may be narrow in focus (Knapp et al. 2006). Examples of certificate programs in the EHS field include attaining the Hazardous Waste Operations and Emergency Response (HAZWOPER) forty-hour training certificate or completing an OSHA thirty-hour general industry or construction training course.

## Value of Certification

Certification programs that adhere to industry best practices tend to raise the bar within a profession and provide a benchmark of professionalism, providing professionals, consumers, and government agencies an assurance of competency in a constantly changing world (Henderson et al. 2012). For the professional, ICE has identified a number of benefits of holding certifications that meet certain standards or conditions, such as greater confidence in professional competence, increased autonomy in the workplace, enhanced marketability, employability, opportunity for advancement, improved monetary factors, and heightened job satisfaction (Henderson et al. 2012).

Some of the benefits reported by those achieving EHS certifications include:

- Recognition from peers, public, and employer
- Satisfaction of achievement
- Career development, growth, and advancement
- Confidence in demonstrating specific knowledge and skills related to the EHS tasks
- Assurance on quality of work
- Reduced liability
- Belonging to a select community
- Recognition of commitment to public safety and the environment
- Identification as distinguished individuals (Snyder et al. 2014)

Specifically, certified OHS professionals report that certification

- is an indication of professional growth;
- enhances professional credibility;
- provides evidence of professional commitment;
- enhances employability and mobility; and
- increases earning potential (Assessment Strategies Inc. 2015).

This increased earning potential of certified EHS professionals is supported through recent salary survey data collected by the Board of Certified Safety Professionals (BCSP), the American Board of Industrial Hygiene (ABIH), the American Society of Safety Professionals (ASSP), the American Industrial Hygiene Association (AIHA), the Alliance of Hazardous Materials Professionals (AHMP), and the Institute of Hazardous Materials Management (IHMM) (Board of Certified Safety Professionals 2015). The survey showed that the median annual base salary for EHS professionals in 2015 was $98,000 (in US dollars) (Board of Certified Safety Professionals 2015).

> Certified OHS professionals report that certification enhances employability and increases earning potential.

Additionally, full-time EHS professionals with at least 1 of the 11 EHS licenses/certifications from the 6 partnering organizations, including BCSP's CSP, Associate Safety Professional (ASP), Certified Environmental Trainer (CET), Construction Health and Safety Technician (CHST), Occupational Health and Safety Technologist (OHST), Safety Trained Supervisor (STS), and Safety Trained Supervisor Construction (STSC); ABIH's CIH; and IHMM's CHMM, Certified Hazardous Materials Practitioner (CHMP), and Certified Dangerous Goods Professional (CDGP) typically earn about $14,000 more per year than those with none of these licenses/certifications (Board of Certified Safety Professionals 2015). CIH and CSP certifications most positively correlate with salary, adding more than $20,000 to the median compared with the salaries of those who have none of the 11 licenses/certifications (Board of Certified Safety Professionals, 2015).

Organizations that engage professionals that hold safety and health certifications reported benefits such as

- improved confidence in the competency of safety decisions;
- improved quality of safety inspections and audits;
- improved trust and confidence from clients in the ability to manage safety at job sites; and
- continued professional development (Wright et al. 2015).

> EHS professionals may need or may use additional credentials beyond their educational degrees to demonstrate competency and to be competitive in the job market.

Research has shown that hiring managers may view holding a certification credential as "a more objective measure of a candidate's skill level than self-reported skills and competency" (Microsoft Corporation 2007). ASSP (ASSE, n. d.) encourages employers to require applicants to hold a respective safety, health, or environmental certification as a way to ensure that the individual they are evaluating has already demonstrated competency in the particular field of EHS for which the candidate is being recruited, which also ensures that the candidate is committed to continual learning and compliance to a code of ethics established by the certification body. Some research indicates that in some parts of North America, up to 70 percent of career advertisements for OSH professionals require or prefer a certified professional (Wright et al. 2015). In addition, many government organizations rely on the certification process to award contracts (Ferguson and Ramsay 2010; Wright et al. 2015). Thus, EHS professionals may need or may use additional credentials beyond their educational degrees to demonstrate competency and to be competitive in the job market. The EHS profession has several established certification programs to provide a means for assessing professional competency.

## Accredited Certification Programs

Approximately three hundred EHS certification programs and titles are available in the United States (Ferguson and Ramsay 2010). However, only a few are actually accredited certifications issued by accredited certification bodies (institutions that are themselves evaluated against international standards). The BCSP, ABIH, and the IHMM are accredited certification bodies that provide the gold standards for credentials most relevant to the EHS professional. The BCSP, ABIH, and IHMM credentialing programs are accredited to the International Organization for Standardization and International Electrotechnical Commission (ISO/IEC) (2012) 17024 standard titled "Conformity Assessment—General Requirements for Bodies Operating Certification of Persons," which provides "a global benchmark for personnel certification programmes to ensure that they operate in a consistent, comparable and reliable manner worldwide, thereby allowing individuals to have skills that translate across national lines." Released in 2003, ISO/IEC 17024 is an international standard designed to harmonize the personnel certification process worldwide. ISO/IEC 17024 is the only internationally recognized standard and is considered "the hallmark of a quality certification program" (American National Standards Institute, n. d.).

Accredited certification programs set standards for minimum requirements for education/training, experience, knowledge, and skill and evaluate people against those standards using methods that conform to the criteria specified by ISO/IEC 17024. The key issues that ISO 17024 addresses can be summarized:

- The competencies (knowledge, skills, abilities) and standardized eligibility requirements must be established through a job-analysis process.
- The examination must be independent from training/training providers.
- The examination must be a valid and reliable assessment tool as determined by psychometric standards.
- The certification scheme must safeguard impartiality.
- An effective management system for continuous quality improvement must be in place. (ISO/IEC 2012)

The ISO/IEC 17024 accreditation process requires that the certifying body be able to prove compliance to the standard through an initial accreditation assessment, including both material/documentation and onsite assessment as well as annual surveillance audits and a full reaccreditation audit every five years.

Accreditation to an international standard is extremely important for certification bodies that have global operations or aspirations. Accreditation of certification programs provides an independent, third-party evaluation to show candidates, certificate holders, employers, government agencies, and the public that a certification program operates fairly, openly, and effectively (Wright et al. 2015). Two organizations commonly awarding accreditation in the EHS field are ICE's administration of the National Commission for Certifying Agencies (NCCA) Standards for the Accreditation of Certification Programs standard and the American National Standards Institute's (ANSI) administration of the ISO 17024 standard (Wright et al. 2015). In Canada, the Standards Council of Canada (SCC) provides accreditation services. Table 11.2 lists EHS certifications and associated accrediting bodies and standards.

**TABLE 11.2.** EHS certifications and associated accrediting bodies and standards

| Organization Offering Certification | Certification | Standard to Which Certification is Accredited |
|---|---|---|
| Board of Certified Safety Professionals | Certified Safety Professional (CSP) | ANSI/ISO 17024 and ICE/NCCA |
| Board of Certified Safety Professionals | Associate Safety Professional (ASP) | ANSI/ISO 17024 and ICE/NCCA |
| Board of Certified Safety Professionals | Occupational Health and Safety Technologist (OHST) | ICE/NCCA |
| Board of Certified Safety Professionals | Construction Health and Safety Technician (CHST) | ICE/NCCA |
| Board of Certified Safety Professionals | Safety Trained Supervisor (STS) | ICE/NCCA |
| Board of Certified Safety Professionals | Safety Trained Supervisor Construction (STSC) | ICE/NCCA |
| American Board of Industrial Hygiene | Certified Industrial Hygienist (CIH) | ANSI/ISO 17024 and ICE/NCCA |
| Institute of Hazardous Materials Management | Certified Dangerous Good Professional (CDGP) | ANSI/ISO 17024 |
| Institute of Hazardous Materials Management | Certified Hazardous Materials Manager (CHMM) | ANSI/ISO 17024 |
| Institute of Hazardous Materials Management | Certified Hazardous Materials Practitioner (CHMP) | ANSI/ISO 17024 |
| National Fire Protection Association | Certified Fire Protection Specialist (CFPS) | ANSI/ISO 17024 |
| Board of Canadian Registered Safety Professionals | Canadian Registered Safety Professional (CRSP) | SCC |

Accreditation by ICE to the NCCA standard or ANSI to the ISO/IEC standard, therefore, demonstrates that the professional credentials meet standards for

- validity and reliability of the certification examination program;
- fairness of the procedures for determining applicant eligibility;
- adequacy of requirements for ensuring maintenance and enhancement of professional qualifications (recertification requirements);
- professionalism, integrity, and independence of the certifying body; and
- openness of the program to public scrutiny.

Not all EHS certifications meet the strict criteria for quality, and many are not accredited to any accreditation standard.

Unfortunately, not all of the over three hundred EHS "certifications" available to the EHS professional meet the strict criteria for quality, and many are not accredited to any accreditation standard (Ferguson and Ramsay 2010). Many of those "certifications" that come from unaccredited organizations can be obtained without possessing the education, training, or experience needed (ASSE, n. d.). It is important to the EHS professional to evaluate the quality of a particular credential, including looking for whether it is accredited to the ISO/IEC or similar standard, before pursuing the credential.

## Certification Examination Development

For more than forty years in North America, a standardized multiple choice examination, developed through a psychometric process, has been used to evaluate potential candidates to determine whether the candidate possesses the requisite knowledge and skills to be awarded the desired mark of certification. The use of such standardized tests ensures a consistent method of scoring/assessment and ensures legal defensibility (Wright et al. 2015). The psychometric process used to develop a defensible examination that measures the skills and knowledge of the individuals being assessed includes the following key steps:

- Job task analysis/role delineation
- Validation survey
- Item development
- Cut score determination
- Statistical analysis
- Continuous improvement (Wright et al. 2015)

### Job Task Analysis / Role Delineation

The first step in the process of developing an examination is establishing the tasks, knowledge, and skills the candidate is expected to have acquired to be considered competent to practice in a field. This process is known as the job task analysis or role delineation process (Wright et al. 2015). This process is performed by gathering a group of subject matter experts (SMEs) from various industries, regions, and demographics who have achieved the certification to develop a consensus of tasks, knowledge, and skills that the "minimally qualified candidate" should have acquired to meet the certification designation. The *minimally qualified candidate* is a term used when developing an exam and represents the person who meets the minimum qualifications and experience to be able to sit for the exam. It is this level of education and experience to which the exam is written. The job task analysis process is reevaluated periodically to ensure that the competencies are reflective of the current practice of EHS professionals (Wright et al. 2015).

### Validation Survey

The next step is to validate the work of the role delineation panel and to establish the importance, criticality, and frequency of the need for or use of the knowledge and skills identified by the SME panel (Wright et al. 2015). This is done by surveying a different group of SMEs and asking them to rate whether a particular task, knowledge, or skill identified by the job analysis team is important for the minimally qualified candidate; how critical that skill or knowledge is for the minimally qualified candidate; and the frequency with which the candidate may need to use that knowledge or skill. The result of this job task analysis / role delineation and validation process is the development of an examination blueprint that identifies both the topics (domains and knowledge or skill competencies) and the weight of importance (how many questions should come from each domain and knowledge/skill area). This blueprint is then approved by the appropriate board of directors or a committee authorized to do so (Wright et al. 2015). These blueprints are generally published and available to both candidates to review when preparing for an examination and to employers to understand the competencies of successful candidates (Board of Certified Safety Professionals 2015; American Board of Industrial Hygiene 2015; Institute of Hazardous Materials Management 2013).

## Examination and Item Development

The content of the blueprint is the basis on which the examination is developed. "Items," or potential test questions for the examination, are developed by another group of SMEs who hold the certification for which the exam is being developed. These test questions are to be designed to evaluate the potential candidate's ability to meet a particular knowledge or skill requirement identified on the blueprint (Wright et al. 2015; Board of Certified Safety Professionals, n. d. b). Items are written utilizing documented, globally-recognized resources and references. Proposed test questions undergo multiple levels of review to confirm that the item is relevant to the certification under review, applicable to a global audience, and linked to the examination blueprint (Wright et al. 2015). Items are reviewed to ensure that the structure of the question is grammatically correct, the answers are all of similar length, there is only one correct or best answer, and there are appropriate and credible distractors (answers that are plausible but not quite the best answer) (Marcham, Turnbeaugh, and Wright 2017).

> The content of the blueprint is the basis on which the examination is developed.

Before the item is used for scoring on an exam, it must go through a beta testing process to be sure it meets certain criteria to appropriately evaluate the candidate's knowledge or skills and the item is not misunderstood by exam candidates. During this beta testing phase, items that are too easy and items that are too hard or are misunderstood are reevaluated and either rewritten or removed. By eliminating both the very easy and the very hard questions, those questions that remain are those that can truly differentiate between candidates who possess the requisite knowledge and skills and those who do not. This process of not including questions on the exam that either all candidates will get right or all may get wrong results in a distribution of questions right around the core competency of the minimally qualified candidate (see figure 11.1) (Marcham et al. 2018). This is an important factor in why the cut score, or passing score, for an examination is relatively low (usually below 70%) compared to a typical academic-style examination, which generally includes several questions the instructor expects all students to get correct (Marcham, Turnbeaugh, and Wright 2017; Marcham et al. 2018).

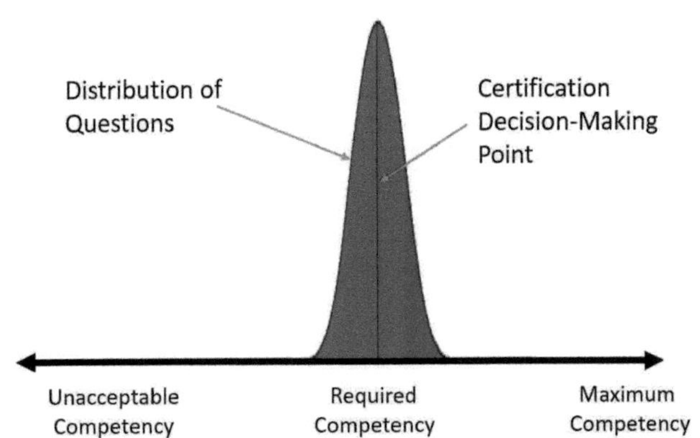


Figure 11.1
Certification testing criteria showing the distribution of test questions around the core competency of the minimally qualified candidate (Marcham et al. 2018)

Therefore, the full cycle of item development includes training SMEs on the process; developing the items; reviewing and fine-tuning the language, content, and difficulty level; testing the items through a beta testing process on the exam; psychometrically evaluating the performance of the item; and then ultimately placing the item on the exam (see figure 11.2). Periodically, the performance of items are statistically evaluated by a psychometrician, and those items that don't fare well in ongoing exams are reviewed and possibly revised or removed.

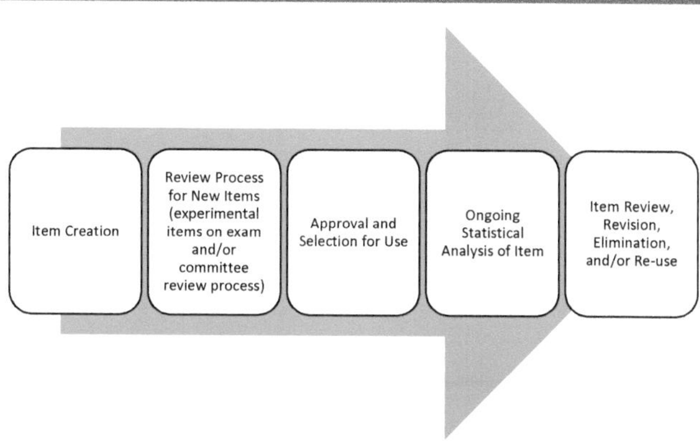


Figure 11.2
This diagram explains the steps in the item development process. (Adapted from Wright et al. 2015)

### Cut Score

In contrast to the traditional setting of a passing grade on a certificate exam or an academic examination (e.g., 90% for an A, 80% for a B, etc.), the psychometric process sets a mathematical cut score, or passing grade, based on the content and the difficulty of the examination questions (Wright et al. 2015). The most commonly used methods for certification or licensure examinations are the Angoff Method and the Modified Angoff Method for setting the cut score (Price 2017). Using the Modified Angoff Method, representative SMEs from various areas of practice review each examination question and rate each item based on the expected performance levels of the minimally qualified candidate (Price 2017). The ratings are then evaluated by a psychometrician, and an Angoff cut score is calculated. Based on the calculated cut score and data from previously administered exams, an appropriate cut score is set by the board of directors or a committee authorized to do so (Wright et al. 2015).

### Statistical Analysis

The reliability and validity of the examination is a key component within the ISO/IEC 17024 requirements. Reliability is defined by the ISO/IEC Standard as an "indicator of the extent to which examination scores are consistent across different examination times and locations," and validity is defined as "evidence that the assessment measures what it is intended to measure" (ISO/IEC 2012). For example, validity would measure whether the inferences being made about a minimally qualified candidate's knowledge and skills in EHS have been appropriately characterized. Reliability is generally measured by the examination's internal consistency or whether there is a correlation between different items (test questions) that intend to measure a particular knowledge or skill produce similar scores (Wright et al. 2015). For the BCSP, ABIH, and IHMM certifications, annual statistical reports are produced by a psychometrician presenting the statistical information on the reliability and validity of the examination and the certification examination process.

### Continuous Improvement

Accredited certification bodies operate in a continuous improvement process in which the definition of a minimally qualified candidate, the examination blueprint content, test questions, and policies are reviewed and updated on a standardized review period to ensure ongoing quality and relevance. In addition, those accredited by third-party agencies such as ICE and ANSI are periodically audited to evaluate whether the process continues to meet the ISO 17024 standard or other national or international standard for certification (Wright et al. 2015).

## Certification Standards and the Impact on the Profession

Because the examination development process involves an evaluation of current issues and relevant knowledge and skills for the EHS practitioner, there is evidence that the certification schemes may influence the practice of safety and health as well as curricula of EHS educational programs. In the United States, the ANSI/ ASSE Z590.2–2003 (R2012) Criteria for Establishing

> The examination development process involves an evaluation of current issues and relevant knowledge and skills for the EHS practitioner.

the Scope and Functions of the Professional Safety Position draws a correlation between the description of the professional safety position outlined in the standard and the BCSP's comprehensive job analysis study of professional safety practice (Wright et al. 2015). In addition, the BCSP offers the designation of becoming a Qualified Academic Program (QAP) to those institutions whose content in required academic courses toward a degree program map directly and completely to the BCSP ASP certification examination blueprint. Graduates of QAP degree programs may apply for a Graduate Safety Practitioner (GSP) designation at no cost and qualify for waiver of the ASP examination requirement toward the CSP eligibility (Board of Certified Safety Professionals n. d. a). As a result, many degree programs strive to ensure that the EHS curriculum contains the requisite components of the ASP blueprint.

Another way that certification standards impact the profession is that the BCSP, ABIH, and IHMM all require certificants to agree and adhere to a code of ethics. This practice of requiring adherence to high standards of integrity and professional competence through an ethical standard is common among certification boards (Wright et al. 2015). Typically, codes of ethics cover areas such as acting within the limits of one's competence; maintaining confidentiality; providing truthful, impartial, and accurate information; and avoiding conflict of interests (American Board of Industrial Hygiene 2007; Board of Certified Safety Professionals 2012). Individuals who are found to have breached the code of ethics may have their certification revoked or suspended.

Finally, to maintain the certification designation, the BCSP, ABIH, and IHMM require certificants to participate in meaningful and relevant continuing education and other activities in the profession to ensure that the certificant remains current with the requisite knowledge and skills to practice in the EHS profession. Failure to comply with this continuing competence program within a certain time period generally leads to suspension or withdrawal of certification of the individual. Requiring certificants to adhere to a code of ethics and participate in lifelong learning contributes to the public's positive view of the profession and the trustworthiness of the professionals involved (Wright et al. 2015).

## Reflection

Holding a certification from an accredited credentialing body is the mark of a true EHS professional. Many EHS practitioners will be entering the field in the years to come, and accredited certification is the primary indicator of demonstrated competency and professionalism. Accredited certification programs not only add value for employers and the EHS professional but also continually raise the bar for the profession.

## Questions

1. Differentiate between certification and certificate.
2. Illustrate some of the benefits of holding an accredited professional certification credential.
3. Describe the process for the development of a certification examination blueprint.
4. Explain the importance of evaluating the quality and accreditation status of an EHS credential before pursuing the credential.
5. Justify why quality credentialing organizations require certificants to participate in meaningful and relevant continuing education and other activities to maintain credentials over time.

## References


American Board of Industrial Hygiene. (2007). *American Board of Industrial Hygiene Code of Ethics.* Accessed August 12, 2016. http://www.abih.org/sites/default/files/downloads/ABIHCodeofEthics.pdf.

American Board of Industrial Hygiene. (2015). *CIH Exam Blueprint.* Accessed August 12, 2016. http://www.abih.org/sites/default/files/downloads/2015%20Domains,%20Tasks,%20%20Knowledge%20and%20Skilll%20Statements%20Final.pdf.

American Society of Safety Engineers. (n. d.) *The Employer's Guide to Hiring a Safety Professional.* Accessed April 7, 2017. http://www.asse.org/assets/1/7/Employer_Handbook_version_5_61.pdf.

American National Standards Institute. (n. d.) Accreditation Program for Personnel Certification Bodies under ANSI/ISO/IEC 17024. Accessed April 29, 2017. https://www.ansi.org/accreditation/credentialing/personnel-certification/Default.

Assessment Strategies Inc. (2011). *Report on the Perceived Value of Certification Survey.* Mississauga, ON: Assessment Strategies Inc.

Board of Certified Safety Professionals. (2012). *Code of Ethics.* Accessed August 12, 2016. http://www.bcsp.org/Portals/0/Assets/DocumentLibrary/BCSPcodeofethics.pdf.

Board of Certified Safety Professionals. (2015). *CSP9 Blueprint.* Accessed August 12, 2016. http://www.bcsp.org/Portals/0/Assets/DocumentLibrary/CSP9_Blueprint.pdf.

Board of Certified Safety Professionals. (n. d. a.) "Graduate Safety Practitioner." Accessed August 12, 2016. http://www.bcsp.org/GSP.

Board of Certified Safety Professionals. (n. d. b.) "How to Shop for Certifications." Accessed August 12, 2016. http://www.bcsp.org/SH-E-Practice/Choosing-a-Safety-Certification.

Board of Certified Safety Professionals. (2015). "SH&E Industry Safety Salary Survey and Calculator." Accessed August 12, 2016. http://www.bcsp.org/SH-E-Practice/Salary-Survey.

Ferguson, L. H., and J. D. Ramsay. (2010). "Development of a Profession: The Role of Education & Certification in Occupational Safety Becoming a Profession." *Professional Safety* 55(10): 24–30.

Henderson, J., M. Biel, L. Harman, J. Wickett, and P. Young. (2012). *A Look at the Value of Professional Certification.* Washington, DC: Institute for Credentialing Excellence.

Institute of Hazardous Materials Management. (2013). *Specification Blueprint for the Certified Hazardous Materials Manager.* Accessed August 12, 2016. http://www.ihmm.org/sites/default/files/doc/2013_CHMM_Blueprint.pdf.

International Organization for Standardization and International Electrotechnical Commission (ISO/IEC). (2012). *ISO/IEC 17024:2012: Conformity Assessment—General Requirements for Bodies Operating Certification of Persons.* Switzerland: International Organization for Standardization and International Electrotechnical Commission.

Knapp, J., L. Fabrey, M. Rops, and N. McCurray. (2006). *Basic Guide to Credentialing Terminology.* Washington, DC: Institute for Credentialing Excellence.

Marcham, C. L., T. Turnbeaugh, and N. Wright. (2017). "OSH Certifications: Behind the Exams." *Professional Safety* 62(7): 44–48.

Marcham, C. L., T. Turnbeaugh, and S. Gould. (2017). "Development of Certification Exam Test Questions: It's More Deliberate than You May Think." *Professional Safety* 63(5): in press (May 2018).

McAdams, M. T., J. J. Kerwin, V. Olivo, and H. A. Goskel. (2011). *National Assessment of the Occupational Safety and Health Workforce.* Accessed August 12, 2016. http://www.cdc.gov/niosh/oshworkforce/pdfs/NASHW_Final_Report.pdf.

Microsoft Corporation. (2007). *The Value of Certification: Connecting the Dots between Employers and Employees.* Accessed August 12, 2016. http://download.microsoft.com/download/e/0/0/e00405a0-1130-47ba-b628-fa2bd0d25d50/MSLEARNING/Value%20of%20Certification%20-%20English%20version.pdf.

National Safety Council. (2017). "2017 Job Outlook." *Safety + Health* (May): 41–45.

Price, L. R. (2017). *Psychometric Methods: Theory into Practice.* New York: Guilford Press.

Snyder, D., T. Turnbeaugh, J. Greenwald, and W. Acha. (2014). "The EHS Professional Credentials." In *Hazardous Materials Management Desk Reference* (3rd ed.), Doyle B. Cox (ed.): 1255–90. Rockville MD: Alliance of Hazardous Materials Professionals.

Wright, N., T. Turnbeaugh, C. Weldon, and D. Lyons. (2015). "Certification of OSH Professionals through an Accredited Competency Assessment Model." Proceedings of the WOS 8th International Conference, Porto Portugal, 2015: 1–9. Accessed August 12, 2016. http://orbit.dtu.dk/files/116635946/Book_of_Abstracts_WOS_2015.pdf.

U.S. Bureau of Labor Statistics. (2015). "Occupational Outlook Handbook." Accessed April 7, 2017. https://www.bls.gov/ooh/.

CHAPTER 12

# CREATING VALUE WITH PROFESSIONAL ASSOCIATIONS: PERFORMANCE AND DEVELOPMENT OF NETWORKING PRACTICES

Garrett Stricker

## Learning Objectives

After studying this chapter, the reader will be able to:

1. Define and describe the various parts of a relationship
2. Identify the benefits of good working relationships through experiences and toward positive personal and organizational growth
3. Explain how networking and relationships can improve the development of an EH&S professional
4. Measure the perception of others through effective management of relationships, using interpersonal skills and utilization of different mentoring approaches
5. Explain multiple interview techniques that can show competence in the profession and lead to new networking opportunities

## Key Terms

**Professional network, networking, relationships, relationship building, American Society of Safety Professionals (ASSP), National Safety Council (NSC), professional development**

## Abstract

This section will focus on professional relationships within the environmental health and safety (EHS) field. Professional associations can have an enormous impact on one's professional development and network; these can be a great benefit throughout a career in EHS. Relationships outside of one's current employer can lead to new opportunities, foster the ability to learn from others, and strengthen professional ties throughout a career.

> The need for knowledge creation and transfer compels organizations to innovate the products and services they deliver to their customers (Kao 2016). This idea of the continuous transfer, practice, and conversion of learning is called knowledge creation.

Professional relationships can be very industry specific, like the Original Equipment Suppliers Association (OESA) within the auto industry, or very broad in focus like that of the American Society of Safety Professionals (ASSP). The important thing to remember is that like many things in life, the benefit out of the relationship is directly proportional to the effort put into the relationship.

## Introduction

As a society, people grow by accumulating and utilizing knowledge. Knowledge can be acquired from experiences, experiments, texts, and daily interactions of individuals. This quest for knowledge can lead professionals to expand their professional circles and seek to network with other individuals within their field. The need for knowledge creation and transfer compels organizations to innovate the products and services they deliver to their customers (Kao 2016). This idea of the continuous transfer, practice, and conversion of learning is called knowledge creation. Knowledge creation and innovations can be applied to professional organizations and networks for today's safety professional. Collaborative creation is a driving force behind social media and professional associations. Studies have shown that even when groups have a non-predefined (or loosely defined) goal, they positively impact the creation of knowledge (Kao 2016). Participating in the creation and transfer of knowledge is a key aspect to understanding where certain types of participation can add value professionally. Exploring and participating in many groups can aid in defining one's personal and professional identity. Understanding one's professional identity is the base to start analyzing group benefits and dynamics.

One's professional identity is considered to be a type of collective identity (Mancini et al. 2015). This collective identity includes the groups and social categories to which EHS professionals belong. Professional identity is the awareness of being a worker doing a specific job and the identification and connection to groups and social categories by virtue of one's job. As an EHS professional, one's professional identity is composed of their job focus of employee/occupational safety and their connection to groups based on that job. Focusing on the connection to groups, the EHS professional will identify with organizations such as the National Safety Council, American Society of Safety Professionals, the World Safety Organization, and so forth.

Modern professional associations and volunteer opportunities are a wealth of value-adding experiences. These connections and relationships serve to not only further the group's goals but can also further one's own. This idea of consciously managing one's career, network, and relationships is another aspect to controlling one's own professional destiny.

*Networking* is another term for the idea of like-focused people interacting and forming relationships. Networking within your profession or career can take many paths, and each can add personal and communal value, respectively. One of the key concepts to networking and professional associations that many people miss is the benefit one receives from the relationship outside of the group's professional services. This benefit is almost always directly proportional to the amount of time and effort that is put into the relationship.

Understanding one's connection to these professional groups has consistently shown that job satisfaction and performance are higher in those who can strongly identify with these groups and organizations (Mancini et al. 2015).

Daily interactions can always be viewed through the lens of networking. Networking is not limited to one's professional circle. One can form bonds with

> It is important to understand that associations with those that hold an opposing view can also be beneficial, as learning often comes from challenging one's mental model of a situation.

any compatible personality that can add *mutual* value to the parties involved. It is equally as important to understand that associations with those who hold an opposing view can also be beneficial, as learning often comes from challenging one's mental model of a situation. A friend that is also an auto mechanic can help when advice is needed around a car issue, and they may come back and seek input on something related to one's area of expertise (hobby, life, or work-related). This is a form of networking that every person is involved in and may not realize. When we look at all our interactions with individuals, society, and companies, they can all be different modes of creating one's personal or professional network. To boil this idea of networking down even further, we need to understand the idea of building relationships.

Due to the changing professional environment, with multiple external pressures to increase one's knowledge and applicable skill, careers are no longer linear processes but a series of learning cycles. Having a wide network, both professional and otherwise, can provide an EHS professional with a variety of different perspectives, knowledge, and skills that are applicable in the active management of their career. It has been said that career development is a contact sport, and it is important to know with whom to connect (Ansmann et al. 2014).

## What Is a Relationship?

Relationships can be described in many ways. The term *relationship* can refer to all sorts of human connections. We as humans connect and create ties to friends, siblings, other family members, coworkers, neighbors, and mentors (DePaulo 2010). Here, we will focus on connections and ties to our professional community. But before we examine these connections, we need to first identify what makes a relationship. There are four key areas to any relationship, and those are communication, respect, transparency, and time/effort.

It has been said that career development is a contact sport, and it is important to know with whom to connect (Ansmann et al. 2014).

Understanding relationships starts with communication. Communication is the ability to share ideas, emotions, and participate in two-way interaction. Communication can be verbal (e.g., speaking), nonverbal (e.g., body language), or written. To create a connection, two parties must be able to communicate. Sharing of ideas and emotions allows people to understand one another. Without communication, relationships would be hard to form and maintain.

Due to the changing professional environment, with multiple external pressures to increase one's knowledge and applicable skill, careers are no longer linear processes but a series of learning cycles.

A second aspect to relationships we will investigate is the idea of respect. Respect can be summarized as admiration for a person's abilities or good qualities (*Cambridge Dictionary* 2016). The idea of treating others the same way that one expects to be treated is another form of respect. The definition of respect can vary from culture to culture based on the cultural norms a their society. For example, in many European cultures, it is customary to kiss the cheek when meeting someone, but in Thailand any physical contact above the shoulders is viewed as disrespectful (Taylor 2014). Respect can be as simple as valuing other people's points of view, regardless of one's personal acceptance. An example of respect is when people are having a disagreement and both sides can express themselves openly without the other immediately shutting them out, allowing a two-directional flow of ideas.

In a professional setting, respect can be treating people in the same manner regardless of their positional authority or rank in a company hierarchy. Professional respect can be thought of as treating a production associate the same way that one would treat the CEO.

A third aspect of professional relationships is the idea of transparency. Relationship transparency is being able to see directly to the core motives of both parties—that is, the ability to identify interactions one has that are not primarily motivated by ulterior or hidden motives. In business, this can often surface as "politics," meaning someone is playing a metaphorical chess game within the office to gain something they want. The person that is attempting to gain something is often motivated by undisclosed or exterior reasons.

Transparency in a business relationship is simply being genuine and truthful about your intentions or motivators. One can strategically manage their involvement in office politics and still maintain a high level of transparency, but this idea is not mutually exclusive. It is important to remember that once someone is labeled as untrustworthy or dishonest, it is very hard to erase that view from someone's mind.

> To advance a relationship, one needs to put in the time and effort to do so. The value one earns from relationships can be seen as a reward for the time and effort put forth.

Finally, we'll look at how time and effort play into the development of a relationship and the strength of that relationship. Time and effort can often be viewed as similar exclusive ideas in regard to relationships. If one does not put forth the necessary effort to advance the relationship and continue the exchange of ideas or two-way communication, the relationship can stagnate and lose value for both participants. To advance a relationship, one needs to put in time and effort to do so. The value one earns from relationships can be seen as a reward for the time and effort put forth.

The composition of relationships—communication, respect, transparency, and time—are just key areas of focus. It is important to note that these areas of focus often overlap. These areas do not have definite starting points and ending points and often have a valuable interplay between them. When an interaction contains these areas, a true relationship is constructed. Understanding the parts of a relationship allows professionals to better control and manage their relationships as they develop in their careers.

## Social Web and Social Networking

In this age of advancing technology, the creation of social network platforms has continued to expand. What was once isolated to high school or college campuses has become increasingly ubiquitous in everyday life across a multitude of industries. Per a Pew Internet and American Life Project, 46 percent of online U.S. adults 18 years and older use some form of social networking site. Social networking sites, with their widespread use, have obvious advantages for efficient communication among both individuals and organizations alike (Landman et al. 2010).

It is important to note that the social web and social networking are often used as synonyms, but the two concepts have decidedly separate meanings. The social web refers specifically to website and web technologies, while social networking is an existing body of theory relating to human interactions (Keenan and Shiri 2009). Currently, perhaps the most well-known professional social web platform is LinkedIn. This site allows a user to create an electronic profile that closely resembles a résumé and then connect to other professionals and their networks. LinkedIn is based on connecting the social web and the users' social network, meaning the website is the tool to help make connections to others and facilitate professional social interactions.

LinkedIn is a great tool to connect to other professionals and virtual groups that interest an EHS professional. The virtual connection to real-world professionals can create another avenue for people to seek and share knowledge within their field. LinkedIn can be used to stay in contact with other professionals whom they may have only met briefly or crossed paths with. Research has shown that most users utilize this platform to connect with the "weak ties" in their network—either colleagues they did not know well or ones they had worked with previously but did not communicate with on a regular basis (DiMicco et al. 2008).

These connections may become helpful when looking for problem-solving solutions, regulation interpretations, or even seeking new employment.

Social web connections create a new landscape for professionals to interact in. As these websites and web technologies become more and more a part of one's networking strategy, it can be important to remember some guidelines that will help to avoid their misuse (Landman et al. 2010):

- Understand institutional or corporate policy—It is important to be aware of and follow any policy that may govern how one utilizes the social web. Policy may hope to limit the scope of what can or should be shared to a public audience. It is important to follow such policy because noncompliance could lead to an undesired situation or even termination, depending on the policy and violation.
- Consider the role social networking plays in issues of human resources—The sharing of information about projects, people, or sensitive company information can lead to disciplinary action.
- Remember the audience—For professional social websites, remember the audience is that of professionals in and related to one's field. The sharing of personal or political views may not be appropriate compared to other social websites.
- Beware of the permanence on online content—Once content is put online, it will be very hard, if not impossible, to remove later.
- Maintain professional boundaries—Treat professional social websites and the connections made on them as professional, and stay away from personal information. There are other social websites that are meant to aid in dating or sharing photos, and it is best to remain focused on the purpose of the specific social web platform.

## Professional Groups and Volunteering

Throughout almost all occupations, we can find groups or associations whose primary goal is to advance their profession or area of focus. There are many professional associations that exist, from the Association for Renaissance Martial Arts (thearma.org) to the American Association of Candy Technologists (aactcandy.org). There are groups for almost every profession and focus.

The key to getting value out of a professional association is to participate. If there are regular meetings, attend them.

Two very prominent organizations within the EHS community are the American Society of Safety Professionals (ASSP) and the National Safety Council (NSC). These organizations operate on national and international levels to advance safety professionals through training opportunities, publications, conferences, and other avenues to personally develop your professional path. The NSC mission is simply stated as "[t]he National Safety Council eliminates preventable deaths at work, in homes and communities, and on the road through leadership, research, education and advocacy" (NSC 2016). ASSP states their mission: "ASSP is a global association of safety, health and environmental professionals dedicated to the advancement of its members and the profession through education and advocacy" (ASSP 2018). Both organizations focus on education and advocacy in the field of EHS. These groups work to advance their mission through the support of their members.

The key to getting value out of a professional association is to participate. If there are regular meetings, attend them. If professional growth conferences or other opportunities are held, attend them. Through participation and attendance, one will start to notice which other individuals are dedicating their time to support an organization. These people understand the value of networking opportunities because they are putting in time and effort because they value the organization and its impact on their field of focus.

To some, professional groups and meetings can seem intimidating or outside of one's comfort zone. People may act as if they have known one another for years or that they have a shared experience. It is important to remember that those relationships started with a simple introduction. Introductions can come from an acquaintance that is already active in the group or from one's personal introduction and networking technique. Another tactic is to volunteer within the group; many times, there is a need for a member to take meeting minutes or suggest options for future meeting places. Recognizing the opportunity to provide value to the group will break the ice with others within the group and give a solid foundation to start conversation.

It is also important to note that volunteering for a cause outside of professional organizations/associations can provide tremendous value. Relationships are easily formed when both parties have a passion for a specific cause. While volunteering for a cause that is important to an individual, that person is surrounded by like-focused people and is expanding their network with others that can share common values.

## Mentors and Coworker Relationships

The relationships that develop within the work environment can add immense value if actively managed. By acknowledging the culture within a company, one can understand how the people within a company react to different scenarios. By paying attention and taking note of different scenarios and situations that are happening every day in the workplace, one could understand a path to success. One of the best ways to learn the culture within a workplace is to utilize a mentor.

The relationships that develop within the work environment can add immense value if actively managed.

The term *mentor* is one that is often used when speaking about professional development. Mentors, in general, come in many different forms and can take many names. In the classic sense a mentor is someone who is there to show less senior professionals how to be successful within the company based on the norms within that company. This can be simple tasks, such as filing an expense report, making travel arrangements, or the process of project review and approval, but a mentor is more than a supervisor. When actively managing one's professional success, it is important to understand the concept of a professional mentor. A professional mentor is someone who is available to discuss and review all aspects, internal and external, to professional success. By studying how someone who is respected within a profession or organization, one can observe a potential path to success. It is important to note that the "path to success" is very different for everybody as everyone may have a different definition to what "success" is to them. Mentors can be very active and have routine meetings or discussions, or they can take the form of study and admiration of our professional role models. Mentors take many different forms, and the relationships that are developed can vary widely. Studies have shown that mentorships and the relationships created between the participants involved lead to greater career satisfaction (Mancini et al. 2015).

Different styles of mentoring may align better with participants' availability, personality, and talents (McBurney 2015). Multiple styles of mentor–mentee relationships exist and have different benefits, depending on what is needed at the time. Three styles of mentorship can be categorized as advisor, coach, and sponsor (McBurney 2015).

Different styles of mentoring may align better with participants' availability, personality, and talents (McBurney 2015). Multiple styles of mentor–mentee relationships exist and have different benefits, depending on what is needed at the time.

An advisor gives advice based on their personal set of experiences. Advisors can share how they have handled situations and elaborate on the outcomes of decisions. This style provides good analysis of specific situations the mentor has faced, but circumstances surrounding current or forward-looking events might be different and provide a challenge to following an advisor's suggested path.

A coach teaches and provides feedback to the mentee and encourages, pushing one's goals and capabilities. Like an athletic coach, a mentor coach is there to help provide guidance, motivation, and support when needed. Coaching is beneficial because the mentor can teach the mentee skills that may be utilized in a broader range of circumstances than other mentoring styles. This type of relationship is about learning different techniques and tools to advance, as well as providing a motivational "push" to reach higher.

Sponsors are mentors who can provide access to formal and informal groups or societies that might otherwise be closed or hard to enter. Sponsors are great for making networking connections and being introduced to more senior-level professionals one may not otherwise encounter. This type of relationship is often purely about making connections, and what one does after the initial meeting is up to the individual. This type of mentor is a great way to connect with those outside one's immediate professional circle(s) and potentially create other mentoring opportunities with different mentors.

Some companies have a very formal mentor program in place to connect new employees with those who are more senior. In situations where there is an employer-guided program, connecting with a mentor may be simple, but if no such program exists, there are many other avenues to connect with a mentor. A very common route to meet a mentor would be with professional or industry groups. Professional associations are often centered on advancing professionals to a higher standard and thus can often easily link a mentor with a mentee. Through networking and participating in one's professional community, the opportunity to learn from a role model is very possible.

Another powerful tool that often gets overlooked is the power of passive observation. When one passively observes others, they pay close attention to details that others may not notice. One can learn a good deal of information by observing the actions of leaders around them in a professional setting. Utilization of this tactic can help one learn from everyone around them. In a professional setting, look at how the people you admire treat others, watch how they react in stressful situations, analyze how they approach problem solving, and so on. Watching and understanding how recognized leaders approach different tasks or situations can then lead to analyzation of one's own methods.

One can learn a good deal of information by observing the actions of leaders around them in a professional setting. Utilization of this tactic can help one learn from everyone around them.

If a mentor program is unavailable or unappealing, one can also work with their coworkers to gain a better handle on their surroundings. Although a mentor can help guide a career, coworkers have a wealth of knowledge that can be helpful. Everyone has a different specialty or area of expertise, so learning from someone who is more skilled or tenured at a certain task can raise the quality of one's output.

## Vendors and Service Providers

It is very likely that in your career you will utilize the services of a vendor or other professional services supplier. This could be for consultation, project management, or general operations contracts (e.g., waste disposal, training resources, or lab testing). These professionals work off of customer service and interaction with a greater number of clients that have the same needs you do. Although initially relationships with vendors can seemingly be finite, it is important to remember their scope of influence. Even if you change jobs, the vendors and service providers in your area may not change, and you could potentially be dealing with the same set of people you were dealing with before. Forming a relationship with vendors and service providers is something that often gets overlooked because the value of a vendor may not be fully understood or appreciated.

A different aspect of vendor relationships that can hold value is the vendor's broad reach within your industry or field. Vendors often see how other companies (sometimes even one's competition) addresses problems. Vendors can be a great link to others that are dealing with the same issues or to others that recently went through a comparable situation. When there is a relationship with a vendor, they can connect you with people who may add value to you immediately or in the future and help solve problems that may arise. Aside from a personal connection, service providers can help link one to existing or developing technology that they may not be aware of.

If there is ever a need to change employers, vendors often hold the knowledge of where positions and opportunities may become available. Vendors can help open lines of communication between a job seeker and the decision-makers. The relationships that are built often transcend employers and can last an entire professional career.

## Government Regulators

When working in a nongovernmental role, government regulators (e.g., Occupational Safety and Health Administration or the Environmental Protection Agency) are often viewed in a potentially negative light. Government regulators generally serve the purpose of enforcement, and with enforcement usually comes the potential of penalties, citations, or a notice of violation. It is important to remember they play a significant role in the lifecycle of compliance.

Government regulators are responsible for a wide set of tasks. They can be responsible for enforcement, consultation, or technical roles. Like other professions, it is important to remember that regulators are governed by different rules and procedures to ensure they interact fairly outside their department. One way to best protect one's interests (company or personal) is to understand the rules regulators must abide by and exercise the rights granted by those rules. For example, if an OSHA inspector shows up for an unannounced inspection, understanding the rights granted to you can help you better control a situation. There are rules in place that spell out the scope of their visit, who they can talk to, who can be present in interviews, and so forth. Knowing these rules and guidelines, which are different for every regulator, is the first step in successfully handling an encounter.

Like other professions, it is important to remember that regulators are governed by different rules and procedures to ensure they interact fairly outside their department. One way to best protect one's interests (company or personal) is to understand the rules regulators must abide by and exercise the rights granted by those rules.

Networking with government regulators is a smart idea. Regulators (usually) have vast knowledge on common problems and solutions. By networking with regulators and forming a relationship, one can turn a potential adversary into a resource. Regulators see a wide range of industries and companies and deal with companies of all sizes. If one can change their point of reference from adversary to teammate, many positive results can happen. By being proactive and communicating with regulators prior to an incident or need, one can attend events that will help in understanding new legislation of enforcement actions. Regulators are also routinely available for consultation and may be able to provide training. Again, it is important to remember that government regulator relationships, like suppliers and vendors, may pop up again and again, regardless of industry.

## Interviews as Networking Opportunities

The last topic of networking we will discuss is viewing a job interview as another opportunity to network and grow one's professional image. Like the discussion on vendors and suppliers, the circle of hiring managers can be small in a specific region. It is important to remember that the one's path could very easily cross again with hiring managers at some point.

A good strategy for interviewing is to promote oneself and create a positive lasting impression. Even if the job one is interviewing for is not a good fit, if you create a lasting impression, you could come to mind later when a better fitting role opens. Viewing an interview as a chance to make a first impression for a future of opportunities can really add value to any interview, regardless of the outcome. Making a lasting impression may not have an immediate payoff, but one never knows when another opportunity may present itself.

## Conclusion

Professional networking is a skill that, when managed appropriately, can be helpful in one's career. Networking is based on human bonds and relationship building. Understanding that all relationships share the common core of communication, respect, transparency, and time/effort is key to forming a strong relationship. Applying these core ideas of relationships to professional interactions will aid in building bonds that can last throughout a career.

The need for knowledge creation and transfer between people is the cornerstone for professional associations and networking. Networking can take many different paths and lead to many fulfilling relationships. Connections to groups and group identity, specifically in the professional setting, have proven to advance individual's skill set and thus potentially advance one's career. Participation is a concrete way to gain value from membership.

Mentoring and the many forms/styles it can take is a fruitful endeavor. A mentoring relationship that aligns with both the mentee and mentor is of meaningful significance to both parties involved. It is important to remember that one can have many mentors that fit one or all the styles discussed in this chapter and that each style has its pros and cons.

Learning through passive observation and networking with regulators and vendors is of substance to a professional as well. These relationships and networks may work positively in one's favor in the near term or further out in one's career. The most important message throughout this chapter is that relationship building and networking are skills that need to be practiced and can impact one's professional career. The best way to gain strength for any skill is to practice it and analyze the outcomes. Some advice for the young professional is to simply get involved with as many volunteer and professional organizations as time allows. Sample several organizations, and then determine which ones are right for you as an individual. Then lend your time and support to those organizations. While you participate, become truly active by volunteering to lead a task, plan an event, or participate in discussion.

## Questions

1. What are the four areas of a relationship highlighted in this chapter, and how are they connected to one another?
2. What is the difference between social networking and the social web?
3. What are the different styles of mentoring described in this chapter?
4. What is a good strategy to ensure value creation and knowledge transfer during interactions with professional groups/organizations?
5. How can vendors and suppliers create value in relationships?

## References

Ansmann, L., T. E. Flickinger, S. Barello, M. Kunneman, S. Mantwill, S. Quilligan, C. Zanini, and K. Aelbrecht. (2014). "Career Development for Early Career Academics: Benefits of Networking and the Role of Professional Societies." *Patient Education and Counseling* 97(1): 132–34.

ASSP. American Society of Safety Professionals. www.assp.org.

Cambridge Dictionaries Online. (2016). Cambridge University Press. Accessed March 8, 2016. http://dictionary.cambridge.org/us/dictionary/english/respect.

DePaulo, D. (2010). "The Meaning of 'Relationship': Notes from a Party." *Psychology Today* (March 13). Accessed March 8, 2016. https://www.psychologytoday.com/blog/living-single/201003/the-meaning-relationship-notes-party.

DiMicco, J., D. R. Millen, W. Geyer, C. Dugan, B. Brownholtz, and M. Muller. (2008). "Motivations for Social Networking at Work." *Proceedings of the ACM 2008 Conference on Computer Supported Cooperative Work—CSCW '08.*

Kao, S.-C., and C. Wu. (2016). "The Role of Creation Mode and Social Networking Mode in Knowledge Creation Performance: Mediation Effect of Creation Process." *Information & Management* 53(6): 802–16.

Keenan, A., and A. Shiri. (2009). "Sociability and Social Interaction on Social Networking Websites." *Library Review* 58(6): 438–50.

Landman, M. P., J. Shelton, R. M. Kauffmann, and J. B. Dattilo. (2010). "Guidelines for Maintaining a Professional Compass in the Era of Social Networking." *Journal of Surgical Education* 67(6): 381–86.

Mancini, T., L. Caricati, C. Panari, and A. Tonarelli. (2015). "Personal and Social Aspects of Professional Identity." *Journal of Vocational Behavior* 89 (2015): 140–50.

McBurney, E. I. (2015). "Strategic Mentoring: Growth for Mentor and Mentee." *Clinics in Dermatology* 33(2): 257–60.

Mourtzis, D., M. Doukas, and N. Milas. (2016). "A Knowledge-based Social Networking App for Collaborative Problem-solving in Manufacturing." *Manufacturing Letters* 10: 1–5.

National Safety Council (NSC). (2016). Accessed March 10, 2016. http://www.nsc.org.

Taylor, L. (2014). "What You Need to Know about Respecting Different Cultures and Customs." *Stunning Places.Net* (September, 10). Accessed April 18, 2017. http://stunningplaces.net/respecting-different-cultures-and-customs/.

Wu, T.-C., P.-C. Lu, N.-W. Yi, C.-H. Chen, S.-C. Yu, and C.-T. Chen. (2016). "Interpersonal Relationships among University Safety Professionals: The Impact of a Safety Department." *Journal of Loss Prevention in the Process Industries* 44: 653–60.

CHAPTER 13

# KEY TOPICS FOR EXEMPLARY OSH PERFORMANCE

Darryl C. Hill

## Learning Objectives

After studying this chapter, the reader will be able to:

1. Evaluate the relationship between serious incidents and fatalities (SIFs) and less serious injuries
2. Describe common SIF precursors and causes and how to improve safety performance
3. Analyze organizational culture and its impact on safety culture
4. Compose a maturity model based upon the organizational goals, methods, and processes for your company
5. Discuss systems thinking and profound knowledge

## Key Terms

**Culture, incident, maturity model, systems**

## Abstract

The pathway to safety excellence is based upon several key elements and concepts. Serious incident and fatality prevention is an important consideration across all industries. Safety culture is a subset of organizational culture. A maturity model provides the framework for a company to have a proactive approach to health and safety. Systems thinking will allow an organization to deploy leading safety practices.

## Introduction

To celebrate fifty years of the *Professional Safety* journal, each issue during 2006 featured an article from a past issue. These articles provide excellent insight into the evolving OSH profession and valuable lessons learned to assist the OSH professional lead their organizations. William Tarrants outlined the importance for engineering solutions and to provide line management with decision-making information for their operations. Furthermore, Tarrants discussed the importance of research as the methods of production become more complex. The OSH professional may use the research results to provide the guidance for optimal safety success (Tarrants 2006). William W. Allison talked about the importance of motivation, as the author viewed motivation as industry's challenge. Studies have shown that the best motivation can only provide a maximum of 30-percent temporary improvement where morale is already average. Finally, Allison stated the need to provide 80–90 percent permanent improvements available through physical changes in conditions (Allison 2006).

As outlined in the "Time to Transform: Assessing the Future of the SH&E Profession" article, behavior-based safety shouldn't be a separate program but part of the overall health and safety process (Hill 2002).

These and other thought-provoking articles republished during 2006 provided the OSH profession with emerging trends and key issues that would guide the OSH professionals during the foreseeable future. Additionally, several key themes began to emerge that are discussed in this chapter. There are four topics we will examine. They include serious injury and fatality prevention, safety culture, maturity model, and systems thinking.

## Serious Incidents and Fatalities

The occupational fatality rate per 100,000 employees was reduced from 17.0 in 1971 to 4.0 in 2005, a 58-percent decline; the rate has been close to stationary from 2006 through 2015. During those 10 years, the rate has ranged from 3.9 to 3.5 (OSHA 2017). There are several initiatives to reduce the number of fatalities and the fatality rate that have resulted in moderate success. There is usually a keen focus for companies to reduce their recordable and lost-time incident rates. As many articles and studies have shown, the strategies that contribute to a lower recordable incident rate do not necessarily lower the fatality rate (Manuele 2014; Martin and Black 2015; Wilbanks 2013).

> It is imperative for the OSH professional to learn and better understand the relationship between their incidents, SIF precursors, and common SIFs. There are many documents, reports, and tools that can assist the OSH professional to mitigate and preferably eliminate SIF potential.

The Indiana University of Pennsylvania (IUP) and the Alcoa Foundation cosponsored a national forum titled "Fatality Prevention in the Workplace" that posited the reliance on traditional approaches to fatality prevention has not always proven effective (IUP 2012). Personal experience has demonstrated a similar result, whereas an outstanding reduction on less-serious injuries did not have similar reduction for serious injuries and fatalities (SIFs). The Campbell Institute sponsored a similar workshop titled "Fooled by Randomness: High-Consequence Events, Proactive Interventions, and the Appetite for Risk" (2014). A panelist shared that the difference between near misses and failures are enabling conditions. The traditional safety pyramid is not accurate predictively in terms of potential for SIFs. Twenty-one percent of all types of incidents have the potential to become a SIF, based on known precursors. Common SIF precursors include the following:

1. Unusual and nonroutine work
2. Nonproduction activities
3. In-plant modification/construction operations
4. Outage work—repair, maintenance, startups
5. High-energy sources are present
6. Upsets occurring

Common SIF causes are the following:

1. Struck by/crushed by objects
2. Operation of/interaction with mechanical equipment
3. Falls from height or same level
4. Electrical contact
5. Contact with nonelectrical hazardous energy
6. Explosions and fires

You will note the similarities between the two lists. It is imperative for the OSH professional to learn and better understand the relationship between their incidents, SIF precursors, and common SIFs. There are many documents, reports, and tools that can assist the OSH professional to mitigate and preferably eliminate SIF potential. Collecting and analyzing incident investigation reports is a good first step. The incident investigations must be comprehensive by assessing the entire system. Incident investigations that use the 8-D problem-solving methodology are usually exhaustive and comprehensive. Furthermore, the incident investigation should not focus on a singular root cause but view the incident in terms of a system and the interdependencies. A sample 8-D problem-solving

**Safety and health: eight-discipline problem-solving**

*Instructions: Complete this form for all incidents. Place cursor in the box and type. Boxes will expand as needed. Where present, begin typing at the red "x." Subsequent pages will be automatically numbered in the header when you close the document.*

*Submit completed form by email to Safety Manager within 8 hours of the incident.*

| **EHSIS Case No.:** | **Date and Time of Incident:** |
|---|---|

| **Location:**<br>*Enter Plant and line/area the incident occurred.* | **Plant Manager:**<br>Name:<br>Tele: | **Local Contact:**<br>Name: |
|---|---|---|
| **Name of Employee:** | **Home Address:** | **Home Phone #** |
| **Date of Birth:** | **Employee ID #** | **Home Department and Shift:** |
| **Job Title:** | **Sex M / F** | **Date of Hire** |

**1. Team Contact:** *Establish a small group of people with the knowledge, allocated time, authority, and skill in the required technical disciplines to solve the problem and implement corrective actions. The team must have a designated champion.*

Champion: *Supervisor of injured employee*

Team: *The name of everyone that was involved in the review.*

**2. Employee Statement of Incident:**

**3. Injury/Illness Description:** *Describe the injury and how it occurred. Use quantifiable terms that answer: What? Why? When? Where? How? etc.*
*What: Injury type*
*When: Date injury occurred*
*Where: Specific location where injury occurred*
*How: Give a detailed description of what the injury/illness is and how it occurred. Give detailed information of what went on and any past history that is relevant.*

| *(Pictures)* | *(Pictures)* | *(Pictures)* |
|---|---|---|

Figure 13.1
8-D problem-solving document *(Continued on next page)*.

**3. Interim Containment Action:** *Define and implement containment actions to prevent reoccurrence in the immediate future while permanent corrective actions are being developed and implemented.*
*Identify short term corrective action to prevent this issue from reoccurring (until the long term corrective action below listed in #5 below is implemented)*
- ❑ *Detailed description of corrective action* ***Resp:*** *(Name of person responsible for corrective action)* ***Due Date:*** *(when will it be completed)*
- ❑ *Detailed description of corrective action* ***Resp:*** *(Name of person responsible for corrective action)* ***Due Date:*** *(when will it be completed)*

**4. Define Root Causes:** *Identify all possible causes, which could explain why the injury/illness occurred. Ask 5 "whys. Isolate the root cause by carefully considering each possible cause. List possible corrective actions.*
*Define all causes that could have created this problem. Think of any systems, procedures, etc. that could have been different to prevent the situation.*
- ❑ *Detailed description of corrective action Resp: (Name of person responsible for corrective action)* ***Due Date:*** *(when will it be completed)*
- ❑ *Detailed description of corrective action* ***Resp:*** *(Name of person responsible for corrective action)* ***Due Date:*** *(when will it be completed)*

**5. Define Permanent Corrective Actions:** *Carefully consider and/or test possible corrective actions and select permanent corrective actions which will assure that the injury will never recur.*
*Define ways that the root causes can be fixed. Determine if new systems need to be implemented. (ex. new machine needed for the job, new disciplined policies, new methods, etc.)*

**6. Implement and Verify Corrective Actions:** *Establish a plan to implement permanent corrective actions, and define ongoing controls to ensure the root cause is eliminated. Monitor the long-term effects and implement contingency actions if necessary.*
*(always insert the following verbiage)*
- ❑ All corrective action will be tracked until closed.

**7. Prevention:** *Modify the necessary systems, practices and procedures to prevent recurrence of this and all similar injuries/illnesses. Identify opportunities for improvement and establish a process for improvement initiative.*
- ❑ *If there are any other areas of the facility where this issue could occur, please identify corrective action to address it.*

**8. Congratulate the Team:** *Recognize the collective efforts of the team.*
*(insert the following verbiage, or something equivalent)*
- ❑ Congratulated the team on a job well done

| **Corrective Action →** | **Complete:**<br>**Yes / No** | **Date Complete:** | **M.E. Signature:** | **Employee Signature:** |
|---|---|---|---|---|
| **Plant Nurse:** | **Supervisor:** | **Unit Manager:** | **Safety Manager:** | **Plant Manager:** |
| **Date:** | **Date:** | **Date:** | **Date:** | **Date:** |

Figure 13.1
8-D problem-solving document *(Continued from previous page).*

document is included (figure 13.1). We will discuss systems thinking later in the chapter.

One issue with SIF prevention is the longtime view that if first aid and recordable incidents are reduced, serious ones would decline as well. This view is a result with the Heinrich pyramid that outlines that a consistent decline in total injuries will be accompanied by a decline in SIFs (Heinrich 1959). The belief that OSHA-related incident rates are a good measurement barometer for serious injury and fatality potential must be discarded. This assertion assumes that most incidents share similar root causes and that less severe injuries will also prevent serious injuries and fatalities.

Also, there is a general view that unsafe acts of workers are the primary causes of occupational incidents. This thinking can have negative impacts as the focus will be on worker behavior and actions versus having a broader view on the system and organizational factors. The article "Time to Transform: Assessing the Future of the SH&E Profession" discusses the great debate in the profession (Hill 2002). "Who is responsible for workplace accidents—employees (who commit unsafe acts) or management (who provides unsafe systems)?" During that time, some behavior-based safety supporters suggested in most cases—80 to 95 percent—accidents were caused by unsafe behavior (Krause 1990). A famous writer stated, "Don't expect people to change their behavior unless you change what they do. Their work must be designed to allow them to work differently" (Champy 1996). Simply, the process designed and controlled by management is responsible for an overwhelming majority of all outcomes. A key learning from the past is a progression to systems thinking (Loud 2016).

An understanding of high-risk exposures and precursors is important to develop an effective strategy for SIF incidents. Events that are considered SIF precursors are significant process upsets, maintenance activities, unexpected changes, high energy potential, and emergency shutdown procedures. Activities that contribute to SIFs are mobile equipment, confined spaces entry, lifting operations, working at height, and hot work permits. The OSH professional has an opportunity to impact their organization by identifying the SIF precursors and to establish a SIF rate and give it the visibility necessary to impact change and, more importantly, the necessary actions to prevent the SIF event. Areas that need more focus for serious injury and fatality prevention include nonproduction activities, unusual and nonroutine work, situations going from normal to abnormal (upsets), high energy sources, and shutdowns for repair and maintenance. Many serious injuries and fatalities have multiple and complex causal factors that are organizational, technical, or cultural in nature. Understanding SIF events and the associated causal factors are key components for eliminating human suffering and improving safety performance and overall safety culture.

## Safety Culture

The organizational disciplines provide the foundation for an effective health and safety management system process. Two key areas are culture and leadership. A conference speaker several years ago stated that the two strongest predictors for safety performance are culture and leadership involvement. In *Zero Index*, culture is defined as the values, beliefs, and unstated assumptions that influence what people do and the way they do it (Duncan 2012). Culture can create the optimal conditions for effective leadership, management, and safe work, or it can be an obstacle to those things. Leadership describes how all leaders are utilized in safety and influences the culture characteristics that contributes to safety outcomes. As our OSH profession evolves, there is a greater need to shift our focus to these organizational disciplines. Leadership influences culture and is demonstrated whenever a decision is made, strategies are developed to solve an issue, and how leadership interacts with employees.

*Safety culture* can be an overused term. For example, how do you define the term? Is safety culture related to organizational culture? Most importantly, how do you measure safety culture, and what is the relationship (if any) to safety performance? The answers to these questions are important for the OSH professional as they navigate through complex operational processes and organization reporting structures. The organization culture sets the tone for safety. Safety culture is a subset and is impacted by the company organization culture. A company that is known to have a positive safety culture has two key attributes: visible leadership involvement and employee engagement. Later we will discuss how you can measure these attributes.

Companies that view safety as a key strategy that is integrated into the organizational strategy and goals are shifting their focus from avoidance-driven and compliance-driven to values-driven. Safety strategies and processes coordinated across other company functions and that complement other business systems are viewed as key enablers to support the organization.

Safety culture surveys can assist an organization to understand safety perceptions and the applicable opportunities for improvement. Companies use the survey results, which may also include interviews and focus group sessions, to develop short- and long-term strategies for safety culture continuous improvement.

## Maturity Model

Safety has historically been defined as a condition where the number of adverse outcomes is as low as possible. Subsequently, safety management attempts to make sure that the number of accidents and incidents is kept as low as possible or as low as is reasonably practicable. The issue with this approach is that safety is measured by counting the number of cases where it fails rather than by the number of cases where it succeeds (Hollnagel 2014). This leads to a reactive approach, focusing on what is wrong. A better approach is to ensure that more outcomes are positive and that what occurs is right. This thinking leads to an organization having a proactive approach to health and safety. Many companies deploy a maturity model to facilitate this concept.

A maturity model allows a company to develop practices in key areas and develop a roadmap for success. Furthermore, a maturity model provides the framework for an organization to outline key actions and, most importantly, is flexible. A company that has multiple sites can provide a template for success and doesn't necessarily penalize a plant for conditions that aren't prevalent at another location. For example, a plant that is operating at a higher efficiency due to experienced leadership and having processes in place for several years is expected to have more mature health and safety processes and systems, whereas a new startup plant with a less experienced plant management staff will most likely have less mature health and safety processes and systems. Therefore, the company maturity model roadmap is the same for both plants, but they can each deploy separate actions based upon their level of maturity to meet specific maturity model outcomes.

A case study illustrates how more than three hundred plants are globally operating with a consistent and standard approach of manufacturing using clear roadmaps to achieve manufacturing excellence and world-class performance by 2018. The Manufacturing Excellence Strategy enabled rapid and sustained development and execution and was formed by a global cross-business unit team during a period of several months (2017). This multi-dimensioned strategy consisted of the manufacturing system, the supporting infrastructure, and people. The strategy was instrumental to achieve the Johnson Controls vision of becoming the most operationally capable company in the world. Figure 13.2 provides an overview of the Johnson Controls Manufacturing System (JCMS). JCMS includes nine

Figure 13.2
Johnson Controls manufacturing system (reprinted with permission by Johnson Controls Manufacturing Excellence).

principles and four foundational elements. Each principle has a maturity model that includes objectives, standards, and key performance indicators (KPIs).

Figure 13.3 displays the foundational elements for manufacturing excellence strategy. These elements ensure a customer focus that exceeds customer expectations. Additionally, a stable operations environment is important. This element is aligned with health and safety initiatives and strategies by expecting standardized processes predictability and repeatability. Zero tolerance for waste is another

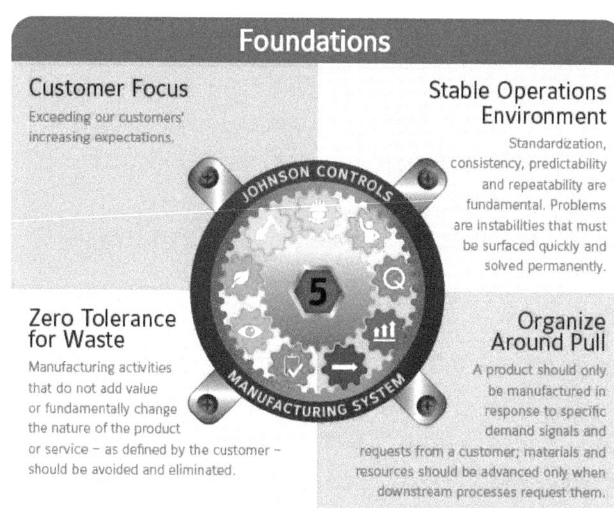


Figure 13.3
Operational excellence foundations (reprinted with permission by Johnson Controls Manufacturing Excellence).

element and consistent with many quality and lean manufacturing principles. Finally, organizing around pull is based upon having the materials, training, and other manufacturing excellence enablers available and accessible to plant personnel when needed.

Johnson Controls deploys a maturity model that includes nine principles. Two of the nine principles are Safe Workplace and Environmental/Sustainability. Each principle has a specific number of objectives. Safe Workplace has several objectives focused in areas like hazard identification, compliance, leadership, management of change, employee participation, monitoring and measurement, audits, and controls. There are five levels for each principle from 1 (not meeting) to 5 (distinguished): not meeting, developing, meets, excellent, and distinguished. Each level has several manufacturing practices (MPs) that must be achieved before receiving credit and moving to the next level. The maturity model also includes metrics and standards. For example, the Safe Workplace Principle has a control of hazardous energy standard. To achieve Level 3, a plant will need 100-percent compliance to the control of hazardous energy standard. The actual maturity model usually has some practices at each level with manufacturing practices met (achieved) as a leading indicator. The indicator can use a total number of MPs met or a percentage (%).

Each manufacturing plant completes an action plan to identify strategies to address gaps in their maturity model. JCMS provides the framework for plants to be successful in nine areas that contribute to manufacturing and operational excellence. A supporting infrastructure enables the maturity model and includes an online assessment tool, learning academy, and performance incentives. Finally, the third dimension is people. It is recognized that having a maturity model alone will not ensure a successful deployment, as all dimensions contribute to operational excellence. The maturity model

**Maturity Model**
Key Success Factor

Aligning the requirements of the maturity model with International Organization of Standardizations, including ISO 9001:2015, ISO 14001:2015, and ISO 45001, will add value by improving organizational work processes and consistency to work processes across multiple plant locations throughout the world. Understanding the framework of the ISO standards and incorporating the Plan-Do-Check-Act actions can help to improve:

* environmental footprint
* increased efficiency
* increased revenue
* employee engagement

(https://www.thebalance.com/top-reasons-to-get-iso-9001–2000-qms-certification-375654)

As a site safety coordinator, utilizing the maturity model roadmap to create consistency and standardization is the first step in creating a successful integrated management system. Expectations for reducing accidents and increasing employee engagement, as well as ISO certification, can be achieved by following a well-written maturity model blueprint.

Tiffany R. Barnett, CSP

provides an excellent framework to transition from lagging to leading indicators and to improve the operating system. Furthermore, the framework sets the foundation for systems thinking and a holistic and sustainable approach for exemplary health and safety performance.

## Systems Thinking

Edward Deming proposed that most accidents (85–94%) are created by faults in the system, and the system is designed, built, and controlled by management, not the workers (Deming 1994). Deming believed that workers have a duty to work safely but explained how the system works and the workers' relationship to the system. Thus, management is ultimately responsible for most outcomes. These outcomes include productivity, quality, and safety. Employees are directly impacted by how management designs and operates the system. Many behavior-based approaches and methodologies focus on the employee and their behavior and assert that most incidents are caused by "unsafe actions." Consequently, safety management aims to address employee behavior.

Traditional safety management has contributed to managers believing that most workplace incidents are caused by worker unsafe actions. Many managers who have a technical background are task oriented and employ single-event thinking. The prevailing wisdom is more a result how traditional safety management has taught them to think and view health and safety in general. The rules for managing safety is developed from the Taylor/Heinrich management paradigm. Frederic Taylor's ideas are based upon command and control, single-event thinking, which dominates American management. Subsequently, Herbert W. Heinrich integrated his views about safety parallel with Taylor's ideas on management, and a safety paradigm was born that prevailed for several decades and still exists today. A familiar Heinrich safety management philosophy includes the ten axioms for industrial safety (Manuele 2002). One famous Heinrich axiom includes the premise that unsafe acts of persons are responsible for most accidents. This is a legacy and unproven myth of Heinrich. A second axiom is the worker who suffers a disabling injury caused by an unsafe act has had over three hundred narrow escapes from serious injury because of committing the same unsafe act. The contributes to the belief that management should monitor employees to see if they can witness them working unsafely and remind them to work safely before they experience a serious injury.

Another familiar statement within the OSH profession is "all accidents are preventable." This assertion is caused by individuals applying nonsystems single-event thinking to a system. Isolated situations, not a system, are conducive to this ideology. Within a system, steps for work are repeatable but are never the same. There is always some variation. Sometimes the variation is quite small and will not make a difference that will lead to an accident. But a greater variation in one or more areas can lead to an accident.

Edward Deming promoted his *profound knowledge* concept. Profound knowledge provides the framework for an OSH professional to make transformational changes in their health and safety processes. Once someone deploys profound knowledge, they can impact positive change throughout their organization. The four areas of the system of profound knowledge include (1) appreciation for a system, (2) knowledge of variation, (3) theory of knowledge, and (4) psychology (Smith 2008). We can understand systems better by understanding the interactions between the parts, not by examining them individually. Systems are wholes defined by the product of the interactions of the parts, not the sum of the parts. A benefit of systems thinking is that it can assist an organization to address inadequate safety rules and procedures that don't relate to actual work conditions. It is important to improve the system by understanding how much variation exists in each process. Once an OSH professional has learned how to measure variation, a strategy is developed and implemented to reduce the variation. Incident rates will vary over time. Without an understanding of variation, a company may treat each data point as a unique and unusual event.

Frequently, a manager may react to each incident and expect a policy, procedure, or standard to address the incident or to prevent reoccurrence. Deming has stated that experience without a theory teaches nothing (Deming 1994; Smith 2008). Without a theory (prediction), you have no way of testing your observations. Obtaining knowledge is a continual process of making a prediction and then using a theory. Then the theory must be tested to determine if what you predicted happens. In *The Logic of Failure*, the bad participants in an experimental study failed to test their hypotheses (Dorner 1996). For them, to propose a hypothesis was to understand reality; testing that hypothesis was unnecessary. Instead of generating hypotheses, they generated truths. Furthermore, the good participants asked more *why* questions as opposed to *what* questions. It is noted that it is important to dig deeper in an analysis. The 5-Whys incident investigative technique supports this approach.

The learning process of a scientific method is key to safety success. The steps include observing, asking a question, developing a hypothesis, and then testing to determine whether it works in a continual process for learning. One key point is the considerable amount of information readily available to everyone. However, information is not knowledge. Information is everywhere on the Internet but usually does not include any knowledge. Knowledge is a result of critical thinking, ability to analyze a situation (or process), ask appropriate questions, and finally utilize a logical thought process to reach a conclusion about what will occur in the future (Blumenfeld 1999). Knowledge will allow someone to make predictions with high confidence.

Psychology allows the OSH professional to understand people and their interaction with each other. Psychology impacts safety management similarly as it influences most management activities. Safety management is influenced by B. F. Skinner's theory of behaviorism. A preferred approach is the elements of achievement orientation. These elements include standards of excellence, cause-and-effect thinking, the importance of individual contributions, self-set goals, and feedback (Smith 2008).

Standards of excellence are a key component for companies that are considered health and safety leaders. Basically, the higher level of achievement in a worker's thinking, the more focused they will be to achieve excellence. This approach includes the worker contributing to a high level of safety success. Cause-and-effect relationships are important for systems thinking. When safety is viewed as fate, luck, or chance, a company will miss an opportunity to study and learn more accurately by cause and effect relationships. Nonsystems, or single-event thinking, assumes that there is a direct connection between cause and effect, which leads people to believing it is sufficient to identify a root cause. The assumption is once you identify the root cause and remove it, the accident will not occur again. One key flaw with this thinking is that most accidents are a result of multiple factors that occur randomly within the system. This is the primary drawback of root cause.

Individual contributions and their achievements are important for health and safety success. Most employees want to contribute to their company's success. A worker that is not engaged (or is disengaged) will not contribute and provide input to improve their company's health and safety processes. Also, allowing the opportunity for employees to set their goals and providing continuous feedback are key elements for leading health and safety organizations.

In *Total Quality Management*, five significant variations are outlined:

1. Variation is normal in every system.
2. The causes of variation lie either within the system (common causes) or outside the system (special causes).
3. Common causes arise out of characteristics of the system, which are determined by management and can only be corrected by management to improve the system. Workers have no control over common causes.
4. When a system that is running consistently within its upper and lower control limits, under statistical control, is left untouched, the variations that occur are due to common causes.
5. The 85–15 rule of system variation applies. In a normal system, 85 percent or more of the

variations is due to common causes; 15 percent or less is due to special causes (Adams 1995).

There are two kinds of accidents in the context of system operation. The distinction between them is in the type of cause involved. The accident outcome is the result of either a common or special cause. Common causes are the interactions between the faults of the system; they are built into it. Special causes are unusual to the system. Special causes are situations that don't usually exist in the system. They occur without warning. Traditional safety management promotes investigating every accident as though something unusual happened. This approach means the company is treating most employee accidents as though they are a result of a special cause when it is more likely variation in the system.

OSH professionals should deploy a systematic approach for their health and safety processes. As Dietrich Dorner stated in *The Logic of Failure: Recognizing and Avoiding Error in Complex Situations*, more astute decision-makers act "more complexly" (Dorner 1996). Their decisions took different aspects of the entire system into account, not just one aspect. This is the preferred approach when addressing complicated systems. High-reliability organizations (HRO) move toward mindfulness and are preoccupied with failure. They treat any mishap as a symptom that there is an issue with the system.

## Conclusion

The OSH profession is evolving, as several emerging trends are the focal point for many health and safety strategies and key initiatives. There are many lessons learned from the past and still a considerable amount of work that needs to occur to move the OSH profession forward. This chapter focused on four key topics. Each topic is complex, and additional research is necessary to advance the understanding and application to improve occupational health and safety. Serious injury and fatality prevention is increasingly a focal point for many health and safety processes. Although safety culture is frequently a topic at safety conferences, there is still much to learn in this area. Maturity models provide companies an opportunity to deploy a consistent and standard approach for operational excellence. Finally, systems thinking is a key area that needs understanding for exemplary safety performance.

## Questions

1. Why are incident precursors the key to addressing serious incidents and fatalities?
2. Why is evaluating a company's organizational culture important to improving safety culture?
3. Is a maturity model a leading or lagging indicator? Explain.
4. Are traditional safety management approaches appropriate for contributing to a world-class safety process?
5. Is Total Quality Safety Management equivalent to a behavior-based safety process?

## References


Adams, E. (1995). *Total Quality Safety Management.* Des Plaines, IL: ASSP.

Allison, W. W. (2006). "Motivation: Industry's Challenge." *Professional Safety* 51(5): 60–63. Reprinted from June 1972.

Blumenfeld, Y. (Ed.). (1999). *Scanning the Future: 20 Eminent Thinkers on the World of Tomorrow.* London: Thames & Hudson, Ltd.

Campbell Institute. (2014). "High Consequences Events, Proactive Interventions, and the Appetite for Risk." San Diego.

Champy, J. (1996). *Reengineering Management: The Mandate for New Leadership.* New York: HarperBusiness.

Deming, W. E. (1994). *The New Economics: For Industry, Government, Education* (2nd ed.). Cambridge, MA: The MIT Press.

Dorner, D. (1996). *The Logic of Failure: Recognizing and Avoiding Error in Complex Situations.* New York: Metropolitan Books.

Duncan, C. (2012). *The Zero Index: A Path to Sustainable Safety Excellence.* Ojai, CA: Behavioral Science Technology.

Heinrich, H. W. (1959). *Industrial Accident Prevention* (4th ed.). New York: McGraw-Hill.

Hill, D. C. (2006). "Time to Transform?: Assessing the Future of the SH&E Profession." *Professional Safety* (December): 18–26. Reprinted from November 2002.

Hollnagel, E. (2014). *Safety-1 and Safety-2: The Past and Future of Safety Management.* Burlington, VA: Ashgate Publishing.

Indiana University of Pennsylvania (IUP). (2014). "Fatality Prevention in the Workplace." Pittsburgh, PA.

Johnson Controls International PLC. (2017). *Johnson Controls Manufacturing System.* Milwaukee, WI: Johnson Controls.

Krause, T., and J. Hidley. (1990). *The Behavior-based Safety Process.* New York: Van Nostrand Reinhold.

Loud, J. (2016). "Major Risk: Moving from Symptoms to Systems Thinking." *Professional Safety* (October): 50–56.

Manuele, F. A. (2014). *Advanced Safety Management Focusing on Z10 and Serious Injury Prevention.* Hoboken, NJ: John Wiley & Sons, Inc.

Manuele, F. A. (2002). *Heinrich Revisited: Truisms or Myths.* Itasca, IL: National Safety Council.

Martin, D., and A. Black. (2015). "Preventing Serious Injuries and Fatalities: Study Reveals Precursors & Paradigms." *Professional Safety* (September): 35–43.

Occupational Health and Safety Administration (OSHA). (2017). *Bureau of Labor Statistics.* Washington, DC: OSHA.

Smith, T. A. (2008). *System Accidents: Why Americans Are Injured at Work and What Can Be Done to Stop It.* Self-published.

Tarrants, W. E. (2006). "Engineering as a Foundation for Optimum Safety Success." *Professional Safety* 51(1): 52–58. Reprinted from October 1961.

Wilbanks, D. W. (2013). "Preventing Major Injuries: Observations on Theory Models & a Path Forward." *Professional Safety* (November): 52–58.

SECTION 3

# PROFESSIONAL DEVELOPMENT

# CHAPTER 14

# SAFETY, LEADERSHIP, MANAGEMENT, CULTURE

Aaron Munoz and Hailey Fulton

## Learning Objectives

After studying this chapter, readers will have a basic knowledge of:

1. Leadership roles and responsibilities in creating a safety culture
2. Management's participation in the safety culture
3. Safety's integral relationship in the process

## Key Terms

**Culture, safety, training, behavior, evolution, management**

## Abstract

This chapter describes the process that can be used to change an organization's culture from one of compliance to one of safety as an intrinsic value held by all individuals within the organization.

Safety is understood worldwide and is becoming noticed on a much larger scale. The definition of safety is "freedom from harm or danger; a state of being safe" (Merriam-Webster n.d.). There are many ways to interpret this definition. For example, at one company, safety is a large portion of the organization. Where employees are treated as more than just the typical worker, they become part of that company's family. The following chapter covers leadership, management, and how it is associated with creating the ideal safety culture.

> "If I am not for myself, who will be for me? If I am only for myself, what am I? If not now, when?"
>
> Hillel the Elder

## Introduction into a Safety Culture

A safety culture is more than just talking about ways the company can keep its employees safe. It is about acting and feeling a certain way about employees, performance levels, and production rates. Behavioral-based safety and its corresponding metrics can be used to achieve goals in safety. There is certain training and behavior individuals need to achieve those goals and get metrics to prove that the safety culture of an organization is working. We could discuss how to create another database, safety application, or website to achieve the numbers we are looking for in an employer's safety record. On the other hand, we could look at what causes those behaviors: the culture. To look at how to create the necessary environment to attain a culture where safety is intrinsic is what this chapter will address—the thing that everyone feels and how important it is in safety.

The connection between safety, leadership, and management is paramount to the organization's credibility. The characteristics of the frontline individual, managers, and top-level visionaries will achieve that organization's culture. Managers will need to identify clear direction for the organization's forward momentum and what every frontline employee needs to sustain a culture of care and concern. Leadership needs to create a vision that empowers managers. The manager then makes it a reality for the organization and for each individual to unite them into one culture. When leaders, managers, and workers align themselves together in a culture of care and concern for every individual, then safety is truly first.

There are many different management styles, including top-down or bottom-up. Top-down management style is when all processes flow from the top management and are filtered down to the front-line employees. There are advantages and disadvantages to this management style. Advantages include:

> In a top-down management style, directions, schedule, functionality and budget are defined by upper management. The project manager communicates those expectations to the project team, who are expected to carry out the plan. The primary advantage for the management team is more control. It is relatively easy to evaluate whether plans have been fulfilled. In operations where the processes and work are very well understood, the top-down management approach is workable. But if there are unknowns, it results in ambiguities and disconnects. (Martinich 2016)
>
> Disadvantages include:
>
> Executive management's failure to think through all the details of the project results in ambiguity. To resolve this ambiguity, the project team needs to submit questions and get answers, slowing down the process. Alternatively, the project team may think it understands the requirements, but interprets them differently than the executive team had intended. Again, this results in delays and rework. Another serious disadvantage is that team members feel undervalued and unheard. (Martinich 2016)

Bottom-up management style is when the frontline employees hear the overall goal, and they get to make the decisions on how to get that goal accomplished. The advantages of this management style include the following:

a. It allows the team more creativity.
b. It provides for team engagement, with everyone's involvement in the planning process.
c. The schedule is more likely to reflect the actual work required. The schedule, budget, and project plan are transparent to the team (Martinich 2016).

The disadvantages include:

a. The bottom-up approach removes a significant amount of control from the executive team.
b. A project can easily veer off in a direction that is not in alignment with the organization's goals.

Although the two different management styles both have pros and cons, a balancing act of both would be ideal in creating a safety culture. It is important that management take leadership in the way they behave so they set an example for the frontline employees. At the same time, frontline employees should have a right to say what is working and what is not working from a safety perspective because they are the people who are working out in the field.

Not only is behavior a way to measure safety within an organization but using statistics can also be helpful. Metrics, statistics (DART and TRIR), experience modification rates, safety application analytics, and the organization's plan on how to accomplish the leader's vision are all documented items for presentation on a boardroom floor. These metrics are valued as benchmarks.

Is that all that is needed? Can you truly define a company's safety through what has been measured? The statement "what can be measured can be improved" goes a long way, yet can we measure how much water a fish needs to survive? If so, how much culture does one company need?

Notice the word *behavior* was used previously, and then later it changes to *culture*. Let's not mix words. In some context they mean the same. Behavior is the way a person acts, whether it is good or bad, while culture is the beliefs of a group of individuals. An issue can also arise in an organized labor force when you mention behavior. The first thought the individual may feel is "check my contract; you cannot tell me how to behave." If you use the word *culture*, the individual can feel you are talking about a collective group, not the individual.

We will review what leaders can do to cause a clear change in the company's culture and how to gauge it. Leadership and its character can define the culture of the company. Each manager should have the willingness to follow the character set forth. *Safety* is the word overused yet so elusive and so important to a company's future, the individual, and those they leave behind.

## Leadership: Visionary, Upper Level, and Frontline

Getting safety on an intrinsic level will not be an overnight undertaking. To accomplish this, the leadership must have the ability to step back and think of the organization not as a whole or a group of units, but as *people*. They are individuals, each with hopes, dreams, and the willingness to do the right thing. "Mothers and fathers will give their children to you willingly, hoping that you will not waste their lives" (Schwarzkopf 1991). When Schwarzkopf stated this in his speech to the core of cadets, he was projecting the true meaning of safety. It is easy to use a slogan such as "safety means go home to your family safe," but it's just a slogan. For persons in that organization with hopes, dreams, and the intent to come to work that day to do the right thing, they must feel the leadership's character. That character is setting the tone for everyone in the organization. Character is what you do when no one is looking. The need for upper-level management to take on the role not only as the leader but also as the example for others to follow is paramount for a safety culture. Changing the culture and maintaining this culture is utmost. Without maintenance, extinction can take place.

Think about the Pavlov theory. Simply put, he rang the bell and fed the dog. He kept this up so that when he rang the bell, the dog would salivate before the food came. The subject "felt" the food would come, so it intrinsically started to salivate. Then, when the bell would ring but no food would arrive, and it continued with no food, salivation stopped.

Extinction. We are not dogs. We all have feelings that are complex. We all have been in areas where we had assurance made, followed for a while, and then stopped. Trust was lost, and extinction took place.

It is the visionary's responsibility to constantly connect themselves with the culture of the company. This can be done on many levels. Some examples are surveys, emails, or by getting to the front line and speaking with the individual.

The television show *Undercover Boss* is popular because it shows the care and concern a top-level individual had to get in the mix with the employees, hear how they feel, see what they do, and understand the need to have the right people in the right seats from the optics of the front line.

Upper-level managers must take that visionary's idea and make it a reality. If the owner/CEO/board/president are the visionaries, then branch managers / vice presidents need to believe in the vision the employer has toward safety, leadership, and management.

These upper-level managers will be responsible to show the frontline managers, by example through communication, rehearsal, and sincere approachability that every individual in the organization is a part of the culture. This would be an example of a top-down management style trait. The visionaries must connect back with the entire organization, and the upper-level managers will need to pause with their groups and ask how they are connecting with every individual. How do they feel? How can we do better? How can we keep this accident from happening again? When the upper level reaches out to frontline managers on a regular basis, the frontline employees feel they are fully engaged in the organization's culture.

All managers from all levels should be able to answer this question on culture: "Whom did you speak with, and what did you talk about?" This short conversation should not have a business tone. How is your day going? How was your weekend? How is your family? If this is difficult for any level in the organization's management, two things need to take place: train through practice and decide on the right people in the right seats. At this point, leaders need to decide if managers "get it." Competencies can be trained, and character can be developed. If character development is beyond control, the question of keeping the employee in the organization must be addressed. Your organization needs to develop its culture, and if an individual will not add to this culture, ask, "Is this the right person for that position?"

Frontline managers are in direct contact with the frontline employees. The frontline employees are the ones who are most at risk for injury, incidents, or other liabilities to the organization (profitability, production, and quality). Frontline managers are responsible for the employee's safety, production, and quality. If the frontline manager is unwilling to carry the message to the frontline employees, all is lost. Managers are most responsible for the execution of the employer's business, credibility, and future sales. These frontline managers have a key role in the future of the company, not only in terms of culture but also in the company's financial status.

One of the largest risks in business is the frontline employee and his frontline manager, who is his direct, day-to-day contact with the organization. This is where communication becomes important between the upper management and the frontline employees. The frontline employees should feel comfortable to be able to bring up their concerns to upper management. Upper management should then take into consideration the request of the employees. This is where some companies involve safety committees. Safety committees are a group within the company made up of management, frontline employees, and normally a safety person. A safety committee should be representative of the company as a whole. Each meeting should consist of the group bringing up issues and trying to solve problems so that the company and frontline employees are happy with the resolution. Although safety committees are used to talk about issues, they can also talk about the positives the company has.

This takes a lot of commitment from not only our managers but also the owners of the company to buy into this safety culture. So how do we get this level of commitment? Through care and concern communicated honestly at all levels.

## Management

The health and safety management system is a formalized approach to health and safety management using a framework that aids the identification and control of safety and health risks (McKinnon 2013). One key factor in a safety culture is management leadership. McKinnon states that it is estimated that 15 percent of a company's problems can be controlled by the employees, while 85 percent can be controlled by the management.

If a frontline employee has a negative attitude toward safety, he or she might say, "Those managers must just sit around all day drinking coffee and going to meetings while we do all the work!" This is not a good attitude toward management or safety. However, if the management style is not setting an example, then the frontline employees may have a right to feel this way. The company must make sure its employees are not feeling this way. To measure the attitude of the employees, a survey could be sent out to make sure they feel management is doing what is expected of them. Employees get evaluated yearly, and so should management.

Another way management can make sure employees are taking the culture seriously is through training. For example, a safety-training center was built in Augusta, Maine. This facility has classrooms for safety training, including fall protection, confined spaces, forklift operation, scaffolding, electrical hazards, ergonomics, and ladder safety. This way, workers can get hands-on training experience, making them feel the company cares for workers and their safety. It is also possible to use willing employees to administer segments of the training.

Although it is good to have safety training courses, it is always good to check in with the morale of the employees when thinking about safety. This could be done through a survey or even just asking a simple question. If the employees do not feel like the company is making safety a priority, the company could take every employee that is responsible for leading another employee through a level of training in safety culture development. This development will take several years and must involve commitment from all levels of management.

## Definition

Definition involves the executive level describing what the vision of that company's safety culture looks like. Many third-party companies can assist, and the best way is to involve someone the executives trust. Skybrary states that a safety culture is "the way safety is perceived, valued and prioritized in an organization. It reflects the real commitment to safety at all levels in the organization" (Skybrary n.d.).

If the organization starts every morning with safety discussions and every meeting with safety discussions and insists all levels do the same, then it is reality, not just perception. This creates the value necessary to have the culture felt at all levels. There will be cynics and pockets of resistance in the organization. However, when the executive branch practices this definition, follows it, and demands the same at all levels, then the culture starts.

## Implementation

Here we start with training. Bringing in employees who assign work to other employees will filter who needs to be in attendance. The first year of training will start by discussing what a safety culture means to every individual, explaining the definition, and performing some activities. Each employee may have different visions of what the culture should look like. Keep the information listed.

An exercise in creating the company's integral analysis done by employees together at all levels (possibly the safety committee) can be another starting point. This analysis can be developed, used to grow the company's culture, and revisited annually to see if there are improvements of the company's cultural setbacks. Training meetings should not have more than fifty in attendance per group and last no more than six hours. These meetings should be led by at least two individuals who have full understanding of the company's vision and *must* be dynamic speakers. Here it is best to hire a third party. Caution needs to be taken when using someone who cannot convey the intended feeling of the meeting because otherwise it will be a waste of time. Third parties can be professionals in the field of bringing vision to the front line. Third parties can also have new ways of presentation, using innovative techniques. Visionaries must attend the speaker's engagement prior to hiring them to see if they will "fit" the suggested implementation training. All employees who attend should walk away with a "wow" feeling. You have made a great start if the employees walk out feeling that not only will they start to make a difference in the way they do daily activities, but they will also change how they view daily activities toward safety at home.

The company has a challenge to keep the momentum moving in this first year. Start all meetings with quick safety moments and discussions and describing good acts that have taken place. The employees should take this change on with great acceptance. When employees feel they are being empowered with care and concern for their frontline workers, then they will have great ideas. Safety committees, improvements in design, and work-flow improvements can be used to rally around the safety culture development. Done right and once the momentum starts, this can be one of the best years for an organization.

## Reconnecting

There must be a system in place to connect with the organization. Ask what all employees concerns are. Getting feedback, good or bad, empowers everyone as part of the cultural solution, and they fully engage with the organization's success. Employees are then able to share their input indirectly with the executive leaders and feel that their voice is heard. When they feel like they are part of the team, individuals will do more for the team than they will do for themselves. Once this is in place, the sky is the limit.

Bringing in new operations, policies, and procedures can be a joy rather than a chore. The team reviews the process and comments and makes improvements where necessary. The naysayers will be overturned by the employees that are fully engaged. Now you are ready for the next process—that is, to move into the action phase.

### Action phase

Have you ever wondered what characteristics make a great worker? Being on time, thinking ahead, understanding the task and thinking of alternative methods, acting safer and quicker, along with many other traits. This question is very easy to answer. Think about all the places you have worked. What did you think of other workers? Everyone has an opinion here. We have all had to work with other employees who may not have been in the right seat at their place of employment. Maybe they were unhappy with their task, unsatisfied with pay or the environment, or felt underutilized. This usually ends with the employee leaving or worse: staying and not being fully engaged. Without full engagement in a task, the possibility of an incident rises.

If you have an employee with great characteristics, then think about what sustains them. Is it a question of nature verses nurture? Is it some value they bring from their upbringing or something they are accustomed to due to their surroundings? Is it things like feeling appreciated, valued, well paid, and considered a part of the team, recognized when things go well, or not being singled out when things go wrong? Most of the things that sustain the characteristics come from the leader. Think back on some leaders that made an impact on your life; is it a parent, coach, or a supervisor whom one may try to emulate throughout their career? A parent, coach, a teacher, or supervisor can do, act, or say something that can carry an impact throughout a person's life while never understanding the meaning or difference they have brought to that person's life.

If we have looked at what characteristics a great worker has and what sustains them, then what characteristics make a great leader? A great leader is one who is able to coach, mentor, and teach the employee and who is fair but firm, knowledgeable, competent, confident, and an example for the employees. A leader is one who leads by example. All these things can circle back to the leader's character.

What defines character? Is it one who does the right thing, even when no one is looking? If a leader does this, his followers will be willing to follow him into any endeavor needed to complete the mission. Machiavelli (*The Prince*) took this down to three reasons why people follow a leader: fear, money, and love. It is easy to use fear as a motivator. Will it have any lasting impact on a person other than they will leave as soon as possible? Or, in a workplace, are their minds somewhere other than the task at hand, like worrying about getting fired? Money is a great motivator. The only problem here is if someone offers more money, and money is their motivator, they are gone, and with that type of characteristic, think about the damage they could do while leaving or what they take to the next employer. Finally, there is love. Employees who truly love what they are doing and can go home at night with the feeling they were happy with the day will look forward to the next day. They are actually happy with their job. Yes, this is possible.

### Evolution

Evolution in your culture is pivotal for the organization's future. New ideas, new programs, and building and maintaining trust in an organization during evolution can either add to or diminish the company's culture. In every phase, we are doing something most companies overlook, which is going beyond what is status quo.

If we think about how we choose our friends—not acquaintances but true friends—we think about trust. You see their actions even when they think you are not looking. You trust them. It is the same at work. Even if the employees think, "Oh boy, another safety thing," at least they feel, internally, that the organization cares so much that they try. Then they will pass this feeling along, discussing the reasons, pro and con, for the new programs or ideas. Communication continues, trust continues, and safety becomes intrinsic.

## Safety

The relationship between safety, management, and leadership should start to become clear. Does the operations visionary group think of the frontline workers as individuals or just a workforce? As a frontline worker, the feeling of being either a number or an individual is one constant. Individuals will feel if the intent to count them as individuals is real or not. If a manager is just going through the motions because the visionaries have brought the program in, the employee can recognize this. Then the worker thinks, "Why should I buy in if they do not believe it?" The secret to safety is that it cannot be faked at any level.

Safety is not something you can buy, rent, or reinforce with a big stick. It is something the individual feels internally. It is intrinsic. I am safe; therefore, I am. This is not a new concept. Maslow's hierarchy of needs has been referred to in many ways. It starts with physiological needs of air, water, food. Such are all needs that keep us alive. The next step up is safety, and then love/belonging, esteem, and finally self-actualization. These are roadmaps we follow in life, whether we follow them consciously or subconsciously. However, other psychological motivators can exist. Only the individual knows what they are.

When managers and leaders are trained to understand the aspects of motivational needs, psychological needs, and virtues and go beyond the individual's surface, then the reason each individual has for safety becomes intrinsic. Think about Erickson's eight stages of psychological development (Erickson 1950). From the first stage of zero- to one-year-old, the infant builds on the virtue of hope. The psychological crisis that may arise is basic trust versus mistrust. Can I trust the world? Do I feel abandoned? If you can connect this with the workforce, you may have started to understand the need to grow safety intrinsically. Erickson's belief is we grow through many stages in life, each connected with different age groups, which can explain a lot in safety of our workforce. It can also explain how individuals can feel about safety. Erickson's eighth stage, ego integrity versus despair , compares the feeling of having done everything you can versus leaving something undone or regretful. If you have the former in your safety culture, you can look in the mirror and be happy.

The younger workforce can have issues that are much different from the seasoned workforce's. To manage this young workforce, understanding their needs and what motivates them is key. Their needs, intelligence, and ways and means as they gain knowledge have grown with the technological forefront. Using these skills to address them in ways they can understand and buy into will assimilate them into the company's culture sooner rather than later. In the past we could say, "Jump," and the response was, "How high?" Now, if you say, "Jump," the question is "Why?" With information at our fingertips, we need to be prepared to answer the why but also to be able to reach out and ask them to assist in the why.

You may be asking yourself, "What does all this jargon have to do with safety?" Safety includes task planning, task training, implementing, monitoring, auditing, rating, evaluating locally as well as nationally, along with a great number of other ways to improve auditing and benchmarking. Evaluating the organization locally as well as nationally will show the number of ways the organization improves in safety.

## Conclusion

What was discussed in this chapter was meant to provide you an insight into what really goes beyond the obvious. It is very easy to fill out a form and show how the frontline, injured employee made the error that lead to the incident. The challenge is to step back and ask how what occurred could be prevented from happening again. Once the culture has evolved in gauging the effectiveness , more can be done by examining the litigation rates and the time lag in reporting. Short lag time in reporting shows that employees demonstrate their true feelings and that they are not afraid to speak up and report quickly. Low litigation rates show minimal legal events tied to injuries and consequently demonstrate employees are happy. Once the culture has evolved, look an employee in the eye and ask how things are going. You will be able to gauge the culture or get a better sense of the place.

## Questions

1. In a company establishing a safety culture, what should be the first question a manager should be asking during a safety audit?
2. How do you define character?
3. Discuss two management styles.
4. Discuss one theory from the chapter.
5. Sum the chapter up in one word.

## References

Erickson, E.H. (1950). *Childhood and Society*. New York: Norton.

Martinich, L. (2016). "Balancing Top-Down and Bottom-Up Management." *IEEE Engineering Management Review* 44(2).

McKinnon, R. (2013). *Changing the Workplace Safety Culture*. Boca Raton, FL: CRC Press.

Merriam-Webster. (n.d.) Safety. Accessed August 12, 2016. http://www.merriam-webster.com/dictionary/safety.

Schwarzkopf, N. (1991). Speech to West Point Corp of Cadets, Part 2. https://www.youtube.com/watch?v=mAIhfw9bY5U.

Skybrary. (n.d.). Safety Culture. Accessed March 30, 2018. https://www.skybrary.aero/index.php/Safety_Culture.

CHAPTER 15

# PROJECT PLANNING AND EXECUTION

Stephanie Helgerman and Mary Hoffman-Pancake

## Learning Objectives

After studying this chapter, the reader will be able to:

1. Explain how applying project management as a business tool can improve business outcomes
2. Identify and describe the four fundamental processes of successful project implementation
3. Describe the five key concepts for project success
4. Define and discuss the steps of preparing a project plan
5. Using the sample template provided, prepare a basic project plan

## Key Terms

**Project, project manager, risk management, scope, stakeholder, time-phased budget, work breakdown structure**

## Abstract

Successful companies have come to recognize the importance of project management because of its positive impact on profitability and operational efficiency in the continually changing environment to compete globally. Project management is a disciplined approach with established processes and, when applied consistently, improves the likelihood of successful outcomes. This approach adds value to the business in meeting strategic objectives within schedule, budget, and quality constraints. Project management can be applied across many business functions, including occupational safety and health (OSH). Successful execution of project management includes several business functions working together to complete a project using the project management framework.

The fundamental processes of a successful project include initiation and planning, execution, monitoring and control, and completion. In addition to these established processes, there are key concepts pertinent throughout the life of a project. The concepts of scope, time management, fiscal planning and control, communications, and risk management are critical to the success of a project.

## Introduction

Project management is an applied business skill OSH professionals will benefit from being familiar with and being prepared to use. Most tasks performed at work are conducted in some organized, structured manner. Regardless of how simple or complex, the steps taken to complete a task can be described within the construct of project management. Understanding and applying the concepts and framework of project management facilitates each task's successful completion, even routine tasks that are not a part of a formal project. Within the realm of occupational safety and health, OSH practitioners may perform these tasks independently, as a part of a project team, or as a project manager.

The dictionary definition (multiple sources combined) of a project is planned work or a task with a specific purpose that requires effort over a period of time. The Project Management Institute, in the Project Management Body of Knowledge (PMBOK Guide 2013), defines a project as "a temporary endeavor to create a unique product, service or result . . . has a definite beginning and end . . . and creates a lasting outcome." This definition helps to distinguish a project from ongoing work, tasks that repeat, or work conducted according to already-defined procedures.

Many project management experts have written about how project management is both a science and an art. The science aspect involves the tools and techniques applied to managing a project throughout the project life cycle, as well as the technical and analytical skills to evaluate information and make decisions. Just as important is the art, or soft skills, of managing a project. The project manager is a leader, integrating resources from across the organization to complete the project. This requires being a liaison between functional management and stakeholders. The art of effective communication, negotiation, relationship management, conflict resolution, influencing, and team building is crucial to successful project management. Understanding the corporate culture is also important in the style of project management implemented within an organization. These soft skills are critical in managing project scope, schedule, budget, and risk.

The art of effective communication, negotiation, relationship management, conflict resolution, influencing, and team building is crucial to successful project management.

## Project Management Overview

### Fundamental processes of successful project management

Project management is a business process that applies a disciplined approach to completing projects. This approach is applicable across a broad spectrum of industries and can be used for projects in most, if not all, aspects of business. The process can be broken down into four phases. This section describes each of the four phases with basic considerations for the understanding of each phase and successful application. The four phases are shown in figure 15.1.

**Table 15.1** Comparison of project and ongoing work

| Project | Ongoing work |
|---|---|
| Develop a new OSH compliance program | Conduct respirator fit testing |
| Install a new process/supply tank | Pre-job or pre-task planning |
| Develop a new training program | Periodic delivery of established training |
| Set up a new safety committee for a division with multiple locations | Conduct a safety committee meeting |

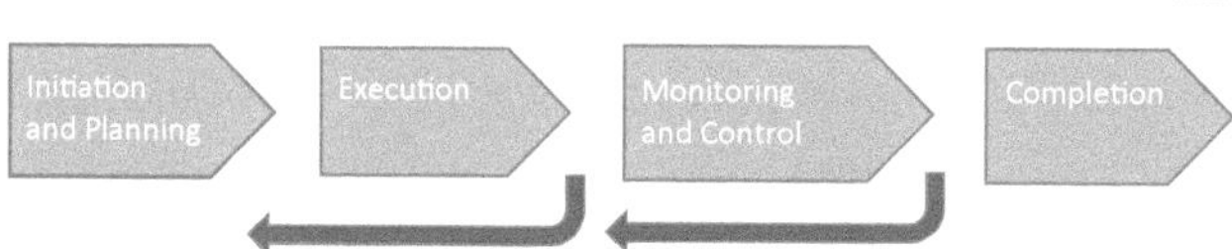


Figure 15.1
Phases of a project

Although depicted linearly, like so many other business processes, these phases are not necessarily executed in a linear manner. Rather, the steps are iterative, with overlap and repetition of phases common. Movement back and forth between phases may be necessary for successful accomplishment of project objectives. Each phase has inputs (information necessary to complete the current task) and outputs or products. Depending on the scope and size of a project, there may be subprojects conducted within a larger project or program.

## First Phase: Project Initiation and Project Planning

Initiation is just what one would assume: the beginning of a project. There is *something* that needs to be done, something not already established, or something that is a significant change from what does exist (table 15.1). Making the decision to call this new work a project brings formal recognition to the need and encourages organizational support. It also recognizes the value in applying a disciplined approach to conducting the work to help ensure success. Depending on the reference, initiation and planning may be identified as separate phases. They are combined here, as the outputs from both are necessary before work on a project can begin. Project initiation and planning includes the following:

- define the project;
- authorize the project;
- define the scope of the project;
- identify project stakeholders;
- define project objectives;
- establish outcomes with criteria for successful project completion; and
- Identify resources necessary to conduct project activities.

The project definition is a high-level description of the project. It is a statement of the basic business need from which a project emerges with an approach to meet the need. Initially, it does not need to be in depth. The development of the scope and objectives is built around the initial definition. Although still somewhat conceptual at this point, the discussion driving the business decision to move forward with a project should consider feasibility and alternatives before a final commitment is made to move forward on the project. OSH input is often critical during this phase.

Consider the example of installing a new process tank in table 15.1. There are several OSH considerations in tank selection, installation, operation and ongoing maintenance. Will the tank contain hazardous materials? Is the tank connected to the process system, or will it be manually filled and emptied? What are the tank design criteria to ensure containment? Is it above or below ground, and will it be inside or outside? Will it be necessary to monitor liquid levels? What kinds of valves are necessary? Is the tank used in a process under the requirements of OSHA Process Safety Management (PSM)? Is PSM change management required? Will contractors be used for the installation? Are any new permits required? Receiving a new permit might be a subproject within the larger project. The list of questions to define the OSH requirements can go on! It is provided to illustrate how OSH input affects the project. Answers to these and many other OSH questions will drive decisions as the project moves forward. (Note: we'll periodically return to this example as we discuss the project management process to give substance to the OSH input and involvement.)

Project authorization is the approval to conduct the project after the business strategic fit and return on investment (ROI) have been justified. It is the commitment to the project on behalf of the organization and provides the authority to proceed with the necessary funding. It provides a formal recognition of the work on behalf of management.

Refer to the OSH questions for tank installation. The answers will impact schedule and project cost and directly affect the ROI.

Project scoping takes the high-level project definition and begins to further develop and refine and build a more detailed definition of the project. Project scope is essential to project planning and is discussed in detail later in the "Key Concepts" section.

Project stakeholders are entities with a vested interest in successful project completion. They are most often recognized as the customer for whom the project is undertaken, but stakeholders represent any part of the business that is impacted by the project. This may include management, OSH, finance, and quality, among others. The members of the project team are also stakeholders as they, too, have a vested interest in success! Defining the scope and objectives are collaborative processes between the stakeholders and the project team. Ensuring the needs of the stakeholders are fully understood so those needs can be met within the project deliverables is a key factor of project success. The communication between the project team and stakeholders is critical to success during all phases of the project and discussed further in the "Key Concepts" section.

Project objectives are built around the final scope. The objectives are the specific and detailed goal(s), outcomes, products, or services of the project. The scope and objectives combined lead to the development of the detailed project plan. It is important to establish outcomes that clearly define successful project completion. A good scope statement and well-defined objectives are used to identify the measurable outcomes/deliverables of the project. The outcomes should include acceptance criteria to verify project completion by the stakeholders. Again, considering the tank installation example, what essential tank attributes are necessary from an OSH perspective? These need to be included in the acceptance criteria. If specific valves are required, were these specific valves ordered and installed? Do they operate as intended?

Once the project objectives and outcomes are defined, a list of project resources is developed. The project manager (PM) is the first key personnel resource. Ideally the PM is identified early in the initiation phase to ensure involvement in developing scope and objectives and identifying resources. The PM has overall responsibility for managing all the resources to deliver the project outcomes. Some technical knowledge is appropriate for the PM, but perhaps more important are the skills necessary to manage the project team and other project resources. This discussion about the roles and responsibilities of the PM here is brief and fairly high level in nature. But in fact, especially on large, complex projects, the importance of this role cannot be overstated. The PM role in business processes has evolved over the years into a recognized specialty that has a rigorous certification, culminating in recognition as a Project Management Professional (PMP Examination Content Outline 2015).

The size and scope of the project will influence the size of the project team. The project team members are selected based on a mix of the technical knowledge, experience, and business skills necessary to accomplish project objectives. If you are on a site with a team of OSH professionals then, consideration of the training and experience of each member of the OSH team matched to the project objectives will influence selecting who will be assigned to the project. People are not the only project resources; equipment, materials, facilities, and software are some of the other resources needed to execute a project.

The project plan is prepared with milestones and key decision points, which outline the actions, activities, resources, budget, and schedule to carry out the project. Internal processes and requirements that will be used to conduct the work are identified according to organization procedures. With the project plan complete and the project team selected, the next phase is project execution. A sample project plan template is shown at the end of this chapter.

## Second Phase: Project Execution

Project execution is, quite simply stated, successful use of project resources to conduct activities to complete the project according to the scope and objectives as defined during the initiation and planning phase. The PM has responsibility for managing the team and the project resources for successful execution and performance according to the project plan. This role is key in keeping the project on schedule and ensuring the project meets stakeholders' expectations. Time management, budgetary control, and communications are key elements of successful project execution and are discussed further in "Key Concepts of Project Management."

The execution phase is where the project team will conduct the work defined in the plan. This may include

- collecting necessary information;
- procuring materials;
- developing and testing requirements;
- validating assumptions;
- identifying processes and procedures to ensure product robustness and sustainability;
- verifying performance; and
- making modifications to ultimately achieve the desired results.

The breadth and depth of project execution is dependent on the size and complexity of the project.

### Third Phase: Project Monitoring and Control

Project controls are processes and tools used to monitor and control the project during the execution phase. Use of an organized approach provides the discipline of periodic monitoring against the plan to ensure activities are being executed according to defined standards. Controls are used when monitoring identifies interim results that are not according to the plan. For example, a cost or schedule variance of ±10 percent from the baseline is an indication of potential issues that may need to be addressed. Issues, when not acknowledged and addressed, can result in delays, unintentional scope change, not meeting project objectives, need for additional resources, and overlooking information that may require changes to the project plan. In extreme cases, project redesign may result.

Controls and monitoring techniques are selectively chosen depending on the portion of the project they are focused on. For example, the project manager should monitor the budget to analyze if spending is according to plan (from both a technical performance and schedule perspective) and determine if the budget is adequate or if additional budgetary resources are necessary. Some replanning may become necessary to complete the project.

Returning to the tank installation example, the OSH professional should verify the safety training of the workers performing the installation. Verify equipment that has been specified with safety requirements is what was received and installed. Verify the equipment is working as intended. Ensure all information has been received from the equipment manufacturer to ensure proper installation, operation, and ongoing maintenance.

### Fourth Phase: Project Completion

Project completion is the delivery of the agreed-upon project deliverables. This phase may also include training to help ensure a successful handoff from the project team to the owner of the project deliverables. Completion activities should also include closeout of project activities and archival of project records. It may also be appropriate to conduct a project review and identify lessons learned that can be applied to improve future projects.

## Key Concepts of Project Management

There are key concepts of project management that are applicable throughout all phases of a project and should be scaled to the project complexity and size. The PMBOK Guide describes ten knowledge areas (concepts); however, in this chapter, five concepts are highlighted and, in some cases, integrated for discussion purposes. Although quality is not discussed as a separate concept, it is expected that quality standards are applied throughout the lifecycle of a project, as stakeholders require quality results. Applicable quality standards are dependent on corporate and industry requirements.

### Scope

Project scope encompasses all the work that is required to successfully deliver the product, service, or result of the project. It must be thoroughly defined to be able to identify all the tasks, resources, timelines, and budget needed to complete the project. It is the basis for all project planning and outcomes. Therefore, the scope must be very clear and unambiguous with stakeholders' buy-in to ensure expectations are met.

Scope definition is part of the project planning process and is written after requirements for the product, service, or project results are defined. To define requirements, the project manager works with the stakeholders—for example, executive management, functional/operational managers, and customers—as well as subject matter experts in technical, business,

> Project scope is the basis for all project planning and outcomes. It should be clear and unambiguous to ensure stakeholders' expectations are met.

regulatory, quality, legal, and safety areas. Gathering requirements may be conducted through interviews, focus groups, workshops, surveys, or a combination of methods. It is critical that buy-in is reached among stakeholders to achieve a successful project outcome. From requirements, scope is defined. Scope defines the expected outcomes of the project. It includes the deliverables, along with acceptance criteria, assumptions, and constraints in achieving the end result.

The next step is to create a work breakdown structure (WBS), which identifies discrete activities to perform the work defined in the scope. The project team, with input from subject matter experts, defines the activities. The WBS may be organized by phases, deliverables, or functional areas. The top level WBS elements are typically deliverable oriented, whereas the lower level elements are activity oriented. Table 15.2 illustrates that the WBS for a tank installation project can be created by either functional area or by engineering phase.

During the project, scope may change based on progress, results, timeline, or funds available. The scope

**Table 15.2** Work breakdown structure examples

| Work Breakdown Structure by Functional Area | Work Breakdown Structure by Engineering Phase |
|---|---|
| 1. Tank Installation<br>1.1. Site<br>1.1.1. Foundation<br>1.1.2. Substructure<br>1.1.3. Access and control<br>1.2. Equipment<br>1.2.1. Tank<br>1.2.2. Pipes<br>1.2.3. Valves<br>1.2.4. Fittings<br>1.2.5. Pumps<br>1.2.6. Controls<br>1.3. Utilities<br>1.3.1. Plumbing<br>1.3.2. Electrical<br>1.3.3. HVAC<br>1.4. Chemicals | 1. Tank Installation<br>1.1. System design<br>1.2. Facilities preparation<br>1.3. Equipment integration<br>1.4. System test and evaluation<br>1.5. Installation and checkout<br>1.6. Operations and maintenance documentation |

defined during the planning process is the baseline for the project budget and schedule. It is imperative that the project remain within the defined scope or that stakeholders are involved in any scope changes and the resulting impacts. At the end of the project, the customer validates the scope by acceptance of the deliverables.

### Time Management

Time management is completing the project within the timeframe established in the scope and agreed upon with the stakeholders. Scheduling is the integration of the time to complete the work breakdown activities within the sequence, duration, and dependencies of those activities with the available resources. Resources include people with the right skills, materials, equipment, facilities, subcontractors, vendors, and regulatory agencies. There are several project scheduling software tools available to help develop the schedule. It is important to understand the interdependence of the tasks and resources as this interdependence contributes to project risk and significantly impacts the project timeline and budget.

The schedule is developed with the project team with input from subject matter experts. Starting with the work breakdown structure, the team breaks the larger WBS elements into tasks and milestones. The PMBOK Guide describes the rolling wave planning method that is typically used, detailing the near-term tasks with greater accuracy than the longer-term tasks. The schedule is regularly reviewed, checked against the plan, and updated as needed. As longer-term tasks approach, they are planned in finer detail and with greater accuracy.

Activities and milestones are identified in the schedule. Activities have a duration, whereas milestones are specific dates by which a task or deliverable is complete. It is important to understand and link activity dependencies, as those dependencies determine the critical path. The critical path determines the minimum time to complete a project. The dependencies help understand flexibility in the schedule so that corrective action and replanning can occur as the project is monitored and controlled to successfully complete the project.

### Fiscal Planning and Control

Management of costs includes estimating, budgeting, and funding for the resources needed to successfully complete the project. The fiscal planning is derived from the scope, WBS, and schedule. Corporate policies and procedures will be followed in developing the project cost accounting since companies may have different accounting methods for what is included in the project budget versus the corporate budget.

A basis of estimate (BOE) documents how the project estimate was established. It includes all the labor, material, travel, subcontractor/vendor, equipment, and supplies planned. The rationale for the estimate should be based on similar projects completed in the past or input from subject matter experts with the project team. A BOE is developed for each WBS element and includes the assumptions used in developing the estimate. For example, if travel is planned, then the number of trips, persons, days with the origin, destination, and purpose should be included in the BOE. Assumptions should address risks and include the associated contingency funds.

> It is important to understand the interdependence of tasks and resources, as it contributes to project risk and significantly impacts the project timeline and budget.

A time-phased budget is developed using the cost estimate and schedule. This enables the project manager to monitor progress of the project. Earned value management is a method to measure progress by monitoring cost, schedule, and technical performance simultaneously. This integrated method facilitates variance analysis of project performance and provides guidance for corrective action and replanning, if necessary. Cost accounts are established to manage and control project costs and are based on the lowest level of the WBS to which the PM needs to manage. The PM provides work authorization to the project team to use the cost accounts and expend funds within the scheduled period of performance for that WBS. Table 15.3 is an example of cost account plan for the tank installation with the cost and schedule variance at a point in time for the project.

**Table 15.3** Variance analysis of cost accounts

| Tank Installation WBS | Cost Account Number | Budgeted Cost for Work Scheduled | Budgeted Cost for Work Performed | Actual Cost for Work Performed | Schedule Variance | Cost Variance |
|---|---|---|---|---|---|---|
| 1.1 System design | 001 | $25,000 | $20.000 | $30,000 | ($5,000) | ($10,000) |
| 1.2 Facilities preparation | 002 | $20.000 | $20.000 | $30,000 | $0 | ($10,000) |
| 1.3 Equipment integration | 003 | $15,000 | $15,000 | $10,000 | $0 | $5,000 |
| 1.4 System test and evaluation | 004 | $10.000 | $8,000 | $11,000 | ($2,000) | ($3,000) |
| 1.5 Installation and checkout | 005 | $5,000 | $3,000 | $3,000 | ($2,000) | $0 |
| 1.6 Operations & maintenance documentation | 006 | $5,000 | $6,000 | $4,000 | $1,000 | $2,000 |
| Total | | $80,000 | $72,000 | $88,000 | ($8,000) | ($16,000) |

Procurement of services, equipment, or materials involves contracts or agreements for delivery in support of project activities. First, an evaluation of whether the team can do this work themselves or purchase it from an external source is conducted. This involves an evaluation of suppliers. The PM should work with the contracting/procurement officer to evaluate, select, and put a contract/agreement in place with the supplier.

## Communications

Communication is among the most important skills of a project manager since the project manager spends the majority of his/her time communicating. Communications cross over all phases and knowledge areas of a project. There are communication exchanges that occur internally within the project team as well as exchanges externally with stakeholders. Formal reports and presentations to stakeholders may be required, in addition to routine or less formal correspondence such as emails and project status meetings.

A communications plan is very useful as it outlines the flow, control, and methods of communication based on the roles and responsibilities documented in the project plan. It is not only important to keep the team informed of project status, issues, and vision, but stakeholder communication is extremely important to the success and acceptance of the project outcome. The project manager must understand the role and level of interest each stakeholder has in the project and the corresponding level of engagement in the decision-making process.

Effective communication needs to be timely, in the appropriate format, and addressed to the appropriate audience. For example, the contracting officer should be included on all contractual / agreement-related correspondence. Formal correspondence to the customer should accompany a deliverable. A project portal is a collaboration tool that enables efficient access to team members and stakeholders for project information, such as schedule, action log, issues, reports, meetings minutes, and other key documents.

Many projects have a virtual team, that is, team members in different locations. There are many issues for the project manager to consider when managing a virtual team. Scheduling teleconferences and video teleconferences provide a way for team members to hear and see each other, but scheduling a time can be challenging if team members are in different time zones. The project manager needs to actively engage all team members for productive meetings, as it is easy for team members to get distracted or multitask during a teleconference.

### Risk Management

Managing risk on projects is analogous to managing safety risks. Risks must first be identified and assessed; then a mitigation plan is put in place to control the risks. Unmitigated risks impact the scope, schedule, cost, and quality of the project output. The project manager needs to proactively manage risks on a continuing basis. A risk assessment should encompass all areas of the project: technical, programmatic, organizational, and external sources. Examples of project risks are listed in table 15.4.

Risk identification can be accomplished in a variety of ways, such as brainstorming with the project team and subject matter experts to create a list of potential risks. The project team, subject matter experts, and stakeholders can participate or be interviewed for input. An analysis is conducted as part of the process, developing and using a probability-versus-impact matrix as the risk register to manage the risks. This is analogous to a failure modes, effects, and criticality analysis probability versus severity-of-consequences matrix.

The budget needs to account for these risks. For known risks, a contingency reserve is budgeted. The project should also have a management reserve held for unknown risks. The management reserve is held in a cost account managed by the PM and allocated only as necessary to resolve the risks.

## Reflection

Project management is relevant to all areas of business, including OSH. As the PM, team member, or corporate stakeholder, OSH professionals should understand project management; this disciplined approach has a positive impact on the organization and its processes and is able to contribute to the success of the project. OSH specialists are often tasked to lead safety initiatives. As project managers of these business initiatives, being able to meet the objectives within schedule, budget, and quality constraints is critical to the successful implementation of OSH programs. The OSH subject matter expert on a project team

**Table 15.4** Examples of project risks

| Technical | Programmatic | Organizational | External |
|---|---|---|---|
| Requirements<br>Specifications<br>Technology<br>Quality | Communications<br>Stakeholders<br>Scope<br>Budget<br>Schedule | Resources<br>Prioritization<br>Occupational safety and health<br>Corporate culture | Regulatory<br>Market<br>Suppliers |

must understand the elements of project management to be able to contribute to the planning, execution, monitoring, and completion of the safety and health tasks and the interaction of those tasks with other project disciplines.

As a corporate stakeholder, it is the responsibility of OSH leadership to ensure the project is conducted in a safe manner. OSH management should work with the PM throughout all phases of the project to ensure compliance with regulatory requirements and safety procedures and conduct necessary training or medical surveillance of team members. Safety must be integrated into the project lifecycle for the safety of all engaged in the work but also to recognize safety issues that lead to risks that negatively impact the scope, schedule, and budget. OSH professionals should be key stakeholders and engaged throughout all phases to ensure a successful and safe project delivery.

## Questions

1. Provide examples of project risks and potential mitigations.
2. Explain the purpose of a work breakdown structure and how it is used in planning and managing a project.
3. Explain what the consequences could be when OSH is not included from the beginning when a new project is being considered.
4. Explain why application of project management concepts would be beneficial when beginning a new safety initiative.
5. Identify the key relationships an OSH professional should have to participate successfully in a project.

## References

Cleland, D. I. (2007). *Project Management—Strategic Design and Implementation*. New York: McGraw-Hill.

Kerzner, H. (2000). *Applied Project Management—Best Practices on Implementation*. New York: John Wiley and Sons.

Project Management Institute. (2015). *Project Management Professional (PMP) Examination Content Outline*. Newtown Square, PA: Project Management Institute.

Project Management Institute. (2013). *A Guide to the Project Management Body of Knowledge (PMBOK® Guide)* (5th ed.). Newtown Square, PA: Project Management Institute.

## Project Plan Template

Below is a sample project plan template. A plan with the detail filled in would be the output of the Project Initiation/Project Planning phase. This example is started for installation of new tank. Tanks are used in a variety of industries for a wide range of purposes depending on the industry. The scope is included for the purposes of providing the detail to the health and safety considerations.

### Project Plan Template*

1. Project Definition—example: installation of a new tank
2. Scope—will include installation, integration with existing system, and operational qualification and checkout
3. Objectives
4. Roles and Responsibilities
   - 4.1 Stakeholders: process operations, ES&H, Q
   - 4.2 Authorization: Plant Manager
   - 4.3 Communications: Project Manager has primary responsibility for periodic status reporting
5. Resources
   - 5.1 Budget
   - 5.2 Personnel
   - 5.3 Other
6. Work Breakdown Structure with Milestones and Schedule
7. Schedule
8. Control and Reporting
   - 8.1 Quality
   - 8.2 Reporting
   - 8.3 Project Meetings and Reviews
9. Risk Management
10. Environmental Safety and Health
    - 10.1 Safety Assessment
      - 10.1.1 Hazards of tank contents
      - 10.1.2 Safety of operations
        - 10.1.2.1 Tank filling
        - 10.1.2.2 Tank cleaning
        - 10.1.2.3 Preventive maintenance
        - 10.1.2.4 Personal protective equipment
      - 10.1.3 Safety controls
        - 10.1.3.1 Tank level indicator
        - 10.1.3.2 Auto fill shutoff
        - 10.1.3.3 Tank over-pressure sensor and controls
    - 10.2 Environmental Assessment
      - 10.2.1 Emissions evaluation—permitting
      - 10.2.2 Identification of potential waste-approval of waste stream(s)
      - 10.2.3 Spill prevention and control—update site plan
    - 10.3 Emergency Planning and Preparedness Considerations—update site plan
    - 10.4 Periodic Maintenance (PM)
      - 10.4.1 Determine PM activities and criteria for Pass/Fail
      - 10.4.2 Determine frequency of PM activities
11. Project Closeout
    - 11.1 Deliverable Acceptance
    - 11.2 Assume Operational Control—complete operator and maintenance training
    - 11.3 Archival of Project Records
    - 11.4 Lessons Learned
    - 11.5 Closeout

*Tailor to complexity of project

CHAPTER 16

# CONNECTING TO EXTERNAL SYSTEMS: INFLUENCE OF INTERNSHIP/CO-OP ON PROFESSIONAL DEVELOPMENT

Todd Loushine

## Learning Objectives

After studying this chapter, the reader will be able to:

1. Justify the need for safety internships and cooperative educational (co-op) opportunities based on current and anticipated expansion of safety and health responsibilities for the profession as well as changes in the generational experiences and attributes of college students
2. Demonstrate the connection between the development of an individual learning technique and problem-solving skills, extending this connection to the need for solving problems in the real world to further develop that learning technique
3. Explore the history of internship/cooperative education programs
4. Define the basic similarities and differences between internships and co-ops
5. Explore attributes of effective internship and co-op programs, particularly the need for an experienced mentor
6. Review search databases of safety degree programs throughout the United States

## Key Terms

**Co-op, internship, diversity, compensation, mentor, career, development**

## Abstract

The business landscape in the United States is changing, and in some cases, rapidly. Traditional (compliance-based) approaches to occupational safety and health (OSH) programs seem have reached peak effectiveness, and therefore OSH innovations are needed to achieve further improvement. At the same time, changes in the US educational system and generational differences in the student population have created a growing and serious gap in expected work experience and self-sufficiency taken for granted in previous generations. An individual's ability to learn is very similar with their ability to solve problems, and therefore the classroom experience fosters development of the learning technique, whereas fieldwork experience extends on that foundation to develop real-world problem-solving skills. Students have the best chance of early career success if they are mentored/coached by experienced OSH professionals during an internship or cooperative educational (co-op) agreement. In order to deal with changing business/OSH issues and changing student backgrounds and to ensure earlier career success, it is essential that OSH students participate in well-planned and mentored internship or co-op experiences.

## The Changing Business, Education, and Student Landscape

Change is a common theme in business and academia, but it can cause anxiety, stress, and errors when the context and magnitude of change are unknown. According to the Office of Disease Prevention and Health Promotion's "Healthy People 2020" (2014), emerging OSH challenges include:

- The workforce, like the US population at large, is becoming increasingly diverse. These demographic changes result in new safety and health issues. For example, some workers—such as racial and ethnic minorities, recent immigrants, younger and older workers, workers with genetic susceptibility, and workers with disabilities—are more likely to have increased risks of work-related diseases and injuries.
- Workplaces are rapidly evolving as jobs in the current economy continue to shift from manufacturing to services.
- Major changes are also occurring in the way work is organized. Longer hours, compressed work weeks, shift work, reduced job security, and part-time and temporary work are realities of the modern workplace and are increasingly affecting the health and lives of workers.
- New chemicals, materials, processes, and equipment that are being developed at an ever-accelerating pace pose emerging risks to occupational health.
- And finally, although improvements in occupational safety and health surveillance are ongoing, there are several emerging areas in which national data systems are not yet available or merit further research. For example, there are recognized data gaps in understanding the safety and health effects of exposure to nanoparticles—the ultrafine, manipulated particles used in many industries. Nanoparticles have numerous applications to areas ranging from medicine to manufacturing. Nanotechnology is anticipated to increase to a trillion-dollar industry employing millions of workers worldwide within the next decade. The National Institute for Occupational Safety and Health (NIOSH) and its partners are conducting research to better understand the health effects of nanotechnology, establish an evidence base on risks and controls, and develop appropriate guidance.

The (above) stated research objectives and recommendations for investment in research and OSH surveillance are in danger of defunding under the current administration, which makes these challenges even more difficult to fully understand and manage. Furthermore, the well-known beacon for emerging OSH issues for research is the National Occupational Research Agenda (NORA). NORA is currently transitioning from its second (2006–2016) to third (2016–2026) decade, and although new information is currently not available on the NIOSH website, here is a list of previous decade's cross-sector focus areas (NIOSH 2016):

- Cancer, reproductive, cardiovascular, and other chronic disease prevention
- Hearing loss prevention
- Immune, infectious, and dermal disease prevention
- Musculoskeletal health
- Respiratory health
- Traumatic injury prevention
- Healthy work design and well-being

The OSH field is evolving from a *compliance focus* to a *risk-based approach* that expands the scope of the safety and health program beyond the hazard identification, assessment, and control and employee training to health and wellness programs and at-home safety and health initiatives. The seemingly ever-expanding scope/role of the OSH professional requires advancements in training and education of its incoming or new professionals. However, due to fundamental changes in generational experiences and expectations, there is a growing need for changes in post-secondary or career training for the OSH field.

The seemingly ever-expanding scope/role of the OSH professional requires advancements in training and education of its incoming or new professionals.

Today's college students are very different than students from the 1980–90s (Generation X) and before the 1980s (Baby Boomers). Millennials have less part-time, summer, and technical work experience than prior generations, and they're the unfortunate recipients of an elementary and secondary education system fixated on student exam scores as indicators of teacher and school performance. These changes in education policy have led to an over-emphasized focus on reading and math test scores, reducing attention to creative and applied problem-solving areas (Jennings and Rentner 2006). Reliance on technology and the Internet has allowed this generation to find answers without thinking through and learning from mistakes, which are trademark experiences for self-improvement and development of critical problem-solving skills. This generation is also taught that achievement is measured in scores and is willing to "bend the rules" to maintain the appearance of better performance (Levin and Dean 2012). However, these are learned behaviors and therefore can be unlearned with training and mentoring.

Standardization of elementary and secondary education with a focus on reading and math test scores is producing a generation of high school graduates with underdeveloped creative and real-world problem-solving skills (Dee and Jacob 2010). Correction of this deficiency is now the responsibility of post-secondary institutions. These state colleges and technical schools are not immune to public policy changes and in many cases are attempting to "do more" with less state funding (Jennings and Rentner 2006). For example, some unfortunate undergraduate institutions (or departments within) are being forced to consider a business model approach to attract more students and increase enrollment to compensate for reduced state funding (Mitchell et al. 2016). Faculty at universities and colleges are reporting "pressure" from administration to increase graduation rates, inflate grades, and lower time/credits to graduation (Katopes 2009). Increased tuition rates and student fees are increasing student loan amounts and therefore student debt, which also increases student expectations for the college experience. Parents of this generation believe that a college degree is a requirement, placing greater expectations on scores and grade point averages (GPA) to get into college and less attention on exposing their children to career options and requiring experience in traditionally part-time or summer teenager jobs, which instill maturity, personal responsibility, and handling finances (Levin and Dean 2012). To deal with these changes in business, academia, and student characteristics, it is vital that OSH degree students participate in internships and co-ops to prepare them for early career success.

Reliance on technology and the Internet has allowed this generation to find answers without thinking through and learning from mistakes, which are trademark experiences for self-improvement and development of critical problem-solving skills.

## Developing a Learning Technique to Improve Problem Solving

> Education thus becomes an act of depositing, in which the students are the depositories and the teacher is the depositor. Instead of communicating, the teacher issues communiques and makes deposits which the students patiently receive, memorize, and repeat . . . Knowledge emerges only through invention and reinvention, through the restless, impatient, continuing, hopeful inquiry men pursue in the world, with the world, and within each other.
>
> —Paulo Freire (1974, p. 58)

> Acquiring the requisite knowledge, skills, and abilities to practice occupational safety and health requires more than instruction; it requires mentoring/coaching with real-world expertise in assessment and critical feedback.

The primary directive of an undergraduate college education is the acquisition of knowledge, skills, and abilities (KSA) required to begin working within a chosen career field. Bachelor's degree curriculum is designed to prepare a practitioner with discipline-based KSAs, and advanced degrees provide users with advanced KSAs while learning the scientific method. Curricular and practice KSAs are defined (and redefined) by the profession's body of knowledge and contemporary or specialized KSAs to address society or business safety and health issues. Within the confines of the university classroom, student learning is limited or "stunted" because it is primarily conducted (and tested) through lectures, labs, and individual/team semester projects. Acquiring the requisite KSAs to practice occupational safety and health requires more than instruction; it requires mentoring/coaching with real-world expertise in assessment and critical feedback (Kolb 1984). In the book titled Academically Adrift (Aram and Roksa 2011), it was shown that four-year college graduates were not developing (actually declining) in their creative and problem-solving knowledge and skills. Although there is clearly a connection between a proficient learning technique and good grades, students have learned to bypass the day-to-day, disciplined approach for learning "short cuts" that include intense studying of lecture PowerPoints hours before an exam, collaborating with more studious classmates to benefit from their disciplined coursework, or cheating/plagiarizing to simply "survive" an assignment deadline or exam. Therefore, instructors should promote, assign, and grade students based on their learning technique, which then promotes its development and ability to self-assess/learn based on instructor assessment and feedback. Classroom research in a safety degree program at a mid-sized university in the upper Midwest mostly agreed with Aram and Roksa's conclusions and indicated that a majority of students were not completing assignments in a timely manner but rather procrastinating and attempting to "cram" for exams and semester projects. In an effort to combat procrastination and improve student-learning skills, a course binder assignment was created. The plan required the development of course binder assignment details and a grading rubric, which was presented to the class on the first day of a semester (lecture). The elements of the course binder attempted to replicate some of the attributes of highly effective people (Covey 2004).

> The basis for assignments and grading rubrics help students to be successful, encouraging them to organize course materials, and prepare for and participate in lectures, among other skills.

The basis for this assignment (and grading rubric) is that successful students need to:

1. Organize course materials by keeping a well-labeled working document (binder)
2. Keep a planner for the semester, along with tracking activities ("to do" lists)
3. Keep a journal, documenting course planning, reflections, and accomplishments
4. Participate in lectures, keep detailed hand-written lecture notes, and demonstrate reading

5. Complete homework assignments by responding to questions and citing the source
6. (Tracked as a secondary measure) Prepare for lectures by visiting the course website

Results of this four-year (and ongoing) research study indicate that in most comparisons, the relationship between individual student GPA, binder score, and exam scores are significant ($p<.001$). Interestingly, in two courses used for these studies, the GPA and binder demonstrate the greatest Pearson correlation scores, meaning that students with higher GPAs likely already mastered their learning technique, and it resembled the binder assignment. Also interesting is the higher Pearson correlation scores for exam score and exam confidence. This means that students have a reliable perception of how well (in general) they know the responses they indicate on an exam are correct. Secondary analysis showed trends indicating that students who entered a course with below average GPA (GPA < 2.50) were able to demonstrate above-average exam and assignment scores if their binder scores were higher. Adopting a semester assignment that requires students to document their learning process/technique over the semester provides them with tools that are vital for their careers and allows students to master their learning technique. In doing so, they are developing problem solving skills. The documentation of their learning technique is the foundation of an internship or co-op portfolio, which documents progress and project work for both grading/feedback but also a demonstration of KSAs for future employers.

> Adopting a semester assignment that requires students to document their learning process/technique over the semester provides them with tools that are vital for their careers.

## Apprenticeships, Internships and Co-ops: A History

> In reality, all arguments from experience are founded on the similarity which we discover among natural objects, and by which we are induced to expect effects similar to those which we have found to follow from such objects. And though none but a fool or madman will ever pretend to dispute the authority of experience, or to reject that great guide of human life, it may surely be allowed a Philosopher to have so much curiosity at least as to examine the principle of human nature, which gives this mighty authority to experience, and makes us draw advantage from that similarity which nature has placed among different objects. From causes which appear similar we expect similar effects. This is the sum of our experimental conclusions.
>
> —David Hume (1748), excerpt from *An Enquiry Concerning Human Understanding*, p 63.

According to a 2009 article in *Time* magazine,

> The importance of internships for securing full-time work has dramatically increased over the years; these days, an internship is less of an opportunity and more of a requirement. In a 2001 survey by the National Association of Colleges and Employers, employers reported offering jobs to 57 percent of their intern class. By 2008 that number had reached 70 percent. There are as many as 300,000 students participating in some form of pre-job apprenticeship in the United States each year, a number that has increased 10 percent over the past five years. (Haire and Oloffson 2009)

> According to Herman Schneider, "If you want to educate a student to become an engineer, then you should provide that student with the opportunity to practice being an engineer".

The same *Time* article chronicles the origins of internships to the long-time apprenticeships and indentured servants of the Middle Ages. For example, "In the trade guilds of 11th century England, a worker would actually pay to learn alongside a 'master' who would teach him a skill like printmaking." Careers were based on knowledge, skills, and abilities passed from master to student over the centuries until the Industrial Revolution of the eighteenth century in which the need for skilled craftsmen decreased and the need for unskilled laborers for factory work increased. According to the Accreditation Council for Graduate Medical Education (ACGME 2007), in the early 1800s most doctors were educated solely through apprenticeships because only about thirty medical schools existed in the United States at the time. In 1861, the Morrill Act (Land Grant Act) provided funding for the establishment of college education in the agricultural and mechanical arts. In 1899, the first cooperative education program was established at Lehigh University in Pennsylvania by Herman Schneider, who once said, "If you want to educate a student to become an engineer, then you should provide that student with the opportunity to practice being an engineer" (CEIA 2015). In 1914, the American Medical Association (AMA) instituted a program of internship approval for hospitals for medical student residency training (ACGME 2007). In the last century, apprenticeships increased with the growth of trade unions and the passing of the 1937 National Apprenticeship Act and the creation of the Bureau of Apprenticeship and Training housed within the US Department of Labor. Thirty years later, the 1965 Higher Education Act (HEA) Title VIII provided additional funding requirements for educational programs, such as co-ops. Federal and state funding fluctuates based on performance of the US economy and fiduciary principles of government leadership.

Currently, there are over 1,000 colleges and universities around the world who collaborate with over 75,000 employers to employ over 300,000 students annually in some form of internship or co-op experience (CEIA 2015).

## Differences between Internships and Co-ops and Compensation

> The improvement of understanding is for two ends: first, our own increase of knowledge; secondly, to enable us to deliver that knowledge to others.
>
> —John Locke (circa 1689)

According to the Cooperative Education and Internship Association (CEIA 2015):

> **Cooperative education** is a structured method of combining classroom-based education with practical work experience. A cooperative education experience, commonly known as a "co-op," provides academic credit for structured job experience. Co-op experiences are either full-time (40 hours per week) alternating periods (semester, quarter) of work and school or part-time (20 hours per week) combining work and school during the same time period. Co-op experiences are paid, supervised by a professional who has followed the same career path of the student and students complete more than one assignment (2 or more) with progressive levels of responsibility.
>
> **Internship** is an experience involving student's working in their expected career field, either during a semester or over the summer. Internships may be paid or unpaid and may or may not carry academic credit. Internships are typically one time experiences. Internships are typically connected to an academic program with course requirements designed and monitored by faculty. Internships generally have related learning outcomes and academic assignments required.

Even with the distinction between co-ops and internships, realize that many employers and universities use these terms interchangeably and may only consider a summer (three-month) work experience an internship and anything work experience during fall or spring semester as a co-op. Due to their extended time at a company, co-op students are likely to gain more depth in their learning and therefore earn greater and more extensive projects, which can give them an advantage over their internship peers (Boyington 2015). Although the longer co-op experience may delay a student's graduation, it can provide much-needed financial relief to the student (and their family).

Some safety and health intern employers offer incentives to get the top students by offering "signing bonuses", moving and/or rent payments, or a stipend to cover their final semester's tuition.

It may be interesting to note that in 1906, engineering interns were reportedly earning eight to ten cents per hour, and in 1934 wages for new engineering graduates was thirty-five cents per hour for a ten-hour work day or an average weekly salary of $13 per week (CEIA 2015). Ongoing assessments of occupational safety internship data at a mid-sized university in the upper Midwest indicate that hourly wages are increasing about a dollar per hour per year. Over spring semester 2017, safety interns reported earning an average over $18 per hour (ranging from $12 to $25 per hour). Additionally, some employers offer incentives to get the top students by offering "signing bonuses," moving or rent payments, or a stipend to cover their final semester's tuition. Some incentives have accounted for over $10,000 to the intern. Figure 16.1 shows average (with trend line), maximum, and minimum internship wages from spring 2015 to spring 2017.

Not all internships are paid. The US Department of Labor, Wage and Hour Division (2010) provides information to employers regarding what is required under the Fair Labor Standards Act. The following subsections provide general information to help determine whether interns must be paid the minimum wage and overtime under the Fair Labor Standards Act for the services that they provide to for-profit, private sector employers (the following is edited for length from fact sheet #71):

> The Fair Labor Standards Act (FLSA) defines the term "employ" very broadly as including to "suffer or permit to work. "Covered and non-exempt individuals who are "suffered or permitted" to work must be compensated under the law for the services they perform for an employer. Internships in the "for-profit" private sector will most often be viewed as employment, unless the test described below relating to trainees is met. Interns in the "for-profit" private sector who qualify as employees rather than trainees typically must be paid at least the minimum wage and overtime compensation for hours worked over forty in a workweek. The Supreme Court has held that the term "suffer or permit to work" cannot be interpreted so as to make a person whose work serves only his or her own interest an employee of another who provides aid or instruction. This may apply to interns who receive training for their own educational benefit if the training meets certain criteria. The determination of whether an internship or training program meets this exclusion depends upon all of the facts and circumstances of each such program.
>
> The following six criteria must be applied when making this determination:
>
> 1. the internship, even though it includes actual operation of the facilities of the employer, is similar to training which would be given in an educational environment;
> 2. the internship experience is for the benefit of the intern;
> 3. the intern does not displace regular employees, but works under close supervision of existing staff;
> 4. the employer that provides the training derives no immediate advantage from the

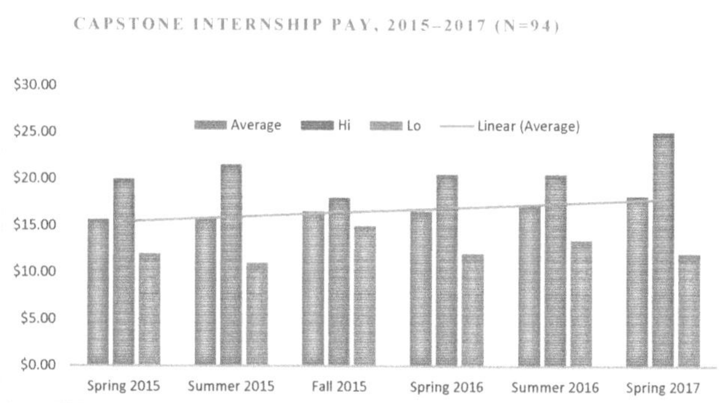


Figure 16.1
Capstone internship pay, 2015–2017.

activities of the intern, and on occasion its operations may actually be impeded;

5. the intern is not necessarily entitled to a job at the conclusion of the internship; and
6. the employer and the intern understand that the intern is not entitled to wages for the time spent in the internship.

If all of the factors listed above are met, an employment relationship does not exist under the FLSA, and the Act's minimum wage and overtime provisions do not apply to the intern. This exclusion from the definition of employment is necessarily quite narrow because the FLSA's definition of "employ" is very broad. Some of the most commonly discussed factors for "for-profit" private sector internship programs are considered below.

In general, the more an internship program is structured around a classroom or academic experience as opposed to the employer's actual operations, the more likely the internship will be viewed as an extension of the individual's educational experience (this often occurs where a college or university exercises oversight over the internship program and provides educational credit). The more the internship provides the individual with skills that can be used in multiple employment settings, as opposed to skills particular to one employer's operation, the more likely the intern would be viewed as receiving training. Under these circumstances the intern does not perform the routine work of the business on a regular and recurring basis, and the business is not dependent upon the work of the intern. On the other hand, if the interns are engaged in the operations of the employer or are performing productive work (for example, filing, performing other clerical work, or assisting customers), then the fact that they may be receiving some benefits in the form of a new skill or improved work habits will not exclude them from the FLSA's minimum wage and overtime requirements because the employer benefits from the interns' work.

If an employer uses interns as substitutes for regular workers or to augment its existing workforce during specific time periods, these interns should be paid at least the minimum wage and overtime compensation for hours worked over forty in a workweek. If the employer would have hired additional employees or required existing staff to work additional hours had the interns not performed the work, then the interns will be viewed as employees and entitled compensation under the FLSA. The internship should be of a fixed duration, established prior to the outset of the internship. Further, unpaid internships generally should not be used by the employer as a trial period for individuals seeking employment at the conclusion of the internship period. If an intern is placed with the employer for a trial period with the expectation that he or she will then be hired on a permanent basis, that individual generally would be considered an employee under the FLSA.

## Effective Internships and Co-ops: Experienced Mentors Needed

> Practice does not make perfect. Perfect practice, makes perfect.
>
> —Dr. Michael J. Smith (circa 2003), UW-Madison Department of Industrial Engineering Graduate Seminar

When recent college graduates are asked about the most important course or the college experience that best prepared them for their first job, a vast majority indicate it was their internship/co-op experience. Students experience accelerated learning because they can focus their full attention and senses on the tasks at hand, which creates more meaningful and complex brain-based connections (Jacobson 2015).

Kolb (1984) provides three basic reasons why experiential learning is superior to "book" learning:

1. Learning is best conceived as a process and not in terms of outcomes.
2. Learning is a continuous process grounded in experience.
3. Learning is a holistic process of adaptation to the world (or work environment).

There is value in the attempt to introduce students to real-world work conditions in a step-wise (and safe) method, but critical to their development for transition to practice, a student needs to be independent.

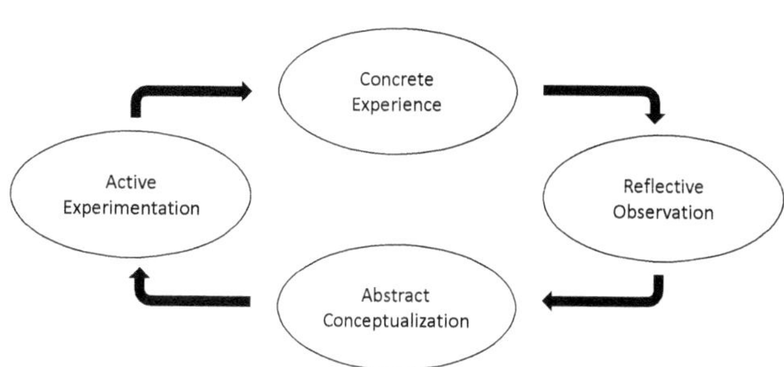


Figure 16.2
Kolb's Experimental Learning Cycle (based on Kolb and Fry [1985]).

Innovative instructors can simulate real-world conditions in labs, bring students on tours of companies, or provide access to a business to complete a semester project, but it is impossible to replicate the depth and texture of the learning experience of an internship or co-op. There is value in the attempt to introduce students to real-world work conditions in a step-wise (and safe) method, but critical to their development for transition to practice, a student needs to be able to conduct their own observations, reflect and theorize on relationships and interactions, collect and analyze data to test their own theories, and pursue changes with anticipated outcomes. This is the type of cyclic learning process indicated by Kolb (1984) and his Experimental Learning Cycle (Kolb and Fry 1975).

In order to facilitate the accelerated/immersed learning experience of internships and co-ops, students need to develop and hone their individual learning technique along with professionalism (ethics, manners, commitment, responsibility) and communication skills (listening, relationship development, documentation/writing, and public speaking). Preparation for internships and co-ops must begin with classroom instruction in the curriculum and coursework where students gain the foundational KSAs of their discipline while they explore and develop their individual learning technique (Matthew et al. 2012). The concept of internships and co-ops is really a "win-win-win" proposal, in that college students gain valuable real-world problem-solving skills through application and critical feedback from an experienced safety professional, the host company assesses and develops a potential future hire, and the degree program produces a more capable graduate who is more likely to be successful early in their career (Velez and Giner 2015). Wan et al. (2013) found that internships that were facilitated by experienced and engaged mentors, along with assistance by degree-program faculty, increased the student's KSAs, problem-solving abilities, and self-confidence. These students also reported higher job satisfaction and an easier and more successful transition into their careers. Velez and Giner (2015) confirmed these outcomes and also found that successful internships and co-ops lead to improved "brand" for the degree program, which led to better and more opportunities for future student internships and co-ops. Innovative degree program faculty can also use feedback from site supervisors and former graduates to continuously improve their internship/co-ops programs and course curriculum and to promote their degree/profession to increase their enrollment.

Innovative degree program faculty can also use feedback from site supervisors and former graduates to continuously improve their internship/co-ops programs and course curriculum, and to promote their degree/profession to increase their enrollment

However, not all internships and co-ops are alike. For an internship/co-op to be truly effective in developing the student and for the company to

> The internship or coop should be an immersed learning experience, in which the intern is supervised by an onsite or host experienced safety professional and by an assigned faculty advisor.

gain valuable work from the student, the internship/co-op needs to be well-planned, with objectives, established review criteria, and documentation of all aspects of the experience (Matthew et al. 2012). If planned and administered properly, the worst outcome would be that the student gained valuable KSA and created a binder/portfolio to be used in future interviews while the company gain some valuable work products and either learned what they really want in a potential new hire (new grad) or how to improve their screening process and management of the internship. The internship or co-op should be an immersed learning experience in which the intern is supervised by an onsite or host experienced safety professional and by an assigned faculty advisor who will grade and provide feedback on an internship portfolio or binder and safety project reports, while acting as a mediator between the intern and site host if there are any disagreements or issues preventing the intern from learning. Ideally, during the internship/co-op experience, the intern gains confidence in their KSAs, develops their professionalism, improves communication skills, and has an easier path to acquiring a full-time position by graduation (Wan et al. 2013).

The American Society of Safety Engineers (ASSE) Education Standards Committee created draft guidelines for an academic internship program (2002). Table 16.1 is a summary of their recommendations to be considered by academic departments and employers participating in internship/co-op programs.

**Table 16.1** ASSE ESC (draft) guidelines for an academic internship program

| 4. General Requirements |
|---|
| 4.1. The purpose of the internship program shall be defined, including objectives and activities. |
| 4.2. An internship program should encourage participation of only qualified students, in accordance with university and department standards. |
| 4.3. A faculty coordinator shall oversee all program activities |
| 4.4. Selection of an internship site shall include a review of the following:<br>• management's overall commitment to safety<br>• commitment to participating students' education<br>• availability of a safety professional on site to act as a mentor<br>• a variety of exposures for standard evaluation/participation<br>• office space for student use and availability of reference materials<br>• travel distance and the possible need for housing<br>• personal protective equipment<br>• security, liability, and insurance issue |
| 4.5. An internship program shall present an orientation program that addresses such issues as:<br>• an explanation of the purpose of the internship<br>• roles of the student, including review of the ASSP Code of Professional Conduct<br>• explanation of the roles of site supervisor and faculty member<br>• an explanation of evaluation criteria |

*Continued*

Table 16.1 ASSE ESC (draft) guidelines for an academic internship program *(Continued)*

| |
|---|
| 5. Development of Evaluation Criteria |
| 5.1. Quality of assignments |
| 5.1.1. Faculty and site management shall work together to develop assignments that will benefit both the student and the organization |
| 5.1.2. Assignments should expose the student to professional responsibility in a variety of areas, such as: occupational safety, industrial hygiene, fire safety, environmental safety, etc. |
| 5.1.3. Daily logs, reports, memos, etc. should be reviewed for technical and grammatical accuracy and clarity<br>• Number of assignments<br>• The number of internship assignments should be balanced to keep the student busy, but not overburdened. It is important to remember that, for most students, this will be their first exposure in the field.<br>• Role of the site supervisor in evaluation<br>• The site supervisory shall be asked to complete appropriate instruments assessing specific criteria, such as timeliness, cooperation, professional ethics, and work quality.<br>• Grading assignments<br>• Faculty with experience in safety, health, and environment shall be responsible for establishing and evaluating assignments in those areas.<br>• Collaboration requirements<br>• The internship program shall include allotted time for students, site supervisors, and faculty to communicate in order to review assignments and perceived issues. |
| 6. Internship Compensation and Legal Implications |
| 6.1. Compensation Issues |
| 6.1.1. Interns should be provided appropriate compensation consistent with local employment conditions, employer ability to offer an equitable honorarium, and the intern's agreement with the compensation package. |
| 6.2. Legal Issues |
| 6.2.1. Individual interns and sponsoring organizations shall have an agreement in writing that states unequivocally the individual's status as either an intern or employee, including:<br>• an outline of the individual's specific responsibilities with regard to defining the intern or employee role; and<br>• an understanding of each party's responsibilities with regard to the Fair Labor Standards Act and relevant state and federal tax laws. |
| 7. Program Evaluation |
| 7.1.1. The internship program shall be evaluated annually to ascertain areas for continued improvement to better meet its goals. |

## How to Find OSH Students for Internships and Co-ops

Although there are many websites that publish "safety-related" degree programs through the United States, this section will focus on databases and search engines provided by the American Society of Safety Professionals (ASSP) and the Board of Certified Safety Professionals (BCSP). The ASSP OSH College and University Directory can be found at http://www.assp.org, and it allows the user to sort the database by state, chapter region, and degree designation. For example, sorting by "bachelor degree" yielded ninety-two options. It also provides a link to "the importance of accreditation" (for OSH degree programs), "safety-related programs accredited by ABET," and a link for available online degrees and online courses. The 2017 listing of ABET-accredited degree programs (including BS, MS, MSPH, MPH) is sorted by "safety programs (n=20)" and "industrial hygiene programs (n=33)."

> There is a real need for OSH students to realize and develop their real-world problem-solving skills to handle the changing business and OSH landscape, and the research literature strongly supports the use of internships and co-ops to achieve those goals.

The BCSP Academic Database can be found at http://www.bcsp.org/Resources/Academic-Database, and it allows the user to sort the database by: field/major, degree type, and state. It also allows the user to designate whether the results are limited to "online options available" or "GSP Qualified Academic Programs." Unlike the ASSP website interface, the BCSP indicates it has 863 degree and certificate options in its database. For example, sorting by "bachelor's degree" yielded 252 options. Selecting the "GSP Qualified Academic Programs" and "Safety" as the field/major yielded 18 options.

Faculty members of OSH safety degree programs should visit these sites to verify information and contact either ASSP or BCSP if their institutions information is outdated or incorrect. Employers should visit these sites to identify possible internship and co-op recruiting opportunities. Both ASSP and BCSP sites are free to use and do not require a login to access the academic databases and search engines.

## Conclusion

Ideally, a well-defined internship or co-op supervised by an experienced OSH mentor increases the employability (value to an employer) and problem-solving skills of the student. Unfortunately, there is little to no research literature to quantify those advantages for OSH students, but the research literature from other technical disciplines does confirm positive outcomes from immersed learning experiences. Regardless, there is a real need for OSH students to realize and develop their real-world problem-solving skills to handle the changing business and OSH landscape, and the research literature strongly supports the use of internships and co-ops to achieve those goals.

The OSH profession needs development and growth in qualified safety professionals and defining what constitutes a qualified safety professional. Qualified safety degree programs need to continue working with professional safety organizations and local/regional safety professionals to continuously improve their curriculum and provide students with applied learning opportunities and real-world experiences.

## Questions

1. Identify some generational and educational system differences between college students of today and those from the '70s, '80s, and '90s.
2. How does the cooperative education (co-op) or internship experience differ and/or compliment classroom learning?
3. What are the basic differences between a co-op and an internship? And what type of compensation can a student expect?
4. What are the elements of a successful safety internship/co-op experience?
5. What are the two primary sources for search and evaluating university safety degree programs in the United States?

## References


Accreditation Council for Graduate Medical Education (ACGME). (2007). *History of Medical Education—History of Medical Education Accreditation.* http://www.acgme.org/About-Us/Overview/History-of-Medical-Education.

Arum, R., and J. Roska. (2011). *Academically Adrift: Limited Learning on College Campuses.* Chicago, IL: University of Chicago Press.

American Society of Safety Professionals (ASSP) (2017). *OSH College & University Directory.* http://www.asse.org/professionalaffairs/directory/.

American Society of Safety Engineers Educational Standards Committee. (2002). *Standard Guidelines for Academic Internship Programs for Safety, Health, and Environmental Curriculum.* https://www.google.com/url?sa=t&rct=j&q=&esrc=s&source=web&cd=3&ved=0ahUKEwjewIbpn_PUAhXl5IMKHZpPBfcQFgg0MAI&url=http%3A%2F%2Fwww.asse.org%2Fassets%2F1%2F7%2FStandard_Guidelines_for_Academic_Internship_Programs.doc&usg=AFQjCNExSQSqPocxOsNRWDqnT-rQmImtRw&cad=rja.

Board of Certified Safety Professionals (BCSP). (2017). *Academic Database.* http://www.bcsp.org/Resources/Academic-Database.

Boyington, B. (2015). "Understanding the Differences between a Co-op, Internship." *US News.* https://www.usnews.com/education/best-colleges/articles/2015/03/31/understand-the-differences-between-a-co-op-internship.

Cooperative Education and Internship Association (CEIA). (2015). *History of Cooperative Education and Internships.* http://www.ceiainc.org/about/history/.

Covey, S. R. (2004). *The 7 Habits of Highly Effective People.* New York: Free Press.

Dee, T. S., and B. A. Jacob. (2010). "The Impact of No Child Left Behind on Students, Teachers, and Schools." *Brookings Papers on Economic Activity* (D. H. Romer and J. Wolfers, eds.). Hanover, PA: Brookings Institution Press.

Haire, M., and K. Oloffson. (2009). "Brief History of Interns." *Time.* http://content.time.com/time/nation/article/0,8599,1913474,00.html.

Jacobson, K. (2015). "Workplace Immersion for Accelerated Learning." *Techniques* (April). http://www.acteonline.org/tech_april15/.

Jennings, J., and D. S. Rentner. (2006). "Ten Big Effects of the No Child Left Behind Act on Public Schools." *Phi Delta Kappan* 88(2): 110–13.

Katopes, P. (2009). "The Business Model is the Wrong Model." *Inside Higher Ed.* https://www.insidehighered.com/views/2009/02/16/business-model-wrong-model.

Kolb, D. A. (1984). *Experiential Learning: Experience as the Source of Learning and Development.* Englewood Cliffs, NJ: Prentice Hall.

Kolb, D. A., and R. E. Fry. (1975). "Toward an Applied Theory of Experimental Learning." In C. Cooper (ed.), *Theories of Group Processes.* New York: John Wiley & Sons.

Levine, A., and D. R. Dean. (2012). *Generation on a Tightrope: A Portrait of Today's College Student* (3rd ed.). San Francisco: Jossey-Bass Higher and Adult Education Series.

Matthew, S. M, R. M. Taylor, and R. A. Ellis. (2012). "Relationships between Students' Experience of Learning in an Undergraduate Internship Programme and New Graduates' Experiences of Professional Practice." *Higher Education* 64: 529–42.

Mitchell, M., M. Leachman, and K. Masterson. (2016). "Funding Down, Tuition Up: State Cuts to Higher Education Threaten Quality and Affordability at Public Colleges." Center on Budget and Policy Priorities. http://www.cbpp.org/research/state-budget-and-tax/funding-down-tuition-up.

National Institute for Occupational Safety and Health (NIOSH). (2016). *Cross-sectors Focus on the Major Health and Safety Issues Affecting the U.S. Working Population.* National Occupational Research Agenda (NORA). https://www.cdc.gov/niosh/nora/crosssectors.html.

Office of Disease Prevention and Health Promotion. (2014). *Healthy People 2020—Occupational Safety and Health.* https://www.healthypeople.gov/2020/topics-objectives/topic/occupational-safety-and-health.

US Department of Labor. (2017). *Fact Sheet #71: Internship Programs under the Fair Labor Standards Act.* https://www.dol.gov/whd/regs/compliance/whdfs71.htm.

Velez, G. S., and G. R. Giner. (2015). "Effects of Business Internships on Students, Employers, and Higher Education Institutions: A Systemic Review. *Journal of Employment Counseling* 52: 121–30.

Wan, C. S., J. Yang, S. Cheng, and C. Su. (2013). A Longitudinal Study on Internship Effectiveness in Vocational Higher Education. *Educational Review* 65(1): 36–55.

CHAPTER 17

# THE APPLICABILITY OF EFFECTIVE SAFETY ADVOCACY PROGRAMS: THROUGH TOP-DOWN AND BOTTOM-UP APPROACHES

Jessica Jannaman

## Learning Objectives

After studying this chapter, the reader will be able to:

1. Understand the complexities of how leadership provides the foundation for building a safety culture in an organization
2. Explain the progression of a safety culture in an organization and identify proactive solutions to prevent incidents to accelerate the evolution of a safety program
3. Recognize how operational excellence interfaces with safety to drive a high-performing and influential safety organization that is integral with the business
4. Comprehend the purpose of establishing a safety program that engages and recognizes employees for their proactivity

## Key Terms

**TPS, muda, leadership principles, operational performance, 5S, unsafe act, active listening**

## Abstract

The purpose of this chapter is to provide insight on building the bridge between structures of a safety program and establishing a safety culture that is founded on leadership. Only providing a structure through programs, policies, procedures, and processes makes up a small portion of what it takes to form a profound safety culture. The primary necessity for creating a strong safety culture is a leadership driven by human values, problem solving, employee engagement, and continuous improvement. After reading this chapter, the reader will understand that a structure is needed for safety, but leadership-based values are the catalyst to transform those necessities into effective approaches, which can be applied in operations with both operators and management.

## Approaches to Leadership and Advocacy

Working in the safety profession, I have found that there are many elements that contribute to an effective and successful safety program, but there is only one underlying and common denominator that contributes to a successful safety culture. That common denominator is leadership and safety advocacy within an organization. There are two approaches for leadership and advocacy, which make a safety program and culture successful.

### Top-Down Leadership

The first approach is top-down leadership and advocacy. Just like all successful principles within an organization, top management requires value in whatever is being driven throughout an organization. A mission and vision must be evident to guide the organization to success in its endeavors. If safety is to be a value to the organization, it begins with senior leadership and top management taking ownership for safety. This means that safety is the highest priority, and senior leadership not only "talks the talk" but "walks the walk." Safety should be apparent as a value cross functionally for all top management through support of programs and key performance indicators (KPIs) and projected as an integral point throughout several discussions. Standing behind the value and need for safety as a leadership principle is only a single portion of what is required for a safety advocacy approach.

### Bottom-Up Leadership

The second approach to leadership and safety advocacy is a bottom-up methodology. This can be described as employees taking ownership for safety and driving it throughout the direct actions and operations necessary to run the organization. I come from a background of manufacturing, and no matter what environment or operation, a culture can be inherently seen through the motions and actions of the employees working out on the production floor. When a culture is strong on the production floor, employees can be seen working as one fluid system. Each person is helping feed what another person is doing, housekeeping is intact, and when a problem arises, all employees show support for one another to resolve the issue in a true team environment.

The Toyota Production System (TPS) first arrived back in the late 1940s with a focus on lean methodology to completely eliminate waste or what can be called *muda*. The TPS system resonates on the notion that every employee is responsible to support in production for one common goal: to eliminate waste and run a successful production system. The same strong culture that can be seen on a production also echoes for safety. This means that employees are not only taking ownership of safety for themselves but the safety of others as well, and when a problem arises, everyone shows support to resolve the issue. But how does a safety professional impact these dynamics?

## The Human Element

Safety leadership has been described in several articles and discussions. These descriptions and discussions are not too different as to how one would define leadership in any profession beyond safety with the exception of one detail: the human element. Dan Petersen once said, "Paper doesn't save people, people save people." This holds especially true for safety since the safety profession is in fact driven by people and their behavior. No matter what profession, leadership will always be founded upon the human element. The safety professional within an organization must be the medium to drive safety throughout the organization as a leader but should not be the only one creating action. This means connecting safety with the top-down management to the employees carrying out the day-to-day activities.

Being the advocate for safety in an organization as a leader is just the same as being a leader for anything. Commonalities between safety leadership and nonspecific leadership are based upon trends ascending through applied principles. The commonality between safety leadership and nonspecific leadership is that each has a guidance and objective to certain target end

> The safety professional within an organization must be the medium to drive safety throughout the organization as a leader but should not be the only one creating action. This means connecting safety with the top-down management to the employees carrying out the day-to-day activities.

goals. At the end of the day, leaders have a vision that they want to see come to fruition whether it be a safe organization or achieving another end goal, such as in business metrics. To successfully achieve a vision, a leader must effectively apply certain characteristics and traits, which can be seen as principles. Through leadership principles, leaders influence and guide to achieve their vision. These influencing principles can be explained and defined as:

1. Creating a vision and effectively communicating the vision
2. Providing a set of clear objectives and targets
3. Establishing value for the vision, objectives, and targets
4. Receiving committed input and buy-in on vision, objectives, and targets
5. Providing the tools and resources to support the objectives and targets set

These commonalities rely upon the basis of human elements as described as:

1. Trust
2. Influence
3. Common interest
4. Self-preservation

To truly accelerate and be successful within the safety profession, a leader must go beyond the essentials of leadership and demonstrate the value of safety to stakeholders. Safety as an intrinsic value can be a challenging commodity to market and sell if one of the human elements is missing between "the buyer" and "the seller." To be effective, safety professionals who are leaders must break down the silos within an organization and understand the value to each defined "customer" in order to look for the end result and value.

If a car salesperson, for example, could not successfully sell a vehicle, the salesperson would not make any money and eventually lose their job; why should safety be viewed differently from a product? Think about the last time you went in to purchase a car. You did not depend solely on walking onto the lot, picking out the car you wanted, and settling with a sticker price. Buying the car was a process and took development with interacting with another individual. You had to establish each one of the human elements with the salesperson, beginning with trust. If you look at each step in the process, you had to develop a certain level of trust with the car salesperson, influence one another as to the limits of purchasing the vehicle, find a common interest or understanding, and find comfort (or self-preservation) on the decision being made.

Each human element is based upon development of relationships, and safety is no different. As a leader in safety, one must have the ability to organize and drive each principle and also have the capability to build the relationships in order to establish the core requirements dependent upon the human elements.

Impacting and developing relationships with a small group of individuals may seem easy, but how does one influence a whole organization?

> Each human element is based upon development of relationships, and safety is no different.

In 1995 DuPont introduced the DuPont Bradley Curve, which outlines the advancement of safety culture within an organization. The concept and development around the DuPont model emphasize progressing the behavior of employees from a reactive state to an interdependent ideal state. The challenge of the DuPont model is that although it may establish the ideal progression and state of a safety culture, it does not implicitly provide the metrics or the business integration necessary for stakeholder involvement. For more information on the DuPont model, visit the following website: https://goo.gl/xXM8qp.

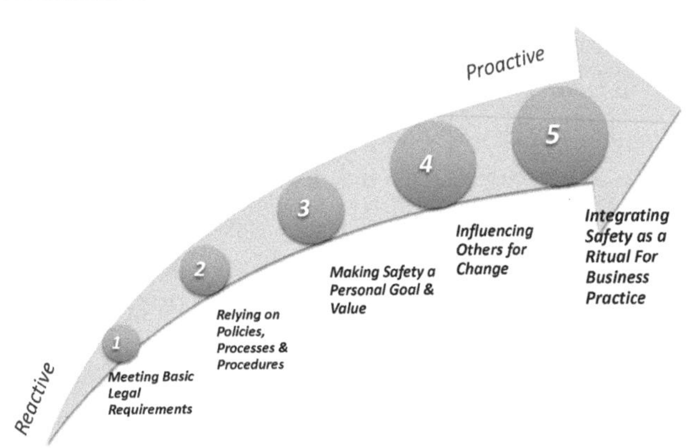


Figure 17.1
The DuPont Bradley Curve.

In 2014 the Aberdeen Group published a report on *Managing Safety to Promote Operational Excellence.* The Aberdeen Group reached out to 175 respondents to examine safety performance and its relationship to operational performance. The report surveyed respondents and defined performance through four metrics:

1. Recordable injury frequency rate
2. Overall equipment effectiveness
3. Unscheduled asset downtime
4. Decrease in total cost of ownership (percent change in total cost of ownership to manage safety system over twelve months)

The report recorded that those organizations that effectively applied cross-functional operational excellence activities and tools, such as 5S, which supports housekeeping, had a lower recordable injury frequency and excelled in overall production (Paquin and Prouty 2014).

Just as the Aberdeen study had concluded, the only effective way to see safety results within an organization is to integrate it into all aspects of the business through operations. Why is this? Correlating business success and a strong safety culture depend on similar models. This is where top-down advocacy meets bottom-up approaches.

## Setting Expectations

An organization must function on structure based upon setting the expectations for every employee and program. Without policies, process, and procedures, there is no basis for the organization to run. Every department and function will simply default to chaos and disorganization. Just as in safety within a business, essential safety policies and procedures must be followed for the minimal expectations for employees to remain safe, and there needs to be a set of basic instructions to follow. Only after the two fundamentals of meeting compliance and setting policies, processes, and procedures can an organization begin to see growth and change. Top management must set the expectation and value for the day-to-day business.

Certain programs, such as 5S (sometimes referred to as 6S), set the policy, process, and procedure for housekeeping. The definition behind 5S can be described as sort, set in order, shine, standardize, and sustain. When applying 6S, the additional "S" stands for safety. In order for good housekeeping to be successful, management has to provide the structure and tools to support the program, but it is up to employees to carry out the actions of the program and ensure good housekeeping is in place. Safety is often tied into the program because good housekeeping can prevent unsafe conditions relating to incident. Setting a program is a fundamental step in safety advocacy, but how does safety culture evolve between top management and employees?

## Challenging the System

The core of an organization begins to grow and transform when the employees begin to challenge the system (including others as well as themselves). When employees begin to challenge the system, problem-solving activities evolve, and employees begin to look for ways to make things better not only for themselves but for the organization as a whole. Part of this challenge also means looking for how the organization can become a safer working environment. By employees establishing challenges, there is also an impact on culture within the workplace. Problem-solving activities

When employees begin to challenge the system, problem-solving activities evolve, and employees begin to look for ways to make things better not only for themselves but for the organization as a whole.

provide employees the opportunity to take personal interest and invest in time and energy. As employees begin to challenge, they allow the opportunity for an organization to grow and expand for improvement. An organization can be seen to be growing when employees become more proactive on recognizing issues and taking the initiative to fix problems and provide follow-up.

When individual employees begin to challenge an organization and seek a need for solutions to problems, they influence the rest of the organization and other employees to do the same. Other employees will then begin to also participate in problem-solving activities and challenge themselves as well as the organization. When top management and leadership support problem-solving activities with employee engagement, this establishes feedback and trust within an organization and begins to evolve culture. It is up to the safety professional to assist in driving these activities to support but also keep the communication and actions intact, based upon the feedback of the employees. The values and beliefs provided by management support culture with the employees performing the work at the operational level. It is through creating a structure and foundation set on values and beliefs that incidents can be prevented.

## Behavior-Based Safety

Herbert William Heinrich wrote the book *Industrial Accident Prevention: A Scientific Approach* in 1931. In his book, Heinrich looks at empirical data to show that as many as 95 percent of all workplace incidents are caused by unsafe acts. It is with this notion that the idea of "behavior-based safety was conceived." Heinrich also implies that for every unsafe condition that was created (such as a missing guard or slippery floor), there is an unsafe act that stemmed from a root cause the majority of the time. Heinrich also stated that for every accident that causes a major injury, there are 29 accidents that cause minor injuries and 300 accidents that cause no injuries (Heinrich 1931).

Employees should be educated on recognition and prevention of unsafe acts and unsafe conditions and empowered to correct them when recognized.

Therefore, if an organization can focus on identifying unsafe acts and unsafe conditions, incidents can be prevented.

It is with this notion of driving values and beliefs through management and setting the program and tools in place for employees to become engaged to recognize, fix, and report these findings that employee engagement and ownership begin to transcend within the operations of the business. Employees should be educated on recognition and prevention of unsafe acts and unsafe conditions and empowered to correct them when recognized.

## Transcending Culture

It cannot be said that an organization can rely solely on the concept of behavior-based safety. Behavior-based safety may drive the bottom-up advocacy for an organization, but top-down management must also provide the guidance from leadership. Without guidance, employees become lost, confused, and complacent to the point of not challenging for solutions to problems. The basis of an organization is so reliant upon structure due to the need for guidance and process. Procedures and systems encompass how the day-to-day operations are set and lay the path for the organization. This structure provides a structure but does not rely on the aptitude of the leadership to influence the beliefs and values of the employees. To provide the structure and tools, leadership must be supportive, but for an organization to truly exceed and be successful, leadership must also provide guidance and assist in transcending culture from processes and procedures to instituting the values and beliefs. By leading safety culture from process to behavior (such as colleagues looking out for one another or believing that incidents are preventable), only then will there be a sustainable safety foundation.

To transcend culture and impact all stakeholders, engagement is crucial and cannot be achieved until the foundation for compliance, policy, process, and procedure is set by leadership. Evolving through the transcendence of culture then begins to push each individual within the organization to become involved. This requires each employee to demonstrate their contribution to the organization and that they are adhering to the policies, processes, and procedures being set. This is not a heavily

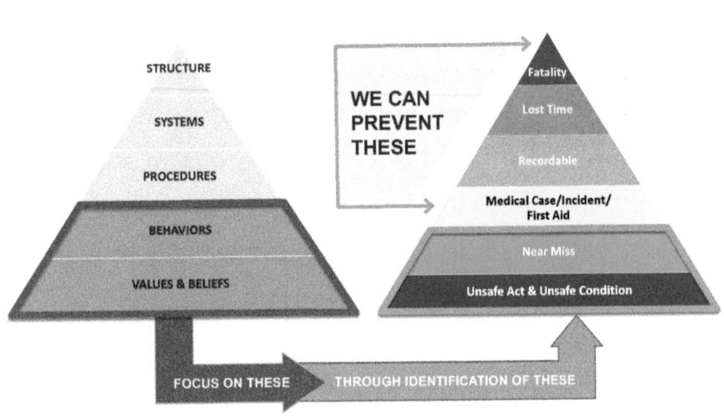


Figure 17.2
Correlation of a safety management system in relation to the Heinrich Pyramid.

weighted element of the transcendence of culture but is a necessary step to ensure there is commitment. Each employee must demonstrate commitment to safety to have a culture that is truly evolved. Every employee may not have value or belief in safety, but they do need to have a commitment to safety within the organization by following the policies, processes, and procedures set.

Once an organization can demonstrate the commitment of employees and ensure that employees are involved with the culture, employee engagement becomes critical. This part of the culture transcendence is where the employees influence the values and beliefs of the organization. Employees start to take ownership and make a contribution to making a better organization as well as a better safety culture. Each employee begins to no longer work independently but as a part of a team. To recognize the impact of employee engagement, the organization can see problem-solving activities begin to take place with employee interaction and contribution. Leaders within the organization must be absolutely supportive in this step of transcendence.

The element of trust must be established in order for employees to feel supported and of value if the organization wants to see progress in the culture. Without the support and trust of leadership, employees will begin to lose common interest and fail to see the necessity to influence others for changes and progression. At this step in the transcendence of culture, safety leadership also becomes persistent to demonstrate business value and leverage the drive for operational excellence. Employee engagement also means working collectively in teams and through cross-functionality. Functions should be able to see the benefits of employee engagement through reflection of employee participation and an increase in performance. Prior to employee engagement within an organization, safety may have been seen as a requirement, a necessity driven by policy—not a value to employees or the organization. With employee engagement, an organization should now see safety influence through the reflection of reduced incidents, which impacts production as well as overhead cost to the organization. The monetary deliverables can now be developed based upon the performance of the employees and activities driving safety culture change. Not only should monetary deliverables be seen within the organization, but the communication of safety should become more visible in the organization as well.

Without the support and trust of leadership, employees will begin to lose common interest and fail to see the necessity to influence others for changes and progression.

As a leader, one has to be able to effectively communicate vision but also the objectives in order to achieve the vision. The most successful people in business had to become effective communicators. Anyone can communicate, but to be an effective communicator is a challenge. Effective communication begins with active listening. Active listening means to not just hear what someone is saying but to be engaged with the conversation and trying to understand what someone is saying through asking questions. How many times can you think of when you were listening to someone talk and you were just waiting for them to finish so that you could begin talking? This is not active listening; active listening is processing what the other person is thinking and asking yourself if you truly understood what the person was trying to convey (restating their point in your own thoughts and words).

Effective communication begins with active listening.

## Recognition of Employees

Recognizing employees for their feedback and effort provides buy-in, trust, and commitment. Rewards and recognition allow the top-down leadership to convey the true value of employees for results from the operations of the organization. The value of results can mean multiple things within an organization. This too can be described in the safety profession. When an organization is effectively communicating, safety can be seen communicated through visuals and results of employee participation. This may be displayed through the results of problem-solving activities and housekeeping and is often driven through the safety professional. The bottom-up approach to effective communication relies upon employee feedback and follow-through of top-down management. Although communication progresses culture and structure, the efforts of employees must be recognized in order to be successful.

> Rewards and recognition allow the top-down leadership to convey the true value of employees for results from the operations of the organization.

Production, finance, and safety can all be results for what leadership defines within an organization. This may be displayed through the results of problem-solving activities and housekeeping. Employee feedback, which is taken and applied, is the result of effective communication. This employee feedback is then taken and translated into activities and results of problem solving, which is guided and supported through leadership, leading to a final step of culture transcendence: rewards and recognition. Rewards and recognition allow leadership to convey the true value of employees for results. The value of results can mean multiple things within an organization. Production, finance, or safety can all be results for what leadership defines within an organization. No matter what the value or the results, if employees are not recognized for their efforts or rewarded through praise, money, or other means, morale and drive within the organization will drastically fall, and continuing excellence will fail. In August of 2016, *New York Magazine* conducted a study on productivity and employee recognition as well as rewards. The study began with sending three out of four employees at a semiconductor factory in Israel messages at the beginning of a week, indicating detailed rewards for meeting production to a specific number of chips each day. The first group was promised a "Well Done!" text message from the manager at the end of the week. The second group was promised a bonus of $30.00, and the third group was promised a pizza voucher. Last, a fourth group received no message or offer.

At the end of the week, the results came back with the percentage of productivity. Most would think that those who received the bonus would have the highest percent of productivity, but this was completely opposite of what the study actually revealed. Money proved a 13.2-percent less effective production incentive than the other groups with the exception of the group that received no reward or recognition. In the end, the "Well Done!" group had the highest productivity, with pizza coming in second for productivity percentage (Dahl 2016). Just as the study concluded, without recognizing and rewarding employees, leadership within an organization cannot expect productive results.

No matter if leadership is defined in safety or within any other profession, the principles are the same, and the human elements must be established and, more importantly, recognizable throughout the organization and others. To achieve excellence, leadership must be able to not only establish the structure for an organization but also be able to influence others

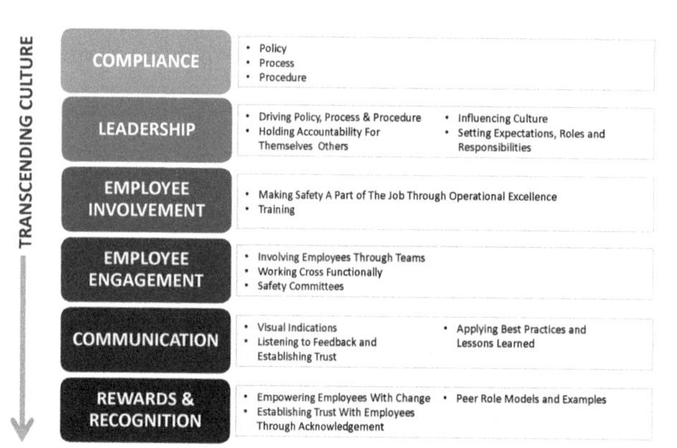


Figure 17.3
Process for establishing a strong safety culture.

> To achieve excellence, leadership must be able to not only establish the structure for an organization but also be able to influence others through beliefs and values.

through beliefs and values. A culture of an organization will only be able to transcend for excellence and achieve a safe work environment with the involvement and engagement of employees through leadership's support. The transcendence of culture can only be achieved with the leadership effectively communicating objectives and recognizing employees for their efforts.

## Conclusion

At the end of the day, a successful safety program in an organization stems from top-down management with a defined structure for policy, process, and procedures from senior leadership and a bottom-up approach through engaging employees with the backbone of effective communication and recognition. Any employee can be the advocate for safety within an organization as long as they recognize and drive the connection between the management and culture for change, but an effective safety professional will lead based upon the principles of the human elements with a clear vision and mission. Safety does not work as a standalone process with one individual but becomes visible through the excellence of an organization and the ability of every employee to be accountable for themselves and influence others for change. The basis of a safety culture lives and dies with the ability to become a cross-functional facet within an organization. Top-down management and bottom-up approach is not just one way for safety advocacy and success; it is the only effective way for safety advocacy and success.

## Questions

1. What are the four human elements that support building an effective relationship as a safety professional and help in "selling safety"?
    a. Communication, influence, self-interest, and impacting others
    b. Trust, influence, self-interest, and self-preservation
    c. Trust, influence, common interest, and self-preservation
    d. Trust, communication, impacting others, and common interest
2. Which was the most effective in influencing others when positively recognizing employees for productivity?
    a. Money
    b. A message of "Well Done!"
    c. Pizza
    d. None of the above
3. Policies, processes, and procedures help set the structure, which is providing basic guidelines to employees.
    a. True
    b. False
4. What does 5S stand for?
    a. Sort, Standardize, Simplify, Shine, and Supply
    b. Sort, Set in order, Shine, Standardize, and Sustain
    c. Set in order, Style, Simplify, Standardize, and Sparkle
    d. Sort, Style, Simplify, Shine, and Sustain
5. In Heinrich's book *Industrial Accident Prevention: A Scientific Approach,* he looks at empirical data to show that as many as 95 percent of all workplace incidents are caused by unsafe conditions.
    a. True
    b. False

## References

Dahl, M. (2016) "How to Motivate Employees: Give Them Compliments and Pizza." *New York Times Magazine* (August 29).

Heinrich, H. W. (1931) *Industrial Accident Prevention: A Scientific Approach*. New York: McGraw-Hill.

Paquin, R., and K. Prouty. (2014) *Managing Safety to Promote Operational Excellence*. Boston: Aberdeen Group.

SECTION 4

# TECHNICAL CONTENTS

CHAPTER 18

# PREDICTIVE ANALYTICS AND BIG DATA FOR CONTINUOUS IMPROVEMENT: CHARACTERISTICS AND APPLICATIONS

Richard Olawoyin

## Learning Objectives

After studying this chapter, the reader will be able to:

1. Integrate information technologies with data analytical methods to extract value from data sets to enhance continuous improvement of an establishment
2. Evaluate safety and business implications, significance, and applicability of observed data patterns and analytical inferences
3. Identify opportunities, needs, and constraints for data analytics within organizational contexts through the use of analytics to inform safety and health strategies, policies, and managerial decisions
4. Provide leadership in analytics teams and projects

## Key Terms

**Big data, analytics, proactive safety management, workplace safety, safety analytics, risk assessment, research.**

## Abstract

There are several challenging aspects in modeling safety risk for operational applications based on inadequate collected data. The advent of the probabilistic model has made it easier to make significant inferences about accidents' causative factors quantitatively. The predictive safety inferences made from the formal and qualitative reasoning data to probable deductions and assumptions allow for the identification of the most significant contributing factors resulting to a risk-factor ranking. This method also enables an analyst to study potential mitigation impacts.

*Big data* is becoming a common term that is even more meaningfully used based on its distinct characteristics as an emerging area of data science. The usage of big data in environmental health and safety (EHS) professional practice is beginning to provide improved solutions to imminent problems affecting individuals and organizations. This chapter explores the progress made and applicability of big data in EHS practice and related fields. The characteristics of big data relative to how it can be applied in EHS are defined. Additionally, the technological tools for processing big data are outlined together with the challenges of big data and best practices management. The chapter also identifies research opportunities with the aim of providing guidance to the readers interested in exploring the usage and improvements of big data in EHS science and engineering.

## Introduction to Big Data

Data is ubiquitous. The term *big data* refers to large or complex datasets that conventional data-processing approaches cannot handle. In context, what volume of data can be categorized as "big"? The answer is not uniform across the board because emergent data do not follow a well-defined structure and can be complex. In our changing world of technological advancements, the amount of digital data currently in existence is growing exponentially, amplified by up to 50 percent annually; these changes directly affect the way we live and process information.

For instance, the geographic positioning system (GPS) built in cars and other devices generate huge amounts of data constantly—at every tick of time. Traffic information is consistently managed through the processing of traffic data and commands, people and vehicles traffic, weather and road conditions, and so forth. These collected data come in a variety of formats, ranging from textual, audio, coordinates, visual, and satellite information. Once the datasets are collected, they may become unpredictably large to process with conventional methods and make quick decisions as needed for regular commuters.

In the workplace, many companies are intensifying focus on improving the working environment for their workers. It is estimated that workplace fatalities, injuries, and illnesses result in economic losses amounting to 4 or 5 percent of gross domestic product (Al-Mutairi and Haight 2009). The World Health Organization (WHO) reported that in 2012, approximately 12.6 million people died from working in unhealthy environments (WHO 2016). These numbers are staggering, and it is extremely important to understand how various workplace demands may influence overall workplace safety. One of the best ways to analyze workplace safety is through the use of analytics to control the outcomes. Throughout the years, companies have begun to use statistics to continuously improve workplace safety by implementing safety protocols. By observing percentages, rates, and trends of injuries and illness among other aspects of safety, companies have been successful in creating safer work environments for everyone. The use of statistical analysis has had a tremendous impact on how safety and health have evolved over the past decades.

> Technological advancement has allowed companies to use past data to figure out why certain injuries occur, forecast trends for future incidents, and develop models for predicting what will happen in the future.

Large corporations often have data available to solve safety issues. For example, the Federal Aviation Authority (FAA), under the Aviation Safety Information Analysis and Sharing (ASIAS) program, used big data to make safety improvement in the sector. Data was collected and aggregated from more than 180 sources, such as governmental agencies and industries (Hughes 2016). Similarly, a company with employees tasked with lifting heavy objects may have a higher number of sprained wrist, back, or sore shoulders injuries. The company can start by keeping track of reported shoulder and wrist injuries and associated resulting factors. Once results are recorded, data can be accumulated and processed to determine the most common causes of the injuries. The variety of the data collected allows for the identification of the prevalent causes of incidents. This data can be helpful to prevent future injuries by identifying the common injury types, frequency of occurrence, and other contributing factors.

Big data has also been used in advancing accident prevention efforts and for predictive modeling. One of the issues with system safety data is that it often comes in amounts too large for individual analysis. Computer systems and programs have been developed to process data that can take years of data collected from a single company, and prevailing trends can be easily identified, using the computer programs. Technological advancement has allowed companies to use past data in order to figure out why certain injuries occur, forecast trends for future incidents, and develop models for predicting what will happen in the future. It is imperative to understand the importance and difficulty of using leading indicators when managing safety (Schultz 2013; Laratonda 2014). Relying solely on lagging indicators results in a reactive approach to safety, while utilizing leading indicators shifts the company's efforts to a more proactive approach. While Laratonda (2014) highlighted the advantages of using leading indicators for predictive analytics, Schultz (2015) recognizes that these sources of data are not always as clear and can be confusing, often resulting in inaccurate interpretations. For these reasons, it is often necessary to rely on computer technology to use algorithms and computer machine learning in order to develop accurate prediction models. The available technology and methods can be used to further advance safety methods. Data and computer programs can provide valuable information, which should be used to fix issues and promote reliable safety protocols.

## Professional Disciplines for Large Datasets

There are three professional disciplines (figure 18.1) relevant to how large datasets can be sorted to identify patterns and establish relationships from the information acquired through data analysis to solve impending problems. It is important to differentiate these three based on their definition, their applications, and required skills for becoming an expert in those areas.

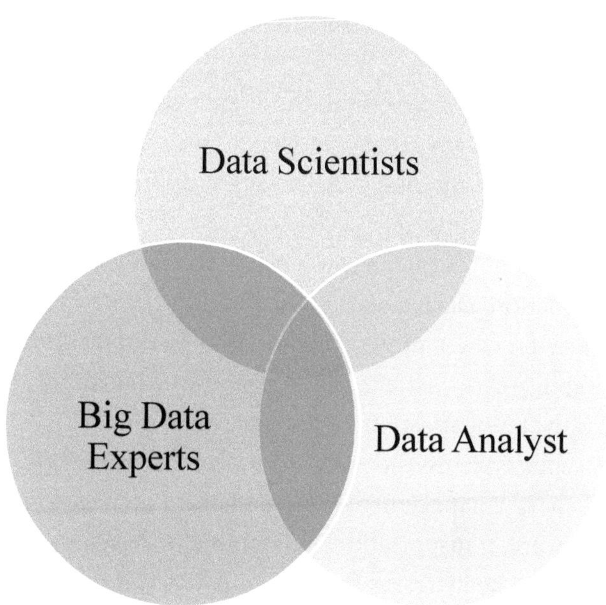


Figure 18.1
Three professional disciplines for large datasets use

The *data science*, also known as "datalogy," is an interdisciplinary field that involves the use of scientific systems, processes, and methods (including data cleansing, data preparation, and data analysis) for knowledge extraction or insight acquisition from unstructured and structured data (Dhar 2013). Data sciences combine concepts and techniques (such as machine learning, data mining, classification, clustering, visualization, and alignment) from broad disciplines, including information science, mathematics, statistics, advanced problem solving, programming, and computer science. Data science algorithms are mostly used in industries, such as in digital advertisements, Internet and web searches, search recommenders, and so on. Data scientists help with identifying leading indicators that can be helpful for making decisions on elimination or substitution of hazards.

The technique of analyzing insights that can result to enhanced decision and organizational strategic move is called big data. The term *big data* is often used to describe the process of analyzing enormous volumes of structured and unstructured data. Big data is applicable in environmental protection, industrial safety, retail, communication, and financial services industries.

*Data analytics* refers to the science of exploring unprocessed data using algorithmic or automated processes and queries, and data aggregation processes to acquire insights into certain datasets of interest, with the aim of reaching valuable conclusions on the information. Data analytics is applicable in several industries, which provide organizations and businesses the ability carry out effective decision-making along with the authentication or invalidation of existing concepts, systems, theories, or models. Environmental and energy management, risk and hazard management, healthcare, transportation, and robotics industries can apply data analytics, as fit for its intended use.

## Characteristics of Big Data

Big data involves the use of predictive analytics based on environmental or user behavior to extract information from available data. It explores data storage methods and the extraction of hidden information embedded in the data. Big-data analytics has found appreciable use for injury and disease prevention, wellness promotion, property protection, hazard and risk mitigations, crime combat, business trends and profitability analysis, cost-benefit analysis, and so forth.

The advancement in technology of health science professions has led to better outcomes that save lives and provide protection, as care has become customizable to personal needs—thanks to big data. Technologies with integrated data processing capabilities in the healthcare industry include monitoring prescription refills based on health parameters and usage and real-time data processing bio-monitors and sensors, which enable care professionals to make prompt decisions with access to patients (e.g. work or home location, medical cards and information, immediate health conditions—blood pressure, pulse, heartbeat, etc.).

Organizations are faced with tremendously complex environments based on organizational dynamics and complexity, rapidly changing technological tools and client behaviors, and an increasing need to be at the competitive advantage. The blast from the vast amounts of data that can be obtained from digital technologies has unlocked many opportunities to gain valuable insights into the most prolific solution. Scientists, engineers, manufacturers, corporate executives, government, medical practitioners, EHS professionals, and marketers frequently face different challenges with big data, including data search and capture without noise, proper storage, analytical procedures, data sharing and transfer, data query, updates, data mining and visualization, data management, and privacy of information.

Obtaining adequate data for especially EHS analytics and modeling can be a challenge due to the fact that most operations rarely collect and preserve accident and incident data; therefore, the alternative modeling methods to conventional risk analysis approaches (fault tree, event tree, and bowtie logic diagrams) are essential, such as real-time simulation modeling, probabilistic analytical approaches, and so forth to reasonably comprehend the situations. The issue of risk in system safety becomes the focus because of the unknown potential hazards relative to different systems. A system safety approach encompasses the identification-analysis-control methodologies of safety.

Datasets grow rapidly in the emerging world due to the fact that information-sensing gadgets are cheap and accessible for use. Smart offices or homes incorporate devices that are able to exchange information quickly through the transfer and processing of data via the Internet of Things (IoT) interface. The IoT components include wireless networks and sensors, mobile devices (e.g., mobile phones, mobile air-quality sensors, mobile scanners, etc.), aerial devices (remote sensing), and so on (Segaran and Hammerbacher 2009).

Success with current business models, unlike conventional practices, largely depends on making intelligent decisions. Making astute organizational decisions requires prompt actions due to the dynamics of the business environment, as business situations develop in quick succession. The digital connectivity makes people, organizations, enterprises, and their stakeholders, near or far, closely connected at all times. Therefore, changes or prompt decisions are transmitted without delay. Smart decision-making requires fast collection and processing of operational or business data.

The distinguishing characteristics of big data from conventional database systems are presented in figure 18.2. Big data that is expanding with capacities to hold patterns and demonstrates the order of existence quantifies the volume of the big data. Data generation from different sources such as networks, sensors, and smart devices, which produce data in either structured or unstructured formats (e.g., text, pictures, graphics, audio, video, logs), can be characterized as data variety (O'Leary 2013).

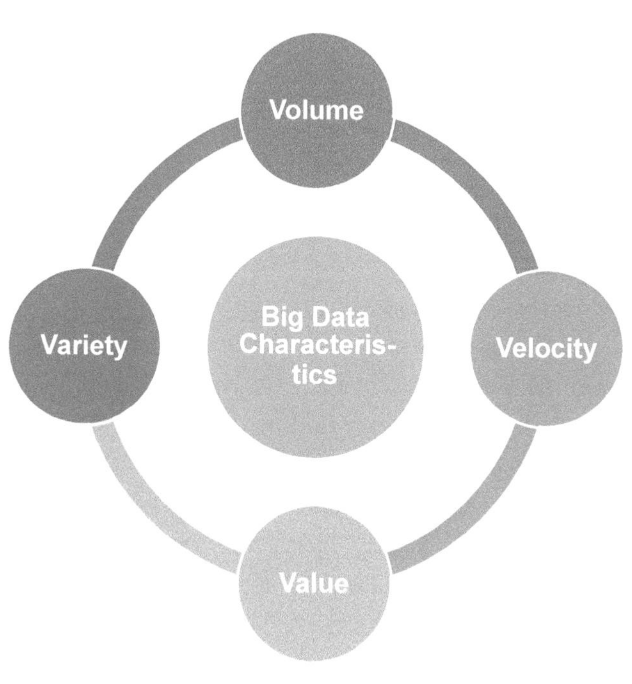


Figure 18.2
Characteristics of big data

The emergence of data through a timeline, together with the rapidity of the data, is called the *data velocity*. This is crucial as there are certain data points generated per tick of time, and the velocity requires that the data is captured without loss. The method of mining embedded information from emerging data is the value of the big data.

## Big Data Classification

Big data can be classified into data sources, storage, format, staging, and processing as illustrated in figure 18.3 (Hashem 2015). The sources of the big data could be a variety of measurement devices (such as combustion analyzer, heat stress or noise meters, dosimeters, toxic gas sensor meters, etc.) that read values and change over time. Other sources may include manual records, IoT, social media or web-based applications, machines with data acquisition, and transmission such as robotics systems and engineering system safety, and so forth. The data content format may be structured, quasi-structured, or unstructured; also the data should be stored to enable quick access when needed. Before the process of mining relevant information from the stored data, preprocessing of the data may be required through the data staging phase, after which a systematic procedure is implemented to process the big data, either in batches or real time.

The advantage of batch processing in contrast to the real-time processing is that it is less time sensitive and involves a three-tier procedure where the collected data is entered and processed and batch outputs are produced. This process is cost effective for organizations since it is also efficient during data auditing; however, the process of batch processing may be slow due to the time delay between data collection. The real-time processing involves continuous input, processing, and output of data in a relatively short period of time (examples include bank ATMs, GPS, point-of-sale systems, online safety data sheets [SDS], etc.). Information on the real-time data processing is always up to date, and this can help organizations detect trends or opportunities that are of interest in a timely manner; however, the real processing of data is more complex and expensive. It requires constant backup, and data auditing may be difficult to carry out.

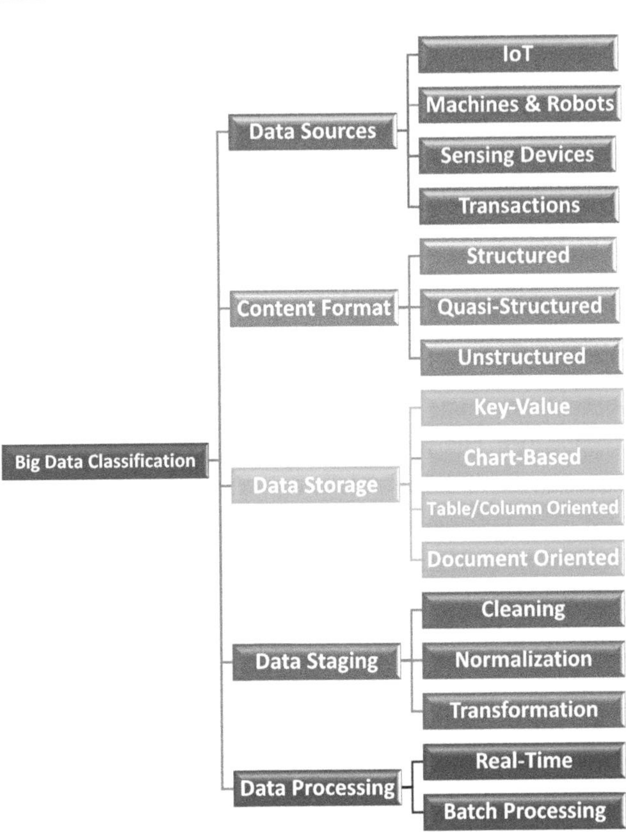


Figure 18.3
Big data classification

## Key Features of Data Analytics

Data mining is a powerful tool used to extract relevant information from big data, and consequently, the intelligent insight gained from the process is used to provide improved services to clients or implement changes that are necessary to protect people, property, and the environment.

Analytics are developed from high-powered numerical methods, such as Bayesian belief networks (BBN), machine learning (e.g., artificial neural networks (ANN), deep learning networks (DLN, etc.), support vector machines (SVM), Hidden Markov models (HMM), and so on. Bayesian analysis can be used for continuous improvement to ensure the safety of workers and environmental and asset protection. Bayesian analysis uses inferences to help achieve this objective. The Bayesian inference method involves a prediction of the number of potential accidents that may occur, the duration of the lost time, impact, as well as the duration of the time they are recovering from the injury (Marcoulaki et al. 2012). Effective predictions using this data can help predict injuries, their frequencies, and the recovery duration.

Data Analytics are used to examine and interpret distinct data features from spatial and temporal data extractions to high-speed data extractions of data streams and sensor data. The characteristics of the four main types of data analytics, together with their potential applications, are illustrated in figure 18.4. Data analytics explores data mining through a timeline of series of collected data and privacy security guarantees the availability, integrity, confidentiality, and the big data security infrastructure.

In qualitative reasoning and analysis of events, trends, or incidents, *text analytics* are applicable for understanding text data, using techniques such as topic modeling, language mapping of linguistic expressions, sentiment analysis, elicitation analysis, and opinion analysis. Text analytics is crucial for information recall (such as query processing and documentation illustration). Word sense disambiguation (WSD), probabilistic context-free grammars (PCFG), and lexical acquisition are all considered as computational linguistics under *text analytics.* Other powerful techniques used in text analytics include the probabilistic retrieval model (PRM), Boolean retrieval model (BRM), and vector-space model (VSM).

Similar to text analytics, *network analytics* are designed for use on sentiment analysis and topic detection with the aim of finding the influencing node or to predict the links between threats and opportunities, which is important for mitigating risk and security concerns. Network analytics are also important for the monitoring of special organizational activities, potential hazards, and safety needs through the integrated computational analysis of network data.

Mobile devices such as cell phones, tablets, and smart watches are capable of hosting mobile applications, integrating users from diverse domains into a bionetwork, executing *mobile analytics.* The main importance of mobile analytics is that it provides location-based data analytics that are capable of making predictions of human presence at a given location, space, and time. It may also predict human mobility based on locational sensing. This may be useful for understanding reoccurring accidents/ incidents and helping with developing effective control measures to avoid reoccurrence.

Insight intelligence is the value acquired from the use of analytics to treat big data. These insights are unbelievably powerful and can be used to implement immediate changes in an organization, with the potential to increase productivity by preventing accidents and reducing injuries and lost time while identifying expanded areas of opportunity.

Successful strategies for the application of big data are illustrated in figure 18.5. It is crucial to be able to apply big data analytics to identify new opportunities. Data by itself without exploration and interpretation is useless. An effective strategy for breaking new grounds is to utilize available data to identify areas of prospects and improvements internally and externally. This can be implemented by initiating end-point thinking, which involves clear definition of issues or challenges of interest and analytical questions that need to be answered.

Exploring data for providing solutions to known or unknown problems and for opening up new areas of opportunities needs creative and innovative thinking. Data analytic tool–development approaches are expected to improve the recognition of operational and safety hazards. Conventional methods of hazard analysis were limited in providing advanced insight and operational intelligence based on functionality, reliability, and accuracy. Data mining through the use of analytics opens a plethora of new opportunities for the identification of potential safety conditions and accident histories.

Big data analytics is expected to improve the safety profile of an organization and consequently will result in higher productivity. Multiple processes, equipment, devices, tools, and emerging technologies are used to meet the needs of the dynamic economy in today's world. Being familiar with the decision drive that works through analytics will help to identify areas needing improvement and lead to success.

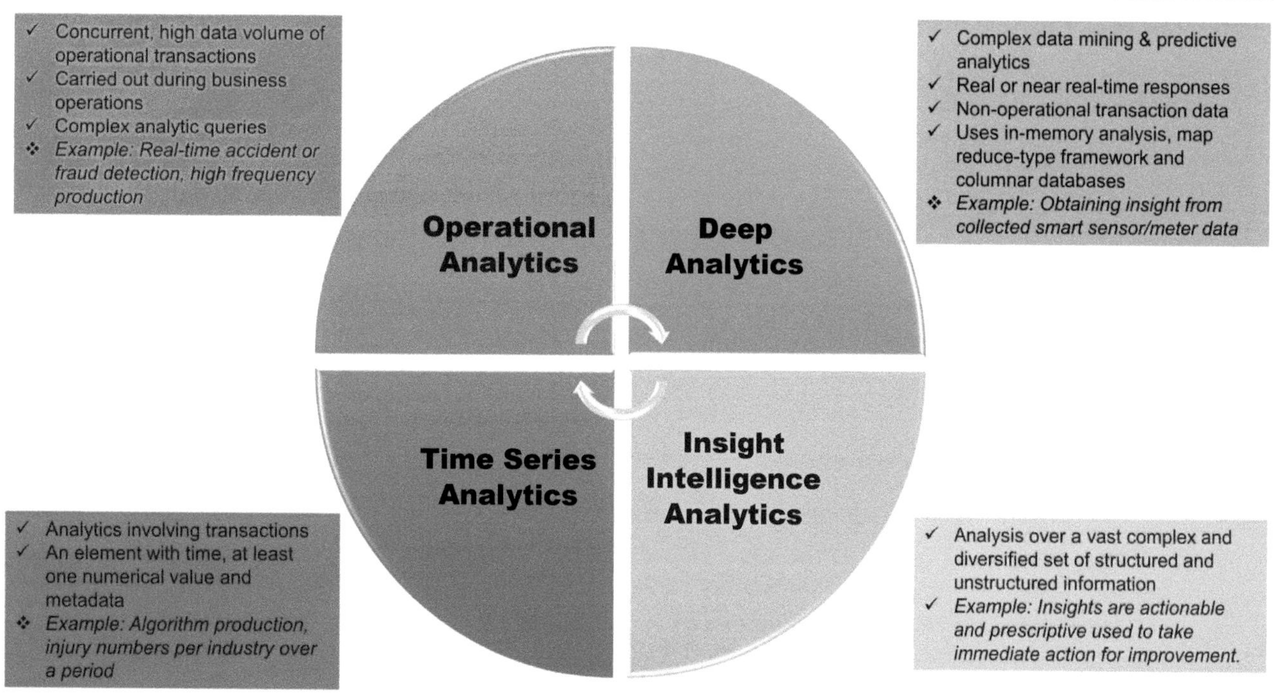


Figure 18.4
Types and characteristics of data analytics

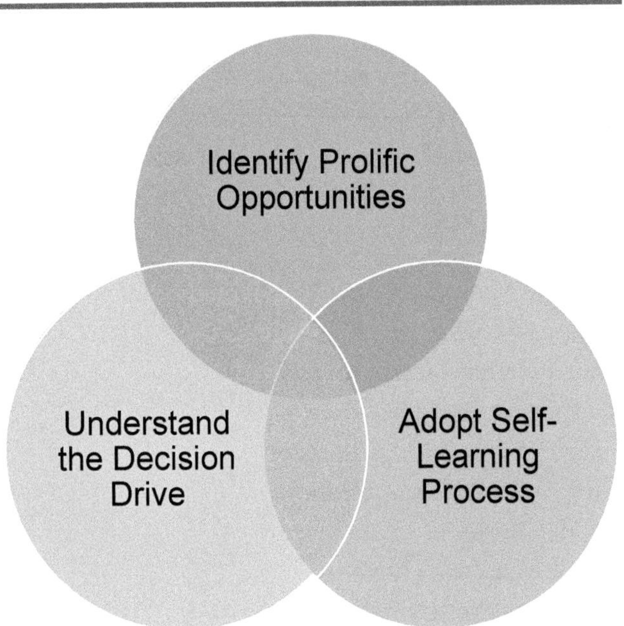


Figure 18.5
Summary tips for big data implementation for success

It will also provide for personalized focus on target areas. Additionally, the use of predictive statistical techniques, such as self-learning machines, can help with identifying issues in real time, carrying out quick comparisons of alternatives and making predictions of the best outcomes. Acquiring insight from data helps with data-driven decision-making. Therefore, analytics derives information from data, helps with understanding the information, provides intelligent insight from the information analysis, facilitates prediction, and guarantees foresight.

Advanced analytics can effectively provide benefits from the line worker and mid-management to upper management. Modernized workforces and the constantly changing global markets are driving many organizations into a new paradigm of flexibility into the business model. For businesses to maintain the competitive market advantage, agility is required with the ability to swiftly and smartly respond to market demands in a customer-centered economy. Maintaining a positive safety climate (keeping people safe) in this fast-paced and demanding environment may be a challenge. Workloads may be increased by higher production flexibility as a result of constant changeovers. Striking a balance between safety, production, and quality becomes a key issue. Interruptions in machine runs are measured per minute, and each minute of downtime means lower productivity, which directly affects profitability. A larger loss percentage is recorded when the operation runs are shorter because operators are focusing on quality and trying to get it right and avoid accidents. With this situation, the measured actual output will be lower than the maximum capacity (negative asset utilization). The self-learning process can be utilized to provide real-time insight per situation and keep the equilibrium between safety, production, and quality.

## Creating Value from Data

The importance of big data cannot be overstated; however, other processes are important when considering the value derived from data. How to collect, capture, transform, and clean the data must also be part of the holistic process for making use of the insight gained to routine analytics. Early big-data analytics have focused mainly on the process of data analysis for businesses, social research, web searches, military strategies, and other high-data-volume sources. This process involves developing independent distinct systems and algorithms for analyzing each dataset by type of data and as individual silos and is lightweight in value. The true value of data, however, is derived through the application of *Metcalf's law* to data, which is a unified approach of integrating multiple processes in a global context to fully maximize the data value and lead to effective learning.

Learning through data analysis is important. For instance, accident and incident data or worker behaviors relative to work conditions have enormously valuable information embedded in them that can be analyzed for insight into how to eliminate/substitute or control hazards.

It is remarkable to analyze accident/incident data and learn that workers that are most frequently involved in occupational incidents are the newly hired (without much training) and long-term workers (with extensive training but have become complacent). Certain work tasks are unsuitable for specific workers due to ergonomics, environmental, biochronological, or skill factors. Big data can also provide insight into how to improve employee experiences, track short- and long-term occupational epidemiology, predict productivity and behavior influencers, enhance the quality of life, and remain strategically focused on organizational goals. The application of integrated analytics, based on the ability to reason with all data by integrating data sources from all departments in an organization and analyzing the data as an integral piece, will provide the best insight and create the best value from the data.

## Applications of Big Data and Analytics in EHS

Big data and analytics are becoming increasing useful in many fields from academia to businesses and organizations with interest in learning more about their processes. Organizations are faced with a highly competitive global marketplace with pressing demands for profitability. The ability to identify efficient ways to operate while ensuring the safety of the workers, environment, and processes (risk minimization) is of prime importance. Toward this end, organizations are focused on using integrated data analytics to derive the business intelligence required to remain competitive.

Some of the applications of big data and data analytics include:

### Risk analysis

Humans have always been eager to be able to predict what will happen next, and based on this knowledge, they have created hopes and fears to meet the situations. Historically, the fear of demonic spirits, devils, ghosts, gods, and witches dominated the human psyche; in recent times, the fears have emerged into fear of accidents, diseases, terrorism, and natural disasters. These are all outside fears known as external risks. Other examples of external risks include economic risks (market volatility and currency fluctuations), geopolitical risks (corruption, political instability, and intercontinental tensions),

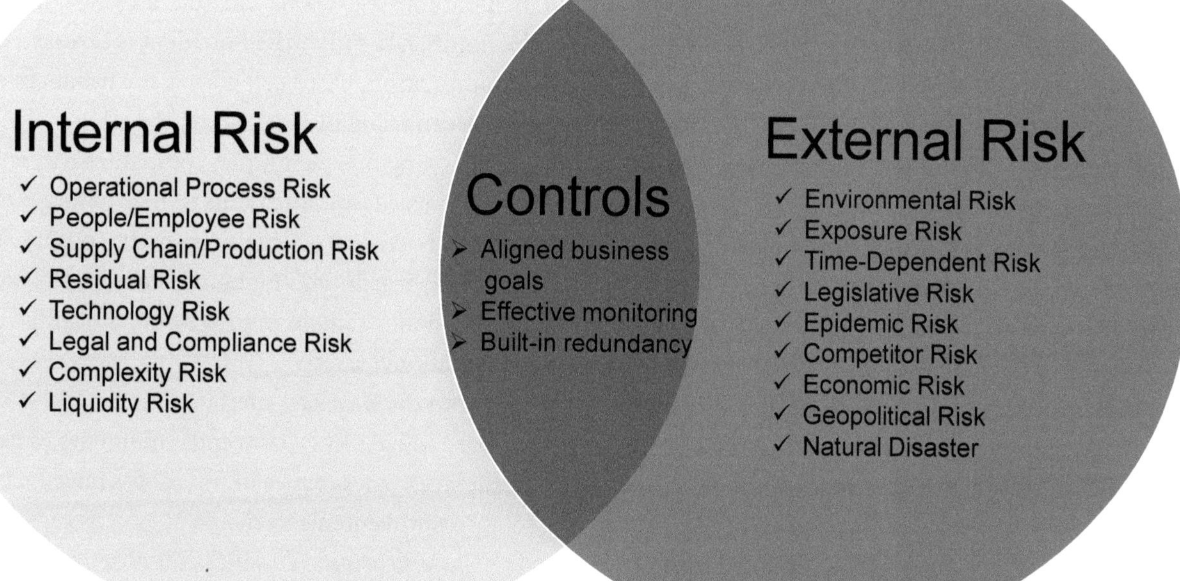


Figure 18.6
Risk categories and controls

and epidemics. Inside risks are called internal risks, which are often unidentified and underestimated and the consequence of which may lead to irreparable damages. Internal risks may be based on quality, workers' health and safety, cost and services, and customer satisfaction. Examples of internal risks include overreliance on figures, forecast accuracy, lack of due process, ineffective design and supply networks, myopic view, or short-term strategy for execution, and so forth. Figure 18.6 illustrates other examples of external and internal risks and examples of effective solutions. Unpredictable risks accounts for about 10 percent of risks in general.

All risks are assessed according to the probability of a risk event occurring and the potential impacts (losses, expenses, or human casualties).

Nolan (2013) defines analytics as observing data and using it to create prevention tools. It plays a vital role in the use of optimizing workplace safety, particularly in the ability to identify high-risk situation areas. Oftentimes, learning from and identifying incidents can become difficult. In most cases a lot of information is incomplete, and it is unclear which incidents are preventable or which intervention strategies are optimal (Anderson et al. 2015). However, through the process of analytics, this type of data can recognize and track key risk indicators (KRIs), including employee attributes and behaviors, environmental factors, and other variables that may impact the risk of different safety incidences (Prescriptive Safety Analytics 2016). Using sophisticated analysis techniques will in turn spot the trending areas that need to be addressed and further work toward the ability of reducing errors and eliminating risks.

Safety analytics can be described in five phases: job hazard analysis, risk management planning and training, safety inspection and observation, incident analysis, and recognition and accountability. Each of these five phases requires the acquisition of safety data, as previously explained. A critical aspect of an effective safety management system is conducting risk assessments. Markowski et al. (2016) reviewed over one hundred articles to develop a workplace assessment tool for determining employees at risk of being injured on the job. It was proposed that information from employees should be collected and analyzed using a screening tool, including the employee's past history of injuries, family history of injuries and illnesses, certain medical conditions, and behavioral or personality traits. Schultz (2012) also discussed the importance of analyzing job processes, environmental conditions, and equipment used when conducting risk assessments. These pieces of information are important for determining weaknesses in systems that can increase the potential for being injured on the job or developing an occupational illness or disease. Safety professionals can effectively integrate data from personal factors in addition to environmental and procedural data, and carry out a more detailed and accurate risk assessment. The risk assessment can then be used to fix the systems to prevent injury in the future.

***PRAT Scale:*** The proportional risk assessment technique (PRAT) is a scaling technique for system prevention used to quantitatively measure the likelihood of occurrence of an accident. It uses a scale of 1–10 and integrates the risk magnitude (R) calculation, likelihood (L), severity (S), and frequency of an incident or injury (Marhavilas 2011). The risk is then put into a 1–1000 scale (table 18.1), and based on the number, the identified incident is assessed deeper for elimination. Once calculated, the numbers can be prioritized using the scale in table 18.1.

By using this technique, companies can rank certain hazards and incidents to help prioritize what needs to be assessed. This assessment companies to focus on hazards with higher severity, likelihood, and frequency to help improve on the overall organizational safety.

Both the Bayesian method and the PRAT scale are used to help find out trends in injuries in certain workplaces. These types of inferences have helped with safety improvements in the past.

***Classification:*** Classification is defined as placing anything into specific groups based on similar characteristics, such as grouping by certain industries, occupations, race/ethnicities, or events (Jens-Erik 2011; Wiatrowski 2013). This process can help prevent

**Table 18.1** Gradation of the risk value versus urgency level of required actions

| Risk value (R) | Urgency level of required actions |
|---|---|
| 700–1000 | Immediate action |
| 500–700 | Required action earlier than 1 day |
| 300–500 | Required action earlier than 1 month |
| 200–300 | Required action earlier than 1 year |
| <200 | Immediate action is not necessary, but it requires event surveillance |

unwanted events by narrowing down the inferences that can be used to track when, where, and why risk events occur.

***Hazard control:*** The most valuable contribution of available big data in risk assessment comes from the ability to determine weaknesses in an overall system in an effort to fix them. Data will reveal weaknesses in an organization; the weaknesses can then be identified and fixed. With advancements in technology, computer programs have been developed that can input a large amount of information, such as the building layout, maintenance records, and other risk factors to determine potential failures that could occur. Dong et al. (2015) demonstrated that by using advanced computer software, potential failure modes could be predicted for a crane system. The system calculated new hazards that could develop from a modification of a crane arm and developed a comprehensive list of potential failures that could arise from this change. These failures brought on by the change would pose a risk for personnel. The data produced by the computer program is an important tool for preparation. This level of rapid evaluation of system factors can be applied to a variety of systems, which can help determine if improvement measures implemented to the system will fix the problems or create new hazards (Deloitte n. d.; Badri et al. 2012). The purpose of the risk assessment is to remove or control the hazards that could contribute to system failures and occupational accidents.

The most valuable contribution of available big data in risk assessment comes from the ability to determine weaknesses in an overall system in an effort to fix them.

Several economic dynamics and compliance requirements influence the necessity to analyze these risks with better insight into potential damages in all situations. Data mining approaches can be used to identify and predict the numerous factors that could lead to the individual attributable risks, or the situations may be analyzed collectively using integrated analytics for all contributory risks. The big data and analytics can help identify potential internal, external, or unforeseeable risks with better contingencies to controlling the risks.

### Trend Predictions

Environmental and occupational health and safety risks have significant impacts on the well-being and income of workers across industrial sectors. In addition, employers also bear the brunt of these risk events after occurrence. For example, slip, trip, or fall injuries rank high among the most common occupational injuries (affecting up to 1 million people annually), which are estimated to cost organizations approximately $40,000 per incident in worker's compensation claims. Hence organizations have recognized the need to adequately develop innovative means of risk and hazard mitigation/control and trend predictions in their operations. Other sources of data relevant to the use of trend projections for data-driven decision-making include obesity, stress, depression, psychosocial issues, alcohol and drug addiction, workplace violence, and so on.

Organizations also collect large amounts of data on equipment functionality, talents, designs, customer's information (age, race, gender, level of technological know-how, interests), market research (sales, production ratio), and employees' information (pre-injury conditions, wellness, welfare, training, technical competence, injury statistics, productivity, and engagement with innovative ideas). Information from these data-mining strategies can help with the identification of where improvements are needed to ensure that the operations are effective, where workers are injured and determine whether the solution will allow workers to return to work more efficiently, or predict future outcomes of potential diseases or reaction to work conditions. The integrated analytics, when carried out using multidimensional tools, can also help visualize the trends in customers' interests, consequently helping to efficiently target the customers' needs and making logistical plans/predictions for growth (increase revenues/profits).

An example of the usefulness of trend predictions as a valuable tool to data analytics was reported in a case study by Schultz (2013). An employee with an arm laceration from a box cutter had to go to the hospital for stitches. The injury was not significant; however, the company was still required to record it as a lost-time incident. This location was identified as the safest within this business, and there were no obvious indicators to suggest increased risk of injury at the location. However, using a proactive model (a red-flag prediction model), it was identified that this location was at high risk of having increased safety incidents. The computer model used the last three months of safety inspection and observation data from the hazard location to predict future accident trends. This is extremely beneficial as no other indicators were suggesting any type of increased risk. The computer model showed trends and nuances in the safety inspection and observation data that allowed for the determination of other potential issues that were beyond the reach of traditional safety measures (Schultz 2013). With increased data collection and the use of analytics, it is expected that prediction models and integrated technology will also be improved to provide more accurate results.

Efficiently allocating resources in the constantly changing global economic environment is a crucial business strategy for organizations. Running an organization effectively requires a sound prediction system using trend analysis to understand the influence of multiple factors and compare several scenarios relative to transactions, operational activities, duration of activities, and logistics for the purpose of maximizing profitability.

### Preventative Maintenance

Preventive maintenance is fundamental, regular, routine maintenance aimed to keep equipment up and running; improve equipment availability, reliability and maintainability; and eliminate excessive maintenance tasks and inspections, while focusing efforts on the most important items: preventing unintended interruptions in equipment failure (before it occurs) and associated costs, reducing day-to-day operational errors, reducing risk of injury, and increasing the overall readiness of a facility relative to an emergency. Preventive maintenance requires thorough planning, scheduling (frequency of activities), and service record-keeping of all maintenance activities to ensure that equipment is properly serviced and repaired to minimize potential failure rates. Companies with much equipment may find preventive maintenance to be an onerous task; therefore, the application of big-data techniques will help to organize and improve equipment life by preventing excess functionality decline, depreciation, impairment, and potential injuries to employees.

The use of robotics cells is prevalent in modern manufacturing industry. Sensors are embedded in the cells and on production lines for efficiency and failure-rate monitoring. This facilitates quick detection of potential issues so as to provide immediate corrective action in order to avoid equipment interruptions. The causative factor may be from multiple interlinked components from various subsystems connected to the production line. Massive amounts of unstructured data collected by the embedded sensors, together with the historic PM records for the different subsystems and production logs at peak capacity, may accrue over time from the continuous operation of the production line. The different subsystems can be effectively analyzed using the aggregated data by applying big data analytics, such as time-series analysis (TSA) and pattern recognition (PR) of the various failure events from the historic data. This can help identify potential failures in the subsystems. Additionally, the probability of failure of components in the subsystems can be forecasted based on the correlation between the aggregated maintenance records, production logs, and sensor measurements using data-analytics approaches, such as the path and criticality analyses. This will help keep equipment in the production lines running without interruptions, and the operations will also run efficiently and productively. Overall, the application of analytics to effectively manage preventive maintenance will result to improved facility safety.

## Research Challenges

Key research challenges potential for improvements to the analytics of big data include identifying new safety data sources and the characteristics of large volumes of diverse datasets; efficiently eliminating duplicate datasets; best practices for integrity, security, privacy and control requirements of big data; developing smarter algorithms to process data irrespective of size in multicore space; and auditing and compliance verification requirements.

The management of huge and rapidly changing data volumes is challenging. Just like everything else in large volumes, big data can be complex, noisy, diverse, dynamic, and unreliable. Research interests in the application of big data continue to be focused on data acquisition, data design, data integration, and data interpretation and representation. Importantly, how to efficiently and intelligently mine the data quickly without discarding useful information in the process must be a key focus. Another important consideration is the development of advanced automated systems that can generate useful data, determine the relevance of the data and what it can measure, and provide accurate difference resolution.

Other challenges of big data with potential research opportunities include data cleaning, data accessibility and reliability, data privacy (social and technical issues involving data sharing, control, and security), data heterogeneity and incompleteness (lack of structure and visualization), big-data algorithms, and computing environments. Research outcomes on data integration (mining and statistical analysis) and human collaboration (crowd sourcing) can potentially provide promising solutions to these challenges. Crowd sourcing or participatory sensing is crucial in the changing world with ubiquitous digital mobile devices. Individuals using these devices, especially in the workplace, can serve as multimodal sensors, rapidly collecting and accumulating data. The downside to this is the reliability of the devices used and the data they will collect, but reaching into the development of technology that can explore the spatial and temporal characteristics of the data can provide enhanced accuracy, precision, and, consequently, quality and reliable datasets.

Prospectively, emphasis should be on fundamental research solutions that researchers can provide to these technical challenges academic curricula refinement to provide a platform for expanded knowledge and research of the applications of analytics and big data in all fields, especially for global safety, and collaboration with legislative and governmental agencies to define policies, develop standards, pass laws, and ensure implementation of the best practices. Industries and organizations must reorganize priorities and reevaluate strategies relative to data sharing, accessibility, and velocity.

Overall, the identified areas of research opportunities outlined above are indicative of the need to improve on the quality of the big-data process.

## Conclusions

Companies and organizations face the same challenge of modern times, which is to efficiently analyze massive historical data that is relevant to their respective businesses and obtain value that will be useful to making productive decisions. Data analytics approaches are quintessential in addressing this challenge by providing fresh and enhanced opportunities to explore new markets, make innovative discoveries, optimize operational efficiency, maintain the competitive advantage, and better target customers' needs so as to be profitable. This chapter presents a bigger picture of different applicable opportunities of big data, data analytics, and data science in the era of technological advancements, especially those which focus on safety, quality, and production. The application of data-driven scientific approaches to boost the bottom line has created value for many corporations and organizations. It is expected that as big data analytics becomes well known across the board, more organizations will harness its beneficial potentials to stay ahead of the curve.

## Questions

1. Discuss the frequent challenges posed by big data.
2. How do you differentiate conventional database systems from big data?
3. What are the characteristics of big data?
4. What is the significance of network analytics and mobile analytics in EHS?
5. Discuss Metcalf's law of data and its relationship with safety analytics.

## References

Al-Mutairi, A., and J. M. Haight. (2009). "Predicting Incident Rates." *Professional Safety* 54(9): 40–48.

Anderson, J. E., and N. Kodate. (2015). "Learning from Patient Safety Incidents in Incident Review Meetings: Organizational Factors and Indicators of Analytic Process Effectiveness." *Safety Science* 80: 105–14.

Badri, A., S. Nadeau, and A. Gbodossou. (2012). "Proposal of a Risk-factor-based Analytical Approach for Integrating Occupational Health and Safety into Project Risk Evaluation." *Accident Analysis & Prevention* 48: 223–34.

Deloitte. (n. d.). "Workplace Safety Analytics Save Lives and the Bottom Line." Accessed July 28, 2017. http://www2.deloitte.com/content/dam/Deloitte/ca/Documents/Analytics/ca-en-analytics-workplace-safety-analytics.pdf.

Dhar, V. (2013). "Data Science and Prediction." *Communications of the ACM* 56(12): 64.

Dong, Q., G. Xu, and H. Ren. (2015). "Risk Assessment of Remanufacturing Arm Structure for Crane Based on Potential Failure Mode." *Journal of Mechanical Science and Technology* 29(12): 5345–57.

Hashem, I. A. T., I. Yaqoob, N. B. Anuar, S. Mokhtar, A. Gani, and S. Ullah. (2015). "The Rise of 'Big Data' on Cloud Computing: Review and Open Research Issues." *Information Systems* 47: 98–115.

Hughes, D. (2016). "The Data's in the Details." Accessed July 28, 2017. http://www.atca.org/Big-Data.

Mai, J.-E. (2011). "The Modernity of Classification." *Journal of Documentation* 67(4): 710–30.

Laratonda, E. (2014). "Predictive Analytics: Using Leading Indicators to Prevent the Next Injury." *Safely Made.* Accessed July 28, 2017. http://www.asse.org/assets/1/7/WR_PredictiveAnalytics_1114.pdf.

Marcoulaki, E. C.,I. A. Papazoglou, and M. Konstandinidou. (2012). "Prediction of Occupational Accident Statistics and Work Time Loss Distributions Using Bayesian Analysis." *Journal of Loss Prevention in the Process Industries* 25(3): 467–77.

Marhavilas, P. K., Koulouriotis, D. E., and C. Mitrakas. (2011). "On the Development of a New Hybrid Risk Assessment Process Using Occupational Accidents' Data: Application on the Greek Public Electric Power Provider." *Journal of Loss Prevention in the Process Industries* 25(5): 671–87.

Markowski, A., M. Watkins, L. Thompson, and J. Vasquez. (2016). "Development of an Injury Risk Assessment Workplace Wellness Screening Tool." *Manual Therapy* 25.

Nolan, S. (2013). "Analytics." *Strategic HR Review* 12(1): 3–4.

O'Leary, D. E. (2013). "Artificial Intelligence and Big Data." *IEEE Intelligent Systems* 28: 96–99.

Roland, H., and B. Moriarty. (1990). *System Safety Engineering and Management* (2nd ed.). New York: John Wiley & Sons, Inc.

Schultz, G. (2015). "Don't Drown in Big Data." *Industrial Safety & Hygiene News* 49(6): 52–53.

Schultz, G. (2013). "Advanced and Predictive Analytics in Safety: Are They Worth the Investment?" Accessed July 28, 2017. http://ehstoday.com/predictive-analytics-safety.

Segaran, T., and J. Hammerbacher. (2009). *Beautiful Data: The Stories behind Elegant Data Solutions*. Sebastopol, CA: O'Reilly Media, 257..

World Health Organization (WHO). (2016). "An Estimated 12.6 Million Deaths Each Year Are Attributable to Unhealthy Environments." Accessed July 28, 2017. http://www.who.int/mediacentre/news/releases/2016/deaths-attributable-to-unhealthy-environments/en/.

Wiatrowski, W. J. (2013). "Using Workplace Safety and Health Data for Injury Prevention." *Monthly Labor Review* 136(10): E1.

Workman, P. A. (1981). "Using Statistics to Manage a State Safety and Health Program." *Monthly Labor Review* (March). Accessed July 27, 2017. www.bls.gov/opub/mlr/1981/03/art6full.pdf.

CHAPTER 19

# IMPLEMENTING A RISK-BASED APPROACH TO BUSINESS: BEST PRACTICE CONCEPTS FOR ENTERPRISE RISK MANAGEMENT

Mark R. Bennett and Jack Ogutu

## Learning Objectives

After studying this chapter, the reader will be able to:

1. Concisely define enterprise risk management (ERM) and effectively communicate its value
2. Discuss key strategies for developing efficient ERM initiatives in an organization
3. Describe how a chief financial officer (CFO) and risk manager can collaborate on an ERM initiative
4. Explain core concepts of an ERM framework
5. Evaluate the significance of traditional risk and ERM in a global economy.

## Key Terms

**Risk assessment process, governance, root cause, risk register, incident management**


## Abstract

The risks that organizations face are many and are broader than what falls within the scope of hazard risk. In addition to hazard risk, which is typically associated with insurance-type exposures, every business process, strategic initiative, and organization goal holds risk. Each risk in an organization is a point of failure that can disrupt revenue streams.

Forward-thinking traditional risk managers realize that they have the skills and experience to support the CFO and the organization in a broader risk platform. This chapter will describe the foundational components of enterprise risk management and give practical insight on what a traditional risk manager can do to take on a broader and more strategic approach to organizational risk.

## Introduction

The objective of this chapter is to challenge how risk is perceived and encourage risk professionals to embrace enterprise risk management (ERM) practices that demonstrate, promote, and drive a broader and more strategic approach to risk.

ERM brings a strategic perspective to risk that can significantly affect an organization's value. It is recommended that risk managers expand their knowledge in ERM principles and find ways to implement foundational concepts in areas of responsibility, with the goal of developing a framework that is transferable to the broader risk an organization faces.

> Many ERM initiatives get started by traditional risk managers first earning creditability in their area of responsibility. They pilot foundational concepts of ERM that can then be transferred to a more global initiative.

Companies that embrace ERM are taking a strategic approach that will affect a company's:

- Profitability
- Protection from Unforeseen & Emerging Risk
- Governance

Figure 19.1
Benefits of enterprise risk management

## Enterprise Risk Management: The End Goals

The "end goals" of ERM are *profitability, protection of the company, and governance.* In terms of *profitability*, ERM puts logic to where organizations put their time and resources. It also takes the organization's most important risks and puts them into actionable plans. In terms of *protecting the company*, it introduces foundational ERM processes that keep organizations from getting blindsided as well as allowing them to be in the forefront of risks that are emerging. In addition, a best practice ERM initiative *puts focused efforts on governance.* It realizes that as companies get larger, silos become more pronounced, and information becomes scattered, thus necessitating focused efforts on continuously improving how organizations approach governance.

## Enterprise Risk Management—What Is It and Why?

Enterprise risk management gives a holistic view of all risk across the enterprise of the organization and allows for executives and process owners to make timely and informed decisions based on apples-to-apples comparisons on the different risks that reside across all business silos. Better decisions are made due to how the risks are consistently collected, organized, and dealt with.

Enterprise risk management provides the platform for operational managers and process owners to contribute strategically, and it requires timely and accurate reporting so that important risk can be in view as the organization is making decisions across silos.

A best-practice ERM initiative then transitions risks that are most important into actionable plans. These plans are supported by consistent processes for applying assessments, mitigation, and monitoring. Companies who engage in ERM typically have a strong competitive advantage. It gives stakeholders the confidence that the management team is applying a structured approach to identifying, assessing, and managing the company's most important risk. It makes a clear statement to the value of appropriate allocation of resources and efficiency in governance.

> By using centralized and consistent processes, ERM platforms cut through organizational challenges and make the obstacles less relevant.

**The Advantages of ERM**

- ♦ It provides a holistic view of organizational risk
- ♦ Enables timely and informed decisions
- ♦ Requires stakeholder engagement
- ♦ Transitions most important risk into action
- ♦ Provides a competitive advantage
- ♦ Provides structure to identifying, mitigating and monitoring risk

Figure 19.2
The advantage of enterprise risk management

## ERM—A Risk-Based Approach to Business

Enterprise risk management is commonly called a risk-based approach to business. As organizations become larger, they become more complex and risks reside in all facets of the business. The make-up of an organization typically involves operations, shared services, and many other dimensions that are put in place to serve the company's mission. Operations include important functions such as sales, service, production, and distribution. Shared services include items such as human resources, IT, and finance. Other dimensions of an organization are made up of things like strategic initiatives, geographic regions, and compliance areas to name a few. A "risk-based approach to business" recognizes that "risk is an overarching theme across all business areas" and there should be a consistent way to deal with it (Minsky 2016a).

Essentially, ERM states that the risks an organization faces drive everything. If you (a) understand the risks and (b) effectively manage the risks, your organization will have the foundation to be successful. Typically, people think of risk as exclusively associated with areas like hazard risk and workers' compensation and other areas often associated with insurance programs. Although these are examples of risk, they are only a part of the risks organizations face. Risk that an organization faces can include things like supply-chain risk, regulation changes, critical skills shortage, and cyber threats, to name a few.

> Risk is seen as being exclusively associated with hazards and workers' compensation, but other forms of risk to an organization may include supply-chain risk, regulation changes, critical skills shortage, and cyber threats, to name a few.

When a company embraces an ERM initiative, they are saying there is value to having a framework to identify and prioritize all the company's risks and put what is most important into actionable plans. They realize it is not healthy for organizations to only have a piece of the information as they make decisions that affect the allocation of time and resources.

**Risk** - An overarching theme across all business areas

| Operations | Shared Services | Other Dimensions |
|---|---|---|
| ❑ Sales | ❑ HR | ❑ Strategic Initiatives |
| ❑ Service | ❑ IT | ❑ Geographic Regions |
| ❑ Production | ❑ Finance | ❑ Functional Organizations |
| ❑ Distribution | | ❑ Compliance Areas |

Figure 19.3
Overarching theme of enterprise risk management

## Foundational Components of Enterprise Risk Management

A best-practice ERM program has a *risk assessment process* and deals with organizational *governance.* A risk assessment process simply means that once an organization captures risk that resides across the enterprise of the organization, this universe of risk needs to be transitioned into action.

Many companies become very good at going through a process of capturing all the risks their organizations face but are not doing anything with

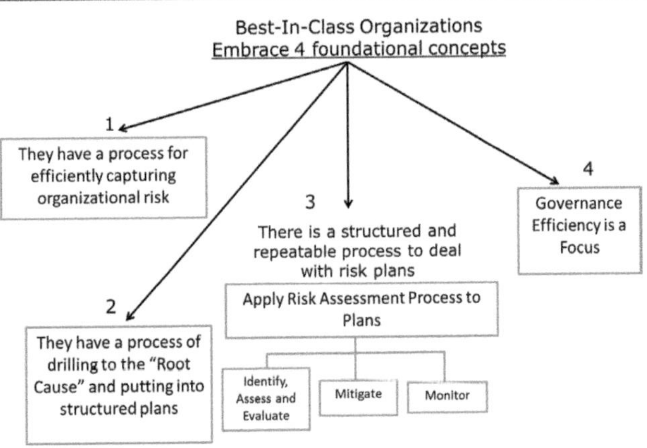


Figure 19.4
Foundational concepts of enterprise risk management

it. A best-practice initiative says as you start pulling risks out of your risk register (collection of all the organization's risk), the risks should be put into structured plans so that they can be made actionable. For example, risks from the risk register may go into financial plans, HR plans, IT plans, workers' compensation plans, business continuity plans, and so forth. These plans are places where a framework is applied to how risks are dealt with.

A best practice states that once you transition risks from the risk register into plans, there needs to be consistency on how plans are functioning. Plans dealing with organizational risks should be consistent in terms of language, assessments, mitigation, monitoring, and how reporting is occurring.

**Risk Assessment Process**

Collect Organizational Risk and put into structured plans to make it actionable.

Plans should include:

- Identifying Risk
- Attaching controls to risk
- Using a risk assessment scale to quantify the risk
- Mitigation of Risk
- Monitoring to make sure what is most important happens

Figure 19.5
Risk assessment process

*Governance* speaks to the ability of a company to operate efficiently as it is growing and becoming more complex. As organizations grow they have siloed activity happening, and there is information scattered in many different places. This type of environment leads to misalignment of priorities and unknown relationships. After an effective risk-assessment process is in place, a next logical step is to allocate time and resources to how the organization can work more efficiently by paying attention to governance.

Within an organization, having an effective risk assessment process in place helps to allocate time and resources to how the organization can work more efficiently by paying attention to governance.

## Breaking through Traditional Obstacles and Getting Started with an ERM Initiative

With the clear value ERM brings, why are so many companies missing the opportunity? Why do they recognize the value but struggle to get their programs up and running? According to Ogutu et al. (2018), research and experience show:

**What is Good Governance and Why Do We Care?**

Governance is defined by the organizational processes used to make and implement decisions. Good Governance is not necessarily making only the "correct" decisions. It's using the best possible risk management processes to informed decision-making, which has the potential to impact employees, customers, other stakeholders, and the community at large.

Optimizing organizational governance is not just recommended, it's a moral and legal obligation. Every company, no matter industry, product, or service, impacts every party mentioned above. Good governance—by holding each part of the organization to a high standard and by enabling surprises to managed before they happen—ensures this impact is possible.

**What Are the Main Characteristics of Good Governance?**

**Good governance creates accountability.**
Accountability is a fundamental requirement of good governance. Businesses have an obligation to identify and assess risk, implement appropriate controls, monitor their effectiveness, and regularly report to the board. Managers throughout the company need to be answerable for the consequences of risks, which impact customers, employees, and investors the organization serves.

**Good governance is transparent.**
As part of the risk management process, any employee should be able to escalate a concern, issue, or complaint for review. This means they'll be able to clearly see:

- The status of an identified risk
- What risk assessment and mitigation activities were reviewed
- Which standard(s) were followed

**Good governance saves money.**
Scandals are caused by negligence, and are therefore 100% preventable. Good governance protects the organization's reputation, avoiding consequences such as lost revenue, higher operating costs, and even class action lawsuits. Such lawsuits, initiated by customers and investors, are often accompanied by regulatory scrutiny and penalties.

**Good governance is responsive.**
Corporations must focus on customer needs while balancing competing interests in a timely, appropriate, and responsive manner. Enterprise risk management is as much about achieving goals as it is preventing scandals.

**Good governance is equitable and inclusive.**
A customer and employee community's wellbeing results from all of its members feeling their interests have been considered by management in the decision-making process. This means all customers, employees, and investors should have opportunities to escalate concerns as part of the risk management process.

**Good governance is effective and efficient.**
Corporations should implement decisions and follow processes that make the best use of available people, resources, and time. This ensures the best possible results for customers, employees, and investors.

**Good governance is participatory.**
Employees, vendors, or contractors performing tasks in a process should have the opportunity to provide subject-matter expertise as part of regular risk, control, and monitoring assessments. This is accomplished by providing a risk assessment to frontline supervisory employees and vendors, which require them to:

- Identify risks in their areas of operations
- Identify what could go wrong
- Provide their expert opinion on impact and likelihood, along with the effectiveness of current controls designed to prevent those risks from happening.

LogicManager – Steven Minsky

Figure 19.6
Governance overview (Minksy 2016a, 2016b)

1. They make it more complex than it needs to be.
2. They spend too much time prepping and not enough time doing.
3. They miss opportunities when it comes to technology.

It is recommended to simplify foundational concepts, streamline the process into immediate action, and use technology to get your program off the ground.

## Make It Simple

Most have heard the terms and concepts of ERM but do not have the time to get their arms around them. To successfully get off the ground and make progress, the first step needs to be *make it simple*, not just initially but for the long haul. Peers at an executive level need to be able to be on the same page, and the message to process owners needs to be clear. If it is not simple and clear, you will waste countless hours with no real value.

A best-practice ERM framework simply means your company has an efficient and effective way to collect risk across the enterprise, a way to quantify risk across business silos, and a way to put what is most important into action. Foundational to the process is identifying what the team looks like that makes up your ERM initiative. It is important to define roles, clearly/concisely communicate the core concepts, and engage stakeholders to be part of the process.

Moving forward, it is recommended that you find simple and efficient ways to capture the team's perspective on risk. Keep the questions straightforward and use technology to gather data in a way that is easy for them. Use simple questions, such as what could hinder their success in reaching objectives; what risk have they encountered over the last year; what have they heard or observed from others; and what is happening externally—in industry, among competitors, regulators, and so on?

The next step of the equation is putting time into dealing with governance obstacles. Things start to slow down when "simple" is not applied to the long haul. Look for opportunities to identify obstacles and apply efficiency.

**Keep It Simple**

- Define roles & responsibilities
- Have a plan to communicate core concepts & engage stakeholders
- Apply logic to collecting risk, quantifying risk and putting it into plans to drive action

Figure 19.7
Keep it simple

> Through simplification and streamlining of the educational process and the early use of appropriate technology, efficient platforms can be developed to collect data, transition risk into structured plans, and transition obstacles into governance efficiency.

## Just Get Started

As companies are attempting to get their ERM programs up and running, they mistakenly think it must be perfectly mapped out before steps can be taken. This, unfortunately, promotes the idea of long, drawn-out committee meetings with no value being realized for upwards of two years down the road.

Take steps that build long-term success; while in tandem, build in steps to capture immediate value. Many companies take too long to capture their top risk and even longer to translate it into action. While the framework is taking shape and you're capturing and organizing your top risks, jump ahead of the process and put a key risk you know will likely end up as a top ten category into an ERM plan. This will be time well spent to pilot a repeatable process to consistently assess, mitigate, and monitor risk that will be transferable to other risk plans.

## Begin with Technology

Unfortunately, some companies get started on an ERM initiative and end up putting their efforts on the shelf. This is a natural outcome of not simplifying and getting started (streamlining the process). Avoid wasted time and efforts by using technology early.

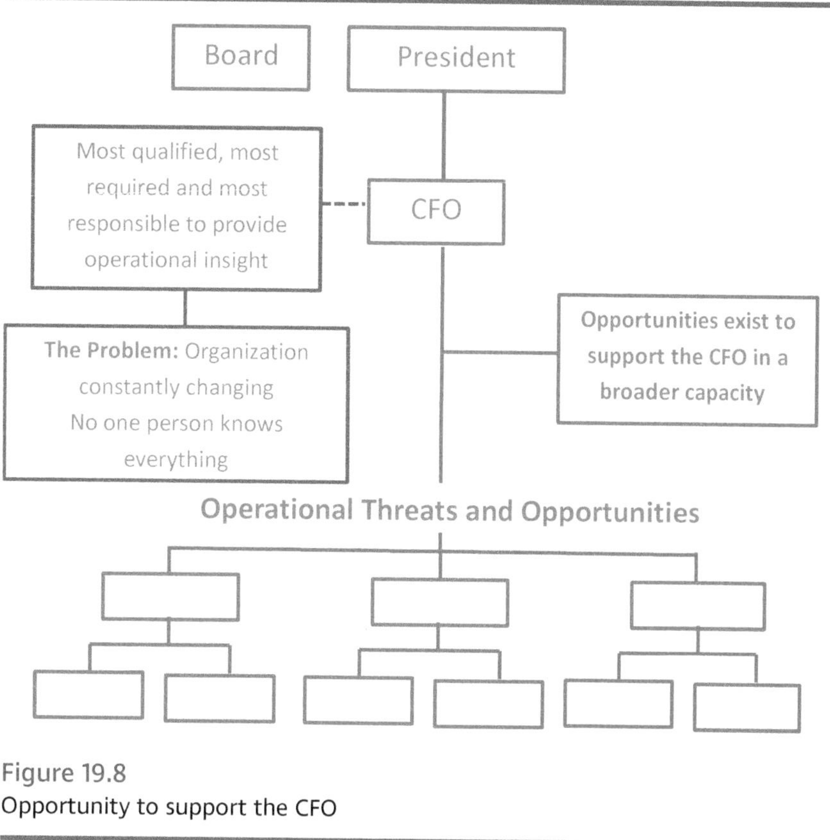


Figure 19.8
Opportunity to support the CFO

Many companies mistakenly think ERM technology comes into play after a mature program is in place. They do not take advantage of tools that can streamline the educational process and allow for efficient platforms to collect data, transition risks into structured plans, and transition obstacles into governance efficiency.

## Risk Managers Should Embrace the Opportunity to Support the CFO in a Broader Capacity

An organizational structure is typically made up of a board, president, CFO, and other executives and managers that need to be in the know in terms of the operational threats and opportunities of an organization. In a typical organizational structure, the CFO is usually the most required, qualified, and responsible to report and provide the president and board with operational insight as it pertains to risk and opportunities. The problem is that as organizations are constantly changing, so no one person knows everything. To effectively report on operational threats and opportunities, the CFO needs a framework and support to capture this risk information and to ultimately deal with it (Otugu et al. 2018).

> Enterprise risk management has three lines of defense (operational manager or process owners, ERM risk manager, and internal audit function) to ensure timely risk collection, action, and reporting.

Risk managers have an opportunity to support the CFO in an expanded capacity. For those professionals who want to support the organization in a more strategic capacity, it is important to first understand the foundational roles that make up an ERM initiative. Enterprise risk management speaks in terms of three lines of defense to ensure timely risk collection, action, and reporting. Risk managers who have an ambition to support the CFO in a broader capacity should embrace the *second line of defense*.

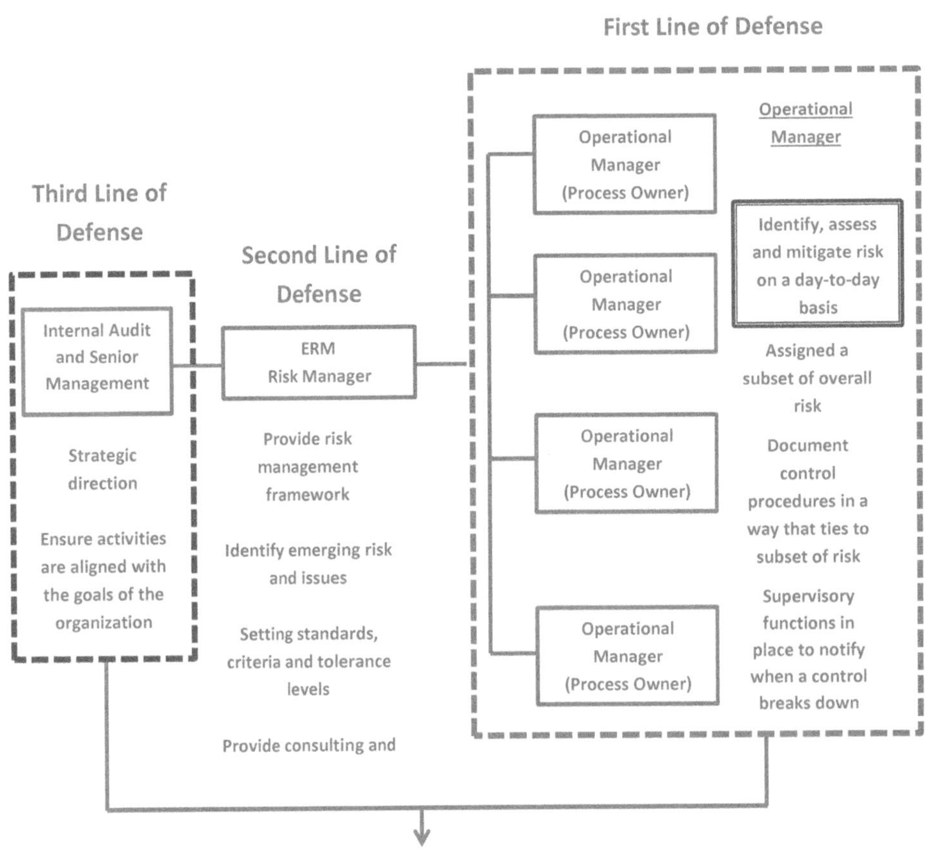


Figure 19.9
Three lines of defense

## ERM—the Three Lines of Defense

*The first line of defense* is the operational managers (process owners). These individuals are responsible for identifying, assessing, and mitigating risks on a day-to-day basis. As they identify risks, they are required to apply controls and monitor this control activity so that what is most important happens. *The second line of defense* is typically the ERM risk manager. This second line of defense takes on a very strategic role. This position needs to focus on the strategic and not be continuously spending large periods of time in the tactical. The second line of defense needs to ensure process owners are effective as possible in their front-line responsibilities. A primary responsibility in this position is to consult and mentor the process owners. This position is also responsible for the framework, and they typically spend time identifying emerging risks and issues. Additionally, they set standards, rating criteria and tolerance levels. *The third line of defense* is typically senior management or perhaps an internal audit function. This third line of defense provides strategic direction and ensures activities are aligned with the goals of the organization.

> Risk managers have an opportunity to support the CFO and organization more strategically.

By embracing the second line of defense, risk managers are able to perform the very valuable role of a strategic facilitator to ensure the gap is being closed between strategic level risks and all other operational risks faced at the front of organizations.

## ERM Is a Collaborative Process

### Three things a CFO can do to get the most from their risk manager

With all the daily tasks required of a risk manager, it can be challenging for them to "get out of the weeds" and support the CFO in broader risk initiatives. CFOs can help bridge this gap by preparing risk managers to be more strategic and implementing just a few simple strategies:

1. **Provide Clarity**—Discuss and agree on initial scope of activities and find ways for the collaborative initiative to grow. Agree on concise ways the risk manager can communicate and report on what is relevant.
2. **Support Education in ERM**—This will be one of your best investments. If the risk manager can support the CFO in an ERM capacity, the organization will have gained strategic support and added value to the organization.
3. **Provide Technology**—Technology is the difference between a long, drawn-out process and taking immediate steps. Provide them with the tools and training they need to support and expedite the process.

### Five things a risk manager can do to support the CFO

As noted previously, the CFO is the most required, qualified, and responsible to know and report operational risks to the president and board. As organizations are constantly on the move, this can be challenging. The CFO typically looks to the risk manager to provide perspective on the insurance program and hazard-type risks the company faces. Other areas of business risks are typically not as defined.

Forward-thinking risk managers recognize the challenges and responsibilities of CFOs and take the position that they are in the best spot to support them. These risk managers can advance their cause by doing five things.

1. **Initiate the Conversation with the CFO**—Risk managers have underutilized skills. An effective process of identifying risks, drilling down to root cause, adding controls, mitigation, and monitoring is valuable and should be consistently applied to all business risks. In this discussion, the goal should be to agree on logical steps to earn credibility in supporting the CFO in the broader risk initiative.
2. **Engage in Enterprise Risk Management (ERM) Education**—For risk managers who want to support the broader risks of the organization, it is essential they (1) gain knowledge in foundational enterprise risk principles and (2) find ways to simplify the concepts so they can be understood and implemented. This knowledge can come through formal classes or a structured mentoring program.
3. **Use Your Area as the Pilot**—As risk managers gain practical knowledge in enterprise risk concepts, it is important to pilot these concepts. The hazard risk and workers' compensation areas are typically a natural landing spot. This is the opportunity to take terms and processes that may be unfamiliar to most and provide a visual display of how it fits and becomes actionable. Your area becomes a clear example that is repeatable.
4. **Use Your Second Line of Defense**—The three lines of defense simply state that the frontline process owners need to be identifying, assessing, and mitigating risk on a day-to-day basis. The third line is senior management, and they provide strategic direction and ensure activities are aligning with the goals of the organization. The second line of defense is one of strategic facilitator. This is a cross-functional role with focus on oversight and facilitation that ensures mitigation and risk analysis are taking place by process owners.
5. **Appropriate Interacting with Business Units**—The CFO needs operational insight on risks. As risk managers gain trust in an expanded role, they need to assume the responsibility of helping managers/process owners identify risks and use the piloted/structured processes to deal with all business risks.

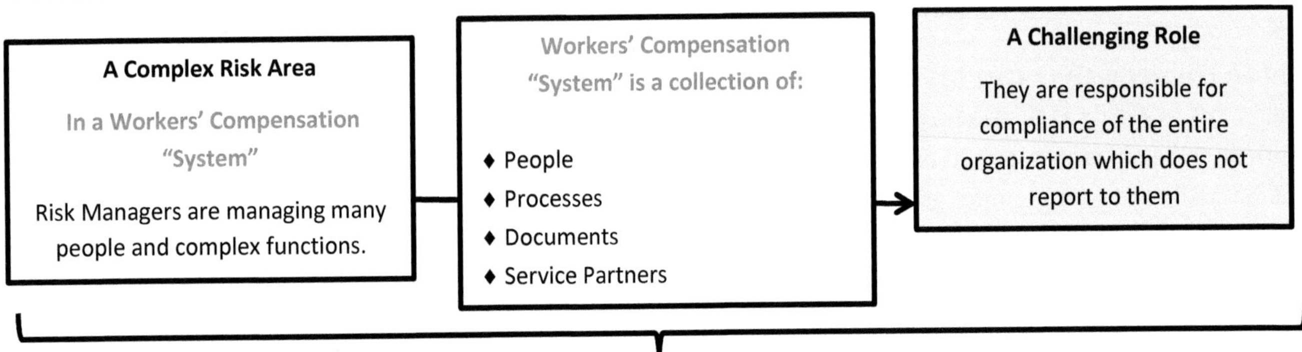


**By effectively putting a framework in place for successful management of a workers' compensation system, a Risk Manager can earn the right to be a champion in supporting a more global ERM initiative.**

Figure 19.10
The complexities of workers' compensation

## Hazard Risk and Workers' Compensation—A Natural Landing Spot to Support Organizations in a Broader Capacity

When risk transitions from the global risk register into plans, the objective is to develop a framework for consistent risk management. As organizations are getting started in ERM, it is recommended to take one area with an identified risk or uncertainty and build early success by starting/piloting a first plan. A natural landing spot for a pilot and to make early progress in an ERM initiative is to put the hazard risk or workers 'compensation (WC) area into a structured ERM plan. This simply means apply *foundational ERM* concepts to your existing hazard or WC system.

This is a natural landing spot because risk managers in these areas "know risk" and, in many cases, have valuable and underutilized skills that are perfect for piloting a plan. As the organization is taking time to capture the more global enterprise risk / universe of risk, it makes sense to get ahead of the global risk collection process and start piloting a plan that can test and demonstrate how some of the core ERM concepts will soon need to be applied consistently across the organization.

> A natural landing spot for a pilot and to make early progress in an ERM initiative is to put the hazard risk or workers' compensation (WC) area into a structured ERM plan.

If a risk manager can take a complex area like hazard or workers' compensation risk and create a win by putting structure to how risk is assessed, mitigated, and monitored, this can become a repeatable process

**ERM Framework**

1. Is there a structured way to capture risk?
2. Is there a structured way to assess risk?
3. Is there a structured way to mitigate and deal with what is most important?
4. Is there a structured way to monitor risk?
5. Is there structured reporting on risk & controls that are in place?

Figure 19.11
Enterprise risk management framework

for handling other risks an organization faces and must deal with. For example, *there is value starting with the workers' compensation (WC) area because it is a very complex area.* Those who manage WC systems are dealing with a complicated system of pulling people, resources, processes, documents, and service partners together to get effective results. Risk professionals face additional challenges because they are responsible for the compliance of the entire organization, most of whom do not report to them. By starting in an area like WC, you are taking a challenging business process area and putting structure to it. If you can effectively apply ERM concepts to a complex area like this, the risk manager is a good candidate to become the champion to support implementation in other areas.

## What Should a Foundational Framework Include?

This initial pilot can become very valuable to the organization. When it is being developed, the risk manager should be thinking in terms of a framework and repeatable processes. For example, if the foundational ERM concepts are built into workers' compensation, the risk manager should be thinking if the "framework" being established and fine-tuned can be transferred to other areas an organization faces risk, such as HR, IT, or the financial area. *When building a repeatable framework, five things should be kept in mind:*

## Foundational Concepts

As companies are getting their ERM initiative off the ground, it is recommended that they stay focused on the fundamentals.

1. A process for efficiently capturing an organization's risks
2. A process of drilling to the "root cause" and putting into structured plans
3. A process to transition root-cause risks into action
4. A process to start putting focus on governance efficiency

### Capturing Organizational Risk and Drilling Down to a "Root Cause"

Risk is typically housed in silos, making it challenging to capture and organize the data. Silos will typically create communication and collaboration problems and sometimes prevent even properly collected data from getting to the right parties. Additional risk can reside in several different silos, which makes it difficult to capture and understand. Because of these obstacles, some companies struggle to capture their risks, or it takes longer to populate their risks into the register than it needs to take.

It is recommended that when capturing organizational risks, there should be an enterprise-wide standard and a common framework that all departments use. An example of a common framework for collecting risk would be a structured root-cause approach. This simply means having a process in place where you can start at a very high level to capture what may drive the risks and then narrow it down to a point where the risks can be made actionable.

> Silos will typically create communication and collaboration problems and sometimes prevent even properly collected data from getting to the right parties, hence companies struggle to capture their risk or it takes longer to populate their risk into the register than necessary.

A first high-level step would be to get the process owners to think what risks exist from an external, people, process, relationship, and systems perspective. This is high level. The next stage is to drill down.

Process owners can hold very valuable information, and it is important to go to the next step of drilling down to capture this information. Below are examples of how drilling down to a root cause takes place.

- ☐ External
- ☐ People
- ☐ Process
- ☐ Relationships
- ☐ Systems

- ☐ Business Environment
- ☐ Economic & Market Conditions
- ☐ Hazard Risk
- ☐ Public Infrastructure
- ☐ Regulatory & Legislative Environment
- ☐ Reputation

**Root Cause**

- ☐ Competition from new or existing business
- ☐ Litigious environment

- ☐ External
- ☐ People
- ☐ Process
- ☐ Relationships
- ☐ Systems

- ☐ Employee Relations
- ☐ Ethics & Integrity
- ☐ Hiring & Termination Practices
- ☐ Management & Supervision
- ☐ Staff Competencies
- ☐ Staffing
- ☐ Training, Education & Growth
- ☐ Workers' Compensation

**Root Cause**

- ☐ Program Foundation
- ☐ Safety Culture
- ☐ Injury Prevention
- ☐ Post Injury System
- ☐ Claims Management
- ☐ Controlling Medical

Figure 19.12
Drilling down to the root cause

A best practice is to begin with pulling risk out of the risk register into ERM plans. Once the root cause risks are integrated into the plans, the risk management becomes actionable.

## From the Risk Register to Plans to Action

To deal with organizational risks, a best practice is to start pulling risks out of the risk register and putting the risks into ERM plans. Once you put root-cause risks into plans, this is where the work takes place to make the risks actionable. Organizations will have numerous ERM plans, so it is important for plans to be consistent in language used and how they are assessed, mitigated, and monitored. Once root-cause risks are put into a plan, a best practice is to do the following:

- Identify, assess, and evaluate
- Mitigate
- Monitor

The identify, assess, and evaluate stage means you are (1) identifying root-cause risk to go into the plan, (2) selecting and implementing controls/mitigation activity for each root-cause risk, (3) attaching owners to each control, (4) assessing each root-cause risk and the controls that are applied with a selected rating criteria, (5) evaluating if immediate action is required, and (6) looking at the root-cause risk/controls to determine what could go wrong.

## A Rating System

An essential part of ERM is an objective rating system. This system should be on a scale that gives perspective on what is most important. This is important because good decisions can then be made in terms of where you put your time and resources. A good assessment process will allow appropriately allocating resources within plans and across silos.

To be able to make objective decisions within plans and across silos, there must be a scale in place that allows for all risk to be evaluated the same way. A best practice is to assess by risk impact, likelihood, and assurance. Impact and likelihood would score a risk, based on no controls being in place. Assurance would be a score, based on controls that have been put in place. Assurance will rate how effective your controls are.

A best-practice rating scale rates the impact, likelihood, and assurance and will take into consideration both quantitative and comparative factors. The quantitative part speaks to a numerical score. This can be as simple as 1 (low), 2 (medium), or 3 (high). A better approach, however, should include a 1–5 or 1–10 scale. The reason is that 1–3 scales have a tendency to score toward the middle. The comparative part speaks to getting everyone on one sheet of music so to speak. You are actually picking the numbers

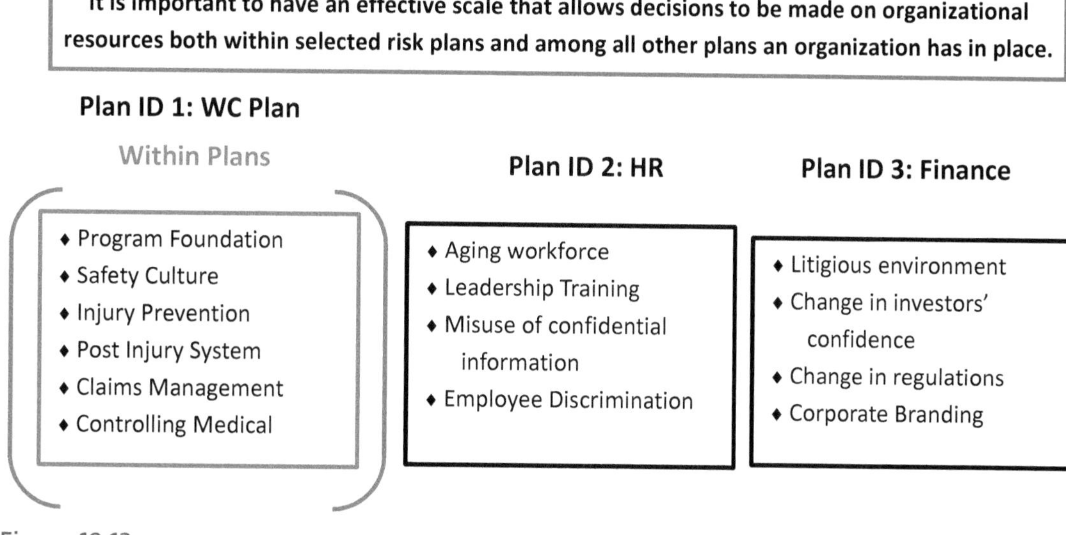


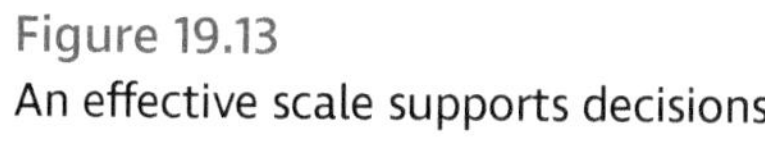

Figure 19.13
An effective scale supports decisions

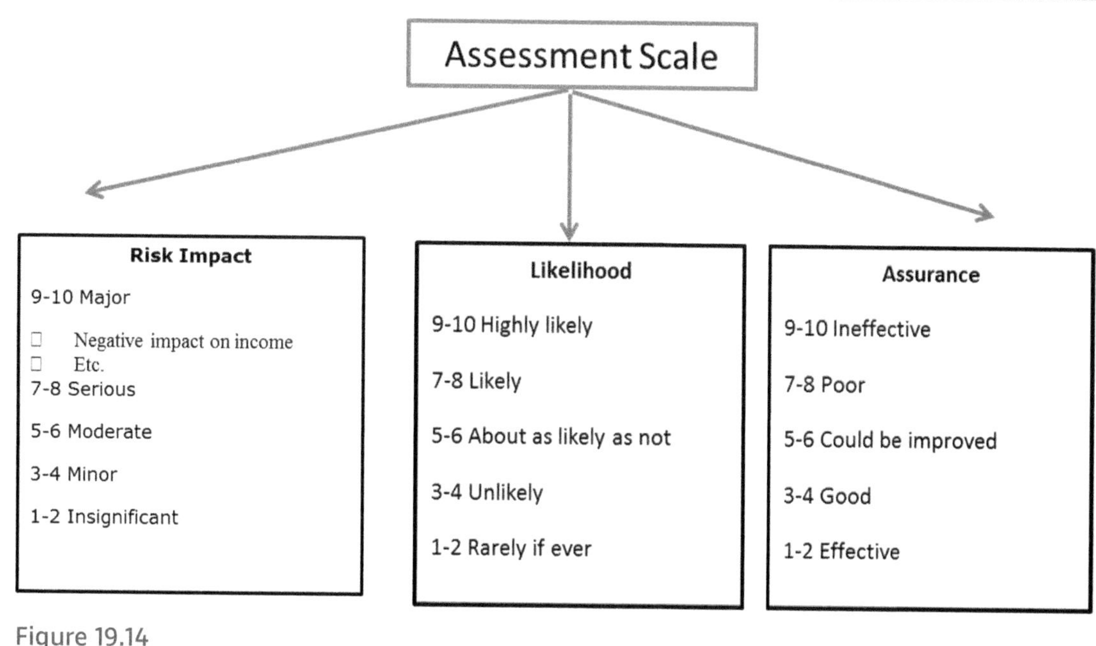


Figure 19.14
Example of a rating scale

based on a pre-established document that defines a number in terms of financial, legal, operations, regulatory, and strategic factors. Regardless of what business process area or business silo is rating a risk, it is using the same comparative document/wording that points to a quantitative score. The process cuts through any biases that may exist and allows for apples to apples comparisons across business silos.

> A beneficial assessment process allows for the appropriate allocation of resources within plans and across silos, which helps to make objective decisions using standardized root-cause risk and controls criteria; which can then be transformed into indexes that can help prioritize activities.

Once root-cause risks and controls are rated/scored by standard criteria; these scores can transition into indexes that can help prioritize activities. Typically, inherent and residual indexes are used. Inherent indexes are a score, based on no controls being in place, and residual indexes provide a score after controls are in place.

## Mitigation and Monitoring

*Mitigation* is where assessment results are put into action. Targeted mitigation needs to happen within every risk plan an organization has in place. Indexes are the end product of an effective rating system and are what create the logic to where time and resources will be allocated to drive effective mitigation.

For a successful risk program, *monitoring* needs to be simplified and made a regular part of the process. Three key items must come into play: testing, metrics, and incident management. Testing refers to making sure what is important is happening—yes or no. Metrics are in place to make sure controls are operating effectively, and incident management refers to learning from controls that have been broken down, building it into training, or adding new or changing existing controls.

## Reporting

Reporting is a key part of a structured plan. This is another area where consistency is important. Reporting needs to be consistent with all the ERM plans that are in place. Having consistent reporting gives the executive team a clearer picture to make cross-siloed decisions.

## Governance Efficiency Needs to Be an Ongoing Focus

As organizations grow and become more complex, it is important to put focused efforts into making the processes more streamlined. Organizations have many components that include people, resources, data repositories, applications, business processes, relationships, and physical assets, to name a few. As these organizations continue to expand, the challenges are dealing with items such as compliance, vendor and policy management, audit management, incident management, and business continuity. Finding solutions to these areas can be complex, but with appropriate technology, solutions that are available to a company can prevent volumes of wasted time and resources.

## Traditional Risk Management versus Enterprise Risk Management

*Traditional risk management* is typically focused on hazard risk—those risks that are most commonly associated with insurance. Because hazard risk is something to avoid, the objective is to eliminate or at least minimize the risk. Additionally, because traditional risk is limited to a specific scope (hazard risk and avoiding it), it does not focus on how this risk compares to other risks the organization may be facing. The risk manager in a traditional risk role is not tasked with quantifying and qualifying the risks in a way it compares to other risks that affect the broader enterprise.

*Enterprise Risk Management (ERM)* is not focused on eliminating or minimizing risks. As noted in the section on "ERM—The End Goal," the focus is profitability, protection of the company, and governance. Enterprise Risk Management typically begins with the strategies, goals, and objectives of the organization and is seeking to obtain "the right amount and kind of risk" that will put the organization in the right position to be successful. The key in ERM is to find the area/range of best possible risk to support the organization's strategic goals. To meet this end goal, ERM pursues managing risk across all business process areas, so it is important to have a rating scale that can evaluate and make comparisons with risks across the enterprise.

Although the focus and scope of traditional risk management and ERM are different, the foundational processes they use should be consistent. Both areas should include the same standardized processes for identifying risk, drilling down to the root cause and putting root-cause risks into plans with owners. From there they should have the same process for risk owners to consistently add controls, assessment, and monitoring; and the rating scale they use should be able to provide management with an objective perspective as they make decisions on risks across business silos.

> The key to ERM is to find the area/range of best possible risk to support the organization's strategic goals.

## Conclusion

Risk managers have an opportunity to take on a broader role in an organization that supports building a framework that deals with all risks a company faces. Because risk managers have backgrounds in foundational risk principles, they are a natural to support the CFO and the executive team in developing a more global risk-based approach to business. To take advantage of this natural opportunity, they should continue education in foundational ERM concepts, they should always be looking for ways to keep these concepts simple so all can understand, and they should be embracing the second line of defense as a strategic facilitator to support process owners to effectively identify, mitigate, and monitor risk on a day-to-day basis.

## Questions

1. What does a risk assessment process look like?
2. Why is governance an important part of enterprise risk management?
3. What can the risk manager do to support the CFO and organization more strategically?
4. What does it look like for a risk manager to embrace the "second line of defense"?
5. What are the components of monitoring, and why is it so important?

## References


Minsky, S. (2017). "What Is Good Governance and Why Do We Care" LogicManager, Inc. www.logicmanager.com/erm-software/2017/04/25/good-governance/.

Minsky, S. (2016a). "5 Characteristics of the Best ERM Program." LogicManager, Inc. www.logicmanager.com/best-practice-erm-programs-ebook/.

Minsky, S.. (2016b). "How to Integrate Governance Areas." LogicManager, Inc. www.logicmanager.com/ebook-how-to-integrate-governance-areas/.

Ogutu, J., M.R. Bennett, & R. Olawoyin. (2018). "Closing the Gap Between Traditional & Enterprise Risk Management Systems." *Professional Safety* 63(4), 42–47.

CHAPTER 20

# USING GAP ANALYSIS IN IMPROVING SAFETY PERFORMANCE

James D. Smith

## Learning Objectives

After studying this chapter, the reader will be able to:

1. Define gap analysis and know how to use it to improve safety performance
2. Begin the process of developing a gap analysis in practical use
3. Assess the benefits and use of a gap analysis to improve safety performance
4. Apply gap analysis as an evidence-based tool for driving safety performance improvement that can lead to injury prevention outcomes

## Key Terms

**Claims, gap analysis, measurement, performance**


## Abstract

This chapter is dedicated to demonstrating the evidence-based practice of using gap analysis to measure injury prevention performance. Gap analysis is an auditing process used to analyze a current corporate injury prevention program, project, business unit(s), or management system with actual practices. The process is used to systematically measure the standard to actual practice while determining the gaps. The results of this process are used to assist in developing intervention strategies to improve safety performance.


## Introduction

To be successful in driving safety performance, safety professionals must not only be technically competent but have the ability to demonstrate the business acumen to advance corporate support for their recommended safety processes or programs. It is important to understand that in order to drive safety performance, the safety professional must enlist the support of others to advance their programs, systems, recommendations, and solutions. To assist in improving safety performance to reduce or minimize injury events, a process can be used to measure current injury prevention programs to the established standards or best practices. This process is called gap analysis. Gap analysis can be used to evaluate and assess an entire safety program or an individual process or method. Gap analysis differentiates itself from a traditional audit process by using the organization's standard of practice as criteria to measure each program element or processes against what is being implemented. The standard is used to compare to the actual practices and measures gaps or differences. The measured gaps in the actual safety performance demonstrate evidence-based results that allow the user to both support and use the results to drive continuous improvement in safety performance.

The main use of gap analysis in a safety program or process is to measure the implementation level of injury prevention programs at the various individual business units. The analysis findings will clearly show what needs to change in the actual practices to improve worker safety outcomes. The role of gap analysis as a measurement process for the safety professional in worker safety is best described in a quote in the American Society of Safety Engineers' *Professional Safety* journal by then-president William E. Tarrants:

> Measurements, perhaps more than any other single aspect, has been the principal stimulus of progress in all professional fields. Measurement is the backbone of any scientific approach to problem definition and problem solution. Without adequate measurement in the safety field we cannot describe the safety state of our operations or determine whether safety programs are really accomplishing anything. Sound measurement is an absolute prerequisite for control and both are necessary for prediction. (Tarrants 1977)

The remaining information in the chapter will define a framework of what constitutes a gap analysis, demonstrate the benefits in the use of this process, establish how to get started using this process, and illustrate some practical application examples in the use of gap analysis. Gap analysis is a management process used by consultants, researchers, and corporate safety professionals in measuring and assessing current practices or programs against established criteria and determining what design changes need to be implemented to improve worker safety performance.

## What Is Gap Analysis in Workplace Safety?

Gap analysis compares the gap between an organization's actual performances against its potential and desired standard of practices in injury reduction. The actual findings, gaps, are reported to show what was assessed in the actual work practices. The gap analysis is performed in the field or work environment through observations/auditing, interviews, document review, claims data analysis, and management review. When performing a gap analysis, you first must create the project objectives as to what you want to measure and analyze. Once the project objectives are determined, the professional must develop the components or elements to be measured and establish a valuation system. A common practice is to create a checklist of questions for the various components or program elements you intend to assess, create a template to capture the information from proper sources, and determine a valuation metric to measure the findings.

In a general utilization, gap analysis can measure current practices; a specific program, project, business unit, or standardization; or integration of program elements in a safety management system. A common use by outside consultants is the use of a gap analysis to conduct baseline assessment of corporate safety/risk program requirements to actual practices in a business unit(s).

Ultimately, gap analysis is to create a business strategy (roadmap) on how to advance or bridge the gap between the current situation and the desired future state of injury reduction performance.

## The Benefits of Gap Analysis

The benefits of using the gap analysis are that it establishes credibility and acceptance of its findings. By using corporate standards of practices or industry consensus standards for comparison to actual practices in the organization, the results are readily accepted by the management team. Furthermore, the results are evidence based and remove doubt from theory or opinion by demonstrating actual fact-finding results using accepted standards.

Another benefit of the gap analysis is that it measures where you are now, where you need to be, and what needs to change to improve performance in worker safety. It provides a roadmap to where you need to spend limited resources in designing or developing changes in various program elements or process to improve injury prevention results. The process allows one to question and understand what is working or not working in the operations. In going through the process, it allows you to fully understand the actual practice complexities in implementing worker safety programs and why programs or elements may fail the desired outcomes. In contrast, it also allows one to understand why program elements and processes work in the operation setting. The experience gained in using the gap analysis method will provide the critical feedback to use in the future to design better methods and programs that have a higher probability of implementation with the desired intervention outcomes in reducing or preventing work injuries.

## Getting Started in Developing a Gap Analysis

Regardless of the level of professional experience you may have, the gap analysis is not as difficult to create as you may think. The more you use and understand the use of gap analysis, the more effective the system becomes. The best way to explain how to get started is to break down the various steps into six main points:

1. Start by defining the specific objectives of the gap analysis along with the desired outcomes you are looking to achieve. The complexity of this depends on the breadth of the gap analysis. If you are looking to conduct a baseline assessment of the entire safety program, the gap analysis will be more complex than reviewing a single method or process.
2. Conduct a claims and trending analysis. It is important to understand the type of injuries occurring in the workplace, the causes of these injuries, and the cost. The data can be secured from the corporate risk management office and/or the workers' compensation carrier or third-party administrator who receives the reports and information from the various business operations units. In a gap analysis of a worker safety program or process the objective should tie the gap analysis results into a business case. The use of workers' compensation claim data that captures worker injury medical cost, wage placement cost, and expenses of the claims is cost information that can be used to make an effective business case. The information is readily available. When possible, capturing the impacts on operations and employee performance will only improve the opportunity for the management team to invest in the solutions to address the various gaps determined in your findings.

   One area of caution is the use of Occupational Safety and Health Administration (OSHA) incident rates used to demonstrate safety program outcomes. Over the years, safety professionals have influenced businesses to rely on and accept this data in lieu of establishing more business-centric metrics. Therefore, our profession will continue to use the OSHA recordkeeping and incident rates until a new measurement of performance is widely accepted. However, OSHA incident rates, which are based on recordkeeping standards first created in the 1960s, cannot demonstrate business cost. OSHA incident rates are based on annualized formulas and are limited when using the data on a quarterly basis in a business year. Moreover, OSHA incident rates are hard to understand by the senior-level management team. Even professionals have difficulty in capturing and explaining the data. Despite OSHA recordkeeping disadvantages, there is one section of the OSHA recordkeeping information that can be used to your advantage: the annual employee work hour data. This data can be used along with the workers' compensation cost to determine cost or business impact on a business unit. Using this combined data, injuries cost can be highlighted in an hourly rate.
3. Establish the criteria for measuring the various components in the gap analysis. In creating the standard for each component being assessed, there are several ways to determine the criteria. For gap

analysis of a safety program element or process measuring the actual practice, one can use the established corporate procedures as the criteria to assess each of the program elements. In a gap analysis comparing the corporate practices to the industry standards, the use of national consensus safety/health standards can be used to establish the criteria for the safety program element. There are various accredited national safety/health consensus standards, such as but not limited to American National Standards Institute (ANSI), National Fire Protection Association Codes (NFPA), National Electrical Codes (NEC), and American Society of Testing Materials (ASTM). There are many more standards established by professional organizations, associations, and standard organization bodies.

The gap analysis criteria must target worker safety program elements used to mitigate or prevent work-related injuries. Therefore, the intervention program elements are categorized and a criterion for each component is developed, using either corporate standards of practice or industry standards or a combination of both (see figures 20.2 and 20.3).

Once this gap analysis criteria and metric is created for various program elements, the next phase is to establish a work group made up of various business units' subject matter experts within the organization to assist in vetting the program's criteria and performance metric. The team review will allow for establishing a viable criterion input from various business units, which will provide a unique understanding, and from various operations to finalize the best intervention programs and acceptable levels of measurement that will offer the outcomes to reduce injuries.

4. Create a management report that captures the essence of information needed to demonstrate the results. The objectives of the management report are to summarize and highlight the results while simultaneously providing information for creating a business plan or strategy to improve injury prevention outcomes. It is important to understand that the senior level management team or client representative(s) wants a concise, easy-to-understand, evidence-based report, along with specific decisions or actions that must be made to address inconsistencies and achieve improvements. Often, management support will be influenced by the findings having a value that relates to their business interest. For credibility, each management report should have an executive summary integrating the findings to business goals. The detailed information is important to capture for your use only. So remember the purpose of the gap analysis, which is to understand what is actually being practiced and what actions are needed to improve the worker safety outcomes.
5. Create a business plan and strategy from the results. It is important to understand that the ultimate reason to use a gap analysis is to create business plan from the results to design changes that need to be implemented to improve injury prevention outcomes. The process allows the professional to concentrate their resources and efforts in improving and addressing gaps. Also, another advantage of gap analysis is to understand what administrative burden is being placed

## Developing Gap Analysis/Safety Measures

Figure 20.1
Gap analysis processes

on operations that have no material effect on improving worker safety outcomes, including those standards of practice that do not apply to the operations as intended.

6. Repeat the gap analysis in the areas needing improvement. Once you have applied the findings and have put the changes in place, then you must repeat the gap analysis process to measure the effectiveness of the changes.

## Real-World Application of Gap Analysis

To provide a means to fully understand the gap analysis processes, it is best to demonstrate a case study in the use of the process. The demonstration of the value of gap analysis that brings action will put the process in better perspective. I will share a gap analysis on a process and one on assessing a safety program.

### Gap Analysis on Review of a Vehicle Safety Program

An organization with multiple locations was developing a corporate written vehicle safety program to address the motor vehicle business risk. The project was tasked to review the procedures and provide input into the corporate procedures as to acceptability and comments for improvement. Ultimately, the corporate procedures will become the standard of practice which each location will be measured against.

What is the best process to use to analyze and measure if the corporate written vehicle safety process meets the best standard of practice in the industry? First, we could look to the regulatory standards. We could choose to use our years of work experience to establish an opinion on the procedure. Perhaps we could look to other companies' written vehicle safety programs and compare. Each of these approaches or combined approaches could be a good start. However, would it lead to the findings using an evidence-based approach or simply be a subject-matter expert's opinion? It was decided the best approach was to use national consensus standards to measure whether their written corporate vehicle safety program was considered acceptable industry practice.

In the following six steps on how to get started in using a gap analysis approach, the established objective of the gap analysis is to determine if the written corporate vehicle safety procedures meet best industry practices. The next step was to evaluate the automobile liability claims data, but the main issue is to manage the business risk exposure of operating corporate vehicles on the road. To create the criteria for the gap analysis to identify and compare the actual written procedures, a national consensus standard was used: ANSI/ASSE Z15.1, *Safe Practices for Motor Vehicle Operations.* A management report was developed in a standard template. The standard sections were used as the framework, and a simple valuation system was used to assess the written vehicle safety standard. The gap analysis measured the actual written procedure against the national consensus standard. If any gaps existed, they were identified in the management report template. We added a management report: the operational program, which allowed for the future planning to assess if each location is applying the written vehicle safety program in their operations. The management report had a program ranking for executive summary of the findings. The program ranking used a heat map or stoplight process, using color coding: green (satisfactory), yellow (inconsistency or caution), and red (not meeting the standard of practice).

### Gap Analysis on Review of Occupational Safety and Health Program (Baseline Assessment)

This is an example of a case study in which gap analysis is used to assess worker safety program in a healthcare setting. In an insurance annual meeting with the C-suite management team, the management team was interested in addressing the impact of workers' compensation costs. Senior management's main interest was both on the impacts on the business cost and worker safety of the caregivers, including the supporting employees. It was clear that in the healthcare industry, the employees work in various units and teams to deliver quality healthcare. The quality and protection of employees is the key in delivering the care. With that said, the industry's

Gap Analysis
Fleet Safety Program

| Program Element | Practices/Procedures | Program Operational | Needs Improvement | Program Ranking |
|---|---|---|---|---|
| Defined Program Responsibilities/Accountability | | | | |
| Leadership Commitment/Engagement | | | | |
| Selection Criteria of Drivers | | | | |
| 1. Job Description | | | | |
| 2. Driver Qualifications | | | | |
| 3. Driver Applicant Form | | | | |
| 4. Driver Transcript Review– Minimum Standards | | | | |
| Driver Testing | | | | |
| Driver Training/Retraining | | | | |
| Operation Rules | | | | |
| 5. Mobile Device Use Policy | | | | |
| 6. Distracted Driver | | | | |
| 7. Aggressive Driving | | | | |
| 8. Personal Use | | | | |
| Incident Reporting – Same Day | | | | |
| Incident Investigation – Management - Cause | | | | |
| New Employee Orientation | | | | |
| Vehicle Inspection | | | | |
| Vehicle Specifications/Standard Equipment | | | | |
| Vehicle Accident Review Board | | | | |
| Disciplinary HR Policy – Poor Driving | | | | |
| Self-Inspection/Hazard Identification | | | | |
| Post -Accident Testing – Drug/Alcohol | | | | |

*Reference: American National Conscensus Standard - ANSI Z15 Standard: Safe Practices For Motor Vehicle Operations"*

Figure 20.2
Vehicle safety program gap analysis using the ANSI/ASSE Z15.1 standard (ANSI/ASSE Z15.1 2012)

prime focus has been on patient safety. Additionally, externally, regulatory agencies and the accreditation process focused on the patient safety area. Meanwhile, worker safety was not a real focus for the local management teams. This is not to state that worker safety was not important; it just was not a focus of constant attention. Senior management wanted to know how they could manage workers' compensation costs or—to better describe it—to reduce work-related injury costs. The objective was clear.

To address the senior management's objective, we needed to have a baseline understanding of the occupational safety and health program within the corporate setting and throughout the individual hospitals in the various states. The use of the gap analysis processes was the best method to accomplish this. Furthermore, the gap analysis would allow the findings to drive a strategic plan for worker injury reduction and mitigation. Measuring is important, but being strategic in the measurement is how you take the data and turn it into information, which in turn yields knowledge to make decisions on reaching the objectives. Thus, the reason for using a gap analysis.

The first step in starting to understand a baseline assessment of the occupational safety and health program was to start with a claims analysis and trends. The focus was to identify loss drivers and the hospitals with the highest frequency of claims and the severity or claims cost. The claims analysis included the type of claims, the occupations, and accident descriptions, along with the various sources contributing to the claim.

The healthcare industry is highly regulated and audited by many outside governmental agencies. As a result of being a highly regulated industry that needs to meet an accreditation process to deliver healthcare, there are well-written corporate procedures in the areas of worker safety. To create the gap analysis criteria, we would use both the corporate occupational safety/health standards and various regulatory provisions. We used the claim data loss drivers on the leading types of claims to create additional program elements or emphasis on existing corporate procedures where applicable. We also discussed with various business unit team members, such as claims, human resources, operations, and risk management, to get feedback on the baseline assessment criteria for the gap analysis.

We created a template format for the management report using the corporate criteria and programs needed to address the leading loss drivers. In conducting a gap analysis of a hospital, the assessment included assessing the established corporate safety/health procedures and best practices to the actual practices being performed. Consistency from hospital to hospital was the primary focus in the gap analysis. The result of the gap analysis can demonstrate how well the hospital has implemented the corporate (established) standards of practice or where the shortfall or gap exists. Additionally, we could address consistency or inconsistency among each hospital. The results of the consistency in the gap analysis would be a good indicator of whether the established corporate procedures were effective in the operations.

In figure 20.3, the gap analysis process was used to compare the established corporate standards of practice to the actual performance in operations. This baseline assessment was applied to nine different hospitals to create standardization of the actual practices of the hospitals to the various corporate written safety/risk standards.

Baseline Site Assessment Preliminary Overview – Worker Safety
Safety Management and Occupational Health Program

| Program Element | Process/Procedures In Place | Operational Efficiency | Input/Need | Comments<br>Green – good<br>Yellow- Improvement<br>Red - Ineffective |
|---|---|---|---|---|
| Defined Program Responsibilities & Accountability | Corporate Procedure | In Place - Limited | Compliance Focus Not WC | |
| Leadership Commitment/Engagement | Corporate Procedure Lacks Focus on Staff Injury | High Interest Need Focus | CEO/Senior Mgr. High Interest - Add to Directors Mgt. | |
| Hiring Practices – Physical/Background | Corporate Procedure | In Place | Minimum Program | |
| Written Safety Procedures/Rules | Corporate Procedure | Corporate Online | Extensive Compliance Drive | |
| Incident/OSHA Reporting | Corporate Procedure | In Place | Effective | |
| Incident Investigation (Review) | Corporate Procedure | Inconsistent | Additional Training | |
| Environment of Care (EOC) Safety Improvement Team | Corporate Procedure | In place | Compliance - Add Employee Safety | |
| New Employee Orientation | Corporate Process | In Place | Add Worker Safety/Comp | |
| In-Service Safety Training | Corporate Process | Effective Calendar | Additional safety courses | |
| Infectious Diseases in the Work Place | Corporate Procedure | Effective | Execution Needed | |
| **Slip/Trip/Fall Prevention Training** | Limited | Add Training | Additional Focus Claims | |
| **Safe Patient Lifting/Handling** | Corporate Process | Inconsistent | Improve Focus Enhance Program | |
| Self-Inspection/Hazard Identification | EOC - Procedure | Limited to Compliance | Compliance Focus – Add WC Focus | |

Figure 20.3
Example using gap analysis (partial) in baseline assessment OSH program

In figure 20.3, we see actual practices results in various intervention areas either inconsistent or fall short of the established corporate standards of practice. There are many reasons for this, but one can make the assumption that simply writing a corporate standard of practices to satisfy the government agency regulations may not reflect the actual practices that are being performed. In the gap analysis "Input/Needs" column, the input from the hospital operations provided for understanding of either the consistency or inconsistency. This information led to taking the measurement and turning it into information, where we could begin to create or improve the effective intervention program elements.

The template was used to create a management report. In the "Comments" column, we ranked the consistency of each of the program elements. We used a color-coding system to report the findings to the management team. The color coding refers to a heat map color coding scheme, or "stoplight" method, to indicate good (green), needing improvement (yellow), and not acceptable (red). The purpose of using this visual graph display was to allow the management team to quickly determine where the areas were that one needed to concentrate their resources to continuously improve the intervention and mitigation processes. It should be noted that when dealing with a senior management team, you have very limited time to present or demonstrate the program results and what strategic decisions are needed from the management team to address program deficiencies.

A management report was presented to the senior management team, along with claims cost data and a phase in business strategy. It was accepted and well received by the senior management team.

## Conclusion

As described, gap analysis is simply an evidence-based process used to measure actual performance to standard of practice or where the organization wants to be. Gap analysis provides the framework to measure processes and create information from the data, which can lead to informed decision-making. The gap analysis, during the process, can be expanded to look for input/needs of the various business units as to why the standards of practice are being implemented or standards are not working or used. A gap analysis allows for the professional to present their findings and create a business strategy from those findings to advance the injury reduction performance outcomes.

## Questions

1. Why is gap analysis used by safety professionals?
2. How is the gap analysis process different from a standard auditing process?
3. What are the benefits of a gap analysis?
4. Name the different steps in creating a gap analysis when evaluating a workplace safety program.
5. What is the essential function of a gap analysis management report?

## References

Tarrants, W. E. (1977). "Measurement of Safety Performance." *Professional Safety* 22(12): 58.

ANSI/ASSE. (2012). *Safe Practices for Motor Vehicle Operations.* ANSI/ASSE Z15.1–2012.

## Further Reading

American Society of Safety Engineers (ASSE). (2011). "Thoughts from ASSE Presidents." *Professional Safety* 56(6).

Hammer, B., S. Pratt, and P. Ross. (2014). "Fleet Safety Developing and Sustaining an Effective Program with ANI/ASSE Z.15.1." *Professional Safety* 59(3).

OSHA. (2015). *Federal Register* 81(92). "Rules and Regulations, 29 CFR Parts 1904 and 1902, Improve Tracking of Workplace Injuries and Illnesses; Final Rule." https://www.gpo.gov/fdsys/pkg/FR-2016-05-12/pdf/2016-0443.pdf.

Ostrowski, K., D. Valha, and K. Ostrowski. (2014). "Gap Analysis Using ICAO Safety Management Guidance." *Professional Safety* 59(7).

Peterson, D. (2005). *Measurement of Safety Performance.* American Society of Safety Engineers: Des Plaines, IL.

Peterson, D. (2007). "Culture of Safety: An Interview with Safety Pioneer Dan Peterson." *Professional Safety* 52(3).

CHAPTER 21

# RESEARCH TO PRACTICE TO RESEARCH (RTPTR): A SUSTAINABLE STRATEGY FOR PROMOTING SAFETY, HEALTH, AND ERGONOMICS

Sang D. Choi and James G. Borchardt

## Learning Objectives

After studying this chapter, the reader will be able to:

1. Define the concept of the research to practice to research (RtPtR) model that encourages both academics and practitioners to continually communicate the "real-world" safety, health, and ergonomic (SH&E) challenges and opportunities
2. Recognize the importance of implementing the RtPtR principle because of the physical, psychophysical, and demographic changes in the workforce.
3. Explain how RtPtR can assist practitioners and academicians in the fields of occupational SH&E
4. Provide examples of academics and practitioners adopting the RtPtR process

## Key Terms

**Research to practice to research (RtPtR), professional development, occupational, ergonomics, safety, risk, management, controls, prevention through design, best practices**

## Abstract

This chapter demonstrates the essential role of transferring occupational safety and ergonomics knowledge and interventions into highly effective prevention practices for improving the worker wellbeing and operational excellence in the workplace. The authors describe effective ways to translate academic research into workplace practices, for example, research to practice (RtP). As an extension of the research-to-practice model, the authors introduce the practice-to-research (PtR) extension by encouraging industry practitioners to communicate real-world exposures to academia, thus narrowing the gap between academic research and practical solutions to workplace SH&E challenges (RtPtR). The authors provide discussions on a variety of topics: bridging the gap by applying the NIOSH revised lifting equation (NRLE), workers' changing psychophysical characteristics, and related SH&E strategies. Furthermore, to meet the challenges of today's changing workforce, such as aging and demographic changes, this chapter also proposes a novel approach called the "Ergonomic Action Level and B Factor" to assist safety and ergonomic professionals to preplan ergonomic controls into construction processes.

## Introduction and Background

Since the early 1980s, the concept of "research to practice" has been applied by various organizations to bridge the gap between researches and practitioners. For example, in 1982, the first Research to Practice Conference (R2P), an informal organization connecting research to practice in education, was held at Northern Illinois University in DeKalb, Illinois. The intent of this annual conference was to bring researchers and practitioners together to discuss and share the impact of research on practice (Berger and Henschke 2013).

In the 1990s, the National Institute for Occupational Safety and Health (NIOSH) encouraged research resources to include real-world applications and eventually evolved into NIOSH's *research to practice* (r2p) model. According to NIOSH (2015), "research to practice" is an approach to encourage collaborations between partners and stakeholders in the use, adoption, and adaptation of knowledge, interventions, and technologies in order to reduce and eliminate injuries, illness, and fatalities in the workplace. It emphasizes working with partners to develop effective products, translate research findings into practice, target dissemination efforts, and evaluate and demonstrate the effectiveness of these efforts for improving worker health and safety (NIOSH 2015).

"Research to practice" is an approach to encourage collaborations between partners and stakeholders in the use, adoption, and adaptation of knowledge, interventions, and technologies in order to reduce and eliminate injuries, illness, and fatalities in the workplace.

In 2008, academic researcher Professor Sang D. Choi and industry practitioner Mr. James G. Borchardt met at the Construction Safety Conference in Rosemont, Illinois. The two authors have collaborated to advocate bridging the gap between academia and SH&E practitioners in an effort to make NIOSH's goal of "research to practice" (RtP) a reality through peer-reviewed papers and professional development conferences. For example, Strategic Goal 7.0 of the National Occupational Research Agenda (NORA 2008) was to *reduce the incidence and severity of work-related musculoskeletal disorders among construction workers in the United States.* The authors have broadened NIOSH's research to practice (RtP) process by adding the practice-to-research (PtR) component. As a result, Professor Choi created the "Research to Practice to Research" (RtPtR) model to encourage practitioners to communicate real-world safety and health (S&H) exposures to academia for future research. The authors continue to discuss how S&H research and resources could be made more useful to practitioners.

It is important to understand the different perspectives of academics and practitioners in order to promote the continuous advancement of ideas for improving the process of research to practice to research.

While NIOSH's research-to-practice initiative has resulted in "practitioner friendly" resources, such as *Simple Solutions—Ergonomics for Construction Workers* (NIOSH Publication 2007-122) and *Ergonomic Guidelines for Manual Material Handling* (NIOSH Publication 2007-131), the authors believe the application of the 1991 NRLE with its various components was neither widely used nor understood by S&H practitioners. For example, in 2012, the authors found a way to translate academic research, using the NIOSH lifting equation, into S&H best practices that practitioners could apply on worksites (Borchardt and Choi 2012; Choi, Borchardt, and Proksch 2012).

Application has always been the goal of both safety and health researchers and practitioners. The authors have advocated the importance of understanding the different perspectives of academics and practitioners in order to promote the continuous advancement of ideas for improving the process of RtPtR. They recognize the RtPtR model encounters both successful pathways and barriers when moving promising ergonomic and safety (E&S) research concepts into good practices and when moving E&S problems from practice to research. The authors have demonstrated the RtPtR model at various national and international conferences. In 2013 the authors were invited to present at the 100th National Safety Council's Research to Practice Track titled "RtPtR: A Roadmap for Safety and Health Practitioners and Academics" (Choi and Borchardt 2013). In 2016 and 2017, the authors presented RtPtR topics *Ergonomics in Construction* and *Prevention through Design* at the US Navy's Annual Joint Safety and Environmental Professional Development Symposium (Choi and Borchardt 2016, 2017).

Figure 21.1 depicts the RtPtR model. This model conveys the concept of *continuous improvement* by translating research findings into best practices (RtP) but then completing the loop where practitioners' feed SH&E problems back to researchers/academicians (PtR).

Figure 21.1
Research to practice to research—RtPtR model diagram. © Sang D. Choi. Used by permission.

## RtPtR Examples

The following examples describe effective ways to translate research findings into workplace best practices intended to bridge the gap between academics and practitioners.

### Example 1: Bridging the Gap: Applying the 1991 NRLE

It is essential that safety and ergonomic (S&E) researchers and practitioners know the weight of materials to be lifted when applying the NIOSH lifting equation (LE) (Waters et al. 1993, 1994) and its European (BS EN 1005-2, 2003) and international (ISO 11228-1, 2003) derivatives.

The recommended weight Limit (RWL) is the result of NIOSH's LE, and its lifting index (LI) defines the relationship of the weight of materials being lifted to the RWL. The European and International "lifting equation" standards (BS EN 1005-2, 2003) and (ISO 11228-1, 2003) are nearly identical to NIOSH's LE, except the ISO equation uses different symbols and the BS EN equation has two recommended mass limits and risk index instead of one LI (HSE 2011–RR901).

> Safety and ergonomic practitioners would use NIOSH's lifting equation and its derivatives often and effectively if the weight of materials could be easily calculated at worksites instead of the current inaccurate "bathroom scale" method.

The weight of materials can be easily measured in a laboratory, but determining the weights of materials at construction worksites is more difficult, especially when they are large, bulky, or irregularly shaped. In the spirit of NIOSH's RtP initiative, the authors believe S&E practitioners would use NIOSH's LE and its derivatives more frequently and effectively if the weight of materials could be easily calculated at worksites instead of the current inaccurate "bathroom scale" method.

While researching a topic for a paper titled "Weight of Common Construction Materials and Related Manual Handling Tasks," the authors recognized the weight of most construction materials is uniform and directly proportional to some easy-to-measure unit (Choi, Proksch, and Borchardt 2009). The authors called this relationship the Borchardt Factor (B Factor) and defined it as the density of materials expressed in units, such as length, width, or thickness, which are easy to measure at worksites (Borchardt and Choi 2012). While the density of construction materials is readily available from manufacturers over the Internet or other resources, such as industry manuals, this information is not easily accessed or in a format that S&E professionals can easily use to calculate the weight of materials at worksites.

For example, the manufacturer's literature on the Internet (US Gypsum Corporation and Georgia Pacific website) shows the density of "light" gypsum board is 0.2279 pounds per cubic inch. Therefore, knowing its density, S&E professionals could calculate the weight of any size, shape, or thickness of gypsum board using the formula weight = volume of the gypsum board × this density. However, determining the volume of construction materials at worksites can be challenging, especially for materials such as rods, dimension lumber, liquids, or dry materials such as sand or gravel in wheelbarrows. The B Factor simplifies the process of determining the weight of materials by using units of area, such as length and width, which are more easily measured on worksites rather than calculating the volume of materials. For example, the B Factor of one-half-inch light gypsum board expressed as B (½" light gypsum board) is 1.368 lbs/sq ft. Therefore, the weight of any size or shape ½" light gypsum board can be determined from the board's area, for example, the weight of one half-sheet of gypsum board would be determined by B (½" light gypsum) times area (length × width) of sheet measured at the worksite = 1.368 lbs/sq ft × (4' × 4') = 21.89 lbs. Likewise, a whole sheet (4' × 8') would be 1.368lbs/sq ft × (4' × 8') = 43.8 lbs, and a double sheet's weight would be 87.6 lbs. Consequently, the weight of any size, shape, or thicknesses of light gypsum board can be determined more easily using the B Factor because the S&E professional needs only to determine the gypsum board area and not its volume.

> The density of construction materials is not easily accessed or in a format which safety and ergonomics professionals can easily use to calculate the weight of materials at worksites, but it is readily available from manufacturers over the internet or other resources, such as industry manuals.

"Simple Solution for Home Building Workers—A Basic Guide for Preventing Manual Material Handling Injuries" (NIOSH Publication 2013-111, 31) provides additional examples of construction materials commonly manually lifted and carried on worksites. The weight of a rebar mat can be calculated using the B Factor concept to determine the number of workers needed to perform the manual task without the risk of overexertion. The density of steel rebar is uniform and is 0.28 lbs/cubic inch (US Concrete Products Corporation website ). However, determining the total volume of rebar rods used to construct a roadway mat in order to calculate its total weight is more difficult than using the B Factor for steel rebar, which uses only the number or dimension of rebar and its easily measured length. For example, B Factor for ½" rebar, for example, B(½" rebar) expressed in imperial units of pounds per linear foot (plf) is 0.668 pounds per linear foot. So a mat of ½" rebar, which has 200 linear feet, weighs 133.6 pounds. The S&E professional could determine a minimum of 3 and probably 4 workers would be needed to lift and carry this rebar mat. (Note: recent psychophysical studies suggest the load constant of the NIOSH LE and its derivatives may need to be lowered to 69 percent—for example, 35 pounds instead of the current 51 pounds).

Another common application of the B Factor on worksites is the manually lifting and carrying of 2" × 4" × 8' dimension lumber studs, which are typically pine or fir for residential construction. If a construction company has a good practice of "don't lift more than 50 pounds," how many 2" × 4" × 8' studs (1⅝" × 3⅝" actual dimensions) should a worker lift and carry? The authors researched the correlation of B Factor for western pine dimension lumber from local lumber yards and compared it to density of 10 percent kiln-dried dimension lumber available on the Internet, for example, 0.0152 pounds/cubic inch (Western Wood Products Association website) . The authors found the *t*-test statistical relationship (Pearson correlation) between the scaled weight at the lumber yards and weight available from the internet to be P value = >0.02. The B (2" × 4" × 8' Pine) = 1.07 lb/lf. Therefore, a typical 2" × 4" × 8' western pine stud would weigh 8.56 pounds. A good manual handling practice for 2" × 4" × 8' would be a maximum of 6 (4 or 5 if the LC of LE is lowered to 35 pounds). The density of Douglas fir used in construction varies depending on harvest location, with an average density of 0.0179 pounds/cubic inch. This means a typical 2" × 4" × 8' Douglas fir stud found on worksites weigh about 10.1 pounds, so a good practice of lifting/carrying of no more than 5 (3 or 4 if the LC of NIOSH's LE is lowered to 35 pounds).

### Example 2: Workers' Changing Psychophysical Characteristics Require New Safety, Health, and Ergonomic Strategies

Researchers studying workers' capacity to perform manual tasks may assume the psychophysical characteristics and demographic makeup of today's workers have remained unchanged. The authors believe these characteristics and demographic changes are shifting faster than researchers can provide scientific conclusions and develop "good practices" for industry.

For example, the physical, psychological, and demographic changes of the US workforce since the 1960s are complex and are expected to continue to change for the foreseeable future (Fox et al. 2015). Snook's Table and the University of Michigan's Biomechanical models were developed in the 1970s and 1980s, NIOSH's Lifting Equation was revised in 1991, and further refinements are suggested by the variable lifting index (VLI) (Waters et al. 1993, 1994, 2016).

Recent studies identified changes in the psychophysical characteristics of today's workers that suggest the set points of current ergonomic (psychophysical) evaluation tools may need to be revised (Snook et al. 1970; Ciriello et al. 2008, 2011). These preliminary studies repeated the psychophysical studies of the 1970s and 1980s (Snook and Ciriello 1991) and showed a significant shift in maximum acceptable weight (MAW) for male workers performing lifting/lowering and carrying tasks (69 percent). It also showed a lesser shift—for example, 82 percent of maximum average force (MAF)—in the pushing/pulling tasks (Ciriello et al. 2008). If confirmed by future research, these suggest the load constant (LC) of 51 pounds for NIOSH LE and its European derivatives (BS EN 1005-2-2003; HSE 2011-RR901) should be reduced to 35 pounds.

The characteristics and demographic changes are shifting faster than researchers can provide scientific conclusions and develop "good practices" for industry.

Lowering this LC to 35 pounds would have implications beyond the United States, since the majority of manual lifting tasks in construction worldwide would exceed this *hypothetical* 35 pounds. A study in 2013 in Nigeria (Adeyemi et al. 2013) shows 76 percent of construction lifting tasks had a lifting index (LI) greater than 1.0 using the current 51 pounds LC of NIOSH's LE, so using the lower LC would mean even fewer lifting tasks could be performed without the risk of overexertion. This study also concluded redesigning work methods are necessary, and construction managers need proactive measures to

Redesigning work methods are necessary, and construction managers need proactive measures to incorporate ergonomics into their job methods to achieve a single task lifting index of 1.0 or less.

incorporate ergonomics into their job methods to achieve single task LI of 1.0 or less. In a 2-year study in 9 construction trades, more than half (i.e., 73%) of workers reported the most important reason for using ergonomic measures was to lighten the load (Boschman et al. 2015).

In 2012, the authors began to consider the implications on changing worker and workforce characteristics on current ergonomic tools. They conducted research culminating in a paper titled "Translating Academic Research on Manual Lifting Tasks Observations into Construction Workplace Good Practices," and the research determined the recommended weight limits (RWL) and lifting index (LI) of manual lifting tasks typically found on construction worksites (Choi, Borchardt, and Proksch 2012). The authors then *hypothetically* revised the load constant (LC) of NIOSH's lifting equation (LE) from 51 pounds to 35 pounds based on recent psychophysical studies suggesting the set point should be "69 percent of guideline values" (Ciriello et al. 2008, 2011). A *hypothetical* LC of 35 pounds was used to determine the potential effect on the RWL and LI of the construction tasks evaluated in 2012. With the *hypothetical* LC of 35 pounds, approximately two-thirds of the trades in the study—for example, ceiling installer, drywall installer, floor finisher, insulator, laborer, painter, plumber, and sod layer—were associated with highly stressful manual-lifting tasks (LI > 3.0, e.g., a significant risk of lower back injury).

### Example 3: Changes to Ergonomics Research Strategies

Tables 21.1 and 21.2 show the change in the average recommended weight limit (RWL) and average lifting index (LI) from the authors' 2012 study when the hypothetical load constant (LC) of 35 pounds is used instead of the current LC of 51 pounds. The average RWL decreased from 16.33 pounds to 11.21 pounds, and the average LI increased significantly from 2.35 to 3.42. From the NIOSH perspective, it is likely that lifting tasks with a LI >1.0 pose an increased risk for lifting-related low back pain for some fraction of the workforce (Waters et al. 1993).

Figure 21.2 shows the changes in the median lifting index (LI) by trade/occupation from the authors' 2012 study, when hypothetical load constant (LC) of 35 pounds is used instead of the current LC

**Table 21.1** 2014 results using LC of 35 lbs

| | | HM | VM | DM | AM | FM | CM | RWL (lbs) | Load Wt (lbs) | LI |
|---|---|---|---|---|---|---|---|---|---|---|
| Observation (*n*=292) | Median | 0.56 | 0.89 | 0.89 | 1.00 | 0.85 | 0.95 | 10.95 | 30.00 | 2.25 |
| | Std Dev | 0.29 | 0.07 | 0.05 | 0.20 | 0.14 | 0.03 | 4.90 | 26.57 | 3.56 |
| | Min | 0.19 | 0.63 | 0.82 | 0.42 | 0.35 | 0.90 | 1.95 | 1.00 | 0.06 |
| | Max | 1.00 | 1.00 | 1.00 | 1.00 | 0.94 | 1.00 | 22.89 | 192.00 | 18.60 |

| | LC | HM | VM | DM | AM | FM | CM | RWL | Load Wt | LI |
|---|---|---|---|---|---|---|---|---|---|---|
| Average | 35.00 | 0.69 | 0.87 | 0.91 | 0.84 | 0.78 | 0.96 | 11.21 | 30.70 | 3.42 |

**Table 21.2** 2012 results using LC of 51 lbs

| | | HM | VM | DM | AM | FM | CM | RWL (lbs) | Load Wt (lbs) | LI |
|---|---|---|---|---|---|---|---|---|---|---|
| Observation (*n*=292) | Median | 0.56 | 0.89 | 0.89 | 1.00 | 0.85 | 0.95 | 15.96 | 30.00 | 1.54 |
| | Std Dev | 0.29 | 0.07 | 0.05 | 0.20 | 0.14 | 0.03 | 7.13 | 26.57 | 2.44 |
| | Min | 0.19 | 0.63 | 0.82 | 0.42 | 0.35 | 0.90 | 2.84 | 1.00 | 0.04 |
| | Max | 1.00 | 1.00 | 1.00 | 1.00 | 0.94 | 1.00 | 33.36 | 192.00 | 12.76 |

| | LC | HM | VM | DM | AM | FM | CM | RWL | Load Wt | LI |
|---|---|---|---|---|---|---|---|---|---|---|
| Average | 51.00 | 0.69 | 0.87 | 0.91 | 0.84 | 0.78 | 0.96 | 16.33 | 30.70 | 2.35 |

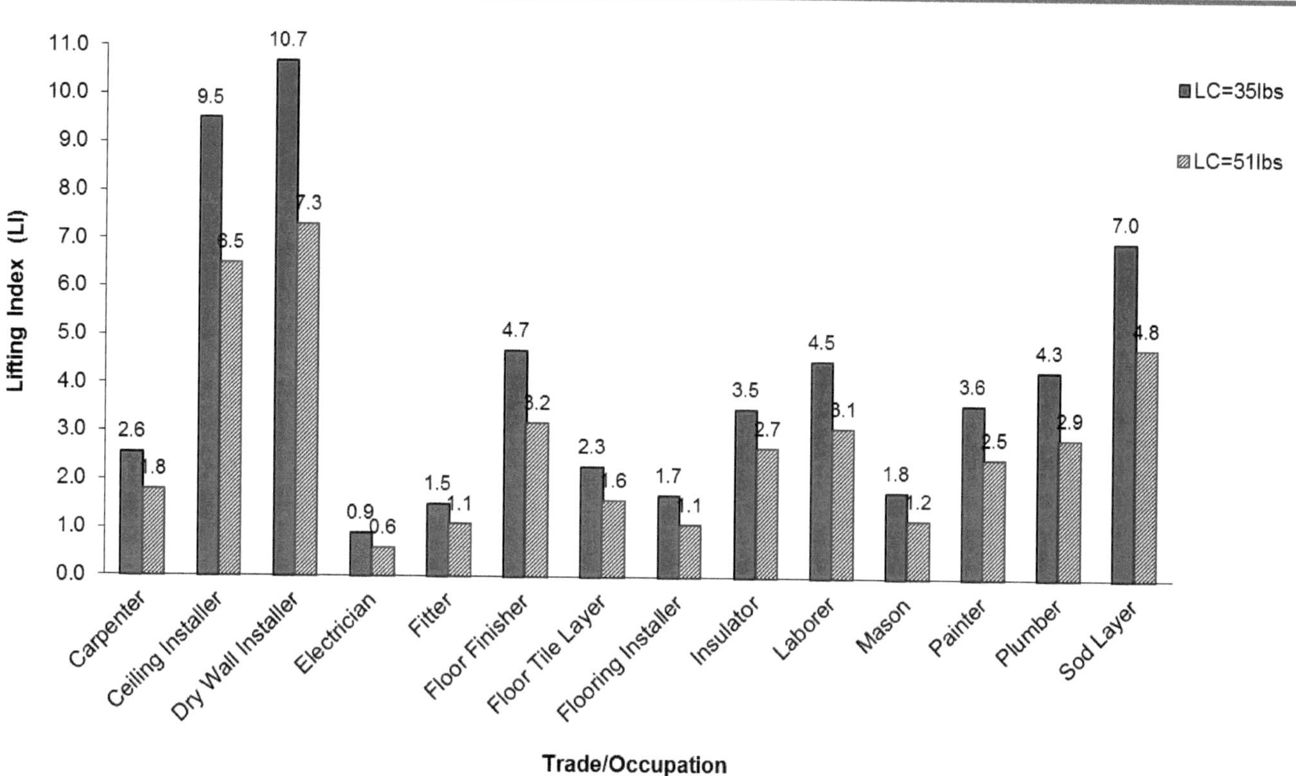


Figure 21.2
Lifting index results comparison by trade/occupation

of 51e pounds. With LC of 51 pounds, one-third (5 out of 14 trades) recorded LI >3.0. However, with the hypothetical LC of 35 pounds, two-thirds of trades, such as ceiling installer, drywall installer, floor finisher, insulator, laborer, painter, plumber, and sod layer, were associated with highly stressful lifting tasks (LI >3.0). According to NIOSH, nearly all workers will be at an increased risk of a work-related injury when performing highly stressful lifting tasks—lifting tasks that would exceed a LI of 3.0 (Waters et al. 1994).

### Example 4: Ergonomic Action Level (EAL) Concept Promotes Prevention through Design Principles in the Construction Industry

Because worker characteristics have changed during past decades of research, assessment tools and good practices may not be applicable for current workers. The authors have proposed a new ergonomic strategy, an ergonomic action level (EAL), similar to the action level used in the industrial hygiene (IH) area to begin to "take action or implement controls at a level below which is known to cause injury" (Borchardt and Choi 2015a,b,c). The *concept of EAL* is similar to the IH "action level" in that it recommends good practices should anticipate changes in worker characteristics and be designed into tasks below the level known or suspected to cause injury to workers. For example, the Informational Appendix D of ANSI/ASSE A10-2007 (2013) *Reduction of Musculoskeletal Problems in Construction* asks contractors to consider "What heavy materials or equipment are being handled on site—anything over twenty pounds?" and "Do workers have to lift more than twenty pounds often?" These "informational only" questions which are not part of the approved standard, suggest contractors should "take action"—for example, identify and consider changes when materials and equipment weighing more than twenty pounds are lifted often. This suggested "action point" is considerably below the fifty-one pounds of load constant (LC) of NIOSH's current LE. The authors believe if a proactive ergonomic action level (EAL) is used as a design guideline, upstream planning will be needed because the weight of common construction materials and equipment will most likely exceed these new guidelines.

Architects, engineers, constructors, manufacturers, and S&E practitioners will need to rethink the manufacturing and construction processes to include increased automation, mechanization, modularization, and prefabrication. The hierarchy of controls per ANSI/AIHA Z10-2005 (R2012) directs the best and most effective controls: eliminate/design out potential hazards, substitution, engineering controls, administrative controls, and, as the last resort, personal protective equipment. To encourage designing engineering controls into workplaces and processes, NIOSH published a National Initiative on Prevention through Design (PtD) in 2011 (NIOSH 2011). PtD is a risk-reduction strategy implemented in the early stages of construction that provides a unique opportunity to identify hazards and reduce exposures to those hazards by preplanning/designing improvements, thereby reducing or eliminating risk (see ANSI/ASSE Z590.3-2011 (R2016)). In 2013, National Institute for Occupational Safety and Health released several PtD publications specific to construction (NIOSH 2013). Changing the way the work process is done to decrease the labor intensity may reduce the amount of overhead work and time it takes to get the job done. Here are some examples to consider.

Architects, engineers, constructors, manufacturers, and S&E practitioners will need to rethink the manufacturing and construction processes to include increased automation, mechanization, modularization, and prefabrication.

It is obvious that a backhoe operator can move more dirt safely than a laborer with a shovel. Landscape contractors have mechanized the sod-laying task by using bulk rolls that are cut and placed mechanically. The 4' × 8' wooden concrete foundation forms weighing over 100 pounds have been replaced by aluminum forms that are lighter and hoisted into place by truck-mounted hoists. The development of insulated concrete blocks (ICB) for foundations and above-ground walls further reduces manual tasks and construction time. Nano particles are beginning to be used to strengthen concrete as a replacement for rebar,

Changing the way the work process is done to decrease the labor intensity may reduce the amount of overhead work and time it takes to get the job done.

eliminating the manual handling and tying at worksites. The removal of asphalt shingles from residential roofs can also be mechanized. The strenuous manual task of roofing with asphalt shingles might be changed by using a large, prefabricated section hoisted in place by crane or the development of a track-mounted, automated "shingling device." Installing embedded concrete inserts into ceiling forms eliminates the need for prolonged overhead drilling that would be needed to place all-thread rods for a ceiling system (Albers and Estill 2007). Requiring employees to use a mechanical lift or hoist to raise themselves closer to their work prevents them from having to raise their arms above their shoulders (Choi et al. 2007). Mechanical placement of kerbs in the United Kingdom could replace manual handling (Bust et al. 2005). Using a mechanical device to hold a heavy tool in place while the employee is using the tool would reduce the physical burden for the worker (Bust et al. 2005).

## Conclusion

In order for safety practitioners and researchers to achieve long-term effective solutions to SH&E exposures at worksites, the authors propose two key strategies that need to be implemented. First, SH&E researchers and practitioners need to collaborate to find and develop solutions and strategies to unknown exposures through the process initiated by NIOSH—for example, RtP but expanded by the authors PtR. Second, known solutions and prevention strategies to SH&E exposures need to be preplanned upstream in the construction process using prevention through design principles. A continuous cycle of SH&E improvement can be achieved when the process of RtPtR is followed. There are many examples/applications of the RtP process attempting to develop control strategies for overexertion of manually handling materials, tools, and equipment, such as Snook's tables (aka Liberty Mutual tables), NIOSH's lifting equation (LE), Water's variable lifting index, and so forth. There are fewer examples of the PtR process where SH&E practitioners have identified real-world exposures and academic researchers have responded. Adding to the body of knowledge, following a strict scientific approach can be a slow and tedious process. Knowledgeable practitioners can improve the research process by offering their real-world insights and possible solutions for researchers to study, test, and then share proven solutions with the SH&E community.

Continuous cycle of SH&E improvement can be achieved when the process of RtPtR is followed to develop control strategies for overexertion of manually handling materials, tools, and equipment.

## Questions

1. Define the concept of Research to Practice to Research (RtPtR) model.
2. What is the B Factor? Provide examples.
3. Describe the importance of implementing RtPtR in regards to the physical, psychophysical, and demographic changes in the workforce.
4. What is the Ergonomic Action Level (EAL)? Explain.
5. What is prevention through design (PtD)? Provide some examples.

## References

Adeyemi, O., S. Adejuyigbe, O. Akanbi, S. Ismaila, and A. F. Adekoya. (2013). "Manual Lifting Task Methods and Low Back Pain among Construction Workers in the Southwestern Nigeria." *Global Journal of Research in Industrial Engineering* 13: 3-G.

Albers, J. T., and C. F. Estill. (2007). "Simple Solutions: Ergonomics for Construction Workers." US Department of Health and Human Services, DHHS (NIOSH) Publication No. 2007-122.

ANSI/AIHA/ASSE. (2012). "Occupational Health and Safety Management Systems." Z10-2005. http://webstore.ansi.org/RecordDetail.aspx?sku=ANSI%2fAIHA%2fASSE+Z10-2012

ANSI/ASSE. (2016). "Prevention through Design Guidelines for Addressing Occupational Hazards and Risks in Design and Redesign Processes." Z590.3-2011 (R2016). http://www.asse.org/ansi/asse-z590-3-2011-r2016-/.

ANSI/ASSE. (2013). "Reduction of Musculoskeletal Problems in Construction." ANSI/ASSE A10.40-2007 (2013)). Des Plaines, IL. http://www.asse.org/ansi/asse-a10-40-2007-r2013-reduction-of-musculoskeletal-problems-in-construction/.

Berger, J., and J. Henschke. (2013). "Perspectives in Adult Education—Research to Practice Conference: Its History, Purpose, and Activities." *New Horizons in Adult Education & Human Resource Development* 26(1): 60–63.

Boise Cascade—Engineered Wood Products. (2016). "Technical Information: Weight of Building Materials." https://www.bc.com/content/uploads/bc-resources/GE-1_Weights_Building_Materials.pdf.

Borchardt, J. G., and S. D. Choi. (2015a). *Workers' Changing Psychophysical Characteristics Require Prevention through Design (PtD) and Safety, Health & Ergonomic (SH&E) Strategies at Construction Worksites*. Australia: International Ergonomics Association.

Borchardt, J.G., & Choi, S.D. (2015b). "Prevention through Design (PtD) and Safety, Health & Ergonomic (SH&E) Strategies Are Needed Due to Changing Psychophysical Characteristics of Construction Workers." Nashville, TN: XXVII International Occupational Ergonomics and Safety Conference (ISOES).

Borchardt, J. G., and S. D. Choi. (2015c). "Psychophysical and Demographic Changes Requires Rethinking Ergonomic Strategies." Dallas, TX: Safety 2015 ASSE Conference.

Borchardt, J. G., and S. D. Choi. (2012). "B Factor and Its Importance to HFE Practitioners—

Applying NIOSH's 1991 Revised Lifting Equation and Its Derivatives." Boston: Proceedings of the 2012 HFES 56th Annual Meeting.

Boschman, J. S., M. H. W. Frings-Dresen, and H. F. VanderMolen. (2015). "Use of Ergonomic Measures Related to Musculoskeletal Complaints among Construction Workers: A 2-year Follow-up Study." *Safety and Health at Work* 6(2): 90–96.

British Standards Institute (BS EN 1005-2). (2003). "Safety of Machinery and Human Performance. http://webstore.ansi.org/RecordDetail.aspx?sku=BS+EN+1005-2%3A2003%2BA1%3A2008.

Bust, P. D., A. G. F. Gibb, and R. A. Haslam. (2005). "Manual Handling of Highway Kerbs—Focus Group Findings." *Applied Ergonomics* 36: 417–25.

Choi, S. D. (2008). "Investigation of Ergonomic Issues in the Wisconsin Construction Industry." *Journal of Safety, Health and Environmental Research* 5(1): 1–19.

Choi, S. D., and J. G. Borchardt. (2017). "Prevention through Design." Norfolk, VA: 25th Annual Joint Safety and Environmental Professional Development Symposium (PDS).

Choi, S. D., and J. G. Borchardt. (2016). "Ergonomics in Construction and Prevention through Design." Norfolk, VA: 24th Annual Joint Safety and Environmental Professional Development Symposium (PDS).

Choi, S. D., and J. G. Borchardt. (2013). "Research to Practice to Research (RtPtR): A Roadmap for Safety and Health Practitioners and Academics." Chicago: 2013 National Safety Council Congress and Expo.

Choi, S. D., and J. G. Borchardt. (2012). "Bridging the Gap between Academic Research and Construction Workplaces Using the NIOSH 1991 Lifting Equation." Denver, CO: ASSP Professional Development Conference.

Choi, S. D., J. Borchardt, and T. Proksch. (2012). "Translating Academic Research on Manual Lifting Tasks Observations into Construction Workplace Good Practices." *Journal of Safety, Health and Environmental Research* 8: 3–10.

Choi, S. D., L. Hudson, P. Kangas, B. Jungen, J. Maple, and C. Bowen. (2007). "Occupational Ergonomics Issues in Highway Construction Surveyed in Wisconsin, United States." *Industrial Health* 45: 487–93.

Choi, S. D., T. Proksch, T., and J. G. Borchardt. (2009). "Investigation of common Construction Materials Weight and Related Manual Lifting Task Observations." Beijing, China: Proceeding of the 17th Triennial Congress of the International Ergonomics Association.

Ciriello, V. M., P. G. Dempsey, R. V. Maikala, and N. V. O'Brien. (2008). "Secular Changes in Psychophysically Determined Maximum Acceptable Weights and Forces over Twenty Years for male Industrial Workers." *Ergonomics* 51: 593–601.

Ciriello, V. M., R. V. Maikala, P. G. Dempsey, and N. V. O'Brien. (2011). "Gender Differences in Psychophysically Determined Maximum Acceptable Weights and Forces for Industrial Workers Observed after Twenty Years."

*International Archives of Occupational Environmental Health* 84(5): 569–75.

CPWR—The Center for Construction Research and Training. (2005). *Work-related Fatal and Nonfatal Injuries among U.S. Construction Workers, 1992–2003.* Silver Spring, MD.

Fox, R. R., G. E. Brogmus, and W. S. Maynard. (2015). "Aging Workers and Ergonomics—A Fresh Perspective." *Professional Safety* 60(1): 33–41.

Georgia-Pacific. (2017). "ToughRock Light and Strong Drywall." http://www.gp.com/build/productgroup.aspx?pid=1490

Health and Safety Executive. (2011). "Prospective Evaluation of the 1991 NIOSH Lifting Equation. Research Report (RR901)." http://www.hse.gov.uk/research/rrpdf/rr901.pdf.

International Organization for Standardization (ISO). (2003). *ISO 11228-1 Ergonomics—Manual Handling—Part 1: Lifting and Carrying.* Technical Committee ISO/TC 159, Ergonomics. Geneva: ISO.

National Gypsum Company. (2013). Specifications092900/NGC. http://nationalgypsum.com/File/111148.pdf.

National Institute for Occupational Safety and Health (NIOSH). (2015). "Research to Practice (r2p)." U.S. Department of Health and Human Services. https://www.cdc.gov/niosh/r2p/.

National Institute for Occupational Safety and Health (NIOSH). (2013). "NIOSH Program Portfolio: Construction Program." http://www.cdc.gov/niosh/programs/const/.

National Institute for Occupational Safety and Health (NIOSH). (2011). Prevention through Design—Plan for the National Initiative. DHHS (NIOSH) Publication No. 2011–121.

National Institute for Occupational Safety and Health (NIOSH). (2007). "Ergonomic Guidelines for Manual Material Handling." DHHS (NIOSH) Publication No. 2007–131.

National Institute for Occupational Safety and Health (NIOSH). (2007). "Simple Solutions—Ergonomics for Construction Workers." DHHS (NIOSH) Publication No. 2007–122.

National Institute for Occupational Safety and Health (NIOSH). (1994). "Workplace Use of Back Belts: Review and Recommendations." U.S. Department of Health and Human Services, DHHS (NIOSH) Number 94-122.

National Occupation Research Agenda (NORA). (2008). "Strategic Goal 7.0—Reduce the Incidence and Severity of Work-related Musculoskeletal Disorders among US Construction Workers." http://www.cdc.gov/niosh/nora/comment/agendas/construction/pdfs/ConstOct2008.pdf

Snook, S. H. (1978). "The Design of Manual Handling Tasks." *Ergonomics* 21(12): 963–85.

Snook, S. H., and V. M. Ciriello. (1991). "The Design of Manual Handling Tasks: Revised Tables of Maximum Acceptable Weights and Forces." *Ergonomics* 34(9): 1197–213.

Snook, S. H., C. H. Irvine, and S. F. Bass. (1970). "Maximum Weights and Work Load Acceptable to Male Industrial Workers." *AIHA Journal* 31: 579–86.

US Concrete Products Corporation. (2017). "Rebar Chart." http://unitedstatesconcrete.com/precast_concrete/index.php/rebar-chart

Western Wood Products Association (WWPA). (2005). "Weight per Linear Foot Model Table 22." Retrieved from: http://www2.wwpa.org/Portals/9/docs/PDF/weight.pdf.

Waters, T. R., V. Putz-Anderson, and A. Garg. (1994). "Applications Manual for Revised NIOSH Lifting Equation." U.S. DHHS (NIOSH) Publication No. 94-110.

Waters, T. R., V. Putz-Anderson, A. Garg, and L. J. Fine. (1993). "Revised NIOSH equation for the Design and Evaluation of Manual Lifting Tasks." *Ergonomics* 36(7): 749–76.

Waters, T., E. Occhipinti, D. Columbini, E. Alvarez-Casado, and R. Fox. (2016). "Variable Lifting Index (VLI): A New Method for Evaluating Variable Lifting Tasks." *Human Factors* 58(5): 696–711.

CHAPTER 22

# BULL'S-EYE HAZARD RECOGNITION SYSTEM

Steve Smith and Richard Olawoyin

## Learning Objectives

After studying this chapter, the reader will be able to:

1. Identify the multiple levels of factors that need to be assessed to accurately evaluate a situation
2. Determine the level of hazard to the people and facilities that may need to be reviewed
3. Evaluate the effectiveness of systems and processes that will guarantee the availability of resources

## Key Terms

**Availability, maintainability, reliability, hazard assessment, turnover rate, system effectiveness**


## Abstract

Bull's-Eye Hazard Recognition System (BEHRS) is a method developed to identify and categorize potential hazards that could impact the safety of people or the use of a property. The method can be used to thin slice information in the process of conducting a thorough hazard assessment. The BEHRS can then provide the opportunity to rank the severity of each hazard found, consequently placing the recognizable hazards into a severity matrix. The matrix assists in designating low or high probabilities of an accident occurrence and provides the capability to handle such accidents. These methods, when used together, should enable safety practitioners to provide the most accurate hazard assessment to interested stakeholders for the purpose of making the best informed decision about a property and its intended use. In addition, these tools are valuable to safety practitioners when developing and implementing corporate-specific safety programs.


## Introduction

Most accident investigations start with an event, and the investigators work outward to determine the cause or causes. They look for evidence around the event, and as soon as they are satisfied that they have an answer, they conclude the investigation. Before an incident happens, there is no defined starting point to work from. Since prevention is more desirable than investigation of an accident, organizations have tried to devise systems to evaluate existing conditions before a loss occurs so that they could modify them and avoid the probable losses. One of the problems with hazard recognition is not that there is insufficient data, but there is too much potential data. Those experienced in hazard recognition can thin slice the data to discard much of what is not relevant (Gladwell 2007). Flanagan and Lybarger (2014) emphasized that when you look at large volumes of data, you must judge the value of the data and then focus on which hazards in the data could have an effect on the possible outcome you are concerned with. The military during the Second World War had developed Program Evaluation Review Technique (PERT). Insurance companies had developed term of reference (TOR) (Ferry 1998), and the space program has developed their own prelaunch review process to eliminate hazards before they occur. Many other systems, such as Job Hazard Analysis (JHA) and Critical Path Method (CPM), require participants with years of experience to identify potential exposures in their area of expertise.

For transitional safety practitioners, the Bull's-Eye Hazard Recognition System (BEHRS), figure 21.1 can be a useful starting point to carry out a logical review of loss exposure before an event occurs or insurance coverage is sought. This method can be used by safety/risk management practitioners with any level of experience to look at an existing situation from the outside inward to select situations with high probable loss potential and restructure the variables of the situation before a loss occurs.

> Through this process of individualizing safety, the leading indicators of any undesirable event will be more discernable.

Experienced safety practitioners may have already developed knowledge that gives them insight into the outer rings of the bull's-eye, so they may progress rapidly to the specifics of the operation. The severity matrix can then be employed to reach a conclusion as to the overall severity of the exposure to an undesirable outcome. It starts with an evaluation of the greater surroundings first. It then works inward, one level of exposures at a time, until an understanding of the whole subject environment is reached. The severity of the hazards versus the probability of occurrence is ranked, and the most serious exposures can be dealt

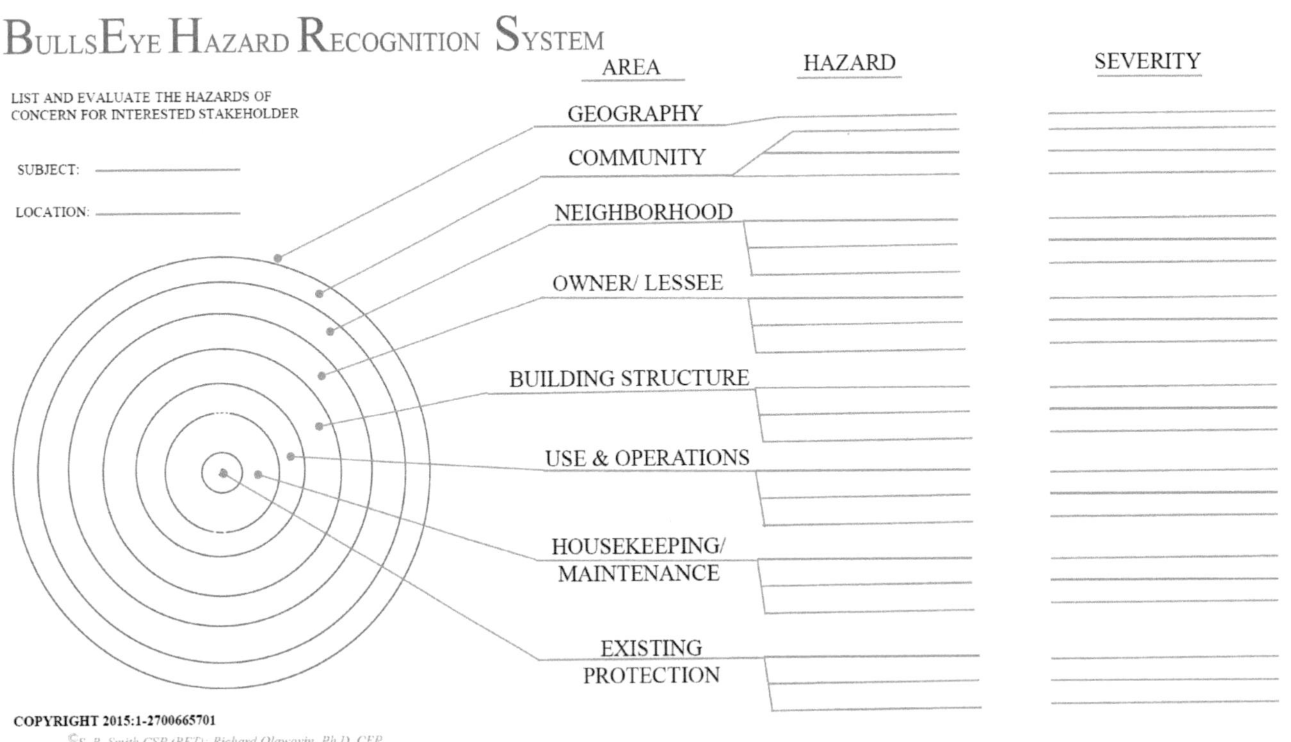


Figure 22.1
Illustration of the Bull's-Eye Hazard Recognition System (BEHRS).

with before a loss occurs. The example used here is an assessment of a property loss exposure, looking at a theoretical plastic parts manufacturer in a theoretical small Midwest town in the United States. The system will go through the bull's-eye, level by level, from a property preservation perspective. The reader may substitute different topics for their bull's-eye to suit the needs of their situation. Think of approaching a site or situation in a vehicle and recording the outermost observations as you approach the location so that the pinpoint conditions do not overshadow broad conditions that may be critical toward allowing a loss to occur or create more severity than is necessary. Remember, as you arrive at a potential loss situation, the most important hazards may be behind you just like when landing an airplane; the most important part of the runway may be that which is behind the plane.

Questions frequently asked are what is hazard recognition, and when should hazard recognition begin and end? This chapter presents the bull's-eye methodology, which is effective in providing the ability to locate and recognize conditions and parameters that are potentially hazardous and cause injury or damage to people, property, and the environment. This is an ongoing process with applicable tools for recognizing and evaluating the severity of hazards. Using leading indicators rather than lagging indicators for safety assurance is crucial, and it all begins with appropriately recognizing the imminent hazards.

## Leading and Lagging Indicators

Leading and lagging indicators are essential parameters to observe in ensuring the success of an organization or a system. However, more attention should be on the leading indicators because these indicators present the opportunity to be proactive in controlling potentially consequential events that have not yet occurred. Leading indicators are measurements used in the safety industry basically for quality and safety improvements (Forest and Kessler 2013). These indicators rely on proper safety training, hazard recognition, safety audits, and employee involvement. The success of using this valuable tool lies with the contributory aptitude of safety practitioners in selling safety to the employees and all stakeholders. Getting to know the employees, seeing them as people, and learning about their value/motivation makes safety personal. The implementation of good housekeeping programs help to reduce the frequency of leading indicators, such as near misses, which are more frequent than reportable accidents. When the root cause of near misses are eliminated, the probability of any minor or major accident occurring will also be reduced (Budworth 2013). Through this process of individualizing safety, the leading indicators of any undesirable event will be more discernable and even more effective with a proactive feedback opportunity. Lagging or trailing indicators are measured by using OSHA rates such as days away and transfer rate (DART), lost work days (LWD), and total recordable incident rate (IR). This data is easier to collect than the leading indicators because it is standardized. It is also a good measure of organizational safety performance, as it provides useful information for selling safety to the management; however, it is always better to have a proactive system that can identify all indicators that may then lead to the trailing indicators.

## Bull's-Eye Hazard Recognition System

The Bull's-Eye Hazard Recognition System (BEHRS) was developed to help identify hazard areas and determine whether potential location and situation require detailed assessment or corrective action. The purpose of this chapter is to present how a safety practitioner can recognize and understand the multiple levels of factors that need to be assessed in order to accurately evaluate a situation and also to determine the level of hazard to the people and facilities that a safety professional may be asked to review.

The hypothetical example is of an evaluation of the fire potential in a midsized plastic parts manufacturer that had just purchased an existing vacant plant in a small Midwestern community with a population of about 5000 people that had previously supplied stamped metal parts for the automotive industry. The plant was equipped with an automatic fire protection system that was installed thirty years prior by the previous owner of the building, a company that stamped metal door

Figure 22.2
Example of a plastic molding plant.

hinges as subcomponents for the auto industry. The fire ignited railcars with chemicals being unloaded from the rail siding adjacent to the plant and serving the grain elevator on the opposite side of the tracks in this small town. The fire from the railcars became so intense that it ignited the raw plastic pellets in the plant and the grain elevator on the opposite side of the tracks.

The town only has an on-call volunteer fire department with one full-time chief. The fire station is modern and only three miles from the site. However, the plant is located on the edge of the town. It is unknown if the firefighters will respond in the event of a fire. Additionally, on-call firefighters may take longer to respond to a fire; a quick response can oftentimes be critical. The on-call fire department is a severity rate of 2. Looking at the volume of water, the community received water from a 400,000-gallon water tower fed by 2 wells installed in the 1950s. The water pressure was insufficient to give the fire department enough pressure to deliver the water to the burning buildings, especially the grain elevator. The volunteer department used a pumper truck from an adjacent community to increase the water pressure from the closest hydrants. The draw on the 50-year-old water system was so severe that the water mains collapsed. As a result the small business district and several adjacent homes had no water available because the water was used to fight the fire, and consequently, the plant and adjacent building burned completely.

> If you are unfamiliar with an area, it is important to inquire from the locals if there are frequent tornados, forest fires, mudslides, sinkholes, or blizzards.

Earlier that same year, a large insurance carrier had been asked to insure the plastic plant for property and liability coverage but had declined to do so. The risk management department of the insurance company had used a bull's-eye evaluation system to evaluate the potential loss. This chapter is an explanation of how that system was used in this hypothetical example and how it could be useful to the safety / loss control person in any organization and adapted to the organizations specific exposures. The steps in a bull's-eye loss potential evaluation (figure 22.1) are (1) the overall geography of the area, including weather and time of day; (2) the characteristics of the community, such as emergency preparedness, municipal water supply, distance to medical facilities, and availability of emergency equipment; (3) the immediate neighborhood where the loss potential is located; (4) the owners, managers, and lessees of the site and the workforce; (5) the buildings and land—is the construction appropriate to the use and the land adequate for the intended operations; (6) what the operational functionality of the site is; (7) what the overall maintenance and hygiene at the site is; (8) is there is a preventative maintenance program in place for all operation critical equipment; a (9) what are the type and level of protection programs currently in place for employee safety, fire protection, or disaster response; and (10) the Hazard Recognition Severity Matrix.

## Geography and Weather

In the plastic plant example, the location of the site in relation to the elevation of the municipal water tower may have affected the available water pressure for controlling the fire.

The geography of an operation and the weather have significant effects on the potential for a loss. The elevation of the site in relation to the overall area along with nearness to rivers, streams, lakes, and very large bodies of water as well as seasonal variations in weather, will impact flooding potential and access to the site by emergency responders. In the plastic parts manufacturer example, a fire during a flood could prevent emergency fire personnel and equipment from reaching the site. If the site is at a higher elevation than the rest of the area, water pressure for firefighting may be inadequate. Also, since lightning does strike twice in the same place, the elevation may make the area more susceptible to damage than locations in a valley. Weather is an important factor in the probability of a severe loss and this can be made even more difficult during hours of darkness. High winds can lead to building and tower collapse. Computer searches can yield significant weather events history. There are tornado maps and earth quake zones that are public knowledge that can give you guidance in evaluating the effect that weather could have and the time of day and time of year that are more prone to the effects of the natural hazards. Consequently, these hazards may make these situations even more difficult. If you are unfamiliar with an area, it is important to inquire from the locals if there are frequent tornados, forest fires, mudslides, sinkholes, or blizzards. Too much precipitation as noted is a potential problem to reckon with, which could lead to flooding. Flooding can lead to unusable roadways and bridge collapse; fast-moving flood water can lead to foundation scour to structures downstream. Many areas are subject to flood insurance based on the floodplain. This is usually set in place by the Federal Emergency Management Agency (FEMA) (Atreya et al. 2015).

Nearby rivers, streams, lakes, and other bodies of water can also contribute to the possibility of floods that can potentially cause damages to the building's landscape. Excess rain can cause these bodies of water to overflow and can also increase the probability of flood occurrence. Other environmental variables such as valleys, mountains, elevation, and climatic conditions are equally important. The elevation difference of the building compared to a mountain, river, or lake can cause a rockslide, taking out building walls and floods. If a building is at a higher elevation, these hazards are avoided. Observation of surrounding buildings for previous water damage and landscaping designed to divert water can provide useful insights into what will happen during severe weather events. The elevation of any building can be obtained by placing a hand-held GPS device at the base of the location in question, then comparing that elevation to readings at the base of surrounding structures. Do remember that everything looks different at night, too. On the alternative, a lack of precipitation, such as draught conditions, can also promote rapid fire spread.

### Community

Many factors in the community are important to the operations of an organization, such as existing plans of action which should include the identification of potential hazards and controls. Why is the community important? The community assesses the influential factors surrounding an operation (e.g., property), including the population. The level of preparedness of the community may determine whether a small problem becomes a big problem.

The emergency response to an event depends on the personnel and equipment a community has to respond to an accident. The access to the water supply to fight fires depends on the capacity of the community to supply water to the area and their capacity to plow snow and keep roads and bridges open during all weather conditions. The ability to care for injured employees depends on the availability of hospitals and medical personnel. It is useful to find out if a community has reciprocal agreements (mutual aid) with neighboring communities to share emergency services.

> The nearness of a fire department, average emergency response time, and availability of extinguishing agents near the operational site of the company should be important considerations as part of the emergency plan.

All fire departments in the United States are rated based on capabilities to respond to emergencies. The ratings range from 1 (highest) to 10 (no fire protection at all). Most fire departments know their rating, and you can stop at a fire station and ask if they are rated and what their class rating is. Very large cities are usually rated class 1 or 2, and most suburbs are rated class 3, 4, or 5. Volunteer fire departments (paid on call) are usually rated class 5 or lower; most rural areas are rated class 8, 9, or 10. The Insurance Services Office (ISO) publishes these ratings. They are called ISO ratings or Town Class ratings, and they have a strong impact on insurance rates in those communities and also are a quick initial measurement of the community's disaster preparedness.

Volunteer fire departments are now usually identified as "paid on call" departments and receive the same training as full-time departments. However many organization locate facilities just outside community boundaries for lower land acquisition cost and taxes. Just because the mail address says "XYZ city" does not mean that community's services are available. It is an important question mark that should be answered. In the plastic plant example, whether the site is actually within the community and whether the closest fire hydrant is actually available to the responding fire department are legitimate concerns. Other relevant questions that should be part of this stage of the BEHRS are has an annual hazardous materials list been furnished to local fire and code enforcement personnel? Are there mutual assistance arrangements with adjacent communities, and is there access to an emergency response team?

The proximity of a fire department, employment status of the firemen (voluntary, part-time, or full-time), average emergency response time, and availability of extinguishing agents near the operational site of the company should be important considerations as part of the emergency plan. Locating the nearest fire hydrant to the building and making sure it is operable and usable is important as well. If there is no access to a fire hydrant, the safety specialist must find out if there is a water tower in the community, the capacity of the tower, as well as how many gallons are readily accessible to the fire department. Having more than one fire station covers more ground for basic calls in a proximate area. The population of the city is another factor of consideration in the community. The more people there are in the community, the higher the possibility that safety and response teams will be on another call. That is why it is important to consider all of these factors during the BEHRS process.

## Neighborhood-Adjacent Structures and Uses

The neighborhood has a big influence on how hazardous the potential event could be. If you are in a building that is surrounded by chemical plants, for example, employees in your organization and the operations could be adversely affected by the impact of events from the neighbors. Alternatively, if you run a small- or moderate-sized operation, it could cause a major loss to the entire community, especially if there are potentials for toxic substance release or fire outbreak.

The safety practitioner carrying out a hazard recognition survey of a site should expeditiously access the presence of security fences and gates adjacent to the site being considered, which will indicate possible crime or theft potential, which could affect the site being considered. Access to the subject site also affects emergency response of all kinds. The site accessor, looking for significant potential hazards, should inspect adjacent structures for unused and discontinued operations that leave behind structures that are clearly abandoned. Radio towers that are no longer in use are often not maintained and could fall on adjacent property should also be observed. The evaluation should consider the height of the tower and distance from the building or operation under consideration. Small locked out-buildings away from main buildings may be dynamite magazines with old, unstable explosives still inside.

The height of adjacent buildings in comparison to a property under review could indicate high potential for fire spread. In the example, fire spread and height of buildings was critical. Fertilizer and grain elevators are hazardous located next to a potential plastic subassembly manufacturing site because of combustibility and flammability and would need to be much farther away. The storage of fertilizer can sometimes be overlooked, but it is important for a safety professional to recognize the risks of improper storage of fertilizer. Ammonium-based fertilizers can detonate under select conditions. This would require a strong source of ignition. Heating under confinement can also be an explosion hazard (Marlair and Kordek 2005). It is important to recognize the storage of fertilizer near a plastics manufacturing site could have severe and fatal consequences in the event of a fire; this would be a severity rate of four on the severity matrix explained in the following sections.

Grain elevators are tall structures that can easily ignite adjacent buildings and railcars. Grain elevators, by their nature, have multiple explosions potential;

they have numerous features in common with airplane fuel tank explosions. The biggest hazard regarding a grain elevator is the grain dust. It has been found that a layer of dust 1/64" thick, with a slight breeze, can create an explosive cloud (Thakur et al. 2011). Having the grain elevator and fertilizer near a plastics manufacturing is hazardous; both of these hazards are at a level four on the BEHRS.

Building location in comparison to city limits can determine whether or not the building is in the fire department jurisdiction. Another consideration for the neighborhood is the fire hydrant. If the nearest fire hydrant is about five hundred feet away from a property, it is questionable whether the fire department's response will be effective in the event of a fire. It has been established that low water supply and a fire hydrant that is five hundred feet away has an impact on water pressure to fight a large fire. Pressure is lost over distance and would likely not combat a severe fire. Large piping and hydrants are also not as common in small communities, which would additionally negatively impact pressure and gallons of water available per minute (Hickey 2008). One fire hydrant five hundred feet away, which is the maximum distance, minimizes the effectiveness of hazard control during an emergency. Therefore, the safety practitioner should recognize this as a potentially severe hazard. The fire hydrant with relative distance greater than five hundred feet should be classified as a level four hazard on the BEHRS.

## Owner/Lessee

Buildings occupied by the owners are generally better cared for. Absentee management often do not respond quickly to unsafe conditions. Short-term or temporary employees are often not invested in the community; therefore an assessment of this ring of the bull's-eye should address these questions:

- Is the facility occupied by the owners of the site or a tenant?
- Is there full-time management on site, or is this a remote location?

It is useful to find out if the employees are full-time, part-time or temporary from an employment agency. Additionally, it is useful to know if employees have a high turnover and if there are adequate, documented training records.

- Are there emergency procedures posted and proper emergency equipment on site?

Another factor to consider is the employee turnover rate. To get an approximate idea of employee turnover rate, investigations into the number of employees and the number of W-2 forms mailed out each year can provide insight into the turnover rate ($T_\varphi$) using equation 1.

$$T_\varphi = \frac{Total\ number\ of\ W-2\ forms}{Total\ number\ of\ employees\ currently\ emplyed} \ldots eq.\ 1$$

Where $T_\varphi$ is the turnover rate (high turnover often means low levels of employee training).

For the plastic plant example, the original owners would know why the existing fire protection was selected. Local managers or long-term employees could answer questions as to whether the protection systems originally installed had been modified and adequately maintained.

## Building Structure: Main Facility, Other Structures, and the Site

Building design and proximity to other structures on the site can be critical to the severity of any unwanted event. Building structure revolves around what the building is made of, the size, and the dimensions of the structure. There are five types of building construction (figure 22.3).

Different building construction types can burn at different rates (Amotz et al. 2013). A wood frame will burn more easily and at a faster rate than a fire-resistive building. A type V construction poses a much more severe hazard than a type I, which makes a difference in whether to invest in a facility or not. Concrete is considered semi-fire resistant and typically has behaved well in fire tests. One full-scale fire test study was performed on a seven-story structure made of concrete, and the structure behaved well. Soffit spalling, or cracks in the ceiling, did occur; however, the building continued to stand in excess of two years after the fire test (Matthews et al. 2006). Concrete is generally thought to be a safe and conservative material to use for a building's frame and foundation, as it is noncombustible and can effectively contain fires. It would have likely contained any fires that occurred when being used for stamping, welding, and assembling door hinges, for example.

In the plastic manufacturing plant example, assuming that the building structure is made of concrete, now that the company that has purchased the plant intends to use it for receiving plastic pellets and manufacturing those plastic pellets into center armrest assemblies, it can be inferred that the building is not safe as is as when the original building was used for its original intent because of the high flammability of plastics and because concrete is not completely fire resistant. If the rear of the structure is constructed with steel beams, it is important to note that steel beams are not fire resistant.

The shear capacity of fire can degrade and melt steel beams exposed to intense fire, which could potentially result in building failures. Steel beams in buildings should have a protective concrete base around them for added support. If absent, the construction of the building is considered a severe hazard, at a level four, because the building should be fully fireproof for manufacturing center consoles from plastics (Kodur and Naser 2014).

The distance from the rail siding, use and maintenance of the siding, and the proximity of the adjacent structure (grain elevator) are crucial to the severity and spread of developed fire. The site being evaluated may have pits or towers, whether in use or abandoned. The construction of the buildings may not be appropriate for the site.

Making sure the facility has fire rooms, fire walls and doors, an integrated fire alarm system, and extinguishers are all aspects of fire protection systems that must be taken into consideration when using the BEHRS.

Contacting the fire marshal to aid in assessing the structural fire rating is also a best practice that can be utilized by safety practitioners during fuzzy

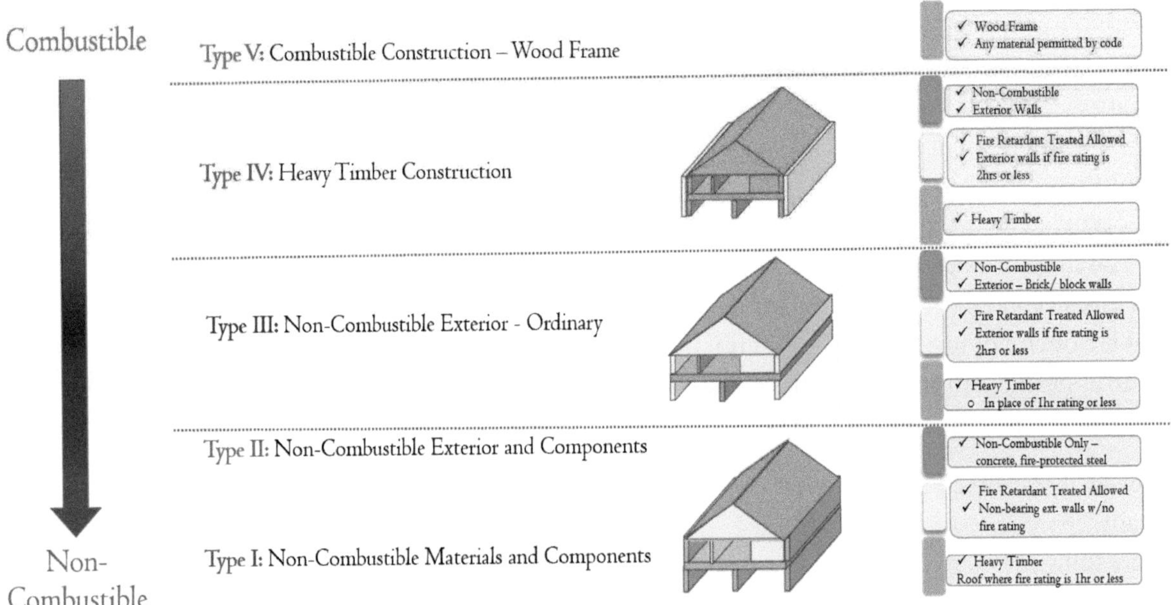


Figure 22.3
Structural material requirements for buildings (adapted from Martin 2013).

circumstances. Many structures have specifically designated rooms that are able to withstand earthquakes, tornadoes, and flooding based on their sturdy design. These rooms should be assessed as far as their protective capabilities if any of these natural disasters were to occur. Based on the occupancy of the building, there must be an adequate number of emergency exits that lead to safe egress. Also, each state has experienced at least one flood or flash flood in the last five years, so it is of upmost importance that there are means to combat this, both from a neighborhood and protection standpoint (NFIP 2015).

Fundamental inquiries should include:

1. Is the site too crowded for the type of operations performed?
2. Is there adequate separation between storage and operation?
3. Are employees working where they cannot exit safely in an emergency?

The NFPA standard 101 (the life safety code) gives valuable guidance in this regard, but a practical way to approach this is asking:

4. "Would I want my children or spouse to work here?"
5. If not, why?
6. Is this site seasonally unreachable?
7. Is it subject to flooding or so isolated that an emergency would go unnoticed in the neighborhood or broader community?
8. Is the site visible to the surrounding area? Isolated sites can be difficult for emergency responders to locate.

A common hazard that has become increasingly threatening in regard to facility and employee protection is the scenario of an active shooter. If an armed intruder enters into the facility, the employees must have a way to exit the building immediately or hide in a type of safe room. These safe rooms are becoming increasingly popular in recent times and should have no windows on any side, as well as a thumb lock that creates a barrier between the shooter and the employees, according to the Department of Homeland Security. As safety specialists, it is important to recognize these kinds of hazard protection that are available in worst-case scenarios and see how a facility can offer protection during each event.

## The Uses, Operations: Materials to Machines

The type of machinery on site and how it is used as well as the raw materials stored on site indicate the type of hazards that will likely be encountered that may potentially set the stage for an accident.

The plastics manufacturing plant from the example had large amounts of combustible plastic raw material along with finished plastic parts and high heat injection molding machines (Rosato and Rosato 2000); see figure 22.4.

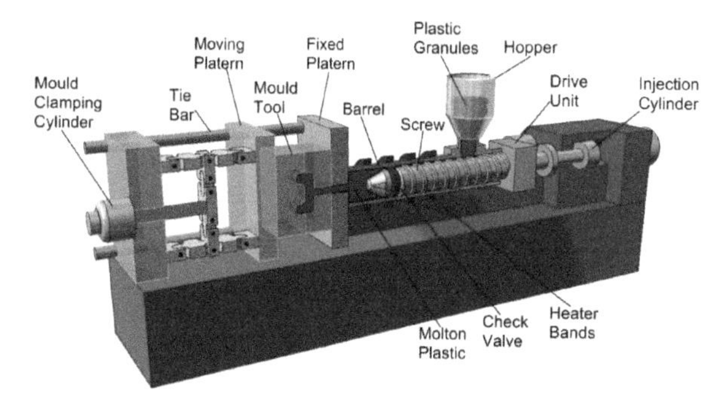


Figure 22.4
Injection molding machine (courtesy Energy Ventures).

Plastics can be very flammable and when burned can emit many toxins into the air in the form of smoke, fumes, and gases. Plastics manufacturing also creates dust. Secondary dust explosions in the plastics industry can and have happened. Secondary explosions can be caused by plastic dust that has accumulated outside of process equipment. If proper ventilation does not exist, then this is a severe hazard (Hayden 2004). Since the plastic, when ignited, will burn with an intense heat (the raw material will feed a fire, and the plastic injection molding machines generate very high temperatures), the fire protection systems have to be especially designed to handle the fire potential they create. A suppression system designed for metal working would be inadequate.

It is beneficial to ask what each machine is for if it is not recognizable. When especially large or complex machines are encountered, the assessor should ask if the machines are unique and whether they can be easily replaced. If the loss of one unreplaceable machine could put a company out of business, this is a severe hazard and should be noted as such.

Therefore, some of the questions to ask in this ring of the bull's-eye are:

1. What do they do? Ask what the operation exists for (i.e., the purpose of the operation)?
2. Is this a place where hazardous or flammable chemicals are used, stored, or processed?
3. What type of equipment is used here?
4. Does it use or produce heat?
5. Are there large amounts of waste produced, and how is it handled?
6. Are there large amounts of material stored on site?
7. Is storage separated from the operations area?
8. Is it flammable, combustible, or toxic?

## Housekeeping and Maintenance

Housekeeping and maintenance is the sixth area of the bull's-eye. Housekeeping is looking at hazards that could be around the building, and maintenance is looking at the quality of upkeep of the facility being analyzed. Although housekeeping and maintenance are two different things, they both indicate the susceptibility to severe loss if not adequately addressed.

The old saying "if it isn't broken, don't fix it" indicates the difference between scheduled and demand maintenance. When companies rely on demand maintenance, this could be considered a severe hazard. All levels of loss potential are increased when housekeeping and maintenance are poor. Simple emergencies become severe when exits are blocked and when fire equipment is inaccessible or not functioning due to lack of periodic maintenance. Some equipment must be checked and tagged on a regular basis by law (i.e., process boilers, fire extinguishers and alarms, and fire suppression systems, both water and special systems such as those found in commercial kitchens and spray-paint operations). Looking for current dates on inspection tags attached to the equipment is a quick way to evaluate this area of the assessment system.

When worksites are not kept clean and stairways are cluttered or blocked, they indicate lack of attention to employee safety. Poor maintenance and housekeeping are often signs of accidents, injury, and disaster potential. Neat and clean walk surfaces reduce the potential for employee, visitor, or customer injuries. A furniture manufacturing plant was destroyed in 1994 by explosions that propagated due to poor housekeeping and inadequate construction (Febo 2011).

Machines that have scheduled maintenance routine and cleaning programs have less loss potential for injury, business interruption, and fire disasters. Scheduled maintenance indicates less downtime and less lost production. Poorly maintained equipment often overheats, breaks down when needed, and possibly explodes. In order to ensure that operations are efficient with the use of machines or components of a system, certain distinct terminologies must be considered, based on the definition from the American Society of Quality Control (ASQC):

a. ***Reliability:*** It is the probability than an item will perform as intended for a specific period under specified conditions. The average time for a system to operate until the next failure is called the mean time between failures (MTBF or μ). There are some cases where the failed system cannot be repaired; this measure is called the mean time to failure (MTTF) or the mean time to first failure (MTFF). If the failing unit can be repaired, the average elapsed time between the unit failing and its repair before returning to service is known as the mean time to repair (MTTR). The number of failures per unit of stress is expressed as

   $\theta = \frac{1}{\mu} \ldots eq.2$, which is the failure rate of the system.

   1. Lusser's product law: The reliability of a series (sub) system is expressed as the product of the reliabilities of the individual contributors to the (portion of the) series.

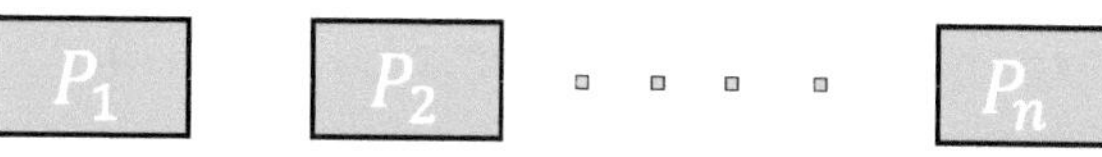


$$R_s = \prod_{i=1}^{N} r_i = r_1 * r_2 * r_3 * \ ... * r_n \ ... eq.\ 3$$

Where $R_S$ is the overall reliability of the system and $R_S$ is the reliability of the $n$th component.

**For example,** if the reliability of fire suppression systems arranged in series, such as check valve, feed main, and water-flow switch, are 0.95, 0.88 and 0.80 respectively, Lusser's law will predict a reliability of;

$$R_s = 0.95 * 0.88 * 0.8 = 0.67$$

which is lower than either of the individual components.

2. For Parallel (Sub) System Reliability: The reliability of a parallel (sub) system is equal to 1 minus the product of the unreliabilities of the individual contributors to that portion.

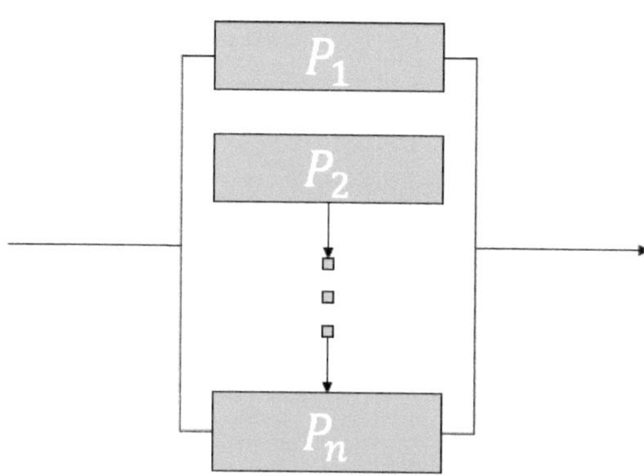


$$R_s = 1 - \prod_{i=1}^{N} (1 - r_i) = 1 - [(1 - r_1) * (1 - r_2) * \ ... * (1 - r_n)] \ ... eq.4$$

**For example:** if the reliability of fire suppression systems arranged in parallel, such as check valve, feed main, and water-flow switch, are 95%, 88%, and 80% respectively, the overall system reliability can be calculated as;

$$R_s = 1 - [(1 - 0.95) * (1 - 0.88) * (1 - 0.80)]$$
$$= 1 - 0.0012$$
$$= 0.9988$$

which is higher than either of the individual components.

3. System Reliability: Any system can be expressed as a combination of series and parallel subsystems. Therefore, by finding the reliability of the distinct components of the system, the overall reliability of the system can then be found as the product of the component reliabilities.

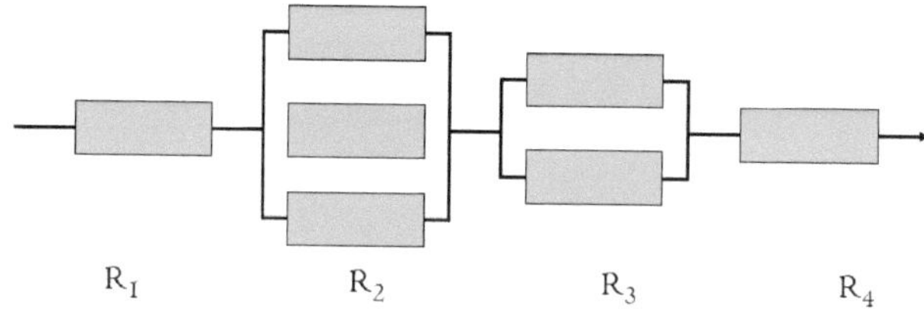


For this system, with segment reliabilities of $R_2$, $R_2$, $R_4$ and $R_4$, the overall system reliability is:

$$\textbf{System Reliability} = (R_1)(R_2)(R_3)(R_4) \ldots eq.5$$

b. ***Availability:*** It is the proportion of time a system is operable, which is only applicable to systems that can be repaired. Availability is expressed in equations 6–9 as,

$$A_1 = \frac{\mu}{\mu + \text{MTTR}} \ldots eq.6$$

$$A_A = \frac{MTBM}{\text{MTBM} + \text{MMT}} \ldots eq.7$$

$$A_o = \frac{MTBM}{\text{MTBM} + \text{MMT} + \text{MLDT}} \ldots eq.8$$

$$MLDT = LDT + ADT \ldots eq.9$$

Where,

$$A_1 = Inherent\ Availability$$

$$A_A = Achieved\ Availability$$

$$A_o = Operational\ Availability$$

$$MTBM = Mean\ time\ between\ maintenance$$

$$MMT = Mean\ maintenance\ time$$

$$MLDT = Mean\ logistic\ down\ time$$

$$LDT = Logistic\ delay\ time$$

$$ADT = Administrative\ delay\ time$$

c. ***Maintainability:*** This is the probability an item or component will conform to specified conditions within a given period when corrective or preventive action is performed in accordance with prescribed procedures and resources.

d. ***$b_{10}$ and $b_{50}$ Life:*** This is the life value at which (10%) 50% of the population has failed, and it is known as the median life.

e. ***System Effectiveness:*** There are three elements of system effectiveness: reliability, availability, and design capability.
The system effectiveness =
$P_{System\ effectiveness} = P_A * P_R * P_C \ldots eq.10$

Where:

$$P_A = A_1\ (from\ eq.6)$$

$$P_R = System\ reliability\ (from\ eq.5)$$

$$P_C = probability\ that\ the\ design\ will\ achieve\ its\ objective$$

Good housekeeping will help reduce hazards of concern and reduce the probability of unwanted outcomes. The knowledge of reliability, availability, and maintainability is crucial in this process.

Inquiring about the maintenance records or talking with maintenance personnel often yields insights into the potential for losses. Poor housekeeping and poor equipment maintenance with high loss potential indicate a high severity rating. In the hypothetical example, the fact that the fire suppression system was for a previous use and may not have been maintained when the plant use was discontinued indicates severe potential for loss. Plastics fires require a special type of fire suppression system (Fire Suppression Systems Association n. d.); reviewing the maintenance and reliability data for each component of the system will be valuable in recognizing all possible hazards in a timely manner.

## Existing Protection

In the plastic plant example, the existing fire protection system was designed for a metalworking operation, which has a much lower fire potential than plastics manufacturing.

During the hazard evaluation process, the severity of the hazard should also be considered. The more existing protection an operation has, the less severe the consequence of any loss occurrence will be. The existing protection can be examined for potential hazards after all other rings in the BEHRS have been analyzed. Existing protection is what is currently in the building that is meant for protection from various hazards, including fire hazards.

There are many questions to explore pertaining to existing protection.

1. What is the fire protection or medical response capability?
2. Is there a federally required emergency response plan?
3. Is the emergency plan properly communicated?
4. Are all emergency response equipment properly cleaned, tagged, and in good repair?
5. Are all hazardous chemicals and their storage areas identified?
6. Are SDS materials available and their location prominently marked for easy, quick access?
7. Are there fire drills and evacuation or shelter in place plans and signage?
8. Do the community responders have a site plan with a contact list of emergency numbers?
9. Are the emergency responders invited in to tour the facility regularly?

The higher the probability of a certain type of disaster (e.g., flooding or forest fire or residential fire), the greater the need for special protection. You can get a clue to this by looking for special equipment as you look at a facility. Look for a high number of fire doors, special storage rooms, such as flammable storage rooms, and special gear, like self-contained breathing apparatus (SCUBA gear).

Considering the example with the plastic molding machines, the facility requires the use of high-pressure hydraulic oils with ready ignition sources. In the event of a high-pressure combustible hydraulic leak, the result could be a fireball type of fire. This is a severe fire and may be one of the most severe in the manufacturing class. Large capacity sprinklers will be required to suppress such fires.

As operations change, the existing protection for all types of loss must change as well. Similarly, discontinued operations may leave behind hazards that still require special protection. Storage rooms may have obsolete process chemicals that still require special equipment and protection. Looking for hazardous warning labels and asking why they are there will help decide if the existing protection is adequate. The application of the Hazard Recognition Severity Matrix can also provide a good means of evaluating the adequacy of existing protection.

### Hazard Recognition Severity (HRS) Matrix

The HRS matrix can be easily constructed by drawing out a simple four-square box with severity on the left side and probability across the bottom. Divide the box with a horizontal line in the middle of the severity line and a vertical line in the middle of the probability line. Figure 22.5 illustrates an example of the HRS matrix.

- If the hazard being evaluated has a low probability of happening and a low severity if it did happen, then a one should be placed in the lower left square of the matrix.
- If the hazard has a low probability of happening but a high severity if it does happen then a 2 should be placed in lower right square.
- If the hazard has a high probability of happening but a low severity if it does occur, then a 2 should be placed in the upper left square of the matrix.
- Finally, if there is a high probability of the hazard happening and the severity of the occurrence is very high, then a 4 should be placed in the upper right square of the hazard recognition matrix.

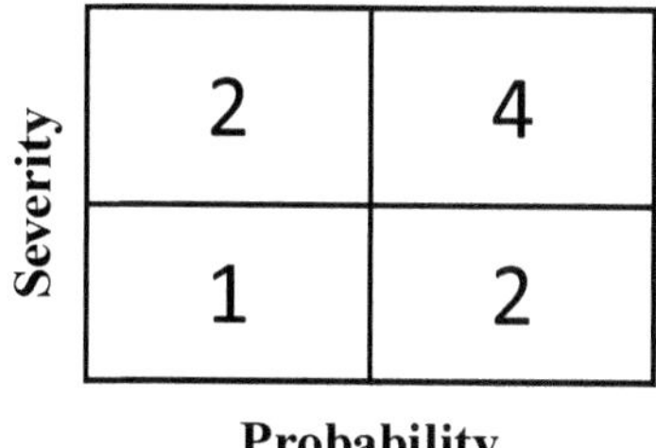


Figure 22.5
Illustration of the hazard recognition severity matrix.

Each hazard for each ring of the BEHRS should have a number in the severity column opposite to the region evaluated. Upon completing the severity column in figure 22.1, simply add all the numbers in the severity ranking column and divide by the total number of items; this will provide a ranking of each circle in the BEHRS.

## Conclusion

Hazard recognition and assessment are crucial as part of the task of a safety practitioner, as they provide the ability to analyze hazards before injuries and accidents occur. Leading and lagging indicators are used together with recognizable hazards through the established safety programs to improve the system. The BEHRS will allow a systematic review of a site or an employment situation, taking into account the unique characteristics of each level of the assessment bull's-eye from the geography to the community, the neighborhood, the ownership of the property, to the building, its use and operation through housekeeping, including an evaluation of the existing controls will lead to an overall rating of the severity of the exposures. A well-conducted hazard assessment using the HRS matrix will lead to a useful summary of the loss potential of most situations. This can be a starting point for decision-making and action to control, avoid, or transfer a hazardous situation or condition to a third party. That task may not be the responsibility of the person using BEHRS. If that is the situation, then a summary of each level of the bull's-eye should include a clear statement of the overall evaluation of the subject (e.g., the statement may read, "based on a review of the overall exposures to XYZ Company, there is an overall low level of loss exposures that appear adequately controlled"). Unless there is an imminent danger, the results of the assessment should only be communicated to the immediate supervisor or the person requesting the assessment. These reports are very useful for accurate decision-making; however, they can become legal documents that can be protected from discovery if distribution is properly controlled.

## Questions

1. List the steps in the BEHRS.
2. What is required for steel beams in buildings to provide support?
3. If the reliability of fire suppression systems arranged in series, such as check valve, feed main and water-flow switch are 0.65, 0.68 and 0.70, respectively, what is the reliability using Lusser's law?
4. The logistic delay time for maintaining a fire suppression system is ten days, and the administrative delay time is two days. Suppose the mean time between maintenance is forty days, and the operational availability is only sixteen hours, what is the mean maintenance time?
5. ***Recommended Exercise:*** You may use the example provided in this chapter to practice your decision-making skills by applying the BEHRS and HRS matrix methods.

   Now, you are prepared to make a decision as to whether the building is adequate for your company's intended use and tell why. You can now write a summary statement beginning with the sentence: "The building at 1234 Side Street, Smallville, MI. is / is not acceptable for our intended use as a plastic molding plant because . . . ," and list the quick summary of each ring on your bull's-eye.

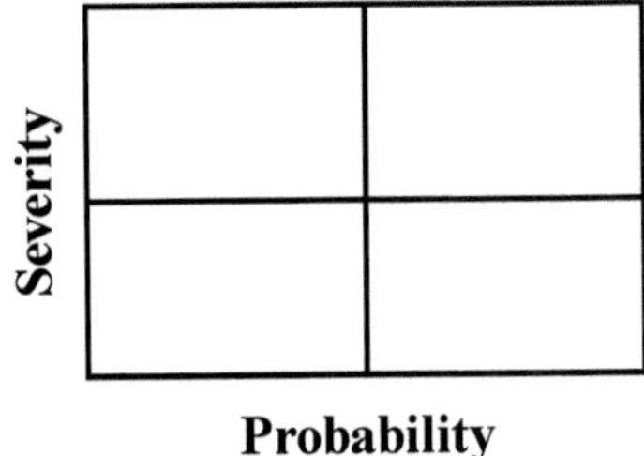


## References


Amotz, P., R. Sacks, and R. Barak, R. (2013). "Hazard Recognition and Risk Perception in Construction." *Safety Science* 64: 22–31.

Atreya, A., S. Ferreira, and E. Michel-Kerjan. (2015). "What Drives Households to Buy Flood Insurance? New Evidence from Georgia." *Ecological Economics* 117: 153–61.

Budworth, N. (2013). "Performance Indicators—The Numbers Game." *The Safety & Health Practitioner* 31(3): 31+.

Febo, H. L. (2011). "Combustible Dust Hazard Recognition—an Insurer's View." *Process Safety Progress* 30: 82–86.

Ferry, T. S. (1998). *Modern Accident Investigation and Analysis* (2nd ed.). New York: John Wiley & Sons.

Flanagan T. A., and J. S. Lybarger. (2014). *Leading Forward: Successful Public Leadership amidst Complexity, Chaos and Change* (with Professional Content). San Francisco: Jossey-Bass Publisher.

Fire Suppression Systems Association. (n. d). *Classifying Fire Extinguishers*. Accessed July 31, 2017. http://www.fssa.net/page/FireExtinguishers/Classifying-Fire-Extinguishers.htm.

Forest, J., and K. Kessler. (2013). "Correlating Process Safety Leading Indicators with Performance." *Process Safety Progress* 32: 185–88.

Gladwell, M. (2007). *Blink the Power of Thinking without Thinking* (1st ed.). New York: Little, Brown and Co.

Hayden, D. K. (2004). "Secondary Dust Explosions: Lessons from the Plastics proceSsing Industry." *Professional Safety* 49(11): 27–30.

Hickey, H. E. (2008). *Water Supply Systems and Evaluation Methods. Volume 1: Water Supply System Concepts*. United States Fire Administration–USFA. Accessed August 29, 2016. https://www.usfa.fema.gov/downloads/pdf/publications/water_supply_systems_volume_i.pdf.

Kodur, V. K. R., and M. Z. Naser. (2014). "Effect of Shear on Fire Response of Steel Beams." *Journal of Constructional Steel Research* 97: 48–58.

Marlair, G., and M. Kordek. (2005). "Safety and Security Issues Relating to Low Capacity Storage of AN-based Fertilizers." *Journal of Hazardous Materials* 123(1–3): 13–28.

Matthews, S., R. Rupasinghe, and T. Lennon. (2006). "Concrete Structures in Fire—Performance in Fire, Design and Analysis Methods." *Concrete* 40(5): 42–43.

Martin, E. (2013). *Multi-story Wood Frame Structures: Introduction to How to Build*. Wood Products Council. WoodWorks. Accessed August 29, 2016. http://www.woodworks.org/wp-content/uploads/2013-May-June-lunch-seminar.pdf.

Rosato, D., and M. G. Rosato. (2000). *Injection Molding Handbook*. New York: Springer, 1457–1457.

Thakur, M., B. J. Martens, and C. R. Hurburgh. (2011). "Data Modeling to Facilitate Internal Traceability at a Grain Elevator." *Computers and Electronics in Agriculture* 75(2): 327–36.

CHAPTER 23

# OCCUPATIONAL SAFETY AND HEALTH PERFORMANCE MEASUREMENT: AN OVERVIEW

Christopher Janicak

## Learning Objectives

After studying this chapter, the reader should be able to:

1. Describe the key components of an occupational safety and health (OSH) performance measurement program
2. Identify safety management systems that can be used as guides for developing OSH performance in the workplace
3. Identify leading and lagging indicators applicable to various industries
4. Establish a system for quantifying OSH performance measures
5. Describe various techniques that can be used to assess OSH performance
6. Track performance and address shortcomings

## Key Terms

**Safety metrics, leading indicators, lagging indicators, OSH performance**


## Abstract

Occupational safety and health (OSH) performance measurement involves the collection of relevant data, evaluating the meaning of that data, and initiating actions intended to improve performance. OSH performance must be managed using valid and established methods. The first step is to select a safety management system that serves as the framework for the performance measurement program. The next step is to identify leading and lagging indicators of OSH performance. Commonly used leading and lagging indicators vary widely from one industry to another, and it is up to the safety professional to identify the performance indicators that are of most importance. OSH metrics are the quantified measures of performance. Safety metrics take performance measures and put them into objective numbers that can be tracked. Finally, OSH performance improvement can only occur when data is collected, evaluated, and applied in action taken to close the gaps between actual performance and acceptable performance levels.

## Introduction

To improve OSH performance, it must be measured using sound methods. An established safety management system can serve as a framework. An underlying concept for many safety management systems is that of continuous improvement. OSH performance measures are observable actions and activities that are designed to improve the organization's safety performance. Broadly classified as leading and lagging indicators, safety professionals have many recognized indicators to choose from. Safety metrics are the quantitative measures of the performance indicators. As varied as the indicators are, the approaches used to put a performance indicator into a number are also widely varied. It is up to the safety professional to identify the performance indicators that are most appropriate for their situation and to determine the best ways to quantify the measures. Program improvement is attained through the continuous improvement process in which performance is measured, compared to an acceptable level of performance, and necessary corrective action taken. This chapter addresses the major aspects of developing an OSH performance measurement program.

Program improvement is attained through the continuous improvement process in which performance is measured, compared to an acceptable level of performance, and necessary corrective action taken.

## Safety Management Systems

An occupational safety and health management system is defined as a set of interrelated elements that establish and/or support occupational health and safety policy and objectives, and mechanisms to continually improve occupational health and safety (American National Standards Institute 2012). A safety management system can be beneficial in providing structure to an OSH performance measurement program. There are a number of recognized safety management systems that have been developed over the years and some currently under development. The most widely recognized of these systems are the American National Standards Institute (ANSI)/ American Society of Safety Professionals (ASSP) Z10, *Occupational Health and Safety Assessment Series* (OHSAS) 18001, and the International Organization for Standardization (ISO) 45001.

### ANSI/ASSP Z10: *Occupational Health and Safety Management Systems*

The ANSI/ASSP Z10 *Occupational Health and Safety Management Systems* standard (OHSMS) provides an overall blueprint for widespread benefits in occupational safety and health, as well as in productivity, financial performance, quality, and other organizational and business objectives. This safety management system consists of five parts:

1. Management leadership and employee participation: An effective OHSMS requires management commitment to the program and the involvement of employees.
2. Planning: Improvements in safety performance occur through careful planning. Planning includes identifying and prioritizing safety activities.
3. Implementation and operation: Activities that are implemented to achieve a successful OHSMS.
4. Evaluation and corrective action: As part of continual improvement, safety performance is evaluated and corrective action taken when necessary.
5. Management review: To ensure a successful OHSMS, management should review the program to ensure program effectiveness.

The design of ANSI/ASSP Z10 encourages integration with other management systems to facilitate organizational effectiveness using the elements of the plan-do-check-act (PDCA) model as the basis for continual improvement (ANSI/ASSP Z10-2012 [R2017] 2017).

### OHSAS 18001: Occupational Health and Safety Management Systems Requirements

This Occupational Health and Safety Assessment Series (OHSAS) 18001 standard specifies requirements for an OSH management system to enable an organization to control risks and improve performance (British Standards Institute 2007). The OHSAS 18001 standard is also based on the PDCA methodology. The OHSAS 18001 components include (British Standards Institute 2007):

**OSH Policy:** Top management shall define and authorize the organization's OSH policy and ensure that within the defined scope of its OSH management system.

**Planning:** The planning phase includes hazard identification, risk assessment, determining controls, and maintaining documented OSH objectives.

**Implementation and Operation:** This phase includes managing resources, defining roles and responsibilities, assigning accountability and authority, training, communication, and employee participation.

**Checking:** This step includes performance measurement and monitoring, conducting audits and incident investigations, and follow up.

**Management Review:** Top management shall review the organization's OSH management system at planned intervals to ensure its continuing suitability, adequacy, and effectiveness. Reviews shall include assessing opportunities for improvement and the need for changes to the OSH management system, including the OSH policy and OSH objectives.

### ISO 45001: Occupational Health and Safety Management Systems

ISO 45001: Occupational Health and Safety Management Systems is an international standard that specifies requirements for an OSH management system, with guidance for its use, to enable an organization to proactively improve its OSH performance in preventing injury and ill-health (International Organization for Standardization 2015). ISO 45001 follows the high-level structure approach that is being applied to other ISO management system standards, such as ISO 9001 (quality) and ISO 14001 (environment). The ISO 45001, approved in January 2018, is intended to replace the OHSAS 18001 standard. This ISO 45001 standard consists of seven major components (AON Risk Solutions 2016):

1. **Context of the organization:** The context of the organization is the key consideration to be taken when developing and implementing an OSH mission statement, OSH policy statement, and objectives. The organization should obtain an understanding of the issues, positive and negative that should be considered when establishing an OSH management system.
2. **Leadership and worker participation:** Leadership and top management have certain responsibilities under ISO 45001, including taking overall responsibility and accountability for worker protection, ensuring the OSH policy relates to the context, integrating the OSH management system into the larger business processes, and providing resources for the OSH management system. Other key considerations for leadership and worker participation include training, communication, worker participation support, and the establishment of audit programs.
3. **Planning:** The planning component defines the need for hazard identification by the organization for both routine and nonroutine activities, emergencies, people and behavior, work area design, work environment under the control of the organization, and situations

not under organizational control, and legal and internationals standards compliance requirements.

4. **Support:** "Support" means that the organization has achieved a level of competence among its workers and systems to successfully drive the outcomes of the OSH plan. Support also includes top management leadership and commitment, providing adequate resources in managing the planned activities including training and communicating information about the safety management system.
5. **Operation:** The operation component addresses the program content necessary to have a successful OSH management system. Areas include systems for creating and managing documentation, incident investigation to identify root causes and initiate preventive measures, management of change to ensure that when planned changes occur they are managed to control risk, and emergency preparedness and response activities to name a few.
6. **Performance evaluation:** The performance evaluation component of the standard addresses the requirements for providing methods for evaluating the overall performance of the OSH management system. Examples of activities include following applicable legal requirements, measuring operational risks and hazards, evaluating the effectiveness of operational controls, and establishing the timeline for conducting the measures.
7. **Improvement:** The improvement component of the standard addresses the concept of continual improvement within the context of the safety management system activities.

## Plan-Do-Check-Act Model

The basis of an OSH management system approach is founded on the concept of plan-do-check-act (PDCA), which requires leadership, commitment and participation of workers, and where they exist, workers' representatives from all levels and functions of the organization (International Organization for Standardization 2014). The PDCA model is an iterative process used by organizations to achieve continual improvement. It can be applied to a management system and to each of its individual elements as follows (International Organization for Standardization 2014):

**Plan**: Establish objectives, programs, and processes necessary to deliver results in accordance with the organization's OSH policy.

**Do**: Implement the processes as planned.

**Check**: Monitor and measure activities and processes with regard to the OSH policy and objectives and report the results.

**Act**: Take actions to continually improve the OSH performance to achieve the intended outcomes.

The basis of an OSH management system approach is founded on the concept of Plan-Do-Check-Act (PDCA), which requires leadership, commitment, and participation of workers, and where they exist, workers' representatives from all levels and functions of the organization (International Organization for Standardization 2014).

## OSH Key Performance Indicators

Key performance indicators (KPIs) are used as a means to collect data and communicate trends, which can then be used to indicate where further improvements and resources are required (Baldauf 2010). Performance indicators are measurable safety program activities and actions one would expect to occur to meet the organizations OSH performance goals.

Performance indicators can be broadly classified as *leading* and *lagging* indicators. Leading indicators are proactive, preventative, and predictive measures that monitor and provide current information about the effective performance, activities, and processes of an EHS management system that drive the identification and elimination or control of risks in the workplace that can cause incidents and injuries (The Campbell Institute 2013). Leading indicators are valuable therefore as they enable organizations to

**Table 23.1** Commonly used OSH performance measures and associated metrics

| OSH performance Measure | Example Metrics |
|---|---|
| Occupational Injuries | OSHA DART Rate, Recordable Case Incidence Rate |
| Safety Audits | Overall Audit Scores, percentage of items corrected |
| Employee Training | Percentage of employees trained, training test/quiz scores |
| Workers' Compensation Losses | Loss severity measured in dollar losses, claims frequencies |
| Safety Observations | Unsafe act rates, number of unsafe acts performed |

identify and correct deficiencies to prevent or mitigate the worst effects of injuries or damage (Sheehan et al. 2016). The main advantages leading indicators include are being proactive, gauging the effectiveness of safety policies, and encouraging a culture of safety among management and workers (The Campbell Institute 2013). Leading indicators are most useful because they allow the organization to make changes to improve performance and induce some sort of pressure to implement corrective actions as revealed by thorough incident investigations, to mitigate possible recurrence of such incidents. However, effective incident investigation and root-cause analysis are prerequisites. Examples of leading indicators include measuring the results of inspections and audits, results from job observations, and employee training measures.

Lagging or trailing indicators are performance measurements linked to the outcome of an accident or an activity. Examples of lagging indicators are injury rates, incident rates, workers' compensation experience modification rates (EMRs), and claims cost (Rajendran 2013). Lagging indicators are after-the-fact measures. They provide the organization with a measure of past performance and induce some sort of pressure to implement corrective actions as revealed by thorough incident investigations to mitigate possible recurrence of such incidents; however, effective incident investigation and root-cause analysis are prerequisites.

## OSH Safety Metrics

A safety metric is a way to define a performance indicator quantitatively. For example, the OSH performance indicator of employee training can be measured a number of ways, such as the percentage of employees trained over a period of time or as a rate in terms of persons trained per full-time employee. It is up to the safety professional to identify measures that are valid, reliable, and meaningful. From a statistical analysis standpoint, metrics measured on a continuous scale, such as the ratio scale, provide the most opportunity for analysis. Some examples of commonly used OSH performance measures and their associated metrics are provided in table 23.1.

## Tracking Performance and Addressing Shortcomings

With the performance indicators identified, acceptable levels of performance should be defined for each. The process for defining what is acceptable can encompass a number of strategies including organization-defined acceptable performance, benchmark-defined performance, and acceptable performance defined through statistical analysis. No matter what processes an organization uses to define acceptable levels of performance, it must be done in order to track performance and make decisions. As discussed previously, the continuous improvement process involves acting upon the results of performance measures and establishing acceptable levels of performance provides the safety professional the criteria by which to act.

Gaps between the current performance measures and the defined acceptable levels provide the safety professional an objective basis when determining if action is necessary. To improve, the goal is to close the gap between current performance measures and the acceptable level of performance. Actions required to close these performance gaps are up to judgment of the safety professional. This requires a thorough understanding of the measures and the potential underlying factors that could be influencing the performance measures. Important factors to examine in the analysis are factors that may be affecting the validity of the performance measures and potential underlying biases in the measures.

## Key OSH Performance Indicators across Industries

It is important to understand that while there are common performance indicators that lend themselves to a variety of industries, there are also indicators that have been found to be more commonly used in some industries than others. The following is a summary of research conducted that identified OSH performance indicators by industry.

### Construction Industry

In a study conducted by Hallowell, Hinze, Baud, and Wehle using face-to-face discussions with a team of construction industry safety professionals, thirteen leading performance indicators were identified as a priority because (1) the team believed that each metric is a strong indicator of future OSH performance, (2) the indicators are measurable forms of efforts that many contractors and owners already implement but do not yet measure or track, and (3) collectively, they represent a diverse group of strategies involving leadership, workers, and vendors (Hallowell et al. 2013). Examples of these key leading indicators include:

1. Evaluation of vendor/contractors' past performance for shortlisting them for the project tender invitation (for limited tenders), and for open tenders, health, safety, and environment (HSE) past performance evaluation of the shortlisted offers based on technical and HSE-related submittals will be done during tender evaluation process.
2. Review and approval of all HSE-related submittal forms from the successful bidder, which includes their HSE manual, project-specific HSE plan, emergency procedure, resource competencies, and HSE site induction to all contractor personnel (progressively as per their reporting date) and so forth during the project mobilization period and maintenance of employees training passports
3. Review and approval of method statements (MS) for their various jobs, including risk assessment studies prior to any specific job commencement
4. Incident reporting, including near misses
5. Project management team safety process involvement
6. Worker observation process
7. Reporting of unsafe conditions observed, which cannot be addressed immediately
8. Stop work authority
9. Housekeeping program
10. Auditing program
11. Pretask planning
12. Owner's participation in worker orientation sessions
13. Foremen discussions and feedback meetings with the owner's PM
14. Scheduled joint (owner, consultant, and contractor) HSE walk-through inspection, documentation, and timely close-out of any noncompliance finding, including, if the need arises, work stoppages (this HSE audit covers all employee facilities at the project site, transportation, and site medical facilities)
15. Periodically holding emergency mock drills
16. Monthly project personnel HSE communication and motivation meetings, presenting briefing of HSE performance and awards to selected members for their best HSE performance (also HSE-selected topics are to be presented for awareness enhancement) (Hallowell et al. 2013)

## Mining Industry

A study conducted by the International Council on Mining and Metals (ICMM) identified the key leading OSH performance measures. The methodology in this study utilized a review of existing literature and the outcomes of various ICMM workshops guided by a semi-structured interview protocol and discussions with mining company representatives involved in OSH management (International Council on Mining and Metals 2012).

In this study, they classified each company into one of three organizational maturity levels: compliance, improvement, and learning. The organizational maturity level is defined as an evolving process whereby an organization (or subset of, such as a system) becomes fully fit for purpose through an internal unfolding of approaches, rather than through externally imposed approaches (International Council on Mining and Metals 2012). Some OSH performance indicators were tied to a specific organizational maturity level while others were found across all levels. Table 23.2 provides a summary of performance indicators by organizational maturity level.

As previously stated, some performance indicators were identified in the study that were not linked to the organizational maturity level. A summary of these measures can be found in table 23.3.

## Chemical Process Industry

A combination of real-time, broad-based leading and lagging process safety management (PSM) metrics is critical to measure the overall "health" and functionality of the process safety risk management program on an ongoing basis, both in a general or macro level within the corporation, and with enough specificity within sites and regions to enable targeted improvement actions (Cummings 2009). Research conducted by the Center for Chemical Process Safety (CCPS) has identified common leading and recommended lagging indicators that should be part of an OSH performance program. Examples of leading indicators in the chemical process industry include measures pertaining to (Center for Chemical Process Safety 2011):

- Maintenance of mechanical integrity
- Action items follow-up
- Management of change
- Process safety training and competency (and training competency assessment)
- Design review and hazard and operability (HAZOP) study
- Project HSE reviews (PHSER)—MOC and action follow-up related to projects are included in PHSER)
- Process operation and HSE audits

It is also recommended that companies adopt and implement leading process safety metrics that include measures of the process safety culture.

For the purposes of the common industry-wide process safety lagging metrics, an incident is reported as a process safety incident if it meets all four of the following criteria (Center for Chemical Process Safety 2011):

1. Process involvement
2. Above minimum reporting threshold
3. Location
4. Acute release

Further, the CCPS defines an incident involving a chemical or chemical process if the following is true:

A process must have been directly involved in the damage caused. For this purpose, the term "process" is used broadly to include the equipment and technology needed for chemical, petrochemical and refining production, including reactors, tanks, piping, boilers, cooling towers, refrigeration systems, etc. An incident with no direct chemical or process involvement, e.g., an office building fire, even if the office building is on a plant site, is not reportable. (Center for Chemical Process Safety 2011)

The CCPS recommends that companies implement and publicly report the following three process safety metrics (Center for Chemical Process Safety 2011):

1. Total count of process safety incidents (PSIC): the count of all incidents, which meet the definitions of a PSI

**Table 23.2** OSH performance indicators by organizational maturity level (International Council on Mining and Metals 2012)

| Organizational Maturity Level | OSH performance Indicators |
|---|---|
| Learning | Agreed responsibilities and accountabilities<br>Jobs/tasks for which risk assessments are performed<br>OSH elements in toolbox talks<br>Perception of a caring organization<br>Effectiveness of OSH briefings/training<br>Improvements shared between sites<br>Effectiveness of visible felt leadership<br>Feedback on positive and negative issues |
| Improvement | Health and safety policy<br>Management commitment to OSH<br>OSH plans and objectives set and achieved<br>Planned risk assessments vs. completed<br>OSH briefings<br>Close-out of audit recommendations<br>Behavior-based task observations |
| Compliance | Health and safety policy<br>OSH legislation addressed by procedures<br>Management system compliant with recognized system<br>Statutory training requirements<br>Behavior-based task observations<br>OSH included in communication |

**Table 23.3** Performance indicators not linked to organizational maturing levels (International Council on Mining and Metals 2012)

| OSH performance Indicators |
|---|
| Occupational health risk assessment<br>Occupational health risk register (linked to critical controls)<br>Occupational health improvement plan (based on risk register)<br>Change in exposure risk categories, e.g. decrease of number of employees in A of B exposure categories<br>Number of at-risk employees that have undergone medical surveillance according to the hazard exposure<br>Number of employees at risk that have undergone appropriate job-related health-risk training<br>Health concerns of employees are formally represented at an appropriate group, e.g. health and safety committee<br>Statutory inspection and test validation requirement for equipment and systems<br>Near-miss reporting and timely completion of incident investigation to gain from lessons learned |

2. Process safety total incident rate (PSTIR): the cumulative (annual) count of incidents normalized by man-hours
3. Process safety incident severity rate (PSISR): the cumulative (annual) severity-weighted rate of process safety incidents

The CCPS committee also recommends that all companies implement a near-miss reporting metric(s). Since a near-miss is an actual event or discovery of a potentially unsafe situation, this metric could be defined as a "lagging" metric (Center for Chemical Process Safety 2011).

## 7.4 Transportation Industry

The National Highway Traffic Safety Administration (NHTSA) and the Governors Highway Safety Association (GHSA) have developed a set of OSH performance measures that each state is required to track beginning in federal fiscal year 2010 (Herbel et al. 2009). The safety performance measures are organized in three categories representing the types of measures often found in practice (Herbel et al. 2009):

- Core measures (also known as outcome measures) relate to the safety goals and objectives established as part of policy or as part of a planning process. These measures allocate resources and measure overall progress. They may include crashes, injuries, and fatalities and can be presented as numbers, rates, percentages, or ratios.
- Behavioral measures provide a link between specific safety activities and outcomes by assessing whether the activities influenced behavior. These may include direct observations of safety-belt use and vehicle speed or self-reported behavior pertaining to program awareness and attitude obtained through surveys.
- Activity measures document safety program implementation and track actions taken by law enforcement, courts, media, education, and others to reduce crashes, injuries, and fatalities.

Examples of each type of measure include (Herbel et al. 2009):

### Core Measures

- Number of traffic fatalities (three-year or five-year moving averages)
- Number of serious injuries in traffic crashes
- Number of unrestrained passenger vehicle occupant for all seat positions

For companies handling transportation by in-house or on contract, like fuel distribution companies, core measures could include the following:

- Heavy-duty vehicles—Number of vehicle in use, total miles driven, number of reportable incidents, number of accidents caused by a third party, and the number caused by company employees and contractors
- Light vehicles—Number of vehicle in use, total miles driven, number of reportable incidents, number of accidents caused by a third party, and the number caused by company employees and contractors
- Incidents affecting the environment—Tracking of major and minor fuel or chemical spills, bumber of spills greater than five gallons, number of spills over one hundred gallons, total number of spills, total quantity of spills
- Number of staff attending HSE-related training in the reporting month and summation for the year
- Number of HSE-related trainings/HSE inspections or audits accomplished in the reporting month with a summation for the year
- IVMS (in-vehicle monitoring system) monthly summary report (a leading event indicator)

### Behavioral Measures

- Observed seat-belt use for passenger vehicles, front-seat outboard occupants, use of cell phone, driving with sleep deprivation, intoxication, and so forth

### Activity Measures

- Number of seat-belt citations issued during grant-funded enforcement activities

- Number of impaired-driving arrests made during grant-funded enforcement

In addition to the OSH performance measures developed by NHTSA and GHSA, some examples of infrastructure-related safety performance measures that can be considered for inclusion in the transportation planning process may include (Herbel et al. 2009):

- Number of run-off-the-road crashes (core measure)
- Number of fixed-object crashes (core measure)
- Number of intersection crashes (core measure)
- Number of signs updated or warning signs installed (activity measure)
- Number of intersections with improved signal timing (activity measure)

Examples of common leading indicators used in the transportation industry include results from driver ride-along observations, measures of driver training, and monitoring vehicle inspection results. Examples of common lagging indicators used in the transportation industry include accident rates in terms of the number of accidents per miles driven, driver injury rates, and measures of motor-vehicle accident severity.

### Manufacturing Industry

Because of the Occupational Safety and Health Administration's (OSHA) influence on safety and health in the manufacturing industry, many performance indicators used today can be traced back to OSHA. For example, the more common lagging indicators used in industry include various OSHA rates such as the days away restricted, transferred (DART) rate, and the OSHA recordable incident rate.

OSHA defines the critical elements of a safety management system as management commitment, employee involvement, worksite analysis, hazard prevention and control, and training for employees, supervisors, and managers (United States Department of Labor 2003). Examples of common safety performance measures applicable to the manufacturing industry include (UL 2013):

- Management support and accountability
- Employee participation and involvement
- New hire orientation, training, and learning
- Inspections/audits/observations
- Incident, near-miss, and observation investigations
- Performance management systems, safety related

Examples of major types of leading metrics that companies have been found to track at the corporate level are (UL 2013):

- behavior-based observations (e.g., safe or unsafe behaviors);
- near-miss incidents (e.g., incidents with serious injury or fatality potential);
- audits (e.g., tracking overdue audit items, monitoring the speed of closing action items);
- training (e.g., EHS training for workers, managers, executives);
- meetings (e.g., EHS committee, management review, action planning); and
- other actions (e.g., noncompliance, incident investigation, EHS ideas and suggestions).

## Application of Key Concepts

Following the concepts presented in this chapter, the process of establishing a safety performance program begins with the adoption of a safety management system, which will serve as the program framework. This chapter presented examples of three such frameworks. Using the ANSI/ASSP Z10 OHSMS as an example, this safety management system consists of five parts that would need to be addressed: management and leadership; employee participation; planning, implementation, and operation; evaluation and corrective action; and management review. Procedures should be developed that address each of these areas and aid in the implantation of the safety performance program. An example of a performance program based upon this framework could be:

1. Management leadership and employee participation: To have a successful program, management must lead in the efforts in safety performance, and employees must play a role. To ensure this is addressed in the program, an organizational structure and the assignment of safety performance

responsibilities that are conducive to the implementation of the safety performance program should be developed. Roles and responsibilities in the OHSMS should be defined and means for holding people accountable established.

2. Planning: For a safety performance program to be effective, it must be well planned. The planning process includes establishing overall safety performance goals, performance objectives that, when met, will result in meeting the overall goals, and defining appropriate safety metrics. The OHS activities that must be carried out to improve safety performance are identified along with the safety metrics, both leading and lagging, that the organization will track over time and measures of safety performance. Included in this planning phase are benchmarks or acceptable levels of performance. These benchmarks will be addressed in the evaluation and corrective action phase of the program.
3. Implementation and operation: With the program planned and the organizational structure in place, the safety performance activities are implemented to achieve an effective OHSMS. The implementation phase includes implementing safety-related activities designed to eliminate risks and control hazards to an acceptable level. A key but often overlooked aspect of a safety performance program is that the activities an organization engages in need to be directly tied to the organizational goals and performance indicators. Overlooking this crucial aspect can result in activities taking place and measures being taken, but no improvement in overall safety performance occurs. To prevent this from happening, care must be taken in the planning phase to ensure the activities carried out in this phase are directly tied to meeting the organizational OHS performance goals.
4. Evaluation and corrective action: To see improvement, safety performance must be continually monitored and compared against expected levels of performance. Again, going back to the planning phase, well-established safety metrics and acceptable levels of performance defined though a benchmarking process are critical to an effective evaluation process. In this phase, data is collected, evaluated, and decisions are made based upon the results. Differences in acceptable levels of performance and actual performance may lead to changes in activities. Each situation is different and requires professional judgment in the type of corrective action that is necessary.
5. Management review: To ensure the OHSMS is functioning properly, a management review should be performed. This review should be conducted on at least an annual basis. Examples of items to review include OHSMS policies and procedures related to program implementation, evaluation, and continuous improvement. The goal of this review is to identify areas of the OHSMS that can be changed and improved.

## Summary

The measurement of OSH performance is critical to ensure safety programs and their interventions are achieving their intended outcomes. Focusing on leading indicators gives the organization a way to monitor activities intended to prevent unwanted events. The concepts covered in this chapter include safety management systems, common OSH performance indicators used by various industries, and safety metrics that can be used to quantify OSH performance.

Safety management systems can be used to structure an OSH performance program. While there are several management systems available, this chapter summarized three. Built on a continuous improvement approach, a safety management system can be useful in identifying the major organizational aspects that should be assessed as part of the OSH performance program. While there are many common leading and

> The measurement of OSH performance is critical to ensure safety programs and their interventions are achieving their intended outcomes.

lagging indicators used across different industries, this chapter provided some insight as to different approaches to OSH performance measurement. Finally, this chapter included examples of safety metrics for various types of performance measures. As part of the continuous improvement process, collecting data, monitoring fluctuations, and acting upon the results are critical for an organization to meet its safety goals and acceptable levels of OSH performance.

## Questions

1. What is the definition of an occupational safety and health management system?
2. How does the plan-do-check-act model relate to safety management systems?
3. What are the major characteristics of leading indicators?
4. Describe is the concept of organizational maturity?
5. What are some examples of common lagging indicators identified in research conducted by the Center for Chemical Process Safety (CCPS)?

## References

ANSI/ASSP Z10-2012 (R2017). *Occupational Health and Safety Management Systems*. Park Ridge, IL: American Society of Safety Professionals.

AON Risk Solutions. (2016). *ISO 45001—Safety Management System Discussion Abstract*. London: AON Risk Solutions.

Baldauf, J. (2010). "Measuring Safety Performance: What Are KPIs?" *EHS Journal*. http://ehsjournal.org/http:/ehsjournal.org/jan-baldauf/measuring-safety-performance-kpis/2010/.

British Standards Institute. (2007). *BS OHSAS 18001:2007: Occupational Health and Safety Management Systems—Requirements*. London: BSI Global.

Center for Chemical Process Safety. (2011). *Process Safety: Leading and Lagging Metrics . . . You Don't Improve What You Don't Measure*. New York: Center for Chemical Process Safety.

Cummings, D. (2009). "The Evolution and Current Status of Process Safety Management Metrics." *Process Safety Progress* 28(2): 147–55.

Hallowell, M., J. Hinze, K. Baud, and A. Wehle. (2013)."A Proactive Construction Safety Control: Measuring, Monitoring, and Responding to Safety Leading Indicators." *Journal of Construction Engineering and Management* 139(10): 1–8.

Herbel, S., M. Meyer, B. Kleiner, and D. Gaines. (2009). *A Primer on Safety Performance Measures for the Transportation Planning Process*. Washington, DC: United States Department of Transportation, Federal Highway Administration.

International Council on Mining and Metals (ICMM). (2012). *Overview of Leading Indicators for Occupational Safety and Health in Mining*. London: International Council on Mining and Metals.

International Organization for Standardization (ISO). (2015). *ISO 45001: Occupational Health and Safety Briefing Notes*. Geneva, Switzerland: International Organization for Standardization.

International Organization for Standardization (ISO). (2014). *ISO/DIS 45001: Occupational Health and Safety Management Systems—Requirements with Guidance for Use*. Geneva, Switzerland: International Organization for Standardization.

Rajendran, S. (2013). "Enhancing Construction Worker Safety Performance Using Leading Indicators." *Practice Periodical on Structural Design and Construction*. Reston, VA: American Society of Civil Engineers.

Sheehan, C., R. Donohue, T. Shea, B. Cooper, and H. DeCieri. (2016). "Leading and Lagging Indicators of Occupational Health and Safety: The Moderating Role of Safety Leadership." *Accident Analysis and Prevention* 92(7): 130–38.

Smith, S. (2012). "ANSI Z10-2012 Standard Provides the Blueprint to Create an EHS Management System." *EHS Today*. http://ehstoday.com/consensus/ansi-z10-2012-standard-provides-blueprint-create-ehs-management-system-0.

The Campbell Institute. (2013). *Transforming EHS Performance Measurement through Leading Indicators*. Itasca, IL: National Safety Council.

UL. (2013). *Using Leading and Lagging Safety Indicators to Manage Workplace Health and Safety Risk*. Northbrook, IL: UL.

United States Department of Labor. (2003). *OSHA Fact Sheet: Effective Safety and Health Management Systems*. Washington, DC: United States Department of Labor.

CHAPTER 24

# UNDERSTANDING AND PREPARING FOR HUMAN BIAS IN THE ASSESSMENT OF RISKS

Jeremy M. Gernand

## Learning Objectives

After studying this chapter, the reader will be able to:

1. Recognize the types and sources of human bias
2. Anticipate the likely effects of different forms of bias on EHS risk assessment
3. Explain how to mitigate bias in oneself or others in the context of risk assessment

## Key Terms

**Anchoring, assessment, behavioral economics, bias, certainty, confidence interval, error, experimental psychology, hindsight, likelihood, mitigation, overconfidence, risk, severity, survivor, uncertainty**

## Abstract

Successful environmental health and safety (EHS) practitioners and managers should be cognizant of the effects that human biases play in their own decision-making process, as well as the decisions and recommendations of their employees, coworkers, and managers. Developments in behavioral economics and experimental psychology provide insights into how and when individuals may be biased and under-predict or over-predict the risk of an uncertain future event. By developing the understanding of when one's own intuition may falsely indicate safety when a situation is dangerous or danger when a situation is safe, EHS personnel can better employ their skills to mitigate risks and communicate about those risks in their organizations. This chapter describes the type and nature of common biases in decision-making, their implications for EHS personnel, and methods for countering or mitigating them.

## Introduction: The Consequences of Biased Risk Assessment

Some human biases are unavoidable, the result of our brains being optimized to pick out patterns even when none exist, depending on scant information to predict the future and enhance our survival or that of our families. Other forms of bias are learned via direct experience (getting hurt as children on playground equipment) or learned from the instruction of family, mentors, and teachers. These differ from motivated biases where we too easily allow ourselves to be persuaded by what we want to be true in the face of contrary evidence, such as the cost and schedule of projects that are regularly underestimated (Brush and Marsden 1982).

The forms of bias we will be discussing in this chapter are entirely unintentional and unmotivated, yet they affect almost every one of us to varying degrees—unless and until we have been trained to counter them. The biases we will discuss in this chapter are ingrained mental shortcuts that all people share. Perhaps they were valuable to our ancestors long ago in helping us to more quickly discern patterns in the world. However, today, as we seek to eliminate worker and public harm due to our uses of technology—harms that thankfully are increasingly rare—these biases can prevent us from correctly identifying problems and solutions and leave us expending resources without any real benefit.

> Biased risk assessment could lead to the wrong decisions on risk mitigation and management.

As EHS personnel and managers, we must be prepared to identify situations where bias is likely to arise and take steps to counter that bias in our own thinking and the judgments of others.

So what happens if we are biased in our risk assessments or we choose to act on the biased assessment of others who work with us? If we think that a particular possibility (say a safety incident, hardware failure, or excessive environmental discharge) is less likely than it really is, we will neglect to focus attention and resources on mitigating that risk.

## Types and Sources of Bias

> "Perceptual bias can affect nut jobs and scientists alike. If we hold too rigidly to what we think we know, we ignore or avoid evidence of anything that might change our mind.".
>
> —Martha Beck (2010)

We should recognize that many tasks in EHS are prone to possible introduction of bias. While strict statistical analysis may not be susceptible, the most critical EHS decisions regard the application or not of specific controls, which have limitations to their effectiveness to potential but not certain future events. Because we often cannot possibly know when and where the next injury, vehicle accident, chemical spill, or fire will occur, the uncertainty surrounding these possibilities is the key determinant of the amount of risk they pose. Our estimates of those future unknowns are then susceptible to errors of thinking—both conscious and unconscious—including systemic biases that may constantly influence our predictions in a particular way.

There are several sources of bias that may influence the decision-making of individuals, and possibly even more if we were to consider biases related to interpersonal and social interactions. They have a variety of names and are relevant to a series of different situational contexts. However, this chapter will discuss four specific individual biases that fall into two categories: assuming we know more than we do and framing our problem or question incorrectly.

> We must be aware of the situations where bias may arise and how that bias may affect our judgment.

One of the most common sources of bias is thinking that we know something to be true when we do not actually have the evidence to back up that claim. Most often, it is a matter of having some uncertain evidence in support of what we believe but then treating that evidence as more conclusive than it actually is. What is most troubling, however, is that our human minds can take entirely unrelated information and use that on which to base a prediction. This chapter will closely examine two main forms of this bias: one called *anchoring bias* and the other called *certainty bias.*

The other typical human bias relevant to risk assessment involves seeking the wrong kind of information either through incorrectly describing the problem or by incorrectly identifying the set of solutions we are looking for. This chapter will describe the implications of two main forms of this type of bias: one called *hindsight bias* and the other known as *survivorship bias.*

Hindsight bias is a particular error observers make when examining the past and imagining, after the fact, that certain eventual outcomes should have been more foreseeable than available data would suggest (Fischhoff and Beyth 1975). Perhaps counterintuitively, this bias is increased when the outcome was unexpected and greatest when that outcome was negative(Schkade and Kilbourne 1991). Certainly safety and environmental incidents fall into this category of being relatively rare and also very negative events.

## Anchoring Bias

> "Once an idea gets into your head, it's probably going to stay there."
>
> —Eliezer Yudkowsky (2007)

Anchoring bias is an error by which we estimate a specific quantitative value as being similar to the last quantitative value that we noticed or studied. This category of errors is also sometimes known as "recency bias," "priming bias," or the "availability heuristic." It is an error based on a tendency of people to modify some value currently in their heads to answer a new question rather than starting with a blank slate, and unfortunately, most people cannot sufficiently adjust the initial value, leaving their estimate biased.

You can demonstrate this bias yourself. In a room of people, divide them into two groups and ask them to estimate how many worker deaths due to falls occurred in the United States in 2014 (the true value is 359) (US Bureau of Labor Statistics 2014). But before you ask that question, provide the groups with different pieces of paper. One sheet will include the fact that the number worker deaths due to electrocution in the same year was seventy-four, while the other group will be informed that the number of deaths in the United States due to diabetes was 75,578 (US Bureau of Labor Statistics 2014; US Centers for Disease Control 2014). Once everyone has made their estimate, compare the resulting guesses. The group provided with the fact about electrocution deaths will probably estimate a lower number for deaths by falls than the group provided with the number of diabetes deaths. Both groups will have been primed to anchor their estimates of deaths from worker falls on the unrelated information on electrocution and diabetes.

> Anchoring bias will lead us to underestimate the common events and overestimate uncommon events.

As M. F. Weiner said, "Don't waste a crisis" (Weiner 1976). We often use recent events and our temporarily changed perceptions about the likelihood or severity of those events to make changes to mitigate real problems. This can be a useful reaction to a point, especially when these severe unwanted outcomes are directly related to much more common outcomes. For example, fatal automobile crashes are vastly outnumbered by nonfatal-injury car crashes and property-damage car crashes, yet all are mitigated by the same countermeasures. However, investment to strengthen roofs to withstand strikes by meteors in the aftermath of a meteorite-caused fatality (Roshni 2016) would likely be a poor allocation of resources when the same level of investment might provide many more buildings with earthquake or fire resistance.

The mistake of anchoring bias will most often lead risk assessors to underestimate the most common occurrence and overestimate the least common occurrences. In general, individual estimates of risk tend to center around certain typical risks because the numbers that any of us may grab as an anchor vary by the day or hour. Overall, this effect means that in the absence of a strong proximate anchor, most people tend to overestimate the likelihood of very rare risks and underestimate the likelihood of very common risks as seen in figure 24.1 (Slovic et al. 1979). This causes a misapplication of resources and attention from common issues that affect large numbers of people to uncommon outcomes that make a more emotional impact because they seem so tragic and unexpected when they do occur.

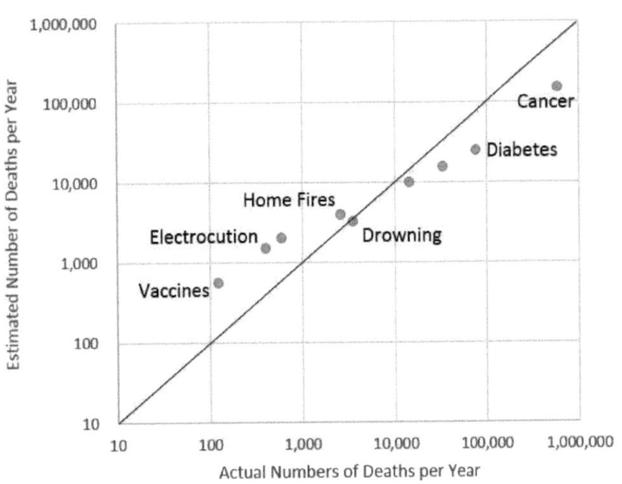


Figure 24.1
Actual annual fatalities due to various causes in the United States in 2014 and mean estimated annual fatalities by a group of undergraduate students in 2015. Commonly occurring risks tend to be underestimated, while uncommon risks tend to be overestimated.

### Mitigating Anchoring Bias with Focusing

The above section discussed the implications of the anchoring bias in risk assessment, but those same cognitive processes that get negatively affected by anchoring can be positively influenced by anchoring if we select the best anchor. This technique can be called *focusing*. For instance, our team may not want to believe that our newly designed and installed redundant process control systems are at any serious risk of failure; however, providing our team the statistical information on past failures of other similar control systems can anchor the assessment of the likelihood of failure and the risk of the new system. It is possible that the new system will perform incrementally better than previous versions, but it is unlikely to perform dramatically better. So, using the power of anchoring bias in a controlled manner with relevant data can improve the ability of EHS personnel to accurately gauge risk. Because clearing one's mind of all numerical values is difficult at best, it is advisable to focus on the most relevant values we can find when evaluating risks.

## Certainty Bias

> "Being deeply knowledgeable on one subject narrows one's focus and increases confidence, but it also blurs dissenting views until they are no longer visible, thereby transforming data collection into bias confirmation and morphing self-deception into self-assurance."
>
> —Michael Shermer (2012)

Certainty bias is an error in thinking an uncertain or initial estimate of a value is more accurate than we have the evidence to suggest. This error is sometimes called "overconfidence bias."

Since uncertainty is one of the main sources of risk, underestimating uncertainty is the same as underestimating risk. Certainty bias is an error of assuming our best guess is a better representation of reality than we ought to. For instance, if we need to plan for an outdoor installation of some equipment that is sensitive to temperature, and we must prepare for the installation months in advance before the weather can be precisely known, we ought to estimate a very wide range of possible temperatures and make plans accordingly. The certainty bias will lead us to minimize that range instead and increase the risk that we will allow our equipment to be damaged.

Figure 24.2 demonstrates how this works for a simple task of estimating the distribution of women's heights in the United States. Data from the US Census Bureau is used to identify the true distribution (US Census Bureau 2011), but without this information, a group of engineering undergraduate students provided their best estimation of the mean and 95 percent prediction interval. As seen, the students' estimates are fairly accurate as guesses of the true mean value, but they display a certainty bias, expecting the range of heights to be closer to the mean than they actually are. Said another way, the estimated range minimizes the size of the distribution tails. In other types of problems, the size of those tails indicate the measure of risk (e.g., strength versus load distributions). When there's a

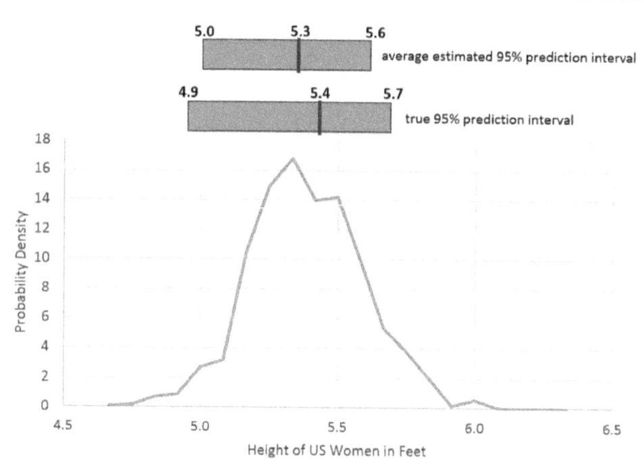


Figure 24.2
Distribution of the heights of US women in 2000 and the actual and undergraduate student estimated 95 percent prediction intervals. The student estimated prediction interval is narrower than true in reality, suggesting overconfidence in each individual's knowledge.

need to predict a future uncertain quantity, certainty bias will lead one to underestimate risk.

Uncertainty in engineered systems, human organizations, and the environment in which they operate is the primary source of environmental, health, and safety risks. If we knew exactly when failures were going to occur and when people would make mistakes, then we could prevent all negative outcomes. Instead, we have some information about the performance of our systems, our employees, the public, and the environment, but uncertainty remains. The certainty bias, however, means that we and others are likely to underestimate this uncertainty. Quantitatively, this means someone may be able to correctly state the average height for adult women, but that person is likely to underestimate the standard deviation, meaning that they believe most women will be closer to the average than is the case in reality. Or, when trying to estimate confidence intervals around an unknown specific quantity (e.g., how many local calls were made by people in the United States in 2007), a person might estimate a range of values that is too narrow, say 30–90 billion local calls, when the actual value was 235 billion (US Census Bureau 2012). If I were to estimate ranges to include unknown values at a 95 percent confidence interval, I should only find 1 in 20 values outside of the estimated range. There is an exercise at the end of this chapter where you can test yourself for certainty bias with questions such as this.

The study of the effects of certainty bias have focused predominately on economics, for example, finding that individuals estimate too narrow a range of possible outcomes and the utility of those outcomes (Werth et al. 2002; McCord and Neufville 1986). Research has also shown that greater expertise does not appear to affect the degree of overconfidence: both novices and experts display similar tendencies toward overconfidence (Fischhoff and MacGregor 1982; Lichtenstein and Fischhoff 1977). While experts do know more and are more likely to select narrower ranges of values somewhat closer to the target, they continue to overestimate how much they know and so are incorrect—the true value falls outside the estimated range—at the same rate as anyone from the general public (Lichtenstein et al. 1982; Armstrong 1985).

Many estimated and uncontrolled values are critically important to understanding the level of risk present in an operation from environmental conditions to equipment degradation to human choices. If we underestimate the range of conditions our equipment and people will be exposed to, we will incorrectly underestimate the level of risk present in the system.

## Mitigating Certainty Bias

A formal approach toward reducing certainty bias in forecasts on currently unknown values is called *expert elicitation.* To ascertain the level of uncertainty that a person actually perceives, it is useful to conduct a formal expert elicitation process whereby they will provide the likelihood or frequency distribution they expect from the value in question. This process involves stating various values and asking the expert for an estimate of probability of the actual value being less than or greater to the estimate. For example, what is the probability that a randomly selected American woman will be taller than five feet, seven inches? As these questions are asked and the shape of the distribution is being completed, the interviewer returns to the tails of the distribution and asks if the expert could posit any scenario whereby the value could be even higher than their previous maximum or lower than their stated minimum. However, if the interviewer only asks for best guesses or confidence intervals, the experts are likely to be overconfident in the same way as any layperson would (Kynn 2007; Rowe and Wright 2001). Requesting the likelihood of a value usually produces more accurate answers than requesting a value for a given likelihood (Slovic et al. 1979). So, walking carefully through the interview with the aim of understanding the tails of the distribution by asking for the probability of certain plausible outcomes is a method for improved ascertainment of the risks. These techniques make the expert elicitation process lengthier and more expensive than many might first suspect, but the level of accuracy has shown to be significantly increased (Morgan 2014; Wood and Ford 1993). Since the goals in the situations where one might use expert elicitation involve significant risks and values that cannot be known (e.g. related to the first time a new technology is operated in space), it is important to maintain this method in the toolbox for these circumstances, and not view it as an easy way to forecast unknowns that might be addressed with better data collection, which is not nearly as susceptible to biases (Morgan 2014).

> Expert elicitation can help us estimate the likelihood of unusual or extreme circumstances.

Response mode changes, another method for improving the elicitation of forecasts and uncertainty from experts, involve altering the way that we request information or estimates from individuals (Cleaves, 1987). This can be as simple as conducting a paper elicitation followed by an in-person elicitation for the same information, or both paper and in-person methods can use multiple question types to address the same unknowns. The *mode effect*, documenting changes in answers depending on how the questions are asked, has been well documented in a number of fields (Aquilino 1994; Gribble et al. 1999; Marta-Pedroso et al. 2007). This technique was originally developed in psychology as a way to ensure that the responses from a person to an interview question were consistent with what that person actually felt or thought (Lonborg et al. 1991). For example, many experts and laypeople will, at first, drastically overstate the probability of a 50 percent likelihood between two events—the "fifty-fifty" response (Auden and Kronenberger 1966). The interviewees make this response to reflect some measure of uncertainty, rather than an accurate depiction of the odds. Changing the response mode during the interview and repeating the process to obtain the same information in a different way can combat some of the biases possible in the expert elicitation process.

## Hindsight Bias

> "Hindsight bias makes surprises vanish."
>
> —Daniel Kahneman (Zweig 2007)

So, how does hindsight bias work? Let's say that I inspect the tires on a truck before driving 100 miles and making a delivery, and I happen to notice that one of the front tires is showing some obvious indications of wear. The measured amount of wear still rates as acceptable with only a 0.01 percent probability of failure in the next one hundred miles, according to our company's maintenance records, and I have personal experience driving 10,000 additional miles on tires with a similar level of wear. So, I make the delivery, but on the return trip, the worn tire experiences a blowout, and I subsequently crash the truck into the concrete barrier wall along the side of the highway but suffer no serious injuries. In an investigation of such an event after the fact, it is a common application of hindsight bias to focus on the decision to drive with the worn tire, and we say that we should have known better. In truth, the risk of a safety critical incident was actually low, but the incident occurred anyway. We may then devote large amounts of resources inspecting for and taking action in response to this particular indicator when the indicator itself is actually a highly unreliable marker of risk.

After the fact, everything seems perfectly clear: what we all should have seen coming and why. Before

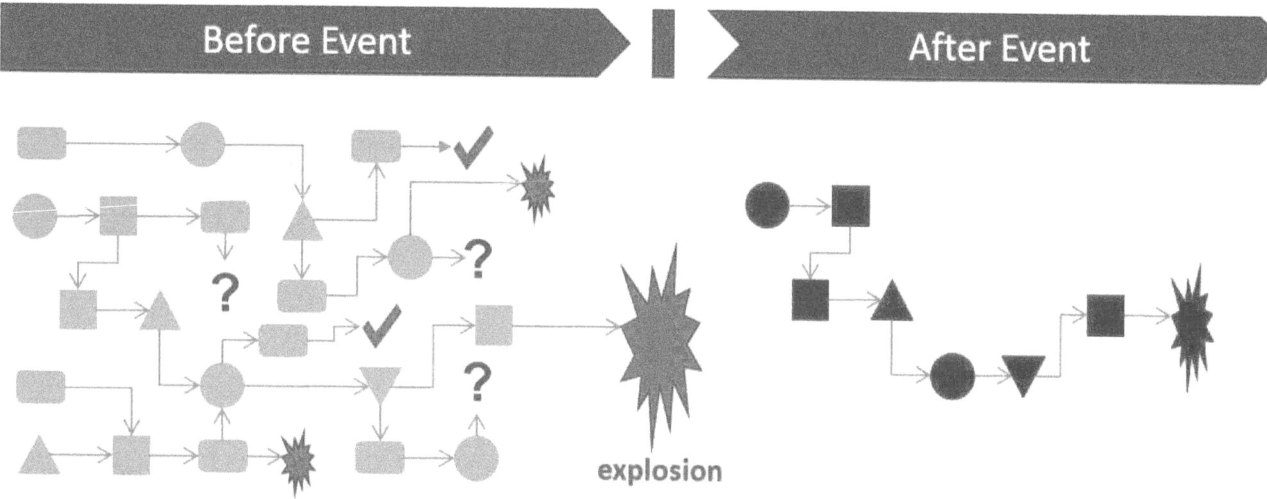


Figure 24.3
Before an event occurs, there exists a complex set of circumstances, indicators, and possible choices, some subset of which may lead to a severe negative outcome (explosion). After this event occurs, hindsight bias leads us to focus on one specific "chain of events" to the neglect of other paths to the same outcome, as well as contradicting indicators and uncertainty that existed at the time.

the fact, we all seek to divine the next outcome from a set of uncertain and constantly changing signals, a cloudy haze of possible but usually unreliable indicators (see figure 24.3). Some EHS disciplines, such as root-cause analysis and other forms of failure or incident investigations, can exacerbate the likelihood of hindsight bias and render our conclusions ineffectual.

Hindsight bias has proven to be especially persistent even when individuals are given access to information on their actual predictive probabilities (Pohl and Hell 1996). While there are researchers who have identified aspects of motivated thinking influencing the degree of hindsight bias (Pezzo and Pezzo 2007; Campbell and Tesser 1983), some researchers believe that this bias is predominately based on the availability of information after an event has occurred (Agans and Shaffer 2010).

While hindsight bias has not been studied in EHS professionals and engineers, it has been studied in business school students making investment decisions (Louie 1999), jurors reviewing corporate audits (Lowe and Reckers 1994), and in medical doctors making diagnoses (Wears and Nemeth 2007; Hugh and Dekker 2009), among others. The effects of hindsight bias on safety management in general tend to focus more attention on behavioral aspects of individual workers (Reiman and Rollenhagen 2011).

It is important to keep in mind that hindsight, in the general sense, is not something to be strenuously avoided. Failure and incident investigations that trace the path from a set of initial conditions through all of the human decisions to an eventual end are a critically necessary part of learning from past accidents and disasters, but as Sydney Dekker explains, hindsight bias makes these investigations prone to judgmentalism and preoccupied with placing blame (Dekker 2004). Careful pains must be taken to structure investigations to avoid focus on decision-making by individuals, which is prone to reinforcing hindsight bias, and instead focus on observations made at the time (Dekker 2004).

The problem arises when we stop considering alternatives that could also have led to the event in question and that could have been present in the minds of the individuals involved. Sometimes called "restoring foresight," techniques have been tested to mitigate this hindsight bias in psychology experiments, legal proceedings, and even technical decision-making on patents (Mandel 2006; Davies 1987; Roese and Olson 1996; Stallard and Worthington 1998). Without mitigating hindsight bias, we place ourselves at risk of learning the wrong lessons from each investigation, and those incorrect lessons learned will do little to prevent the next occurrence.

### Mitigating Hindsight Bias

Hindsight bias has been mitigated when people are most familiar with the causes and related outcomes of particular events and the probability at which those outcomes occur (Christensen-Szalanski and Willham 1991). Of course, knowledge and experience can just as easily lead to jumping to the wrong conclusions as well as any untrained and inexperienced person as we have seen. So, how can that expertise be put to positive use? Through a series of techniques called *structured investigation* (Agarwal and Tanniru 1990). These techniques are taught through effective team design courses and Six Sigma courses but not always consistently applied in the course of root cause investigations, where many begin with an assumption of human error (Dekker 2004). As the field of medicine has incorporated more systems safety processes to reduce medical errors, these techniques have become more prominent there (Spath 2012; Wu et al. 2008). The key in these investigations is to focus on the complex web of inputs and outcomes without assigning blame or responsibility to individual decisions or equipment failures, only seeking to understand each piece of the puzzle—what could have happened and why. A review of this web of causes and effects can identify weaknesses in the current system and permit decision-makers to reduce the number of critical failure points and make the system more robust.

> Hindsight bias puts us at risk of learning the wrong lessons.

## Survivorship Bias

> "All of us show bias when it comes to what information we take in. We typically focus on anything that agrees with the outcome we want."
>
> —Noreena Hertz (2013)

Survivorship bias is an error of focusing on an incomplete set of events and then using characteristics of that incomplete set to make generalizations about a larger population. It is important to note that survivorship bias in EHS could also be known as "negative selection bias," since in many cases we are examining a small population of failures or problems rather than a small population of good outcomes. Survivorship bias comes from looking at a small population of survivors like people who live to one hundred years of age, or companies that have consistently returned profits for each of the last forty years and then misattributing the unusualness of their survivorship to any common characteristics among those centenarians or high-performing companies—we ascribe the observed outcome to a particular circumstance or set of circumstances that are, in fact, unrelated to that outcome. That is, most noncentenarians and most failed companies may also have these characteristics. Instead, we need to know the differences between the two groups, rather than what is common among the "special" group of interest.

In EHS, survivorship bias could operate something like this (see figure 24.4): at a chemical processing facility, we have experienced 20 valve failures in the last year resulting in small releases of chemicals. There is a population of over 500 valves of similar design in total at the facility, which have not experienced leakage. Seeking to understand the problem, we disassemble the failed valves and identify metal oxide particles from corrosion covering the valve seals as well as pitting and cracking in the seals. There are other signs of wear on the valves that are not in common among all of the failed units.

If one looks at a set of machines that outlived all their peers and then looks for commonalities between them to explain how they survived so long, he or she is falling victim to the survivorship bias. What is common among the survivors may also be common among the failures as in figure 24.4. It should be noted that this bias works in the same way if one is only considering failures or only considering situations where worker injuries occurred. The issue is that in training attention on only the failures or only the survivors, which are often in the minority, one is

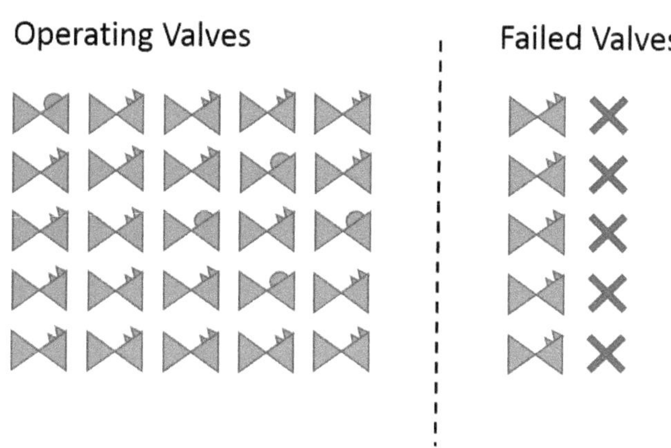


Figure 24.4
Out of twenty-five valves, the five failed valves share a common feature (indicated by the triangles). Negative selection bias might lead one to conclude that this commonality is the cause or at least an indicator of the reliability problem. All the alternative valves survived (indicated by half circles). Do they represent a truly better product, or is it just an effect of the small sample size?

neglecting the majority of the available information. This is important in EHS, since we might incorrectly target an entirely unrelated indicator that is not at all predictive of the true risk being faced.

This process will usually play out in one of several ways: the first being that EHS personnel focus on something in common among worker injuries (e.g., they all occurred on days when it rained) that sounds plausible, and so the investigation stops prematurely without continuing to identify the true causal factors in the injuries, which may have been because there was a 50 percent higher workload on those same days. If the common factor among the injuries is not tested against all the cases where injuries did not occur (i.e., EHS personnel do not bother to check all rain days and compare the injury rates to the injury rate on dry days), then the true cause and method for reducing risk will remain hidden until more costly injuries have occurred. The second common manifestation of this bias occurs when considering successes, such as evaluations of investment in risk-reducing products (e.g., safety monitors or high-reliability components). If successful survivors of field trials happen to mostly be all of one brand, are those components truly more reliable than their counterparts? In controlled laboratory investigations, this question may be easy to answer, whereas in the field it can be difficult to track and record differences in the environment and use profile of all tested components. It could be that ease-of-use issues led to the survivors accumulating less wear than the alternatives. Careful evaluation of the use and environment of all surviving and failed systems is necessary to counteract the tendency toward survivorship bias and prevent the associated waste of resources and lost opportunity for risk reduction.

### Mitigating Survivorship Bias

Survivorship bias is based on an incorrect demarcation of mental borders we draw around a problem. So, the mitigation for survivorship bias is a rule of thumb in any investigation to widen those borders until it is no longer logical to do so. People often call this *stepping back* like in the context of stepping back in search of a broader perspective—a bigger picture. Ensuring that we or our coworkers are not carried away by survivorship bias requires constant challenges to step back and make certain that we are not too narrowly focused. If one person is injured when performing a certain task, even while dozens or hundreds of others completed the task without problem, or when one monitoring device fails at the same time fifty others continue their functions without a problem, the issue may not lie solely with the injured person or the failed device. If we focus on finding differences or indicators related to that one device or that one person or among a small number of unusual cases, we increase the chance that we will be misled by survivorship bias and come to the wrong conclusion. Stepping back to look at the risk in the context of all the monitoring devices or all the personnel performing the task will help to counter this bias.

> If we focus too much on the unusual cases, we increase the chance that we will be misled by survivorship bias.

## Practical Examples

1. A guide cable breaks during a lift at a construction site, injuring a worker when the load turns on the

main cable. A forensic investigation shows that the cable had a manufacturing defect. The company operates nearly thirty lift cranes at various worksites and uses the same cables for all of them and has been using the same manufacturer for years. The safety department had been in the process of investigating a series of fires and near fires that have occurred in the storage areas of three different construction sites. None of these fires or possible fires had led to any serious damage or worker injuries. The owner, however, tells his safety manager to put all safety personnel on the lift cable investigation so it can be solved as quickly as possible.

The safety manager notes that this request is likely due to anchoring bias—the owner has reevaluated the probability of a cable problem based on the recent issue. The real probability of another problem with the cables in the near future is lower than he is currently estimating. The safety manager prepares data on the company's use of the cables and their own safety tests and brings that to the owner along with information on the potential severity of the unresolved fire problem. The safety manager succeeds in getting the owner to keep most safety personnel on the fire problem, while they also continue the investigation on the cables.

2. Some liquid drips onto the sleeve of a maintenance worker at a chemical plant, damaging her protective clothing. She was uninjured but reported the incident to her supervisor and the safety representative, and they initiate an investigation and find a second flange seal that is currently leaking. Both seals are replaced, and the leaking seals are examined in the lab. Both seals appear to be contaminated with silica particles (sand). Some of the maintenance personnel interviewed tell the investigators that the seal materials sometimes attract sand particles due to static charge created when removed from the packaging. The investigators report back to their manager and recommend that antistatic measures be taken on future flange installations.

   The manager warns the investigators against survivorship bias and asks them to take a wide random sample (at least twenty) of other seals in the plant as they are removed for maintenance and compare their characteristics and environments to the failed seals. This line of investigation reveals that over half of the seals have similar sand particle contamination, and the factor that sets the failed seals apart is their higher-than-average operating temperatures (only one of the other twenty seals operated at such high temperatures). The operating temperature was within the manufacturer's specifications, but queries to maintenance contractor companies suggests that the seals may be less reliable near their maximum operating temperature.

3. An engineering team is designing a lightning protection system for an airport radar that will help reduce the odds of any aircraft–aircraft or aircraft–ground vehicle collisions on the runways and taxiways. One of the engineers calls a local meteorologist to request information on the electrical current typical in local lightning strikes. The meteorologist looks up information from the last year on recorded lightning strikes and tells the engineer that at the airport, lighting strike current has been averaging 30,000 amps, with the top recorded strike being 150,000 amps last year. The engineer reports back to the team that the design should be able to withstand 150,000 amps to ensure protection of the system. The design proceeds forward on that basis until the formal customer design review.

   At the design review, the chief engineer for the airport recognizes the weak assumption occurring due to certainty bias and asks a series of questions about the lightning protection system, including: Why were only strikes at the airport considered and not anywhere in the country or the state? How many strikes were included in the data set of strikes at the airport? What is the estimated probability of a strike with more than 150,000 amps? Is there strong confidence that no changes in lightning intensity will occur in the next 30 to 40 years (the lifetime of the radar system)? These questions lead the engineers to realize they may have underestimated the likelihood of a strike with greater than 150,000 amps, and they modify the design accordingly.

4. A consumer purchases a tie-down strap to hold his dirt bike in the bed of his pickup truck. Before a trip, he loads the bike into his truck and installs the tie-down strap, connecting it to eye bolts mounted in the bed. One of these is corroded, but no more than is common with this type of hardware. During the man's trip, the truck travels over a large pothole in the road at highway speeds. The bolt breaks, letting the dirt bike roll out of the back of the truck, striking the road and a following vehicle. There was significant damage to the bike and minor damage to the following passenger car, but there were no injuries. When the man examines what has happened to the previously thought secure bike, he notices that the corroded bolt was the one that broke.

   The consumer replaces all the eye bolts in his truck bed, and later tells his friend that he should have known that the corroded bolt was too weak. But, the man knew in advance about the corrosion and had evaluated it to be no more indicative of a problem than any other. He relies on hindsight bias to make a new rule about replacing the bolts at the first sign of corrosion, without any evidence that the observed corrosion was the actual cause of the problem. His friend notices the logical shortcut and tells him that there are other possibilities including a manufacturing defect or an inadequate design for the tension in his new tie-down strap. This informal structured investigation step of brainstorming other possibilities for the failure helps to not narrow the problem too quickly to the possibly unrelated corrosion observation.

## Conclusion

"Fortunately for serious minds, a bias recognized is a bias sterilized."

—Benjamin Haydon (Fitzhenry 1990)

"Two quite opposite qualities equally bias our minds—habits and novelty."

—Jean de la Bruyere
(Auden and Kronenberger 1966)

As we have seen in this chapter, bias in assessing an uncertain future event is common and affects all of us unless we are specifically aware of that bias and take preparations to work against it. These are not the only biases that EHS professionals may be affected by. Other interpersonal and group biases may also affect the assessment of risk in complex situations, but the biases discussed in this chapter affect individual judgments about risks. Though currently lacking, future research may focus on the particular effects these biases have among engineers and EHS professionals when evaluating risks as well as the best mitigation techniques for these biases in the context of the unique, rare, and potentially severe negative outcomes we seek to protect against. Understanding when these biases occur is critical to self-calibration and good decision-making to best protect the safety and health of workers and the public.

### Further Reading

*Why We Make Mistakes* by Joseph T. Hallinan (2009) is an approachable book discussing how people make errors in a variety of different circumstances and the types of situations that most often set people up for making mistakes.

*The Field Guide to Understanding Human Error* by Sidney Dekker (2014) points out why determinations of "human error" are often wrong and nearly always unhelpful to the prevention of future accidents, and how investigators can move beyond this as a conclusion.

*Human Error* by James Reason (1990) is a discussion of human error from a systems perspective, including cognitive biases as well as human-machine interfaces. Numerous case studies populate its pages, outlining the opportunities for intervention.

*Risk Communication* by Regina E. Lundgren and Andrea H. McMakin (2013) specifically addresses the planning, design, and visual and verbal communication techniques proven to most effectively provide the public and decision-makers with information on risks.

## Exercises

1. Without doing any research, estimate what you believe is a 90 percent confidence interval around the following values:

    a. The number of passenger cars in the United States in 2014
    b. The average annual number of sunny days in Pittsburgh, Pennsylvania
    c. The average annual number of sunny days in Phoenix, Arizona
    d. The number of jobs created in in the United States in July 2007
    e. The number of named Atlantic hurricanes and tropical storms in 2011
    f. The number of inches of rainfall over the year 2006 in Atlanta, Georgia
    g. The total number of words in the English language
    h. The number of votes cast for the US presidential election in 1992
    i. The number of twin births in the United States in 2014
    j. The total number of buses in the United States in 2000

    Now, check your intervals with the true values. If more than one actual value falls outside your confidence intervals, then you have displayed overconfidence.

2. Find a small group of people and divide them into two subgroups. Provide each group with the following prompt and question:

    a. In 2014, the state of North Dakota produced more than 394,000,000 barrels of oil and 462,000,000,000 cubic feet of natural gas. What do you estimate is the probability of experiencing a fatal car crash in North Dakota (expressed as 1 in N chance)?
    b. The state of Mississippi experiences an average of 113 sunny days and 54 inches of rainfall per year. What do you estimate is the probability of experiencing a fatal car crash in Mississippi (expressed as 1 in N chance)?

    Statistically analyze the responses of both groups and evaluate whether either or both of the groups displayed any anchoring bias.

3. Your team needs to assess the risk of severe weather at a new location. No monitoring equipment has been installed previously at this location. Describe and research a set of statistics that could provide a useful "good anchor" to your team's analysis of the severity and likelihood of this hazard.
4. Interview a classmate or colleague and elicit their range of travel times between the two major cities that they travel most often between (by car or by air). Begin with an estimate of the mean travel time, and then ask for a 90 percent confidence interval. Follow this by performing a likelihood estimation of various values you select for large travel times beyond their initially reported maximum value. Ask the interviewee to imagine a possible scenario whereby this higher value could be exceeded, and if they can imagine one, to estimate its likelihood. Construct a graph of this probability distribution.
5. Consider that you work for a forklift manufacturer. In conducting a risk assessment for a new model of forklift, you identify the need for a tilt gauge and alarm that is later implemented in the design. Previous forklifts experienced rollover incidents in 1 in every 12,000 worker-days, and the new indicator and alarm is expected to drastically reduce this risk if implemented correctly. Design an effective 1-page risk communication that counteracts the potential biases of the engineers and managers involved with the project.

## Questions

1. How would certainty bias decrease worker or product safety?
2. Does anchoring bias lead to overestimates or underestimates?
3. Stepping back to reexamine the big picture is a mitigation for what type or types of cognitive bias?
4. Expert elicitation techniques are most focused on what part of value estimation?
5. Which cognitive bias leads investigators to overemphasize human error as the cause of incidents?

## References

Agans, R. P., and L. S. Shaffer. (2010). "The Hindsight Bias: The Role of the Availability Heuristic and Perceived Risk." *Basic and Applied Social Psychology* 15(4): 439–49.

Agarwal, R., and M. R. Tanniru. (1990). "Knowledge Acquisition Using Structured Interviewing: An Empirical Investigation". *Journal of Management Information Systems* 7: 123–40.

Aquilino, W. S. (1994). "Interview Mode Effects in Surveys of Drug and Alcohol Use: A Field Experiment." *Public Opinion Quarterly* 58: 210.

Armstrong, J. S. (1985). *Long Range Forecasting: From Crystal Ball to Computer*. Hoboken, NJ: Wiley-Interscience.

Auden, W. H., and L. Kronenberger. (1966). *The Viking Book of Aphorisms: A Personal Selection*. Dorchester, UK: Dorset Press.

Beck, M. (2010). "Secret to Finding Unexpected Miracles." CNN. Accessed January 1, 2016. http://www.cnn.com/2010/LIVING/11/30/o.secret.finding.miracles/.

Bruine de Bruin, W., P. S. Fischbeck, N. A. Stiber, and B. Fischhoff. (2002). "What Number is 'Fifty-Fifty': Redistributing Excessive 50% Responses in Elicited Probabilities." *Risk Analysis* 22: 713–23.

Brush, R. M., and S. S. Marsden. (1982). "Bias in Engineering Estimation." *Journal of Canadian Petroleum Technology* 34: 433–39.

Campbell, J. D., and A. Tesser. (1983). "Motivational Interpretations of Hindsight Bias: An Individual Difference Analysis." *Journal of Personality* 51: 605–20.

Christensen-Szalanski, J. J. J., and C. F. Willham. (1991). "The Hindsight Bias: A Meta-analysis." *Organizational Behavior and Human Decision Processes* 48: 147–68.

Cleaves, D. A. (1987). "Cognitive Biases and Corrective Techniques: Proposals for Improving Elicitation Procedures for Knowledge-based Systems." *International Journal of Man-Machine Studies* 27: 155–66.

Davies, M. F. (1987). "Reduction of Hindsight Bias by Restoration of Foresight Perspective: Effectiveness of Foresight-encoding and Hindsight-retrieval Strategies." *Organizational Behavior and Human Decision Processes* 40: 50–68.

Dekker, S. (2014). *The Field Guide to Understanding Human Error* (3rd ed.). Dorchester, UK: Ashgate.

Dekker, S. W. A. (2004). "The Hindsight Bias Is Not a Bias and Not about History." *Human Factors and Aerospace Safety* 4: 87–99.

Fischhoff, B., and R. Beyth. (1975). "I knew It Would Happen: Remembered Probabilities of Once-future Things." *Organizational Behavior and Human Performance* 13: 1–16.

Fischhoff, B., and D. MacGregor. (1982). "Subjective Confidence in Forecasts." *Journal of Forecasting* 1: 155–72.

Fitzhenry, R. I. (1990). *Chambers Book of Quotations*. Chambers, Edinburgh.

Gribble, J. N., H. G. Miller, S. M. Rogers, and C. F. Turner. (1999). "Interview Mode and Measurement of Sexual Behaviors: Methodological Issues." *Journal of Sex Research* 36: 16–24.

Hallinan, J. T. (2009). *Why We Make Mistakes*. New York: Broadway Books.

Hertz, N. (2013). "Why We Make Bad Decisions." *New York Times* (October 19).

Hugh, T. B., and S. W. A. Dekker. (2009). "Hindsight Bias and Outcome Bias in the Social Construction of Medical Negligence: A Review." *Journal of Law and Medicine* 16: 846–57.

Kowalewski, M. R., and K. D. Henson, and D. Longshore. (1997). "Rethinking Perceived Risk and Health Behavior: A Critical Review of HIV Prevention Research." *Health Education and Behavior* 24: 313–25.

Kynn, M. (2007). "The 'Heuristics and Biases' Bias in Expert Elicitation." *Journal of the Royal Statistical Society Series A* 171(1): 239–64.

Lichtenstein, S., and B. Fischhoff. (1977). "Do Those Who Know More Also Know More about How Much They Know?" *Organizational Behavior and Human Performance* 20: 159–83.

Lichtenstein, S., B. Fischhoff, and L. D. Phillips. (1982). "Calibration of Probabilities: The State of the Art to 1980." In D. Kahneman, P. Slovic, and A. Tversky (eds.), *Judgment under Uncertainty: Heuristics and Biases*. Cambridge, UK: Cambridge University Press, 306–34.

Lonborg, S. D., J. A. Daniels, S. G. Hammond, et al. (1991) "Counselor and Client Verbal Response Mode Changes during Initial Counseling Sessions." *Journal of Counseling Psychology* 38: 394–400.

Louie, T. (1999). "Decision Makers' Hindsight Bias after Receiving Favorable and Unfavorable Feedback." *Journal of Applied Psychology* 84: 29–41.

Lowe, D. J., and P. M. J. Reckers. (1994). "The Effects of Hindsight Bias on Jurors' Evaluations of Auditor Decisions." *Decision Sciencies* 25: 401–26.

Lundgren, R. E., and A. H. McMakin. (2013). *Risk Communication* (5th ed.). Hoboken, NJ: Wiley.

Mandel, G. N. (2006). "Patently Non-Obvious: Empirical Demonstration that the Hindsight Bias Renders Patent Decisions Irrational." *Ohio State Law Journal* 67: 1391.

Marta-Pedroso, C., H. Freitas, and T. Domingos (2007). "Testing for the Survey Mode Effect on Contingent Valuation Data Quality: A Case Study of Web Based versus In-person Interviews." *Ecological Economics* 62: 388–98.

McCord, M., and R. de Neufville. (1986). "'Lottery Equivalents': Reduction of the Certainty Effect Problem in Utility Assessment." *Management Science* 32(1): 56–60.

Morgan, M. G. (2014). "Use (and Abuse) of Expert Elicitation in Support of Decision Making for Public Policy." *Proceedings of the National Academy of Sciences of the United States of America* 111: 7176–84.

Payne, E. A., and R. J. Ramsay. (2005). "Fraud Risk Assessments and Auditors' Professional Skepticism." *Mangerial Auditing Journal* 20: 321–30.

Pezzo, M. V., and S. P. Pezzo. (2007). "Making Sense of Failure: A Motivated Model of Hindsight Bias." *Social Cognition* 25: 147–64.

Pohl, R. F., and W. Hell. (1996). "No Reduction in Hindsight Bias after Complete Information and Repeated Testing." *Organizational Behavior and Human Decisions Processes* 67: 49–58.

Reason, J. (1990). *Human Error.* Cambridge, UK: Cambridge University Press.

Reiman, T., and C. Rollenhagen. (2011). "Human and Organizational Biases Affecting the Management of Safety." *Reliability Engineering and System Safety* 96: 1263–74.

Roese, N. J., and J. M. Olson. (1996). "Counterfactuals, Causal Attributions, and the Hindsight Bias: A Conceptual Integration." *Journal of Experimental Social Psychology* 32: 197–227.

Roshni, M. (2016). "India Meteorite? Man Killed by Falling Object." CNN. Accessed August 4, 2016. http://www.cnn.com/2016/02/08/asia/india-meteorite-man-killed/.

Rowe, G., and G. Wright. (2001). "Differences in Expert and Lay Judgments of Risk: Myth or Reality?" *Risk Analysis* 21: 341–56.

Schkade, D. A., and L. M. Kilbourne. (1991). "Expectation-outcome Consistency and Hindsight Bias." *Organizational Behavior and Human Decisions Processes* 49:105–23.

Shermer, M. (2012). "Wrong Again: Why Experts' Predictions Fail, Especially About the Future." Huffington Post. Accessed January 1, 2016. http://www.huffingtonpost.com/michael-shermer/wrong-again-why-experts-p_b_1181657.html.

Slovic, P., B. Fischhoff, and S. Lichtenstein. (1979). "Rating the Risks." *Environment* 21: 14–20.

Spath, P. L. (2012). "Error Reduction in Health Care: A Systems Approach to Improving Patient Safety, Second Edition." *Journal of Nursing Regulation* 2: 60.

Stallard, M. J., and D. L. Worthington. (1998). "Reducing the Hindsight Bias Utilizing Attorney Closing Arguments." *Law and Human Behavior* 22: 671–83.

US Bureau of Labor Statistics. (2014). "Census of Fatal Occupational Injuries." Washington, DC.

US Census Bureau. (2012). "Telephone Systems—Summary." In *Statistical Abstract of the United States.* Washington, DC, table 1147.

US Census Bureau. (2011). *Statistical Abstract of the United States.* Washington, DC.

US Centers for Disease Control and Prevention. (2014). "National Diabetes Statistics Report." Washington, DC.

Wears, R. L., and C. P. Nemeth. (2007). "Replacing Hindsight with Insight: Toward Better Understanding of Diagnostic Failures." *Annals of Emergency Medicine* 49: 206–9.

Weiner, M. F. (1976). "Don't Waste a Crisis—Your Patient's or Your Own." *Medical Economics* 53(5): 227

Werth, L, F. Strack, and J. Förster. (2002). "Certainty and Uncertainty: The Two Faces of the Hindsight Bias." *Organizational Behavior and Human Decisions Processes* 87(2): 323–41.

Wood, L. E., and J. M. Ford. (1993). "Structuring Interviews with Experts During Knowledge Elicitation." *International Journal of Intelligent Systems* 8:71–90.

Wu, A. W., A. K. M. Lipshutz, P. J. Pronovost, et al. (2008). "Effectiveness and Efficiency of Root Cause Analysis in Medicine." *JAMA: The Journal of the American Medical Association* 299: 685.

Yudkowsky, E. (2007). "We Change Our Minds Less Often Than We Think." In *LessWrong.* Accessed January 1, 2016. http://lesswrong.com/lw/jx/we_change_our_minds_less_often_than_we_think/.

Zweig, J. (2007). "Your Money and Your Brain." *Wall Street Journal* 320.

CHAPTER 25

# EMERGING TECHNOLOGIES IN ENVIRONMENTAL HEALTH AND SAFETY PRACTICE: SUCCESS STRATEGIES FOR IMPLEMENTATION

Richard Olawoyin

## Learning Objectives

After studying this chapter, the reader will be able to:

1. List types of technologies that are pertinent to the field of environmental health and safety (EHS)
2. Develop foundational skills on virtual environments (VE) that can be used as extensive reference tool applicable to the virtual world
3. Describe the applicable utilization of VE tools (such as computer-based training), and their applications for EHS practice
4. Evaluate emerging trends in the VE world relative to applicability in EHS practice for societal benefits

## Key Terms

**Environmental health and safety, technology, virtual EHS, computer-based training**

## Abstract

Technological advancements and innovation in computing have increased access to new application domains in virtual environments (VE). Expenses of running a facility-based safety training or similar instructional modules have been reduced, while the effectiveness/quality of the training methods are retained. Over the years, innovations in data management systems (DMS) and telecommunications technology have facilitated data collection, storage, analysis, and dissemination, which can be invaluable in the environmental health and safety (EHS) practice.

New software applications, devices connected on the Internet of things (IoT), and computer-based training (CBT) tools are examples of programs that can be used in EHS practice. This document discusses various technologies and software that are available to EHS professionals and how to select the appropriate technology for the applicable business need. This chapter discusses the opportunities available in VE for professional training and effective transition from the VE of learning into real-world practice.

Figure 25.1
Immersive virtual reality © 2018 Oculus VR, LLC. Used by permission.

## Introduction

The advent of technology-mediated learning (TML), also known has e-learning, provides enormous opportunities for effective knowledge transfer to the learners or trainees. These opportunities include technological interactions that provide learning—at a desired location and at one's own pace and time—of predesigned and customized topics. In recent times however, improvement to the TML environment has brought about the concept of virtual learning. The VE, which is mostly Internet or web-based, provides the means for openly effective communication and access to other resources in real time. Important elements in the VE are sense of presence (SoP) and copresence (Hendaoui and Limayem 2008). Sense of presence is categorized as the consciousness of being in a VE due to individual's focus on the environment and the loss of awareness of external environment and the psychological sense of virtual habitation (Lee 2004; Jerome and Singer 2005). It has been described as situated and embodied cognition, which may also involve body's interaction with the environment (Shapiro 2010). Extant studies have shown that the social gap and distance between learners are reduced when SoP exists, which improves the outcome of the learning experience, enhances the acquisition of technical skills, boosts knowledge transfer between learners and from instructors to learners through collaborated learning, exploration of multiple perspectives, and situated performance (Palloff and Pratt 1999; Dede 2009). However, when an individual is conscious of the fact that others are present in the VE shared, the state is called copresence. Organizations around the world are revolutionizing the VE for different purposes. Some have adopted the concept of virtual commerce for their goods and services, while others have utilized the VE for recruitment, conferences, meetings, product design, innovative collaborations, and training.

The VE, which is mostly Internet or web-based, provides the means for openly effective communication and access to other resources in real time.

Extant studies have established that in VE, SoP facilitates learners' achievement of learning outcomes through learning engagement and stimulus, providing for dedicated and realistic interactions with the learning activities and materials (Mikropoulos 2006; Persky et al. 2009). Other studies have highlighted the relationship between presence and the level of immersion (Bystrom et al. 1999; Faiola et al. 2013).

The level of "subjective impression that one is partaking in a comprehensive, realistic experience" and "the semi-voluntary experience of expedition into an alternate context for a prolonged period" is known as *immersion* (Buchanan 2006). Advances in computer technology have made it practicable to integrate three-dimensional–virtual reality (3D-VR) and the Internet to develop an immersive VE (I-VE) (Gregory et al. 2013) as shown in figure 25.1.

Currently, opportunities exist for implementing 3D-VR as platform of preference for formal and informal learning support tools (Jou and Wang 2013). For example, the Microsoft Kinect sensor technology provides unmatched value and excitement for the implementation and exploration of situated and embodied cognition with the goal of developing a significantly dynamic learning environment. The fundamental interactions with the VE that promote embodied presence are the demonstration of directional movement of the body in the VE (Bailenson et al. 2008). According to Dalgarno and Lee (2010), VR is characterized by genuine reliability relative to learner's interaction, which adequately supports immersive practice and psychosomatic SoP, leading to personified engagements and enhanced experiential learning.

> VR is characterized by genuine reliability relative to learner's interaction, which adequately supports immersive practice and psychosomatic sense of presence, leading to personified engagements and enhanced experiential learning.

Immersive VR learning environment promotes situated learning by providing learning activities within a framework, and it can offer a virtual space to recreate teaching challenges, therefore serving as a valuable instructional tool that aids with the development of effective collaborative educational programs and facilitating proper transfer of learning to practice (Bailenson et al. 2008; Bossard et al. 2008; Quintana and Fernandez 2015). Additional benefits of using the VR learning environment include the ability to track subject's performance, reconstruction of accident scenarios, recreation of jobsite conditions, and review of jobsites for potential hazards and applicable controls (Miles 2012). Factors affecting SoP include interactivity, user characteristics, and vividness. Interactivity is the level of participation by users to transform the content of a facilitated environment in real time. The effect of users' characteristics originates from the individual differences in the SoP when users are faced with identical VE. The range of individual differences includes age, gender, cognitive or motor abilities, and so forth. Vividness is the depictive significance of facilitated VE defined by its formal characteristics, which is the process for which an environment presents information to the senses.

> Factors affecting SoP include interactivity, user characteristics, and vividness. Interactivity is the level of participation by users to transform the content of a facilitated environment in real time.

Augmented Reality (AR), also known as "mixed reality" (MR), are fundamentally different from I-VE due to the capability of the AR to overlay illustrations, charts, schematics and other visualization information directly in front of the user. The AR technology can be gainfully used in EHS like an interactive hologram for routine workplace operations and trainings. The importance of the AR for simulated training sessions cannot be overstated, as it can help employees gain meaningful skills needed to control hazardous conditions, identify system flaws, and prevent the occurrence of accidents.

## Technology Use in Environmental Health and Safety

The role of an EHS professional is constantly changing and adapting. In recent decades, the EHS discipline has made some vast improvements that have helped to reduce injury rates throughout many fields. One of the main reasons for these improvements has been the use of technology. Advancements in technology have provided EHS professionals with tools to help better manage the safety and health of people and the environment. Innovations in data management systems (DMS) and telecommunications technologies have provided means to collect and interpret large volumes of data, communicate more effectively with employees, and develop stronger safety programs. Furthermore, EHS professionals are collaborating with technology and software developers to help companies and communities to manage safety and health better.

A cornerstone of an effective safety and health program is collecting, analyzing, and reporting data. This includes employee monitoring and hazard analysis, as well as incident recording and reporting. Moreover, compliance with various regulatory agencies can require extensive documentation and reporting of recorded data, which can become cumbersome to maintain. Invention of the Internet of things (IoT) and the various devices that connect to it have created opportunities to streamline data collection processes, such as wearable devices that collect and monitor biometrics (this is useful for effective lock-out, tag-out procedures). Once data is collected, advancements in software provide robust applications for storage, organization, and analysis of vast amounts of data or information.

Another vital component of safety and health programs is ensuring employees possess the knowledge necessary to perform their work safely. Often, the task of employee training is the responsibility of the EHS professional. Advancements in telecommunication technology have allowed for the development of CBT and e-learning, which provide enormous opportunities for effective knowledge transfer to the learners or trainees. These opportunities include cost-savings, customizable curriculum, and flexibility in training location and timeline. As with the many choices available for EHS software and IoT-connected devices, the EHS professional has many options to choose from for CBT programs. This chapter will detail many of the available possibilities for all three types of emerging technologies. Additionally, once the EHS professional is knowledgeable on the various technology options, including VR technologies, it is necessary to choose which will best suit the needs of the business. This chapter also identifies the steps necessary to accomplish this task.

## Computer-Based Training

Effective EHS training is crucial to every organization since employees who are inadequately trained are at a greater risk of accident/illness/diseases or even fatalities. Training schemes are constantly evolving and with the dynamic nature of the global marketplace, technically current and relevant EHS trainings are required for the workforce and the trainings are mostly delivered on computer systems. The training scheme move to more CBT indicates a significant transformation on how employees are equipped to stay safe on the job and keep the environment safe at the same time.

Globally, the importance of developing more meaningful learning experiences that meet the desired goals of public and private organizations cannot be overemphasized. Training goals typically include the facilitation of learners' engagements and the improvement of the learning processes and outcomes. There are two major types of training approaches: strategy-based and process-based training methods. Existing cognitive training methods are intended for improving cognitive functions and skills by teaching strategies (Caviola et al. 2009). Strategy-based training usually is composed of task identification by which strategies are introduced to training a group of participants with abysmal performance with the goal of helping them develop skills, consequently improving their performance. Whereas, when participants are trained on a set of tasks with emphases on a particular cognitive process in comparison to an untrained set of tasks, it is known as process-based training. The practicality and significance of a specific training method could also be dependent on the integration of learners' levels of proficiency and the cognitive tasks load; therefore, individuals' cognitive process capabilities and domain-specific knowledge base are quintessential.

Many studies have explored the correlation between learner's attitude, information technology, and the overall benefits to the learners and the

The practicality and significance of a specific training method could also be dependent on the integration of learners' levels of proficiency and the cognitive tasks load.

organizations for which they work. Information technology applications have been integrated into the learning strategies in different CBT framework, including the enhanced traditional classroom, blended (online/hybrid) e-learning, and fully online learning.

Employee training is often the responsibility of the EHS professional. This can entail a range of tasks from developing curriculum and conducting training sessions to hiring outside training consultants and securing training facilities and resources. Providing effective training to employees can be challenging because it requires taking employees out of work functions/production for long periods of time. Conducting multiple training sessions across different locations or for different groups of workers can lead to inconsistencies in instruction and training experiences. The use of CBT can effectively provide consistent training to employees, while reducing the time away from job functions. Different forms of CBT include software applications through corporate intranet or web-based platforms.

> Computer-based training helps to calibrate learners' understanding of the training contents, which effectively integrates the concepts with the desired learning outcome.

CBT programs *normally* do not require an instructor, which gives the employer the flexibility to schedule training sessions at opportune times for the organization without incurring costs associated with hiring trainers for multiple sessions (Kilbourne 2010). Moreover, using CBT in this way ensures every employee is receiving consistent content, while still allowing the employer to tailor the module to the target audience. This type of program is useful while training employees who are in multiple business locations, are out of state or country, work nontraditional shifts, or have disabilities and gives the employee access to the training that is needed without having to be in a physical classroom. In addition, these types of training create a stress-free environment for trainees by providing them the time to learn at their own pace.

The military has also used CBT to train servicemen and women, and in the military training system, there are numerous instructional strategies that have been developed for better improvement and greater efficiency (Vogel-Walcutt et al. 2013). Computer-based training helps to calibrate learners' understanding of the training contents, which effectively integrates the concepts with the desired learning outcomes. Organizations such as the United States military service have employed newly developed CBT training strategies, such as the metacognitive prompts (McP), together with retrospective confidence judgment (RCJ) and operator action performance (OAP) feedback, for training novices and measure their learning effects (Fiorella et al. 2012; Kim 2018). The McP concept is about thoughts about thoughts, or it's the knowledge and regulation of personal cognition with the ability to control what one knows (Van Overschelde 2008; Kim 2018). Like for other training needs with today's technological advancement and with the variety of programs to choose from, CBT continues to play a significant role in workplace safety training. The selection of suitable learning strategies and management of cognitive resources will help meet the training objectives using CBT.

### CBT Resources and Tools

Adequate and appropriate resources for CBT facilitate learners' development of cohesive learning strategy linked to greater attention to details of personal progression toward attaining learning outcomes and properly evaluate individual response to performance and improvement. Learners who are availed with appropriate CBT resources have been shown to develop higher levels of McP skills (Kim 2018), and they have

> Learners and instructors benefit from computer-based training when used appropriately, which facilitates instructors' teaching improvements, instructional engagements, and real-time assessment which help to provide efficient course/lesson organization, just-in-time grading, assessment, and evaluation of learners' performances, and proper implementation of continuous quality improvement.

better self-awareness of how well they have grasped the contents in the training material based on easy evaluation of personal performance.

Online-based and computer-based training and testing tools are mostly used for providing more engaging and interactive learning experiences for learners (such as verbal guidance, behavioral modeling, multiple trials and attempts on problems, and real-time feedback) (Hardin et al. 2014). They also facilitate instructors' teaching improvements, instructional engagements, and real-time assessment, which help to provide efficient course/lesson organization, just-in-time grading, assessment, and evaluation of learners' performances and proper implementation of continuous quality improvement. Learners and instructors benefit from these tools when used appropriately.

Short-term memory (STM) also called "working memory" is the allotment of the cognitive processing system that is used for processing received information, but it can only process limited information at a time (Sweller and Chandler 1994), after which the information is transferred to long-term memory (LTM), also called "explicit memory," of which the information is potentially stored in the temporal cortex and are consciously available for recall. Computer-based training often presents information to learners in a number of formats, which includes narrations through texts, voice/sound, graphics/illustrations/pictures, and so on. The understanding of these information sources entails the use of verbal and visual processing mechanisms (Baddeley 1999). Sufficient working memory is essential for processing CBT instructional information; therefore, constant practice, due to the availability and accessibility of CBT, can minimize the working memory deficits, which may constrain certain learners from understanding complex information because they may be unable to perform batch-information processing.

There is a variety of resources available for developing EHS courses or training as a CBT. A combination of the methods is presented in figure 25.2, which shows the developmental process and the feedback process. Process step one entails the development of the training goals, objectives, and learning outcomes, while step two is based on a process that accurately evaluates the learners' knowledge base, strengths, and weaknesses. Similarly, the learners'

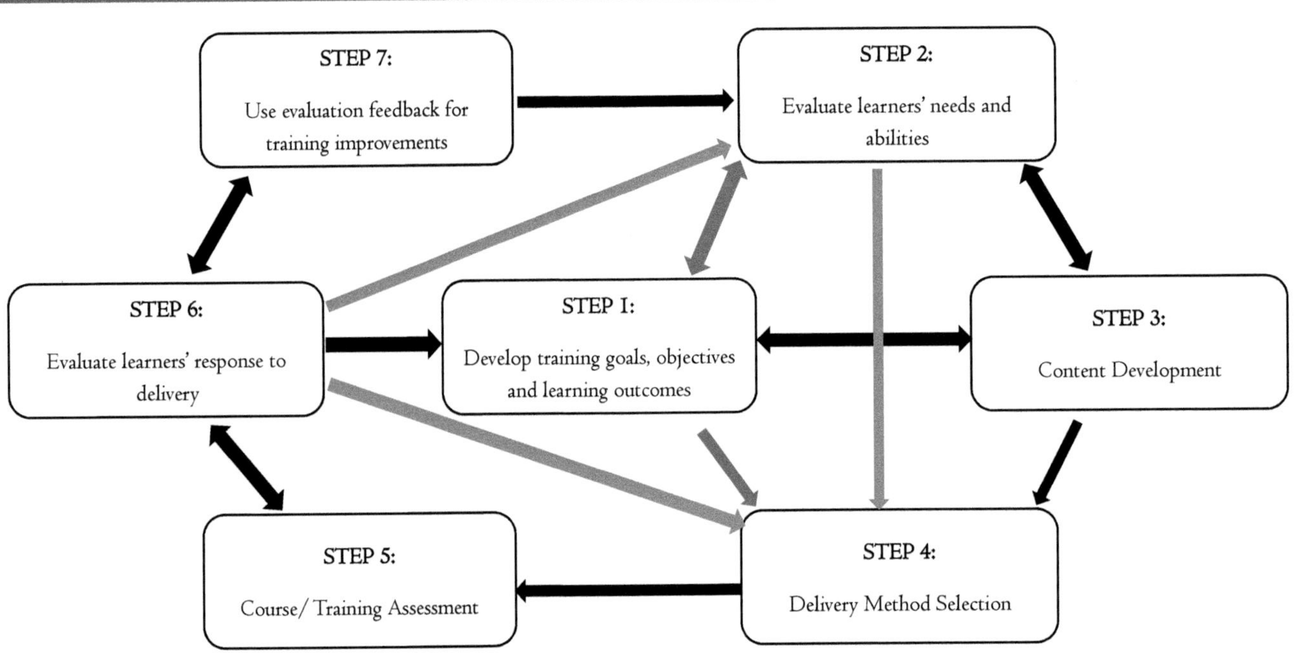


Fig. 25.2
Conceptual training development and evaluation model

qualities may necessitate the modifications and revision of the initially defined goals, objectives, and outcomes.

The course/training developer(s) will then gather information relevant to the intended training using trusted materials with good references (e.g., peer-reviewed articles) or seek the assistance of other professionals with extensive related experience on the topic, and other subject matter experts (SME) may be consulted for the development of the content for the training.

Professional trainers may have the aptitude to develop their own training modules, selecting the CBT method using tools, such as intelligent tutoring systems (ITS), a software that customizes itself to learners' needs and diagnoses individuals' problems and is able to adapt instructions based on the learner's preferred learning modes. Interactive multimedia training (IMT) integrates animation, sound, graphics, videos, texts, and photos for the training presentation. The IMT is very interactive, self-paced, useful for on-the-job skills training, and also effective when used in instructor-facilitated training.

The selection of an appropriate learning management system (LMS) is key. An LMS is a software that basically integrates training management functions (the functions may include assessment) and learning tools with the developed training program. Examples of LMS that can be used to develop and deliver an effective EHS training include Blackboard, Desire2Learn, Moodle, Canvas, and Google Classroom.

Other available CBT tools include: Adobe Captivate, Articulate Storyline 3, and PowerPoint (PPT), and so forth. Adobe Captivate specializes in responsive content, including simulations, assessment modules, and product demonstrations, and can easily adapt desktop courses into mobile-friendly courses (Adobe Systems Incorporated 2017). Similarly, Articulate Storyline functions very much like Adobe Captivate in allowing for creation of a fully interactive CBT program with mobile and desktop computer functionality. PowerPoint is a tool used to facilitate CBT, as images and videos can be incorporated into a slide show presentation that can then be imported into programs such as Adobe Captivate and Storyline 3.

The training effectiveness should be measured through an appropriate assessment plan (step five) integrated in the CBT platform. This promotes learning and retention among learners. The assessment results must be evaluated to identify any potential gaps in the training process (step six). The evaluation results are used as feedback mechanisms following step seven to make informed choices about needed changes and for continuous quality improvement of the training scheme. Throughout the process, each step should be constantly reviewed so that where modifications are needed, they can be made timely, to improve the quality of the training program.

### CBT Advantages and Disadvantages

The advantages and disadvantages of CBT are listed in table 25.1. The use of CBT should be considered when the cost benefit analysis (CBA) suggests that if used, the benefits will outweigh the disadvantages that is if it is cost-effective. Another important factor to take into consideration is the potential for the materials to require frequent updates. When other training methods are available for use alongside the CBT, and if there is an experienced facilitator/trainer available to coordinate the training, it will be safe and effective to use the CBT delivery method.

## Internet of Things

The Internet of Things (IoT) is an emerging global, Internet-based information service architecture facilitating the exchange of goods in global supply chain networks and is developing on the technical basis of the present domain name system. It is the network of physical devices, such as smart devices, vehicles, wearable devices, and other items containing electronics, software, sensors, and network connectivity allowing the collection and exchange of data (Manoukian 2016). The Internet of Things envisages a future in which digital and physical things can be connected through telecommunication technologies to enable a range of applications and services (Razzaque et al. 2016). In the field of EHS, connected devices include smart sensors and other equipment that are used to collect and monitor EHS data to improve the health of individual workers,

Table 25.1 Advantages and disadvantages of computer-based training

| | |
|---|---|
| Advantages | • It helps with maintaining effective control of the learning process.<br>• It provides different learning groups with consistent learning experience.<br>• The differences that exist between the levels of preparedness of trainees are taken into account.<br>• It is effective for training that leads to knowledge acquisitions, skills development, and behavioral changes.<br>• It is efficient, and it can reduce the time required for regular training and the learning time. |
| Disadvantages | • It is expensive to develop, purchase, and implement.<br>• It limits the availability for substantive discussions, question & answer sessions and accommodation of trainees' concerns.<br>• It may not be effective if used exclusively without a facilitator.<br>• The required training materials to cover may be burdensome if the process is not properly paced.<br>• It requires other training exercises and materials. |

to mitigate safety hazards, and to reduce harmful environmental impacts.

Smart sensors can capture data to monitor emissions and water usage. Geographic information systems using grid-based data collection is less time-consuming than collecting data manually, which can be useful in EHS scenarios such as a chemical spill, where an immediate cleanup response is needed. Wearable devices, sensors, moving cameras, and mobile apps can be used in a variety of ways in EHS. For example, a mobile device can scan a barcode from a chemical container, thus enabling an audit of chemical inventory, and that can be transferred to a safety data sheet (Hardcastle 2015). Wearable devices can also be used for health and environmental monitoring to protect workers, such as monitoring for high-temperature environments and unsafe sound levels, alerting the worker and the employer. The Internet of Things will make wearable technology a must-have tool for EHS management (Leavoy 2014).

For example, in 2015, Honeywell Industrial Safety and Intel demonstrated a prototype of an IoT-connected device that provides safety intelligence that will reduce worker injuries and help prevent loss of life. This device would collect data from a variety of sensors, such as a sensor on a self-contained breathing apparatus, a heartrate monitor, a toxic gas monitor, or an activity detection device. The device would then analyze the data locally and would provide high-level insights to the remote operator as well as to the worker himself (Hardcastle 2015). Particularly for workers going into high-risk environments, such as firefighters, these devices could store critical information about the activities and the environment of the worker, which could be analyzed, used for training purposes, or for continuous remote monitoring at a centralized command center (Smith 2015).

> The use of CBT should be considered when the cost-benefit analysis (CBA) suggests that if used, the benefits will outweigh the disadvantages (that is, if it is cost-effective).

## EHS Software Applications

A vast number of software applications are available for EHS professionals. Each of these software programs is uniquely designed and geared toward a specific aspect of EHS. These range from occupational health to ergonomics software. With a growing need for safety oversight in the workplace, the need to take safety to a digital, quantifiable level is increasing in importance.

Many software applications are web-based, meaning the software is contained entirely on the Internet without having to be installed on the computer or device, while others are a combination of installed software with some web-based operations. There are many advantages of using web-based software systems. Data stored in a central location can be updated automatically, allowing users to have access to the same up-to-date information to ensure consistency in key areas of concern. They are available for a multitude of operating systems and have high levels of security, backup systems, and resiliency

Many software applications are web-based, meaning the software is contained entirely on the Internet without having to be installed on the computer or device, while others are a combination of installed software with some web-based operations.

(Santos 2013). Some software applications are too robust to be contained entirely web-based, so the bulk of the software is installed on the device but regularly connects to the Internet for cloud storage and data updates. The next few paragraphs give a detailed explanation of programs such as Enablon, EMEX, Enviance, Intelex, Medgate, regAction, and others.

## Enablon

Enablon provides EHS professionals an opportunity to use their "Sustainability, EH&S and Operational Risk Management Software" (Enablon 2017). It provides organization solutions and helps manage procedures needed to meet EHS rules and regulation, improve sustainability, and reduce the severity of work-related risks by monitoring threats. The program provides a step-by-step process, and the software also gives helpful advice when developing financial planning, which also provides users "solutions to manage their environmental and social performance, minimize risk and improve profitability." The program is useful in green facilities to assist with brand protection, finding solutions for automotive, healthcare, and even oil and gas. The program can also be applied for audit and compliance (ISO 19001), air quality management to product compliance (ISO 9001), and stewardship.

## EMEX

EMEX provides EHS software specifically in environmental management systems, with ISO 14001, which involves environmental management systems, including products, services, and processes. The multifaceted program helps with incident management, audits, risks, and safety observations (EMEX 2016). The software program enables companies to reduce the costs of compliance and compliance failures, prepare performance reports, and KPIs. Processes managed by software include risk and audit management, incident and event management, carbon management, and compliance software. Combining the software with other applications with Internet presence can be effective for organizations intended to ensure that safety is at the forefront of their endeavors.

## Enviance

Enviance provides EHS cloud-based software that can centrally manage a broad range of compliance activities with minimal burden on IT resources (Enviance 2016). Since the technology is cloud based, it can deliver enterprise resource planning (ERP) solutions in real time, anywhere, and company-wide. This software allows companies to access many different programs that assist in making it much easier for their business to keep track of their operations, from inventory to waste management. It makes it easy for companies to master multiple types of management systems in order to keep the business running efficiently and economically. The software provides solutions in four areas: environmental, health, safety, and sustainability, and each area offers specific subgroups that benefit companies based on their needs. It involves a huge database of information on how to keep employees healthy, to strengthen the workplace environment, and how to integrate and understand safety-related data.

*Environment*: Environmental solutions offered by the program include air compliance, permit management, greenhouse gases and emissions inventory, water compliance, waste management, audits, assessments and inspections, chemical inventory management, incident management, management of change, and action tracking. Many companies use the environmental aspect of Enviance (Alliance Resource Partners). The software can be used to "track environmental data for water, greenhouse gas inventory, and air emissions. An automated system connects administrative offices with emission-producing units to alert if a problem occurs" (Wiedemann 2008).

*Health:* Solutions provided for health includes office ergonomics, behavior-based safety, job hazard analysis, and action tracking, which help improve employee health while strengthening management systems.

*Safety:* Solutions provided under safety include job hazard analysis, hazards communications, audits, assessments and inspections, management of change, incident and near-miss, process safety management, and action tracking.

*Sustainability:* Solutions offered under sustainability include metrics and corporate responsibility reporting and carbon management and reporting; these allow companies to improve financial performance while complying with regulations.

In addition to the software, other useful programs include the *EHS Audit Action Manager,* which allows users to "manage facility audits on almost any device" ("Bloomberg BNA" 2014). This application uses hypertext markup language (HTML), which is the backbone. It allows the creating of documents and the use of images. The program is user friendly, with an icon-driven interface, which allows easy recording of findings, corrective action, and scoring of performance.

The benefits of software programs in EHS cannot be overstated. Workstations could utilize ergonomics programs for task analysis and improvements. The software programs are user friendly with the graphical user interchange (GUI), which makes the program easier to learn, understand, and use. ERP solutions may very well be the future of safety and this can only make EHS goals more achievable.

### Intelex

Intelex EHS provides a cloud-based interface for environmental, health and safety, quality, and business performance management (Intelex Technologies 2016). The cloud-based system allows users to access this software on multiple devices including computers, tablets, and smartphones. The system is broken up into a few different fields of focus, which offer features that allow for illness and injury management, document control, compliance requirements, and reporting on environmental management operations. With these features, users can effectively look at every aspect of safety through a single window and allow for tracking information to use to mitigate future risks, as well as improving processes. Users can measure their metrics (leading and lagging indicators), such as incidents, injuries, safety objectives, the company's safety policy, and vehicle accidents. It also helps to improve companies that use their software by using JSAs, explaining behavior-based safety and tracking ergonomic hazards and human factors. The software is capable of providing different management systems, such as training management, communication management, safety meetings management, and audits management. With the ability to help communicate safety to workers and management, EHS professional can use such software and similar kinds to improve their business practices and avoid future safety risks.

### Medgate

Medgate is an EHS software solutions program that is designed to collaborate with organizations around the world to effect meaningful change in the way that EHS systems are managed (Medgate, Inc. 2017). The main objective of this software is to reduce EHS risks and create healthier workforces. This program is particularly designed for safety professionals, industrial hygienists, medical directors, and EHS directors. Furthermore, this type of software will be configurable to meet the needs of any company's requirements.

### regAction

regAction is an EHS professional web tool that deals with the organization of data for environmental management, such as air, waste, and water, as well as occupational safety management (regAction 2017). This application is used to centrally organize all of the data that encompasses waste, air, and water management and allows the user to access the records on a mobile device as well as a desktop. The suite of

EHS management solutions aids the EHS professional by streamlining many regulatory compliance needs, such as data analysis and reporting, regulatory alerts, and centralized data storage.

### SAP

Systems Applications and Products (SAP) has an extensive portfolio of products that offer solutions for a variety of business processes (SAP SE 2017a). Suites of products include cloud and data platforms, procurement, analytics, customer engagement and commerce, IoT and digital supply chain, EHS-SAP, human resources (HR), and finance. These products provide the capability for a company to manage many different aspects of business operations, such as financial assets, cost accounting, production operations, materials, personnel, plants, and archived documents. The company also has many interfaces that deal with web-based interactions and products and services that use the IoT, which can help to increase productivity with both internal and external business partners and customers. Additionally, SAP has an EHS management software that provides solutions for risk assessment, safety inspections, incident investigations, safety and health program administration, and compliance with safety and health regulations.

### Ex3

Ex3 is an advanced software with many different measuring systems that help with workflow management and help uncover unanticipated data correlations (Efficient Enterprise Engineering, Inc. 2017). The software offers an EHS data management system (DMS) that is a multimodule cloud system used to track occupational injuries and illnesses affecting the organization. The software is capable of graphics, reports, statistics, OSHA regulations, workers' compensation requirements, and so forth, which allows for easier data flow and management.

### NordSafety

The platform packages health, safety, environment, and quality (HSEQ) management tools through the Internet (NordSafety 2017). The program can be used across all mobile and desktop devices to track analytics of a safety company, provide administrative security of data, use of public reporting, learn from near-miss accidents, and apply safety audits to real-time inspections. It provides an easier and safer way of storing all the information necessary to conduct safety inspections and changes of businesses all around the world. With the information being cloud-based and mobile-friendly, the EHS professional could use this data wherever they are at in the world as long as there is an Internet/data connection.

### Quarks Safety

Inventory management and traceability give this application the ability to manage stock input/output, trace product use, and generate simple Safety Data Sheets (SDS ) (Quarks Safety 2017). Safety Data Sheets management allows EHS professionals to download SDS from suppliers, track version histories, conduct compliance reviews and exposure scenarios, and have all information organized and readily available for any issue that may arise.

## Technology Selection

With the large variety of programs, systems, and software, there are many options for the EHS professionals to consider when shopping for the right technology to suit their needs. Furthermore, as technology continues to evolve, those within the EHS profession will continue to see a vast array of advancements within the discipline. Therefore, the role of the EHS professional will always be improving.

> Organizations should prioritize their functional or nonfunctional needs and requirements to be able to achieve the set goals and objectives.

Proper procedures for the selection of the appropriate technology must always be considered. Since there are many EHS software packages available, selecting the right one that is fit for purpose may be complicated, and the wrong choice can lead to poor results and cause future problems. Picking a CBT program, IoT-connected device, or software application requires preparation and planning. There are six crucial steps that a business should follow to select the technology that would best fit their needs:

1. The first step is to identify the organization's needs and then set some goals and objectives that should be achieved by implementing the new safety technology. A company's goals can either be broad or general in nature but should give a direction for them to work toward.
2. Once the organization has a clear understanding of what the overall goals and objectives are, the organization should think about what they may need in order for them to be able to achieve those goals and objectives. They should prioritize their list of requirements as either functional or nonfunctional. Functional means what a business needs that particular technology to do in order for them to achieve their required goals and objectives Nonfunctional means it describes things that a business may find important, but it is not something that must be performed by the technology. It is also wise for a business to discuss the application with their staff so they can provide feedback in regard to the functionality of the application.
3. Organizations should choose a suitable technology type that will promote their goals. For example, smaller organizations usually prefer single-user systems, which can be installed on a computer, and larger organizations find that enterprise systems are helpful because it allows multiple users to access a single.
4. They should evaluate and compare the different technology solutions offered. When comparing the different technology types that are offered, a business should mainly focus on the requirements that they have established for their organization. The organization should reject a technology provider if they cannot meet mandatory requirements that they need in order to run their business and should accept the provider that gives the most features, such as advantageous for saving time and things that might be useful to have, but are not essential, all for an affordable price. Also, the organization should select a technology provider that is flexible in catering to any changes or additions to their requirements after the initial implementation. This is because during the evaluation process, things such as "internal processes, local and international legislation and international standards are subject to change and often require changes to a business's [EHS] management system" (SAI Global, Ltd. 2011).

One rule is that organizations should not make cost a primary issue; prices can always be negotiable. The important thing is for an organization to find a technology provider that is relatable and form a partnership.

5. Select a supplier and product that suits your needs. One rule is that organizations should not make cost a primary issue; prices can always be negotiable. Also selecting the cheapest solution can end up costing more by not achieving the intended goal, or product or supplier may become incapable of growing with the organization's requirements. The important thing is for an organization to find a technology provider that is relatable and form a partnership.
6. Implement the technology chosen. It is important to note that even if the organization chooses the best technology available, the initial goals and objectives may not be achievable unless a well-planned implementation is produced with the correct configuration and training. The organization should discuss the amount of time that they are allowed to spend on managing the implementation and training process, which will help the business get a good understanding of the amount of assistance they will need from their technology provider. The technology supplier should be able to provide any services that are required and should have the experience for providing it. A business must talk with their supplier to determine how the software should be rolled out (SAI Global, Ltd. 2011). They should then run a test pilot to determine if everything works properly, at which time the company can finally implement the new technology.

## Conclusion

New safety technologies including virtual learning environments are becoming the norm of the day. These technologies make it easier for companies to organize safety information, communicate with employees, comply with standards, and improve their safety programs. Since applications being used are Internet/cloud based, information can be sent real time to all members of an organization. It also allows organizations to make sure that everyone uses the same protocols. Doing this allows individuals to quickly decipher the company's safety progress by individual site.

While virtual and computer technologies are beneficial, improvements can always be made. Software applications and CBT should be made available for all devices. This includes computers, tablets, and phones. These EHS virtual software companies do not want to ostracize potential clients based on the type of electronics that are made available to employees. For example, the program should not strictly be made for Android but not iOS (e.g., available for Samsung products but not Apple) or vice versa. They should not just be computer based. When doing safety audits or inspections, it is much easier for investigators to have access to tablets rather than a computer due to size and convenience constraints.

Safety technology will continue to evolve and adapt as new challenges and responsibilities are placed on today's EHS professionals to be more innovative in providing solutions to emerging problems. It is critical that safety engineers, employers, and software and technology developers continue to communicate and collaborate. The possibilities for improving safety in the VE through technology are endless and will have a tremendous, and hopefully positive, impact on how safety is managed in the future.

## Questions

1. What are the factors that could affect sense of presence in virtual reality?
2. Spell out the following abbreviated computer terminologies in full:
3. Discuss some of the resources available for CBT.
4. List five applications of EHS software programs.
5. Briefly describe the steps for selecting the appropriate technology.

## References


ASCII (American Standard Code for Information Interchange). (n. d.). Accessed September 15, 2016. https://www.allbusiness.com/barrons_dictionary/dictionary-ascii-american-standard-code-for-information-interchange-4943214-1.html.

AT&T. (n. d.). Accessed September 15, 2016. https://www.att.com/global-search/search.jsp?App_ID=HOME&autoSuggest=FALSE&tabPressed=FALSE&q=DSl#!/All/.

Baddeley, A. D. (1999). *Essentials of Human Memory*. Boston: Allyn & Bacon.

Beal, B. V. (n. d.). Domain name. Accessed September 14, 2016. http://www.webopedia.com/TERM/D/domain_name.html.

Bharti, N. (2002). "Multi-Purpose Internet Mail Extension (MIME)." Powershow.com. Accessed September 12, 2016. http://www.powershow.com/view/a819d-ZGRjN/Multipurpose_Internet_Mail_Extension_MIME_powerpoint_ppt_presentation.

"Bloomberg BNA and Enviance announce the release of EHS audit action manager." (2014). *Information Technology Business* 68.

Caviola, S., I. C. Mammarella, C. Cornoldi, and D. Lucangeli. (2009). "A Metacognitive Visuospatial Working Memory Training for Children." *International Electronic Journal of Elementary Education* 2: 122–36.

Davis, T. (n. d.). "What Everyone Should Understand about JPEG." General Glyphics, Inc. Accessed September 12, 2016. http://www.glyphnotes.com/gn-jpeg.cfm.

DBMS. (n. d.). Accessed September 14, 2016. http://techterms.com/definition/dbms.

Efficient Enterprise Engineering, Inc. (2017). "EHS Software Solutions: Efficient Improvement Company—EX3." http://www.ex3.com/

EMEX. (2016). "EMEX Provides a Most Complete Solutions for Incident, Safety and Risk Management According to Global EHS 2016 Industry Report." http://emex2.herokuapp.com/verdantix_report/

Enablon. (2017). "About Enablon—EHS, Risk & Sustainability Software." http://enablon.com/company.

Enviance. (2016). "Environmental, Health, Safety EHS Software." https://www.enviance.com/.

"Enviance Recognized for Carbon Management Software by Groom Energy Solutions." (2011). *Entertainment Close-Up* (February 10).

Fiorella, L., J. J. Vogel-Walcutt, and S. Fiore. (2012). "Differential Impact of Two Types of Metacognitive Prompting Provided during Simulation-based Training." *Computers in Human Behavior* 28: 696–702.

Geier, E. (2015). "DNS Services Protect against Malware and Other Unwanted Content." Computerworld from IDG. Accessed September 15, 2016. http://www.computerworld.com/article/2872700/6-dns-services-protect-against-malware-and-other-unwanted-content.html.

Hardcastle, J. L. (2015). "Leveraging IoT to Improve EHS Management." http://www.environmentalleader.com/2015/11/leveraging-iot-to-improve-ehs-management/.

Hardin, A. M., C. A. Looney, and M. A. Fuller. (2014). "Self-efficacy, Learning Method Appropriation and Software Skills Acquisition in Learner-controlled CSSTS Environments." *Information Systems Journal* 24(1): 3–27.

Hendaoui, A., and M. Limayem. (2008). "Understanding Consumer Virtual Shopping Behavior in 3D Virtual Worlds: A Theoretical and Empirical Investigation." *Proceedings of the Twenty Ninth International Conference on Information Systems, December 14–17, Paris, France, paper 78.*

Henry, A. (2012). "Why You Should Start Using a VPN (and How to Choose the Best One for Your Needs)." Accessed September 14, 2016. http://lifehacker.com/5940565/why-you-should-start-using-a-vpn-and-how-to-choose-the-best-one-for-your-needs.

Holmes, N. (2013). "What's the Difference between GIF, PNG, JPEG, and TIFF?" Accessed September 12, 2016. http://www.computerhope.com/jargon/h/html.htm

Intelex Technologies. (2016). "EHS—Health & Safety—Quality Management Software—Intelex." http://www.intelex.com/.

Ketpichainarong, W., P. Laosinchai, P. Panjaburee, H. Piyayodilokchai, and P. Ruenwongsa. (2013). "A 5E Learning Cycle Approach-based, Multimedia-supplemented Instructional Unit for Structured Query Language." *Journal of Educational Technology & Society* 16(4): 146.

Kilbourne, C. (2010). "Reap the Benefits of Web-based Safety Training." EHS Daily Advisor. http://ehsdailyadvisor.blr.com/2010/01/reap-the-benefits-of-web-based-safety-training/.

Kim, J. H. (2018). "The Effect of Metacognitive Monitoring Feedback on Performance in a Computer-based Training Simulation." *Applied Ergonomics* 67: 193–202.

"LAN vs WAN." (n. d.). Diffen. Accessed September 12, 2016. http://www.diffen.com/difference/LAN_vs_WAN.

Leavoy, P. (2014). "4 Ways Wearable Tech Will Transform EHS Dynamics." LNS Research. Accessed January 21, 2016. http://blog.lnsresearch.com/blog/bid/199852/4-Ways-Wearable-Tech-Will-Transform-EHS-DynamicsLister, J. (n. d.). "Difference between LAN and WAN in Wireless Routers." *Houston Chronicle*. Accessed September 11, 2016. http://smallbusiness.chron.com/difference-between-lan-wan-wireless-routers-73466.html.

Manoukian, J.-G. (2016). "The Technology-enabled Future of EHS." Enablon. https://enablon.com/blog/2016/11/10/the-technology-enabled-future-of-ehs.

Martin, L. (2016). "What Is LAN Used for?" *Houston Chronicle*. http://smallbusiness.chron.com/lan-used-for-26613.html.

Medgate, Inc. (2017). "Mission & Vision." http://www.medgate.com/about-us/mission-and-vision/.

Menus, B. (2015). "Voice over Internet Protocol (VoIP)." Federal Communications Commission. Accessed September 9, 2016. https://www.fcc.gov/general/voice-over-internet-protocol-voip.

Miles, H., S. Pop, S. Watt, G. Lawrence, and N. John. (2012). "A Review of Virtual Environments for Training in Ball Sports." *Computers & Graphics* 36(6): 714–26.

Mohammad, A. R., M.-J. Marija, P. Andrei, and C. Siobhán. (2015). "Middleware for Internet of Things: A Survey." *IEEE Internet of Things Journal* 3(1): 70.

NordSafety. (2017). "The Smart Mobile Solution for HSEQ—NordSafety." https://www.nordsafety.com/.

Patton, S. B. (n. d.). "What Is a Buffer in Electronics?" *The Arizona Republic*. Accessed September 15, 2016. https://yourbusiness.azcentral.com/buffer-electronics-20738.html#.

PC Glossary. (n. d.). PC.net. Accessed September 14, 2016. http://pc.net/glossary/.

Pickel, F. (2014). "Why Is RAM So Important and What Does It Do?" PhoenixTS. Accessed September 15, 2016. http://phoenixts.com/blog/why-is-ram-so-important-and-what-does-it-do/

Pot, J. (2016). "WTF Is FTP? The File Transfer Protocol, Explained." Digital Trends. Accessed September 14, 2016. http://www.digitaltrends.com/computing/what-is-ftp-and-how-do-i-use-it/.

Prasad, D. (2011). "How to Identify Various Ports of an SAP System?" SAP Basis Tutorials. Accessed September 15, 2016. https://sapbasisdurgaprasad.blogspot.com/2011/09/how-to-identify-various-ports-of-sap.html.

Quarks Safety. (2017). "EHS Responsible Chemical Risk and Chemical Products Stock Management: Quarks Safety." http://www.quarks-safety.com/ehs-responsible-chemical-risk-and-chemical-products-stock-management/.

Razzaque, M. A., M. Milojevic-Jevric, A. Palade, and S. Clarke. (2016). "Middleware for Internet of Things: A Survey." *IEEE Internet of Things Journal* 3(1): 70–95.

regAction, Inc. (2017). "regAction—Solutions." Accessed September 12, 2016. http://www.red-gate.com/.

Rouse, M. (2016). "Virtual Private Network (VPN)." SearchNetworking. Accessed September 14, 2016. http://searchenterprisewan.techtarget.com/definition/virtual-private-network.

Rouse, M. (2011). "CAD (Computer Aided Design)." WhatIs.com. Accessed September 12, 2016. http://whatis.techtarget.com/definition/CAD-computer-aided-design.

Rouse, M. (2010). "What Is Portable Document Format (PDF)?" WhatIs.com. Accessed September 12, 2016. http://whatis.techtarget.com/definition/Portable-Document-Format-PDF.

Rouse, M. (2005). "What Is MIME?" SearchMicroservices. Accessed September 13, 2016. http://searchsoa.techtarget.com/definition/MIME

SAI Global, Ltd. (2011). "EHS Management Software—Making the Right Choice for Your Business." https://www.saiglobal.com/compliance/resources/whitepapers/2011-11-EHS-Whitepaper-Buyer-Checklist-Global.pdf.

Santos, J. M. D. (2013). "What Is Web-based Software and How It Can Help Your Team." Project-Management.com. https://project-management.com/what-is-web-based-software-and-cloud-apps/.

SAP SE. (2017a). "About SAP SE." https://www.sap.com/corporate/en.html.

SAP SE. (2017b). "Protect the Health and Safety of Your Employees—and Your Business—with Our EHS Management Software." https://www.sap.com/products/ehs-management-health-safety.html.

SearchWinDevelopment. (2006). "HTTP (Hypertext Transfer Protocol)." Accessed September 7, 2016. http://searchwindevelopment.techtarget.com/definition/HTTP.

Smith, S. (2016). "IoT: Reducing Back Injuries and Costs, Improving Productivity." EHS Today. Accessed January 21, 2016. http://ehstoday.com/construction/iot-reducing-back-injuries-and-costs-improving-productivity.

Smith, S. (2015) "Worker Safety Intelligence at the Edge." EHS Today. http://ehstoday.com/industrial-hygiene/worker-safety-intelligence-edge.

Specialty Technical Publishers. (n. d.). "International EHS Protocols." Accessed September 14, 2016. http://www.stpub.com/publications-global-international-ehs-protocols.

Sweller, J., and P. Chandler. (1994). "Why Some Material Is Difficult to Learn." *Cognition and Instruction* 12(3): 185–233.

Techopedia. (2016). "Extranet." Accessed September 14, 2016. https://www.techopedia.com/definition/2401/extranet.

Techopedia. (2016). "Wide Area Network." https://www.techopedia.com/definition/5409/wide-area-network-wan.

TechTarget. (1999–2016). "Database Management System." http://searchsqlserver.techtarget.com/definition/database-management-system.

Training Industry, Inc. (2017). "Computer-based Training." http://www.trainingindustry.com/taxonomy/c/computer-based-training-%28cbt%29.aspx.

United States Census Bureau. (2016). "Portable Document Format (PDF) Files." Accessed September 15, 2016. http://www.census.gov/main/www/pdf.html.

Upenn. (2016). "What Is a URL?" Accessed September 14, 2016. https://www.cis.upenn.edu/~bcpierce/courses/629/papers/Java-tutorial/networking/urls/definition.html.

Van Overschelde, J. P. (2008). "Metacognition: Knowing about Knowing." In D. Hacker, J. Dunlosky, and A. Graesser (eds.), *Handbook of Metacognition in Education.* New York; Psychology Press, 47–71.

Vogel-Walcutt, J. J., L. Fiorella, and N. Malone. (2013). "Instructional Strategies Framework for Military Training Systems." *Computers in Human Behavior* 29: 1490–98.

WhatIs.com. (n. d.). "Fast Guide to DSL (Digital Subscriber Line)." Accessed September 14, 2016. http://whatis.techtarget.com/reference/Fast-Guide-to-DSL-Digital-Subscriber-Line.

Wiedemann, L. (2008). "Enviance Helping Utilities Meet Pollution Regs." *San Diego Business Journal* 29(30): 6.

William, D. (2016). "What is a GIF?" Small Business Trends. Accessed September 14, 2016. http://smallbiztrends.com/2016/03/what-is-a-gif.html.

# Appendix

## Computer Terminologies

In recent decades, EHS has made some vast improvements and expansions. These improvements have helped to reduce injury rates throughout many fields, which is evidence that safety is making a big difference since the creation of the OSHA Act in 1970. One of the main reasons for these improvements has been the use of technology, which aids the health and safety professionals. EHS professionals typically utilize training modules when a training session is longer than one or two hours. A training module is a specific block of continuous training that is focused on a specific skill or concept. During training sessions, EHS professionals will also utilize simulation models to allow trainees to experience a concept and develop specific skills. In order to achieve an objective, most simulations will use real-life situations. However, there are many other additional tools used within the EHS profession. These types of technologies and software have helped introduce new training techniques, hazard communications, and material handling.

Some of the technologies that have allowed EHS professionals to become connected better in safety are Graphics Interchange Format (GIF), hypertext markup language (HTML), and uniform resource locator (URL). Using these and more, health and safety has been able to expand throughout the Internet so that workers have access to more materials than ever. Health and safety professionals are using these emerging technologies to enhance safety and health processes.

## Terminologies defined

With the rapid expansion of technology and its capabilities, there are copious amounts of technology and platforms that can be used to suit the needs of a variety of EHS professionals.

The American Standard Code for Information Interchange (ASCII) is the combination of 1s and 0s that are assigned to letters, numbers, and characters that can be communicated over various types of computers. This type of program is helpful to EHS professionals because it provides a unique and company-specific way to code and organize information within that system, allowing professionals the ability to create, customize, and quickly recognize the information that is present. Information interchange is required sometimes for importing files because computers are more accustomed to the ASCII format. This makes sharing information easier. In today's world of technology, there are a vast number of devices that exist. Microsoft and Apple use two different word-processing programs. Some devices may not understand the language from one program to the next. ASCII is the language used that all computers understand when displaying information on different devices. This means that Apple and Microsoft (and other computer manufacturers) can coexist. This makes it convenient to train when a variety of devices can be used by trainees to view the information in the programmed training. ASCII is also used in sending and receiving emails. Thus the reason why sharing files using attachments is required—because information that is non-ASCII cannot be viewed on all computers.

Buffers are a necessary component when dealing with technology. Buffers provide a "holding area, enabling the CPU (central processing unit) to manipulate data before transferring it to a device" (Patton n. d.). Having a buffer can create, literally, a buffer when transiting from one processing unit to another to arrange data to suit the user's needs or to just store data that may be needed.

## File Format

In the health and safety work environment, many safety specialists use digital cameras to take pictures of their place of work such as offices, factories, product design, ergonomics, workstations, and so on. These pictures can show safety hazards, safety improvements, examples of safe equipment, and more. There are a variety formats that data files can be saved as, each format different in its application. Pictures and images are typically saved using Tagged Image File Format (TIFF), Joint Photographic Export Group (JPEG), or Graphics Interchange Format (GIF). In the EHS field, it is common to see these types of images in presentations, especially in PowerPoint presentations. This type of graphic can emphasize a statement or illustrate a specific concept or product.

JPEG is the most common way to store and transfer photos/images on the Internet. JPEG files are capable of being stored in cameras and computers. Being able to compress digital photos, store them, and send them easily is important. JPEGs can compress photographs and reduce the size of their storage by 90 percent (Davis 2016). This allows safety workers to store large quantities of photos on their devices. Second, JPEG files make it easier and faster to email pictures due to their small megabyte size. Safety professionals benefit from the use of JPEGs, making it easy to apply pictures to training programs, PowerPoints, and even sending pictures of possible OSHA violations. Most of the online images are saved under the JPEG format because they can be easily opened by most devices, and the size of the file can be kept down (Holmes 2013).

A TIFF is an image file for larger images with varying color depths. It is a commercial and professional image standard for higher-quality images that require editing. TIFF exchanges raster graphics (bitmap) images between programs, including those used for scanner images. While a JPEG image creates a small file in terms of memory, a TIFF image can support much more texture and resolution for more precise viewing. Safety professionals looking to make large signs for the workplace should look at using TIFF images to avoid any distortion while making the file bigger. TIFF images can also be used in training programs to allow easy visuals of the information being distributed. TIFF is supported by Mac, Windows, and UNIX. TIFF format is now part of Adobe software. Microsoft and Hewlett-Packard were among the contributors to the format. TIFF files are commonly used in desktop publishing, faxing, 3-D applications, and medical imaging applications.

GIF is an image file format that is an animated clip or movie. It is produced by combining multiple other images or frames into one single file (William 2016). GIF files are the smallest of all three formats and can be loaded the fastest. However, the color range and quality is limited for this type of format (Holmes 2013).

A Portable Document Format (PDF) allows documents such as articles, images, brochures, PowerPoints, spreadsheets, and so forth to be stored as a file (Rouse 2010). According to the United States Census Bureau (USCB), a PDF is "a self-contained cross-platform document. In plain language, it is a file that will look the same on the screen and in print, regardless of what kind of computer or printer someone is using and regardless of what software package was originally used to create it" (USCB 2012). PDFs are the easiest way to save, store, and send documents while keeping their original format. They are used in the EHS field quite frequently. Many of the documents that OSHA has published are in PDF, making it very convenient for anyone who needs to send, receive, or print published information.

### Design Diagrams

Computer-aided design (CAD) is a program that allows the user to design and draft 2D and 3D models of a variety of products. CAD can be used to help with the envisioning process of a product and can provide measurable figures. Before a product, tool, or machine is put into production, CAD can be used to create multiple models to fix any problems with the prototype before starting production (Rouse 2011). Even though this tool is used by engineers and architects, understanding the use of CAD can be beneficial to an EHS Professional. In EHS, CAD is typically used for troubleshooting areas in a plant that have space restrictions, understanding how a product is assembled, how a product affects the operation of the line and the deadlines that need to be met, and to design a process with safety considerations (prevention through design). CAD replaces hand drafting with an easier process. When CAD is used, safety must be in mind in the process. Hazards must be engineered out to keep things safe. Guard rails for buildings or shields for equipment can all be designed through CAD.

### File Memory

Storing files and data requires a combination of both temporary and permanent computer memory. The temporary memory for virtual software is found in the random access memory (RAM) and is lost after the power is turned off. The long-term, permanent memory is called the read-only memory (ROM). A single safety software program may have to store millions of data files within its ROM.

RAM is one of the most important components of a computer. RAM is useful to EHS professionals for many reasons. RAM is the memory used when applications are loaded from a long-term memory storage device like a hard drive. These applications would be very intermittent if a program ran strictly from a long-term storage device because it takes a lot longer for a computer to find and run from a device, such as a hard drive. RAM takes over the function of these open applications, allowing them to run fluidly with little pause. RAM indicates the speed and overall performance of a computer. Applications require minimum amount of space and memory to be able to run smoothly .With multiple applications open, RAM can be overrun if too much memory is being used. If a computer does not have enough RAM to support all the software systems that are running, then it will run slower, or it could crash (Pickel 2014). When using applications relative to EHS, if these applications run slow or take long to open, upgrading the amount of RAM in your device can substantially help the processing speed, allowing positive workflow.

ROM is the memory in a computer that contains the programming needed to start a computer, and it performs major input/output tasks. It is not edited by the user. It guides your computer through startup, as well as the startup of certain applications. In the field of EHS, ROM would be present not only on the computers a safety professional uses but in a lot of the powered machines a workplace uses. Actions to be performed by a machine, like press down and ignite, can be programmed using ROM. Pressing a specific button would activate ROM to complete a task. ROM retains all its information, even if the power source in removed. It supplies the instructions on how a device communicates with various hardware components.

A buffer is a region in a computer system's memory that temporarily stores data so that it can be transferred from place to place. This is important in computer programming so that different processes can be coordinated together without interfering or slowing down the other processes needed for the program to function. This is utilized by safety professionals when creating certain types of programs. Often found on YouTube videos, the video must buffer or temporarily store video data (commonly referred to as loading) so that it can play without interruption. When using videos in a presentation, to avoid losing participant focus, make sure all videos are buffered before playing them.

## File Sharing

*File Transfer Protocol (FTP)*: File sharing is extremely important regardless of industry because it allows individuals to come together to work on projects and keep everyone updated on current status. File transfer protocol (FTP) is used to share files via a computer network between a client and server. FTP is a convenient way for EHS professionals to transfer files online. FTP programs provide a wide array of directories and subdirectories that allow users to connect to servers and download and upload files (Pot 2016). EHS employees will be able to move information such as safety project files, data, and so forth from their computers to company directories. Even though FTP is not a typical cloud-like program, files and information may still be transferred between colleagues and superiors. There are other cloud-based alternatives to FTP, such as Dropbox, Google Drive, and OneDrive.

*Universal Serial Bus (USB):* A USB is a protocol using devices that can be connected to transfer files. This allows any file from documents to programs to be transferred between computers. USB devices come in a variety of sizes, which will limit the amount of data one can hold. The USB is plugged into the computer and automatically configures to the computer's specifications. Once configured, the user can manage files and drag/drop information from the desktop of the computer directly to the USB. The USB is useful in the field of EHS because documentation is key in the process of safety and health. Any citation, penalty, or record of an injury needs to be kept together by the EHS professional, and a USB can help them bring their files, such as PowerPoint presentations or spreadsheets with safety statistics, with them on the go.

Safety professionals will most often use USB ports for transferring information from place to place.

### Data Management and Navigation

Database management systems (DBMS) are software programs that catalog and retrieve data. They organize incoming data and provide ways for the data to be extracted through other programs. DBMS are used automatically when opening programs and trying to access data for a specific program. Protocol is the set of rules that control communication. Regardless of which protocol a system uses, the data within a program's database is managed through Structured Query Language (SQL). SQL is designed to search through the database and access specific information for the user (Ketpichainarong et al. 2013). A DBMS has many uses. A company can store safety statistics like medical records, innovated concepts, program updates, and other information, like workers' compensation claims and accident/incident information. Storage of training programs can be pulled for certain needs in the workplace.

SQL is one of the ways for updating, deleting, and requesting information from databases. One database product that supports SQL is Microsoft SQL Server. In a distributed database system, a program runs constantly on a server, interpreting the data on multiple servers as a standard database. Programs on client computers allow users to input data using tables, columns, rows, and fields. Client programs send SQL statements to the server. The server then processes these statements and returns result the result.

### Graphical User Interface

A graphical user interface (GUI) is a human–computer interface. "GUI's [sic] allows the use of icons or other visual indicators to interact with electronic devices, rather than using only text via the command line" (Computer Hope 2016). EHS professionals benefit from GUIs due to the fact that GUIs enable them to control, view, and manipulate multiple things at once. A GUI ultimately yields higher productivity while facilitating a lower cognitive load. GUI icons and menus were first found on Apple Macintosh (Mac) and Windows computers (TechTarget 2016). In 1970, Xerox was the first company to develop a GUI. Apple implemented GUIs into their Macintosh computers in 1984, and Windows followed soon after, in 1985 . (LINFO 2004). Without GUIs, safety professionals would not be able to easily research safety programs online and would have to resort to researching books or magazines.

### Email Exchange

Emails are a big part of any workplace. Many safety specialists work around the world. Emails allow them to communicate with other workers from anywhere. Most organizations utilize an application, such as Microsoft Outlook, to manage email accounts, contacts, and scheduling. Outlook is a convenient tool since it allows multiple users to share mailboxes, calendars, meeting schedules, and contact lists. Many companies have their own custom email addresses (e.g., @companyname.com). The purpose of having a custom email address is to help the receiver identify the sender as being affiliated or working for a specific company.

Multipurpose Internet Mail Extensions (MIME) are extensions to the Internet mail standard known as Simple Mail Transfer Protocol (SMTP) (Bharti 2002). MIME allows workers to share multimedia information across the Internet. These include spreadsheets, Word documents, videos, pictures, and so on (Bharti 2002). Hence safety specialists can send training programs, safety programs, safety statistics like graphs and tables, and so forth. Any email attachment that ends in .mim or .mme has been sent using the MIME file format (Rouse 2005).

## Connectivity and Network Technologies

### Domain Name Systems

Domain name systems (DNS) provide different registrations for domain names. These types of domains are used to identify one or more particular Internet Protocol (IP) addresses (Beal 2016). For the EHS professional, this type of system can supply access to specific websites or email accounts. This then makes it possible to search within your browser to find a specific site, making researching for EHS employees more accessible. Having DNS can ensure that companies' documents are secure from unwanted viruses and other unwanted technology troubles that may come their way. Anytime you search the web, you use DNS, which ultimately pulls up the IP address of what you searched (Geier 2015). As said earlier, EHS professionals are always searching for new regulations and standards as well as training programs that will ultimately improve what they currently use. As new technology and new standards come along through the years, companies will need the Internet to help keep up with this. DNS helps ensure that these sites (OSHA, other training sites) are safe to use and protected. Along with DNS, Extranet is a system that allows companies to keep their files and documents secure. Extranet helps companies allow authorized users to access certain information. Safety professionals can utilize this by putting training documentation and other documentation in the extranet file so that only authorized users can see it. For example, OSHA uses an extranet login to authorize certain people to view certain information (DOL 2016). This helps them keep certain information secure virtually, rather than having to use paper documentation in physical secure draws.

### Digital Subscriber Line

Digital subscriber line (DSL) is a type of technology that brings high-bandwidth information to homes and small businesses over copper telephone lines (WhatIs 2016). The technology behind this allows the transmission of data between phone lines and computers. With DSL, an EHS professional will have access to the web either from work or home. DSL has helped organizations advance through the use of the Internet. For example, a company can spend $15 per month with AT&T and receive broadband high-speed DSL Internet (AT&T n. d.). With this, companies can "surf" the OSHA website for standards and regulations. Companies can use DSL Internet to track their chemicals and hazard communication programs through websites like MSDSonline and Site Hawk.

### Extranet

Extranet is a company's intranet with limited access. This controlled, private network allows customers, partners, vendors, suppliers, and other businesses to obtain information on a specific company or institution without granting access to the organization's entire network (Techopedia 2016). For EHS employees, this provides the possibility to exchange data among companies or business partners, which can further expand different collaborations and training processes among these various groups. However, extranet may have some downfalls. If there is ever a breach within the intranet, sensitive information may become compromised, giving access to competitors.

### HyperText Markup Language

HyperText Markup Language (HTML) is the authoring language used to create documents, or pages, in the World Wide Web. It has codes and text that enable Internet browsers such as Google Chrome to read and relay the website content. HTML defines the structure and layout of a web document by using a variety of tags. These tags are commonly used to specify hypertext links, which allow web developers to direct users to other pages with just a simple click of the mouse on either an image or words (Beal 2016). HTML was created in 1989 by Tim Berners-Lee (Computer Hope 2016). HTML can be used to create websites that can be used for training programs. Safety professionals can access OSHA standards, training samples, and contact other safety engineers by using the websites available through HTMLs. With the use of HTML, EHS professionals can assist web developers in creating a webpage for various safety-related pursuits.

### Protocols

Protocols are rules and procedures for communicating. In other words, protocol is a set of algorithms that a sending computer and a receiving computer must follow in order, step by step, to communicate or interact with one another. Computers that follow correct protocol keep the Internet running smoothly and quickly. Without protocol, computers would not be able to connect, send messages, or interact with each other. EHS programs have their own protocols. "EHS protocols are available for jurisdictions worldwide. They include environmental regulations and general safety and health requirements" (STP 2016). EHS protocol is the way health and safety professionals communicate with each other properly. Without proper protocol, it would be very hard for EHS professionals to discuss important details involving safety over the Internet.

### Hypertext Transfer Protocol

Hypertext Transfer Protocol (HTTP) is considered the foundation of data communication for the World Wide Web. HTTP is "the set of rules for transferring files (text, graphic images, sound, video, and other multimedia files) on the World Wide Web" (Rouse 2016). HTTP is a way for clients to request information from a specific web server. HTTP has been improved over the years, with new versions created to improve images when browsing the Internet. HTTP can be used when we access a computer, which links the user to the desired webpage. HTTPs are not secure, so information from websites or the server can be hacked (Term 2016). HTTPs are usually used with uniform resource locators (URL) starting with "www." One way to improve HTTPs is to enforce a security system so that important information does not get stolen.

### HyperText Transport Protocol Secure

HyperText Transport Protocol Secure (HTTPS) secures data as it travels between the server and the client, meaning all communications between one's browser and the website are encrypted. Using HTTPS rather than HTTP will ensure that the website is secure, and any data that is entered will only be recognizable by the computer and the web server. HTTPS gives safety and health professionals a sense of comfort knowing that their personal and financial information cannot be accessed online. HTTPS are used by mortgage companies and banks. They use the URL that starts with "https" (TechTerms 2016). An example of a secure website is https://www.osha.gov.

### Uniform Resource Locator

Uniform Resource Locator (URL) is the reference used to show the address of the website that is being accessed. The URL consists of two parts: the protocol identifier and the resource name. The protocol identifier is used to show which protocol is accessed for information (such as HTTP). The resource name is the complete address of the resource used. This typically consists of four parts: host name (the name of the machine the resource lives on), filename (the pathway to the file in the computer), port number (the port number to connect to), and reference (UPenn 2016). There are many different types of resources you can find through the URL besides the websites. Included are databases, queries, and command input, among others. The URL makes it easy for EHS professionals to access documents and regulations quickly and easily through the Internet.

### Structured Query Language

Structured Query Language (SQL) is the language used mostly to develop dynamic webpages from databases. An EHS professional who is proficient in web design could use these commands to allow different actions to happen each time a webpage loads. Webpages, which are designed for a workplace that might want to get different types of information out on the main page, might use this language so that users could see new ideas each time they load the page, getting more information across than a standard webpage (PC glossary).

### Internet Service Provider

An Internet service provider (ISP) provides customers with Internet access. Each time you connect to the Internet, the connection is routed through an ISP. Health and safety professionals utilize ISPs to communicate with one another through Internet access and telephone services. ISPs also allow professionals to virtually host and build their own websites (Rouse 2016).

### Transmission Control Protocol/Internet Protocol

Transmission Control Protocol/Internet Protocol, or (TCP/IP), is a set of rules governing communications among all computers on the Internet. They dictate how the packets of data should be packaged, sent, and received. They are built into all major operating systems, and this allows the user to communicate over long-distance networks. The IP tells packets where to go and how to get there. IP lets any computer on the

Internet forward a packet to another computer that is closer to the packet's recipient. The TCP is responsible for ensuring transmission of data across the Internet. TCP checks packets for errors and submits requests. The three most common TCP/IP protocols used are HTTP, HTTPS, and FTP. There is a variety of different TCP/IP used in the systems, applications, and products (SAP) software system. Each of these protocols is associated with a SAP port. The two major ports SAP uses are HTTP and HTTPS (Prasad 2011, 3). Basically, this is what allows an EHS professional to communicate information over a network. From sending an email to loading a webpage, these protocols allow you to send and receive information over the Internet. Without these protocols, it would be hard for a safety professional to relay information to workers about hazard communication and would also make electronic training not probable, or a very slow process.

### Voice over Internet Protocol

Voice over Internet Protocol (VoIP) is used to for connecting to a phone network using the Internet connection of your computer. A VoIP can be used to make calls from the Internet. It converts the Internet signal into a phone signal (Menus 2015). Using a VoIP service is useful for users for many reasons, the main reason being that it is much cheaper than getting another phone service. Also, another useful reason to use the VoIP service is because it is much more functional than a normal phone line. If you have a VoIP app installed on a computer, it can be used wherever an Internet connection is available. This makes the VoIP apps useful for anyone on the go, including EHS professionals.

### Virtual Private Network

A virtual private network (VPN) is an encrypted network set up on a lower security network. A VPN is important because they secure a computer's Internet connection to guarantee that all the data that is being sent and received is encrypted and secured (Henry 2012). An application usually can set up this type of network, and it ensures safety of information through the VPN rather than just on the regular network being used. EHS professionals would use VPN for the ease of access that it provides instead of a private connection that can only be used at a certain area (Rouse 2016). The VPN can be set up on any Internet connection and provides a safe and secure area for the user to do his or her work without the possibility of a security risk. This can be useful for EHS professionals because being on the go and doing inspections at different workplaces may not always provide as safe a connection as used in the office or home. The VPN can give an EHS professional security to the data while handling important resources on the field.

### Networks

Two of the most important parts of the VE are local area networks (LAN) and wide area networks (WAN). LAN and WAN were created to link multiple devices together, such as computers, printers, servers, monitors, and so forth.

*Local Area Network*: A LAN is a networking system that connects multiple computers provided by an institution such as a school, workplace, or even a restaurant to each other. LANs can be very helpful in the EHS. Since LANs are usually used to connect computers to a local network via WiFi or Ethernet, EHS professionals can communicate quickly and efficiently in the workplace. LANs are used to link offices together so that every device can work more efficiently. "Devices connected to a LAN are able to access data from any machine that's connected to the network" (Martin 2016). LANs make it possible to connect to devices like printers and fax machines, allowing safety professionals to easily send to other organizations safety policies and requirements that may need some adjustments or tweaks, or even to change their whole safety program.

*Wide Area Network*: A WAN is the connecting network of LAN and Metropolitan area network (MAN) connections throughout a large geographical area (Techopedia 2016). WAN is useful in any industry because communication between professionals is key. Without a WAN connecting the many different LANs in the area, the computers could not share the data that they want to outside of that LAN. EHS professionals need WANs to be set up so that they can transmit and access all the different types of resources needed daily.

CHAPTER 26

# EVOLUTION OF HUMAN FACTORS AND ERGONOMICS IN SAFETY ENGINEERING

Mary Asher, Geena Tacconelli, and Erika Cleary

## Learning Objectives

After studying this chapter, the reader will be able to:

1. Describe early examples of ergonomic principles seen in ancient civilizations
2. Explain the history of human factors and ergonomics (HFE) in America from the premodern period to the fully modern era
3. Define musculoskeletal disorder (MSD) and how human factors and ergonomics (HFE) plays a role in reducing risks
4. Examine cultural design considerations for international ergonomic needs
5. Describe the different HFE challenges for developed and developing countries
6. Identify and explain the different HFE specialties

## Key Terms

**Human factors, ergonomics, job hazard analyses, Taylorism, ergonomic design, human factors engineering, musculoskeletal disorders, anthropometry, safety engineering**

## Abstract

The purpose of this chapter is to describe the development of human factors and ergonomics (HFE) throughout the years as well as explore the field of HFE. Ergonomics, also known as HFE, is simply the study of work. Ergonomics integrates different scientific disciplines, such as physiology, biomechanics, psychology, anthropometry, industrial hygiene, and kinesiology (OSHA 2000). The history of HFE can be traced back as early as the Neolithic period, and it has evolved over time into a multifaceted discipline. There are now a variety of HFE specialties and branches. These include biomechanics, industrial ergonomics, safety, system design/development, training, aging, human functions, and visual performance. HFE challenges include obesity, the aging population, and the labor-intensive nature of production in industrially developing countries (IDCs). The ergonomic design process must meet these challenges and strive for inclusivity.

## Introduction to Human Factors and Ergonomics (HFE)

Forcing a worker's body to fit the job has long been known to cause problems for the worker, particularly musculoskeletal disorders (MSDs). Musculoskeletal disorders are soft tissue and nervous system disorders mainly affecting the arms and backs of humans. In an effort to protect workers against MSDs, it has become common to implement a comprehensive ergonomics program in the workplace. Ergonomics, also known as human factors engineering, is simply defined as the study of work. The Occupational Safety and Health Administration (OSHA) defines ergonomics as "the science of designing the job to fit the worker, rather than physically forcing the worker's body to fit the job" (OSHA 2000). Fitting the task to the worker helps decrease muscle fatigue, reduce the frequency and the severity of MSDs, and increases overall productivity for the task (OSHA, n.d. a).

Ergonomics integrates different scientific disciplines such as physiology, biomechanics, psychology, anthropometry, industrial hygiene, and kinesiology (OSHA 2000). With the integration of the aforementioned disciplines, best-practice ergonomic tools and programs have been developed. Once developed to be workplace-specific, an effective ergonomics management system can reduce or eliminate strain and injury to the muscles, nerves, ligaments, tendons, and blood vessels. This is accomplished through the effective design of a workplace that limits repetitive motion, awkward and stationary postures, heavy or awkward lifting, use of excessive force, and exposure to extreme conditions, temperatures, or vibration. With the reduction in these types of risk factors, the incidence of MSDs will decrease. Common workplace MSDs include carpal tunnel syndrome, tendinitis, rotator cuff injuries, epicondylitis, trigger finger, muscle strains, and lower back injuries. MSDs are common issues in the workplace today despite the fact that research and technology are available for the reduction and elimination of these disorders. In fact, according to the Bureau of Labor Statistics (BLS), MSDs are one of the most common causes of lost or restricted work time; in 2013 MSDs accounted for 33 percent of worker injury and illness cases (OSHA n.d. a).

An effective ergonomics management system can reduce or eliminate strain and injury to the muscles, nerves, ligaments, tendons, and blood vessels.

### Ergonomics Management System

In order for an ergonomics management system to successfully reduce MSDs and contribute to the overall wellbeing of employees and the success of the workplace/business, there are seven key components that must be implemented. These include management support, involvement of workers, training, problem identification, early reporting of symptoms, implementation of solutions, and progress evaluation (OSHA n.d. a). Gaining management support is crucial in the implementation of any type of safety program/system. Organizational management should set clear and defined goals for the system, communicate the importance and direction clearly to workers, and assign ergonomic responsibilities to staff who are best educated to handle the responsibilities. Providing opportunities for workers to be directly involved in tasks, like jobsite assessments and the development and implementation of recommendations, are effective means of building a successful ergonomics program. Specifically, workers can identify and provide feedback about ergonomic risk factors at their respective jobsite/workstation and recommend improvements as a follow up to changes implemented. Proper organizational structure and the establishment of effective safety policies, to include well-designed training programs for the workforce, are essential to ensuring that workers are engaged with hazard identifications and corrective actions.

The training should be specific to the job type, such as recognizing ergonomic risk factors, the use of appropriate control techniques, effective communication with the workers on the benefits of the ergonomics program, and the importance of reporting signs of MSDs as soon as they are recognized. Problem identification, job hazard analyses (JHA), and ergonomic risk assessments are all key elements in preventing the occurrence of MSDs. Without problem identification, JHA, and risk assessments, the progression of MSDs could only be slowed after onset, not prevented. Proper identification and assessment of each task that may present an ergonomic issue for the worker should be conducted in the form of a JHA or similar method. To keep the ergonomics management system running and effective, evaluation and, if need be, corrective action should be conducted on a regularly scheduled basis. This process will aid in the continuous improvement of the management system and determine if newly implemented engineering or administrative controls are effective (OSHA n.d. a).

> Problem identification, job hazard analyses (JHA), and ergonomic risk assessments are all key elements in preventing the occurrence of MSDs.

## Ergonomic Controls

Traditionally the hierarchy of ergonomic controls begins with elimination, substitution, and engineering controls (OSHA n.d. b). If engineering controls are not suitable, then administrative controls may be considered, and if neither are an option, as a last resort, personal protective equipment (PPE) would be utilized. Engineering controls are used to physically change things in the workplace to reduce or eliminate the task-specific hazard. Examples of engineering controls include using a device to lift a heavy object to reduce force exertion and repositioning a work table to eliminate work in awkward postures and excessive reaching. Administrative controls are those controls that establish effective processes/procedures. Examples of these controls include employee training, requiring two people to lift heavy loads, establishing a work rotation system that focuses on different muscle groups and minimizes repetitive motions and awkward postures, and allowing additional breaks between the normal scheduled breaks. PPE is used to reduce exposure to ergonomic hazards and risk factors. Some ergonomic PPE includes padding that decreases the amount of contact with vibrating or hard surfaces and thermal gloves that reduce exposure to cold temperature while still allowing workers to easily grasp items (OSHA n.d. b).

In recent years, a slightly different model has been developed regarding the descending order of controls. This model is based off the idea that if the hazard is addressed earlier in a process, such as the design phase, addressing the hazard will be less costly and more feasible, and the entire process will be overall more effective. See the descending order of controls below:

a. Eliminate hazard through design selection: Ideally, the risk of a hazard should be eliminated. This is often done by selecting a design alternative that removes the hazard altogether.
b. Reduce mishap risk through design alteration: If the risk of a hazard cannot be eliminated by adopting an alternative design, design changes should be considered that reduce the severity or the probability of a harmful outcome.
c. Incorporate engineered safety features (ESF): If unable to eliminate or adequately mitigate the risk of a hazard through a design alteration, reduce the risk using an ESF that actively interrupts the mishap sequence.
d. Incorporate safety devices: If unable to eliminate or adequately mitigate the hazard through design or ESFs, reduce mishap risk by using protective safety features or devices.
e. Provide warning devices: If design selection, ESFs, or safety devices do not adequately mitigate the risk of a hazard, include a detection and warning system to alert personnel to the presence of a hazardous condition or occurrence of a hazardous event.
f. Develop procedures and training: Where other risk reduction methods cannot adequately mitigate the risk from a hazard, incorporate special procedures and training. Procedures may prescribe the use of personal protective equipment. (US Department of Defense 2005)

This model can be used in a workplace to achieve acceptable risk levels. Each step should be considered in descending order, starting with eliminating the hazard, to effectively move down the hierarchy of controls to mitigate or quantify the hazard as an acceptable risk (Manuele 2008).

## History of Human Factors and Ergonomics

### Ancient History

The history of HFE dates back as early as the Neolithic period. HFE history begins with the use of tools (Brennan 1999). From the beginning, it can be inferred that there have always been challenges in matching the human to the tool (Meister 1999). Despite the science of ergonomics emerging as a discipline in the twentieth century, evidence suggests that ergonomic principles were known and followed more than twenty-five centuries ago (Marmaras et al. 1999). Origins of HFE can be traced back to primitive societies that learned tool manufacturing relative to specific jobs, which therefore expanded the possibilities of the human body. Archeological findings indicate that from the second interglacial period, the improvements in tools were made for handling convenience and for the adaptability to the human body. In prehistoric times, convenience as well as a correspondence to human needs were vital for survival—a poor weapon maker would not survive. Specifically selected pebbles, scoops made from bone, and tools and utensils were the result of distinct, intelligent reactions to the interaction between humans and the environment (Moray 2005).

Despite the science of ergonomics emerging as a discipline in the twentieth century, evidence suggests that ergonomic principles were known and followed more than twenty-five centuries ago.

### Ancient Sri Lankan Lumbar-Supported Seats

In the United States, HFE was not a major consideration until World War II; however, ergonomic principles can be observed in some ancient societies centuries before. In South Asia, ergonomically designed seats which predate World War II by about 1,500 years were found in ancient island Sri Lanka. Ergonomic seats appeared early in Sri Lanka and further progressed in design over a span of three to four centuries. Ergonomically designed stone seats were found in and around Sri Lanka's first capital city, Anuradhapura. The fifth century CE Sigiriya palace fortress had two stone seats with lumbar support that curved where the spine arches. At this stage, the seats were semicircular and convex. A Buddhist meditation monastery that dates to the eighth and tenth centuries had buildings with ergonomically carved stone seats as well. Furthermore, in a tenth century CE temple, a stone seat with lumbar-hugging characteristics was found near a monk assembly hall. These examples portray the evolution of lumbar seats in Sri Lanka from fifth century CE to their final spine-hugging form in the eighth to tenth centuries CE (Goonatilake 2014). Seat contouring, such as that described, is used to distribute pressure over a larger area and rotate the pelvis forward, promoting better posture (Stensland n.d.). These ergonomic developments likely occurred because Buddhists considered the mind and body intertwined, which enabled its practitioners to appreciate proper posture. Due to Buddhist beliefs, the world's first ergonomically designed seats that we know of came to fruition (Goonatilake 2014).

### Ancient Greek Ergonomic Principles

The ancient Greeks had keen focus on ergonomic principles. Ancient Greek design was human-centered, and the Greeks were knowledgeable of human characteristics and utilized said characteristics for the purpose of design (Marmaras et al. 1999). Substantial evidence shows that Hellenic civilization in the fifth century BCE used ergonomic principles when designing tools, jobs, and workplaces (Oluwafemi 2012). "Man is the measure of all things" is the translation of an apothegm by the famous Greek Philosopher Plato and serves as the theoretical basis for ancient Greek design being human-centered (Marmaras et al. 1999). The names and magnitudes of measurements for length came from the human body: finger, forearm, and foot are all examples of accepted measurements of length. This measuring system meant that many building elements were proportional to the human body (Marmaras et al. 1999). The rules of proportion for columns were based on the human body as the accepted model of strength (Coulton 1997). For example, the height of temple columns was eight times the diameter of their base. This ratio is similar to the relation between a tall woman's height and foot length (Marmaras et al. 1999). Human-centered design is also evident when examining burial practices. Ancient Greeks put personal objects and utensils in graves that matched the age of the deceased: miniature objects for babies, small objects for children, and regular-sized objects for adults.

"Man is the measure of all things" is the translation of an apothegm by the famous Greek Philosopher Plato and serves as the theoretical basis for ancient Greek design being human-centered

Formal consideration of the interactions between people and their work environments can be found in ancient Greek writings (Wilson 2000). A remarkable example is Hippocrates's (the father of medical science) description of a surgeon's workplace design (Oluwafemi 2012). Hippocrates recommended that surgeons may stand or sit depending on the type of operation, but the surgeon must always adopt the most comfortable posture. Regarding tools, he stated that they had to be placed near the operating hand of the surgeon in such a way as to not obstruct movement (National Technical University of Athens 2006). This is similar to ergonomic principles today that state that arms and hands should be in a position to easily reach objects that are used frequently (Marras and Karwowski 2006). Workload minimization was also utilized during construction. Marble was the main material used for important buildings, which is difficult and heavy to manipulate (Marmaras et al. 1999). Techniques to reduce this workload included sculpting at ground level, which decreased the weight of the marble blocks during transportation. Additionally, sledges and carriages pulled by animals or workers were utilized. When marble blocks had to be lifted to the top of hills, a heavy-duty pulley was used. Furthermore, the tools used to sculpt marble came in various shapes and sizes; the metal parts of select tools were also harder and more efficient than those used today. Hand drills utilized a sawing movement, which is arguably just as comfortable, if not more, as the circular movement necessary for modern hand drills (Marmaras et al. 1999).

In the ancient Greek home, everyday objects, such as pots for cooking, were designed with ergonomic principles in mind. Pots were designed for ease of use, task fitness, and minimization of the user's effort. Various different shapes and sizes were used depending on the use of the pot and body size of the user. Pot handles are a particular example of the ergonomic concern for the time period. For example, the bi-handled bronze urn was used as a water container. One handle was positioned at the neck of the urn, near the point of water flow. A second handle was horizontally placed at the bottom. The upper handle allowed fine control over the flow of liquid while the lower one allowed the necessary force to lift the water container, utilizing the power grip (National Technical University of Athens 2006). Neither hand had to exercise both force and accuracy. This bronze urn dates back to the sixteenth century BCE. The clay urn from the eighth century BCE has three handles. Two horizontally opposed handles were in the middle of the urn's body, and the third was vertically placed in the middle of the urn's body. When the urn was full of liquids, two hand lifts utilized the horizontal handles. When empty, the urn could be used by lifting the vertical handle; this handle could also be used for handling the urn when carried on the shoulder.

For entertainment outside of the home, ancient Greeks attended the theater. Construction details of theaters point to concern for ergonomic design. The bench seats had an inward curve to fit the shape of the lower leg. This facilitated idle movements of feet during the performance, which increased blood circulation and prevented numbness. Additionally, the lower part of the foot was supported farther back, providing leverage to stand up easily despite the lack of hand rests

Pots were designed for ease of use, task fitness, and minimization of the user's effort.

(Marmaras et al. 1999). Through these examples, it is demonstrated that ancient Greeks utilized various ergonomic principles.

### Modern Period and HFE

Starting in the Middle Ages, production of swords, armory, and other weaponry took into consideration the anthropometry of warriors. This also demonstrates the relationship between military and ergonomics, which is still relevant today. Prior to World War II, to fit the human to the machine required trial-and-error approaches. Either the human was able to function with the machine, or the human could not and was then rejected. This process was ongoing until a successful candidate was selected. During the American Civil War, there was a shift in concern for the human in a technological context. There was concern with ensuring that mass-produced uniforms and guns fit soldiers and that soldiers were able to use the newly designed weaponry (Meister 1999). *Hunley* was a submarine used by the Confederate States of America. Its developer considered what could be referred to as primitive human factors when designing the submarine. Men who were shorter than average with greater than average strength were needed for the submarine. However, this is an example of fitting the human to the machine, and no efforts to design the machine to fit the human were made. This machine dominance when considering human and machine operations would reign for many years (Meister 1999).

#### Taylorism

A major turning point for HFE was the rise of Taylorism, or the scientific study of the worker. Taylorism attempted to increase human efficiency in the workplace. Characteristics of Taylorism include time and motion studies, strict division of labor, detailed preplanning, and specific job and task descriptions (Bjorkman 1996). In 1898, Taylor reconfigured an ingot-loading task at a steel-producing company named Bethlehem Steel by modifying selection, training, and work-rest schedules; the result was moving 47.5 tons of steel per worker versus the 12.5 tons each worker moved before. Of significance, Taylor developed and employed data collection and statistical analysis methods close to those used by HFE professionals today. It has also been suggested that Taylor's principles of work design and time and motion studies are the basis for today's task analysis methods (Meister 1999). Taylor's main work was *Principles of Scientific Management*, a book published in 1911 (Caldari 2007). Despite these gains, Taylorism also led to poor work conditions marked by fatigue, monotony, and poor utilization of worker capabilities because Taylorism relied on the principle of "one best way" (Salvendy 2012). To find the one best way, Taylor proposed these time studies to discover the most efficient way to execute each motion and to distinguish best conditions, machines, tools, and more. The one best way was not always best for the worker. The essence of Taylorism is minute division of labor, repetition of simple movement, predetermined methods of work, minimum training requested, incentive of a merely monetary nature, time optimization for each operation, and high production above everything—including the workers' needs (Caldari 2007).

#### American HFE: World War I

With World War I came more development of sophisticated technology; for example, modernized aircrafts called "fighters" were introduced (Meister 1999). Looking back at early military aviation, many aircrew were lost from what can be called human performance issues and individual deficiencies. This highlights the importance of selecting the appropriate worker for hazardous tasks. Therefore, identifying physical and psychological characteristics of successful aviators became a large focus (Shorrock and Williams 2017). Aviation psychology was of particular interest during this period. The first tests to predict flying aptitude were developed, and the first psychological testing center for the military was established in 1915 for selection of motor transport drivers. Tests were used to select pilots, detector operators, and anti-aircraft gunners (Meister 1999).

#### American HFE: World War II

The start of World War II in 1939 brought upon a large need to allocate workers and their skills to the most appropriate jobs needed for the war effort (Shorrock and Williams 2017). With the United States's involvement in World War II came extraordinary advancements in technology. Highly advanced aircrafts were developed, and pilots with complex physical and mental skills were needed to operate these aircrafts. Additionally, radar and photographic systems required specialized perceptual skills, and sonar technology required individuals with the ability to discriminate pitch exceptionally well. However, with the sheer number of individuals participating in the war, it was impractical to only select a few specialized individuals to fit an existing job. Equipment design now had to take advantage of human capabilities and avoid negative effects of human limitations (Meister 1999). A study by Fitts and Jones (1947) aimed to establish the most effective configuration of control knobs to be used in aircraft cockpits. Research was also conducted by Wright Field to determine human tolerance limits for high-altitude bailout, automatic parachute operating devices, breathing equipment, and more. This type of research allowed for psychologists to work with design engineers to utilize HFE research. Slowly, as psychologists and engineers worked together, applied experimental psychology started to transition to HFE (Meister 1999). Immediately following the war, the office of Naval Research sponsored a text on human engineering authored by Chapanis, Garner, and Sanford in 1947 that was developed into the first text describing the new discipline of HFE for general use in 1949 (Meister 1999). Due to the practical problems of using military equipment in World War II, HFE was officially recognized as a discipline in 1949 (Rutherford 2013). In the United States, human factors were developing with input from both psychology and engineering (Gainer 2008).

Due to the practical problems of using military equipment in World War II, HFE was officially recognized as a discipline in 1949.

## American HFE: Post–World War II

The technological development beginning in World War II continued after the war. A number of questions were raised regarding human performance that led to the need for continued research. In 1953, the Department of the Army established the Human Engineering Laboratory, presently known as the Human Research Laboratory. Additionally, each of the service branches developed human performance research laboratories during or immediately after World War II. A majority of human factors research at this time was military sponsored. Studies performed took into consideration larger equipment, workstations, or entire systems for the first time in American history.

In the civilian industry, numerous large organizations in aviation established human factors groups as part of their engineering organization. Electronics and communications also employed HFE professionals. An example is Bell Laboratories, which established a human factors group in 1946. The group worked with designers on topics such as the layout of keys for telephone handsets (Meister 1999). The group was characterized by an empirical approach relying heavily on laboratory and field simulation (Hanson 1983). Post-war research began to expand into industries, such as space systems, consumer products, industrial and office settings, and computer systems (Gaddy et al. 2017). With the introduction of HFE to industry, there was a transition from a research-oriented discipline to HFE being an interactive, integral element of system design. Thus, there became a division between HFE research and those who participated in application work (Meister 1999).

The US government awarded human performance research contracts to departments of psychology and industrial engineering in universities throughout the country. To bid on said contracts, private companies were formed, and these companies employed many HFE professionals. This research was for profit, and it led to maturation of the discipline. During World War II, human-technology relationships were overlooked at the fundamental state; due to government-sponsored research, the opportunity to explore human-technology on a fundamental level was now possible. An example is task analysis, which was developed by R. B. Miller under contract in 1953 (Meister 1999). Task analysis was popularized within psychological and ergonomics communities by R. B. Miller; he believed that all task investigations should start by breaking down a complex task into a series of subtasks or task elements (Karwowski 2006). Various activities during this period led to the number of HFE professionals growing from a small number during World War II to over 5,000 professionals. The connection that was only vaguely anticipated during World War II is now fully recognized (Meister 1999).

> With the introduction of HFE to industry, there was a transition from a research-oriented discipline to HFE being an interactive, integral element of system design. Thus, there became a division between HFE research and those who participated in application work.

### American HFE: 1965 to the Present

The fully modern era started after the 1960s with the development of computers and automation and the integration of social science and ergonomics-human factors as it is currently known. The ergonomics discipline is accepted in a number of industries and internationally when considering the regulation of safety and health (Moray 2008). In the United States, a major milestone showing commitment to ergonomics was the development of the MANPRINT Program, which focused on integrating human element for the military in the 1980s. The goal of the MANPRINT program was to demonstrate the integration of manpower, personnel capabilities, and training efforts early in the design process would make a huge impact on the development of new systems (Savage-Knepshield et al. 2014). Work on modeling continuous human-machine systems continued on with the development of Optimal Control Theory in 1970, which laid the framework for detailed real-time prediction of control of surface vehicles, aircrafts, and ships. Now, there are a large number of models of both quantitative and qualitative nature that are available that did not exist at the start of the 1960s (Moray 2008).

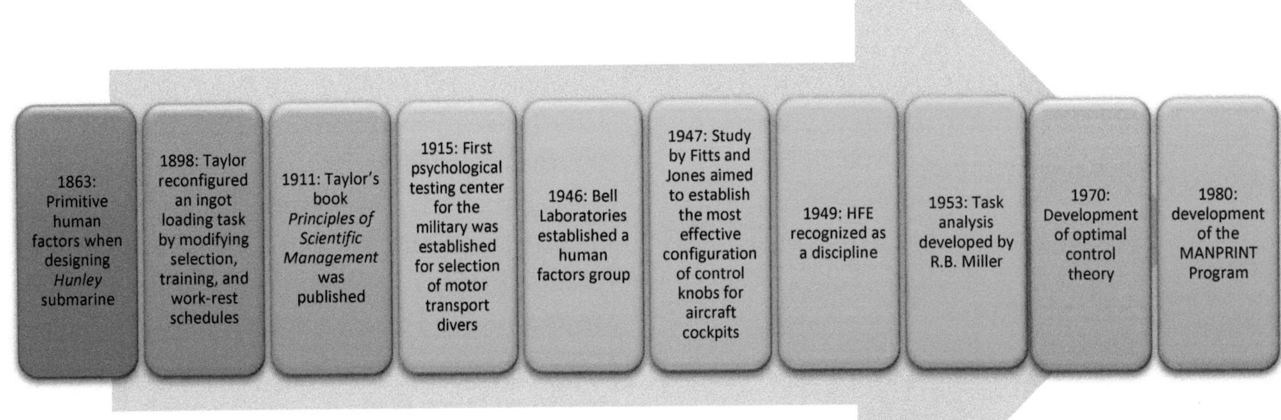


Figure 26.1
Timeline of HFE American history

## International and Cultural Ergonomics

### HFE Design Considerations

Cultural ergonomics investigate variations based on interactions and experiences among cultures (Lin et al. 2016). The research, design, and evaluation of inclusive ergonomic systems and technologies in global contexts are necessary to find the needs of all workers. Those living in industrialized and affluent nations, including North America, Europe, and Australia, have been the primary focus of ergonomic design, excluding minority populations in industrialized and developing nations (Smith-Jackson et al. 2014). It is paramount for ergonomists and engineers to understand the importance of cultural differences in the design phase that impact the preferences and user requirements of all workers.

When designing ergonomic products for international populations, the following items should be considered: language, anthropometry, climate, and cognition (Smith-Jackson et al. 2014). Translating from the original language into other predominant languages in each location where the organization wants to deliver the product or service should be considered to avoid any misinterpretations. Anthropometry is a study which deals with body dimensions (size, shape, strength, and working capacity) for design purposes and can help individuals work comfortably and reduce MSDs (Taifa and Desai 2017). Anthropometry varies between citizens of different countries worldwide and should be considered when designing ergonomic products. Hot and cold climates also need to be a factor in the design stage because individuals conducting work in cold climates may have less tactile sensitivity and motor coordination due to the use of gloves. Finally, cognition must be considered when designing ergonomic products and services because cognitive differences materialize from cultural differences in experiences, education, and training worldwide.

### HFE Challenges in Developed and Developing Countries

Factors influencing HFE in developing countries differ from those in developed or industrialized countries. Increasing obesity prevalence in developed countries along with the aging population has proven to be a challenge for HFE due to these individuals being less capable of performing normal work. These personal factors increase the risk for musculoskeletal injury, fatigue, and psychological strain due to the higher prevalence of metabolic disorders and sedentary lifestyles of these demographic populations (Bridger 2012).

Increasing obesity prevalence in developed countries along with the aging population has proven to be a challenge for HFE due to these individuals being less capable of performing normal work.

The ergonomic needs of the aging population and the obese population must be considered to ensure health and safety for these worker demographics, especially in industrialized nations due to the increased prevalence of these issues. According to the US Department of Labor, workers aged 45 to 55 compose 44 percent of the workforce, and more than 1 in 5 workers is over the age of 55 (Lassila 2017). See figure 26.2 for the projected change in the US civilian workforce between 2016 and 2026 for selected age groups.

It is projected that between 2016 and 2026, the percent of workers 55 and older will increase by 17.9 percent and the percent of workers 75 and older will increase by 91.5 percent (BLS 2017). These projections stress the need to accommodate the aging population in the workplace.

Since older workers experience physical changes, including decreased aerobic capacity, flexibility, dexterity, and overall strength, ergonomics plays a crucial role in ensuring the safety and health of the aging population (Fox et al. 2015). Established ergonomic principles already consider the aging worker by including guidelines for manual materials handling and repetitive motion. It is advised that older workers be given jobs that involve working in neutral postures and jobs that allow for frequent posture changes to reduce musculoskeletal strain (Middlesworth n.d. b). It is also advised that physically demanding jobs be engineered out and hazard

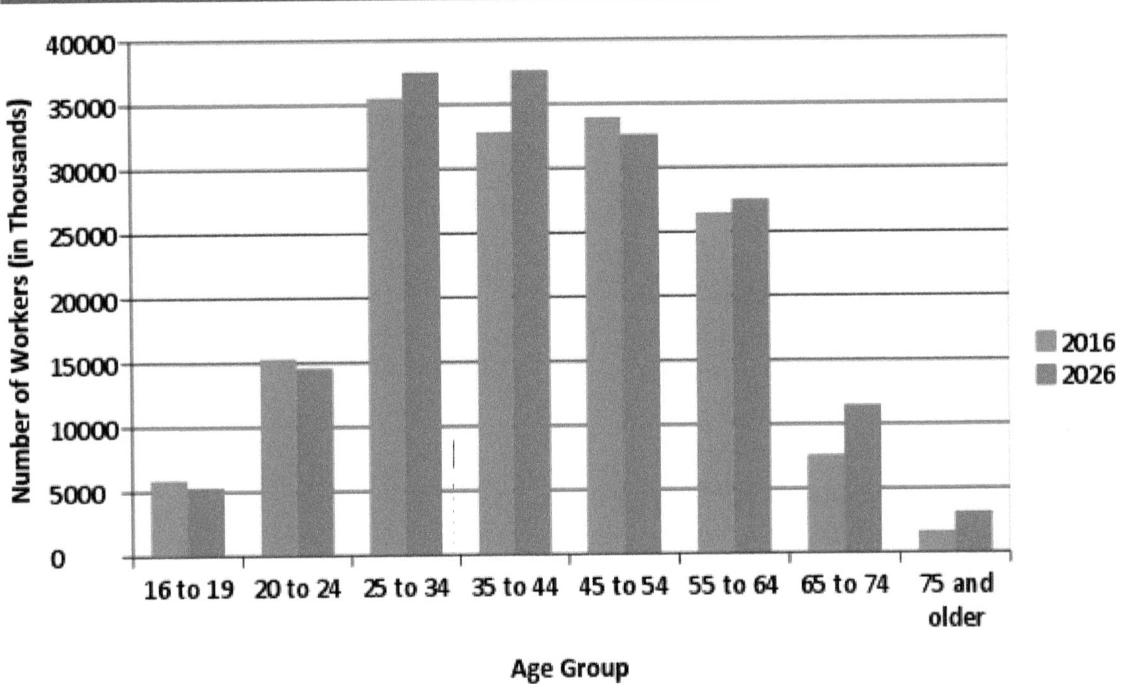


Figure 26.2
Civilian labor force by age. Source: Bureau of Labor Statistics (BLS) 2017.

recognition training be employed to ensure workers, supervisors, and engineers can identify and correct injury hazards in the workplace.

Obesity is a prevalent epidemic worldwide that shows no signs of slowing, which is exacerbated by the sedentary nature of occupational sitting in modern offices. Data recently collected from the National Health and Nutrition Examination Survey (NHANES) show that 35 percent of US adults (78 million) were obese in 2011–2012, with approximately 40 percent of middle-aged (40–59) adults in the obese category (Gu et al. 2016). Table 26.1 illustrates injury prevalence during the past 3 months (at time of questionnaire) and the mean BMI of those that participated in the National Health Interview Survey (NHIS) from 2004–2012. This increasing public health issue stresses the need to apply ergonomic approaches to address this challenge in the workplace.

Obesity leads to increased sick leave and workplace injuries, which increases health care costs, ultimately impacting the performance and productivity of an organization (Cavuoto and Nussbaum 2014). Therefore, consideration is needed to redesign the work to account for the needs of the increasingly obese workforce. To control ergonomic risks for the overweight and obese workforce, the following design considerations are recommended: appropriate chairs, workstations, anti-fatigue mats, and sit/stand workstations (Middlesworth n.d. a). Additionally, weight and placement of material should be evaluated to reduce overhead and forward reaching, along with low-level lifting. When engineering controls are not practical, job rotation should be considered to reduce prolonged static work and accommodate the needs of overweight or obese employees (Buckle and Buckle 2011).

Due to the labor-intensive nature of production in industrially developing countries (IDCs), ergonomics education and practices often focus on physical ergonomics, along with a conscious improvement of working conditions (Bridger 2012). The influx of new information and communications technology in IDCs offers new opportunities for ergonomics research. However, these countries often lack the research capacity needed to build and implement ergonomic solutions needed to find new and better ways to deliver

Table 26.1 Prevalence of injury during the last three months by obesity category

| BMI | Workers | | Injury | |
|---|---|---|---|---|
| | No. at risk (=participants) | % | No. of injured workers | % of total (no. at risk) |
| Normal (18.5–<25) | 51,310 | 36.3 | 319 | 0.62 |
| Overweight (25.0–<30) | 51,879 | 36.7 | 417 | 0.80 |
| Obese I (30–<35) | 23,901 | 17.0 | 232 | 0.97 |
| Obese II (35+) | 14,145 | 10.0 | 152 | 1.07 |

Source: Gu et al. 2016

basic services in the workplace. Because of this need, the International Ergonomics Association (IEA) was founded to promote ergonomic education, research, and practices in developing countries mainly in Asia, Central and Latin America, and the Baltic countries (Caple 2012). The IEA helps to support research projects in these countries by advancing the practice of ergonomics internationally and enhancing the ergonomics contribution to the global society (IEA 2017).

## HFE and Technology

### Technology and Emerging HFE Risks

With the global societal needs for production constantly changing from more agricultural to service economies, equipment needs are changing. Additionally, the use of computers, cell phones, and other similar electronic devices has greatly increased both at work and at leisure globally. Along with the use of computers and other technologies at a workstation, the computer chair and desk are integral parts as well. An uncomfortable workstation can cause health and productivity issues. Discomfort caused by improper sitting positions can lead to musculoskeletal pain in the neck, shoulders, lower back, wrists, and legs, along with reduced productivity caused by these discomforts (Workineh and Yamaura 2016). Greater stress on the importance of how increased technology usage can impact ergonomics and human health is needed to reduce risk at work and at leisure.

Increased concerns over MSDs related to computer use have led to the development of standards for computer workstation design, including the International Organization for Standardization *ISO-9241* adopted in Europe, Australian Standard *AS-3590.2* adopted in Australia, Canadian Standard *Can/CSA-Z412-M89* adopted in Canada, and the American Standard *ANSI/HFES-100* adopted in the United States. These standards generally incorporate the following requirements and best practices for computer workstations: sitting posture, monitor position, seat requirements (including seat pan height, width, depth, and tilt angle), backrest requirements (height, width, and tilt angle), lumbar support requirements, armrest requirements (height, length, and width), work surface requirements (height and area), and leg space requirements (Woo et al. 2016).

The use of standing workstations has increased over recent years to reduce the amount of time sitting at work. There is evidence showing that high levels of overall sitting time are linked to adverse health outcomes, including type 2 diabetes, cardiovascular diseases, some cancers, and depression (Coenen et al. 2017). Reducing seated work and frequently rotating between sitting and standing can reduce discomfort and increase performance in the workplace (Callaghan et al. 2015). However, changing from sitting to standing does not completely eliminate musculoskeletal issues from sedentary work. Although there are existing OSHA guidelines for sitting computer workstations and general standing work, there are no specific guidelines for standing office computer work. Therefore, developing guidelines in the future oriented toward standing office computer work will help to reduce workplace discomfort.

There is evidence showing that high levels of overall sitting time are linked to adverse health outcomes, including type 2 diabetes, cardiovascular diseases, some cancers, and depression.

Considering the increased usage in recent years, there is limited research in the long-term effects of tablet usage and ergonomic recommendations or guidelines have not been developed to ensure the safety and health of tablet users. When using a tablet computer, head and neck flexion angles are greater than those typically occurring the use of a desktop or laptop computer (Vasavada et al. 2015). This increased flexion can cause the neck muscles to experience fatigue, which often results in increased reports of neck pain. Additionally, studies suggest that typing on a tablet may lead to more extended and less ulnar-deviated wrist postures than typing on a laptop computer. Awkward wrist postures (wrist extensions over 30 degrees or ulnar deviation over 15 degrees) are considered problematic because it increases carpal tunnel pressures (Lin et al. 2015). Therefore, ergonomic recommendations for tablet usage must be created in the future.

Another growing technology that may cause ergonomic concerns is touchscreens. Touchscreen interfaces are used every day on smartphone mobile devices, tablets, and computers. Interactions with computer touchscreens requires movements of the entire arm without hand or arm support, which is more than just finger and wrist movements required for mobile device use (Kang and Shin 2017). Studies have found that placing touchscreens lower reduces arm elevation but results in increased neck flexion to look down at the screen. However, when the computer touchscreen interface is placed at worker's level, neck flexion is reduced, but greater arm elevation is needed to reach the computer screen. Along with computer touchscreens, mobile touchscreen usage can present ergonomic risks, particularly on the right thumb. Increased thumb movement results in fatigue in the muscle abductor pollicis longus (APL) at a fast speed (Xiong and Muraki 2014). With the growing use of devices with touchscreen interface, there is a greater concern for ergonomic risks associated with these devices.

## Technology and HFE Risk Reduction

Advances in technology over several decades have helped to reduce ergonomic risks in the workplace. For example, industrial robots in manufacturing environments have been used to conduct repetitive and monotonous assembly steps. Although humans are not able to share their workspace with robots due to the hazards associated with the equipment, there are still opportunities for direct collaboration with humans and robots (Scholer et al. 2015). Robot velocity and acceleration, robot size, and distance between robot and human are considered in human-robot interactions (HRI) to ensure safety of the worker (Trzcieliński and Karwowski 2013). Overall, the use of robot systems results in higher efficiency in the workplace and enhanced ergonomics by reducing the need for humans to perform repetitive motions and manual materials handling.

Surface electromyography (sEMG) is an important tool and new technology that can be used for the evaluation of risks related to work activity. This technique can be used to quantify muscular involvement and force, along with fatigue and evaluate the strain of tendons or ligaments, which is useful in the design of ergonomic workstations, improvement of assembly lines, and the prevention of MSDs (Gazzoni

2010). A study by Ohu et al. (2016) of ergonomic impact on grocery store workers during stocking activities using normalized sEMG data found that the highest muscle force groups were erector spinae and the triceps, while muscle activations on erector spinae were reduced when a mobile cart was used to perform job duties. The use of this technology to detect ergonomic risks can help to identify and eliminate potential causes of musculoskeletal accidents that have huge financial impacts on organizations and impacts on employee safety and health.

## Specializations

Because human factors engineers have such a broad range of work duties they may participate in, there are areas that a human factors engineer can specialize in. These include the process-oriented specialties like biomechanics, industrial ergonomics, safety, system design/development, and training as well as the behaviorally oriented specialties such as aging, human functions, and visual performance. There are also ergonomists that specialize in certain industries, which will be explained later (Meister 1999).

In regard to process-oriented specialties, if an ergonomist specializes in biomechanics, the focus is on human physical strength and how it is used in working activities like lifting and pulling. A focus on industrial ergonomics means that there is a concentrated emphasis on the manufacturing processes and problems that arise with those processes, such as carpal tunnel syndrome. When an ergonomist is focused on safety, their main concern is similar to that of an industrial ergonomist, but there is a strong emphasis on prevention and analysis of accidents. Those focused on system design/development are concerned with the process of analyzing, creating, and developing systems to prevent ergonomic issues. The last specialty regarding process-oriented specialties is training. Those who concentrate on training focus on teaching workers to perform tasks safety with a human-machine interface (Meister 1999).

As for the behaviorally oriented specialties, those concentrated on aging work on understanding the effect of aging on work performance and how aging changes the worker's ability to perform their duties. The ergonomists focused on human functions have a good understanding of perceptual, motor, and cognitive functions. Those who specialize in visual performance are focused on how people see and how that affects the job they are doing (Meister 1999).

As mentioned, ergonomists can also specialize in a certain industry. The system-/technology-oriented specialties include aerospace, automotive, communication, computers, consumer products, displays, and environmental factors/design. The aerospace specialty is concerned with civilian and military aviation activities. The automotive specialty deals with automobiles, buses, railroads, and transportation functions. Communication has to do with telephone, radio, and direct personal communication. The computer specialty is anything dealing with the hardware and software for computers. Displays are focused on equipment used to present information. The environmental factors/design specialty focuses on the environment around human-machine system functions (Meister 1999).

## Other Domains of Specialization

The International Ergonomics Association (IEA) also classifies domains of specialization. These specializations are similar to the ones mentioned above but are more current for the types of specializations ergonomists may have today. The three specializations defined by IEA are:

- Physical ergonomics
- Cognitive ergonomics
- Organizational ergonomics

Physical ergonomics deals with human anatomical, anthropometric, physiological, and biomechanical characteristics in relation to physical activity. Topics that ergonomists who focus on the physical aspect study are working postures, work-related musculoskeletal disorders, safety and health, workplace layout, materials handling, and repetitive movements. Cognitive ergonomics focuses on mental processes like perception, memory, reasoning, and motor response. How these mental processes affect interactions of humans and system elements is key to cognitive ergonomics. Cognitive ergonomists spend time examining mental workload, skill performance, human reliability, work stress, decision-making, and training and how these relate to human-system design. Finally, organizational ergonomics concentrates on optimizing sociotechnical systems and the accompanying organizational structures, policies, and processes. Main topics for focus within organization ergonomics include communication, crew resource management, quality management, telework, virtual organizations, new work paradigms, cooperative work, work design, designing of working times, teamwork, and participatory design (International Ergonomics Association (IEA) 2017).

## Future Agenda in HFE

The advancements of HFE throughout the decades have been significant; nonetheless, there are still challenges to overcome. The readiness and willingness of the market to develop and maintain HFE best practices is still lacking. Additionally, the ability to influence stakeholders/company owners on the importance and fundamental characteristics of HFE needs to be developed. In order to continue to increase wellbeing of workers and achieve performance outcomes, workplaces will need to continually change and adapt to the new design systems that fit people to the job, as experts indicate that systems are changing (IEA Future of Ergonomics Committee 2012).

It is thought that those who act on the system (the main stakeholder group) are being served well by the current HFE systems. However, HFE systems need improvement in serving the other stakeholders, the system experts, and system decision-makers. The experts and decision-makers are more influential in the design of the system and have an investment in performance. While they are more influential, they may not understand all of the aspects on what HFE has to offer. In the future, HFE must move in a direction that expands to system experts and decision-makers. There should also be a stronger emphasis on reaching performance goals and diversifying application areas.

The IEA Future of Ergonomics Committee proposed a strategy to strengthen the demand for and application of high-quality HFE for all stakeholders:

1. **Strengthening the demand for high quality HFE** by enhancing the awareness of stakeholders' need for quality HFE (in particular, for system experts and system decision makers, emphasizing performance) by:
   a Communicating with specific stakeholders about the value of high-quality HFE in the language of the stakeholder
   b Building partnerships with these stakeholders and their representing organizations
   c Educating stakeholders to create awareness of high-quality HFE and its contributions to system design
2. **Strengthening the application of high-quality HFE** by:
   a Promoting the education of HFE specialists to apply high-quality HFE
   b Ensuring high quality standards of HFE applications and HFE specialists
   c Promoting HFE research excellence at universities and other organizations

(IEA Future of Ergonomics Committee 2012)

The two work together in improving overall HFE. Higher demand for high-quality HFE can lead to implementing more high-quality HFE.

By communication with stakeholders, building partnerships, and educating stakeholders, the awareness, strength, and prosperity of HFE programs can increase. This will increase demand for high-quality HFE and boost the cycle shown in figure 26.3. In order for this to be successful, HFE specialists must integrate the desired objectives into the stakeholders/companies strategies, policies, and actions. Additionally, stakeholder education, ensuring high-quality applications, encouraging HFE research, and best practice implementation can increase program future success (IEA Future of Ergonomics Committee 2012).

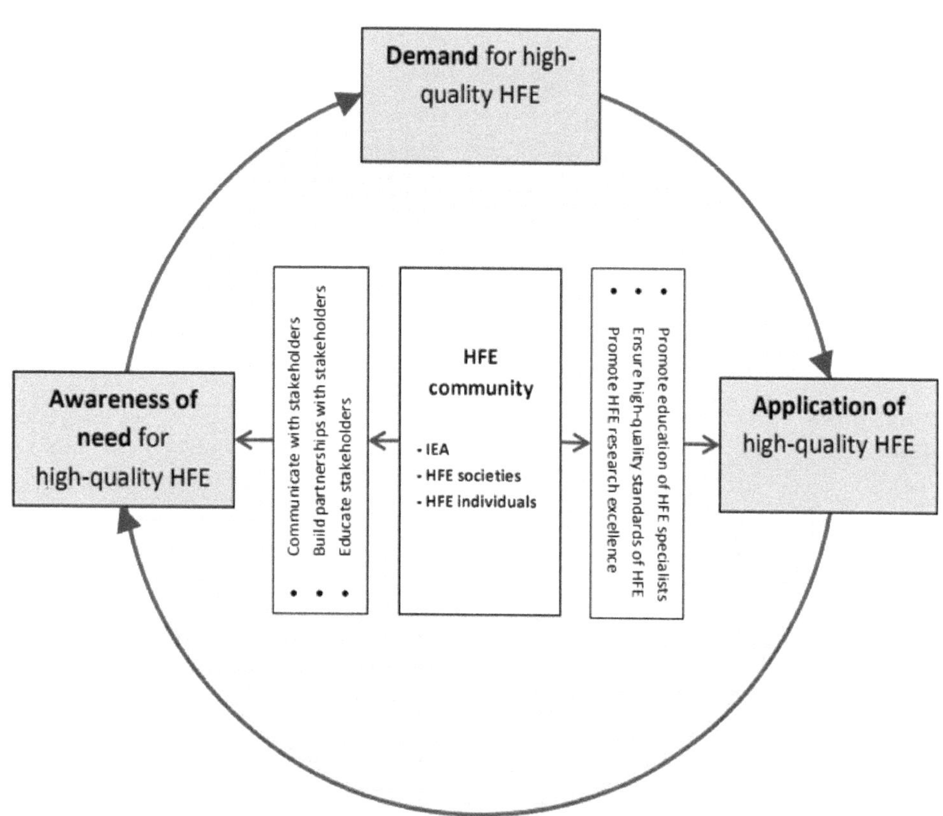


Figure 26.3
HFE demand development cycle. Source: IEA Future of Ergonomics Committee 2012. Used by permission.

## Conclusion

In this chapter, the history of HFE was discussed, and the drivers of its necessity in the workplace were identified. Ergonomics as we know it today integrates physiology, biomechanics, psychology, anthropometry, industrial hygiene, and kinesiology. However, HFE had humble beginnings in the Neolithic era with primitive tools, was embraced in ancient Greece and Sri Lanka, and was eventually accepted as a discipline in the twentieth century. Since then, HFE has advanced in the present day with emerging safety improvement technologies, including industrial robots and sEMG to help reduce employee exposure to workplace hazards.

The diversity of workers around the globe demands accommodation. As the population of aging and obese workers increases, ergonomic control principles, including elimination, substitution, and engineering and administrative controls must be implemented to meet the needs of these growing demographics. Additionally, the advances in technology used in the workplace, including tablets and touch screens, have introduced unique challenges and new risks. As the issue of technology changes gains prominence, the need for ergonomic specialists is critical to facilitate in the prevention and analysis of accidents. Despite the significant advancements in HFE throughout the past decades, the future challenges include serving the system experts and system decision-makers to ensure that high-quality HFE is available.

## Questions

1. What type of body movements in the workplace can increase the risk of musculoskeletal disorders?
2. What are the suggested ergonomic controls used to accommodate the aging and obese populations?

3. Improper sitting positions can lead to what kinds of discomfort issues in the workplace?
4. What year was the first text describing the new discipline of HFE for general use published?
5. The International Ergonomics Association (IEA) classifies three different domains of specialization. List and describe all three domains.

## References

Björkman, T. (1996). "The Rationalisation Movement in Perspective and Some Ergonomic Implications." *Applied Ergonomics* 27(2): 111–17.

Brennan, J. (1999). "Workspace Design, Ergonomics and Gender." Paper presented at the 162 –70.

Bridger, R. S. (2012). "An International Perspective on Ergonomics Education." *Ergonomics in Design: The Quarterly of Human Factors Applications* 20(4): 12–17.

Buckle, P., and J. Buckle. (2011). "Obesity, Ergonomics and Public Health." *Perspectives in Public Health* 131(4): 170.

Bureau of Labor Statistics [BLS]. (2017). "Civilian Labor Force by Age, Sex, Race, and Ethnicity." US Department of Labor. Accessed December 19, 2017. https://www.bls.gov/emp/ep_table_304.htm.

Caldari, K. (2007). "Alfred Marshall's Critical Analysis of Scientific Management." *European Jouranl of the History of Economic Thought* 24(6): 55–78. http://classes.engr.oregonstate.edu/mime/winter2011/ie366-001/Bibliography/Alfred%20Marshall's%20critical%20analysis%20of%20scientific%20management.pdf.

Callaghan, J. P., D. De Carvalho, K. Gallagher, T. Karakolis, and E. Nelson-Wong. (2015). "Is Standing the Solution to Sedentary Office Work?" *Ergonomics in Design: The Quarterly of Human Factors Applications* 23(3): 20–24.

Coulton, J. J. (1997). *Ancient Greek Architects at Work: Problems of Structure and Design.* Ithaca, NY: Cornell University Press.

Caple, D. C. (2012). "Globalization of Ergonomics through the International Ergonomics Association." *Ergonomics in Design: The Quarterly of Human Factors Applications* 20(4): 18–21.

Cavuoto, L. A., and M. A. Nussbaum. (2014). "The Influences of Obesity and Age on Functional Performance during Intermittent Upper Extremity Tasks." *Journal of Occupational and Environmental Hygiene* 11(9): 583–90.

Coenen, P., G. N. Healy, E. A. H. Winkler, D. W. Dunstan, et al. (2017). "Pre-existing Low-back Symptoms Impact Adversely on Sitting Time Reduction in Office Workers." *International Archives of Occupational and Environmental Health* 90(7): 609–18.

Dempsey, P. G., and S. E. Mathiassen. (2006) "On the Evolution of Task-based Analysis of Manual Materials Handling, and Its Applicability in Contemporary Ergonomics." *Applied Ergonomics* 37(1): 33–43. Centrum för belastningsskadeforskning, & Högskolan i Gävle (Translation: Center for Musculoskeletal Research & University of Gävle).

Ergonomist. (2017). National Careers Service. Accessed May 18, 2017. https://nationalcareersservice.direct.gov.uk/job-profiles/ergonomist.

Fitts, P.M., and R.E. Jones. (1947). *Analysis of Factors Contributing to 460 Pilot-error Experiences in Operating Aircraft Controls.* Memorandum Report TSEAA-694-12, Dayton, OH: Aero Medical Laboratory, Air Material Command.

Fox, R. R., G. E. Brogmus, and W. S. Maynard. (2015). "Aging Workers and Ergonomics: A Fresh Perspective." *Professional Safety* 60(1): 33.

Gaddy, C., P. Kobor, and B. Wanchisen. (2017). "Ergonomics: The Science for Better Living and Working." Accessed July 15, 2017. http://www.apa.org/about/gr/issues/workforce/ergonomics.aspx.

Gainer, R. D. (2008). "History of Ergonomics and Occupational Therapy." *Work* 31(1): 5.

Gazzoni, M. (2010). "Multichannel Surface Electromyography in Ergonomics: Potentialities and Limits." *Human Factors and Ergonomics in Manufacturing and Service Industries* 20(4): 255–71.

Goonatilake, S. (2014). "Ancient Sri Lankan Lumbar-supported Seats." *Ergonomics in Design: The Quarterly of Human Factors Applications* 22(1): 27–30.

Gu, J. K., L. E. Charles, M. E. Andrew, C. C. Ma, T. A. Hartley, J. M. Violanti, and C. M. Burchfiel. (2016). "Prevalence of Work-site Injuries and Relationship between Obesity and Injury among U.S. Workers: NHIS 2004–2012." *Journal of Safety Research* 58: 21–30.

Hanson, B. L. (1983). "A Brief History of Applied Behavioral Science at Bell Laboratories." *Bell System Technical Journal* 62(6): 1571–90.

International Ergonomics Association (IEA). (2017). "About IEA." Accessed July 14, 2017. http://iea.cc/about/index.html.

International Ergonomics Association (IEA). (2017). "What Is Ergonomics? Domains of Specialization." Accessed July 10, 2017. http://www.iea.cc/whats/index.html.

International Ergonomics Association (IEA) Future of Ergonomics Committee. (2012). "A Strategy for Human Factors/Ergonomics: Developing the Discipline and Profession." Accessed January 2, 2018. http://www.iea.cc/project/recent.html.

Kang, H., and G. Shin. (2017). "Effects of Touch Target Location on Performance and Physical Demands of Computer Touchscreen Use." *Applied Ergonomics* 61: 159–67.

Karwowski, W. (2006). *International Encyclopedia of Ergonomics and Human Factors* (2nd ed., vol. 1). Boca Raton, FL: Taylor and Francis Group.

Karwowski, W., and W. S. Marras. (2006). *Interventions, Controls, and Applications in Occupational Ergonomics.* London: CRC Taylor & Francis.

Lassila, S. B. (2017). "Engagement Is Key to Improving Safety, Ergonomics and Wellness for Aging Workers." *EHS Today* (March 14). Accessed February 9, 2018. http://www.ehstoday.com/safety-leadership/engagement-key-improving-safety-ergonomics-and-wellness-aging-workers.

Lin, M. Y. C., and J. T. Dennerlein. (2015). "A Psychophysical Protocol to Provide Ergonomic Recommendations for Standing Computer Workstation Setup." *Proceedings of the Human Factors and Ergonomics Society Annual Meeting* 59(1): 1288–90.

Lin, M. B., R. Hong, J. Chang, and X. Ke. (2015). "Usage Position and Virtual Keyboard Design Affect Upper-body Kinematics, Discomfort, and Usability during Prolonged Tablet Typing: E0143585." *PLoS One* 10(12).

Lin, C., S. Chen, W. Hsiao, and R. Lin. (2016). "Cultural Ergonomics in Interactional and Experiential Design: Conceptual Framework and Case Study of the Taiwanese Twin Cup." *Applied Ergonomics* 52: 242–52.

Manuele, F. (2008). "Prevention through Design: Addressing Occupational Risks in the Design and Redesign Processes." *Professional Safety*. Accessed July 10, 2017. http://www.safetybok.org/prevention_through_design_addressing_occupational_risks_in_the_design__redesign_processes/.

Marmaras, N., G. Poulakakis, and V. Papakostopoulos. (1999). "Ergonomic Design in Ancient Greece." *Applied Ergonomics* 30(4): 361–68.

Meister, D., and I. NetLibrary. (1999). *The History of Human Factors and Ergonomics.* Mahwah, NJ: Lawrence Erlbaum Associates.

Middlesworth, M. (n.d. a). "Ergonomics and Injury Prevention Strategies for an Overweight and Obese Workforce." *Ergonomics Plus*. Accessed May 19, 2017. http://ergo-plus.com/ergonomics-injury-prevention-overweight-obese-workforce/.

Middlesworth, M. (n.d. b). "Ergonomics and the Aging Workforce—Designing a Safe and Productive Workplace." *Ergonomics Plus*. Accessed July 14, 2017. http://ergo-plus.com/ergonomics-aging-workforce-design/.

Moray, N. (2005). *Ergonomics: The History and Scope of Human Factors.* London: Taylor & Francis.

Moray, N. (2008). "The Good, the Bad, and the Future: On the Archaeology of Ergonomics." *Human Factors: The Journal of the Human Factors and Ergonomics Society* 50(3): 411–17.

National Technical University of Athens. (2006). "Ergonomics in Ancient Greece." Accessed July 14, 2017. http://ergou.simor.ntua.gr/research/ancientGreece/AncientGreece.htm.

Occupational Safety and Health Administration (OSHA). (2000). "Ergonomics: The Study of Work." United States Department of Labor. Accessed May 18, 2017. https://www.osha.gov/Publications/osha3125.pdf.

Occupational Safety and Health Administration (OSHA). (n.d. a). "Ergonomics: Prevention of Musculoskeletal Disorders in the Workplace." United States Department of Labor. Accessed May 18, 2017. https://www.osha.gov/SLTC/ergonomics/.

Occupational Safety and Health Administration (OSHA). (n.d. b). "Ergonomics: Solutions to Control Hazards." United States Department of Labor. Accessed May 18, 2017. https://www.osha.gov/SLTC/ergonomics/controlhazards.html.

Ohu, I. P. N., S. Cho, D. H. Kim, and G. H. Lee. (2016). "Ergonomic Analysis of Mobile Cart–Assisted Stocking Activities using Electromyography. *Human Factors and Ergonomics in Manufacturing and Service Industries* 26(1): 40–51.

Oluwafemi, J. (2012). "Ergonomics: An Important Tool for Organizational Success." https://ssrn.com/abstract=2140808

Rutherford, D. (2013). "Ergonomics." *Routledge Dictionary of Economics* (3rd ed.). London: Routledge. http://huaryu.kl.oakland.edu/login?url=http://search.credoreference.com/content/entry/routsobk/ergonomics/0?institutionId=218.

Salvendy, G. (2012). *Handbook of Human Factors and Ergonomics.* Hoboken, NJ: Wiley.

Savage-Knepshield, P., C. Paulillo, J. Thomas, J. Davis, D. Quarles, N. Gaither, and D. Mitchell. (2014). "The U.S. Army Acquisition Process and Close MANPRINT Encounters of the 'Early' and 'Agile' Kind." *Proceedings of the Human Factors and Ergonomics Society Annual Meeting* 58(1): 2270–74.

Scholer, M., M. Vette, and M. Rainer. (2015). "A Lightweight Robot System Designed for the Optimisation of an Automotive End-off Line Process Station." *Industrial Robot: An International Journal* 42(4): 296–305.

Shorrock, S., and C. Williams. (2017). *Human Factors and Ergonomics in Practice: Improving System Performance and Human Well-being in the Real World.* Boca Raton, FL: Taylor and Francis Group.

Smith-Jackson, T. L., and M. S. Wogalter. (2000). "Applying Cultural Ergonomics/Human Factors to Safety Information Research." *Human Factors and Ergonomics Society Annual Meeting Proceedings* 44(33): 150–53.

Smith-Jackson, T. L., M. L. Resnick, and K. T. Johnson. (2014; 2013). *Cultural Ergonomics: Theory, Methods, and Applications.* Boca Raton, FL: CRC Press.

Stensland, J. (n.d.). "Sitting and Chair Design." Accessed July 14, 2017. http://ergo.human.cornell.edu/dea3250flipbook/dea3250notes/sitting.html.

Taifa, I. W., and D. A. Desai. (2016; 2017). "Anthropometric Measurements for Ergonomic Design of Students' Furniture in India." *Engineering Science and Technology, an International Journal* 20(1): 232–39.

Trzcieliński, S., and W. Karwowski. (2013; 2012). *Advances in Ergonomics in Manufacturing* (1st ed.). Boca Raton, FL: CRC Press.

Vasavada, A. N., D. D. Nevins, S. M. Monda, E. Hughes, and D. C. Lin. (2015). "Gravitational Demand on the Neck Musculature during Tablet Computer Use." *Ergonomics* 58(6): 990–1004.

Woo, E. H. C., P. White, and C. W. K. Lai. (2016). "Ergonomics Standards and Guidelines for Computer Workstation Design and the Impact on Users' Health—a Review." *Ergonomics* 59(3): 464–75.

Wilson, J. R. (2000). "Fundamentals of Ergonomics in Theory and Practice." *Applied Ergonomics* 31(6): 557–67.

Workineh, S. A., and H. Yamaura. (2016). "Multi-position Ergonomic Computer Workstation Design to Increase Comfort of Computer Work." *International Journal of Industrial Ergonomics* 53: 1–9.

Xiong, J., and S. Muraki. (2014). "An Ergonomics Study of Thumb Movements on Smartphone Touch Screen." *Ergonomics* 57(6): 943–55.

# SECTION 5
# CULTURE

CHAPTER 27

# IMPROVING WORKPLACE CULTURE THROUGH INDIVIDUAL SAFETY LEADERSHIP

Donald Groover

## Learning Objectives

After studying this chapter, the reader will be able to:

1. Discuss the relationship between safety leadership and culture
2. Identify how to leverage safety as an agent for culture change
3. Describe culture as a product of relationships between people
4. Establish safety as a fundamental component of relationships
5. Evaluate how a leader and peer commitment to safety is linked to employee perceptions of leadership capabilities
6. Review organizational factors that impact change efforts
7. Discuss the approach for developing leadership skills through safety improvement

## Key Terms

**Leader–member exchange, organizational change, organizational climate, organizational culture, organizational citizenship behavior, perceived organizational support, procedural justice, safety leadership, transformational leadership, upward communication**

## Abstract

This chapter explores a model for how leaders can leverage the power of safety to drive cultural change. Not only does the model produce a measurable change in culture, but research (Krause 2005) suggests it also improves safety metrics and other non-safety-specific outcomes. Generally, for an individual leader who is trying to change the culture of their workgroup, this means leveraging the power of transformational leadership. Inherent in transformational leadership is the leader's personal concern for the physical and psychological safety of others. By leveraging transformational leadership, the individual leader changes the beliefs and actions of his or her followers. For organizational change, this transformative process is still applied, except on a broader scale. The power of using safety as the lever for change is that it is the one personal and cultural attribute that is a shared value. Additionally, by having everyone focused on using safety for learning and development, it speeds up leadership learning and cultural transformation. In either a personal or organizational change situation, the first step is the identification of the barriers that prevent buy-in and change and a strategic plan for change.

## Introduction

How do we know if a leader has arrived at understanding their role in changing culture through their own safety leadership? It is when an incident happens and instead of the first question being, "Why did the employee do that?" the leader asks, "What could we as leaders have done to prevent this incident? What is it about our culture, leadership, or systems that made the employee believe that we expected or accepted that they do it that way?"

> The individual leader determines, for the most part, the cultural experience employees have each and every day.

In this chapter, we explore the relationship between safety leadership and culture and examine safety as an agent of culture change. It is the author's experience that many organizations have successfully used safety as the beachhead for change, whether that change is related to how an individual impacts direct reports or how an executive leadership team develops and drives a strategy of transformation by leveraging the power of safety. Regardless of the breadth of the effort, safety is an effective vehicle for change because no reasonable person can take a stand against improving safety. People may challenge the methodology for change, but the objective of getting everyone home safely every day can't be reasonably rejected.

## Leadership Creates Culture

Within any organization, there are multiple cultures. Each leader creates a subculture for their workgroup. The individual leader determines, for the most part, the cultural experience employees have each and every day. While individual leaders create a subculture, each individual workgroup influences, and is in turn influenced by, the overall organizational culture and the systems that reinforce the wider cultural norms.

In the process of driving culture change, individual leaders must stop and consider how their actions or decisions will impact others and, as importantly, what change they would like to see in others as a result. Culture changes one leadership behavior at a time, but individual actions aren't enough. If leadership activity is not coupled with a change in the systems that tell people in the organization what is really valued, then a short-term climate change will result—but it will not ultimately lead to culture change. The more often employees experience climate change without it sustaining, the less likely they are to buy in to and support the next change. A few of the systems that can delay, derail, or stop the change include:

- selection process for hiring and promotions;
- the focus of training and development;
- how raises and bonuses are administered; and
- organizational structure (reporting relationships and reporting ratios).

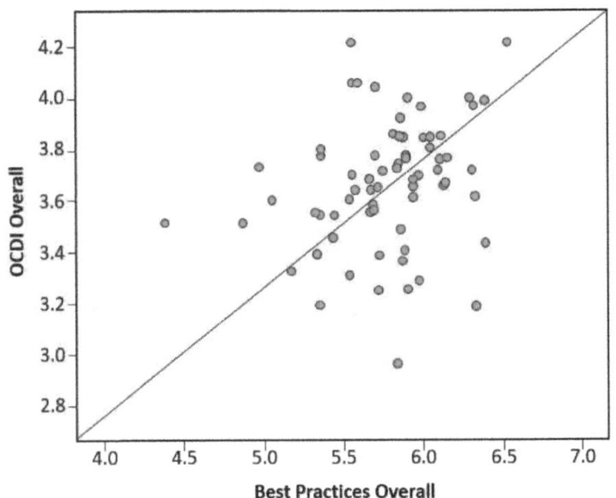


Figure 27.1
Sixty-eight sites with higher leadership best practice scores have higher scores on the nine culture factors.

> Organizational culture change requires a broad level of sustained engagement across most of the leadership. When all the leaders of an organization are learning and working together through a single focal point like safety, they are able to accelerate the pace of change.

Culture change in an organization can only be accomplished by leadership. Employees can't really change the culture because they are unable to transform the systems that continue to reinforce the old culture and norms. Employees can cause a shift in climate, but ultimately culture change is decided by leadership. The crucial first step for a leader is to understand that they own the culture—no matter how new they are to the situation or how poorly they view the cultural norms. Leaders must understand that it is their job to transform the culture so the attributes they desire become reality.

Finally, culture change is a long process, often taking years. It is the author's experience from working with hundreds of organizations that change is rarely accomplished in months. Just when you think you have succeeded in the change, someone or something will remind you that you are not there yet. Some people are patiently biding their time, so they can revert back to the old ways. In other cases, some systems, agreements, or operational realities make the change nearly impossible. It is not until these items are fully understood and addressed that the change process can be completed. Organizational culture change requires a broad level of sustained engagement across most of the leaders. When all the leaders of an organization are learning and working together through a single focal point like safety, they are able to accelerate the pace of change.

## Culture or Safety Culture?

There has been a lot written about culture and specifically about safety culture. The idea that safety culture actually exists is open to debate. If safety culture stands alone, then it begs the question: What other standalone cultures exist? Consider the potential list of cultures for a typical organization: customer service, environmental, occupational health, operational excellence, personal health, production, and quality. The list could continue. Moreover, safety itself could be two different cultures: personal and process safety. The implication is that there is really just one culture. That culture values certain factors and tends to have an organizational focus on certain performance measures or aspects of organizational life.

> Safety itself could be two different cultures: personal and process safety. The implication is that there is really just one culture.

Edgar Schein (Schein 2004) presents culture as a series of assumptions a person makes about the group in which they participate. These assumptions are grouped into three levels, each level becoming more difficult to articulate and, more importantly, more difficult to change. Schein suggests that these assumptions can be seen through:

1. artifacts (what is experienced via your senses, such as language, styles, stories, and published statements);
2. espoused beliefs and values (ideals, goals, and aspirations); and
3. basic underlying beliefs (conditions that are taken for granted).

This chapter discusses the basic underlying beliefs and the cultural assumptions. It is these beliefs and assumptions that represent the greatest barrier to change. Often, they are unspoken and, in my experience, there is a sensitivity when they are brought up for discussion. In some instances, the resistance to accepting these assumptions is so strong, they prevent leaders from moving forward, and instead they seek to deny their existence. Some of these assumptions pivot around:

> Consider the following situation. A friend asks you what it is like to work for your company. The pivot point regarding how you phrase your answer likely has less to do with the job task you perform than it has to do with your perception of how the company, the company leaders, and your peers treat you.

- What is truth? What is the reality of the situation? How do we know what is really happening? Is it because someone says so, because everyone agrees, or because we all prove it to be so?
- Space: How is everyone situated? How is the work environment laid out? Is there a point when someone is invading personal space, or is intimacy generally accepted?
- Human nature: Are people only there to get work done, or are people considered more as complex individuals more than as the position they hold?
- Appropriate human activity: Are we here to take control of our environment? Are we here as slaves of circumstances to simply coexist with our environment, or do we develop ourselves to work in harmony with our environment?
- Nature of human relationship: Are we individuals or are we a collective? What is the difference in power between members, and how is that power leveraged?

## Culture Is about Relationships

Consider the following situation. A friend asks you what it is like to work for your company. What races to the front of your mind? What are the things you quickly want to talk about? How you think about your employer is based on three primary components: the work, the working conditions, and the workplace culture. More often than not, your mind would quickly race beyond the nature of the work and conditions, and you would consider the nature of the workplace culture. The pivot point regarding how you phrase your answer likely has less to do with the job task you perform than it has to do with your perception of how the company, the company leaders, and your peers treat you. When we are faced with uninteresting or unchallenging work, with working conditions that are unpleasant, and we do not feel connected to the company, its leadership, or its mission, what we are thinking about is escape. In this configuration, what we would share with our friend would be less than complimentary.

When we are faced with uninteresting or unchallenging work, with working conditions that are unpleasant, and we do not feel connected to the company, its leadership, or its mission, what we are thinking about is escape.

Woven into Schein's assumptions is the fundamental idea of relationships. As an individual in the culture, what is my relationship to my company, my management team, my immediate supervisor, and my peers? How I think about these relationships has a significant impact on my level of commitment to the organization, the leadership, company goals, and the rules. The more "connected" I am to the organization, the more likely I will try to fit in and make a commitment to help the organization and the leadership achieve their goals and objectives. If leadership has demonstrated a commitment to safety, then I will more likely act safely and try to keep not only myself but others safe.

Many organizations attempt to measure an employee's orientation based on their level of engagement. A highly engaged employee will perform more actions that would be deemed as organizational citizenship behavior. Organizational citizenship behaviors are those actions an employee willingly takes on that are beyond their job descriptions or the requirements of their position. Generally looking after the safety of a coworker is not in a job description; however, an engaged employee who is working in an organization that values safety would take on this responsibility willingly.

## Relationships Have a Foundation in Safety

Relationships are based on social exchange theory and the law of reciprocity. Social exchange theory explains how our perceptions of fairness enter into the relationship we have with another person (Hofmann 1999). The law of reciprocity has to do with a social principle that if you do something for someone else, you expect them to reciprocate. When someone does

The law of reciprocity has to do with a social principle that if you do something for someone else, you expect them to reciprocate.

something for us, we feel a slight pull to reciprocate and do something in return. The more one does for someone else, the more they feel the pull. Relationships break down when one side breaks this social exchange, and there is no reciprocation. In business relationships, the reciprocity principle holds the same; however, it is not a 50/50 relationship. Leadership must often stretch further to see a reciprocation.

When we consider our strongest and deepest relationships, they are built on a foundation of safety—not just physical safety but also psychological safety. If we come to believe that another person is not interested in our physical or mental wellbeing, the foundation breaks down.

Consider the situation where a leader suggests that you violate a lifesaving rule or policy so that they have a better chance of hitting their production targets, or consider a leader that almost never lets you know whether you are doing good work or poor work and never provides success feedback or encouragement. In the first situation, we would come to believe that the leader is willing to sacrifice our physical wellbeing. In the second, we are left in a state of uncertainty and doubt (psychologically unsafe). When either situation exists, the safety foundation was never built or has crumbled. Without this foundation, the relationship is much different. It is one where we become focused on ourselves, organizational citizenship behaviors evaporate, and we disconnect from the leader.

The concept of safety being foundational to relationships is crucial when we consider leadership and, most critically, safety leadership. We will return to this topic once we finish exploring culture.

From research (Krause 2005) there are nine culture factors that correlate with safety outcomes: procedural justice, leader-member exchange, management credibility, perceived organizational support, teamwork, workgroup relations, organizational value for safety, upward communication, and approaching others. These factors can be measured with an organizational culture diagnostic instrument (OCDI) significantly and are inversely correlated to safety outcomes.

The concept of safety being foundational to relationships is crucial when we consider leadership and, most critically, safety leadership.

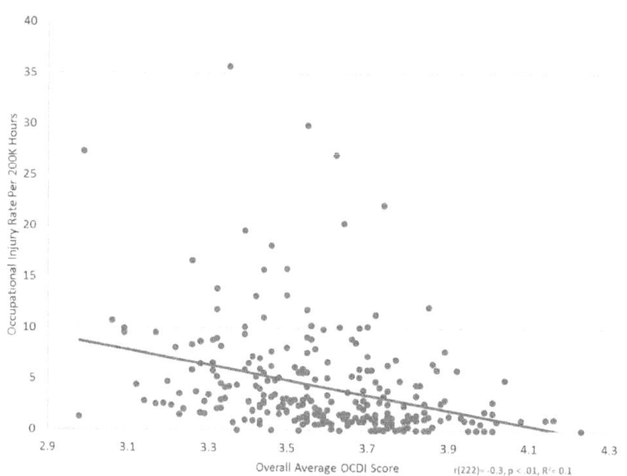

Figure 27.2
Sites that scored higher on the nine culture factors had lower injury rates.

What is interesting about the nine culture factors is that six of them are not safety specific and have little if anything to do with safety, yet they are predictive of safety performance. They can be broken out as follows.

## Employee's Relationship with the Company

The basic idea underlying the relationship an employee has with the organization is whether the employee perceives their company is concerned about his or her needs and interests. This factor is called perceived organizational support (POS). POS relates to Edgar Schein's cultural assumptions related to human nature: Are people only there to get work done, or are they considered as complex individuals more than as the position they hold? With respect to POS, the key is the perception that the favorable treatment is discretionary on the part of the organization. Employees do not give the company credit for those things that are done because they are required by law or contract to do so. Instead, employees look for evidence that the employer actually considers them as an individual versus a badge number (Rhoades 2002).

Examples of POS can include free coffee, popcorn Fridays, managers standing at the gate thanking employees for their contributions, family safety day events, providing employees tickets to the local fair, matching retirement contributions, and access to training or education that is not specifically tied to the person's current job assignment. While some of these seem minor, they all add up for the person as they are making a judgment about their employer.

## Workers and Their Relationship with Management

As employees, we have a relationship with the leaders (management) that are two or three levels above our immediate boss. This relationship with management is generally based on brief interactions where assumptions are made about their true intent and whether we consider management trustworthy. We might only see a manager once or twice a month, depending on our job, work schedule, and responsibilities. During these brief interactions, we form our beliefs. Of all the judgments we are making, two measure the health of this relationship and predict safety performance. They are organizational value for safety and management credibility.

When the level of effort matches the words, management is seen as credible in safety. When there is significant mismatch, the leader's credibility and ability to communicate about other important topics are severely hindered.

Organizational value for safety measures the extent to which workers believe leadership is committed to safety. This relates to Edgar Schein's cultural assumptions about truth and perceptions about the reality of the situation. Employees listen to the leader's words and compare those words to the level of effort and resources they see being applied specifically to safety. When the level of effort matches the words, management is seen as credible in safety. When there is significant mismatch, the leader's credibility and ability to communicate about other important topics are severely hindered.

The second area is management credibility, which is basically the degree to which employees feel they can trust management. Perceptions that a manager is competent are not a sufficient basis for the development of trust. Employees are unlikely to trust an incompetent

Trust is built through a wide variety of actions, like following through on commitments, being transparent, admitting to a mistake, and treating others with dignity and respect.

manager, but competence alone does not lead to trustworthiness. Trust is built through a wide variety of actions, like following through on commitments, being transparent, admitting to a mistake, not being accepting of toxic leaders or individuals in the workplace, and treating others with dignity and respect.

## Workers and Their Relationship with their Immediate Supervisor

There are three dimensions to the supervisor/employee relationship: upward communication about safety, procedural justice, and leader-member exchange (Krause 2005).

Upward communication about safety relates to the supervisor's openness to listen to employees' safety concern. It also relates to the beliefs an employee has about whether the supervisor will do something about their concern. This willingness to listen and respond establishes a foundation of trust that the supervisor genuinely is concerned about a direct reporter's wellbeing.

Procedural justice refers to decision-making processes. An employee may accept a decision that gives a less-than-desired outcome if the procedures used to make the decision are considered fair. A fair procedure can compensate for bad outcomes. Fair procedures are characterized by the following:

- Consistency—across groups, people, and time
- Lack of bias—avoidance of personal self-interest by the decision-maker
- Accuracy—use of good information and informed opinion
- Correctable—ability to appeal decisions
- Representativeness (or "voice")—the procedure reflects the basic concerns, values, and outlook of those affected
- Ethicality—the procedure is compatible with the fundamental moral and ethical values of those affected

The third and final factor in the supervisor/employee relationship is leader-member exchange. The leader-member exchange concept is predominantly a measure of the supervisor's use of transformational leadership. Transformational leaders exert influence through the building of relationships. The relationships develop, based on a series of "exchanges." The supervisor takes a risk and gives a member an assignment. If performance is good, the supervisor develops trust in the worker and over time gives him or her more latitude for decision-making (delegation). The member also tests the relationship by seeing if the supervisor follows through on commitments made, backs up the worker, and is willing to accommodate to the worker's needs. These factors relate mostly to Edgar Schein's attributes of human nature, truth, and the nature of relationships.

Workgroup relations is based on the notion that social relationships within the workgroup influence important safety-related variables.

## Workers and Their Relationship with Their Peers

The factors that are important in peer-to-peer relationships are approaching others about safety, workgroup relations, and teamwork.

Approaching other's about safety relates to people's willingness to speak up to one another about at-risk situations. This factor gets at what is sometimes called the "brothers' keeper" atmosphere in the workgroup. As a basis of a relationship, we want to be working around people who are willing to look out for our physical wellbeing.

Workgroup relations is based on the notion that social relationships within the workgroup influence important safety-related variables. This is fairly easy to picture. In a group where people do not get along well together, individuals are less likely to go out of their way to speak up to coworkers about safety. Speaking up can be risky—one cannot be certain how the other person will react. Likewise, raising a safety concern in a safety meeting is risky—other group members might ridicule the concern.

Teamwork and team functioning are affected by many factors, including design of the work and the team (socio-technical considerations), team composition, the general organizational context in which the team operates, and internal group processes. The teamwork dimension represents an overall assessment of group cohesiveness and functioning, the result of the various influences.

These factors relate to all of Edgar Schein's assumptions listed previously.

The teamwork dimension represents an overall assessment of group cohesiveness and functioning, the result of the various influences.

## Interdependent, Not Independent

The culture factors are interdependent, not independent. This is important to understand for two reasons. First, doing poorly in one area can cast a negative pall overall, and second, working on improving significantly in one area can have positive impact across multiple factors.

For example, the author worked with one chemical plant where employees were awarded a meal ticket for working over a twelve-hour shift. But the supervisor distributed meal tickets in a way that was not perceived to be procedurally just. Some employees (the favorites) got more than one ticket, while others (who had worked beyond twelve hours) didn't receive any. When asked about procedural justice, employees had significant concerns, and it was discovered that the impact of the meal ticket awards exceeded loss of respect and trust for supervisors. The affected employees' perception of injustice led to a breakdown in teamwork and workgroup relations. The favorites were disliked by those out of favor, and the favorites knew they were favorites and treated the others with disrespect. Those in disfavor had no intention of watching out for the safety of the favorites. In fact, when one of the favorites got hurt, there was not a lot of pity felt by those who were not favorites. This injustice also impacted management's credibility. While evidence suggested that management had no knowledge of this practice, the employees believed (this was their truth) that they did and believed they were condoning the action.

There were other examples of unjust procedural decisions found from the interviews and focus groups, but this particular one was so blatant and had so much passion around it, that it triggered the management team to take action. It was not a safety-specific issue that was stopping the organization from moving the culture forward. Sometimes working on safety excellence means working on culture more generically. Good leaders understand this.

Sometimes working on safety excellence means working on culture more generically. Good leaders understand this.

## Relationships, Commitment, and Organizational Citizenship Behaviors

Let's consider the impact all these factors have on the way workers perceive the workplace and, more important, how their perceptions impact their level of commitment to the organization. Consider the following answers to the same question about different companies.

Worker A reports the following when asked *What is it like to work for Company X?*

> I am just a number to this company; regarding safety, my supervisor doesn't listen to my concerns, and management lets safety problems go unresolved. Management around here always makes promises about change, but nothing happens. My supervisor has favorites in the crew and they get special treatment, and the supervisor never gives me opportunities to show how much more I can do. I get along with my workmates okay, but I can't count on anyone outside my department to do what needs to get done. In fact, when I am having machine problems and parts are getting backed up, the maintenance team just stands by and watches. They never help out.

Worker B reports the following when asked *What is it like to work for Company Y?*

> Company Y is really a good company; they are helping me with school tuition, and they do lots of things to demonstrate they care about the employees and our wellbeing. When it comes to safety, my supervisor continually asks if we have any safety concerns. We are told we have the authority to stop the work if we are concerned about safety, and management is always talking about the importance of everyone getting home safely. I am constantly being challenged in my job and allowed to do new things. I get along with my workmates, and we have each other's back when it comes to safety.

As you consider the answers, think about the burden Worker A carries to work each day. What level of commitment would this person have to the organization? How committed would he be to follow the procedures? What is very concerning is that this employee is less likely to follow the safety rules and procedures. He would also be unlikely to focus beyond his own safety to the safety of others. This employee is interested in one thing: escape. While he may be forced to stay working at Company X (because of the wages or location of the job), the employee will still find a way to escape. In this culture, "eight and the gate" becomes the mantra. Safety performance, productivity, quality, and employee satisfaction are some of the outcomes that suffer.

Worker B is experiencing a much different culture. It is clear that leadership is investing in the relationship, and they will be repaid through greater discretionary effort and a higher level of compliance to rules, procedures, and systems. An organization with the culture described by Worker B typically has better performance across the board.

Regarding the answers from both Workers A and B, the author has found nearly these exact answers coming from employees working for the same company but in different operating locations.

**Table 27.1** Cultural and organizational factors relating to worker attitudes

| | Cultural Factor | | | |
|---|---|---|---|---|
| Organizational Factor | Procedural Justice | Leader-Member Exchange | Perceived Organizational Support | Management Credibility |
| Commitment | .57* | .41** | .67** | .59* |
| Satisfaction | .62* | .50* | .62** | .65* |
| Performance | .36* | .26** | .20** | .17* |
| Org. Citizenship Behavior | .27* | .38* | .28** | .12* |
| Turnover Intention | −.26** | −.31* | −.51* | −.47* |
| Absenteeism | −.28* | | −.69** | |
| Turnover | −.36** | −.11* | −.11** | |
| Withdrawal | −.46* | | −.26** | |
| Stress | −.16* | | −.32** | |

*Indicates significance at $p < .05$
**Indicates significance at $p < .01$

Procedural justice, leader-member exchange, perceived organizational support, and management credibility are positively correlated to employee commitment, satisfaction, performance, and organizational citizenship behavior. These cultural factors are negatively correlated to turnover intention, absenteeism, turnover, withdrawal, and stress.

Table drawn from data compiled from Burton et al. 2008; Cohen-Charash and Spector 2001; Colquitt et al. 2001; Kirks and Ferrin 2002; Illies et al. 2007; and Rhoades and Eisenberger 2002.

The working conditions, schedule, and pay were nearly identical in the two locations, yet the cultural experience the employees were having was totally different. In other words, most organizations and leaders are deserving of the culture they have. When you run into a high-functioning culture, it is because leadership has made the investment in demonstrating their care for the people.

The question for many leaders is what can they do to cause a turnaround in a culture?

## Safety Leadership as a Foundation for Culture Change

In the content provided above, we have made the case for how safety is foundational to relationships, how the strengths of relationships are predictive of a strong culture, and how having a strong culture leads to better performance in safety. Also, in the beginning of the chapter, we questioned whether safety culture is a unique culture unto itself or just a product of the overall culture. What we need now is a roadmap for how to leverage this understanding to create change. The roadmap is simple: make safety a cornerstone of the change. Whether you are trying to create change within your workgroup as an individual leader or move an entire organization as a leadership team, use safety as the beachhead and the focal point for learning and development. Help leaders get good at safety leadership; then allow them to generalize the learning to other areas. Before you jump to the solution, below is a model for change the author has successfully followed for years. This model requires being patient and going slower; however, in the end, the pace of change is faster, with more sustainability.

Steps to using safety leadership to drive workplace culture:

1. define the desired attributes of safety you want to see in the culture;
2. assess the organization;
3. identify the crucial few targets that need to be addressed;
4. pull together a strategic safety improvement plan; and
5. implement the plan.

Stacks of books have been written on change management and implementing change. This chapter focuses on explaining the first two steps of the change process. Getting these first two steps right positions leaders to develop a sound strategic safety plan.

### Step 1: Defining Attributes of Safety

Many organizations have safety visions that tend to be some form of statement that represents achieving zero injuries. These vision statements are really more of an objective declaration than they are of a vision. They infer that as long as zero injuries is reached, the organization has achieved its vision, there is nothing beyond zero injuries, and it is unimportant how the organization achieves the vision. Other organizations have safety mantras or overarching slogans. Again, many of these tend to lean toward some zero-injuries goal or objective; a few focus on a specific cultural attribute. What is needed is a description of the safety attributes leadership desires in the culture they want to achieve. Safety attributes need to be clarified by the individual leader at the team level or, for a broader-based organizational change, by a leadership team. For an individual leader, defining these attributes is the foundation for clearly communicating the culture he or she wants to see. If the change involves many leaders or an organization, it is important to provide clarity on where the leadership team desires to move the culture.

> Safety attributes need to be clarified by the individual leader at the team level or, for a broader-based organizational change, by a leadership team.

While identifying attributes is not difficult, many people struggle because they continue to focus on safety outcomes versus the attributes of the culture. The process involves facilitating a discussion about what leaders believe they would see and sense in an organization that has world-class safety. (Note: Avoid trying to define world class—this is a distraction to the real task.) The next question to ask is when you walk into a location, what would you see or experience that would make you say, "If we keep doing this, we will send everyone home safely today"?

These questions generate a discussion about what attributes we would see in our desired future state. Let me provide two common attributes that arise from this discussion:

- "We watch out for each other and step in and say something if someone is doing something at risk."
- "We take pride in the workplace and use good housekeeping practices."

> Cultural change and safety improvement seldom result from a focus on just one area or aspect of safety.

You can use whatever process you are familiar with to condense the list, but it is recommended that the list not exceed ten short and concise attributes.

Having these attributes is crucial for doing a sound assessment. In order to understand the gap between current state and future state, you have to understand where you are going.

## Step 2: Assess the Organization

Cultural change and safety improvement seldom result from a focus on just one area or aspect of safety. All the factors that contribute to dysfunction, dissatisfaction, and increased exposure need to be understood. As part of the strategy and safety-plan development process, all of these factors must be considered, not only as stand-alone items but also as to how they interact and influence each other.

For a widespread organizational change effort, it is important to understand the myriad of organizational elements and factors that could hinder progress and success. These include:

1. leadership's current role in the change effort and in safety;
2. health of relationships across the levels and departments;
3. alignment of performance management systems to the desired culture and safety outcomes;
4. the effectiveness, level of perceived value, and level of acceptance of the existing safety systems;
5. the organizational reporting structure, ratio of leaders to employees;
6. the type of safety data and analysis available, metrics tracked, and how this information is leveraged;
7. the focus and structure of the safety organization; and
8. the types of exposures at the point where employees interact with the processes, procedures, equipment, and other factors that can influence risk-taking behavior, like fatigue or the level of organizational urgency.

A focus on safety leadership as a mechanism for organizational culture change is about making the changes and adjustments necessary to create the environment where change can occur.

A focus on safety leadership as a mechanism for organizational culture change isn't just about increasing and more fully leveraging the power of transformational leadership in safety; it is about making the changes and adjustments necessary to create the environment where change can occur. For example, consider the following organizational situation, which has to do with Edgar Schein's assumption of space:

- A supervisor-to-employee ratio of 50 to 1
- Supervisors working on a different shift rotation than the hourly workers
- Supervisory job requirements that require them to spend 75 percent of their time on the computer

So, if an assessment finds that the relationship between supervisors and the employees is stressed, the reason may not be a lack of safety leadership capabilities with the supervisors. The three issues identified above are barriers to change. If one of my expectations as a senior leader is that my supervisors will be more accessible and engaging with their direct reports as a way to drive organizational change, then these barriers set the supervisor up for failure unless they go to extremes.

In another instance, workers were routinely working over twelve hours a day for ten or more days in a row. If this work schedule is the result of operational issues, then the supervisor is going to produce little change by focusing on becoming a better safety leader. What the supervisor needs to do is address the operational issues that are creating this situation and increasing safety exposure. It is after the supervisor has stepped up to deal with the barriers to change that he can truly focus on honing his safety leadership skills.

By integrating the teaching of a specific safety activity with leadership best practices, organizations can improve functioning around that activity at the same time they cultivate capabilities in the leader.

## Developing Leadership Skills through a Focus on Safety Leadership

There are several common findings from organizational safety assessments the author has led. These include that the frontline and middle management leaders are not afforded much in the way of leadership development. In addition, the selection systems for filling these positions are heavily weighted toward technical competency. These common findings do lead to the identification of an opportunity to enhance the leadership capabilities of these leaders.

There are an innumerable number of ways that leadership development can be done. The most impactful approach in the author's experience is to focus the leadership knowledge and skill building on safety. The key is to identify a safety activity (observation, inspection, verification audits, leading safety meetings, incident investigation, etc.) that, when done effectively, will move the culture forward and toward the desired attributes. By combining the teaching of a specific safety activity with leadership best practices, organizations can improve functioning around that activity at the same time they cultivate capabilities in the leader. In other words, a single activity accomplishes two objectives.

## Case Study: One Railroad's Journey to Culture Change

In 2006, my firm was approached by a major class 1 railroad to help with the implementation of a peer-to-peer observation system. The organization reported that safety performance was not acceptable and, even more troubling, leaders were struggling to get employees to engage in safety efforts. With over 35,000 employees spread across half of the United States, including operations in Canada and Mexico, the railroad carried the legacy of a culture that had roots 150 years in the past.

Instead of jumping to a solution (peer-to-peer observations), leadership made the decision to conduct an organizational safety assessment. Some of the key findings from the assessment included:

- an "us versus them" culture;
- employees that were disconnected from their company, the leadership, and supervisors;
- a heavy-handed approach to safety, which was described as doing safety to the employees rather than doing safety with them;
- supervisor-to-employee ratios in some situations of 100 to 1;
- employees that didn't know their supervisor's name, only their title;
- wide variation in leadership skills across all levels; and
- an employee population that generally worked independently and had little contact with leadership that wasn't viewed as negative.

Based on the assessment findings, railroad executive leadership did a complete about-face on the strategy for change. The decision was made that the focus would be on enhancing leadership skills and addressing some of the systems that were creating a rift between leaders and workers. Because the culture was not yet ready, the leaders decided to back away from trying to advance peer-to-peer interventions.

All leaders from the executive level to the frontline leaders went through classroom instruction on safety leadership. To assure that the classroom knowledge was understood and the new skills developed, each leader was given individual coaching. The leader would go into the field and conduct the desired safety activity and be observed by the coach. The coach would reinforce the desired behaviors and actions and provide guidance coaching on the opportunities for improvement. This coaching process continued until the leader demonstrated competence. Coupling this safety leadership development with making the safety and labor-relations systems more worker-friendly resulted in major advancements.

Coupling safety leadership development with making the safety and labor-relations systems more worker-friendly results in major advancements.

First was a significant improvement in safety performance as characterized by one leader: "Had I suggested that we could be below a 1 on the reportable incident rate several years ago, they would have thought I was crazy."

What was rewarding to the leadership of the company was that all their effort in improving their own leadership skills and enhancing safety systems drew significant interest from union leaders and employees. This interest was reflected in an expressed desire to be more involved in the safety process. Trained hourly workers rolled out, approaching other workshops that were so successful they were soon expanded to other topic areas. This success led union leaders to allow their people to participate in a formal peer-to-peer process. Currently over fifty peer-to-peer steering committees have been assembled and trained. These committees have trained hundreds of peer observers and have conducted hundreds of thousands of observations, reinforcing safe behaviors while coaching and mentoring others on safer ways to accomplish a task.

## Questions

1. Why is organization culture more the direct outcome of leadership than the hourly team members?
2. Why is focusing on safety an excellent starting point for overall culture change?
3. How can treating some employee unfairly impact teamwork and management credibility?
4. What are the limitations of thinking more narrowly about safety culture versus more broadly about culture?
5. How long does it take to change culture?

## References


Burton, J.P., C.J. Sablynski, and T. Sekiguchi. (2008). "Linking justice, performance, and citizenship via leader-member exchange." *Journal of Business and Psychology* 23(1-2): 51–61.

Cohen-Charash, Y., and P.E. Spector. (2001). "The role of justice in organizations: A meta-analysis." *Organizational Behavior and Human Decision Processes* 86: 278–321.

Colquitt, J.A., D.E. Conlon, M.J. Wesson, O.L. Porter, and K. Yee Ng. (2001). "Justice at the millennium: A meta-analytic review of 25 years of organizational justice research." *Journal of Applied Psychology* 86(3): 425–445.

Dirks, K.T., and D.L. Ferrin. (2002). "Trust in leadership: Meta-analytic findings and implications for research and practice." *Journal of Applied Psychology* 87(4): 611–628.

Gerstner, C., and D. Day. (1997). "Meta-analytic review of leader-member exchange theory: Correlates and construct issues." *Journal of Applied Psychology* 82(6): 827–844.

Hofmann, D. (1999). "Safety-Related Behavior as a Social Exchange: The Role of Perceived Organizational Support and Leader-Member Exchange." *Journal of Applied Psychology* 84: 286.

Illies, R., J.D. Nahrganag, and F.P. Morgeson. (2007). "Leader-member exchange and citizenship behaviors: A meta-analysis." *Journal of Applied Psychology* 92(1): 269–277.

Krause T. (2005). *Leading with Safety*. Hoboken, NJ: Wiley-Interscience.

Rhoades, L., and R. Eisenberger. (2002). "Perceived Organizational Support: A Review of the Literature." *Journal of Applied Psychology* 87: 689–714.

Schein, E. (2004). *Organizational Culture and Leadership*. 3rd ed. Hoboken, NJ: Jossey-Bass.

CHAPTER 28

# CHARACTERISTICS OF EFFECTIVE SAFETY LEADERSHIP

Kevin Slates

## Learning Objectives

After studying this chapter, the reader will be able to:

1. Discuss the characteristics of effective safety leadership and how it influences organizational culture, and safety performance
2. Describe how leadership style can influence organizational culture and safety behaviors
3. Discuss how utilizing a transformational leadership style can change employee attitudes, values, and beliefs
4. Explain the relevant concepts of leadership, safety, and safety performance
5. Describe recommendations for organizational culture change
6. Identify the differences between management and leadership traits and discuss recommendations for managing safety activities

## Key Terms

**Safety culture, safety climate, transactional and transformational leadership, safety management system**

## Abstract

Many environmental, health, and safety (EHS) professionals believe that the identification and control of workplace hazards and the implementation of safety policies will lead to a reduction in workplace injuries and increased safety performance. However, hazard identification and written policies and programs won't address the antecedents associated in poor safety performance. It is my hope that this chapter will offer insights derived from a solid and sufficiently broad knowledge base of theory, research, and practice. To help the reader understand the root causes of workplace accidents and develop a strategy to achieve increased safety performance, this chapter will review the general literature and issues on effective leadership behavior and its influence on culture, employee behavior, and safety performance. The overarching goal of this chapter is to help EHS practitioners achieve their occupational safety and health-related goals and objectives.

## Introduction

In the past several years, during the researcher's career first as a professor of occupational safety and health and as an inspector for the Kentucky Labor Cabinet's Occupational Safety and Health Program, he has witnessed firsthand many workplace injuries and illness caused by slips, trips, falls from elevated surfaces; struck by and caught in-between incidents; and exposures to physical, chemical, and biological hazards. After conducting hundreds of accident investigations, reviewing incident reports, and interviewing managers and employees, this researcher suggests that many of the debilitating injuries and illnesses could have been prevented if the employer understood the relationship between leadership and safety-related outcomes.

Consequently, it is essential that safety and health professionals are cognizant of the rapidly changing workplace. Today, leaders of organizations, including EHS professionals, are under immense pressure to understand the complexity of workers' motivations, while ensuring that their businesses meet requirements of their consumers and regulatory agencies (Tseng et al. 2010). As a result, its vital that EHS professionals understand how to best motivate employees and achieve organizational goals and objectives. This chapter's focus will be transformational leadership since it is the leadership theory that has been most readily applied to workplace safety and health (Kelloway et al. 2002). Previous research studies have since ensued that demonstrate that leadership style has an effect on safety performance (Mearns et al. 1997; Parker et al. 2001).

## Characteristics of Effective Leadership

EHS professionals should ask themselves the question why some companies have effective safety performance while others do not. Perhaps the answer has more to do with organizational leadership. According to Stogdill, a noted leadership researcher, the definition of leadership is one that has been variously defined over the years, often depending upon the researcher.

> Safety leadership is defined as the process of motiving followers to achieve established safety goals.

In the past there have been many questions regarding the nature of leadership and its influence on follower behavior and organizational culture. Scientific research exploring this topic did not take place until the late twentieth century. At one time many asked why some followers in organizations meet articulated goals and objectives while some others did not. After conducting a literature review, Stogdill concluded that the definition of leadership could be defined in terms of influence, behavior norms, role relationships, and traits (Yukl 1998).

> Follow the Leader: Best practices related to safety management systems and programs that promote hazard control and safety performance should be shared among safety professionals.

A leader must first establish a vision for the organization and articulate this vision to the organization (Lock 1991). Cohen (1990) mentioned in his book *The Art of Leadership* true leadership is about communicating one's vision and having it accepted by others in the organization. The fact of the matter is that nothing can be accomplished by leaders alone without the help of others. A study published in *Professional Safety* by researchers Findley, Smith, Kress, Petty, and Enoch (2004) identified leadership commitment as the essential program element that contributed to up to a 65-percent reduction in incident rate and a 350 million–dollar savings. Recently, researchers have gained interest in studying the many aspects of leadership's influence on organizational culture and followers through analysis of transformational and transactional leadership.

Transformational leadership refers to the overall value-based social exchange between the follower and leader empowering them to meet organizational objectives and goals. Previously, many theorists of transformational leadership also analyzed how cultures of organizations are changed to reflect the new goals and objectives established by new leadership (Yukl 1988).

Burns, an eminent social psychologist, viewed transformational leadership as a process in which follower and leaders elevate one another's motivation and morality to higher levels. Leaders may seek to appeal to follower morals and values such as justice, liberty, and equality. Consequently, follower consciousness is raised by the leadership's ability to appeal to emotions, and thus followers work harder to meet leadership expectations (Yukl 1988).

The use of transformational leadership theory to explain leadership behaviors has its critics. Van Knippenberg and Sitkin (2013) noted several problems that may require reexamination of the validity of this leadership theory. The primary issue identified is that transformational leadership lacks a clear definition with meaningful boundaries, allowing for any element of leadership to be clearly seen as either transformational or not.

The next problem identified is that transformational leadership theory has an underdeveloped and overly inclusive causal model (Van Knippenberg and Sitkin 2013). Furthermore, most transformational leadership measurement tools, in particular surveys, are invalid and fail to achieve empirical distinctiveness. These criticisms certainly raise opportunities for future research on transformational leadership theory. It has been this researcher's experience that when EHS managers and supervisors establish safety policies and articulate to employees that they are established out of genuine concern for the employees' wellbeing, employees are more likely to follow their safer work practices and meet employer expectations.

Transactional leadership style is defined as a leadership style guided by the task and rewards based on performance. It's important to mention that leaders and management under this leadership style are motivated only by self-interest. This motivation is in stark contrast to transformational leadership which is guided by the concern for the welfare of others. This leadership style can be characterized as either passive or active. For instance, if a leader waits until something goes wrong in a process and if leadership responds in a reactive manner with the appropriate consequence, this is considered an example of transactional behavior (Avolio 1999). In general, all transactional leadership traits, which have been called by many as job-oriented leadership, are essentially conservative behavior.

> Many researchers believe transformational leadership style is considered an effective leadership style to motive employees to accept and accomplish safety goals.

Now that we have defined both leadership behaviors/styles, you need to ask yourself this fundamental question: which one is a better predictor of safety performance? According to the literature on leadership style and safety outcomes, transformational leadership has a much higher level of safety performance than transactional leadership style (Avolio 1999).

Despite the fact that there are several types of leadership styles or behaviors that can be displayed in an organization, it is clear that effective use of various leadership styles should be situational, depending on the characteristics of the organization. Both leadership styles are summarized by the following (Krause 2005):

### Transactional leadership traits

- Highly individual
- Based on performance and rewards
- Task oriented
- Focuses only on getting the job done
- Best used in unstable environments

### Transformational leadership traits

- Team focused
- Person focused
- Lower employee turnover

## Safety Culture

Previous sections of this chapter have established the importance in achieving organizational goals and objectives and its association with effective leadership. However, we have yet to discuss issues related to culture and its influence on safety performance. How is

> A strong culture is characterized by using leading indicators to assess safety performance and management committing time and resources to communicating organizational values and principles to employees.

culture defined, and how is it influenced by leadership? "Culture is the aggregate total of beliefs, attitudes, values, assumption, and ways of doing things that is shared by members of an organization and taught to new members" (Lussier and Achua 2004, 410). Let's first make a distinction between safety culture and safety climate. In the literature, the terms *safety culture* and *safety climate* are often used without regard to differences in meaning. The beliefs, attitudes, and values held toward the organization are used to define or describe safety culture (Williamson et al. 1997; Cox et al. 1998; Glendon and Stanton 2000; Reiman and Oedewald 2002). For the remaining part of this section, safety culture is the preferred term used.

In summary, these attitudes, norms, and beliefs guide employee behavior by indicating to workers what will be rewarded or punished by the leadership (Biggs et al. 2005). Safety climate, conversely, is considered a snapshot of the organization's perceptions of safety at a particular point in time (Cavazza and Serpe 2009). Consequently, culture can influence how an employee perceives workplace risks (Cooper 2003). Krause (2005) identified and compared the following attributes associated with climate and safety culture:

### Culture

- Changes more slowly
- Unstated
- How we do things
- Applied to many areas of functioning
- Common values that drive
- Organizational performance

### Climate

- Change more rapidly
- Stated
- What we pay attention to
- Applied to a specific area of functioning
- Perception of what is expected, rewarded

> If leadership's actions and behaviors match expected organizational values and beliefs, employees' behaviors are more likely to match the espoused culture.

## Leadership and Its Influence on Organizational Culture

Lussier and Achua (2004) suggested that each organization has its own distinctive organizational culture, distinguished by its own values, behavioral norms, and beliefs about how it makes organizational decisions and priorities. An organization's culture can usually be observed in the attitudes, beliefs, and values displayed by individuals in leadership positions. Lussier and Achua (2004) indicated that organizational cultures can vary in behavior norms displayed by leadership, management, and employees. For example, these behavior norms or cultures can be considered effective or ineffective. Ineffective organizational cultures are characterized by the nonconformity of values, beliefs, and norms. More importantly, ineffective organizational cultures are characterized by the leadership's inability to get employees to accept, support, and carry out the leader's vision.

An effective culture is characterized by management committing significant time and resources to communicating organizational values and principles to employees and customers. In an effective culture, the leader is able to communicate a clear vision and inspire individuals from top management to employees to buy in to the vision (Lussier and Achua 2004). Scholar and author Earl Blair (2003) described the safety culture of an organization as a procedure model composed of four elements: inputs, process activities, outputs, and results.

> a. Inputs are composed of the attitudes, vision, and mission of the organization, as well as leadership, adequate resources, assumption, and engineering controls.
> b. Processes activities are composed of education and training, teamwork, workplace inspections, employee behavior, and open lines of communication.
> c. Output is composed of overall safety performance.
> d. Results are able to be measured by the following indicators of safety performance: inspection conducted, behavioral observations, employees trained, reduction in lost workdays, and restricted work activities. (Peterson 2005)

Blair further indicated that in the past, there were many misconceptions regarding the actual root cause of workplace injuries. For example, in the past, the blame for many workplace injuries was placed upon employee negative attitudes and risk-taking behavior in the workplace. However, the output of poor employee attitudes and values would be associated with lack of leadership's ability to develop a strong safety culture, which in turn, contributes to the output of poor safety performance (Blair 2003). It's the responsibility of leadership to establish and create the safety culture of the organization. He contended that an ineffective safety culture is an indicator of ineffective leadership (Blair 2003).

## Recommendations for Culture Change

Now that foundations and constructs of leadership and safety culture have been discussed, the chapter will now focus on practical recommendations for change. Lussier and Achua (2004) stated that changing a company's culture can be a very difficult and daunting task. They suggest several options leaders can take to successfully change organizational culture. First, leaders must be able to recognize which aspects or beliefs, values, or behavior norms of the current culture are supportive or counterproductive to its achieving organizational goals and objectives. Second, the leader must be able to communicate to all employees which values, behaviors, or beliefs need to be changed to achieve a strong organizational culture.

Third, the leader has to be seen by employees as modeling the new expected behaviors or policies suggested by management. If the leader's actions and behaviors match expected organizational values and beliefs, employees are more likely to match the espoused culture (Lussier and Achua 2004). Lussier and Achua (2004) proposed that there are substantive and symbolic actions that leadership can utilize in shaping the organizational culture they desire. Substantive actions include:

- New facilities design
- Replacing old members with new organizational members
- Developing written values and mission statements
- Creating new and changing old dysfunctional policies

Symbolic actions include:

- Leadership serving as role models and mentor to new employees
- Special recognition of employee achievement and appearances by leaders
- Organizational structure and establishing rewards and incentives

## Supervisor and Management Contributions

To properly treat the subject of leadership and safety performance, some discussion should be provided about the role of supervisors and management contributions to effective leadership and the differences between the two. Having the first-line supervisor actively involved in a safety program is essential to establishing a safety program. Heinrich (1959) was the first to postulate that the key to accident prevention in the workplace was supervisor involvement. Since supervisors are considered to be line management, they have a direct influence on employee behavior and attitudes in the workplace. Previous research studies have since ensued that demonstrate that leadership style and the behaviors of supervisors are have an effect on safety performance (Mearns et al. 1997; Niskanen 1994; Parker et al. 2001). If, for example, the supervisor neglects to wear a hard hat in construction areas, employees working under the supervisor's direction usually neglect wear them also. According to social learning theorist Albert Banduar, people learn from observing the actions and outcomes of others' behaviors as well as from the concept of modeling. Modeling can be seen in two different ways: live or symbolic. The live

> First-line supervisors usually have the most experience and training regarding the nature of the job and usually are aware of the hazards associated with it. The first-line supervisor usually sets an example for other employees.

model is best described as the live actual observable behaviors displayed by an individual. The symbolic model is described as viewing the actions or behaviors of an individual in a medium, such as videotapes, and television actors (Sims and Manz 1982).

For instance, employees can observe the manager or supervisor participating in toolbox talks, attending safety committee meetings, following safety work practices, and wearing personal protective equipment when working with or near mobile cranes, material hoists, elevated working surfaces, excavation, demolition, and steel erection. Bandura indicated four ideal conditions that better enable individuals to model expected behaviors of others. They include the following (Blair 2003):

1. Attention: The observer must observe in detail the actions and behaviors of the model.
2. Retention: The displayed behaviors must be remembered by the observer. This process is strengthened if the behavior is retained.
3. Reproduction: The repetition of the expected behavior increased the observer ability to successfully replicate the behavior displayed by the model.
4. Motivation: The observer has to be self-motivated to replicate what he or she has observed and reproduce the desired behavior.

In summary, Bandura's model of reciprocal determinism can be defined as a state in which the individual and the environment influence each other and can be used to examine organizational safety culture because it reflects situational, psychological, and behavioral factors that contribute to accident rates. This model for safety culture explains that individuals are not solely controlled or influenced by self-determination or their environments. Instead, a state exists between the individual and the environment called *reciprocal determinism* in which the individual and the environment influence one other (Henry et al. 1982).

Jack Welch (2003), former chief executive officer of General Electric, said that he preferred avoiding the term *manager* during his tenure as CEO at General Electric. Instead he felt that the term *leader* was well suited for the job activities of managers. When employees observe supervisors' attitudes toward safety, they see a direct reflection of upper management's commitment to providing a safe and healthful workplace (Phillips et al. 2001). The behaviors of managers and supervisors can be modeled by employees if management sets a good example by following safety and health policy. Anton (1997) remarked that supervisors should be responsible for developing positive attitudes toward safety at workplace. Supervisors serve as the direct link between top management and employees by sharing, enforcing, and communicating the vision of a safety culture. Supervisors can develop employee attitudes toward safety in the following ways;

- First, they should readily accept and become advocates of management vision and commitment regarding the company safety program.
- Second, supervisors should never violate company safety rules or condone employees who do so.

As can been seen in earlier section of this chapter, management commitment to safety can be considered an antecedent to employee behavior. Management support of safety efforts constitutes a positive psychological environment that encourages safe behavior (Neal & Griffin 2004). Collective safety management practices, such as safety training and enforcement efforts are precursors of the employees' perceptions about the importance of safety in their organization (Hoffman et al. 1995).

These managerial safety behaviors and communication efforts reflect a genuine sense of how the organization values safety and motivates employees toward not just complying with safety policies but to be aware of hazardous conditions within their work environment (Dejoy et al. 2004; Hoffman et al. 1995). For example, according to Bailey (1989), using the Minnesota Perception Survey in the railroad industry finding of his case study showed that employees who perceived management commitment to safety recorded a low rate. Therefore, management commitment to safety efforts such as effective safety training must result in observable activity and, more importantly, be demonstrated in their behavior as well as their words (Hoffman et al. 1995). Table 28.1 reflects differences between safety leadership and management traits.

**Table 28.1** Distinction between safety leadership and safety management traits

| Management Traits | Leadership Traits |
|---|---|
| Management involves coping with process and complexity | Leadership involves coping with change |
| Management communicates policy to employees | Leaders persuade employees |
| Management is responsible for work procedures and practices | Leaders set the vision for the future for the organization |
| Management is responsible for planning and organizing | Leaders guide people through challenging times |
| Management ensures plans are achieved by solving problems | Leaders align people, and set the direction for the organization |

Modified from Kotter (1990).

## Recommendations for Safety Performance

Incorporating management principles based on safety can be a challenge for environmental, health, and safety professionals. The following is a summary of how safety activities should be managed. Dan Peterson (2003) suggested the following three recommendations for how safety should be managed:

- Safety should be managed similar to any other business function, with management commitment and strong leadership.
- In general, an unsafe behavior or hazardous condition in the workplace is a symptom of a failure in the management system.
- It is management and leadership's job to change the environment and organizational culture that leads to hazardous conditions and at-risk behaviors.
- Safety professionals must first evaluate the existing culture.
- Evaluate the organization's attitude toward occupational safety and health goals and objectives. Integrating safety into the culture requires accountability at all levels of the organization.

## Safety Management Systems

Now that foundations and constructs of transactional leadership have been discussed, the chapter will now focus the importance of safety management systems. Managing the organizational safety system has received increased attention in the published safety literature. However, there appears to be no universal definition or criteria of what constitutes an effective safety management system (Hale et al. 1997; Santos-Reyes and Beard 2002), although previous studies have stressed the importance of a having an effective safety management system (Hale et al. 1997). This disparity is partly due to differences in organizational safety culture, history, company size, as well as other variables. Kirwan (1998) defines the safety management system as a set of written policies, strategies, practices, procedures, roles, and functions associated with safety.

Safety management systems are concerned with improving safety outcomes by influencing employee attitudes and behaviors with regards to risk, thereby reducing unsafe employee behaviors (Fernández-Muñiz et al. 2007). Examples of safety management systems include vision and mission statements, employee responsibilities, and goals, which set into

> Traditionally, a major flaw with most safety management systems is related to their use as criteria for the measurement of safety performance outcomes. For example, safety management systems are typically determined by lagging safety performance indicators, such as worker compensation (WC) claims, Occupational Safety and Health Administration (OSHA) incident rates, and post-accident investigations.

place acceptable standards of employee behavior. Employees who perceive that the organization's safety management system as ineffective will be more likely to not follow policies or procedures outlined in their safety program (Lu and Yang 2010).

This type of data can only prevent repetition of a similar accident rather than proactively predicting or preventing the accident (Booth and Lee 1995). WC information and OSHA incident reports always trail behind an accident, whereas effective safety management system policies and procedures are trying to prevent accidents from occurring initially by using leading indicators of safety performance. A leading indicator of safety performance is defined as what employees are doing today to prevent workplace injuries (Peterson 2005).

Prominent theorist and researcher Peterson (2005), in his book titled *Measurement of Safety Performance*, gave the following examples of leading indicators of safety performance: behavioral observations and employee perception surveys. It's important to mention that since employee behavior has been found to play a larger role in workplace accidents, it is insufficient to judge the success or failures of the organizations' safety management system. As a result, a safety management system approach to improving safety performance must include a behavioral component and also an assessment method for a more complete understanding of workplace safety behavior. Self-reporting of safety behaviors and perceptions of safety are alternative or complementary methods to evaluate safety management systems (Hoffman et al. 1995).

## Conclusion

This chapter highlights the critical role leaders, managers, supervisors, and employees play in establishing positive safety performance. Understanding that effective leadership behavior has a direct influence on culture, which in turn increases safety performance within the workplace, should not be disregarded. Furthermore, evidence in this chapter suggests that leadership—in particular, transformational leadership—is a positive driver for the safety behaviors in the workplace. Several implications can be drawn from the findings of this chapter.

> Safety leadership is a significant factor influencing safety culture in organizations and should be taken into consideration by hiring managers and human resources professionals when selecting candidates.

In conclusion, by understanding this, EHS professionals can develop effective policies, procedures, and training programs to influence ineffective organizational culture, in turn changing the attitudes, values, and beliefs of the employees. It is self-evident that people's actions and behavior can be influenced by their positive or negative perception of the leadership. How employees are perceived to be treated is one of the major indicators of the level of safety performance in a company. Whether employees are considered a valuable resource or simply as a cost of doing business will, in large part, determine if the company will or won't achieve positive safety outcomes.

## Questions

1. This chapter identifies and describes recommendations for culture change. Discuss recommendations for culture change.
2. Define transformational and transactional leadership.
3. The safety culture of an organization can be described as a procedural model. List and discuss the four major elements of this model.

4. Describe the attributes associated with safety culture and climate, and discuss the differences between the safety culture and climate.
5. Identify management and leadership traits and discuss how each can affect safety performance.

## References


Anton, Thomas J. (1979). *Occupational Safety and Health Management*. New York: McGraw-Hill.

Avolio, B. J. (1999). *Full Leadership Development: Building the Vital Forces in Organizations*. Thousand Oaks, CA: Sage Publications, Inc.

Biggs, H. C., D. P. Dingsdag, D. Cipolla, V. L. Sheahan, and W. Artuso. (2005). "Utilizing a Safety Culture Management Approach in the Australian Construction Industry." *QUT Research Week*. Queensland, Australia: Queensland University of Technology.

Blair, E.. (2003). "Safety Performance Culture and Leadership." *Professional Safety*: 18.

Cavazza, N., and A. Serpe. (2009). "Effects of Safety Climate on Safety Norm Violations: Exploring the Mediating Role of Attitudinal Ambivalence toward Personal Protective Equipment." *Journal of Safety Research* 40: 277–83.

Cohen, W. (1990). *The Art of Leadership*. Upper Saddle River, NJ: Prentice Hall.

Cooper, D. (2003). "Psychology, Risk and Safety." *Professional Safety*: 11, 39–44.

DeJoy, D. M., B. S. Schaffer, M. G. Wilson, R. J. Vandenberg, and M. M. Butts. (2004). "Creating Safer Workplaces: Assessing the Determinants and Role of Safety climaTe." *Journal of Safety Research* 35(1): 81–90.

Eckenfelder, J. D. (2003). "Getting the Safety Culture Right." *Occupational Hazards*. Accessed October 12, 2004. www.occupationalhazards.com.

Fernández-Muñiz, B., J. M. Montes-Peón, and C. J. Vázquez-Ordás. (2007). "Safety Management System: Development and Validation of a Multidimensional Scale." *Journal of Loss Prevention in the Process Industries* 20(1): 52–68.

Findley, M., S. Smith, T. Kress, G. Petty, and K. Enoch. (2004). "Injury and Cost Control Safety Program Elements in Construction." *Professional Safety*: 14, 18.

Guldenmund, F. (2000). "The Nature of Safety Culture: A Review of Theory and Research." *Safety Science* 34(1-3), 215–57.

Hale, A. R., B. H. J. Heming, J. Carthey, and B. Kirwan. (1997). "Modeling of Safety Management." *Safety Science* 26(1/2): 121–40.

Hall, M. (2006). *Measuring the Safety Climate of Steel Mini-mill Workers Using an Instrument Validated by Structural Equation Modeling*. Doctoral Dissertation, Tennessee University.

Harrell, K. (2003). *The Attitude of Leadership*. Hoboken, NJ: John Wiley & Sons, Inc.

Heinrich, H. W. (1959). *Industrial Accident Prevention* (5th ed.). New York: McGraw-Hill.

Hoffmann, D. A., R. Jacobs, and F. Landy. (1995). "High Reliability Process Industries: Individual, Micro and Macro Organizational Errors Influences on Safety System Performance." *Journal of Safety Research* 26: 131–49.

Kotter, J. P. (1990). "What Do Leaders Really Do?" *Harvard Business Review* 68: 103–11.

Kelloway, K. E., and J. Barling. (2010). "Leadership Development as an Intervention in Occupational Health Psychology." *Work and Stress* 24(3): 260–79.

Krause, T. R. (2005). *Leading with Safety*. Hoboken, NJ: Wiley-Interscience.

Lock, A. E. (1991). *The Essence of Leadership*. New York: Lexington Books.

Lu, C. S., and C. S. Yang. (2010). "Safety Leadership and Safety Behavior in Container Terminal Operations." *Safety Science* 48(2): 123–34.

Lussier, N. R., and C. F. Achua. (2003). *Leadership: Theory, Application, Skill Development* (2nd ed.) Stamford, CT: South Western Thompson Corp.

Mearns, K., R. Flin, M. Fleming, and R. Gordon. (1997). *Human and Organizational Factors, Offshore Safety Report (OTH 543)*. Norwich, UK: HSE Books.

Neal, A., M. A. Griffin, and P. M. Hart. (2000). "The Impact of Organizational Climate on Safety Climate and Individual Behavior." *Safety Science* 34: 99–109.

Parker, S., C. Axtell, and N. Turner. (2001). "Designing a Safer Workplace: Importance of Job Autonomy, Communication Quality and Supportive Supervisors." *Journal of Occupational Health Psychology* 6: 211–28.

Petersen, D. (2005). *Measurement of Safety Performance*. Chicago: American Society of Safety Engineers.

Hagan, P. E., J. F. Montgomery, and J. T. O'Reilly. (2001). *National Safety Counsel Accident Prevention Manual for Business and Industry Administration and Programs*. Itasca, IL: National Safety Council.

Santos-Reyes, J., and A. L. Beard. (2002). "Assessing Safety Management Systems." *Journal of Loss Prevention in the Process Industries* 15: 77–95.

Seo, D. C., M. Torabi, E. H. Blair, and N. T. Ellis. (2004). "A Cross Validation of Safety Climate Scale Using a Confirmatory Factor Analytic Approach." *Journal of Safety Research* 35: 427–45.

Sims, H. Jr., and C. C. Manz. (1982). "Social Learning Theory." *Journal of Organizational Behavior Management* 3: 4, 55–63.

Tseng, H. C., H. L. Tung, and C. H. Duan. (2010). "Mapping the Intellectual Structure of Modern Leadership Studies." *Leadership and Organisation Development Journal* 31(1): 57–70.

Van Knippenberg, D., and S. B. Sitkin. (2013). "A Critical Assessment of Charismatic-transformational Leadership Research: Back to the Drawing Board?" *The Academy of Management Annals* 7(1): 1–60.

Welch, J. (2002). *The Jack Welch Lexicon of Leadership*. New York: McGraw-Hill.

Williamson, A. M., A. Feyer, D. Cairns, and D. Biancotti. (1997). "The Development of a Measure of Safety Climate: The Role of Safety Perceptions and Attitudes." *Safety Science* 25(1–3): 15–27.

Yukl, G. (1998). *Leadership in Organizations* (4th ed.). Upper Saddle River, NJ: Prentice Hall.

Zohar, D. (2002). "The Effects of Leadership Dimensions, Safety Climate, and Assigned Priorities on Minor Injuries in Work Groups." *Journal of Organizational Behavior* 23: 75–92.

CHAPTER 29

# RISK LEADERSHIP: A MULTIDISCIPLINARY APPROACH

Tania Van der Stap

## Learning Objectives

After studying this chapter, the reader will be able to:

1. Discuss the two types of risk (residual risk and entropic risk) that negatively impact productivity, work quality, and EHS performance, using an incident/loss causation model (entropy model).
2. Apply a multidisciplinary approach to effectively manage the two risk types and achieve productivity, quality work, and EHS incident mitigation concurrently
3. Evaluate EHS management systems, the organizational culture, leadership, and risk management capability, which are subject to degradation and negatively impact the business's capacity to manage risk effectively and achieve the desired performance outcomes
4. Recognize that a shift has occurred from safety to risk management as a result of changes to international standards, legislation, the focus of risk-related disciplines, and industry's need for increased productivity without compromising EHS performance
5. Evaluate the critical role of the EHS professional in providing sound technical knowledge and capacity to build a risk-based organization culture aligned to the Journey Maturity Model
6. Encourage organizational leaders to seek opportunities from EHS management systems and practices in addition to understanding and effectively managing the business's total risk profile

## Key Terms

**Entropy model, risk management, management system, resilience engineering, alignment fallacy**

## Abstract

This chapter presents a multidisciplinary approach to risk management written with the practical needs of the environmental health and safety (EHS) professional in mind. Regardless of whether a professional's job role is EHS or a combination of these disciplines, the models and principles presented here can be applied in any workplace.

## Introduction

The EHS profession has undertaken a significant journey in the last fifteen years. Historically, safety and environmental management were seen as separate organizational functions and were managed accordingly. Safety and human resource management were also standalone. The concept of a fully integrated approach to risk management addressing all systems risks within processes, technologies, the work environment, human resources, and the interfaces between such systems was not considered feasible. Within hazardous industries with a profit motive, it was not readily accepted that risk could be managed to achieve production, quality output, and EHS incident mitigation concurrently. Production and associated pressures, whether real or perceived, were issues out of bounds to the EHS professional.

A holistic, risk-based approach to achieving production, quality work, and EHS incident prevention was presented in *Productive Safety Management* published by Butterworth Heinemann in 2003. This chapter presents the foundation tools of such work, provides a contemporary update, and explains the role of the EHS professional as a risk leader and subject matter expert within a multidisciplinary management team. An evolving perspective on the nature of risk is included in the discussion, along with strategies for effective risk management.

## The Nature of Risk

Risk is associated with negative outcomes such as regret and loss; however, there is no reward without risk. Risk is fundamentally a choice of cost or consequence against the benefit. Financial management embraces both ends of this spectrum, whereas traditionally, EHS management has tended to focus on negative outcomes.

Risk is generally understood as a singular concept; in other words, categories of risk have not been defined except to say that once risk has been reduced, there remains a residual risk. In recent years, however, a number of researchers have correlated the concept of *entropy*, the tendency of systems to shift to a state of chaos, which has its origins in thermodynamics, to safety. For instance, Liu Dunwen, Y Lei, and Li Bo (2012) undertook a study of mathematics, referred to as "fuzzy" mathematics using entropy theory, to building construction safety.

> In order to improve the safety management level of construction site, a new kind of safety evaluation method using the combination of fuzzy mathematics and the entropy theory was put forward . . . The results show that the hybrid method, which can overcome the shortcomings of each single method, is feasible, practical and operational in construction site safety assessment.

Likewise, Nurwulan and Jiang (2016) apply this mathematic approach to evaluate the distracting effect of mobile phones on pedestrians. Murat (2011) undertook a study of traffic safety level determination for black spots.

> Fuzzy mathematics demonstrates that entropy (the tendency of systems to move to a state of chaos) is a risk that affects safety.

> The safety levels of black spots and center of black spots are determined and classified using Shannon Entropy approach. Geometrical and physical conditions, traffic volume, average speed and accident rate are considered as effective parameters on safety level determination . . . The results can be used for decision makers who are trying to find optimum investment assignment.

The research done using Shannon's entropy approach with the correlation to safety and risk exposure lends weight to entropy as a category of risk. Larranaga (2013) refers to this concept as "disaster creep" and states:

> Many modern energy, industrial, transportation, health care, telecommunications, and political systems are highly vulnerable to small changes that

propagate and develop into major disasters. This systemic tendency to unravel, decay uncontrollably, or move from order to disorder (e.g., disaster) is a characteristic of all natural and human-made systems and is defined by Newton's Second Law of thermodynamics as 'entropy.' Before one can overcome this entropic tendency of all systems to unravel, one must understand the nature of system failure across multiple disciplines.

These contemporary research studies support the concept of entropy as a risk factor, if not a risk type. This theory was introduced in the entropy model in *Productive Safety Management* as a means of illustrating incident causation and the relationship between risk and business objectives, specifically production, quality, and EHS incident mitigation. It is explained in the following section.

## The Entropy Model

The entropy model presents two types of risk: residual risk and entropic risk. Everything humankind does has some risk associated with it. In business, energy is used to source product and to transform, transport, and consume. The amount of energy involved is the inherent risk associated with the process that is being undertaken. As a day-to-day example, when driving a car at sixty miles per hour, there is inherent energy that cannot be reduced under a given time constraint for the journey.

By establishing controls, this inherent risk is reduced to as low as reasonably practical. For instance, when driving at sixty miles per hour, the energy level is still present, but by designing and manufacturing cars with safety features, the residual risk has been reduced. By design, society can lower residual risk through technological improvements, which generally occurs over the longer term through innovation and economies of scale as these improvements become more affordable and standardized.

Figure 29.1 shows the first part of the entropy model, which is applied to a diagrammatic form, rather than mathematical representation. Residual risk is present and cannot be reduced in the short term due to technological and resource constraints. As a result, the probability of an incident or loss is never zero; in other words, it is above the perfect system's risk level shown by the red line in the first column. In hazardous industries, such as mining, oil and gas, transportation, and manufacturing, this residual risk is relatively high compared to non-energy-dependent businesses, and therefore, there is always the potential for an undesirable event or loss of productive output.

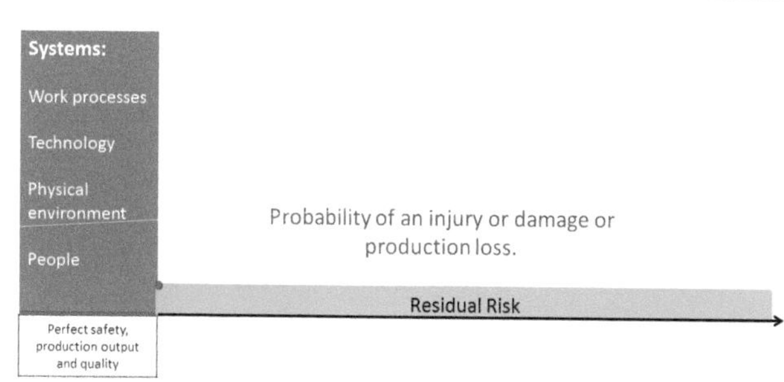


Figure 29.1
Entropy model, part 1: Residual risk (adapted from Mol 2003, figure 1.5, page 13).

As a small detour from the model, where does "zero harm" fit? From a risk perspective, it does not because residual risk cannot be eliminated; therefore, all unwanted events or losses cannot be eradicated. Zero harm should be understood as a cultural driver, not a reflection on the reality of risk. It is possible for an organization to achieve a zero-harm hour in terms of EHS incidents, then another hour, which becomes a day, which becomes a month, thus perpetuating this target until broken. Zero harm is a statement of underlying beliefs and values.

The entropy model posits that residual risk is inherent in the four systems that combine when businesses operate. These are processes (how the work is done), technologies, the physical environment, and human resources. In addition, these four systems degrade over time, sometimes gradually and at other times rapidly. This is referred to as *entropic risk.*

Figure 29.2 shows the systems degrading as the blue dotted line, and concurrently as this downhill slide occurs, the probability of an incident or loss to the business rises, shown by the red line. Importantly, while this entropic risk may be related

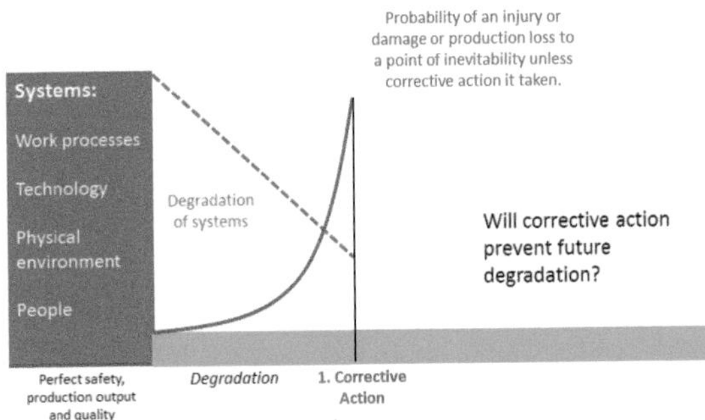


Figure 29.2
Entropy model, part 2: Entropic risk (adapted from Mol 2003, figure 1.5, page 13).

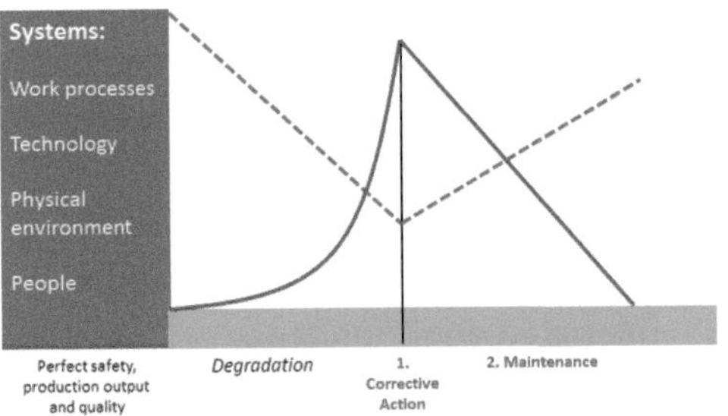


Figure 29.3
Entropy model, part 3: Corrective action and maintenance practices (adapted from Mol 2003, figure 1.5, page 13).

to the probability of EHS incidents, it also impacts production and work quality.

For instance, plant and equipment degrade as a result of wear and tear or due to damage. Hydraulic hoses in a critical production plant are a good example. Where a company has repeat hydraulic bursts, then degradation has reached the point of failure. Is this a safety issue? Not necessarily, provided that no one is "in the line of fire." It is, however, an important issue for production and quality as degradation of critical parts is a business risk. The model indicates that EHS incidents are an outcome of escalating risk.

Note in figure 29.2 that the probability of an incident or loss rises from the residual risk level (not zero) and then escalates as systems degrade. The entropy model shows that when system standards are in decline, this needs to be recognized and corrective action taken promptly. Such action prevents further degradation and thereby circumvents future incidents or losses, remembering that escalating degradation makes losses inevitable.

At the strategic level, corrective actions can be responses to red flags or identified risks to production—for instance, threats to the supply chain or EHS incidents that require shutdown and draw the attention of the regulator. The level of action required can range from local issues management to crisis management, depending on the overall impact to the business.

Corrective action, both strategically and operationally, is critical at any point along the degradation continuum. When companies go through a cycle of red flags, quick fixes, operate as normal, red flags, and more quick fixes, it is often because of the failure to recognize degradation and take corrective action until the undesirable outcome becomes evident.

The model also illustrates, in figure 29.3, that proactive maintenance practices are required in all system areas to prevent degradation. System factor standards are raised while concurrently the probability of incidents and failures is lowered to the nonreducible residual risk level. This is the best that can be achieved in the short term due to resource and technological constraints.

The root cause of entropic risk is the tendency of organizational systems to shift toward a state of chaos. Proactive maintenance is the counter-action to chaos. Corrective action is reactive while proactive maintenance practices are a managed response to recurrent issues and known risks. Both are required and set the standards of performance by which a company operates strategically and also at the individual worker level. The model promotes monitoring practices and data analysis. For example: "Why are repeat occurrences of burst hydraulic hoses on production critical plant occurring? At what point in the product lifecycle should hoses be replaced to prevent failures?"

Another example is when workplace inspections regularly report poor housekeeping standards. Corrective action can involve a campaign to get work areas back to an orderly and safe condition; however, will that prevent recurrence? The key questions to be asked are "What systems need to be in place to

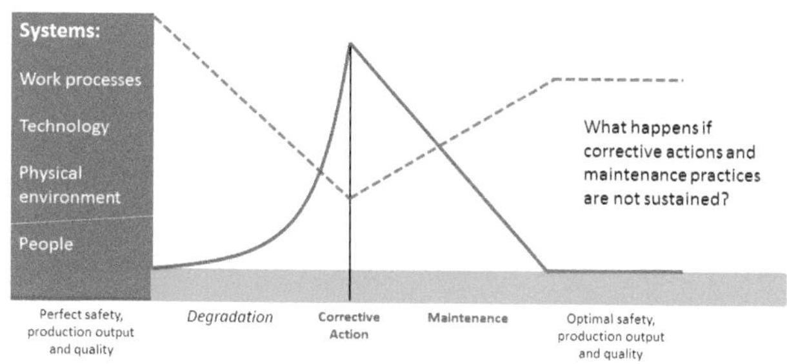


Figure 29.4
Entropy model, part 4: risk optimization. (Adapted from Mol 2003, figure 1.5, page 13).

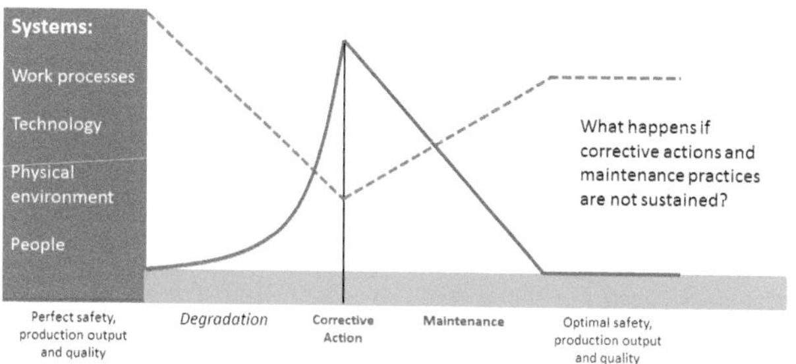


Figure 29.5
Entropy model, part 5: degradation creep and the four-fold strategy. (Adapted from Mol 2003, figure 1.5, page 13).

encourage the desired housekeeping standards? What changes can we make to set a higher standard of safety, quality work, and efficiency?" Logically, any modifications would involve the input of the people who are responsible for the workplace.

Looking more broadly at recurrent issues that require corrective action, the key questions for the EHS professional within a multidisciplinary team are: *"Can it be measured? Can the status of degradation in the product/workplace lifecycle be determined?"* If it can be measured, if it can be inspected and assessed to refine and inform the decision-making process, then degradation can be prevented from escalating to failure. The model promotes EHS in design, engineering solutions, monitoring, and data analysis of faults and failure rates.

Figure 29.4 illustrates the level of risk that a company should be aiming to stabilize. Degradation is prevented by reactive corrective action as needed and implementation of proactive maintenance practices. The company achieves optimization when the risk level is brought down to the residual risk level. Under these conditions, what is the probability of incidents and losses? The answer is "as low as reasonably practical." Accordingly, a compliance outcome is also achieved.

There is no room for complacency in the organization. In figure 29.5, the entropy model provides a reminder that systems have a tendency to degrade, so if decision-making and behaviors do not sustain the focus on risk management, systems will go into decline again, and the probability of incidents and failures will escalate.

The EHS practitioner has a vital role to play in coaching managers and supervisors to promote corrective action and proactive maintenance as an organizational discipline. These two steps, shown in red in the model at 1 and 2, are the first steps in the "four-fold strategy." These aim to counter complacency about entropic risk and drive the desired operational behaviors.

Likewise, because of the depth of risk mitigations in most first-world hazardous industries, the workforce may be lulled into a false sense of security and safety. Residual risks associated with energies are contained, guarded, isolated, or controlled in such a way to prevent the worker from being "in the line of fire." It is assumed that personnel can concentrate on the task at hand, alert only to more minor hazards. The modern, seemingly well-controlled workplace allows complacency to creep in despite residual risk. This is also evident within society generally—for example, in relation to driving of motor vehicles. While safety in design has improved significantly over the last fifty years, respect for the energies involved has diminished. This is evident in behavioral factors such as risk-taking choices, including intoxication, fatigue, distraction, and speeding (Fitch et al. 2013).

The entropy model shows that residual risk cannot be reduced in the short term. It provides step 3, indicating that workers must remain alert. The higher the total residual risks of the four systems in combination, the greater the need for vigilance and operational discipline in implementing required controls. Examples include heavy vehicle road transport in hazardous conditions, remote oil and gas platforms, and underground mining operations with difficult geotechnical conditions.

The level of residual risk that is acceptable is a strategic decision driven by cost-benefit analysis and availability of alternatives. The front end of a project where design, construction, and commissioning decisions are made will determine the level of residual risk inherent during the operations lifecycle. The model shows that residual risk can be reduced in the longer term through technological innovation and economies of scale. This is shown as the fourth step required for effective risk management.

The four-fold strategy is a tool for both management decision-making and individual behaviors. The steps are:

1. take immediate corrective action to eliminate entropic risk;
2. establish maintenance strategies to prevent future entropic risk;
3. manage residual risk in the short term by remaining alert and exercising operational discipline when implementing required controls; and
4. reduce residual risk in the longer term through investment, technological innovations, and economies of scale.

## Building a Total Risk Profile

The two types of risk are found in the four system factors that combine when work is done. This methodology provides a comprehensive risk profile for the business. A detailed breakdown of risks for processes, technologies, the physical environment, and human resources is provided in *Productive Safety Management.* A summary table is included here to give the reader general understanding of the risk interfaces or sources and indicative controls.

The need for a multidisciplinary approach becomes evident with the need to address EHS in design for processes, the physical workplace, and technologies. Human resource management (HRM)–related strategies are required to address cultural and behavioral issues. EHS management systems provide a procedural foundation and cover traditional practices, including but not limited to risk assessments, emergency planning, and auditing and inspection regimes.

**Table 29.1** Residual and entropic risks and indicative controls by system factor

| SYSTEM FACTOR | RESIDUAL RISK | ENTROPIC RISK |
|---|---|---|
| Processes<br><br>Controls for all interfaces<br>• Process safety<br>• Risk assessments of all phases of process lifecycle and management of change | Process/technology interface<br><br>Process/physical environment interface<br><br>Process/human resource interface | Process/technology interface<br><br>Process/physical environment interface<br><br>Process/human resource interface |

*Continued*

| SYSTEM FACTOR | RESIDUAL RISK | ENTROPIC RISK |
|---|---|---|
| Technology | Design and manufacturing shortcomings<br>• Pre-purchase evaluation<br>• Supplier information<br>• Performance monitoring and big data<br>Technology/physical environment interface<br>• Design and planning of work environment<br>• Hazop studies<br>• Installation standards<br>• Major hazard standards<br>Technology/process interface<br>• Standardization of technologies<br>• Risk assessment<br>Technology/human resources interface<br>• Ergonomic design<br>• Job design<br>• Task modification | Wear and tear<br>• Proactive scheduled maintenance<br>• Inspection and monitoring regime<br>• Planned replacements<br>• Reactive maintenance<br>Technology/operator interface<br>• Pre-operational training<br>• Organizational culture and desired behaviors<br>• Correction of undesirable behaviors |
| Physical Environment | Site design shortcomings<br>• Site environmental studies<br>• Documentation of residual risks<br>Physical environment/process interface<br>• Site assessment and selection<br>• Site design and layout<br>Physical environment/technology interface<br>• Design and planning of workplace<br>• Pre-installation risk assessment<br>• Safe work practices<br>Physical environment/human resources interface<br>• Modifications to fit worker<br>• Flexible work practices<br>• Monitoring of worker health<br>• Residual awareness training | Natural degradation<br>• Regular monitoring<br>• Emergency response and crisis management<br>• Maintenance regime<br>Physical environment/process interface<br>• Monitoring and inspection regime<br>• Safe work practices<br>• Proactive scheduled maintenance<br>• Reactive maintenance<br>Physical environment/technology interface<br>• Monitoring and inspection regime<br>• Proactive scheduled maintenance<br>• Reactive maintenance<br>Physical environment/human resources interface<br>• Monitoring for person fit<br>• Inductions and training<br>• Housekeeping<br>• Culture of desired behaviors |

*Continued*

| SYSTEM FACTOR | RESIDUAL RISK | ENTROPIC RISK |
|---|---|---|
| Human Resources | Incomplete competencies<br>• Inductions and training ongoing<br>• Risk awareness training ongoing<br>• Change management<br>• Communication systems<br>Physical limitations<br>• Physical environment modifications<br>• Matching capability to task<br>• Sick leave entitlements<br>• Job rotation and enrichment<br>• Safe work procedures<br>• Preventative health measures | The new employee<br>• Value-based recruitment<br>• Mentoring<br>• Supervision<br>• Hazard monitoring (person is hazard)<br>Fatigue<br>• Workplace, technology and process modifications<br>• Job rotation<br>• Fatigue monitoring<br>• Training<br>Ill health<br>• Training and self-assessment<br>• Healthy lifestyle programs<br>• Monitoring of worker wellbeing<br>Stress<br>• Education and training<br>• Employee assistance programs<br>• Dispute resolution<br>• Right sizing of staffing levels<br>Safety violations and drug and alcohol breaches<br>• Organization culture<br>• Disciplinary procedures<br>• Risk identification and management training<br>• Communication processes<br>• Pre-employment testing<br>• Random testing<br>Healthy lifestyle programs<br>Employee assistance programs |

The total risk profile approach is helpful in highlighting interdependencies that exist within organizations. For instance, the rate of wear and tear of truck components will be affected by the behavior and competencies of the operator from the production department. The mechanical reliability of the truck will be affected by the behavior and competencies of the tradespersons from the maintenance department. The two departments are therefore both responsible for preventing technology-related entropic risk.

> There are four steps for managing risk to achieve production/productivity, quality work, and EHS incident mitigation concurrently.

The entropy model assists personnel to understand *why* the quality of their work is critical to overall risk management. Substandard work practices and a culture of complacency contribute to production losses, quality deficiencies, and increased risk of EHS incidents. The four-fold strategy is thus a cultural and behavioral driver for operational discipline. With a risk-based focus, interdependencies between functions can be identified and, concurrently, organizational silos broken down.

## Sustaining a Risk Management Culture

The EHS professional needs the competencies to span the "helicopter view" to the granular detail of the risk profile, to lead the risk management function. The big picture is that a business that builds risk management capability will achieve productivity, quality output, and EHS incident mitigation concurrently.

The foundation strategy to achieve effective risk management is to build and embed a robust risk-based management system in consultation with stakeholders. The EHS professional at this early stage of the journey tends to be the "process owner" or "subject matter expert" of this system, and initially it will be centralized within the EHS Department. However, the longer-term strategy should be to decentralize to the extent that optimizes operational ownership of frontline supervisors and workers at the risk face. The transition from centralization to right-sized decentralization is therefore a journey of continuous improvement.

The organization's risk management capability can be mapped to the safety journey maturity model. Hudson's model identifies five steps from a "pathological" stage where systems are underdeveloped and the culture is "no care" to "generative" where managing risk is a way of life (Hudson 2003; Hudson 2007; Foster and Hoult 2003). Systems are fully integrated and sustainable. The stages have been described here in relation to risk management as opposed to safety management to align to the entropy model:

- Pathological—Uncontrolled risk is a problem caused by workers. The main drivers are production/profit and a desire not to get caught by the regulator or external stakeholders who will hold the business and its management to account.
- Reactive—Organizations start to take risk management seriously, but there is only action after incidents or significant losses.
- Calculative/Compliant—Risk management is embedded within the management system only to the level of compliance. Risk management is primarily top-down and imposed rather than the workforce having operational ownership.
- Proactive—Compliance is the norm and signs of continuous improvement through risk management are occurring. Unexpected events may still be a challenge. The workforce's involvement starts to translate into bottom-up, along with the top-down leadership already in place.
- Generative—There is active participation at all levels. Risk management to achieve production/productivity, quality work, and EHS incident mitigation is a key driver of business performance. The organization maintains a chronic unease as a counter to complacency and degradation. A culture of learning is espoused with a desire for leader-leader interactions rather than leader-follower, which was based on outdated command-and-control management.

Some organizations have identified specific activities and behaviors to these stages of the maturity journey and captured these in an audit tool, for instance using ISO 18001 or ISO/DIS 45001.2:2017 Occupational Health and Safety (OH&S) Management System Standard. The results of the first audit are used to benchmark the business unit and provide a basis for improvement.

A cautionary word needs to be provided in relation to these tools, however, particularly when ascribing results into "proactive" and "generative" categories. High scores can simply mean that well-embedded calculative/compliant EHS management systems are in place. This tends to be tangible with a body of evidence in the form of documents and records that demonstrate the business is meeting its legal obligations and internal assurance requirements.

The complexity with "proactive" and "generative" labels, when it comes to risk, is that visible leadership, observable worker behaviors, and symbols reflecting desired cultural values can be deceptive; specifically, "talking the talk but not walking the talk." The entropy model, although not specifically depicted, would caution that leadership, the culture, and desired behaviors are also subject to degradation, as are the underlying values, which are not visible to management, that drive them. For instance, to achieve proactive status, an ownership culture needs to be in place. Operational ownership of frontline supervisors can be eroded when other drivers are cascaded from the middle management level because of contextual changes. This is referred to as the "alignment fallacy" (Mol 2003). Just because a company has a safety-first policy and supporting values, it does not ensure that safety first becomes an operational reality. For instance, following boom economic times, which allow for more resource allocation to EHS efforts, post-boom constraints can filter to the operational level and have an undesirable effect.

> Maintaining "boom" levels of commitment to safety is more difficult when there is an imperative to produce and a tendency towards overreaction to the market. It can lead to a focus on doing what has to be done rather than what should be done. (Cliff, Harris, and Bofinger 2016)

> The alignment fallacy explains why a safety-first strategy seldom becomes an operational reality, especially in production-driven organizations.

The organization needs to ensure that the business strategy is aligned to the external environment in the face of changes, including economic forces. However, concurrently, internal strategic alignment to achieve the right balance of human, physical, and financial capital needs to be maintained. Cutting workforce numbers too deeply results in loss of capacity to manage risk as valuable competencies and internal knowledge are lost.

In addition, internal goal alignment, being compatibility of organizational goals and values with employee goals and values, needs ongoing attention to prevent degradation of the psychological contract between employees and employers (Mol 2003). The concept is important because the risk is that external factors can erode the organization's progress and cause regression on the culture journey. This in turn creates a cycle, illustrated by the entropy model, of corrective action and proactive maintenance practices to reinstate the desired culture followed by degradation again.

Production creep can also occur. For instance, economic conditions that drive production over EHS management can cause degradation of internal leadership as managers are pressured to increase output with fewer resources. The workforce's confidence to make sound risk-based decisions on a day-to-day basis can also be eroded. As found by McLain and Jarrell (2007), safety-production compatibility versus conflict was linked to safe work behaviors and the extent to which hazards interfered with the tasks performed.

Under such economic conditions, the workers can become increasingly concerned about their job security. Masia and Pienaar (2011) concluded that job insecurity had an inverse relationship with safety compliance. Job stress encourages employees to avoid safe work behaviors, which increases the likelihood of workplace injuries. Uncertainty can indirectly lead to employees becoming less job-involved (Maiti et al. 2004; Paul and Maiti 2008), which is a human resources risk as engagement and attentiveness are essential for managing residual risk and preventing entropic risk.

> EHS professionals need to have business acumen and build the risk management culture top-down and bottom-up concurrently.

The upshot is that the EHS professional needs to have business acumen to understand how business dynamics can change at the macro level, which can then cascade to the operational level. This top-down effect can cause degradation of the risk management culture; however, there can also be a bottom-up impact as external labor market conditions influence how personnel perceive the company's priorities, that is, production versus EHS incident prevention.

Although not entirely economically driven, similar dynamics were identified during the investigation into the space shuttle *Columbia* disaster.

> The Space Shuttle Program had been built on compromises hammered out by the White House and NASA headquarters. As a result, NASA was transformed from a research and development agency to more of a business, with schedules, production pressures, deadlines, and cost efficiency goals elevated to the level of technical innovation and safety goals. (CAIB 2003, 198)
>
> Under these conditions, NASA management was fixated on making the target launching the Columbia on time and adhering to the February 19 target date of the International Space Station. (Starbuck and Farjoun 2005)

Disasters such as the *Columbia* provide root causes that are often beyond the boundaries of the organization itself. If the EHS manager is not the custodian of these lessons learned heading into the future, then who is? The challenge, however, is to have a more strategic place at the executive management table and for the executive to champion effective risk management focused on achieving balanced business objectives in a manner that is sustainable.

The EHS manager must therefore have the technical knowledge and interpersonal skills to positively influence the organization's leadership and to rally support from other disciplines with competencies to gather and analyze objective data supporting risk-based decisions. The intent is to promote sustainable risk management and a culture that is sufficiently resilient to adapt to external forces without losing traction. The underlying values related to protecting workers' safety and health and the environment remain steadfast as founding principles of the EHS profession.

## Leveraging Opportunity

As mentioned earlier, the EHS discipline has traditionally been skewed toward prevention of negative business outcomes on the basis of risk. Where there is risk, however, there is often also opportunity. This part of the chapter touches on some of the key trends affecting EHS management with the intent of building the knowledge of the profession and capacity to deliver service with high levels of professionalism. Optimism about the value of discipline to the employer's bottom line and more broadly, the community, is also encouraged as part of the EHS professional's personal journey through their career.

First, while the external environment can be a threat as discussed earlier, it can also be a driver of improvements in risk management within organizations. For instance, the shift in legislation and international standards to a greater emphasis on risk management (Lozier 2016) rather than prescriptive measures provides the basis for a multidisciplinary approach. The alignment of ISO 9001 and 14001 illustrates this point in this extract from *ISOfocus*.

> One very important factor has been the greater alignment of structure, content and terminology for all ISO management system standards, particularly evident when looking at the new versions of ISO 9001 and ISO 14001. . . . This is intended to make life easier for organizations needing to address the requirements of several standards in a single management system.
>
> Identifying risks adds value and opportunities for improvement, and the engagement of top management enhances the chance of success on all levels. . . . Introduction of the term "risk-based thinking" along with the term "risks and opportunities" will encourage an organization to be more proactive. (International Standards Organization, Nov–Dec 2015)

Regardless of whether an organization elects to achieve accreditation, the principles of the ISO Standards, particularly the risk-based approach, the need for leadership, and the integration of management systems, provide a solid foundation for contemporary organizations. The EHS professional has the opportunity to align management systems to such standards to ensure that risk is managed effectively. Importantly, the standards require that critical tools, such as the risk register, are kept "live" and updated following change management and in light of new hazards and lessons learned. Effectively, alignment to the standards ensures the fundamentals of compliance are maintained.

In the early sections of this chapter, the emergence of entropy and fuzzy mathematics was introduced. The process engineering discipline is exploring a mathematical basis for measuring entropy as it relates to safety and risk. The Internet provides a wealth of information readily available to the EHS professional—for example, Google Scholar (https://scholar.google.com.au/) and Entropy Journal (http://www.mdpi.com/journal/entropy). The EHS professional is increasingly able to source more objective data about risk from the work of other disciplines.

The smartphone, while having its distracting disadvantages, also provides benefits in data capture. Major companies, particularly in the oil and gas sector, are pioneering the application of advanced analytics and cognitive computing. Information is being gathered from their operations to leverage collective knowledge and to pursue operational excellence.

> The biggest challenge of making the evolution from a knowing culture to a learning culture—from a culture that largely depends on heuristics in decision making to a culture that is much more objective and data driven and embraces the power of data and technology—is really not the cost. Initially, it largely ends up being imagination and inertia. (McKinsey 2016)

From an operational risk management perspective, the smartphone with the use of apps is a useful tool for capturing information that ordinarily is overlooked. For example, when workers input corrective actions and make suggestions for proactive maintenance practices, the organization gets a better understanding of its entropic risk exposure and trends. Such tools also contribute to a proactive risk management–based culture. Safety, rather than being negatively focused, shifts to opportunity and positive behaviors that can be recognized and rewarded. Safety becomes a partner of efficiency and quality work.

The EHS professional can also leverage off the significant work being undertaken in the area of resilience engineering.

> The term Resilience Engineering is used to represent a new way of thinking about safety. Whereas conventional risk management approaches are based on hindsight and emphasise error tabulation and calculation of failure probabilities, Resilience Engineering looks for ways to enhance the ability at all levels of organizations to create processes that are robust yet flexible, to monitor and revise risk models, and to use resources

proactively in the face of disruptions or ongoing production and economic pressures. (Resilience Engineering Association 2017)

For instance, research has been undertaken for the construction industry to develop a resilient safety system that is proposed to predict future risk and prevent it in advance. The methodology uses simulation modeling, based on workers' movements and behaviors (Han et al. 2009). Again, new types of data are being used to better understand operational risk and required controls.

The depth and breadth of resilience engineering is beyond the scope of this chapter; however, the EHS professional is encouraged to understand the fundamentals. According to Woods (2012), resilience engineering should adjust the balance across the sets of acute production goals and chronic safety risks. He also refers to the Columbia accident as an example where pressure on acute goals eroded attention to controlling safety risks.

> The dilemma of production pressure/safety trade-offs is that we need to pay the most attention to, and devote scarce resources to, potential future safety risks when they are least affordable due to increasing pressure to produce or economize. As a result, organizations unknowingly act riskier than they would normally accept. The first step is tools to monitor the boundary between competence at designed-for-uncertainties and unanticipated perturbations that challenge or fall outside the envelope. (Woods 2012)

Production pressure is a risk requiring a strategic approach to mitigate productivity losses, poor work quality, and EHS incidents.

Clearly, the argument for managing risk as a strategic and operational discipline is reinforced, together with the need for an uneasy awareness that leadership, capability, and the desired culture can degrade if the organization is not sufficiently robust to buffer against external forces. In addition, production and associated pressures are now within scope for the EHS professional to address within the broader risk management strategy.

The final area of consideration for the EHS professional is to take a fresh look at the discipline itself and the theories that have underpinned EHS programs to date. The key questions are "Knowing what is known now, are the EHS programs in place still relevant? Are all current strategies and programs justifiable with a risk basis?" For instance, what value is a peer-to-peer behavioral observation program in a workplace populated by engineers and other highly skilled, risk-educated personnel? On the other hand, where the human resource residual risks are relatively high—that is, profiled by low workforce competencies and experience—there is a sound case for coaching by experienced personnel using workplace observations and feedback.

The EHS profession is continuously under self-reflection and scrutiny. For instance, in relation to behavioral-based safety:

> "That's the evolution," said former ASSE President Skipper Kendrick. "In the beginning, BBS was the magic bullet and folks thought that's all they had to do. BBS was their safety program, and that was a mistake. Over the years safety pros have learned to use BBS as one element, one piece of the puzzle, of their overall safety program." (Johnson 2013)

A cautionary word is therefore offered, particularly in a climate of increased demands for business to be fast, efficient, accountable, and resilient. Naturally, this expectation will cascade to the EHS manager. The profession is recognizing that some programs and the structure of the EHS management system may be ill-directed. There have been misplaced priorities with most of the management system elements, such as performance measures, audits, and behavior modification aimed at low-severity, high-frequency/probability events rather than major hazard accidents, which are high-severity, low-frequency/probability

(Ivensky 2017). The call to the profession is therefore that programs must be risk based and contribute to the triple bottom line for the EHS professional to gain and maintain credibility with senior management.

Traditional paradigms of safety need to be challenged. The mindset change from safety to risk management is already underway and gaining momentum with the recognition that a multidisciplinary approach to risk management is required. The opportunity is to apply this holistically to achieve production/productivity, work quality, and HSE incident mitigation concurrently. A significant value-add is to continue the organizational and professional maturity journey with the people the EHS management system is designed to protect in the first place—frontline supervisors and workers. The challenge for business is how to tap into the depth of knowledge that exists at all levels of the organizational hierarchy and to gather the data to make well-informed, risk-based decisions at both strategic and operational levels.

## Questions

1. What is entropic risk?
2. What evidence is there that entropic risk is real?
3. Why is the entropy model important to the EHS profession?
4. The chapter talks about the alignment fallacy. What is that?
5. What is the future of the EHS profession?

## References


Cliff, D., J. Harris, and C. Bofinger. (2016). "Ensuring Health and Safety through the Entire Mining Cycle." *The AusIMM Bulletin* (August). Minerals Industry Safety and Health Centre, Sustainable Minerals Institute, University of Queensland. https://www.ausimmbulletin.com/feature/ensuring-health-and-safety-through-the-entire-mining-cycle/.

Fitch, G. A., S. A. Soccolich, F. Guo, J. McClafferty, Y. Fang, R. L. Olson, M. A. Perez, R. J. Hanowski, J. M. Hankey, and T. A. Dingus. (2013). "The Impact of Hand-held and Hands-free Cell Phone Use on Driving Performance and Safety-Critical Event Risk." *Report No. DOT HS 811 757*. Washington, DC.

Foster, P., and S. Hoult. (2003). "The Safety Journey: Using a Safety Maturity Model for Safety Planning and Assurance in the UK Coal Mining Industry." *Minerals 2013*: 3(1): 59–72.

Han, S., S. Lee, and F. Pena-Mora. (2009). *"System Dynamics Modelling of Safety Culture Based on Resilience Engineering."* 2010 Construction Research Congress. Edmonton, Alberta, Canada.

Hudson, P. (2007). "Implementing a Safety Culture in a Major Multi-national." *Safety Science* 45: 697–722.

Hudson, P. (2003). "Applying the Lessons of High Risk Industries to Health Care." *Quality and Safety in Health Care* 12: i7–i12.

International Standards Organization. (2015). "Sustainable Success." *ISOfocus* 113: 2–13.

Ivensky, V. (2017). "Optimizing Safety—Engineering, Systems, Human Factors: Part 1." *Professional Safety* (January): 36–45.

Ivensky, V. (2017). "Optimizing Safety—Engineering, Systems, Human Factors: Part 2." *Professional Safety* (February): 46–51.

Johnson, D. (2013). "Is Behaviour-based Safety Dead?" *Industry Safety and Hygiene News* (June 27). http://www.ishn.com/articles/96240-is-behavior-based-safety-dead.

L. Dunwen, Y. Lei, and L. Bo. (2012). "Fuzzy-Entropy Theory Comprehensive Evaluations Method and Its Application in Building Construction Safety." International Symposium on Safety Science and Engineering in China ISSE-2012, SciVerse Science Direct. *Procedia Engineering* 443: 137–142.

Larranaga, M. D. (2013). "Issue 71: Disaster Creep—Why Disaster and Catastrophe Are the Norm—Not the Exception." *SFPE*. http://www.sfpe.org/?page=FPE_ET_Issue_71.

Lozier, T. (2016). "What Is Risk-Based Thinking?" *Quality Digest* 16: 28. https://www.qualitydigest.com/inside/risk-management-column/030216-what-risk-based-thinking.html.

Maiti, J., S. Chatterjee, and S. I. Bangdiwala. (2004). "Determinants of Work Injuries in Mines—an Application of Structural Equation Modelling." *Injury Control and Safety Promotion* 11(1): 29–37.

Masia, U., and J. Pienaar. (2011). "Unravelling Safety Compliance in the Mining Industry: Examining the Role of Work Stress, Job Insecurity, Satisfaction and Commitment as Antecedents." *SA Journal of Industrial Psychology* 37(1).

McKinsey and Company. (2016). "How Companies Are Using Big Data and Analytics." http://www.mckinsey.com/business-functions/mckinsey-analytics/our-insights/how-companies-are-using-big-data-and-analytics.

McLain, D. L., and K. A. Jarrell. (2007). "The Perceived Compatibility of Safety and Production Expectations in Hazardous Occupations." *Journal of Safety Research* 38: 299–309.

Mol, T. (2003). *Productive Safety Management.* Oxford, UK: Butterworth Heinemann.

Murat, Y. S. (2011). "An Entropy (Shannon) based Traffic Safety Level Determination Approach for Black Spots." Science Direct. *Procedia Social and Behavioral Sciences*: 786–95.

Nurwulan, N. R., and B. C. Jiang. (2016). "Possibility of Using Entropy Method to Evaluate the Distracting Effect of Mobile Phones on Pedestrians." *Entropy* 18: 390.

Parker, D., M. Lawrie, and P. Hudson. (2006). "A Framework for Understanding the Development of Organisational Safety Culture." *Safety Science* 44: 551–62.

Paul, P. S., and J. Maiti. (2008). "The Synergic Role of Sociotechnical and Personal Characteristics on Work Injuries in Mines." *Ergonomic* 51(5): 737–67.

Resilience Engineering Association. (2017). "About Resilience Engineering." http://www.resilience-engineering-association.org/.

University of Queensland. (2008). "Minerals Industry Risk Management Maturity Chart." Brisbane, AU: University of Queensland Minerals Industry Health and Safety Centre. http://www.mdpi.com/2075-163X/3/1/59/htm.

Woods, D. D. (2012). "Chapter 2: Essential Characteristics of Resilience." In N. P. W. D. D. Leveson, *Resilience Engineering*. Farnham, UK: Ashgate Publishing.

CHAPTER 30

# ENVIRONMENTAL HEALTH AND OCCUPATIONAL SAFETY IN THE INFORMAL SECTOR: AN ESSENTIAL COMPONENT OF THE GLOBAL ECONOMY

Oladapo Okareh

## Learning Objectives

After studying this chapter, the reader will be able to:

1. Evaluate the benefits of the concept of the informal sector
2. Discuss the occupational safety problems of the informal sector
3. Analyze some of the environmental impacts of the informal sector
4. Assess common strategies to achieving total workplace safety in the informal sector

## Key Terms

**Informal sector, environmental health and occupational safety, global economy, working conditions**

## Abstract

The informal sector constitutes an employment platform on which individuals with no formal employment seek to earn an income. Globally, informal workers are a large group, and the primary aim of these individuals is simply geared toward economic empowerment. The sector is growing rapidly because of the global economic decadence and the necessity for individuals to survive. However, this important sector of the global economy has been grossly neglected in relation to monitoring the working conditions of those employed in this sector. There is a dearth of information on the environmental and occupational safety of the informal sector workers. Safety is increasingly becoming more important in the world's dynamic environment. A systematic review on this subject globally revealed that safety awareness or training is rarely practiced, and where it is being practiced, standards are compromised. Common safety issues of concerns are related to the type of job or routine activities. At the global level, the informal sector growth rate is attributed to a decline in formal employment opportunities. Therefore, safety education and use of appropriate safety policy and regulations are necessary to improve the health and welfare of workers in the informal sector.

> The informal sector has become a growing source of employment for large numbers of youth and also for older workers pursuing entrepreneurial goals.

## Informal Sector in the Sphere of Globalization and Widespread Economic Restructuring

Globally, the informal sector is steadily growing. Bacchetta et al. (2009) reported that globalization and widespread economic restructuring over the past three decades have facilitated an increase in the growth of the informal employment sector and changed the way people are connected to the formal labor market. This economic pattern is the result of governments' failure to plan for sufficient formal jobs in the face of expanding global economy, communication, and competition. Academics and policymakers regard the informal sector with conflicting views. Some believe the informal sector fuels entrepreneurialism and provides a cushion during economic crises. Others argue that the informal sector undermines taxation and regulation and thereby weakens the overall economy.

In contrast to the formal sector, the laborers, businesses, and activities that make up the informal sector are not registered with or taxed by the government. For this reason, scholars sometimes refer to the informal sector as the black market, shadow economy, or underground economy. Originally, the term referred to self-employed small enterprises like street vending, sewing, artisans, and small farming. It now also includes wage-earning jobs like crop-harvesting, cleaning, and any other unprotected occupation.

Fox and Gaal (2008) initially viewed the informal sector as a safety net for those unable to find employment in the modern sector. However, this image of the sector has changed with time. People now view the informal sector not as a temporary stop while searching for employment in the formal wage economy, but as a preferred destination, offering opportunities to those wanting to become entrepreneurs (Adams 2008). In sub-Saharan Africa, the informal sector has become a growing source of employment for large numbers of youth and also for older workers pursuing entrepreneurial goals and others adjusting to structural changes in the region's employment (ILO 2004).

## Concepts of the Informal Sector

Several studies have attempted to define the informal sector. Most of these studies, however, only distinguished it with the legal definition and government recognition of the formal sector as activities, which have neither legal status under existing legislation nor fall under the formal institutional regulation of any public sector bureau or administration (Tagnman 2006). Another publication from ILO (2004), according to the Fifteenth International Conference of Labour Statisticians, stated that the informal sector enterprise is unincorporated enterprise with no complete sets of accounts available, owned and operated by an individual/self-employed person or unpaid household members, not registered under national legislation including tax, and goods and where services produced are meant for sale or barter.

> Unlike formal employment, informal jobs are not subject to national labor legislation, income taxation, social protection, or certain benefits (advance notice of dismissal, severance pay, paid annual or sick leave, maternity leave, retirement/pension, etc.).

The informal sector in Nigeria refers to economic activities in all sectors of the economy that are operated outside the purview of government regulation. This sector may be invisible, irregular, parallel, nonstructured, backyard, underground, subterranean, unobserved, or residual (Magbagbeola 1996). Informal economic activities in Nigeria encompass a wide range of small-scale, largely self-employment activities. Most of them are traditional occupations and methods of production. Others include such financial and economic endeavors of subsistence nature, such as retail trade, transport, restaurant, repair services, financial intermediation, and household or other personal services (Adamu 1996). Activities in the informal sector in Nigeria are difficult to measure; they are highly dynamic and contribute substantially to the general growth of the economy and personal or household income.

> Informality is described as a "way of doing things characterized by ease of entry, reliance on indigenous resources, family ownership, and small-scale operations."

Unlike formal employment, informal jobs are not subject to national labor legislation, income taxation, social protection, or certain benefits (advance notice of dismissal, severance pay, paid annual or sick leave, maternity leave, retirement/pension, etc.). In a nutshell, the informal worker is defined as an individual engaged in informal employment while the informal sector is a constellation of all remunerative work that is not recognized, regulated, or protected by existing legal or regulatory frameworks and nonremunerative work undertaken in an income-producing enterprise (ILO 2011).

The International Labour Organization (ILO) in its Kenya mission report introduced the concept of the informal sector in 1972. This concept described informality as a "way of doing things characterized by ease of entry, reliance on indigenous resources, family ownership, and small scale operations." It also involves labor-intensive and adaptive technology, skills acquired outside of the formal sector, and unregulated and competitive markets. The informal sector covers a wide range of labor market activities that combine groups of workers with different natures. One of such is the informal sector, which is formed by the coping behavior of individuals and families an in economic environment where earning opportunities are scarce.

In 1999, The ILO/ICFTU international symposium on the informal sector also categorized informal sector workforce into three broad groups via (a) owner-employers of micro enterprises, which employ a few paid workers, with or without apprentices; (b) own-account workers, who own and operate a one-person business, who work alone or with the help of unpaid workers, generally family members and apprentices; and (c) dependent workers, paid or unpaid, including wage workers in micro enterprises, unpaid family workers, apprentices, contract labor, homeworkers, and paid domestic workers.

Operationalizing the concept of informality for the purpose of measurement is not easy both because the categories of informal sector overlap and because the border between the informal and the formal sector is blurry. An unregistered one-person, low-profit street trader can be considered to be an informal sector worker. If the street trader, however, registers her enterprise, the enterprise and the trader herself could be categorized as belonging to the formal sector if the profit is considered above the survival level.

> An unregistered one-person, low-profit street trader can be considered to be an informal sector worker

## Characteristics of Informal Sector

The informal sector since the early 1970s has become a focus of increased attention in international discussions on economic development. The ILO and other multilateral agencies such as the World Health Organization (WHO) and United Nation Development Programme (UNDP) have played a major role in understanding the phenomenon of informal sector. The informal sector is characterized largely with limited job security, low and unstable incomes, lack of occupational health service coverage, lack of work compensation and retirement benefits, less social protection for workers, particularly women and girl children, and inadequate provision of personal protective equipment (PPE) (Atienza 2007).

It is also characterized by poor working conditions, which include unregulated working hours, long working hours, poor housekeeping, inadequate welfare facilities, poor ventilation and lighting, poor work posture and work methods, unregulated exposure to environmental hazards of biological, chemical, and physical natures, and absence of occupational safety standards. In addition, absence or low statutory benefits to government (taxation) and workers as reported by ILO (2011) and work that is not recognized, regulated, or protected by existing legal or regulatory frameworks and nonremunerative work undertaken in an income-producing enterprise are typical characteristic of informal sector.

The informal financial subsectors are mostly underground, unofficial, irregular, informal, shadowy, and parallel

The informal sector may be categorized into the production subsector, service subsector, and financial subsector. The informal production subsector encompasses all economic activities involving the production of tangible goods, such as agricultural production, mining and quarrying (excluding petroleum), small-scale manufacturing, and building and construction. In developing countries, they are in food production, woodworking, furniture making, garment making, and welding and iron works, among others. The informal service subsector includes repairs and maintenance, informal education services, health services, and counseling services as well as labor for menial work. Repairs and maintenance services include tailoring, vehicle repairs and maintenance, tinkering, carpentry, and servicing of various household and commercial tools. Informal health services, especially in the rural areas, include traditional birth attendants, herbalists, and other traditional medical practitioners. There are also traditional spiritualists who offer counseling services. These services are rendered for a fee.

The informal financial subsectors are mostly underground, unofficial, irregular, informal, shadowy, and parallel. The most predominant type of informal finance in most developing countries is the local

Informal workers number 1.8 billion (60% of the global workforce) and comprise a diverse population in terms of type of occupation and social and legal status.

cooperative groups, or fixed contribution groups. Some groups operate with written laws while others operate with unwritten laws but on oath of allegiance and mutual trust. The general practice is that the associations contribute a fixed amount periodically and give all or part of the accumulated funds to one or more member(s) in rotation until all members have benefited from the pool.

Informal workers number 1.8 billion (60% of the global workforce) and comprise a diverse population in terms of type of occupation and social and legal status (Rockefeller Foundation 2013). They face greater job insecurity and stress than workers who are formally employed, and they have little to no access to affordable, quality health care. These conditions increase informal workers' vulnerability to poor health, injury, and illness. Furthermore, working conditions are often unsafe and unhealthy.

Accessing health care requires leaving work, which reduces the income of informal workers and adds health care expenses. However, most informal workers have few resources. More than one-third receive less than $1.25/day for their labor (Palash 2016). Informal worker vulnerability is exacerbated by political systems that do not recognize them, global economic conditions that hurt the formal sector, national economic systems that see informal work as a drain on resources, inconvenient and underfunded health systems, poor education and training systems, and sociocultural norms that permit gender discrimination.

## Informal Work Activity in the United States

A clear deduction from the review of literature is that informal work activities are substantial in the US economy (US Department of Labor 1992a). New businesses are expanding in urban areas, but costs of starting up enterprises are high, causing some entrepreneurs to operate in the informal sector and pay lower wages to minimize expenses (Schneider 2002; Williams 2011). According to Nightingale and Wandner (2011), individuals in both informal and nonstandard employments have relatively high poverty rates and low earnings, and women represent a disproportionate share of the workers. The poor, who work mainly in the informal sector, may find it even more difficult than low-wage formal workers to raise themselves and their families out of poverty through work alone because informal wages are lower and there is less chance for wage increases. Informal employment in the United States tends to be overlooked in policy circles. When it is considered, it is often viewed in terms of black market (i.e., criminal and illegal) activities, undocumented immigrants, or white-collar tax evasion (Nightingale and Wandner 2011).

Informal employment in the United States tends to be overlooked in policy circles, and when it is considered, it is often viewed in terms of black market activities, undocumented immigrants, or white-collar tax evasion.

Informal employment is not captured by official government statistics and reports because individuals and employers involved in the informal sector are not likely to report all economic activity (Kalleberg et al. 1997). Estimating the size of the informal economic sector is difficult, and cross-national estimates are particularly challenging if one attempts to distinguish between licit and illicit activities. Some research also suggests that informal work has increased significantly in the United States, beginning in the 1980s, because of a growing immigrant population reliant on nonstandard work, usually informal arrangements (Tanzi 1999), and an increasingly decentralized labor movement (Houseman and Osawa 2003). The scale of informal economic activity in monetary terms is difficult to estimate. Despite a body of literature linking informal and nonstandard work with a prospering and even vibrant underground economy (de Soto 1989; Thomas 1992) and research indicating a trend among middleclass Americans to pursue contingent labor as a supplement to standard work (Mattera 1985), in reality, informal and nonstandard work is concentrated at the lower end of the wage scale and represents a disproportionate share of female, Black, and Hispanic workers (Horowitz 2000).

The high prevalence of informal work participation among part-time employees and the economic significance of such work to this group suggest that a substantial share of them may be willing to supply additional hours to formal jobs as labor demand improves.

Bracha and Burke (2013) designed a survey aimed at describing the nature and extent of participation in informal work activities in recent years and measuring its economic importance to participants. The result of the survey shows that roughly 44 percent of respondents participated in some informal paid work activity during the past two years, not including survey work.

The most common reason given for engaging in an informal paid activity is to earn money (rather than to pursue a hobby, meet people, or maintain job-related skills). Among the participants, 35 percent say that informal work helped them either "somewhat" or "very much" in offsetting negative shocks to their personal financial situation experienced in hard times. Individuals with a part-time (formal) job are both most likely to participate in informal work (compared with full-time employees, the unemployed, and those outside the labor force) and most likely to report that such work helped them "very much" in surviving the season of hard times. The high prevalence of informal work participation among part-time employees and the economic significance of such work to this group suggest that a substantial share of them may be willing to supply additional hours to formal jobs as labor demand improves. Yet, because most of those who engage in informal paid activities do so online and because the number of applications that facilitate informal work is likely to continue to increase, there is high expectation of participation in the peer-to-peer economy to grow even as labor market conditions improve. It is established that as formal wages increase in an improving labor market, individuals may switch from informal to formal work. The informal sector as facilitated by new technologies is likely to grow in terms of participation and economic value in coming years, possibly changing the labor market in some professions.

## Informal Work Activity and Occupational Safety in the United States

Recently, the US National Institute of Occupational Safety and Health (NIOSH) provided brief information on the response to work-related health needs of informal sector workers in the United States. It was noted that this important topic is not often discussed. However, it is a pertinent issue because low-wage jobs represent nearly one-half of all new jobs that are created in the United States, and evidence from research shows that workers in low-wage jobs are at an increased risk of work-related injuries and illnesses

The informal sector as facilitated by new technologies is likely to grow in terms of participation and economic value in coming years, possibly changing the labor market in some professions.

(Forum on Public-Private Partnerships for Global Health and Safety 2016). There are some channels for accessing federally funded Occupational Health and Safety (OHS) services. These include federally qualified health centers administered by the Health Resources and Services Administration that sponsors community and migrant health centers that provide services to individuals who are frequently employed in the informal sector in the United States. The Patient Protection and Affordable Care Act, which was passed in 2010, provides a special fund over the first five years to support the expansion of these clinical centers and their services to increase the number of patients served by this population (Forum on Public-Private Partnerships for Global Health and Safety 2016). NIOSH is assisting these centers by helping them to provide preventive health services, but in the crush of providing rescue medicine, it is often very difficult to add preventive occupational health services despite recognition of their values. NIOSH established that it is working in several different areas to improve the diagnosis and management of and patient education concerning occupational health in the health centers.

Accidents are so common that they are considered an inevitable part of the work.

A study of profitability and occupational injuries in US underground coal mines showed that some financially stressed mines might be so focused on survival that they forgo investing in safety (Abay et al. 2012). Safety and health concerns that are commonly associated with informal sector in the United States and also common in other developed countries are as given below:

- High occupational hazards—Workers in the agricultural sector often face hazards; according to the ILO, at least 170,000 agricultural workers die every year as a result of workplace accidents.
- Pesticide exposure—Pesticides exposure affects many workers annually in the United States. Acute pesticide poisonings are common. Pesticide poisonings disproportionately affect women due to their higher levels of body fat (where pesticides accumulate) and have been documented to produce birth/reproductive defects.
- High incidence of injuries from accidents is the most common health risk, resulting from unsafe worksites and lack of appropriate protective equipment and training. Considerable numbers of informal construction workers are exposed to occupational hazards. Accidents are so common that they are considered an inevitable part of the work.
- Chemical exposures are common and can cause metal poisoning.

- Musculoskeletal injuries and disorders, including back injuries from carrying heavy loads, and joint pain are also common.
- Respiratory diseases from inhaling dust have been documented.
- Poor living conditions.
- Physical, sexual, and psychological abuse.
- Health problems from poor working conditions and postures.
- Eye-related problems and blurry vision caused by dust and pollution.
- Strains and joint pains from inappropriate work posture and heavy lifting.
- Stress-related diseases including migraine, hyperacidity, hypertension, and high blood pressure.
- Hearing damage from prolonged loud noise exposure, and so forth.

These and many others are the critical safety concerns of the informal work activity in the United States.

Informal workers have limited access to affordable and appropriate health care for themselves and their families, and they may not seek care if they have insecure legal status or due to the potential expense or loss of income

## Occupational Safety Problems of the Informal Sector

Informal workers face substantial risks and vulnerabilities due to insecurity surrounding their employment status and lack of control of the conditions of their employment. In addition, informal workers have limited access to affordable and appropriate health care for themselves and their families, and they may not seek care if they have insecure legal status or due to the potential expense or loss of income. The combination of high vulnerabilities and inadequate social protections (including insufficient access to affordable health services) results in high incidence of injury, illness, susceptibility to chronic diseases, and out-of-pocket expenditures, which may result in poverty (OECD 2009).

Informal employment is often invisible, as workers are mostly excluded from national labor laws and regulations, social protections, and high-level discussions. As a result, they fall through the cracks in systems, including most universal health coverage (UHC) schemes that serve formal workers on the one hand and the unemployed on the other. Employment insecurity and inadequate health care are common to all informal workers and increase health vulnerabilities; specific health issues vary in prevalence among informal workers because of differential working conditions, exposures, and health risks.

Over 700 million informal workers live in extreme poverty and often cannot bear the financial or opportunity costs of receiving health services and losing a day's work.

Over 700 million informal workers live in extreme poverty and often cannot bear the financial or opportunity costs of receiving health services and losing a day's work. Women make up the largest proportion of the most vulnerable informal workers due to a combination of factors; they occupy the lowest-paying informal jobs, maternal health needs are not met by employment conditions, and working conditions often subject them not only to bodily harm but also psychological and sexual abuse. No one-size-fits-all solution will address the geographic, health, and occupational differences among informal workers. Some countries (especially in Asia and Latin America) are addressing healthcare accessibility via national or tailored insurance. In Asia, Latin America, and (less so) in Africa, countries have devised worker-specific programs, particularly in urban areas (Rockefeller Foundation 2013; Hove et al. 2013).

Opportunities for engagement on workplace safety and informal worker issues include population-level or worker-level efforts. Scattered funding and variable interests have led to a patchwork of policies and programs focused on national interest or type of worker. According to Rejoice et al. (2013), safety awareness or training is not being practiced in most informal sectors, and where it is being practiced, standards are compromised.

Often, the potential exposure of informal workers to hazards or health vulnerabilities of the informal workers are addressed as one small component within a broad range of activities. The invisible nature of informal work results from and contributes to the dearth of systematic data, especially in the developing countries. Informal workers are not "seen" so are not counted, limiting estimates of scale and scope, and exacerbating the practice of overlooking this population and their needs. Similarly, systematic health data generally does not designate employment status and reveals very little about specific "heath vulnerabilities" (Rockefeller Foundation 2013). Studies have shown that workers in this sector are at risk of exposure to several hazards, like body injuries from road accidents and harassment from police, task force environmental officials, and so on (Oluyomi 2012).

Safety awareness or training is not being practiced in most informal sectors, and where it is being practiced, standards are compromised.

The workers in the informal sector are exposed to physical, mechanical, chemical, biological, ergonomic, and psychosocial hazards. Physical hazards are those risks affecting physical safety. According to a WHO (2001) report, they arise primarily from sources, such as noise, vibration, fire, poor sanitation, radiation, and extreme temperatures. In study by Rejoice et al. (2013), informal sector workers are exposed to physical hazards such as noise, vibration, burns, fire, and filthy environment; chemical hazards, such as smoke, dust, fume inhalation, and ergonomic hazards, such as poor posture, psychosocial and sexual abuses, stress, and so forth. Several harmful exposures occur among informal sector workers. Mechanics use a lot of paint additives, such as binders, solvents, pigments, and other additives. Most exposure to these substances causes serious respiratory problems (Brown 1990). Drivers are commonly exposed to fumes from vehicle exhaust pipes (Doug et al. 2007). The chemical composition depends on the reactors. Exposure can cause eye, nose, and throat irritation, fever, chills, headache, nausea, shortness of breath, and coughing. Sitting in the driving position exerts considerable forces on the spine and can cause many problems with the musculoskeletal system, in particular backaches, neck problems, pulled muscles, and general stiffness (Rejoice et al. 2013). Beauticians use shampoo, neutralizers, styling gels, and setting lotion, including hairsprays and mousses, relaxers, nail polish remover, and rubber gloves. All these pose various levels of health risks to beauticians exposed to them (Brown 1987).

The informal sector must be properly integrated into the global economy; the occupation health and safety programs of informal workers must be given global attention

Welders are exposed to both chemical and physical hazards. Common chemical hazards include metal particles, fumes, and gases, such as carbon oxides, nitrogen oxides, and ozone (Jafari and Assari 2004; Ayman 2014). Physical hazards include electrical energy, heat, noise, vibration, and radiation (Luo et al. 2006; Antonini et al. 2003). The traditional women weavers in developing countries are also commonly exposed to various hazards, especially physical and ergonometric hazards *(Awoyemi and Abdulraheem 2003).* Bricklayers are exposed to lifting of blocks and other heavy materials that result in musculoskeletal disorders (Adele et al. 2001). Tailors are exposed to vibration from their sewing machines (Sonya et al. 2001). Farmers are exposed to physical, mechanical, chemical, biological, ergonomic, and psychosocial hazards, depending on the scale of their practice. The local illegal miners of different mineral resources are exposed to dust and other hazards (Ana and Jinky 2016). The list is endless, but principally, informal workers are exposed to unsafe conditions as is the case with the formal workers. The scale and magnitude of the exposure may differ, including the response to the unsafe conditions in the workplace (Menya 2012). According to Rejoice et al. (2013), the major psychosocial hazards identified with informal workers relate to stress and sexual abuse. Therefore, if the informal sector must be properly integrated into the global economy, the occupation health and safety programs of informal workers must be given global attention.

## Environmental Impact of Informal Sector

Due to numerous numbers of informal-sector or small-scale industries within every marginal neighborhood of cities and communities, informal firms or small-scale industries contribute greatly to air, noise, and water and land pollution, especially in the aspects of solid and liquid waste generation. Effluents from activities of informal firms are often channeled to streams or nearby rivers, polluting the water and sometimes causing thermal pollution. In most cases, the surface water is the available source of water for domestic use. The informal sector encompasses a wide range of areas of informality, which may include informal settlements that also serve as workplace. For instance, residential areas are often widely used for small businesses, in complete disregard of the zoning arrangements that require separate areas for presumed incompatible activities. These have been associated with incessant unsafe acts and conditions, including accidents and deaths. Given the heterogeneity of informal-sector activities, generalizations about their environmental impacts are likely to be misleading. In some developing countries, the majority of informal activities are retail oriented and create few environmental problems beyond litter and congestion (Perera and Amin 1996).

> Some evidence suggests that informal sources are more pollution intensive than larger sources because they use inputs relatively inefficiently, lack pollution control equipment, lack access to basic sanitation services, such as sewers and waste disposal, and are operated by persons with little awareness of the safety, health, and environmental impacts of pollution.

Documented studies revealed that certain types of informal activities can create severe environmental pollution problems. Among them are the leather tanning, electroplating, metal working, brick and tile making, printing, auto repair, wood and metal finishing, mining, charcoal making, textile dyeing, dyestuffs manufacture, and food processing (Bartone and Benavides 1993; Kent 1991). Informal sector enterprises engaged in these activities can have environmental impacts that are contrary to the sizes of the firms for a number of reasons. Most important, they are often quite numerous. Secondly, some evidences suggest that informal sources are more pollution-intensive than larger sources because they use inputs relatively inefficiently, lack pollution control equipment, lack access to basic sanitation services, such as sewers and waste disposal, and are operated by persons with little awareness of the safety, health, and environmental impacts of pollution (Kent 1991). Thirdly, by nature, informal sectors are highly competitive (since barriers to entry are relatively low) and therefore are under considerable pressure to cut costs, regardless of the environmental impacts. In addition, informal sectors are usually significant sources of employment and are often situated in poor residential areas. As a result, their emissions directly affect a considerable population.

> Informal sectors are usually significant sources of employment and are often situated in the midst of poor residential areas

In most developing countries, towns' and cities' water supply and sanitation are grossly inadequate for domestic and personal hygiene. In many informal settlements, waterborne and sanitation-related diseases, especially diarrhea and cholera are common. People commonly defecate and urinate in the open or in nearby bushes so that food and water can be easily contaminated from exposure to human waste. This unsafe environmental condition, in no small measure, affects the informal sector in relation to health and safety. Ameyibor et al. (2003) stated that unregulated construction of houses with no drainage systems has obstructed many natural water ways, which has led to recurrent floods during the rainy seasons. Flooding or unguided flow of storm water may result in the overspill of pit latrines and septic tanks, which will pollute surface water sources and marine environments. Lack of proper drainage system in such environments could generate big ponds that become breeding places for mosquitoes that cause malaria. Most of the informal houses used for informal businesses are characterized by high housing density that causes natural discharge of storm water more difficult to control.

Safe and nutritious food is the foundation of good health. In most cases, especially in informal settlements, food contamination and foodborne diseases are major factors in the high incidence of diarrhea and dysentery.

Proliferation of unplanned houses used for informal work often result to high generation of liquid and solid wastes, but poor disposal practice causes water pollution (Cole 2000). Due to lack of established collection points, piles of garbage are scattered in and around residential areas, which leads to environmental and health problems (Mohammed et al. 2013). There have been frequent outbreaks of waterborne diseases, particularly during high rainfall seasons, due to contamination of the drinking water (Cole 2000). Potholes in the streets, pools of stagnant water, and waste gushing from bathrooms and kitchens provide breeding sites for malarial mosquitoes and other vectors of disease. Large volumes of rubbish are generated by the activities of informal sector and left to litter the streets or to accumulate in open dumps where flies and rats, including other disease-carrying insects and rodents, proliferate. Most communities or even cities have open drains and narrow, shallow trenches, which are often clogged with discarded appliances from domestic and industrial sources, sand, and refuse transported by flooding. When the drains are not cleaned, they are unsightly and exude unpleasant odors (Geoffrey 2005).

Safe and nutritious food is the foundation of good health. In most cases, especially in informal settlements, involved in informal work, food contamination (unsafe food) and foodborne diseases are major factors in the high incidence of diarrhea and dysentery. Food poisoning often occurs in open marketplaces, slaughterhouses, and in the extensive ready-to-eat street food industry in the informal sector, widely patronized by workers and others. In developing countries, the primary source of air pollution is exposure to toxic fumes from cooking fires and stoves inside poorly ventilated homes, which may also serve as workplaces. This is sometimes responsible for a wide variety of respiratory infections and chronic lung diseases (Doug et al. 2007). Noise pollution is also a major environmental problem. Loudspeakers from churches and mosques; bells rung incessantly by peddlers, hawkers, and other salesmen to advertise their wares; highly amplified music from record shops; and noise from private electricity-generating plants and grinding machines all help to cause irritation and can in extreme cases even impair hearing. As a matter of necessity, therefore, if the informal sector must be properly integrated into the global economy, the environmental health and safety of informal workers must be given a global attention for improved status.

Safety awareness and sensitization are key components to robust workplace safety in informal sector.

## Strategies to Achieve Total Workplace Safety in the Informal Sector

Safety awareness and sensitization are key components to a robust workplace safety in informal sector. A simple pre-implementation checklist to cover preventable hazards will help to reduce accidents and deaths rate in workplaces. The more times an enterprise in the informal sector observes or detects unsafe conditions and acts, the more opportunities it has to correct them before they turn into actual injuries. Rather than being reactive and waiting for injuries to occur, those in the informal sectors can be proactive and prevent them from occurring in the first place.

Essentially, informal sectors have to ensure absence of risks in workplaces or to employees and others so far as is reasonably practicable by ensuring a system in place to manage safety (plan, organize, control, monitor, and review preventative measures); identify hazards; and assess risks (the probability that significant harm will occur), risk-control measures, and backup measures.

There are underlying requirements to reduce or eliminate these hazards at the source or isolate people from them, for example, by placing guards on machinery. Most of these requirements are often not practiced by the informal sector because of poor knowledge about them or their lean resources.

Relying on the use of personal protective equipment—like respirators or protective footwear—is a last-resort measure and is only acceptable when all other options have failed.

Although resources might be a factor with the informal sector operators, there is the need to inform, train, and supervise employees. Relying on the use of personal protective equipment—like respirators or protective footwear—is a last-resort measure and is only acceptable when all other options have failed. Regrettably, this option is not available to many informal sector workers, as they are usually unaware of them or cannot afford to purchase them. Fundamental safety practices should be encouraged, such as reporting and recording of accidents, providing certain basic workplace first aid and welfare facilities, notifying the local authority of their existence, and consulting workforce and their representatives.

Finally, informal-sector operators require support and should be supported for improved economy from local to global level. Informal sector operators should pool resources through "clustering" and other ways of cooperating that foster mutual support to work in safe and healthy environments and help their businesses to grow and mature. Collectively they must curb practices and socially unacceptable "coping strategies," or unsafe acts and conditions that could result in incidents, accidents, and death in workplace.

## Conclusion and Recommendations

The informal sector plays an important role in the global economy, but it also carries numerous safety concerns. It provides jobs and reduces unemployment and underemployment, but in many cases the jobs are low paid and the job security is poor. It bolsters entrepreneurial activity but at the detriment of state regulations compliance, particularly regarding tax and labor regulations. It helps alleviate poverty, but in many cases informal sector jobs are low paid, and the job security is poor. Its size and role in the economy increases during economic downturns and periods of economic adjustment and transition. This sector should be given prominent recognition and support at global level. Comprehensive safety education for informal sector operators, therefore, should be encouraged.

The protection of the health and wellbeing of workers in the informal economy is a challenge that should be faced with a coherent and integrated approach involving policies for environmental health and occupational safety and health promotion, skills development, social protection, and employment creation. To promote more global attention and support for the informal sector, the following factors should be considered:

- Provision of education
- Use of effective training gear toward employment in the informal sector
- Generate rationale(s) for promoting self-employment and small-scale enterprises
- Adopt general policy lessons from programs to promote the informal sector
- Adopt sound and sustainable management and entrepreneurial training
- Encourage sound occupational safety programs in informal sector
- Encouragement of entrepreneurship backed with political will
- Create an enabling environment for the sustainability of the informal sector

## Questions

1. List and discuss the occupational safety problems of the informal sector.
2. Identify some of the environmental impacts of informal sector in global economy.
3. Explain, in clear terms, the strategies that could be used in achieving total workplace safety in the informal sector.
4. Discuss vividly the importance of safety in the informal sector of global economy.
5. Differentiate between the occupational safety challenges in the formal and informal sectors of global economy?

## References

Adams, A. V. (2008). *Skills Development in the Informal Sector of Sub-Saharan Africa*. Washington, DC: World Bank.

Ametepeh, R. S., D. Adei, and A. A. Arhin. (2013). "Occupational Health Hazards and Safety of the Informal Sector in the Sekondi-Takoradi Metropolitan Area of Ghana." *Research on Humanities and Social Sciences* 3(20): 1–13.

Antonini, J. M., A. B. Lewis, J. R. Roberts, and D. A. Whaley. (2003). "Pulmonary Effects of Welding Fumes: Review of Worker and Experimental Animal Studies." *American Journal of Industrial Medicine* 43: 350–60.

Asfaw, A., C. Mark, and R. Pana-Cryan. (2013). "Profitability and Occupational Injuries in U.S. Underground Coal Mines." *Accident Analysis and Prevention* 50: 778–86.

Atienza, T. V. (2007). "Pursuing a Remedy: Occupational Safety and Health in the Informal Sector." *Philippine Journal of Labor and Industrial Relations* 27: 1–2.

Awoyemi, O., and I. S. Abdulraheem. (2003). "Occupational Health Problems Associated with Traditional Cloth Weaving in Ilorin, Nigeria." *Sahel Medical Journal* 6(1): 6–9.

Bacchetta, M., E. Ernst, and J. P. Bustamante. (2009). "Globalization and Informal Jobs in Developing Countries." http://www.wto.org/english/res_e/booksp_e/jobs_devel_countries_e.pdf.

Bartone, C. R., and L. Benavides. (1993). "Local Management of Hazardous Wastes from Smallscale and Cottage Industries." Presented at the 5th Pacific Basin Conference on Hazardous Waste, Pacific Basin Consortium for Hazardous Waste Research, East-West Center, Honolulu, HI.

Bracha, A., and M. A. Burke. (2014). "Informal Work Activity in the United States: Evidence from Survey Responses." Accessed April 30, 2017. http://www.bostonfed.org/economic/current-policy-perspectives/index.htm.

Brown, N. J. (1987). *Health Hazard Manual for Cosmetologists, Hairdressers, Beauticians and Barbers*. Ithaca, NY: Cornell University, Chemical Hazard Information Program.

Brown, N. J. (1990). *Health Hazards Manual for Autobody Shop Workers*. Ithaca, NY: Cornell University, Chemical Hazard Information Program, 37–41. http://digitalcommons.ilr.cornell.edu/manuals/7.

Brugge, D., J. L. Durant, and C. Rioux. (2007). "Near-highway Pollutants in Motor Vehicle Exhaust: A Review of Epidemiologic Evidence of Cardiac and Pulmonary Health Risks." *Environmental Health* 6: 23.

Bylund, S. H., L. Burström, and A. Knutsson. (2001). "A Descriptive Study of Women Injured by Hand–Arm Vibration." *Annals of Occupational Hygiene* 46(3): 299–307.

Cole, G. A. (2000). "Organizational Behavior: Theory and Practice Cengage Learning EMEA." *Business and Economics*: 1–381.

de Soto, H. (1989). *The Other Path: The Invisible Revolution in the Third World*. New York: Harper & Row.

Department for International Development. (2007). "Working Together for Better Health." London.

Development Centre. (2009). "Is Informal Normal? OECD 2009; based on ILO LABORSTA database and ILO Global Employment Trends." The Organisation for Economic Co-operation and Development.

Ekram Fahim, A. (2014). "Chemical Elements in Welding Fumes." *African Newsletter on Occupational Health and Safety* 24: 64–65.

Forum on Public-Private Partnerships for Global Health and Safety. (2016). Board on Global Health; Institute of Medicine; National Academies of Sciences, Engineering, and Medicine. In *Approaches to Universal Health Coverage and Occupational Health and Safety for the Informal Workforce in Developing Countries: Workshop Summary*. Washington, DC:

Fox, M. L., and M. S. Gaal. (2008). *Working Out of Poverty*. Washington, DC: World Bank.

Horowitz, S. (2000). "New Thinking on Worker Groups' Role in a Flexible Economy." In F. Carré, M. A. Ferber, L. Golden, and S. A. Herzenberg (eds.), *Nonstandard Work: The Nature and Challenges of Changing Employment Arrangements*. Champaign, IL: Industrial Relations Research Association, 393–98. http://digitalcommons.ilr.cornell.edu/manuals/6: 54.

Houseman, S., and M. Osawa. (2003). "The Growth of Nonstandard Employment in Japan and the United States:

A Comparison of Causes." In S. Houseman and M. Osawa (eds.), *Nonstandard Work in Developed Economies: Causes and Consequences.* Kalamazoo, MI: W. E. Upjohn Institute for Employment Research, 175–214.

Hove, M., E. T. Ngwerume, and C. Muchemwa. (2013). "The Urban Crisis in Sub-Saharan Africa: A Threat to Human Security and Sustainable Development. Stability" International Journal of Security and Development 2(1): Article 7.

International Labour Organization (ILO). *Cities at work, employment promotion to fight urban poverty 2004.* Turin, Italy: International Labour Organization.

International Labour Organization. (2011).. "100th ILO Annual Conference Decides to Bring an Estimated 53 to 100 Million Domestic Workers Worldwide under the Realm of Labour Standards" (Press Release June 16). http://www.ilo.org/ilc/ILCSessions/100thSession/media-centre/press-releases/WCMS_157891/lang--en/index.htm.

International Labour Organization. (1999). ILO/ICFTU: International Symposium on the Informal Sector.

Jafari, A. J., and M. J. Assari. (2004). "Respiratory Effects from Work-related Exposure to Welding Fumes in Hamadan, Iran." *Archives of Environmental Health* 59: 116–20.

Kalleberg, A. L., E. Rasell, N. Cassirer, B. F. Reskin, K. Hudson, D. Webster, E. Appelbaum, and R. M. Spalter-Roth. (1997). *Nonstandard Work, Substandard Jobs: Flexible Work Arrangements in the US.* Washington, DC: Economic Policy Institute and Women's Research and Education Institute.

Kamruzzaman, P. (2016). "A Critical Note on Poverty Eradication Target of Sustainable Development Goals." *European Journal of Sustainable Development* 5(2): 87–110.

Kent, L. "The Relationship between Small Enterprises and Environmental Degradation in the Developing World (with Emphasis on Asia)." Review prepared for USAID 1991, Washington, DC.

Luo, J. C., K. H. Hsu, and W. S. Shen. (2006). "Pulmonary Function Abnormalities and Airway Irritation Symptoms of Metal Fumes Exposure on Automobile Spot Welders." *American Journal of Medicine* 49: 407–16.

Marie, A., R. Leung, and J. L. D. P. Lu. (2016). "Environmental Health and Safety Hazards of Indigenous Small-Scale Gold Mining Using Cyanidation in the Philippines." *Environmental Health Insights* 10: 125–31.

Mattera, P. (1985). *Off the Books: The Rise of the Underground Economy.* New York: St. Martin's Press.

Menya, D., C. Walekhwa, P. Koskei, R. Too, and R. S. Carel. (2012). "Occupational Risk Factors in the Jua Kali Industry, Eldoret, Kenya." *African Newsletter on Occupational Health and Safety* 22: 46–50.

Mohammed, Y. U., M. David, and T. W. Seow. (2013). *International Journal of Physical and Human Geography* 1(2): 31–46.

National Academies Press (US). (2016). "Responding to Work-Related Health Needs of Informal Sector Workers." https://www.ncbi.nlm.nih.gov/books/NBK373407/.

Oluyomi, O.-D. (2012). "Occupational Health and Safety for Informal Sector Workers: The Case of Street Traders in Nigeria." IAABD 2012 Conference Proceedings.

Perera, L. A. S. R., and A. T. M. N. Amin. (1996). "Accommodating the Informal Sector: A Strategy for Urban Environmental Management." *Journal of Environmental Management* 46: 3–14.

Reid, A., A. Pinder, and S. Monnington. (2001). "Musculoskeletal Problems in Bricklayers, Carpenters and Plasterers: Literature Review and Results of Site Visits." *Health and Safety Laboratory* 19.

Schneider, F. (2002). "Size and Measurement of the Informal Economy in 110 Countries around the World." Paper presented at the workshop of the Australian National Tax Centre, Australian National University, Canberra.

Tajgman, D. (2006). "Extending Labour Protection to the Informal Economy: Bringing Together Three Country Experiences. http://www.who.int/occupational health/regions/en/oehemhealthcareworkers.pdf.

Tanzi, V. (1999). "Uses and Abuses of Estimates of the Underground Economy." *Economic Journal: The Journal of the Royal Economic Society* 109(456): F338–47.

The Rockefeller Foundation. (2013). "Health Vulnerabilities of Informal Workers" https://www.rockefellerfoundation.org/.../Health-Vulnerabilities-of-Informal-Workers: 4.

Thomas, J. J. (1992). *Informal Economic Activity.* London: Harvester Wheatsheaf Press.

Williams, C. C. (2011). "Formal and Informal Employment in Europe: Beyond Dualistic Representations." Paper presented at the European Union Conference on Informal/Undeclared Work, Brussels, May 21, 2003.

World Health Organization (WHO). (2001). "Occupational Health: A Manual for Primary Health Workers." http://www.who.int/occupational_health/regions/en/oehemhealthcareworkers.pdf.

World Health Organization. (WHO). "Working Together for Better Health." www.who.int/pmnch/activities/advocacy/workingtogether.pdf.

CHAPTER 31

# DECODING THE HUMAN ERROR BLACK BOX: INTEGRATING PSYCHOLOGY AND SAFETY

Erin Bowen

The majority of accidents across industries are not due to intentional action or catastrophic and unexplainable equipment failure but are instead a result of human errors at varying stages in the organizational system (not just the often-blamed "user" error at a visible point in the accident chain). Human error resides not just in the realm of lists of accident causes, but more often is symptomatic of deeper flaws and failures in an operational system. These flaws and failures combine in both additive and multiplicative ways to increase the likelihood of an accident or incident; unfortunately, articulating and measuring the error system presents an ongoing challenge. For example, areas that may contain flaws or failures that in turn influence individual, team, and organizational actions in the system include everything from the international regulatory and political context and the physical working environment to organizational policies and procedures, all the way down to individual worker variables. At each of these system points, it is the human in the loop who influences the quality, reliability, and validity of the practices and processes in use. When safety is considered from this perspective of humans in overlapping and entwined loops, influencing one another's behavior, the fundamental reality must be recognized that safety cannot be maintained or enhanced without an understanding and integration of psychological principles and practices.

Areas that may contain flaws or failures that in turn influence individual, team, and organizational actions in the system include everything from the international regulatory and political context and the physical working environment to organizational policies and procedures, all the way down to individual worker variables.

Why must psychology and safety go together? To reflect, it makes sense to start with an understanding of the term *safety*. While numerous variations of definitions exist, often specific to various technical specializations such as the American Society of Safety Professionals (ASSP) and the Human Factors and Ergonomics Society (HFES), for the present discussion the web-based Google dictionary definition will be considered. Safety as a basic construct should be discussed from the standpoint of what the average employee, manager, or policymaker understands—and Google is certainly something the public appears to understand. If one thus defines safety (as Google's dictionary does) as "the condition of being protected from or unlikely to cause danger, risk, or injury," then safety is inherently based upon a psychological premise—that is, one's individual or organizational-level perception of what is likely or unlikely to cause danger, risk, or injury. This includes the perception of what constitutes danger, risk, or injury (is the occasional paper cut at an office job an acceptable risk or evidence of an unsafe work environment?), whether policies in place truly reduce the risk, and whether the risk is worth accepting. By extension, if safety as a construct is inherently based in individual and shared perceptions of the nature of various dangers and even whether a certain protective action is in fact a protection from said dangers, then it is imperative for those in the safety disciplines to have at least a rudimentary understanding of basic behavioral science principles. To go further, I advocate that practitioners benefit from collaborations with applied psychologists (i.e., those who focus their science and practice on application of theory and research to organizational or other relevant settings for specific benefit). Much can be written on failures in safety—the training program that becomes another "flavor of the month," the policies that no one abides by, the careless mistakes that cost time, money, and harm workers. These are but a sample of the psychological attitudes and behaviors that the safety professional must manage.

The notion of bringing psychology into safety (inasmuch as safety appears to be a particular application of larger psychological theories and techniques) is certainly not a novel one. The Association for Aviation Psychology has existed since 1964, focusing on applications in aviation performance and safety. Among the most widely-recognized texts on the topic is *Human Factors Engineering* (Wickens et al. 2004), which takes a comprehensive approach to the role of understanding human perception, ability, and behavior at all phases of the organizational system. Others (e.g., Cooper 2003; Dejoy 1985; Fischoff et al. 1978; Geller 1998) have for years been putting forth scientific studies, documenting the numerous advantages to organizations, regulators, and individual employees when data on behavior and mental processes (like thought and perception) are taken into account in the planning, implementation, and maintenance of safety policies, procedures, and culture. However, despite the ongoing research and the various case study examples of successful integration of behavioral and cognitive data into policies, procedures, and organizational cultures, there still remains a substantial gap between what has been documented in research and the practices of many safety practitioners.

How frequently can one think of safety colleagues who have opted to include a survey or conduct an assessment to gather data on their current safety programs, or have developed or paid for a new safety training series, or attempted to understand why employees are not following current safety policies? Each of these is an example of the work that applied psychologists (particularly industrial/organizational psychologists) perform, and yet how rarely they are contacted directly by safety managers for assistance! Safety leaders at all levels owe it to themselves to become more familiar with applied psychologists, especially those who may specialize in their industry or in a particular problem that they have (e.g., training design and evaluation, policy noncompliance, safety culture, as just a few examples), and not hesitate to reach out to them. Many university I/O psychology programs offer corporate consulting at a fraction of the cost of a professional firm—and produce high-quality results for organizations. Internships or other opportunities for students in these types of programs give safety departments low-cost access to expertise and resources.

What is the future of safety and psychology as integrated disciplines? This author remains cautiously optimistic. Scientists often struggle to effectively communicate their work to practitioners and industry partners or even reach out to adapt their research findings into tools, strategies, and techniques for practitioners. The onus should not have to be on the safety practitioner to take densely worded scientific work outside their discipline area and identify how it can be applied in various organizational contexts. Conversely, safety practitioners have a duty to reach out to their psychology counterparts when they recognize that they are moving into the realm of describing or predicting human thought and behavior. For example, many poorly designed and executed "surveys" of safety topics have been seen and put through organizations. There is a large scientific body of knowledge solely dedicated to the development of questionnaires, assessment tools, and other data metrics, and very few safety specialists take the time to find someone to assist them in this regard. It is helpful to keep in mind this thought: "It is easy to write a survey. It is incredibly hard to write a *good* survey." While most are familiar with the notion of "garbage in, garbage out," that seems to be forgotten when the safety manager or coordinator decides they want to find out what employees *think* about safety. The partnership of disciplines is essential to success.

Perhaps the best advice to share with colleagues in safety is this: If you want to understand or change the what, how, why, or when of people acting or thinking about safety—then learn more about psychology and partner with a psychologist. And to those in applied psychology or human factors psychology: We can always do more to meet safety experts halfway. Their jobs are incredibly challenging and, in many cases, the consequences of failures are significant if not deadly. The successful integration of safety and psychology informs and improves each discipline and frankly, saves lives.

## Questions

1. Why is it so difficult to write a good safety survey? What are the consequences of using poor-quality questionnaires in safety evaluations?
2. What does it mean to integrate psychology and safety effectively?
3. What are common misconceptions regarding the integration of psychology into safety (e.g. assuming it means offering counseling or mental health services)? How can these be overcome by safety practitioners?
4. How does the integration of psychology and safety enhance the effectiveness of safety programs?
5. What is the role of behavioral or perceptual data (such as that studied by psychologists) in the success or failure of safety initiatives?

## References

Cooper, D. (2003). "Psychology, Risk and Safety." *Professional Safety*: 48(11): 39–46.

Dejoy, D. M. (1985). "Attributional Processes and Hazard Control Management in Industry." *Journal of Safety Research* 16: 61–71.

Fischoff, B., et al. (1978). "How Safe Is Safe Enough? A Psychometric Study of Attitudes towards Technological Risks and Benefits." *Policy Sciences* 9: 127–52.

Geller, E. S. (1998). *The Psychology of Safety: How to Improve Behaviors and Attitudes on the Job.* Boca Raton, FL: CRC Press.

Wickens, C. D., J. D. Lee, Y. Liu, and S. E. Gordon Becker. (2004). *An Introduction to Human Factors Engineering* (2nd ed.). Upper Saddle River, NJ: Pearson Education.

CHAPTER 32

# EFFECTIVELY LEADING EHS CHANGE

Kathy A. Seabrook and Tom Reeves

## Learning Objectives

After studying this chapter, the reader should be able to:

1. Evaluate the complex nature of an EHS organizational change initiative
2. Recognize the importance of the EHS professional's role in a change initiative
3. Discuss the positive and negative ramifications of taking leadership on a critical EHS change initiative
4. Consider how cultural norms, political climates, regulatory environments, global standards, and other factors affect successful change

## Key Terms

**Safety culture, integrated management systems, business integration, workplace safety, context safety, ISO 45001, safety strategy, risk mitigation, commercial excellence, operational excellence**


## Abstract

Leading environmental, health, and safety (EHS) change is complex, challenging, and rewarding. The technical skills required to be an EHS professional are not enough. EHS professionals must master the skills of a C-Suite executive, a marketer, a public relations manager, and a master coach if they are to be successful in leading organizational EHS change in today's rapidly evolving global setting.


## Introduction

Leading EHS change sounds simple, doesn't it? It is anything but. Leading any organizational change is complex, challenging, and rewarding. There are many unintended consequences that can arise if we don't approach organizational change with the proper mindset: being cognizant of the complexity of change initiatives.

Most EHS professionals lack solid grounding and skills in other disciplines, which further complicates EHS change initiatives. Although EHS underpins the change the organization is planning to implement, it does not provide all the tools necessary to align the organizational levers, such as culture, top management (executive leaders), commitment, and organizational engagement and mindset.

Executive leaders drive EHS, and its success is a result of the organizational culture. For example, do executive leaders (C-Suite) embrace EHS, and are they willing to provide the resources necessary to achieve the EHS goals? So, the EHS professional must look at the change as the C-Suite would and answer questions such as:

- Will our financial performance suffer if we don't change?
- How could staying on our current course affect our competitive position?
- Are there other business impacts if we don't begin an EHS change?

Additionally, EHS professionals need to utilize the skillset of the marketer, as well as that of the public relations specialist. No easy task for someone with limited background in either discipline.

In this chapter, we will discuss the challenges and barriers to EHS change, as well as explore the complex nature of organizational change, particularly one driven by an EHS change agent.

> Early in my career, I spent a lot of time trying to develop the ideal programs and tinkering with the strategy to get it "just right." But these efforts didn't facilitate buy-in from senior management. You may have the best message in the world, but if you haven't connected with your organizational leaders on an emotional level and created a coalition for change, your chances of success are greatly diminished. (Mike Belcher, CSP, Vice President Risk and Safety, DS Services)

## EHS Professional as Organizational Change Agent

Even though the daily mission of an EHS professional is managing EHS risk within their organization, the premise of this chapter focuses on the overarching role of an EHS professional as an organizational culture change agent (Manuele 2014, 271–89).

What does it mean to be a change agent? EHS professionals assess current conditions, identify gaps or deficiencies, and develop a plan to improve their organization's systems or processes. In this broader capacity, the EHS professional is a catalyst, driving planned organizational change that reduces risk to the business and promotes continuous improvement.

Organizational culture is one of the key barriers to the success of any organizational change. An IBM Study found that 60 percent of change initiatives failed. Forty-nine percent of study participants reported that corporate culture was among the highest rated challenges when implementing change initiatives (IBM Global Business services Strategy and Change Practice 2010).

The EHS professional must have a deep understanding of the overall organizational culture and how EHS fits into this culture prior to beginning any change project. Understanding the business environment and organizational culture in which the EHS professional operates is essential to the success of the organizational change and the EHS professional. EHS success is a product of organizational culture, which is a top-down driven organizational element.

Top management owns and influences the culture of an organization and must fully support any change if it is to be a success. Ninety-two percent of the respondents in the IBM study agreed that top management sponsorship was the most important factor in the success of an organizational change initiative (IBM Global Business Services Strategy and Change Practice 2010).

Another challenge to successful change is determining the true nature of top management's commitment to EHS. Top management may establish solid EHS policies and procedures, but their actions may indicate the company is not truly committed to EHS. Consequently, employees may perceive that their expected performance is not judged on what written policies, procedures, and manuals say (Manuele 2014, 81–97).

Affecting organizational change, whether the organizational culture is positive or negative, requires the EHS professional to get buy-in from top management, employees, and other organizational stakeholders. It necessitates developing a compelling story that helps management understand the implications if the situation continues.

Once top management is committed, engaged, and fully supportive of the change, the important storyteller role continues as they motivate employees at all levels of the organization to embrace and adopt the change. Sometimes sacrifices are required by members of the organization in order to achieve improvement. Understanding a compelling reason why the change must occur will make the sacrifice more palatable. Employees must trust that top management has fully committed to an overhaul of the system and resulting performance (Manuele 2014, 81–97).

Organizational factors must be considered when leading change. When organizations change directions or expectations change dramatically, workers and leaders in the organization can experience tremendous stress. New expectations may create fear, uncertainty, and doubt. In Kurt Lewin's famous three-step model of change (figure 32.1), he points out that organizations must "unfreeze" prior to changing and refreeze in a future state. Lewin recognized in the 1940s that organizations may attempt to change too quickly without adequate preparation for change. The "unfreezing" step creates dissatisfaction with the current state and performance of the organization. In the next step, "changing," the organization executes the change. In the final step, often interpreted as "refreeze," the organization solidifies in a new, future state (Lewin 1947). It is critical that EHS professionals recognize the importance of "unfreezing" the organization prior to beginning to change organizational factors, such as culture or mindsets.

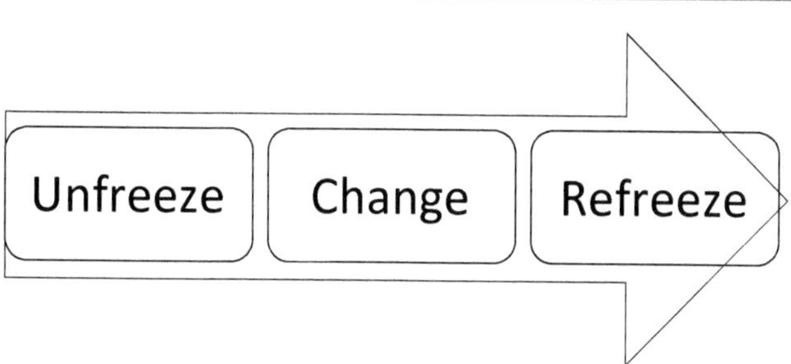


Figure 32.1
Three-step model of change (Lewin 1947)

Increasingly, EHS professionals are charged with leading EHS change in their organizations, whether on a jobsite, plant, or on an enterprise-wide scale. Some EHS professionals are asked to lead culture change directly. Other EHS professionals are tasked with leading complex initiatives, such as implementation of occupational health and safety management systems, without the senior leaders in the organization realizing the depth or complexity of the organizational change.

An EHS leader discussed the risks a safety professional takes when leading change, even when senior leaders state they want the change:

> I joined a company as safety director and very quickly, I was charged with leading an enterprise-wide "safety culture change." The initiator of the change was my direct boss. While we had great intentions, we didn't realize how large of a change this would be for the organization, especially for leaders who had grown up inside the company. Our task was to transfer ownership of health and safety from the safety department to the line leadership and we started several initiatives to accomplish this. Some of the initiatives made progress—most did not. We struggled to break old habits, especially when we were behind schedule or our costs started to rise. As things got harder, my relationship with my boss suffered. I thought he was too focused on the minute details and change can be messy. He thought I was too focused on the people and relationship challenges. I eventually left the company. In retrospect, it wasn't the relationship with my boss that led us to part ways. Our downfall actually started much earlier than that and is rooted in two things. First, we didn't really understand the complexity of the change within the business culture of our company or what levers we would need to pull to drive change. Second, we didn't plan the change. We simply described the future state we wanted to see and expected things to move. Ultimately, this created tremendous pressure on me and my boss. Later, someone told me that water boils at different temperatures under different pressures and so do people. I think that's what happened to us. We

> boiled under the pressure because we didn't have a strong strategy for change. (Anonymous 2016)

## Leadership Courage

Leading as a change agent is not for the weak-hearted. The EHS professional must comprehend the profound nature of taking leadership on a critical transformation of the corporate EHS culture. Most EHS professionals know how resistance to changing the status quo feels. And there will be resistance. It sounds like this: "We have been doing this for fifteen years without an accident."

Leaders inspire, take decisive actions, and often are rewarded well. Those leaders who take risks also may lose their jobs, derailing their careers and personal lives. It takes courage to lead organizational change.

In some areas of life, courage manifests as a sudden, impulsive action with little thought given when attempting the heroic act. In the business world, courage is typically less impetuous. It is usually more deliberate and demands more thorough preparation before making a risky move. Deliberate business risk-taking requires the courageous change agent to follow a process, particularly if in a leadership role without authority, typical for EHS professionals. Process steps include:

- Identify clear goals and objectives
- Prioritize the goals and understand what is most important
- Identify the organizational influencers on organizational culture and EHS issues (with or without authority)
- Analyze costs and benefits
  - Who will benefit from this change?
  - Who will lose from this change?
  - Consider what resistance may be created by those who may lose from the change.
- Determine the best time for implementation
- Develop alternative options (Reardon 2007)

Driving organizational change requires the EHS professional to disturb the status quo, sometimes turning it on its head and uncovering hidden conflict. That's why following a deliberate process is important. When disruption happens, there will be pushback, and the conflict can become personal. If the change is truly critical, the EHS professional must stay the course, finding ways to smooth the conflict and lead with courage despite the opposition (Linsky 2002, 3–5).

Leading courageously requires the EHS professional to be deeply committed to the planned change while understanding the change may fail in the face of resistance.

## Equal Business Partnerships

As change agents, EHS professionals must establish that they have the same business stature and bring as much value to the business as everyone else involved in the change initiative. This is particularly true if they don the mantle of leadership but lack corporate-level authority.

This requires acting with confidence and avoiding deferring to colleagues who are older or who have more imposing corporate titles. Expertise in EHS change makes the EHS professional a consultant to the business.

Tom Reeves, CEO of Engaged Change Solutions and one of this chapter's authors, shares his experience:

> Several years ago, when I started my health and safety consulting practice, I attended some sales training. While I was an experienced safety professional, I knew little about how to market and sell my consulting services. Little did I know that I would learn a valuable lesson for safety professionals. The instructor, a veteran sales professional, began the class by talking about this concept of "equal business partnerships." He encouraged us to establish ourselves as equals to anyone we visited on a sales call. This meant that if we met with a CEO, we were just as self-assured and confident as if we were meeting with a production employee. Even though this was a sales class, I immediately thought of my experience as a safety professional. I thought, "How many times have I deferred to an executive, instead of holding myself as their equal? How many opportunities have I missed because I thought my position was lower in the organization (or worse, higher) than

**John Farris, vice president and general manager at Nucor Steel Gallatin has been the plant manager at three VPP Star worksites. He discusses his expectations of safety professionals leading change:**

Safety is the most personal thing we do at work. No person should ever die or be injured working in service to themselves and their families. Ken Iverson, the first CEO of what became our modern steel company said we run Nucor so that our children and grandchildren will have a place to work. None of that is possible unless we're working safely, and in a manner that protects our health. In order to achieve this end, organizations often need to change in significant ways.

While I hold my line managers and supervisors accountable for ensuring their departments identify hazards, assess risks, and implement highly effective controls, the role of the safety professional is critical to this mission. My first expectation for my safety director is to challenge me to fully live my responsibility to health and safety. If I'm not leading the way I should, or if I'm missing something, my safety director must have the courage to challenge and coach me. They must also be able to challenge and coach department managers. This is called 'leading up' and it takes tremendous leadership courage. I also expect the safety professional to be an expert organizational influencer. They must be able to influence and coach at every level of the organization. With that influence, I expect safety professionals to help our organization identify and implement the appropriate mindsets, processes, and structures to ensure the highest level of safety performance. They must be capable of being a leader, a coach, a technical advisor, a teacher, and an advocate to the entire organization.

At an organizational development level, I see tremendous opportunities to employee health and safety to develop leaders and teams. Safety is a lever we use to grow decision-making, ownership, and empowerment throughout our organization. Safety professionals who understand how to develop leaders and teams are immensely valuable. It's also critical for safety professionals to understand how to lead complex, adaptive change and be able to deploy any resource to move the organization forward. This requires both strategic thinking and hands-on application. Growing organizational development capabilities adds to the value and impact safety professionals can have on the organization. By targeting organizational factors, we help ensure health & safety is more deeply ingrained into the way we work and not simply a bolt-on business function we abandon under pressure.

Make no mistake, helping our team members work safely and return home to their families each shift is our highest responsibility. Everything else follows from this responsibility.

someone else?" At the time, I had a corporate client working through a safety related organizational change and I was scheduled to facilitate a workshop with all the regional safety managers. I immediately incorporated the concept of "Equal Business Partnership" into the session and encouraged those safety professionals to view themselves as equals of everyone in the organization. Through some exercises and ongoing coaching, those professionals grew to think of themselves as equals of everyone in their organization. Over time, the organization began to change its perceptions of these safety professionals–from "safety cops" to "go-to problem solvers and organizational influencers." (Reeves 2018)

## Global Fluency

Today's companies are becoming what are known as "Velcro organizations" as they push the innovation envelope. That means their parts and people can be rapidly rearranged to meet new business goals, expand markets into new regions, and keep up with the digital revolution. For Velcro organizations, the pieces move around, but major structural changes are not required.

Agile leaders need to be fluent in new business imperatives in these volatile times. This is particularly true of organizations working on a global scale.

The United States Army War College coined a term that perfectly captures the chaos of the twenty-first century: VUCA. VUCA stands for volatility, uncertainty, complexity, and ambiguity. In the face of VUCA, an EHS professional in a global organization must be concerned with the complicated web of technical and personal networks as well as with organizational structure. Further complicating matters, global aspects of culture, norms, customs, and hierarchy also must be considered in EHS change strategy creation (Horney 2010).

The necessity of having a global view becomes clearer to the EHS professional involved in a change initiative that impacts corporate strategy and corporate social responsibility in a multinational organization. Although the multinational organization may have its own business culture and vernacular that is accepted and used by stakeholders worldwide, those stakeholders (including workers) may still be embedded in the traditions of their local culture, which impact EHS strategies such as risk control methodologies (Seabrook 2012). Contemplating change on a global scale requires the change agent to consider how unique cultural norms, political climates, regulatory environments, nongovernmental organizations, and global standards may affect successful change. This adds to the complexity of an already complicated process (Galbreath 2006).

## Resilient Leader

Leading change takes resilience, grit, empathy, and emotional intelligence.

Because change often causes discomfort, those happy with the status quo sometimes rebel against the agent of change. Dissenters may try to marginalize change agents with personal attacks, throw up barriers to divert them, and even try to seduce them into agreement.

The prepared EHS professional will keep the focus on the issue. One must be resilient and have enough grit to overcome personal attacks and negativity (Linsky 2002).

The EHS professional must also possess the emotional intelligence to discern why stakeholders are resistant to change. When one understands this, one can often disarm the naysayers by listening for, understanding, and empathizing with their concerns. One can then reframe the change to help them understand the benefit it will have on them as well as the business.

A safety professional from a Fortune 100 company shares an experience:

> In the mid-2000s, I accepted a safety leadership role at a Fortune 100 manufacturing company. In the interview, the plant manager warned me this would be an extremely difficult assignment. The plant was nearly 100 years old and had a history of fatal and serious injuries. The plant had just been purchased by an extremely safety conscious company who wanted to immediately turn things around regarding health and safety. In the interview for the job, I was told that the expectation was nothing less than world-class safety performance and an OSHA VPP quality culture and safety management system. As a reference point, employees at this plant didn't even have locks for lockout-tagout at the time of the acquisition. We were starting from scratch and this massive organizational change involved improvements to systems, programs, plant conditions, infrastructure, culture, and leadership development. We very quickly designed a multi-phased strategy to begin to implement the change. Our first mission was to implement basic safety programs like lockout-tagout, confined space, fall protection, mobile equipment, etc. We got employees involved in the development of these programs and did a lot of training. After that, we began to involve employees in the development

of safety management systems all while building a more "actively caring" culture where people would look out for each other. Getting people involved ensured that our practices matched our programs and procedures. We conducted extensive audits to correct and control hazardous conditions in the plant. We worked solid for two years getting things turned around and the work was beginning to show. Employee perceptions of safety were changing. We were performing better in audits. Supervisors were taking a much more active role in leading safety.

Not that the change was easy. There were tough choices. Some supervisors and department managers didn't buy into the change and had to be removed from their roles. Some employees struggled to do their work differently or even actively resisted the change. It seemed like we often took a few steps forward only to fall a few steps back. And, yet, through all that, we made progress.

Then, almost exactly two years after the acquisition, we were in a plant maintenance turn-around. I was walking into the shop to see the project and check on a few things when I heard a nearby employee's radio—someone was severely injured on an overhead crane. My heart sank. As I made my way to the crane, it was obvious the man had been killed. I'll never forget the devastation this death had on the man's family and his friends. I only know a small part of that pain and, for me, it was unbelievably hard.

As hard as it was emotionally for our entire team, we had to move forward. And I give credit to the employees at that plant—they redoubled their efforts. They wanted safety to be different. At the same time, many thought it might just be impossible to turn this plant around—an understandable response after all the hard work of the last two years.

As a safety professional, I had a hard time separating my emotions from the responsibility I had to the rest of the team to continue to lead us forward in the change. And I wasn't the only one who felt this way among the plant leaders. All of us had to look ourselves in the mirror and commit—truly commit—to the improvement.

I think we all banded together and carried each other through the tragedy. While we can't bring that team member back, we did continue on the journey so no one else would have to experience the loss of a loved-one who was working in service to her or his family.

Less than two years after that tragic day, this plant successfully completed its' VPP Star evaluation and I'll never forget the spouses of the employees who came for the VPP flag raising ceremony. Many of those spouses had tears in their eyes as they thanked the plant leaders for turning things around. But it wasn't us—it was the workers who truly wanted things to be different—to be better—to be safer. (Anonymous 2017)

## Strategic Learning

The PDCA (plan, do, check, act) strategic approach to the continuous improvement cycle has stood the test of time since its beginnings in the 1950s. But in our tumultuous, global VUCA times, it is not sufficient as a driver of change because it doesn't adequately consider the human element or the complexity of today's world.

Comparing the PDCA, VUCA, and VUCA Prime models helps one see the evolution of approaches to continuous improvement. With these models as tools in hand, EHS professionals can see how to utilize strategic learning to help convert their organizations into adaptive enterprises. Let's further explore these models.

PDCA evolved to help manage and continually improve industrial processes. The *plan* phase in PDCA begins with identifying the problem, developing a clearly defined problem statement, setting measurable, attainable goals, determining the stakeholders, and developing communication channels to reach them. Second, one must analyze the problem and formulate a hypothesis based on the analysis. The hypothesis will verify the problem statement or provide more information so the problem statement can be revised for clarity and relevance.

The *do* phase in PDCA establishes criteria that determine experimental success. An experiment to test the hypothesis is designed, and approval is gained from stakeholders. The experiment is then implemented.

In the *check* phase of PDCA, the results of the experiment are evaluated. If the hypothesis is validated, move on to the *act* phase of PDCA. If not, cycle back to revise the hypothesis and repeat until the hypothesis is validated.

Once the hypothesis is confirmed, the *act* phase of PDCA provides an opportunity to identify changes necessary to put the new processes in place (Johnson 2002).

The VUCA model is helpful in identifying the internal and external conditions that affect the organization. This is a requirement for organizations implementing the ISO 45001.2 *Occupational Safety and Health Management Systems* (International Standards Organization 2017) and ISO 14001:2015 *Environmental Management Systems* standards, which is known as the "context of the organization" (International Standards Organization n. d.). The VUCA model looks at four unique types of problems (volatility, uncertainty, complexity, ambiguity), each demanding a different type of response.

The VUCA Prime model, developed by Bob Johansen, distinguished fellow at the Institute for the Future, turns VUCA on its head, making it solution oriented, not problem oriented. So, the VUCA acronym becomes vision, understanding, clarity, and agility, all traits the EHS professional needs for addressing organizational change (UNC Kenan Flagler Business School 2014).

Vision trumps volatility in VUCA Prime. With a solid understanding of the organization's vision, leaders determine the steps to take so that they can weather volatile changes from market fluctuations and economic declines to ramp up competition.

Leaders in a VUCA business environment must develop their ability to stop, look, and listen. Determining how uncertainty is affecting all areas of the organization is key, and once this is understood, it can be addressed.

Clarity is the antidote to the chaos caused by complexity. In this case, the leader needs to have the ability to quickly make sense of all the details in the chaotic environment. Only then can solid, informed decisions be made with clear, direct communication of those decisions throughout the organization.

Ambiguity surrounds us since we can't foretell the future. Like the relationship of clarity to complexity, one can counter ambiguity with agility. This requires a leader to take more risks, more quickly (UNC Kenan Flagler Business School 2014). This is where communication mechanisms and early adopters to help with the communication are essential. Whether it is changing the name of a risk-assessment process, introducing a new incident investigation model aligned with the principles of learning organizations, or introducing a new member to the change initiative steering team, never underestimate the importance of communication. Agility and communication go hand-in-hand, and one cannot communicate enough. If in doubt, communicate and check for understanding of those affected by the course correction, process, team, tools, or initiative.

The critical skills necessary for a successful leader are no longer function specific but situational. More than ever a leader needs the ability to assess and think through complex challenges strategically (Horney 2010).

## Strategy Overview and Three Levels of Strategy

How does one learn to think strategically about EHS? First, there are three hierarchical levels of strategy to consider.

Corporate strategy is the level at which the organization answers foundational questions of what it wants to achieve and where it wants to compete. Business strategy is focused on how to develop and sustain a competitive advantage. The focus of functional strategy is to align operational methods to meet the goals laid out at the corporate and business levels. EHS is a functional strategy that occurs within the context of a business and corporate strategy.

Many organizations are looking at the three levels of strategy in a new way, moving from the *strategy as planning* methodology into the *strategy as learning* approach. Using this method, leaders can transform their organizations into adaptive enterprises. There are five critical skills that must be mastered if the organization is to become adaptive:

1. Insight
2. Focus
3. Alignment
4. Execution
5. Renewal

The first four competencies aim at producing specific outputs. The fifth competency gives the EHS professional the ability to become a dynamic, ever-evolving change leader. Traditional strategy focuses on a one-time change, while strategic learning continuously senses and responds to change (Pietersen 2010, 9).

## Conducting Strategic Situational Analysis: Current State

Strategic learning, as we have seen, is key to defining a successful, dynamic strategy. This is not done in isolation by just the top-level executives. Employees at every level should provide input. Our first step in the strategic learning process is to perform a situational analysis. The situational analysis helps leaders gain a keen perception of the organization, as well as the customers, competitors, other stakeholders, industry dynamics, and the wider business environment.

During this analysis phase, leaders are gathering and analyzing information to gain a deep understanding of the internal and external realities the organization faces. Gathering reams of data to sit unused on a shelf is not the aim. The aim is to turn information into insight. We challenge the status quo by looking for trends and probing for root causes. Typically, this means the process does not begin by developing a vision. The insights the EHS professional gains from asking probing questions lead to the strategic vision, not the reverse (Pietersen 2010).

The elements of the situational analysis include a review of the organization's business and corporate strategies.

1. Organizational Performance
   a Environmental, health, and safety performance
   b Financial performance
   c HR performance
   d Operational performance
2. Industry factors
3. Broader factors
4. Regulatory and consensus standards
5. The organization's reality

Understanding strategic context is important, so start by reviewing the organization's current corporate and business strategies before assessing business and functional plans and performance information.

### Organizational Performance

Next comes an assessment of organizational performance. Understanding organizational realities requires a consideration of the trends that relate to measures the organization deems critical to driving performance. For example, how does EHS performance affect the bottom line? Are there customer, investment community, or regulatory EHS requirements based upon sustainability performance expectations? Consider financial strengths and weaknesses. Where are there competitive advantages, and where is there room for improvement? Look at revenue streams. Ask what's profitable and what is not. How are human resource issues, such as turnover, absenteeism, and high medical costs affecting performance? What are the trend lines? What are the root causes?

On the operational side of the business, ask about productivity and efficiency. Are there product quality issues? Are costs reasonable? Are environmental issues considered? Are there maintenance issues, planned or unplanned downtime, affected productivity, product quality, or other operational factors?

### Industry Factors

Are there industry-specific factors to consider? Are there evolving trend lines to consider? How are competitors gaining advantages in the marketplace? Are there new, nontraditional competitors taking market share? How are they doing it, and what can we learn from them? Have customer views of us and our competitors shifted? Where are customer expectations heading? Are customer needs identified, and how well are they being met?

### Broader Factors and Regulatory/ Consensus Standards

What is happening in the broader environment politically, economically, technologically, and socially? Are there global issues to consider? Are there market-specific issues that must be addressed? What innovations are driving performance? Are nongovernmental organizations affecting our operations? Are new or proposed regulations threatening the business?

As part of the situational analysis, we look at reality inside the company. Is proper leadership in place, and is the next generation ready to move up? Is our culture stable or eroding? What hazards and risks are we facing? Do we have adequate management systems?

These are just a few questions EHS professionals might ask during the situational analysis. The more questions asked and answered, the better the quality of the insights that will be developed. A set of insights is the most important outcome of a situational analysis. These should be clearly and simply articulated into diagnostic statements anyone can understand (Pietersen 2010).

## Creating Strategic Focus

There are two ways to influence human behavior: through manipulation or by inspiration. Consider how Apple Computer communicates:

> Everything we do, we believe in challenging the status quo. We believe in thinking differently. The way we challenge the status quo is by making our products beautifully designed, simple to use and user-friendly. And we happen to make great computers. Want to buy one? (Sinek 2009)

Manipulation doesn't last. Inspiration, like Apple's, does.

People will accept change and even embrace it if EHS professionals provide an inspiring reason. Author Simon Sinek refers to this inspiring reason as a compelling *why*. Everyone has a compelling *why*: a purpose, a cause, or a belief that makes them want to go to work in the morning. The best organizations—the ones with the strongest cultures—have clear values that are lived every day. Those organizations have the most motivated employees. Leaders at these organizations inspire followers by giving them that sense of purpose. Tell people a captivating story about why anything is necessary, and they will be motivated to act because it becomes personal to them (Krogue 2015).

People will accept change, and even embrace it, if EHS professionals provide an inspiring reason.

The *why* should be developed for any change initiative, one firmly tied to the organization's culture, if the initiative is to succeed. There will be resistance to change, even if there is a compelling story. So, proactively anticipate and consider possible reasons for potential resistance and how to overcome it. After doing this, develop a simple, inspiring leadership message to win over hearts and minds. The inspirational message must explain why the change is necessary, and it must be continually repeated. Communicate, communicate. communicate.

Lead with the compelling reason, the *why*, before answering the other questions people will have, such as:

- What's in it for them?
- What will change, and what won't change?
- Who is affected by the change?
- How will the change manifest itself?
- When will the change begin?

### Defining Future State

A good way to overcome resistance is to maximize participation in what needs to be done (Pietersen 2010). This includes involving people throughout the organization in developing a shared vision of how the future will look—the future state.

Having management go behind closed doors to write a vision statement is efficient but not collaborative or effective. The future state is not truly shared until people connect with it on an emotional level, which makes widespread engagement critical.

> If you want to lead change that reaches the culture down to the floor level, you need to start with the "why." Once you have established the "why," it is critical to develop a great operational plan, utilizing operational management to drive the change. And finally, you have to implement processes that engage employees which is the engine that drives continuous improvement. (Michael Sinclair, Corporate Safety Manager, McKee Foods Corporation)

## Aligning Culture and Organization

The Beckhard-Harris Change Model specifies there are three critical and necessary components that must be in place before change can begin. There must be:

- dissatisfaction with the current state;
- a clear and shared vision of the preferred future; and
- acceptable steps outlined to achieve the vision.
- In completing the situational analysis, determine whether there is dissatisfaction with the current state. If so, define the changes desired and write the vision of the preferred future state.

To evaluate the forces favorable and unfavorable to change, Kurt Lewin created a *force field analysis*. To begin the analysis, brainstorm the forces that are favorable to change. These driving forces should be recorded on the left side of a force field diagram. Perform the same brainstorming process and analysis of the restraining forces, and place these on the right side of a force field diagram. Then, evaluate and rate each force from 1 (weak) to 5 (strong). Total the driving forces and the restraining forces to see where the balance lies. The balance between the forces must be upset if the change is to be driven in the organization (Lewin 1948).

Review the forces to determine which can be influenced. Then, develop a strategy to strengthen driving forces, weaken restraining forces, or both.

Develop actionable steps, and prioritize them based on which will achieve the greatest impact. Reducing the restraining forces is sometimes more effective than attempting to strengthen the driving forces. Now, identify the resources necessary and decide how to implement the action steps.

Communication is critical in change management. Successful change management begins with people. First, engage opinion leaders to help carry the message forward that will drive the desired change. There are three types of influencers, and each plays a different role. They are:

- Cassandras
- Networkers
- Influencers

Cassandra, in Greek mythology, had the ability to accurately foretell events, but no one would listen to her. Cassandras are often seen by organizational management as complainers, but they can be helpful in pointing out where resistance to change will arise or what reaction a specific tactic might provoke. Networkers are like journalists. They know what is happening, what people are saying, and are willing to report this information to management. Influencers have the ability and the desire to sway public opinion. Others in the organization seek them out to see what they think about an issue. Think of them as the op-ed page in a newspaper.

### Aligning Organizational Levers

Everything is now in place to begin implementing the strategy. It may seem a huge task, particularly if the EHS professional is in a large, global organization, but there are guiding principles to follow that ease the job. An overview of four key areas or organizational levers will help clarify how an EHS change initiative is managed. The areas are:

- Measurements and rewards
- Structures and processes
- People
- Culture

### Measurements and Rewards

Organizations measure things for two reasons. One is to announce that this metric is important. The other is to gauge performance against that metric. So, legacy measurements and rewards left in place that are no longer important will almost guarantee the failure of the change initiative. The system of measurements and rewards must act in concert with other business system elements (Pietersen 2010).

### Structures and Processes

The new strategy may necessitate changes in organizational structures and processes. Organizational structures include leadership hierarchies, digital systems, and resources. Processes include all business processes, which affect EHS. This includes aspects of the occupational health and safety and environmental management systems. It may also include other business processes, such as capital allocation or mergers and acquisitions (Pietersen 2010).

### People

Focused, skilled, and motivated people drive organizational success. Clear, simple communication helps provide the focus for people at all levels in the organization, making the success of the change management initiative more likely (Pietersen 2010).

Recruitment to fill jobs necessary for implementing the new strategy should be considered. Job training may also be necessary to upgrade skills of existing employees. The need for severances should not be overlooked (Pietersen 2010).

Organizations with a high commitment to change have been shown to outperform those in which employees display lower levels of motivation. This motivational effort is a crucial responsibility of leadership (Pietersen 2010).

### Culture

Managing the culture aspect of change is considered the most critical and difficult factor in successful change management. Culture is observable and is not as mysterious as some think. It is a set of beliefs and behaviors that are integral to the organization. Fostering change is impossible without having a culture in place that supports it (Pietersen 2010).

## Execution

Executing change can be described as a journey of 10,000 steps where the steps continually change. While steadfast focus on the goals and vision of the change are critical to success, it is also critical to employees to have nimble methods to execute the change. Executing a transformational change in an organization requires an understanding of the way the organization works, its culture, and an application of various project management techniques.

In their 2012 book, *The 4 Disciplines of Execution,* Chris McChesney, Sean Covey, and Jim Huling identify four principles necessary for execution. Their findings included:

- Create clear, measurable *goals* that are critical to the organization's success. Focusing on a small number of measurable goals creates organizational focus. As the number of goals increases, so does the chance for failure.
- Goals are the lag measure—the result. Develop *leading measures, which* are the activities and behavioral levers that drive change, increasing the likelihood that goals will be achieved.
- If you were to watch kids playing basketball, can you tell if they're keeping score? Keep a meaningful *scoreboard* that measures progress to the goal and tracks progress on the leading measures. A scoreboard also gives members of the rest of the organization an instant view into the progress being made.
- Establish a *rhythm of accountability*. Change leaders must to establish a regular cadence of meetings where teams report-out on their progress toward goals and lead measures by reviewing progress on the scoreboard. In an accountability meeting, teams will report on their previous commitments, review the scoreboard to see if the team is winning, check the project milestones or other lead measures, and then make new commitments to be accomplished before the next meeting (Covey et al. 2012).

In addition to the four disciplines of execution, the authors identify the key reason they determined execution fails: the whirlwind of actively described as the *day job*. Change involves work that is in addition to these day jobs. Balancing day-to-day responsibilities with activities related to the change execution is a key consideration for change leaders. Often, failing to execute on the day job comes with significant consequences, so the day job often wins the tug of war for a team's time, energy, and focus. As strategic execution unfolds, tremendous opportunities to learn and improve the process may exist. Strategic change leaders leverage key learnings throughout the execution process and adjust their methods as necessary.

While structuring a change process is important, it is even more critical the EHS professional develops into a master change coach. Coaches help people solve their own challenges while growing and developing. While a team is growing and developing, the EHS professional leading the change efforts must also grow and develop. Some coaching competencies to consider:

- Relating and engaging—understanding another's perspective before challenging their mental models, specifically when communicating the "why" of the change
- Coaching presence—showing up, listening, and working through another person's concerns, challenges, and potential barriers to the change
- Leveraging diversity—understanding differences in background and culture and leveraging these differences to open possibilities and expand opportunities
- Listening—listening for understanding and empathy. An active, deep listening is challenging but provides insights into how the change is going, the effectiveness of the change strategy, and how well the "why" of the change is being communicated. Listening to others also exposes deeply held resistance to the change.
- Questioning—asking the right questions provides an opportunity to understand context, test assumptions, and identify the underlying causes of resistance. It also adds to the learning and provides a platform for honest feedback on the change.
- Testing assumptions—elevating and challenging underlying mental models, mindsets, and worldviews throughout the organization that may be enabling or limiting the organization's capacity for change.
- Reframing—getting others to see the change or their issues in a different context allows them to begin to reframe their understanding or to develop another perspective on the change.
- Contributing—engaging and empowering others to make decisions and be a part of the change leads to embracing and adopting the change going forward.
- Business acumen—holding the bigger picture, aligning business strategy and continually communicating why the change is important for the future of the organization helps the business leaders and workers embrace and adopt the change (Maltbia 2007, 2016).

By mastering these coaching competencies, EHS professionals can help people at all levels of their organization navigate and succeed in transforming their EHS performance.

## Summary

EHS is an exciting profession that challenges on many levels, particularly when it is the job of professionals to ensure the health and safety of their colleagues with minimal impact to the surrounding community and environment. While the EHS professional's primary role is to manage their organization's EHS-related risk, EHS professionals are increasingly asked to take on the role of change agent. Becoming a change agent requires EHS professionals to demonstrate leadership courage, establish equal business partnerships, and be resilient in the face of challenges and setbacks. EHS professionals increase their value to their organizations by helping their leaders identify successful change strategies. Successful change efforts include strategic learning, clear focus, organizational alignment, and execution. To succeed in these challenges, EHS professionals can adopt tools and methods from other professions, such as marketing, public relations, and organizational development. While emotionally and intellectually challenging at many levels, leading an organization through a transformative improvement effort can be one of the most satisfying aspects of the EHS professional's career.

## Questions

1. What is one of the key barriers to the success of any organizational change?
2. Why is it valuable for EHS professionals to understand the principles and practices of leading organizational change?
3. What other business functions might you explore to be better prepared to lead organizational change?
4. How do you envision expectations of EHS leaders changing in the future?
5. Name and describe four key organizational levers that will help clarify how an EHS change initiative is managed?

## References

Anonymous. (2016). Interview with the author.

Anonymous. (2017). Interview with the author.

Burke, W. W. (2017). *Organization Change: Theory and Practice.* Washington, DC: Sage Publications.

McChesney, C., S. Covey, and J. Huling. (2012). *The 4 Disciplines of Execution: Achieving Your Wildly Important Goals.* New York: Free Press.

Galbreath, J. (2006). "Corporate social Responsibility Strategy: Strategic Options, Global Considerations." *Corporate Governance: The International Journal of Business in Society.* Bingley, UK: Emerald Group Publishing Limited.

Horney, N., T. O'Shea. (2010). "Leadership Agility: A Business Imperative For a VUCA World." *Human Resource Planning* 33(4). *Chicago, Illinois: HR People & Strategy.*

IBM Global Business Services Strategy and Change Practice. (2010). "Making Change Work." Somers, NY: IBM. Accessed February 18, 2018. https://www-07.ibm.com/au/pdf/making_change_work.pdf.

International Standards Organization. (n. d.) ISO 14001:2015 *Environmental Management Systems—Requirements for Guidance for Use.* Geneva, Switzerland: International Standards Organization.

International Standards Organization. 2018. ISO 45001 *Occupational health and safety management systems—Requirements with guidance for use.* Geneva, SUI: International Standards Organization.

Johnson, C. N. (2002). "The Benefits of PDCA." Milwaukee, WI: *Quality Progress: The Official Publication of ASQ.*

Krogue, K. (2015). "Start with Why: How Great Leaders Inspire Everyone To Take Action." *Forbes.* Accessed February 18, 2018. https://www.forbes.com/sites/kenkrogue/2015/07/06/simon-sinek-says-start-with-why-but-sales-experts-disagree/#5054ce374b82.

Lewin, K. (1948). *Resolving Social Conflicts.* New York: Harper and Row Publishers.

Lewin, K. (1947). "Frontiers in Group Dynamics: Concepts, Method and Reality in Social Science; Social Equilibria and Social Change." *Human Relations* 1: 5–41

Linsky, M., and R. A. Heifetz. (2002). *Leadership on the Line: Staying Alive through the Dangers of Leading.* Brighton, MA: Harvard Business Review Press.

Maltbia, Dr. T. E. (2007–2016). "Faculty Director." *The Columbia Coaching Certification Program's External Coach Intensive.* Columbia University.

Manuele, F. A. CSP, P. E. (2014). "Safety Professionals as Culture Change Agents." In *Advanced Safety Management Focusing on Z10 and Serious Injury.* Hoboken, NJ: John Wiley & Sons.

Pietersen, W. (2010). *Strategic Learning Overview.* Accessed February 18, 2018. http://williepietersen.com/wp-content/uploads/pdf/Strategic_Learning.pdf.

Reardon, K. K. (2007). "Courage as a Skill." Brighton, MA: *Harvard Business Review.*

Reeves, T. (2018). Personal account of the author.

Seabrook, K. A. (2012). *The Safety Professional's Handbook: Management Applications.* J. M. Haight (ed.). Des Plaines, IL: American Society of Safety Engineers.

UNC Kenan Flagler Business School. (2014). "Leadership Development in a VUCA Environment." Chapel Hill, NC: UNC Executive Development, University of North Carolina.

# AFTERWORD

## Daniel H. Anna

Safety work is today recognized as an economic necessity. It is the study of the right way to do things.

—*Robert W. Campbell, 1914.*

Over the decades since Robert Campbell's declaration that safety was the right thing to do, the perceptions of safety and health in the workplace have evolved. Despite the historic importance of personal ethics and the reliance on regulatory requirements, they are simply components of the factors that guide the decisions, actions, and policies of an organization. The combination of topics addressed in the preceding chapters speak to the next wave of changes for OSH professionals and the potential future for the OSH profession: the successful integration of safety and health into the culture-based decisions of an organization.

The development and maturation of academic programs that provide degrees in OSH-related areas have created a network of professionals dedicated toward ensuring safe and healthy workplaces throughout the world. Improving the academic rigor through accreditation of those degree programs continues to strengthen the OSH profession. Increasing the number of graduates from OSH degree programs and the number of OSH professionals who pursue accredited professional certifications will help address the predicted shortage of professionals.

Although essential, the skills and technical expertise gained through academic preparation and professional certification do not automatically result in success as an OSH professional. Business, leadership, management, and finance skills have become essential companions to technical expertise. Integration of OSH subject-matter expertise throughout the lifecycle of a project, process, or facility requires the ability to effectively communicate expectations within a multidisciplinary team. Safety and health issues need to be addressed comprehensively with solutions that integrate with other production or process goals and expectations. Safety and health successes need to be measured in conjunction with other project performance aspects; clear metrics to measure success are expected. The ability to collect high volumes of complex data related to safety performance and health data provides the opportunity to make data-based decisions but also presents the same "big-data" challenges faced by other professions.

The regulatory environment has become increasingly difficult to navigate with the combination of new regulations, outdated regulations, the lack of regulations, and the variety of regulations encountered in a global industrial environment. In many instances these issues prevent the reliance on regulatory requirements and result in the need to develop alternative methods to support safety- and health-related recommendations. However, increased emphasis and interest in corporate social responsibility has provided a new opportunity. Corporate social responsibility can influence development of occupational safety and health management and contribute to integration of safety and health into a company's management systems. The evolution of occupational safety and health management into the framework of corporate social responsibility is helping increase visibility of the positive contributions of a strong safety and health culture to organizations' productivity and profitability.

Major improvements in worker protections have resulted from the use of risk assessments, advances in training methods, enhancements to personal protective equipment, and innovations in engineering control design and implementation. At the same time, OSH professionals continue to be asked to solve more complex problems. New manufacturing technologies, such as additive manufacturing, including 3-D printing, robotics, and nanotechnology, result in new, previously undefined hazards. Advances in the assessment and quantification of risks and in the technologies used to control risks have provided the most significant push for OSH professionals to develop leadership, management, and communication skills. The use of risk assessments and the ability to quantify risk has resulted in the ability to make data-based decisions about acceptable safety and health risk as part of a broader business decision about enterprise risk. Participation in enterprise risk discussions and decisions requires a combination of OSH subject-matter expertise, business skills, and effective communication capabilities.

The future of the OSH profession is filled with opportunities. Through continuous learning and the development of leadership skills, OSH professionals can develop into OSH leaders and transition into business leaders, making it easier to integrate safety and health principles into the goals of an organization. The unique expertise that OSH professionals bring into a leadership role will positively influence organizational culture and impact business decisions to increase productivity, improve working conditions, and ultimately protect worker safety and health.

Daniel H. Anna, PhD, CIH, CSP
President, 2015–16
American Industrial Hygiene Association

# ANSWER APPENDIX

## Chapter 1

1. Motivations, culture, beliefs, expectations, learned professional experiences, and education
2. Reflective learning
3. Moral values, behavioral criteria, coordinated action, and time
4. Support for professional codes of ethics, continuous training and education, encouragement of open dialogue, shared experience of pain and suffering, proximal ethics mentors, leadership responsibility, community resources, effective organization, and team building
5. Workplace dishonesty, harassment, assault, fraud, intentional malice, wasting resources, defamation, aggression, and hostility

## Chapter 2

1. Transparency is operating in such a way that it is easy for others to see what actions are performed.
2. Safety culture is a reflection of the organization's values, norms, expectations, etc., whereas safety climate consists of the organization's perceptions of safety as measured by tools such as safety perception surveys. Safety climate should be thought of as a leading indicator of safety culture and is measurable.
3. OSHA identifies management commitment and worker involvement as two of the key elements of an effective safety and health management system; the other elements are hazard prevention and control, worksite analysis, and training. Both management commitment and worker involvement contain elements of transparent leadership, while the other elements do not.
4. In organizations where transparent leadership has broken down at the first level supervisor, value conflicts between the perceived organizational priorities for safety and productivity may result in risk-taking behaviors.
5. Kirstin Ferguson identifies four specific components of safety leadership relevant to the most senior leaders of an organization (the CEO or president and their teams and the board). These components include vision, personal commitment, decision making, and transparency.

## Chapter 3

1. The focus of accident prevention has been associated with what safety professionals recognize as the three E-words:
   - Engineering—designing the safest equipment, environmental setting, or protectives devices
   - Education—educating people regarding the use of engineering interventions
   - Enforcement—using discipline to enforce compliance with recommended safety work practices

   People-first safety environments focus on creating quality work environments, which can boost productivity and the bottom line. Safety culture reflects attitudes, beliefs, perceptions, and values that employees at all levels share with a deep sense of purpose. A strong belief in people—employees—shapes a people-centered safety culture, which is crucial for leaders to understand and embrace.

   The people-centered approach to organizational safety culture leads to sustained high-level performance and profits over an extended period of time. Flexible, innovative, adaptive, and safety focused, these organizations are quick to adapt to changing market dynamics by leveraging the talent of their employees through ideas and brainstorming, and they assist and support employee success through the integration of technology
2. People-centered cultures share the following key elements:
   - leveraging people-first core values
   - leadership that walks the talk
   - open communication
   - high levels of trust
   - aligned operations and work environments focused on HR and talent development practices
   - change responsiveness
   - organizational resiliency
3. Inspirational leaders are those in the organization who can inspire the others around them to exceed their personal best. Such leaders are tenacious, committed, and driven by a passion and sense of personal responsibility, not rules and

regulations. They are open to new ideas, always pushing the envelope, yet watching and observing. They are people catalysts, coaching and guiding, benevolent yet demanding, and revered for their knowledge.

4. PHWs are integral because:
   - PHWs are workplaces that are dedicated to promoting and supporting the physical and psychological health and well-being of their employees while simultaneously incorporating solid business practices, to remain as an efficient and productive business entity and having a positive impact on their clients and community.
   - PHWs provide opportunities for employees to provide feedback to management.
   - PHWs make goals and actions committed to by the organization clear.
   - PHWs determine employee needs and resources needed to enable them to efficiently and effectively perform their job duties.
   - PHWs communicate information about the outcomes of various workplace practices.
5. Employees have a right to just and equitable treatment, and safety professionals have a responsibility to all employees to ensure that the right to employment does not endanger workers' physical welfare or jeopardize their moral integrity.

   There is inherent dignity associated with labor, and employees are humans deserving dignity and are not merely means of production; thus, employers and employees should treat all people with consideration.

   There is a moral imperative for safety professionals to care for others; safety professionals are required to remove hardships, regardless of the cost.

   Companies that invest in instilling ethical principles in their organizational culture demonstrate a strong commitment to their organizational values, empowerment, and trust. Ethics provides standards in an organizational culture and the framework for decision-making
6. Critical aspects of CSR are:
   - maintaining a good relationship between employees and management, respecting industry rules and regulations
   - ensuring good relations in the workplace
   - properly compensating employees for overtime
   - ensuring appropriate working conditions (including occupational safety)
   - maintaining a proper relationship with local communities
   - caring for the natural environment and recognizing its influence on working conditions

## Chapter 4

1. If you understand how an organization works and the responsibilities of each of the different parts, departments, groups, and reporting relationships, then it is much easier and more efficient to communicate directly with the right person in order to get recommendations implemented in a timely manner.
2. You can learn much about the safety culture of an organization by observing visual performance measures, observing what topics are covered at management meetings, and most importantly by talking to employees at all levels of the organization.
3. Relationships are important because they determine and affect the extent and nature of communications. Relationships need to be based on trust. When a leader is trusted, the people he or she works with are much more likely to listen as well as share important information. In many cases, workers have information that they do not have to share but that is very valuable in resolving safety and health issues.
4. The ideal role for the EHS professional is one of an expert consultant. It is someone who has or can easily obtain the right information about specific aspects of occupational safety and health or protecting the environment and provide the most effective and efficient solutions to EHS problems and issues.
5. You must set priorities because of limitations on your time and energy. Typically there are more daily demands on a leader than can be done that day. Determining which of those demands may have the biggest or most serious impact is crucial in making a positive impact on worker safety and health. In a sense, establishing priorities is a way of performing a risk assessment. Attacking the highest risk items first only makes sense.

## Chapter 5

1. Very few professionals will be able to spend their careers in the vacuum of only national boundaries, regulations, and standards of practice. Even the smallest enterprises interact internationally with vendors and supply chains, and the role of developing countries in manufacturing and services is growing rapidly. It is not unusual for large organizations to have production facilities and employees in many different countries around the world. The OHS professional will play a role in standardizing and coordinating health and safety practices. It will be increasingly important to understand the environments and cultures where workers will be performing to ensure efficient operations and the best possible conditions for worker health and safety.
2. One of the problems in comparing the safety records for different countries is that each country uses its own accident and injury reporting schemes. The methods are not often comparable between countries. Different countries keep records on different types of employees, and they may only track certain illnesses but not others. Many countries have incomplete health registries, and as a result the actual global burden of occupational disease is largely underestimated.

3. The short answer is "everyone." Of course workers and their families should care that they come home from work each day in the same condition they departed, and modern efficient organizations now know the value of health and safety programs that keep their workers healthy and safe as a means to improve productivity and profits. Additionally, sophisticated governments understand the economic benefits of a having a healthy and strong workforce. Health and safety regulations and governmental support systems can have a positive economic effect on national systems.
4. The European Union believes that treaties and agreed-upon directives can be an effective means to support associated action programs for disseminating information, exchanging research results, supporting smaller organizations, and helping developing countries.
5. The ILO is a tripartite organization composed of representatives from governments, workers, and employers. The ILO's mission is to set labor standards, develop policies, and promote fair and decent work for all people.

## Chapter 6

1. Ethics is a branch of philosophy focused on the study of values and morality. The word ethics is derived from the Greek work *ethikos* ("of or for morals"). Ancient philosophers were concerned with the functioning society as a whole and the individual's role in it. Furthermore, the Merriam–Webster Dictionary defines ethics as "the discipline dealing with what is good and bad and with moral duty and obligation."
2. Most of the historical religious texts (Qu'ran (Koran), Torah, Bible) include some version of the Golden Rule. The basic idea is to teach other people decently.
3. A multitude of factors can impact a specific ethical behavioral issue. Possible influencing factors include the person could be new to the discipline and specific ethics code, the action was intended for the greater good, and not everyone views a situation the same way.
4. The four actions are:
   - Learn the rules of the organization or society you are a member of so you are not caught unaware.
   - Do your work as if you would have to defend it in a court. Many EHS practitioners will do just that. Even if you never end up in court in defense of your professional work, you will be better able to withstand challenges to previous work you have done. Just because you are honest and try to be ethical in your work, that does not mean you will not be challenged.
   - Upper management sets the culture for an organization. Be selective in choosing the organization you work for. Interviews for employment should be a two-way street. Assess how passionate the organization is about ethical behavior. If you find you made a mistake and determine that changing the culture is unlikely, start looking for a new place to work.
   - Continue to immerse yourself in activities that focus on ethics, such as reading and participating in professional society meetings at both the local and national level.
   - Maintain a network of trusted colleagues that you can depend on for advice and counsel.
   - Never let money be the overriding factor in the company and job you select for your employment.
5. No, legal issues and ethical issues are not identical. An action may be legal but go against an ethical code.

## Chapter 7

1. Identification of hazards, exposures, and noncompliance is at the core of EHS professionals' work. Risk management provides a structured process to set priorities, execute strategies, and allocate resources based on industry-accepted methodologies. Risk management enables effective communication of EHS issues at all levels and functions of the enterprise.
2. Recommendations on ethical issues are:
   - Learn the enterprise's process flow(s). If products are made, visit the areas and meet the people responsible for managing inputs, processes, and outputs. If services are sold, meet the stakeholders and learn about the information flow and services sold.
   - Tour areas, and observe maintenance and operations personnel performing their work. Specifically watch the tasks with hazard and potential exposure.
   - Develop and maintain relationships with key decision makers, function leaders, and internal and external stakeholders. Learn about business changes with potential EHS impact. Be proactive about change management and continual improvement.
   - Learn about the applicable industry-specific associations and standards that apply to the business. Benchmark best practices, develop contacts, and share relevant information with managers and supervisors.
3. The three necessary areas are:
   - Technical expertise
   - Personal effectiveness
   - Functional expertise
4. Resources for initial self-assessment are:
   - OHS Professional Capability Framework, A Global Framework for Practice, Roles, Knowledge, and Skills
   - Certified Safety Professionals Blueprints and Study Sources
5. EHS leadership is much more than presenting technical information correctly. In most situations, complex issues have many challenges, perspectives, and solutions. Effective EHS

leaders build support and facilitate action through positive interactions and well developed skills such as listening to stakeholders, soliciting diverse thought, building consensus, resolving conflict, and empowering others to take action, while integrating technical information. Leadership skills are situational, and require continual focus and personal commitment to skill development and improvement through on-going training, practice, self-reflection, and feedback.

## Chapter 8

1. Although the author acknowledges several definitions of system, he presents two from the published literature: "A system can be considered to be a grouping of interrelated and often interdependent components that are brought together in an industrial environment meant to help generate or achieve a common objective or perform a common function" (Haight et al. 2013). Common attributes of a system that show up most often in the literature are interrelatedness or interdependence in system components with and between each other. The literature also often notes a common objective. An example of a natural system is a respiratory system, made up of the trachea, bronchioles, lungs, alveolar ducts, and so forth. These components all work together to oxygenate the blood and remove carbon dioxide. An example in the manufacturing world might be an electric power supply system that includes the power supply, wiring, circuit protection, switches, and outlets.

   A collection of components, such as material, labor, capital, and knowledge, go into the manufacture of a product. How this collection of components is put together in any specific situation defines the particular system.

   Another definition of a system proposed by Eisner (2002, 3) is "any process that converts inputs to outputs."
2. A management system can be described as a structure and set of processes, procedures, policies, or actions that are implemented within an organization to achieve a defined objective or perform a common function in an efficient and structured way (Haight et al. 2013).
3. The American National Standards Institute (ANSI) ANSI/ASSE/AIHA Z10 standard titled Occupational Health and Safety Management System defines an HSMS as "a set of interrelated elements that establish or support occupational health and safety policy and objectives, and mechanisms to achieve those objectives in order to improve occupational health and safety (ANSI/ASSE/AIHA Z10–2010). The British Standard (BS OHSAS 18001:2007) and its guidelines for implementation (BS OHSAS 18002:2008 Occupation Health and Safety Assessment Series for health and safety management systems) define an HSMS as "part of an organization's management system used to develop and implement its OH&S (Occupational Health and Safety) policy and manage its OH&S risks." There are also three notes associated with the definition and they read, (1) "A management system is a set of interrelated elements used to establish a policy and objectives and to achieve those objectives," (2) "A management system includes organizational structure, planning activities (including, for example, risk assessment and the setting of objectives), responsibilities, practices, procedures, processes and resources," and (3) "Adopted from International Standards Organization (ISO), ISO 14001: 2004" (Haight et al. 2013).
4. Quantify and measure both key leading indicators as well as key lagging indicators so one can do a statistical comparative analysis between the two over time. This is in order to determine a mathematical relationship between the two so that when one makes a change in the system, if reflected in any of the leading indicators, one can determine the mathematical effect on the lagging indicators.
5. ISO-450001 *Occupational Health and Safety Management Systems*

## Chapter 9

1. Mature disciplines share the following common characteristics: a professional code of conduct; peer reviewed journals and professional conferences; professional certifications that exemplify ongoing continuing professional development; and peer reviewed, recognized academic program accreditation. Last, and potentially most important, mature disciplines/professions are characterized by occupation closure—that is, the ability through mechanisms like licensure to identify those who legally can practice and use the discipline title from those who cannot or should not practice or use the discipline title.
2. At the moment, it is debatable and difficult to precisely characterize the OSH discipline. At one level, OSH does have many of the characteristics of mature professions as discussed above. However, it lacks two things: a complete integration of accreditation (i.e., a minority of OSH programs use recognized accreditation) and a lack of occupational closure (i.e., a lack of some sort of licensure that can separate those who can and should practice from those who cannot and should not).
3. All mature disciplines should be able to say at least three things: first, that higher education (i.e., at least an undergraduate degree) is essential to entry into the profession. Second, all programs should convey a minimum set of education standards that are consensus knowledge, skills, and behaviors deemed appropriate for *every* practitioner of a profession. Third, all mature disciplines have a mechanism that enforces occupational closure, such as licensure. Licensure in turn should require that candidates have graduated from an accredited academic program. In

this way, these three characteristics reinforce the professional sovereignty of the discipline.

4. The management of modifiable risk is central to successful OSH programming and, by extension, organizational success. The OSH profession represents expertise that can identify, anticipate, recognize, and control both life and occupational risk in the workplace. Through use of mindful and effective policy and procedures, work processes are modified and employees are empowered to mitigate risk while the organization supports risk mitigation overall. Modern OSH efforts transcend compliance to state and federal mandates, rules, and regulations and work to build health and empower employees in order to minimize turnover, absenteeism, injuries, and illnesses and thereby optimize the organization's competitive poster in the marketplace.

   Modification of the answer in number 2 above may include a characterization of OSH as a "risk management"-oriented profession, as opposed to a "compliance or legalistic" profession.
5. This is a discussion question for class and has no real "correct answer." Rather, encourage participants to discuss whether and to what degree licensure can occur, whether there is an adequate and universally understood code of professional ethics and how best to integrate accreditation standards into *all* OSH programs.

## Chapter 10

1. The term *accreditation* differs from certification and licensure in that it refers to the assessment of academic programs or educational institutions, while the latter terms are used to recognize individuals' accomplishments or credentials.
2. Peer review is the evaluation of scientific, academic, or professional work by others working in the same field. For safety, it means program evaluators who have subject matter expertise in safety or environmental health and safety.
3. Under outcomes-based assessment, institutions and programs define the mission of the institution and the program and then tailor the educational objectives for the program to meet the needs of the program's constituencies and stakeholders. The outcomes are aimed at preparing the graduate for professional practice. It is up to the program to demonstrate how the criteria are being met and that they are actively engaged in continually improving their student outcomes. To do so requires the programs to involve their constituencies, with emphasis on advisory committees, formalizing the process of engagement. ABET has been refining its process on an ongoing basis since it embraced outcomes-based assessment, involving its Academic Advisory Council and its Industrial Advisory Council in the process. The model allows programs and institutions to define their own constituencies and stakeholders and tailor their programs accordingly, rather than taking a one-size-fits-all approach.
4. ASSP provides the program criteria that are used to evaluate safety programs and environmental health and safety programs and then provides subject matter experts in safety to be the program evaluators.
5. The plan contained two objectives: certifying safety practitioners and accrediting degree programs in various safety specialties.

## Chapter 11

1. Certification is a process by which a professional is evaluated against a psychometrically established industry standard of required knowledge, skills, and abilities. The successful candidate is awarded the use of a certification designation for a given time period during which the certificant is held accountable for continuing professional development and complying with a defined code of ethics. A certificate program generally results from an educational process (a class or series of classes with a specific focus) and is an end result (no continuing professional development is required to maintain the certificate), and assessment tools are typically not set through a psychometric standard-setting process but instead are established by the program instructor to measure knowledge of listed program outcomes.
2. Some of the benefits include:
   - Recognition from peers, public, and employer
   - Satisfaction of achievement
   - Career development, growth, and advancement
   - Confidence in demonstrating specific knowledge and skills related to the EHS tasks
   - Assurance on quality of work
   - Reduced liability
   - Belonging to a select community
   - Recognition of commitment to public safety and the environment
   - Identification as distinguished individual

   In addition, the certification is an indication of professional growth, enhances professional credibility, provides evidence of professional commitment, enhances employability and mobility, and increases earning potential.
3. First, a job task analysis or role delineation process is performed by SMEs holding the credential to determine the tasks, knowledge, and skills that the "minimally qualified candidate" should have acquired to meet the certification designation. Then, that list of tasks, knowledge, and skills is validated by another set of SMEs holding the credential to determine how critical a skill or knowledge is for the minimally qualified candidate and the frequency with which the candidate may need to use that knowledge or skill. The

result of this job task analysis / role delineation and validation process is the development of an examination blueprint that identifies both the topics (domains and knowledge or skill competencies) and the weight of importance (how many questions should come from each domain and knowledge/skill area). This blueprint is then approved by the appropriate board of directors or a committee authorized to do so.

4. Unfortunately, not all of the over three hundred EHS "certifications" available to the EHS professional meet the strict criteria for quality, and many are not accredited to any accreditation standard. Accreditation demonstrates that the professional credentials meet standards for
   - validity and reliability of the certification examination program;
   - fairness of the procedures for determining applicant eligibility;
   - adequacy of requirements for ensuring maintenance and enhancement of professional qualifications;
   - professionalism, integrity, and independence of the certifying body; and
   - openness of the program to public scrutiny.
5. This is to ensure that the certificant remains current with the requisite knowledge and skills to practice in the EHS profession.

## Chapter 12

1. There are four key areas to any relationship and those are communication, respect, transparency, and time/effort. The linkages are created by the interdependency of these areas. Communication is linked with respect and time/effort because these are required to have effective communication and thus a relationship.
2. The social web refers specifically to website and web technologies, while social networking is an existing body of theory relating to human interactions.
3. An *advisor* gives advice, based on their personal set of experiences. Advisors can share how they have handled situations and elaborate on the outcomes of decisions. A *coach* teaches and provides feedback to the mentee and encourages pushing one's goals and capabilities. Like an athletic coach, a mentor coach is there to help provide guidance, motivation, and support when needed. *Sponsors* are mentors that can provide access to formal and informal groups or societies that might otherwise be closed or hard to enter. Sponsors are great for making networking connections and being introduced to more senior-level professionals one may not otherwise encounter.
4. Answers may vary; active participation, volunteering, and putting effort into attendance, and contributions.
5. Vendors/suppliers have a wide audience and people they interact with. This connection can be used to help problem solve, connect to career opportunities, emerging technologies that can help create value.

## Chapter 13

1. Understanding incident precursors provides an opportunity to develop and deploy strategies to prevent or mitigate serious injuries and fatalities.
2. Safety culture is a subset of organizational culture. The factors that contribute to organizational culture will have an impact, positive or negative, on safety culture and ultimately safety performance.
3. A maturity model is viewed as a leading indicator. Maturity model deployment allows an organization to proactively develop strategies and initiatives to prevent incidents.
4. While traditional safety management components, including safety committees, audits, and posters, will increase safety awareness, to sustain an exemplary safety process, an organization must develop and implement innovative approaches to safety. Examples include maturity model, systems thinking, and serious incident and fatality (SIF) prevention strategies.
5. Total Quality Safety Management is a comprehensive, systematic approach to reducing industrial accidents through the process of continuous system improvement. A behavior-based safety process is an application of science of behavior change to improve safety by aligning management and employees.

## Chapter 14

1. Whom did you speak with, and what did you talk about?
2. One who does the right thing even when no one is looking
3. Top-down and bottom-up
4. Pavlov or Erickson
5. Character

## Chapter 15

1. Project risks are organized into four categories: technical, programmatic, organizational, and external. OSH risks fall under the organizational category. As a part of the project, risks should be assessed and a mitigation plan determined based on the assessment. The mitigation(s) is specific to the risk identified.
2. The WBS identifies discrete activities to perform the work defined in the scope. The WBS is used to develop the project schedule and budget.
3. Key OSH compliance elements could be overlooked, creating risk for the company.
4. PM concepts provide structure and organization. This helps ensure the implementation will be thorough, ensuring all aspects are considered and implemented effectively.
5. The OSH professional should have relationships with each of project team members and with project stakeholders.

# Chapter 16

1. Millennials have less part-time, summer, and technical work experience than prior generations, and they're the unfortunate recipients of an elementary and secondary education system fixated on student exam scores as indicators of teacher and school performance. These changes in education policy have led to an over-emphasized focus on reading and math test scores, reducing attention to creative and applied problem-solving areas (Jennings and Rentner 2006). Reliance on technology and the Internet has allowed this generation to find answers without thinking through and learning from mistakes, which are trademark experiences for self-improvement and development of critical problem-solving skills.
2. Curricular and practice knowledge, skills, and abilities (KSAs) are defined (and redefined) by the profession's body of knowledge and contemporary or specialized KSAs to address society or business safety and health issues. Within the confines of the university classroom, student learning is limited or stunted because it is primarily conducted (and tested) through lectures, labs, and individual/team semester projects. Acquiring the requisite KSAs to practice occupational safety and health requires more than instruction; it requires mentoring/coaching with real-world expertise in assessment and critical feedback (Kolb 1984). Adopting a semester assignment that requires students to document their learning process/technique over the semester provides them with tools that are vital for their careers and allows students to mastery their learning technique. In doing so, they are developing problem-solving skills. The documentation of their learning technique is the foundation of an internship or co-op portfolio, which documents progress and project work for both grading/feedback and also a demonstration of KSAs for future employers. According to a 2009 article in *Time* magazine

   The importance of internships for securing full-time work has dramatically increased over the years; these days, an internships is less of an opportunity and more of a requirement. In a 2001 survey by the National Association of Colleges and Employers, employers reported offering jobs to 57% of their intern class. By 2008 that number had reached 70%. There are as many as 300,000 students participating in some form of pre-job apprenticeship in the U.S. each year, a number that has increased 10% over the past five years. (Haire and Oloffson 2009)
3. According to the Cooperative Education and Internship Association (CEIA 2015):

   *Cooperative education* is a structured method of combining classroom-based education with practical work experience. A cooperative education experience, commonly known as a 'co-op,' provides academic credit for structured job experience. Co-op experiences are either full-time (40 hours per week) alternating periods (semester, quarter) of work and school or part-time (20 hours per week) combining work and school during the same time period. Co-op experiences are paid, supervised by a professional who has followed the same career path of the student and students complete more than one assignment (2 or more) with progressive levels of responsibility. *Internship* is an experience involving student's working in their expected career field, either during a semester or over the summer. Internships may be paid or unpaid and may or may not carry academic credit. Internships are typically one time experiences. Internships are typically connected to an academic program with course requirements designed and monitored by faculty. Internships generally have related learning outcomes and academic assignments required.

   Even with the distinction between co-ops and internships, realize that many employers and universities use these terms interchangeably and may only consider a summer (three-month) work experience an internship and anything work experience during fall or spring semester as a co-op. Due to their extended time at a company, co-op students are likely to gain more depth in their learning and therefore earn greater and more extensive projects, which can give them an advantage over their internship peers (Boyington 2015). Although the longer co-op experience may delay a student's graduation, it can provide much-needed financial relief to the student (and their family).
4. Wan et al. (2013) found that internships that were facilitated by an experienced and engaged mentors, along with assistance by degree program faculty, increased the student's KSAs, problem-solving abilities, and self-confidence. These students also reported higher job satisfaction and an easier and more successful transition into their careers. For an internship/co-op to be truly effective in developing the student and for the company to gain valuable work from the student, the internship/co-op needs to be well-planned, with objectives, established review criteria, and documentation of all aspects of the experience (Matthew et al. 2012). If planned and administered properly, the worst outcome would be that the student gained valuable KSA and created a binder/portfolio to be used in future interviews while the company gain some valuable work products and either learned what they really want in a potential new hire (new grad) or how to improve their screening process and management of the internship. The internship or co-op should be an immersed learning experience, in which the intern is supervised by an onsite or host experienced safety professional and by an assigned faculty advisor who will grade and provide feedback on an internship portfolio or binder and safety project reports, while acting as a mediator between the intern and site host if there are any disagreements or issues preventing the intern from learning.
5. The American Society of Safety Professionals (ASSP) and the Board of Certified Safety Professionals (BCSP).

## Chapter 17

1. C—Trust, influence, common interest, and self-preservation
2. B—A message of "Well Done!"
3. A—True
4. B—Sort, Set in order, Shine, Standardize, and Sustain
5. B—False; Heinrich looks at empirical data to show that as many as 95 percent of all workplace incidents are caused by unsafe acts, not conditions.

## Chapter 18

1. Some of the challenges include data search and capture without noise, proper storage, analytical procedures, data sharing and transfer, data query, updates, data mining and visualization, and data management and privacy of information.
2. See figure 18.2: volume, velocity, variety, and value.
3. See figure 18.3—characteristics of big data.
4. They are used in sentiment analysis and topic detection for predicting links between threats and opportunities, which is important for mitigating risk and security concerns as well as monitoring special organizational activities, potential hazards, and safety needs through the integrated computational analysis of network data.

   Mobile analytics provides location-based data analytics that can predict human presence at a given location, space, and time. It may also predict human mobility based on locational sensing, which is helpful in determining reoccurring accidents/incidents and can help with developing effective control measures to avoid reoccurrence.
5. Metcalf's law is a unified approach of integrating multiple processes in a global context to fully maximize the data value and lead to effective learning. Accident and incident data or worker behaviors relative to work conditions have enormously valuable information embedded in them that can be analyzed for insight into how to eliminate/substitute or control hazards

## Chapter 19

1. A risk assessment process is a framework for organizations to deal with risk that they face. A best practice process will be made up of three components. They are as follows:
   a **Identify, Assess, and Evaluate:** In this stage the risk is identified and drilled down to the root cause. Controls are added to each root-cause risk (current and anticipated), and the risk is assessed. This simply means it is given a rating based on an established rating system. This could include things like impact, likelihood, and assurance. This stage also includes doing an evaluation to determine if immediate action is required and identifying what could go wrong.
   b **Mitigate:** This is where the actual work takes place to ensure the identified risks do not play out. In a best practice process, the rating translates into "indexes," which applies logic to where it is most beneficial to put time and resources.
   c **Monitor:** This is where you make sure what is most important actually plays out. It involves test, metrics, and incident management.
2. In enterprise risk management you are dealing with all risks an organization faces. As risk is an overarching theme across all business process areas, you have differing and non-aligned priorities, lack of coordinated decision-making, lack of information flow, and redundancies, to name a few obstacles. Continuous efforts and resources toward governance efficiency support better and timelier decisions as well as accountability, transparency, and participation toward achieving company goals.
3. Risk managers can use their area of responsibility, hazard risk, as a platform to pilot and demonstrate foundational concepts of enterprise risk managers. As they show progress and earn credibility, they can support the CFO as a champion, introducing a more global risk framework that includes capturing, housing, organizing, and transitioning organizational risk into actionable plans.
4. Risk managers make the connection that they are not the person to be identifying, assessing, and evaluating risk on a day-to-day basis. There is not enough time for them to operate in a first-line capacity. The risk manager needs to identify who his first line of defense is and put targeted efforts into supporting and mentoring the first line. To operate in a second line of defense capacity, the risk manager needs to remain a strategic facilitator.
5. The components of monitoring are test, metrics and incident management. Tests are used to make sure controls are working and typically yield a yes-or-no response. Metrics are in place to answer how effective controls are and are used to look for a percentage of compliance with an acceptable tolerance level. Incident management is a process of tracking back to the control that has failed and either identifying training or additional controls to correct the issue.

   Monitoring is important to the process to ensure that controls put in place are actually working to protect the organization, its people, and its assets.

## Chapter 20

1. Gap analysis can be used to evaluate and assess an entire safety program or an individual process or method. It is generally considered an evidence-based approach as it measures the

actual practices against a standard and reports on the gaps. For safety professionals, gap analysis criteria can use program elements used to mitigate or prevent work-related injuries. Gap analysis is a process often used as a tool in developing a baseline understanding of an occupational safety and health program.

2. Gap analysis differentiates itself from a traditional auditing process by using the organization's standard of practice as criteria to measure each program element or processes against what is being implemented. The gap analysis compares actual practices against the standard and measures gaps or differences from the standard.
3. A benefit of the gap analysis is that it measures where you are now, where you need to be, and what needs to change to improve performance in worker safety. It provides a roadmap to where one can spend limited resources in designing or developing changes in mitigation efforts to improve injury prevention outcomes.
4. Gap analysis starts with identifying the objective of the analysis. It establishes the criteria or standard for each intervention program to be measured. The criteria can be the established corporate policies/procedures or industry standards. It then creates a process to assess the actual practice against the program elements standard and develops a management report that reports on the findings or program gaps.
5. It creates a management report that captures the essence of information needed to demonstrate the results. The objectives of the management report are to summarize and highlight the results while simultaneously providing information for creating a business plan or strategy to improve injury prevention outcomes. It is important to understand that the senior-level management team or client representative(s) wants a concise, easy-to-understand, evidence-based report along with specific decisions or actions that must be made to address inconsistencies and achieve improvements

## Chapter 21

1. RtPtR encourages both academics and practitioners to continually communicate the real-world SH&E challenges and opportunities. The RtPtR model encounters both successful pathways and barriers when moving promising ergonomic and safety (E&S) research concepts into good practices and when moving E&S problems from practice to research. This model conveys the concept of continuous improvement by translating research findings into best practices (RtP) but then completing the loop where practitioners' feed SH&E problems back to researchers/academicians (PtR).
2. The B Factor simplifies the process of determining the weight of materials by using units of area such as length and width, which are more easily measured on work sites rather than calculating the volume of materials. For example, the B Factor of 1/2 light gypsum board expressed as B(1/2" light gypsum board) is 1.368 lbs/sq ft. Therefore, the weight of any size or shape 1/2" light gypsum board can be determined from the board's area—for example, the weight of 1/2 sheet of gypsum board would be determined by B(1/2" light gypsum) times area (length × width) of sheet measured at the worksite = 1.368 lbs/sq ft x (4' × 4') = 21.89 pounds. Likewise, a whole sheet (4' × 8') would be 1.368 lbs/sq ft x (4' x 8') = 43.8 pounds, and a double sheet's weight would be 87.6 pounds. Consequently, the weight of any size, shape, or thicknesses of light gypsum board can be determined more easily using the B Factor because the S&E professional only needs to determine the gypsum board area and not its volume.
3. The characteristics and demographic changes are shifting faster than researchers can provide scientific conclusions and develop good practices for industry. For example, the physical, psychological, and demographic changes of the US workforce since the 1960s are complex and are expected to continue to change for the foreseeable future. Snook's table and the University of Michigan's biomechanical models were developed in the 1970s and 1980s, NIOSH's Lifting Equation was revised in 1991, and further refinements are suggested by the Variable Lifting Index (VLI). Recent studies identified changes in the psychophysical characteristics of today's workers, which suggest the set points of current ergonomic (psychophysical) evaluation tools may need to be revised. These preliminary studies repeated the psychophysical studies of the 1970s and 1980s and showed a significant shift in maximum acceptable weight (MAW) for male workers performing lifting/lowering and carrying tasks (69%). It also showed a lesser shift—for example, 82 percent of maximum average force (MAF) in the pushing/pulling tasks. If confirmed by future research, these suggest the load constant (LC) of 51 pounds for NIOSH LE and its European derivatives (BS EN 1005-2-2003; HSE 2011-RR901) should be reduced to 35 pounds.
4. The ergonomic action level (EAL), similar to the action level used in the industrial hygiene (IH) area, is that level at which one begins to take action or implement controls at a level below which is known to cause injury. The concept of EAL is similar to the IH action level in that it recommends that good practices should anticipate changes in worker characteristics and tasks should be designed below the level known or suspected to cause injury to workers. For example, the Informational Appendix D of ANSI/ASSP A10-2007 (2013) Reduction of Musculoskeletal Problems in Construction asks contractors to consider "What heavy materials or equipment are being handled on site—anything over twenty pounds?" and "Do workers have to lift more than twenty pounds often?" These "informational only" questions, which are not part

of the approved standard, suggest contractors should "take action"—that is, identify and consider changes when materials and equipment weighing more than twenty pounds are lifted often. This suggested action point is considerably below the fifty-one pounds of load constant (LC) of NIOSH's current LE. The authors believe if a proactive ergonomic action level (EAL) is used as a design guideline, upstream planning will be needed because the weight of common construction materials and equipment will most likely exceed these new guidelines.

5. PtD is a risk-reduction strategy implemented in the early stages of construction that provides a unique opportunity to identify hazards and reduce exposures to those hazards by preplanning/designing improvements, thereby reducing or eliminating risk—see ANSI/ASSP Z590.3-2011 (R2016). In 2013, National Institute for Occupational Safety and Health released several PtD publications specific to construction. Changing the way the work process is done to decrease the labor intensity may reduce the amount of overhead work and time it takes to get the job done. Here are some examples to consider. It is obvious that a backhoe operator can move more dirt safely than a laborer with a shovel. Landscape contractors have mechanized the sod-laying task by using bulk rolls that are cut and placed mechanically. The 4' × 8' wooden concrete foundation forms, weighing over 100 pounds, have been replaced by aluminum forms that are lighter and hoisted into place by truck-mounted hoists. The development of insulated concrete blocks (ICB) for foundations and above-ground walls further reduces manual tasks and construction time. Nano particles are beginning to be used to strengthen concrete as a replacement for rebar, eliminating the manual handling and tying at worksites. The removal of asphalt shingles from residential roofs can also be mechanized. The strenuous manual task of roofing with asphalt shingles might be changed by using a large, prefabricated section hoisted in place by crane or the development of a track-mounted, automated "shingling device." Installing embedded concrete inserts into ceiling forms eliminates the need for prolonged overhead drilling that would be needed to place all-thread rods for a ceiling system. Requiring employees to use a mechanical lift or hoist to raise themselves closer to their work prevents them from having to raise their arms above their shoulders. Mechanical placement of kerbs in the United Kingdom could replace manual handling. Using a mechanical device to hold a heavy tool in place while the employee is using the tool would reduce the physical burden for the worker.

## Chapter 22

1. (1) The overall geography of the area; (2) the characteristics of the community; (3) the immediate neighborhood; (4) the owners, managers, and lessees of the site and the workforce; (5) the buildings and land; (6) operational functionality of the site; (7) overall maintenance and hygiene at the site; (8) preventative maintenance program in place; (9) existing protection; and (10) the Hazard Recognition Severity Matrix.
2. Protective concrete base around the beams
3. Using Lusser's law

$$R_s = \prod_{i=1}^{N} r_i = r_1 * r_2 * r_3 * \ldots * r_n \ldots eq.\ 3$$

$$R_s = 0.65 * 0.68 * 0.70 = 0.31$$

4. Using the operational availability equation

$$A_o = \frac{MTBM}{\text{MTBM} + \text{MMT} + \text{MLDT}}$$

$$A_o = 16\ hours\ or \left(\frac{16}{24}\right)\ days\ or\ \left(\frac{2}{3}\right)\ days$$

$$MTBM = 40\ days$$

$$MLDT = LDT + ADT$$

$$MLDT = 10\ days + 2\ days = 12\ days$$

$$\text{MMT?}$$

Rearranging the formula:

$$\text{MMT} = \left(\frac{MTBM}{A_o}\right) - (MTBM + MLDT)$$

$$\text{MMT} = \left(\frac{40}{2/3}\right) - (40 + 12)$$

$$\text{MMT} = 60 - (40 + 12)$$

$$\text{MMT} = 8\ \text{days}$$

5. Now, you are prepared to make a decision as to whether the building is adequate for your company's intended use and tell why. You can now write a summary statement beginning with the sentence: "The building at 1234 Side Street, Smallville, MI. is / is not acceptable for our intended use as a plastic molding plant because . . . ," and list the quick summary of each ring on your bull's-eye.

## Chapter 23

1. An occupational safety and health management system is defined as a set of interrelated elements that establish and/or support occupational health and safety policy and objectives, and mechanisms to achieve those objectives to continually improve occupational health and safety.
2. The plan-do-check-act (PDCA) model for continuous improvement is underlying premise of many safety management systems. Incorporating this process into safety management systems provides the safety professional with a way to continually improve safety performance.

3. Leading indicators are proactive, preventative, and predictive measures that monitor and provide current information about the effective performance of a safety program.
4. The organization maturity level is defined as an evolving process whereby an organization (or subset of, such as a system) becomes fully fit for purpose through an internal unfolding of approaches, rather than through externally imposed approaches.
5. Total count of process safety incidents (PSIC)
   Process safety total incident rate (PSTIR)
   Process safety incident severity rate (PSISR)

## Chapter 24

1. Certainty bias leads individuals to underestimate the complete range of possibilities, making systems and processes unprepared for high or low extremes.
2. It depends on the anchor and whether that anchor is greater or less than the true value being estimated. On average, anchoring bias tends to push individuals' estimates toward the mean (for example, the average probability of all accidents).
3. This method is most effective at mitigating survivorship bias, but it can also be useful in counting hindsight bias.
4. Expert elicitation is most focused on the tails of the distribution and the likelihood thereof. The probability of the more extreme or unlikely events tend to be underestimated initially due to certainty bias.
5. Hindsight bias tends to cause this effect, as it makes previous intuition regarding uncertainty about a situation seem less significant in retrospect.

## Chapter 25

1. Interactivity, user characteristics, and vividness
2. Full computer term names are:
   a GUI—Graphical User Interface
   b MIME—Multipart Internet Mail Extension
   c DNS—Domain Name Systems
   d DSL—Digital Subscriber Line
   e USB—Universal Serial Bus
   f ASCII—American Standard Code for Information Interchange
   g GIF—Graphics Interchange Format
   h URL—Uniform Resource Locator
   i CAD—Computer-Aided Design
   j HTTPS—HyperText Transport Protocol Secure
   k TCP/IP—Transmission Control Protocol/Internet Protocol
   l VPN—Virtual Private Network
3. Adobe Captivate, Articulate Storyline 3, PowerPoint (PPT), and so forth.
4. All of the below are applications of ERM software:
   a Audit and compliance (ISO 19001)
   b Air quality management to product compliance (ISO 9001)
   c Environmental management systems, (ISO 14001)
   d Water compliance and management
   e Chemical inventory management
   f Incident management
   g Management of change
   h Process safety management
   i Training management
   j Communication management
   k Safety meetings management
5. Six steps:
   1. The first step is to identify the business needs and then set some goals and objectives that should be achieved by implementing the new safety technology.
   2. The business should think about what they may need in order for them to be able to achieve those goals and objectives.
   3. The business should choose a suitable technology type that will promote their organization's goals.
   4. The business should evaluate and compare the different technology solutions offered.
   5. The business selects a supplier and product that suits their needs.
   6. The business should implement the technology chosen.

## Chapter 26

1. Repetitive motion, awkward and stationary postures, heavy or awkward lifting, use of excessive force, and exposure to extreme conditions, temperatures, or vibration (from the "Introduction to Human Factors and Ergonomics" section)
2. It is advised that older workers be given jobs that involve working in neutral postures and jobs that allow for frequent posture changes to reduce musculoskeletal strain, physically demanding jobs be engineered out, and hazard recognition training be employed to ensure workers, supervisors, and engineers can identify and correct injury hazards in the workplace. To control ergonomic risks for the overweight and obese workforce, the following design considerations are recommended: appropriate chairs, workstations, anti-fatigue mats, and sit/stand workstations. Additionally, weight and placement of material should be evaluated to reduce overhead and forward reaching along with low-level lifting. When engineering controls are not practical, job rotation should be considered to reduce prolonged static work (from the "HFE Challenges in Developed and Developing Countries" section).
3. Discomfort caused by improper sitting positions can lead to musculoskeletal pain in the neck, shoulders, lower back,

wrists, and legs, along with reduced productivity caused by these discomforts (from the "Technology and Emerging HFE Risks" section).

4. 1949 (from the "American HFE: World War II" section)
5. Physical ergonomics—deals with human anatomical, anthropometric, physiological, and biomechanical characteristics in relation to physical activity

   Cognitive ergonomics—focuses on mental processes like perception, memory, reasoning, and motor response

   Organizational ergonomics—concentrates on optimizing sociotechnical systems and the accompanying organizational structures, policies, and processes (from the "Specializations" section)

## Chapter 27

1. Leadership establishes the values of the organization and set the organizational priorities. Leaders also determine the performance management system, which generally aligns with what is truly valued. The hourly employees typically have little input into these decisions and systems. One could argue that there are locations where employees have a strong voice in the values, priorities, and systems. However, what is often forgotten is that leadership allows this type of input and participation, and they control whether this type of culture remains the norm.
2. No normal or logical person can argue with an objective of doing what it takes to get everyone home safely every day. So the process of change can start with a point of agreement. Additionally, when an employee is not convinced that their leadership has their safety and well-being in mind, they are less likely to want to be engaged in other meaningful discussions or change.
3. Treating people unfairly is related to procedural justice. Procedural justice means that when decisions are made regarding a person, they are free of bias and favoritism. When a leader treats some members of their team unfairly, then those team members think negatively of the team members that are perceived to be receiving preferential treatment. These affected employees also believe that management knows that the supervisor is making biased decisions and are condoning those actions.
4. Anytime we place a qualifier (like the word *safety* in front of *culture*) it can cause people to limit their thinking about how to improve safety. People will naturally lean toward thinking about those systems or elements that are safety specific. We know that getting leaders to think more generally about whether their culture supports safety and what prevents people from fully engaging in the organization and the leadership allows everyone, no matter what group or department they belong to, find a meaningful role in safety. Finally, the research shows that non-safety-specific cultural factors strongly predict safety performance.
5. It depends. It depends on the gap between current state and desired future state. It depends on the level of energy and resources the organization is willing to apply to the culture change effort. We do know that a climate change can happen in an organization in a matter of weeks, and climate change is the precursor to culture change. For most organizations it will take at least three years before people to truly believe that the climate change is permanent.

## Chapter 28

1. Leaders must be able to recognize which aspects, beliefs, values, or behavior norms of the current culture are supportive or counterproductive to its achieving organizational goals and objectives. Second, the leader must be able to communicate to all employees which values, behaviors, or beliefs need to be changed to achieve a strong organizational culture. Third, the leader has to be seen by employees as modeling the new expected behaviors or policies suggested by management. If the leader's actions and behaviors match expected organizational values and beliefs, employees are more likely to match the espoused culture. Leadership authors, Lussier and Achua, proposed substantive and symbolic actions, which leadership can utilize in shaping the organizational culture they desire.

   Substantive actions include:
   - New facilities design
   - Replacing old members with new organizational members
   - Developing written values and mission statements
   - Creating new and changing old dysfunctional policies

   Symbolic actions include:
   - Leadership serving as role models and mentor to new employees
   - Special recognition of employee achievement and appearances by leaders
   - Organizational structure and establishing rewards and incentive

2. Transformational leadership refers to the overall value-based social exchange between the follower and leader, empowering them to meet organizational objectives and goals.

   Transactional leadership style is defined as a leadership style guided by the task and rewards based on performance.
3. Scholar and author Earl Blair described the safety culture of an organization as a procedure model composed of four elements: inputs, process activities, outputs, and results.
   a Inputs are composed of the attitudes, vision, and mission of the organization, as well as leadership, adequate resources, assumption, and engineering controls.

b Processes activities are composed of education and training, teamwork, workplace inspections, employee behavior, and open lines of communication.
c Output is composed of overall safety performance.
d Results are able to be measured by the following indicators of safety performance: inspection conducted, behavioral observations, employees trained, reduction in lost workdays, and restricted work activities.

It's important to note that the output of poor employee attitudes and values would be associated with lack of leadership's ability to develop a strong safety culture which in turn contributes to the output of poor safety performance. It's the responsibility of leadership to establish and create the safety culture of the organization. Furthermore, an ineffective safety culture is an indicator of ineffective leadership.

4. Answer: In the literature, the terms *safety culture* and *safety climate* are often used without regard to differences in meaning. The beliefs, attitudes, and values held by the organization are used to define or describe safety culture. Safety climate, conversely, is considered a snapshot of the organization's perceptions of safety at a particular point in time. Consequently, culture can influence how an employee perceives workplace risks. Noted researcher Krause identified and compared the following attributes associated with safety climate and safety culture:

### Culture

- Changes more slowly
- Unstated
- How we do things
- Applied to many areas of functioning
- Common values that drive
- Organizational performance

### Climate

- Changes more rapidly
- Stated
- What we pay attention to
- Applied to a specific area of functioning
- Perception of what is expected, rewarded.

5. Both management and leadership traits contribute to increased safety performance. Management traits can affect safety performance by creating policies and procedures related to safety, communicating safety polices to employees, and establishing responsibility for planning and organizing. Leadership traits can affect safety performance by persuading employees to accept safety goals, encourage individuals to cope with change, set the vision for the organization, and leaders align people who set the direction of the organization.

## Chapter 29

1. Entropic risk is the tendency of organizational systems (processes, technologies, physical environment, human resources) to shift to a state of chaos or degradation. This risk negatively impacts production/productivity, the quality of work outputs, and capacity to mitigate EHS incidents. Entropic risk also applies to degradation of EHS management systems, leadership, and capacity (collective organizational competencies), with resulting consequences for EHS performance.
2. The mathematical concept of entropy originated from thermodynamics but was later applied by Claude E. Shannon to communication. The work is highly technical; however, this "fuzzy mathematics" has been applied more recently to evaluate safety construction, individual's intuitive attitude to risk, gantry crane reliability, traffic management, and other areas of safety-related risk. These studies lend weight to the concept that systems degrade and that this has a negative impact on safety. In the organization, entropic risk can be related directly to housekeeping standards. Poor standards have a negative impact on productivity, work quality, and EHS incident mitigation. Entropic risk can also be identified using reliability engineering through monitoring of safety critical systems and collection of data that triggers replacements ahead of equipment failures.
3. The entropy model illustrates that residual risk is fixed in the short term because of technological and financial constraints faced by the organization (equal to concept of ALARP). In addition, systems tend to degrade, referred to as entropic risk. Unmanaged residual and entropic risks result in production/productivity losses, poor-quality work, and EHS incidents. The model contributes to the profession's understanding of loss causation. It presents four steps to manage risk to pursue incident prevention and other business objectives concurrently.
4. The alignment fallacy explains that just because an organization has a safety-first policy, it does not mean that this will become an operational reality. The book *Productive Safety Management* talks about this in detail. In this chapter, one factor is the boom-bust cycle faced by organizations in difficult economic times. This results in cost cutting that erodes capacity to manage risk effectively. Also, whenever production and schedule pressures drive the business, safety tends to be overridden by output key performance indicators. The alignment fallacy highlights the need to manage risk in a sustainable manner to achieve production, quality, and EHS incident mitigation concurrently. It flags the loss of capacity to manage risk in a climate of cost cutting and retrenchments. This supports the cyclical pattern shown by the entropy model of degradation, occurrence of incidents and losses, followed

by corrective action and maintenance, and then degradation again. There are opportunities for further research in this area.

5. The profession is undergoing a transformation from safety-based thinking to risk-based thinking. This requires the EHS professional to develop business acumen and become a strategic partner in the success of the organization. Safety performance traditionally has been presented as a business driver. This is incorrect as organizations do not exist to deliver on safety as such. They exist to provide products, services, and value to stakeholders. The transformation is that EHS performance is an outcome of effective risk management along with other business objectives. The future of the EHS profession therefore is to lead the management of risk to achieve production/productivity, quality work, and EHS incident mitigation concurrently engaging through a multidisciplinary approach.

## Chapter 30

1. There are so many occupational safety problems of the informal sector. These problems can be discussed vividly under the following categories that are elements of unsafe conditions, acts, and risks in the informal workplaces.
   a Socioeconomic problems
   b Health problems
   c Environmental problems
   d Psychological problems
   e Level of education
2. Biophysical impacts and socio-environmental impacts
3. Workplace safety can be attained through:
   - Education
   - Use of pre-implementation safety checklist
   - Plan, organize, control, monitor, and review preventative measures
   - Use of personal protective equipment
   - Fundamental safety practices
   - Social support networks
4. The benefits of safety in informal sector in global economy include the following:
   - Safe workplaces contribute to sustainable development, which is the key to poverty reduction.
   - The processes of protecting workers, surrounding communities, and the environment for future generations have important common elements, such as pollution control and exposure reduction.
   - Much pollution and many environmental exposures that are hazardous to health arise from industrial processes that can be beneficially influenced by occupational health and safety programs.
5. There are many differences between the occupational safety challenges in formal and informal sectors of global economy. Some of the differences are given below:
   - Evidence from research showed that workers in low-wage (informal) jobs are at an increased risk of work-related injuries and illnesses than the workers in the higher-wage (formal) jobs.
   - Exposures to high occupational hazards are known to be more associated with informal than the formal workers.
   - Unsafe work sites and lack of appropriate protective equipment and training in the informal sector results in higher incidence of injuries, while there is relatively safer work sites and provision of appropriate protective equipment and training in the formal sector.

   Musculoskeletal injuries and disorders, including back injuries from carrying heavy loads, and joint pain are more common in the informal sector than in the formal sector.

## Chapter 31

1. Valid survey writing involves understanding and incorporating a number of human factors, psychological, and mathematical principles. A "good" survey is one that has met standards for reliability and validity, is written at a reading level appropriate for the intended audience, utilizes proper assessment and item-writing methodology (e.g., lack of double-barreled questions, avoiding words with loaded meanings or multiple interpretations, etc), and meets human factors design principles for length, delivery format, question order, and item layout. Many safety professionals are technical experts in safety, not in questionnaire design and psychometrics, thus it is often difficult to write a safety survey that can be considered a useful, valid, and reliable indicator of the attitude or behavior attempting to be measured.

   The use of poor-quality questionnaires can result in a number of consequences, from the minor to the catastrophic. A poorly designed survey may cause safety professionals to miss high-risk attitudes or behaviors growing in the organization, or misidentify root causes of an accident/incident. It can cost the organization and its employees both time and money in completing a questionnaire that ends up having little real applicability, which in turn may make employees less likely to participate in future questionnaires. Data collection via poor-quality surveys leads to a "garbage in, garbage out" situation in which the survey produces meaningless or misunderstood data, which is then converted into invalid or even harmful interventions in the organization.
2. Effective integration of psychology and safety includes identifying the unique perspective that each discipline brings to a situation or organization, and building upon these complementary skills to create something greater than either

could design independently. Psychologists are not safety professionals, and vice versa, but in organizations each is often asked to play some of the other discipline's roles (e.g., asking a workplace psychologist to conduct a safety audit or interviews after an incident because it's "people related," or asking safety experts to assess attitudes or perceptions that are preconditions for incident/accident trends in the workplace).

3. A majority of the general (non-trained) public view psychology as a "helping" or "medical" discipline, focused on clinical assessment, community mental health, or personal counseling. Despite advocacy by the American Psychological Association, there remains a lack of popular understanding about the variety of different technical sub-disciplines within psychology. This misunderstanding can potentially hinder safety experts who are aware of psychology's sub-disciplines and are attempting to integrate them into safety practice. Employees may be wary of psychologists joining a safety assessment team, fearing they are going to be "psychoanalyzed"; they may be concerned about safety meetings turning into "feelings sessions" or that employers are concerned about their mental health rather than task performance.

   Safety practitioners can overcome some of these challenges primarily through transparency and communication. Transparency means clearly articulating the rationale and motives behind integrating psychology into the safety team, the goals involved, and how the psychologist is going to assist in meeting these goals. Communication includes explaining (and allowing the psychologist) to explain their expertise in clear, non-technical language, to clearly communicate how any data will be used, and to create a structure or system in which employees can safely raise concerns or questions about this new component to safety.

4. Safety programs that include an integrated psychological component can be enhanced in several ways. Psychological data (such as employee perceptions and attitudes) before and after safety training programs (particularly those focused on human factors contribution to errors) can assist in documenting ROI of training or other safety culture initiatives that are primarily driven by indirect metrics. Human error based on training, perception, situational awareness, or other psychologically based misapplications cause a significant number of accidents and incidents across industries. Integrating enhanced awareness and training on the role and limitations of human perception (for example, role of fatigue and stress in injuries or accidents) can aid in safety program reduction. Psychological expertise on the design of training for maximum retention and application (transfer of training) can aid the efficacy of safety program initiatives as well.

5. Safety initiatives are similar to many other organizational change initiatives—they are an attempt to change the culture, attitudes, or behaviors in an organization. These are data points usually studied by psychologists; thus, perceptual and behavioral data at various points in the initiatives can be strong contributors to evaluating the success or failure of a safety initiative. This is especially true in industries in which the actual accident rate is generally quite low (like aviation), but the rate of high-risk behaviors, incidents, risky attitudes toward safety, or near misses is much higher. Psychological data can aid in identifying the high-risk attitudes and behaviors before they result in a major injury or accident.

## Chapter 32

1. organizational culture
2. Executing on any EHS initiative means leading an organizational change. Therefore, understanding and executing the principles and practices of leading an organizational change will greatly influence the success of the EHS initiative.
3. maintenance, finance, marketing and sales, operations, quality, purchasing, engineering and design, sustainability, leadership/management team (foremen, supervisors, managers, VPs, C-suite, board of directors)
4. The EHS professional must have/develop the skills of a change agent, C-Suite executive, a marketer, a public relations manager, and a master coach. They are organizational influencers, identifiers of early adopters to support EHS initiatives, and they understand the people (social) side of implementing EHS initiatives, such as an EHS management system. They must be willing to develop leadership courage to be resilient in the face of assured resistance to change within their organization.
5. See Section 10: Aligning Culture and Organization descriptions. The areas are:
   - Measurements and rewards
   - Structures and processes
   - People
   - Culture

# GLOSSARY

**5 S.** Sort, set in order, shine, standardize, and sustain

**ABET.** Accreditation body that assures programs meet standards to produce graduates ready to enter critical technical fields that are leading the way in innovation, emerging technologies and anticipating the welfare and safety needs of the public.

**academic program.** A combination of courses and/or requirements leading to a degree or certificate, or to a major, co-major, minor or academic track and/or concentration.

**actionable plans.** Structured plans that are put together to apply mitigation activity to root-cause risk and monitored activity to insure what is most important happens.

**active listening.** To not just hear what someone is saying but being engaged with the conversation and trying to understand what someone is saying through asking questions.

**Accreditation.** The act of granting credit or recognition, especially to an educational institution that maintains suitable standards.

**AIHA.** American Industrial Hygiene Association (AIHA) – A professional association that provides information and resources to Industrial Hygienists and Occupational Health professionals.

**alignment fallacy.** Operational ownership of front-line supervisors can be eroded when other drivers are cascaded from the middle management level because of contextual changes.[1]

**analytics.** The systematic computational analysis of data or statistics.

**anchoring.** Basing an estimate of an unknown value on another known value whether or not the two are actually related to one another.

**Angoff Method.** A process for determining how often a minimally qualified performer would answer a test item correctly

**ANSI.** American National Standards Institute (ANSI) - A premier source for timely, relevant, actionable information on national, regional, international standards and conformity assessment issues.

**ANSI-Z10.** Occupational Health and Safety Management Systems Standard (OHSMS) which provides an overall blueprint for widespread benefits in occupational safety and health, as well as in productivity, financial performance, quality and other organizational and business objectives.

**anthropometry.** The scientific study of the measurements and proportions of the human body.

**assessment.** An analysis that aims to evaluate the causes, consequences, and likelihood of a potential future event or the nature, quality, or ability of someone or something.

**ASSP.** American Society of Safety Professionals (formerly known as the American Society of Safety Engineers), a professional society for people employed in the occupational safety and health field.

**availability.** Suitable or ready for use; of use or service; at hand, having sufficient power or efficacy; valid.

**behavior.** The way in which one acts or conducts oneself, especially toward others.

**behavioral economics.** The study of how individual psychological processes lead to economic decisions, usually focused on choices that seem to be irrational under traditional economic understanding.

**best practices.** Commercial or professional procedures that are accepted or prescribed as being correct or most effective.

**bias.** A tendency to consistently misestimate an unknown value to be higher or lower than its actual value.

**big data.** A term that describes the large volume of data, both structured and unstructured, that inundates a business on a day-to-day basis.[2]

**blueprint.** Something that acts as a plan, model, or template.

**BS OHSAS 18002:2008.** British Standards Occupational health and safety management systems (BS OHSAS) 18002:2008 provides guidance for the use of BS OHSAS 18001, including application and explains the principles and intentions in terms of inputs, processes and outputs and addresses occupational health and safety rather than product and services safety.[3]

---

* Some other definitions on the list were retrieved from: http://www.businessdictionary.com/definition/hazard.html

1 Mol, T. 2003. Productive Safety Management. Butterworth Heinemann. Oxford.

2 SAS (2018). Statistical Analysis System. Big Data. Retrieved February 9, 2018 from https://www.sas.com/en_us/insights/big-data/what-is-big-data.html

3 BSI (2018). British Standard Institutes (BSI). OHSAS 18001 Occupational Health and Safety Management. Retrieved on February 9, 2018 from https://www.bsigroup.com/en-US/OHSAS-18001-Occupational-Health-and-Safety/

**business integration.** A technique used to align the technical components of a company with its business goals in order to create a smoothly running system.

**business value.** Value that determine the health and well-being of the firm in the long run, this establishes a standard measure of value used to determine the business worth.

**career.** An occupation undertaken for a significant period of a person's life and with opportunities for progress.

**certainty.** A measure of how accurately a value is known at a given point in time.

**certificant.** A person who has been certified or has received a certification.

**certificate.** Document containing a certified statement especially as to the truth of something; specifically: a document certifying that one has fulfilled the requirements of and may practice in a field.

**change.** The act or instance of making or becoming different.

**circle of influence.** Those concerns that we can do something about. They are concerns that we have some control over.

**claims.** An application for compensation under the terms of an insurance policy.

**commercial excellence.** An area in which many companies can improve and use to create increased customer loyalty and more revenue, without significantly changing their business model.[4]

**compensation.** The action or process of awarding someone money as a recompense for loss, injury, or suffering.

**competencies.** A cluster of related abilities, commitments, knowledge, and skills that enable a person (or an organization) to act effectively in a job or situation.

**computer-based training.** This involves the use of a personal or networked computer for the delivery and access of training programs either synchronously or asynchronously, using online, web-based, mobile, and distance learning platforms.

**confidence interval.** A range of values such that there is a specified probability that a population parameter (for example, and average or mean) lies with that interval.

**continuous improvement.** On-going effort and process to make instructional-improvements that unfolds progressively, that does not have a fixed or predetermined end point, and that is sustained over extended periods of time. These require organizational or professional commitment to an ongoing process of learning, self-reflection, adaptation, and growth.*

**context.** The circumstances that form the setting for an event, statement, or idea, and in terms of which it can be fully understood and assessed

**controls.** The situation of being under the regulation, domination, or command of another:

**co-op.** Cooperative education (or co-operative education or co-op) is a structured method of combining classroom-based education with practical work experience. Academic credits are provided for structured job experience.

**corporate management.** Process of leading, administrating and directing a company through strategic planning, resource allocation and management and applying these for the attainment of the organizational objectives.

**cross-functional.** A group of people with different functional expertise working toward a common goal. It may include people from finance, marketing, operations, and human resources departments. Typically, it includes employees from all levels of an organization. Members may also come from outside an organization.*

**CSR.** Corporate social responsibility (CSR) refers to a growing appeal asking organizations to take a broader social responsibility into account, behaving accordingly in an accountable manner, thus behaving as good corporate citizens.*

**culture.** See Safety Culture.

**curriculum.** The subjects comprising a course of study in a school or college.

**cut score.** These are selected points on the score scale of a test. The points are used to determine whether a particular test score is sufficient for some purpose.

**development.** The act or process of growing or causing something to grow or become larger or more advanced

**distractor.** An incorrect option in a multiple-choice question.

**diversity.** The condition of having or being composed of differing elements: variety; especially: the inclusion of different types of people (such as people of different races or cultures) in a group or organization.

**DuPont Bradley Curve.** A model produced in 1995 by DuPont which outlines the advancement of safety culture within an organization.

**educational standards.** These define the knowledge and skills students should possess at critical points in their educational career. Standards serve as a basis of educational reform across the nation as educators and policy makers respond to the call for a clear definition of desired outcomes of schooling and a way to measure student success in terms of these outcomes.[5]

**EHS.** Environmental health and safety (EHS): is a discipline and specialty that studies and implements practical aspects of environmental protection and safety at work.

**EHS leadership.** See leadership

**EHS student.** See student

**EHS young professionals.** See professionals.

**engineering.** Application of scientific knowledge and mathematical methods to practical purposes of the design, analysis, or operation of structures, machines, or systems.

**enterprise wide.** Encompassing an entire organization, rather than a single business department or function.

---

4 Madsen M.S., Struck T., Braae J. (2016). What is Commercial Excellence? Sales White Paper, September 01. Retrieved February 9, 2018 from http://sandmadsen.com/wp-content/uploads/2017/03/sales-white-paper-01-febr2017.pdf

5 Setting Performance Standards: Concepts, Methods, and Perspectives. Gregory J. Cizek, ed. Mahwah, NJ: Lawrence Erlbaum Associates, c2001. (371.260973 Se784)

**entropy model.** The means of illustrating incident causation and the relationship between risk and business objectives, specifically production, quality, and EHS incident mitigation.

**ergonomics.** The study of people's efficiency in their working environment.

**ergonomic design.** The applied science of equipment design, as for the workplace, intended to maximize productivity by reducing operator fatigue and discomfort. Also known as; *biotechnology, human engineering, human factors engineering.*

**error.** A measure of the difference between a prediction for a value and the actual value.

**ethical codes.** A code of ethics document may outline the mission and values of the business or organization, how professionals are supposed to approach problems, the ethical principles based on the organization's core values and the standards to which the professional is held.

**ethical dilemma.** Also called moral dilemma, is the situation where there is a choice to be made between two options, neither of which resolves the situation in an ethically acceptable way.

**ethics.** Moral principles that govern a person's behavior or the conducting of an activity.

**ethos.** Represents principles, decision-making frameworks, and habits that systematically define the concept of right and wrong conducts.

**evolution.** The gradual development of something, especially from a simple to a more complex form.

**experimental psychology.** The study of mental processes and behaviors under controlled conditions.

**framework.** Broad overview, outline, or skeleton of interlinked items which supports a particular approach to a specific objective, and serves as a guide that can be modified as required by adding or deleting items.

**gap analysis.** A technique used to determine what steps need to be taken in order to move from its current state to its desired, future state. Also known as; *need-gap analysis, needs analysis, needs assessment.*

**general industry.** All industries not included in agriculture, construction or maritime, which are regulated by OSHA's general industry standards, directives, and standard interpretations.

**global.** Operating or applying through the whole of a file, program, or relating to or embracing the whole of something, or of a group of things or of worldwide significance.

**global economy.** World-wide economic activity between various countries that are considered intertwined and thus can affect other countries negatively or positively. *

**governance.** Governance is the set of processes, customs, policies, laws, and institutions affecting the way an enterprise is directed, administered or controlled. Corporate governance also includes the relationship among the many stakeholders involved and the goals of the company involved.

**graduate.** Someone who has been the subject of a graduation, namely, someone who has completed the requirements of an academic degree.

**hazard.** Dangerous event or situation that may lead to an emergency or disaster. It could also be a biological, chemical, or physical agent in (or a property of) an environment that may have an adverse health effect, or may cause injury or loss.*

**hazard assessment.** Evaluating and ranking potential hazards by their estimated frequency and intensity, and determining a margin of safety.*

**hindsight.** The act of considering a particular outcome and tracing the history of how that outcome came to be.

**HSE.** Health, safety and environment (HSE), Same as EHS

**HSEQ.** Health, safety, environment and quality (HSEQ), same as EHS with the inclusion of quality.

**HSSE.** Health, safety, security and environment (HSSE), same as EHS with the inclusion of security.

**HSSEQ.** Health, safety, security, environment, and quality (HSSEQ), same as HSSE with the inclusion of quality.

**human element.** Human behavior and psychology factors, in various aspects, such as; 1) Trust 2) Influence 3) Common interest 4) Self-preservation, etc.

**human factors.** Also known as *ergonomics*, it is the study of human physical and psychological behavior relative to particular environments, products, or services.

**human factors engineering.** Also known as *ergonomics or human engineering,* science dealing with the application of information on physical and psychological characteristics to the design of devices and systems for human use.

**incident.** An event or occurrence.

**incident management.** Activities and process of an organization to identify, analyze, limit and correct hazards to prevent potential disruption caused by such an event and a future re-occurrence, followed by a return to business as usual.[6]

**incident rates.** These are used to show the relative level of injuries and illnesses among different industries, firms, or operations within a single firm.

**informal sector.** Sector which encompasses all jobs which are not recognized as normal income sources, and on which taxes are not paid.*

**integrated management systems.** An Integrated Management System (IMS) integrates all of an organization's systems and processes in to one complete framework, enabling an organization to work as a single unit with unified objectives.[7]

**international standards.** International standards are standards developed by international standards organizations. International standards are available for consideration and use worldwide.

6 The National Archives (2018). Incident Management. "What qualifies as an 'incident'? UK, Small Business Service, Retrieved February 9, 2018 from webarchive.nationalarchives.gov.uk.

7 The Integrated Standards Store (2018). What Is An Integrated Management System? Retrieved February 8, 2018 from http://integrated-standards.com/articles/what-is-integrated-management-system/

**internship.** The position of a student or trainee who works in an organization, sometimes without pay, in order to gain work experience or satisfy requirements for a qualification.

**ISO.** International Organization for Standardization (ISO) - An independent, non-governmental international organization with a membership of 161 national standards bodies which brings together experts to share knowledge and develop voluntary, consensus-based, market relevant International Standards that support innovation and provide solutions to global challenges.[8]

**ISO 14001.** Environmental management systems. The other standards in the ISO 14000 family focus on specific approaches such as audits, communications, labelling and life cycle analysis, as well as environmental challenges such as climate change.

**ISO 45001.** Occupational health and safety management systems - Requirements with guidance for use.

**item.** An individual article or unit, especially one that is part of a list, collection, or set.

**item writing.** Test item writing is an activity based on a learner's participation in the pre-publication development and review of any type of test-item (e.g., multiple choice questions, standardized patient cases).

**job hazard analysis.** A job hazard analysis (JHA), also known as a job safety analysis (JSA), is a technique to identify the dangers of specific tasks in order to reduce the risk of injury to workers.

**job task analysis.** The Job Task Analysis (JTA) is a process used for determining valid job content and employment requirements, for constructing accurate and valid job descriptions and defining valid and defensible position duties and responsibilities.

**lagging indicator.** A measure of a company's incidents in the form of past accident statistics. Examples include: Injury frequency and severity OSHA recordable injuries Lost workdays Worker's compensation costs.[9]

**Leader-Member Exchange.** Leader-Member Exchange Theory (LMX) or Vertical Dyad Linkage Theory, describes how leaders in groups maintain their position through a series of tacit exchange agreements with their members.

**leadership.** The action of leading a group of people or an organization which involves taking bold steps to create solutions and monitor progress to foster safety practices and morale in the workplace.

**leadership principles.** Creating a vision and effectively communicating the vision; providing a set of clear objectives and targets; establishing value for the vision, objectives and targets; receiving committed input and buy-in on vision, objectives and targets; and providing the tools and resources to support the objectives and targets set.

**leading indicator.** A measure preceding or indicating a future event used to drive and measure activities carried out to prevent and control injury, such as; Safety training, Ergonomic opportunities identified and corrected, Reduction of MSD risk factors, Employee perception surveys, Safety audits etc.[10]

**likelihood.** The probability of an event occurring over a certain amount of time.

**maintainability.** Characteristic of design and installation which determines the probability that a failed equipment, machine, or system can be restored to its normal operable state within a given timeframe, using the prescribed practices and procedures.

**management.** (1) The organization and coordination of the activities of a business in order to achieve defined objectives. (2) The directors and managers who have the power and responsibility to make decisions and oversee an enterprise.

**management system.** The way in which an organization manages the inter-related parts of its business in order to achieve its objectives.[11]

**maturity model.** A tool that helps people assess the current effectiveness of a person or group and supports figuring out what capabilities they need to acquire next in order to improve their performance.

**measurement.** Values made meaningful by quantifying into specific units. Measurements act as labels which make those values more useful in terms of details.

**mentor.** An experienced and trusted adviser.

**mitigation.** Reducing the severity of a potential negative event such as a worker safety incident.

**moral distress.** The physical, emotional and psychological response to the feeling of constrained from executing ethically appropriate action or to ethically challenging situations.

**MQC.** Minimum Qualified Candidate (MQC): Those who meet the qualification standard as well as the minimum level of all selective placement factors.

**muda.** Muda (non-value added – usually translated as waste) refers to those elements of production that add no value to the product and only raise costs.[12]

**musculoskeletal disorders.** Musculoskeletal Disorders (MSDs) are injuries and disorders that affect the human body's movement or musculoskeletal system such as; *Carpal Tunnel Syndrome (CTS). Tendonitis. Muscle / Tendon strain.*

**networking.** The exchange of information or services among individuals, groups, or institutions; specifically: the cultivation of productive relationships for employment or business.

---

8 ISO (2018). International Organization for Standardization (ISO) – About ISO. Retrieved February 9, 2018 from https://www.iso.org/about-us.html

9 Ergonomics plus (2018). A Short Guide to Leading and Lagging Indicators of Safety Performance. Retrieved February 9, 2018 from http://ergo-plus.com/leading-lagging-indicators-safety-preformance/

10 Ergonomics plus (2018). A Short Guide to Leading and Lagging Indicators of Safety Performance. Retrieved February 9, 2018 from http://ergo-plus.com/leading-lagging-indicators-safety-preformance/

11 ISO (2018). International Organization for Standardization (ISO) – Management Systems Standards. Retrieved February 9, 2018 from https://www.iso.org/about-us.html

12 Toyota Production System (TPS) Terminology- University of Kentucky – Lean Systems Program, Retrieved on January 4, 2018 from https://www.lean.uky.edu/reference/terminology/

**national Safety Council.** The National Safety Council (NSC) is a non-profit, nongovernmental public service organization promoting health and safety, eliminating preventable deaths at work, in homes and communities, and on the road through leadership, research, education and advocacy in the United States of America.

**occupational.** Relating to a job or profession.

**occupational health.** Identification and control of the risks arising from physical, chemical, and other workplace hazards in order to establish and maintain a safe and healthy working environment. Same as OHS.

**OHS.** Occupational health and safety (OHS): Multidisciplinary field concerned with the safety, health, and welfare of people at work.

**operational excellence.** A philosophy of the workplace where problem-solving, teamwork, and leadership results in the ongoing improvement in an organization. The process involves focusing on the customers' needs, keeping the employees positive and empowered, and continually improving the current activities in the workplace.*

**operational performance.** Operational performance management (OPM) is the alignment of all business units within an organization to ensure that they are working together to achieve core business goals.

**organization.** An organized body of people with a particular purpose, especially a business, society, association, etc.

**organizational change.** Organizational change is about reviewing and modifying management structures and business processes.

**organizational citizenship behavior.** Organizational citizenship behavior (OCB) is a person's voluntary commitment within an organization or company that is not part of his or her contractual tasks.

**organizational culture.** Involves values and behaviors that "contribute to the unique social and psychological environment of an organization.

**OSH.** Occupational safety and health (OSH), same as OHS.

**OSH performance.** See Safety performance

**overconfidence.** Believing one's information or opinion to be truer and more specific than a strict examination of the evidence would suggest.

**people-centred.** An approach that focuses on improving local communities' self-reliance, social justice, and participatory decision-making.

**perceived organizational support.** Perceived Organizational Support (POS) denotes employees' perception relative to the extent to which the organization values their contribution and cares about their well-being.

**performance.** The accomplishment of a given task measured against preset known standards of accuracy, completeness, cost, and speed.

**personal effectiveness.** Making good use of personal and professional resources such as; talents, strengths, skills, energy and time, for achieving set goals.

**PHW.** Psychologically healthy workplace fosters employee health and well-being while enhancing organizational performance and productivity.

**policy.** Action or procedure conforming to or considered with reference to prudence or expediency.

**prevention through design.** Process of preventing and controlling occupational injuries, illnesses, and fatalities by "designing out" or minimizing hazards and risks.[13]

**proactive Safety Management.** A risk management strategy that includes identifying hazards before they materialise into incidents or accidents and taking the necessary actions to reduce the safety risks.[14]

**procedure.** An established or official way of doing something.

**procedural justice.** Procedural justice emphasizes on how law enforcement and other legal authorities interact with the public, and how the characteristics of those interactions shape the public's views of law enforcement, their willingness to be law abiding, and actual crime rates.

**process owners.** The person who has responsibility and accountability over a particular business area. In an Enterprise Risk Management platform this person is responsible to coordinate the identification, mitigation and monitoring of risk on a day-to-day basis.

**profession.** A paid occupation, especially one that involves prolonged training and a formal qualification.

**professional.** Characterized by or conforming to the technical or ethical standards of a profession, exhibiting a courteous, conscientious, and generally business-like conduct in the workplace.

**professionalism.** The conduct, intentions, or virtues that distinguish or symbolize the profession.

**professional development.** Process of improving and increasing capabilities of individuals through access to education and training opportunities in the workplace, through outside organization, or through watching others perform the job.

**professional network.** This involves using personal, professional, academic or familial contacts to assist with a job search, achieve career goals, or learn more about one's field, or another field of interest.

**professional organization.** A body of persons engaged in the same profession, formed usually to control entry into the profession, maintain standards, and represent the profession in discussions with other bodies.

**project.** Planned set of interrelated tasks to be executed over a fixed period and within certain cost and other limitations.

**project manager.** An employee who plans and organizes the resources necessary to complete a project.

**project management.** The body of knowledge concerned with principles, techniques, and tools used in planning, control, monitoring, and review of projects.

**project teams.** A group of individuals assembled to perform activities that contribute toward achieving a common task related

---

13 CDC (2018). Center for Disease Controls. Prevention through design. Retrieved February 9, 2018 from https://www.cdc.gov/niosh/topics/ptd/default.html

14 Skybrary (2018). Safety Management. Retrieved February 9, 2018 from https://www.skybrary.aero/index.php/Safety_Management

goal. Many business operators will put together a project team consisting of skilled workers from the same or different function areas to work on an important project.

**psychometry.** The supposed ability to discover facts about an event or person by touching inanimate objects associated with them.

**QHSE.** Quality, health, safety, and environment, same as (HSEQ),

**QHSSE.** Quality, health, safety, security, and environment.

**relationship.** The way in which two or more people or organizations regard and behave toward each other.

**relationship building.** Ability to identify and initiate working relationships and to develop and maintain them in a way that is of mutual benefit to all.

**reliability.** The degree to which the result of a measurement, calculation, or specification can be depended on to be accurate.

**research.** The systematic investigation into and study of materials and sources in order to establish facts and reach new conclusions.

**Research to Practice to Research (RtPtR).** Looping process of proper conduct of research and implemented in practice and continuous evaluation of the effectiveness through research.

**resilience engineering.** Resilience Engineering looks for ways to enhance the ability at all levels of organisations to create processes that are robust yet flexible, to monitor and revise risk models, and to use resources proactively in the face of disruptions or ongoing production and economic pressures.[15]

**risk.** A measure of exposure to negative outcomes calculated as the severity of an event multiplied by its likelihood.

**risk assessment.** A systematic process of evaluating the potential risks that may be involved in a projected activity or undertaking.

**risk management.** The process of identifying, assessing and controlling threats or risks to an organization, including; accidents, natural disasters, financial uncertainty, legal liabilities, strategic management errors, capital and earnings.

**risk mitigation.** A systematic reduction in the extent of exposure to a risk and/or the likelihood of its occurrence. Also known as risk reduction.*

**risk mitigation strategy.** This is an overall approach to reduce the risk impact severity and/or probability of occurrence

**risk register.** The collection of all the risk an organization faces. This information typically comes from a facilitated effort of collecting information from stakeholders throughout the organization.

**roadmap.** A plan or strategy intended to achieve a particular goal.

**role delineation.** Description of those tasks critical for competent job performance by identifying the minimum amount of knowledge and skills required to perform job-related functions.

**root cause.** A factor that caused a non-conformance and should be permanently eliminated through process improvement.

**safety.** The condition of being protected from or unlikely to cause danger, risk, or injury.

**safety analytics.** Predictive analytics used by safety professionals to predict and prevent workplace fatalities, injuries, diseases and accidents.

**safety climate.** Organization's perceptions of safety as measured by tools such as safety perception surveys.

**safety culture.** A reflection of the organization's values, norms, expectations, etc.

**safety engineering.** An engineering discipline that assures that engineered systems provide acceptable levels of safety and a life-critical system behaves as needed, even when components fail. Similar to *industrial engineering/systems engineering,* and *system safety engineering.*

**safety leadership.** Safety leadership is defined as the process of interaction between leaders and followers, through which leaders can exert their influence on followers to achieve organizational safety goals.[16]

**Safety Management System (SMS).** A systematic approach to managing safety, including the necessary organizational structures, accountabilities, policies and procedures.[17]

**safety metrics.** These are measures that are used to evaluate and track the safety performance programs.

**safety performance.** Safety achievement as defined by the safety performance targets and safety performance indicators.[18]

**safety performance indicators.** Data-based parameter used for monitoring and assessing safety performance.

**safety performance target.** Planned or intended objective for safety performance indicator(s) over a given period.

**safety strategy.** This is a high level safety plan to achieve one or more goals.

**scope.** Sum of all individual jobs comprising a contract, employment, program, or project.

**scope of work.** The division of work to be performed under a contract or subcontract in the completion of a project, typically broken out into specific tasks with deadlines.

**severity.** A measure of the consequences of a particular outcome.

**SHE.** Safety, health and environment

**silos.** A silo mentality occurs when a team or department shares common tasks but derives their power and status from their group or area. They find it difficult to share resources or ideas with other groups or welcome suggestions as to how they might improve.

**stakeholders.** A person or organization that has interest or concerns in an organization.

---

15 Resilience Engineering Association (2018). About resilience engineering. Retrieved February 9, 2018 from http://www.resilience-engineering-association.org/

16 White C. (2018). Safety Leadership is NOT Safety Management. Safety Perspectives, Select International Inc. Pittsburgh PA, Retrieved February 9, 2018 from http://www.selectinternational.com/safety-blog/bid/185973/safety-leadership-is-not-safety-management.

17 International Air Transport Association (IATA) - 2018 Support Consistent Implementation of SMS. Retrieved February 9, 2018 from http://www.iata.org/whatwedo/safety/Pages/safety-management.aspx

18 Leite J. (2017) Safety Performance Indicators (SPI) Safety Performance Targets (SPT) and Measuring Criteria. Tap Maintenance and Engineering. Retrieved February 9, 2018 from https://flightsafety.org/wp-content/uploads/2017/03/09.-Jorge-Leite.pdf

**strategic element.** Characteristic of a strategy used for defining organizational strategy, or direction, and making decisions on allocating its resources to pursue this strategy, and used as control mechanisms for guiding the implementation of the strategy.

**student.** A student is a learner or someone who attends an educational institution.

**survivor.** A discrete set of units or outcomes that have not experienced a particular negative outcome.

**system.** A set of connected things or parts forming a complex whole, in particular.

**system effectiveness.** Extent to which a system may be expected to achieve its objectives within its specified environment. System effectiveness is a function of system availability, capability, and dependability.*

**system safety.** It is the application of engineering and management principles, criteria and techniques to optimize safety.

**Taylorism.** The principles or practice of scientific management.

**technical competency.** Behaviours directly related to the nature of training and the technical proficiency required to exercise effective control.

**technology.** The application of scientific knowledge for practical purposes, especially in industry.

**time-phased budget.** The distribution of activities, tasks, milestones and resources over a suitable time for the scheduled completion of a plan, project or program and the cost baseline for the project and allows tracking and reporting of actual results for the project.

**TPS.** Toyota Production System (TPS) is the production system developed by Toyota Motor Corporation to provide best quality, lowest cost, and shortest lead time through the elimination of waste.[19]

**training.** The teaching, instruction, or developing of a person or others, with any skills and knowledge that relate to specific useful competencies.

**transformation.** Thorough or dramatic change in form or appearance.

**transformational leadership.** It is a style of leadership approach that causes change in individuals and social systems, where a leader works with subordinates to identify needed change, creating a vision to guide the change through inspiration, and executing the change in tandem with committed members of a group.[20]

**transparency.** Implies openness, communication, and accountability.

**transparent leadership.** Characteristics of leaders that are open, available for communication from a variety of organizational pathways and sources, and being perceived as accountable for their actions.

**turnover rate.** A human resources metric which expresses the number of employees lost through firing, attrition and other means compared to the total number of employees in the company.*

**uncertainty.** A measure of how much variability an unknown value may have.

**unsafe act.** An activity or task conducted in a manner that unnecessarily increases the likelihood of an injury, accident or other incident.

**upward communication.** The transmission of information from lower levels of an organization to higher ones; the most common form is employees communicating with managers.

**validity.** The quality of being logically or factually sound and the extent to which a concept, conclusion or measurement is well-founded and corresponds accurately to the real world.

**validation survey.** The process of assessing the survey questions for their dependability.

**virtual EHS.** Use of virtual reality through immersive videos and graphics to improve safety, discover system flaws, and simulate trainings.

**work breakdown structure.** A deliverable-oriented hierarchical decomposition of the work to be executed by the project team to accomplish the project objectives and create the required deliverables. It organizes and defines the total scope of the project.

**working conditions.** The conditions in which an individual or staff works, including but not limited to such things as amenities, physical environment, stress and noise levels, degree of safety or danger, and the like.*

**workplace safety.** See Safety and OSH

19 Toyota Production System (TPS) Terminology- University of Kentucky – Lean Systems Program, Retrieved on January 4, 2018 from https://www.lean.uky.edu/reference/terminology/

20 Deinert A., Homan A.C., Boer D., Voelpel S.C., Gutermann D. (2015). Transformational leadership sub-dimensions and their link to leaders' personality and performance. The Leadership Quarterly 26 (2015) 1095–1120

# INDEX

Note: *f* indicates a figure; *t*, a table.

## F



## G

## N



## O

MW00630159

# 100 HERBS TO GROW

# 100 HERBS TO GROW

A comprehensive guide to the best culinary and medicinal herbs

JEKKA McVICAR

Hardie Grant
QUADRILLE

**To my family, Mac, Hannah and Alistair, with love and gratitude for supporting my passion for herbs over the past four decades.**

**Page 2** *Malva moschata*, Musk Mallow
**Left** *Monarda fistulosa*, Wild Bergamot

# Foreword

Thirty years ago I was presenting gardening for Granada's daytime *This Morning* and somehow persuaded them to film in my garden. This was something of a confidence trick because in fact, despite having just moved into the two-acre empty field where the garden now is, back then it existed mostly in my head and the the only bit that had begun to be planted was a small walled area in front of the house.

We were to do a short film about growing herbs and it was suggested that I might like to be advised on the development of my own rather scant collection of herbs by a brilliant young herb grower from Somerset called Jekka. Jekka duly arrived and, hiding her dismay at the limitations of my garden, quickly charmed us all as well as being a natural on television. Within minutes of her arrival she was making lavender biscuits in our building-site kitchen with flowers from the couple of scraggly lavender plants I had growing in pots.

Funny, clever, effervescent and with a deep well of horticultural knowledge, I was and still am in awe of her. Jekka has gone on to be rightly recognised as one of the horticultural great and good but has never lost that impish gleam in her eye nor the streak of rebellious joy of the young woman playing flute on the stage at Glastonbury.

The other point of connection between us was our shared commitment to organic growing. Thirty years ago it was viewed by the horticultural establishment as at best fringe and often as a form of incompetence. But Jekka never wavered and although often the sole organic exhibitor at Chelsea, she has won over 60 RHS gold medals as well as every other award that horticulture has to bestow, serving as a shining example of what can be achieved without resorting to chemicals – and despite all these accolades remaining the least reverential or self-important person that you might ever meet.

No one has done more to both educate and enthuse the nation in the appreciation and use of herbs as part of both our gardens and kitchens. Herbs tend to be sidelined as also-rans alongside the more established institution of vegetable growing, but Jekka has shown us that the wide range of herbs that we might grow in a very limited space has culinary, health and aesthetic possibilities most of us barely touch upon. No other aspect of gardening has such a broad influence on our lives and yet herbs can be grown in almost any situation, even if you do not have any kind of garden.

This book summarises a lifetime of expertise in one beautiful volume. I sincerely hope that it is not the last but as a testament to her gift of sharing her deep knowledge in an accessible, encouraging manner it is unsurpassable. And do make lavender biscuits – they are delicious.

**Monty Don**

**Right** *Lavandula angustifolia 'Folgate'*, Lavender Folgate

# Introduction

It is a dank, grey winter's day. I have come back into the cottage, having spent the day in the glasshouse propagating lavender; my hands and clothes all smell delicious. The scent of lavender reminds me of the summer and the sound of bees. Very soon spring will be on our doorstep and even now the evenings are slowly getting lighter. I keep writing lists of what I need to sow, what needs to be divided and what has enough material for me to take cuttings. Even after over 40 years of growing herbs commercially, I am as enthusiastic today as I was when I first started learning with my mother over 65 years ago. My mother had a very productive garden and used herbs to make the simplest meal taste wonderful. I vividly remember smelling the food that she was cooking wafting over the garden, where I was tending my own tiny garden in which I grew radishes, sorrel and chicory. Being the eldest child in the family, it was my job to pick the herbs that my mum required for meals. I could tell the difference between apple mint and spearmint before I started school – you could say that herbs are in my DNA.

On leaving school I went to art college in Somerset, where I met a progressive pop group. Having been classically trained to play the flute and clarinet, it was a whole new world that lasted for a few years. I left the group in high dudgeon and hitched across Europe, ending up on Crete, where I got a job busking in a taverna. One day I got acute food poisoning, but the owner of the taverna gave me a dittany tea and within a few days I had recovered. Today I grow that beautiful herb here at the Herb Farm – it is *Origanum dictamnus* – and it transports me back to that magical island, where sadly due to development it is now becoming endangered.

When Mac, my long-suffering husband, and I bought our first house in Filton I had my own herb garden, which I turned to every day when I cooked the evening meal. The herbs filled our house with delicious aromas reminiscent of my childhood.

The Herb Farm started in that tiny herb garden in Filton. It was all because a girlfriend asked me for some French tarragon as she was cooking an Elizabeth David recipe, and unlike today the supermarkets only had dried herbs. Before we knew it, we had orders from shops, garden centres and Fortnum & Mason. The demand for the herbs very quickly outgrew our small back garden so I had a choice between stopping, or moving to South Gloucestershire. We moved to a derelict cottage with one acre of neglected land, and into a mobile home with our children who were then three and four years old. In those days very few people knew about herbs and I soon realised that I would have to share the wonder and delight of these amazing plants so I wrote my first book, *Jekka's Complete Herb Book*. Now, three decades later, it is time for a new book that encompasses everything I have learnt over the past four decades and the benefits of growing herbs not only for oneself and the family but also for the planet as they are some of the most beneficial plants for increasing biodiversity. It is also very exciting to know that herbs are being taken seriously, not only in the garden and the home, but also medicinally, where they are undergoing research into their medicinal properties.

In this book I have chosen my top 100 herbs to grow – they are the ones that have most inspired me in the kitchen and in the garden. The aim of this book is to give you the confidence to grow and use herbs. Once you embark on this journey, your life will never be dull, and it will help you transform a meal into a feast and your garden into a haven for bees, butterflies and charms of finches.

**Top left** *Origanum vulgare*, **top right** *Hypericum perforatum*, **bottom left** *Calendula officinalis* 'Indian Prince', **bottom right** *Echinacea purpurea*

# Botanical plant names

Why can't we use the common name for all plants? I have been asked this question on numerous occasions and my answer is that if you are eating it or using the plant for medicinal purposes it is important that you are certain you know what you are putting in your body. By using the scientific botanical name, you can be specific and succinct and you minimise confusion because many common names are ambiguous. For example, the following are the common names for *Plectanthus amboinicus*: Cuban oregano, Jamaican broad leaf thyme, Indian borage, Spanish thyme, and banga banga. These common names come from around the world, including Malaysia, India, Cuba and Jamaica. Even greater confusion can occur when a common name in different parts of the world refers to a different plant. For instance, in the UK, meadowsweet – *Filipendula ulmaria* – is often called queen of the meadow, while in the USA, queen of the meadow is in fact *Eupatorium purpureum* – gravelroot or Joe pie weed; they are two totally different plants which have completely different attributes.

The system used today is known as the 'binomial system', which was derived by the famous 18th-century Swedish botanist Carl Linnaeus (1707–78) – each plant is classified by using two Latin words. The first word is the name of the genus, e.g. *Thymus*, and the second is the specific name (epithet) e.g. *Thymus vulgaris*. Together they provide a universally known name, which translates as 'thyme common'.

The Linnean system of plant classification has been developed so that the entire plant kingdom has been divided into a multi-branched family tree according to each plant's botanical characteristics. Plants are gathered into particular families according to the structure of their flowers, fruits or seeds. A family may contain four genera and seven species, e.g. the family *Saururaceae*, of which *Houttuynia* is a species, or many, e.g. the family *Asteraceae*, of which there are over 1,900 genera, including *Achillea*, *Artemisia* and *Calendula* to name a few, and over 32,000 species.

Plants are cultivated for the garden from the wild either to improve their leaf or flower. This can be done by selecting the strongest seedling and propagating from it or by spotting an interesting mutation, from which you can also propagate. These are known as cultivars, 'a combination of cultivated varieties'. Propagation from these varieties is normally done by cuttings or division. Cultivars are given vernacular names, which are printed within quotes. i.e. *Mentha* 'Berries and Cream', which distinguishes them from wild varieties in the Latin form that appear in italics i.e. *Mentha suaveolens*. Sexual crosses between species, usually of the same genus, are known as hybrids and are indicated by a multiplication sign, i.e. *Mentha* x *gracillis*.

With the advance of research and scientists sequencing plant DNA, reading the genetic code of a plant is regarded as the most reliable way to identify its species. This had led to many plants being reclassified and therefore long-established names are being changed. For example, *Rosmarinus officinalis* (rosemary) has been reclassified to *Salvia* so the botanical name is now *Salvia rosmarinus*. In this book I have used the latest information available, but I am very aware that the plant world is evolving.

Using scientific botanical names may appear complicated to those unfamiliar with horticulture. However, despite the changes, it does greatly simplify communication; it also avoids potential confusion which means that we can share information around the world, knowing we are all talking about the same plant.

*Lamiaceae*
Family

*Mentha*
Genus

*Thymus*
Genus

*Lavandula*
Genus

*Mentha spicata*
Species

*Mentha aquatica*
Species

*Mentha x piperita*
Hybrid

*Mentha x piperita*
'Black Mitcham'
Cultivar

*Mentha x piperita*
'Logee's'
Cultivar

*Mentha* x *piperita* 'Black Mitcham', Black Mitcham Peppermint

# Climate and temperature

The climate and temperature are major factors in determining which herbs you can grow successfully.

When I started herb farming four decades ago, I was not aware of climate change. One knew roughly when the first and last frosts were; now trying to predict this is much more precarious. The consequence of the rising global temperature is that it has altered the consistent weather patterns and it has increased precipitation and drought periods. The growth patterns, pests, flowering periods and water used by plants are all affected by changes in their environment. For example, I was used to what was commonly known here in the West Country of the UK as soft rain – gentle, wetting rain – which is good for the soil and good for the plants. Now we have deluges that can happen at any time in the year, including in the summer. These are often damaging, especially when the lavender is in flower. We have had plants literally split in half by the force of the rain. What's more, if this happens after a drought the water simply runs straight off the land rather than into the soil. The other problem with the deluge form of rain is that it drowns plants, and Mediterranean plants, which are in the main shallow-rooted – bay, thyme, oregano, sage, rosemary, etc. – hate prolonged and wet, cold winters.

Mild, warm winters can also upset herbs that are grown from bulbs and those that are deciduous. This is because the plants need to hibernate and die back during the winter months to give the plant time to rest and regenerate.

*Filipendula ulmaria*, Meadowsweet

| RHS rating | USDA zone | Type | Climate | Temperature |
|---|---|---|---|---|
| H1a | 13 | Heated greenhouse | tropical | Warmer than 15°C (59°F) |
| H1b | 12 | Heated greenhouse | subtropical | 10–15°C (50–59°F) |
| H1c | 11 | Heated greenhouse | warm temperate | 5–10°C (41–50°F) |
| H2 | 10 | Tender | cool or frost-free greenhouse | 1–5°C (34–41°F) |
| H3 | 9 | Half-hardy | unheated greenhouse/mild winter | -5–1°C (23–34°F) |
| H4 | 8, 9 | Hardy | average winter | -10– -5°C (14–23°F) |
| H5 | 7, 8 | Hardy | cold winter | -15– -10°C (5–14°F) |
| H6 | 6, 7 | Hardy | very cold winter | -20– -15°C (-4–5°F) |
| H7 | 6 | Very hardy | lower than | -20°C (-4°F) |

In the A–Z section I have indicated the hardiness of each herb. I have chosen to follow the Royal Horticultural Society's (RHS) and the United States Department of Agriculture's (USDA) hardiness ratings (see chart above), which will assist gardeners in determining more clearly which herbs are hardy in their local area.

I live in an H4 typical winter area so growing *Aloysia citrodora,* lemon verbena (see page 50), which is classed as an H3 plant, outside in winter is pushing it. So, I grow it in a container and winter it in a cold polytunnel. When the temperature is below 1°C (34°F) I cover it in horticultural fleece. Then in the spring, I pot it up, and sink the pot into the ground for the growing season, returning it to the polytunnel in the autumn. This is much easier that struggling to keep it alive outside in the vagaries of the weather.

The unpredictability of the seasons makes it much more difficult to know when to sow seeds and when to harvest. A good rule of thumb is to get two, if not three, weather forecast apps onto your computer or phone. You can then regularly check them and take a mean average. Where I live, the last hard frost is usually at the end of spring and the first serious frost is mid-autumn therefore I do not start planting out annuals until the end of spring or start of summer, and complete harvest of seeds by mid-autumn. I wish it was as simple as that but to hedge my bets I keep a watch on the weather forecast. I also have a roll of horticultural fleece at hand to cover the seedlings, or annuals, if the weather decides to be awkward.

# Propagation

I know I have said this on numerous occasions, but there is nothing better than going into the glasshouse in early spring to check the seed trays, to see which herbs are emerging. The reward is doubled when you see the seed that you have stratified pushing its way through the soil. And later in spring taking cuttings that are basically just a twig and seeing them root, then grow on to become a strong healthy plant is quite simply a joy.

In this chapter I go through the elements for successful propagation, which include growing mediums and composts. Then I cover the techniques for sowing seeds and for taking successful cuttings as well as the propagation methods of layering and division.

## The essential elements for successful propagation

Growing herbs under protection is a different technique to growing herbs outside in the open ground. The main difference being 'the ecosystem' as you do not have the living soil, nor the natural rain or wind. You have to control four essential elements – light, temperature, water and air – to create the most natural environment for the plants to germinate and grow.

### Light

Plants need light for photosynthesis to take place. However, seedlings and cuttings do not like the direct, hot midday sun because this can cause scorching of the new leaves. If you do not have a shaded position in your greenhouse or if you're using a windowsill in your home or shed that gets direct sun, especially at midday, then cover your seedlings or cuttings with a lightweight horticultural fleece at that critical time.

### Temperature

Every seed has an optimum temperature for germination. Although many seeds will germinate within a fairly wide temperature range some are limited, so it is worth checking the range for your chosen herb in the A–Z section. Cuttings need warmth to encourage the roots to form and grow.

**Left** *Anethum graveolens*, Dill

### Water

Seeds need water to penetrate the outer seed coat as this causes the endosperm to swell, which in turn causes the embryo to grow. Cuttings require water to replace moisture lost by transpiration, for photosynthesis and to encourage root growth.

### Air

Air is needed to encourage growth and to avoid disease. Oxygen is needed for respiration and carbon dioxide for photosynthesis. This is why it is most important to open the window of the shed or greenhouse, especially in winter or early spring, during the warmth of the day. This will increase air circulation and prevent the young plants sitting in too humid an atmosphere, which can cause mildew and/or damping off (see pages 276 and 274).

## Compost and growing mediums

Just as the soil is the engine for the plants in your garden, the growing medium you choose is the start of your seed or cutting's journey into becoming a flourishing herb, so it is worth choosing a quality seed or cutting compost.

Do not use soil taken directly from the garden as it is not sterile and your seeds may have to compete with weed seed, while old compost may contain pests and disease that will attack and damage your cuttings. You can either buy a good peat-free seed compost from a garden centre or online or I make my own using the following mix, which is ideal as it helps to retain water, but has good drainage and allows air flow round the immature roots. My mix is as follows: two parts coir (coconut fibre) + one part composted fine bark + one part perlite.

For cuttings, the mix is two parts coir + one part composted fine bark + one part vermiculite. No fertiliser is added because the seed has its own store and cutting roots happily grow without. Both only need feeding once they start growing. For those who live near a good garden centre you can now buy good peat-free seed compost. In the A-Z of herbs I have mentioned which mix is best for seed sowing and cuttings and how to adapt bought peat-free seed compost by adding appropriate growing mediums.

### Coir

Coir is the outside layer of husk that surrounds the shell of the coconut. It consists mainly of fibres that have traditionally been used to manufacture rope, carpets and brushes. Between these fibres is the corky substance known as coir which is a recognised growing medium. The inherent quality of coir provides optimum water/air availability and is ideal for quick rooting and propagation. Watering can cause a problem as the upper surface often appears dry while lower down in the container it is still wet.

### Composted fine bark

Tree bark is available in many different grades from any good garden centre or store. You will need the composted fine or propagating grade bark for seed sowing. If you are using your own collected and composted bark, make sure that it has been composted for a minimum of 6–9 months. This will get rid of the ammonium nitrate that green bark contains, which, if still in the bark, will either burn the seedlings or stunt their growth.

### Perlite

Perlite is not a trade name but a generic term for naturally occurring siliceous rock, which has been heated to make sterile, light, expanded granules. It is available in fine, standard or coarse grades. Root cuttings can be taken in 100% perlite and it is ideal for hydronic systems. It has a neutral pH which makes it ideal for mixing with compost, for extra drainage or used as a covering over the seeds instead of soil or other composts.

### Vermiculite

Vermiculite is the mineralogical name given to hydrated laminar magnesium-aluminium-iron-silicate that resembles mica in appearance. When heated, it expands and this is the substance that it used in horticulture. It is similar to perlite, but holds more water and less air. It comes in various grades from fine to coarse. It can be added to composts for extra drainage or aeration. It can also be used as a covering over the seeds instead of soil or substrate but, as it holds water, it is not as good as perlite as a general seed covering.

### Sand and grit

Horticultural sand, also called coarse sand or horticultural grit, can include various materials, such as quartz, crushed sandstone or crushed granite. This composition means it is lime-free, so it will not adversely affect the pH balance of soil. If you cannot get horticultural grade you can use building sand or grit but make sure it is washed before you use it.

## Containers for seed sowing

### Plug or modular tray

These are multi-celled trays with 6 –200 cells made from plastic, polystyrene, recycled tyres or pressed peat. Plastic trays are the easiest from which to remove the rooted modules. These trays are very useful if you have a small amount of seed, or for plants that hate having their roots disturbed when pricked out. The disadvantage of these trays is that they dry out much more quickly than seed trays so need to be checked regularly in hot weather.

### Seed tray

These trays should be 5–7cm (2–3 in) deep and sturdy enough not to lose shape when full of wet compost or bend when you pick them up or move them. The major disadvantage of using these trays is that when you prick out the seedling, it is very difficult not to damage the fine roots. When replanted the seedlings growth is checked until the roots are repaired.

### Pot

There is now a huge range of pots available. Plastic, clay or decomposable ones made from cardboard, miscanthus or coir all have their merits. If you have limited space, sowing directly into pots is ideally suited for large seeds. To prevent the seedlings breaking when you prick them out, it is better to thin them in the pot and allow the strongest to grow on before planting out or potting on.

## How to prepare seeds

When sowing seeds, it is important to consider the plant's native habitat. Does it come from a mountainous region or the tropics or does it originate from the Mediterranean? Understanding where a plant originates and attempting to create a similar environment will improve your chances of successfully raising the plant from seed. In spring germination is triggered in many types of seeds by the temperature change. However, some seeds require additional triggers, so we need to fool the seed by mimicking nature.

**Right** *Calendula officinalis*, Pot Marigold

### Scarification

Scarification is the process of intentionally damaging the outer case of the seed to encourage germination. This is because some seeds have a hard outer coat that is impervious to water. In the wild this can be broken by the seed falling from the tree, by temperature change or if it passes through the digestive tract of an animal. It may be difficult for the gardener to mimic nature, so one has to resort to mechanical methods. You can break down a seed coating by soaking it in vinegar, however, it is easy to get the timing wrong. A simpler method is hot water scarification. Bring some water to a boil in a pan with a lid, remove from the heat, place the seeds in the water, then cover. Allow the seeds to soak until the water cools to room temperature, then remove the seeds from the water and sow them directly into a prepared pot or module. Other methods include rubbing the seed in sandpaper, or putting a little nick into the outer coating, being careful not to damage the 'eye' or hilum which is a little depression or mark where the seed is attached to the ovary. Scarified seeds do not store well and should be planted as soon as possible after treatment.

### Stratification

Stratification is the breaking down of the seed's hard outer protective coating by subjecting it to changes in temperature, for example, cold temperatures followed by warm, i.e. winter followed by spring. Or warm temperatures followed by cold, which in most cases is followed by a period of second warmth, i.e. summer followed by autumn and winter followed by spring.

### Natural stratification

Where the temperature in winter drops below 0°C (32°F) for at least 3 weeks over the 3 months of winter, natural stratification is possible. Sow the seeds in a container and leave them outside to experience the weather. The fluctuating temperatures will help break down the outer protective coat.

### Artificial stratification

Where the temperature remains warm in winter, you may need to apply artificial stratification. This is simply done by placing the seed in the refrigerator for a period of time. On average the seed should be kept at 0–5°C (32–41°F) for 3–4 weeks. Mix the seed with some damp vermiculite, sand or coir (not wet, otherwise it will rot the seed). This helps to make the seed colder by coming into continuous contact with the cold damp substance. It also makes it a lot easier to sow. Place the seed mixture into a plastic bag, label it clearly and place it in the refrigerator. Turn the bag from time to time to allow the air to circulate.

## How to sow seeds

**Once you are ready to sow your seeds:**

**1** | Fill the pot with the compost, firm and water in well. You water before adding the seed, so the water does not wash away the seed.

**2** | Use scissors to open the seed packet, avoid tearing as it is harder to seal the packet afterwards.

**3** | Sow the seeds.

**For small seeds:** Sow the seeds thinly on the top of the compost. We use a label bent lengthways to dispense the seeds, which helps to avoid touching them. Once sown, cover with perlite.

A useful technique when sowing very fine seed is to mix it with fine silver sand so that you can see the seed. Then place this mixture into the crease of a folded piece of card. Gently tap the card to sow the seeds in thin lines across the surface of the compost. You can also use this method when sowing directly into the garden as it makes it much easier to sow the seeds thinly.

**For medium-sized seeds:** Space the seeds out evenly onto the surface of the substrate, then gently press them into the surface of compost before covering with a thin layer.

#### SEED SOWING CHECKLIST

- washed pots, trays or modules
- prepared soil if sowing directly into the garden
- seed compost for sowing under cover
- seeds prepared for sowing
- paperclip or rubber band to reseal the seed packet when you have finished
- waterproof box, with lid, for storing seed packets
- perlite, grit or sand for covering the seed (and fine silver sand if sowing tiny seeds)
- labels, piece of card and a soft pencil or waterproof pen

**For large seeds:** Use a dibber to make a hole in the soil or compost about 1½ times the size of the seed, pop the seed into the hole and cover with soil or compost.

4 | Label with plant name and date.

5 | Place the pot in a warm light place, 18 °C (65°F), not full sun.

6 | Keep watering to a minimum until germination has taken place, which takes 10–20 days.

7 | Once the seedlings start germinating, make sure the container gets as much light as possible. If you live in a frost-free environment, when air temperature does not go below 7°C (45°F), place the container outside during the day, bringing in at night.

8 | Continue until the third leaf starts to appear, then the container can be left out all night. This is to harden them off in order to acclimatise the young plants to the outdoors before planting out.

## When to cover your seeds

I have found perlite wonderful to cover most seeds as it helps protect the seed from too much moisture, reflects light, adds warmth and is totally sterile so will not affect the seedlings as they emerge. This is also useful when sowing in drills outside as it makes it very easy to see where the row is so you can monitor germination and watch out for pests.

**There are two situations when you might not wish to cover with perlite:**

- Very tiny seeds are usually sown on the surface of the compost and/or soil. They should not be covered with compost or perlite which will allow the maximum light, air and water to contact the seed.
- Herbs that would naturally self-seed in the wild benefit from being sown in a darker environment and should be covered with compost. This is because the leaves would have fallen after the seeds, covering them and protecting them through the winter and omitting the light. When sowing, only cover with additional compost equal to the diameter of the seed.

Sowing allium seeds, using a folded label

## Where to sow

### Inside with extra warmth

Using a propagator to start the seeds' germination allows you to adjust the humidity, temperature, air flow and light to suit specific seeds, thereby giving the best chance of germination. There are many different propagators available – small ones holding four pots that can be placed on the windowsill, or larger propagators with a heating element that provides the seedlings with extra warmth. All are useful but whichever you choose make sure the lid has a vent that allows you to control the excess humidity.

### Windowsill

Trays or pots can be placed on a windowsill, preferably not south facing as this could get too hot when the seedling emerges. Rotate the tray once a day to stop the seedling bending towards the light.

### Conservatory

This is very similar to growing plants in a greenhouse, however it is often considerably hotter. If this is the case you must keep an eye on the watering, especially if you are using coir as your substrate. Also be diligent about opening the window to stop the build-up of humidity.

### Greenhouse

This is an ideal environment in which to germinate as in most cases it has all-round light. However, if it is unheated and frost is forecast after the germination of the seedlings, protect them with horticultural fleece.

### Outside with protection

If you want to get an early start in spring or prolong the season in autumn then cloches, cold frames and crop covers give valuable temporary or long-term protection to seedlings and salad herbs. They are also far cheaper than a greenhouse and much more flexible.

### Cold frames

I started my farm with cold frames, which were simply made from an old wardrobe and polycarbonate sheeting. These frames are ideal for wintering seeds that need to have some cold to germinate and for protecting hardwood cuttings. In spring they are great for starting early salad crops.

### Cloches

These are now available in all shapes and sizes. You can create mini cloches from sawn-off plastic bottles, which are good for protecting single plants, or you can use replica Victorian glass cloches which look attractive in any garden for protecting specimen plants. Alternatively, you can use the A-shaped cloches for starting seeds in the ground or protecting low-growing herbs like sweet marjoram.

There are many other uses for cloches: helping to establish young plants; protection from flying pests; extending the season of salad herbs like coriander, dill and chervil; protecting hardy herbs for winter picking, such as thyme and sage. Their disadvantage is that they do need to be removed from time to time so that you can control the weeds and remove the slugs.

### Horticultural fleece

This fleece is sometimes called agricultural fleece and is available in many different weights depending on how much protection you wish to provide. In extremely hard conditions you will need a fleece of 30gm (1oz), in sheltered sites or in a cold frame you will need a fleece of 17gm (0.6oz). If you were to visit my farm on an early cold spring morning you would see neat small white beds. This is because the pots of herbs are tucked up in 2 x 1.2m (6 ½ x 4ft) sections and covered with fleece to protect them through the night when frost is forecast. Later in the morning, after we have lifted all the fleeces off and hung them to dry, the farm looks like an old Victorian wash house. By lifting the fleece during the day it prevents the plants becoming soft; we can also see if there are any weeds starting or slugs. Fleece is not only good for frost protection, it is a very useful pest barrier protecting herbs like *Petroselinum crispum* (parsley) from carrot root fly and *Diplotaxis muralis* (wild rocket) from flea beetle. It can also be used as a windbreak, protecting young stock that has been brought out of the cold frames.

Horticultural fleece covers the herbs in winter

## Once the seed has germinated

The most important element in germination and growing seedlings well is watering. Before germination you must keep watering to the minimum. Do not allow the compost or soil to dry out, but do not let it get soaking wet as this will rot the seed. On average germination takes 10–14 days, but it varies from plant to plant. Once the seedlings have emerged, water them in the morning rather than the evening, as this will give them a chance to dry, which is especially important if the night temperatures are still fluctuating. Try and water the compost or soil not the seedlings, as this will help prevent fungal disease.

*Borago officinalis*, Borage

## Pricking out and potting on

Having nurtured your seedlings through the germination stage, it is time for pricking out and potting on. The seedlings in the modules and pots are ready for potting on or planting out when they have formed their second leaves and are well rooted. If you are unsure, you can check by lifting up the container and looking to see whether the roots are peeping out of the bottom. Alternatively, you can gently tap the seedlings out of the pot or ease them out the module. If the roots are well formed it is time to move on to the next stage. A word of warning, if you have sown in a seed tray or in a pot and leave the seedlings too long they will need to be carefully separated before potting on or planting out. If you leave the seedlings in a module for too long the root ball will become too tight for the seedling to grow and you will have weak, stunted plants.

*Thymus* cuttings ready for potting up

Before you start potting on you will either need to buy a peat-free potting compost or make your own. You can of course purchase good commercial organic fertilisers already mixed – and add one to your chosen compost mix at the recommended rate.

When potted on you will find that herbs raised in the modules will grow twice as fast as those grown in the seed trays or pricked out from pots – this is because the root ball has had very little disturbance so the plant does not feel threatened. When potting on, do not compress the substrate at any time, as this will crush the air out and make it more difficult for the root system to develop. Once potted the plants need to be watered, then placed under a certain amount of protection to harden off for a week. This again is to prevent the young plant being stressed, as it will have come from a nurtured environment into the cruel world.

## Cuttings

Nature never ceases to amaze me. There is something quite miraculous about creating a plant from a leaf or a small shoot. There are four types of cutting used in herb growing:

**1** | Softwood cuttings taken in spring – the best way to get a plant to produce successful rooting material is to prune hard in the autumn, which will encourage rapid growth when the temperature rises in the spring. Average rooting time 2–4 weeks.

**2** | Semi hardwood cuttings taken in summer, usually taken from shrub herbs towards the end of the growing season from midsummer to mid-autumn. Average rooting time 4–6 weeks.

**3** | Hardwood cuttings taken in mid- to late autumn. These can take up to one year to root so be patient.

**4** | Root cuttings that can be taken in spring and autumn. This method is suitable for a number of herbs – mint and comfrey are both prime examples. Check the A–Z for more herbs in this category. Average rooting time 2–3 weeks.

If I know I am going to be spending the morning taking cuttings, the evening before I always get everything ready so that I do not have the cutting material waiting and wilting while I assemble all the equipment. My recipe for a good general cutting mix is two parts coir + one part fine bark + one part vermiculite. For more information see the Compost and Growing Mediums section on page 15 because in the A–Z I do change the cutting recipe depending on the herb – *Origanum* (oregano), for example, uses a soil-based compost mixed with perlite.

**CUTTINGS CHECKLIST**

- washed pots, trays or modules
- cutting mix (check A–Z of herbs for guidance)
- hand spray bottle filled with water
- labels and a soft pencil or waterproof pen
- small watering can

*Origanum dictamnus*, Cretan Oregano cuttings

Mint root cuttings

**Right** Cuttings on the propagation bench

### Taking cuttings

The best time of day for selecting the material is in the morning before the sun has started to dry the plant. Choose sturdy shoots with plenty of leaves, approximately 12–15cm (5–6in) in length – some herbs will be shorter so check the A-Z of herbs for guidance. The best results come from non-flowering shoots. Once you have picked the cuttings, place them in a small waterproof bag (it's a great way to re-use the biodegradable plastic bags you get from the supermarket), add a label with the herb name and then close. If it is a hot morning it is worth using a hand mister to wet the inside of the bag to create a humid atmosphere as this will prevent the material from drying out. If you are doing softwood or green shoot cutting you will notice that the stem is much paler than the previous year's growth. The best material is not floppy and has a certain amount of rigidity so that when you pick it the tip stays upright. As soon as you have taken enough material, keep it cool, which will prevent the cutting from drying out; the crisper drawer of the refrigerator is great, especially when you cannot start propagating immediately.

**1** | Fill your modules or small pots with your chosen propagating compost.

**2** | Remove the leaves from the bottom third of the cutting, leaving at least two or three leaves on top with the growing tip. The reason for leaving the leaves is that the plant feeds through them as it sets root.

**3** | Use sharp snips or a knife to remove lower leaves, making sure that you do not tear the stem as torn stems attract disease. A good average length for the final cutting is the growing tip plus a pair of leaves, plus a stem for rooting, which is roughly 10cm (4in).

**4** | Using a sharpened chopstick (this is finer than a bought dibber), make a hole in the compost.

**5** | Using sharp snips or a sharp knife on a ridged surface, cut the stem just below a leaf node. Do not touch this with your fingers. There is no need for rooting hormone if you take cuttings at the right time of year.

**6** | Gently put the cutting into the hole in the compost, keeping the leaves above the surface, then using the chopstick back fill round it so that it is firm and straight.

**7** | Once the tray or pot is finished, label, with the label you created when you took the cutting material. I put two labels in a tray just in case one falls out.

**8** | With a very small watering can water the compost (this will make the compost settle around the cutting).

**9** | Mist the leaves using the spray bottle.

**10** | Softwood cuttings can be rooted in a propagator at 15–18°C (59–64°F), no higher. Alternatively cover the cuttings with a sheet of plastic, this is ideal for semi hardwood and hardwood cuttings.

**11** | When growing cuttings under plastic, each morning remove the plastic sheet and turn it over, checking the compost has not dried out – it needs to be damp but not waterlogged. Before covering hand mist the cuttings.

**12** | In the early evening, especially in late spring when the daytime temperature is rising, check the cuttings, and hand spray with water if required (as number 11).

**13** | Once the cuttings have rooted, remove them from under the plastic sheet or from the propagator if you're using one.

**14** | Grow on until they are fully rooted: if you're using modules, you'll see the roots protruding from the bottom; if you're using small pots you will see that the cutting is growing and putting on new growth. When this happens, tease the cuttings apart and pot up into small pots following the instructions in the A-Z of herbs.

**Top left** Taking thyme cuttings, **top right** *Myrtus communis* subsp. *tarentina* 'Microphylla Variegata' cuttings, **bottom left** Taking thyme cuttings, **bottom right** *Tagetes lucidia*, Winter Tarragon

## Root cuttings

There is something immensely satisfying about propagating plants from root cuttings.

**ROOT CUTTINGS CHECKLIST**

- washed pots, trays or modules
- Cutting compost (check A–Z of herbs for guidance)
- labels and a soft pencil or waterproof pen
- watering can
- cutting material

There are two techniques you can use to take herb root as cuttings: from deep tap roots or the creeping rhizomes. Both produce invasive plants in the garden – the deep tap root will grow from any piece of root that is left in the soil, which is why it is nearly impossible to move comfrey. Mint, which reproduces via its creeping rhizome, is renowned for rampaging around a garden. Please check the individual propagation guidelines in the A–Z of herbs where it will say if root cuttings are possible. Root cuttings can be taken in spring and autumn.

### Slicing of a deep tap root

1 | Wash any excess soil from the root. On a hard clean surface, use a sharp knife to slice the root into neat circles, approximately 1.5–2cm (½–¾in) thick.

2 | Using the standard cutting compost mix, fill your chosen container two-thirds full with the substrate. Make a small hole in the substrate with your finger, drop the cutting in and cover with further substrate to just below the rim of the pot or module. Water in well, label and date.

3 | Put the container somewhere warm, do not let the compost dry out. It should start shooting in 7–10 days depending on light levels.

### Cutting between nodes of a creeping rhizome

1 | Having selected your roots, wash them well to remove excess soil and so that you can see the growing nodes. These nodes are definite swellings in the root, sometimes they have roots to one side, others you can actually see a shoot starting. Using either a sharp knife or sharp scissors, divide the cuttings up so that each piece has a growing node.

2 | Using the cutting compost half-fill a module tray. Then lay the root cuttings on the surface of the substrate. Cover the cuttings with more substrate to just below the rim of the tray. Do not compress the substrate as this could damage the growing node. Water in well, this will adequately compress the compost over the cutting.

3 | Put the container or tray in a warm place, do not let the compost dry out. Shoots will appear in 7–10 days.

*Mentha cervina* rhizomes

## Layering

This is a very simple, old-fashioned method of propagation. It does not require anything other than a healthy plant, which is well established in the garden and has strong growth that either hangs down towards the earth or is touching the earth. This method of propagation encourages the plant to form roots while still attached to the parent plant. If you look closely at shrubby herbs you can quite often see this happening naturally – where the lower branches touch the ground they start to root. All you are doing is enhancing the plant's natural habits. The best time for layering the plant is in the autumn when the soil is warm or in the spring when the soil has started to heat up. Check all round the chosen plant to make sure it is healthy. Check the main stem, making sure it has not been damaged, if it has, it may become diseased before your layer has rooted.

**1** | Choose a strong healthy stem that can touch the ground and remove all the side shoots and leaves for about 30cm (12in) for large shrubs so the stem is bare where it touches the soil. For smaller herbs like *Thymus*, thyme, remove only 10–15cm (4–6in).

**2** | Prepare the ground where the stem is going to be growing for the next year. Dig it over well, removing all weeds and stones. For woody herbs like *Salvia*, sage, feed with fertiliser to give the cutting extra nutrients. However with *Thymus*, thyme, this is not as crucial as drainage is more important, so it is worth adding fine grit or sharp sand to the prepared site.

**3** | Remove a slither along the side of the stem that is going to touch the earth. Peg the cutting into the soil. Some old books describe having to make trenches to put your layering in; this is fine for trees or large shrubs, but for herbs, where space is a premium and the stems are never that thick, you will find this method more than adequate.

**4** | Cover the cutting with the soil, leaving the growing tip exposed. Herbs like *Thymus*, thyme, will root within one growing season, for example, if you make the layer in spring you will be able to separate it from the parent plant by the autumn. If this is the case, do not replant in the garden, instead remove the layer and pot up. Winter the cutting in a cold frame and plant out in the following spring.

## Division

Dividing established herbaceous herbs is a very useful way not only of producing more stock but also of keeping the plant healthy. Quite often herbaceous plants become invasive and as the plant ages the centre can die out. Division allows you to control both these problems. You can divide plants in the early autumn when they start to die back or the early spring, before they grow away too much. If you leave it too late in the spring you could inhibit flowering. Refer to the A–Z of herbs to find out if your chosen herb likes to be divided in the spring or autumn.

**1** | Dig up the plants that are to be divided in spring or autumn.

**2** | Either shake the excess soil off the root prior to dividing or hold the root ball under a running tap to loosen the soil.

**3** | Gently ease the plant apart, you can choose if it is one or two plants or even more if you want to plant it around the garden.

**4** | Replant the divisions into a prepared site as soon as possible to prevent them drying out. Always water in well, even if it is raining. Divisions can also be potted up either for insurance against bad winter weather or for creating a container plant. Use a soil-based potting compost.

# Planning the herb garden

The first principle of a good garden is to work with the environment. Every garden is unique. When looking over your neighbour's wall you may wonder why they can grow certain plants, yet you can't. Maybe your garden is in the lee of their house and therefore does not get as much rain. Or it could be exposed to a prevailing wind that dries the soil. Alternatively, the place you live in might be prone to excessively wet conditions, which are leaching all the nutrients from the soil.

Before you start planning a new garden it is a very good idea to walk all the way around the existing garden noting its basic plan – the weeds, native trees and shrubs that are growing well and happily, as this is a good indicator of soil type. Horsetail and comfrey indicate damp, heavy soil; rhododendrons and azaleas point to acid soil; while scabious and beech trees mean the soil will be chalky. Note where the sun is first thing in the morning and watch it throughout the day. Note the shady points – these could again be the result of next-door's water butt, garage or tree. If there is a tree, where do its roots spread, for not only do they cast shade, they draw water and nutrients from the soil. Where is the hottest part of the garden, as this is good for Mediterranean culinary herbs. If your garden has not been touched for a number of years, see if there are any dips or raised areas where there could be old paths. Visit your local authority and ask to see the old maps of the area. When I checked the garden at the Herb Farm, I found that the old ordnance survey maps called the fields either side of the cottage 'clay fields'. This has proven to be very apt and highly relevant. Ask your neighbours what they have had success with and, if you get on well with them, what they have failed with. Armed with all this information you will have the necessary knowledge to plan a thriving garden.

## What condition is your soil in?

The easiest way you can tell what condition your soil is in is by picking up a handful and examining how it forms in your hand. Does it fall through your fingers? Is it a big lump? Does it have large pieces of flint? Smell it: good soil has a sweet, warm earthy smell. Poor soil either has no smell or smells sour. A good healthy soil is teeming with life and it should have lots of worm channels. These channels not only show that it is well balanced, it also indicates that the soil is not compacted.

Good plant growth is not only dependent on how much you feed the soil. It is also dependent on the structure. Sandy soil is often low in nutrients because the rain permeates the soil and washes them away. Clay soil can be rich in plant food but, because it is heavy and waterlogged, it only produces small plants because the roots are not growing well. Improving the structure of the soil with bulky organic matter will allow sandy soil to retain water and air to permeate clay soil. Either way, it will give you healthier crops.

The pH of the soil refers to its acidity or alkalinity. It is a vital factor in a plant's ability to obtain all types of plant foods and essential chemicals via its root system. For example, an alkaline soil can produce stunted plants with yellowing leaves. This is because the minerals, especially iron, have become locked in the soil. At a neutral pH of 7, most of the essential chemicals and plant foods become available to a plant, which means it will be healthy.

To test your soil, buy a soil-testing kit from any good garden centre or store. The majority of amateur soil-testing kits are very simple and rely on colour rather than a numerical scale. Acid soils turn the solution yellow-orange, a neutral soil will turn it green, while alkaline will cause it to be dark green. Most herbs will tolerate a pH of between 6.5 and 7.5, which is fairly neutral. There are always exceptions: *Rumex scutatus* (sorrel) will tolerate acid soils and *Sambucus nigra* (elder), alkaline. The following four basic soil types (overleaf) are the most suitable for growing herbs.

**Right** Herb garden with Poppies, Cardoons and Atriplex

**Clay pH 6.5**
This soil is composed of tiny particles that stick together when wet and make the soil heavy and difficult for the roots to penetrate. In summer, when dry, it sets rock hard. Even though it can be rich in plant nutrients, because of its characteristics it is improved by working in extra well-rotted leaf mould or compost. This will improve the structure and allow young plants to become more easily established.

**Chalk pH 8.5**
This soil is light with lumps of flint or chalk, well drained and often shallow. It has a high pH making it very alkaline. It is possible to increase the nutrient content by adding loads of compost but it is difficult to lower the pH. A large amount of herbs will tolerate chalk however; considering the characteristics of this soil, to give it depth and help it retain moisture it may be easier to grow the herbs in a raised bed.

**Loam pH 5.5-8.5**
This is often considered the ultimate garden soil in which most herbs will grow. There are various types of loam depending on the content of clay or sand. A sandy loam is the best soil for growing the largest range of herbs as it is rarely waterlogged in winter and dry in summer and it is naturally high in nutrients.

**Sand pH 4.5**
This soil feels rough and gritty when handled. It is very free draining, which means that the plants' nutrients are quickly washed away. A plus point to this soil is that it is quick to warm up in the spring so sowing and planting can be started earlier than in clay soils. To help it retain moisture it needs to be fed in winter with leaf mould to retain moisture and with well-rotted manure for an extra source of nutrients.

**Left** Herb garden with Blackcurrant Sage and Lemon Bergamot

## Preparation

Before you start planting a new herb garden it is very important to prepare the ground well by eradicating all the weeds, especially perennial ones. A weed is basically an invasive plant in the wrong position. Sometimes before you dig it up, it is worth trying to identify it as it may just be a herb that has self-seeded in the wrong place. Once you have checked what is growing and if there is anything you want to save, cover the area with cardboard, this will block out the light and stop any weed seed germinating; it also gives you a surface to cover with a good mulch of well-rotted compost or well-rotted manure. The worms will then munch through the cardboard to the compost, and from the compost to the soil, and they will do all the work for you in preparing the soil by aerating, moving and feeding it. When it is time to start planting use a wooden plank from which to dig the planting hole. Do not stand or walk on the soil as compacted soil has little air which makes it difficult for the roots to penetrate.

## History of a herb garden

There are historical records showing that herbs have been cultivated for thousands of years. Not only were they used for medicine and as a food, but they were also planted near or around temples, as they were required for ritual and worship. *Chamaemelum nobile* (chamomile) was identified by its pollen in the tomb of the Egyptian King Ramses II who died in 1237 BC. By the 3rd century BC practical market gardens had become established, combining herbs and vegetables, usually with a well or pond central to the garden. By 1066 European monasteries were the custodians of the medicinal herbs. The gardens within the monasteries were laid out in simple rectangles, one of which was a dedicated physic garden, and was situated next to the infirmary. After the dissolution of the monasteries by Henry VIII in 1509, herbs became the province of the lady of the manor house and by Elizabethan times (1558) herb gardens had become very formal. The first botanic garden was constructed at Oxford University in 1621, linking medicine and botany for the study of medicine. The Chelsea Physic Garden in London was started by the Society of Apothecaries in 1673, and it still retains the name and the formality of design. By the 18th century and with the advent of the industrial revolution and the small back-to-back town houses, herbs left the town and become part of the cottage garden within the border and in the vegetable plot. Today herbs are grown both in the vegetable plot and within the formal herb garden, the modern design of which often reflects much of their history.

## Herb garden styles

### Physic

The design of this herb garden is influenced by the old monastic gardens. The beds are rectanglular in shape and divided by grassy paths, giving easy access to each bed. It was usual that each bed either comprised of a plant family, i.e. *Lamiaceae*, or plants that were specifically for healing parts of the body, i.e. head, heart, circulation. At the botanic garden in Edinburgh there are four beds: one for the early herbalists, for example, Pliny and Dioscorides; the second bed focuses on the 16th and 17th centuries, the third bed the 18th and 19th centuries and the final bed celebrates the herbs from the 20th and for the 21st centuries which includes such herbs as *Chrysanthemum parthenium*, feverfew; *Melissa officinalis*, lemon balm; *Salvia rosmarinus*, rosemary and *Ginkgo biloba*, maidenhair tree.

### Formal knot

In the early 16th century, knot gardens became very fashionable. The basic feature of knot planting is that regular geometric and symmetrical patterns are picked out by evergreen herbs, such as *Santolina chamaecyparissus*, cotton lavender; *Thymus vulgaris,* thyme; *Hyssopus officinalis*, hyssop or *Teucrium* x *lucidrys*, hedge germander, planted in continuous ribbons. An 'open knot' was filled with flowers, a 'closed knot' was a more complicated pattern with no flowers but sand or brick dust to enhance the pattern. *Buxus sempervirens*, box, was not introduced as a hedging plant until the 17th century and is not commonly used.

### Culinary

Over 400 years ago herbs were a staple of daily life. At that time the word 'herb' had many different meanings. Vegetables were known as pot herbs because they gave bulk to the cooking pot. There were salad (salet) herbs and sweet herbs that were used for flavouring, and simples, which were the medicinal herbs. The culinary herb garden has evolved from being primarily a vegetable and herb garden combined to a garden that now contains just evergreen and annual herbs. The design of this ensures that the plants are easily accessible to the cook, either by the use of stepping stones or narrow beds.

## The herb garden at home

The joy of designing a herb garden is that there are herbs for every situation in the garden and in the home. So, whether you are planning to convert the whole of your garden to herbs or you want to plant up a window box, it is well worth taking a bit of time to work out what you want to use the herbs for. Do you want to be able to pick herbs all year round for use in the kitchen, in the home or to take medicinally, or do you simply want annuals for salads? Having decided how you wish to use the herbs, before planning or planting it is essential to find out how your chosen herbs grow. For example, how tall do they get? Angelica can reach 2.5m (8ft 2in). How far do they spread? Mint could take over a window box in one season. Are they short-lived? Salad rocket is only productive for a few months. By their very nature herbs are survivors, not only they will spread, they are renowned for self-seeding – borage is a classic for doing this. All the information on specific herbs can be found in the A–Z, which begins on page 40. Also consider when planting, which herbs go well together, which are good companion plants, and which attract birds, bees or butterflies. Think of your ecosystem: what insects, animals or predators do you wish to attract to the garden to maintain the garden's ecosystem. If you are revamping an existing herb garden do not be afraid to replace old plants that have become woody and are now no longer productive. Equally, if you do not like a certain herb, remove it so that you are creating more space for herbs you do like and which will be useful to you and the home. If you have time, go and see some established herb gardens – The Herb Society is always a good source of information as to which gardens are open in your area. Visit flower shows and look at the show gardens. These gardens quite often have novel ideas regarding edging, hedging and structure plants. Armed with all this information, the only other choices left are when are you going to start and where.

## The planting plan

I have found that the time I take in creating a planting plan is never wasted. It not only gets my thoughts about what I want in the garden clear, it also makes sure that I do not overstock the garden, giving the plants a chance to grow and show off their shape, flowers and/or produce enough leaves so that one can create a feast. Here and overleaf are a few ideas of some basic garden designs that will enable you to create your own herb garden.

| Symbol | Herb | |
|---|---|---|
| | *Amaranthus tricolor* 'Red Army' | Amaranth 'Red Army' |
| | *Allium schoenoprasum* | Chives |
| | *Allium tuberosum* | Chives Garlic |
| | *Aloysia citrodora* | Lemon Verbena |
| | *Anethum graveolens* | Dill |
| | *Artemisia dracunculus* | Tarragon French |
| | *Borago officinalis* | Borage |
| | *Calendula officinalis* | Calendula |
| | *Foeniculum vulgare* 'Purpureum' | Fennel Bronze |
| | *Hesperis matronalis* | Rocket Sweet |
| | *Hyssopus officinalis* subsp. *aristatus* | Hyssop Rock |
| | *Laurus nobilis* | Bay |
| | *Lavandula x christiana* | Lavender Christiana |
| | *Lavandula angustifolia* 'Miss Muffet' | Lavender Miss Muffett |
| | *Melissa officinalis* | Lemon Balm |
| | *Mentha spicata* 'Moroccan' | Mint Moroccan |
| | *Mentha spicata* 'Tashkent' | Mint Tashkent |
| | *Mentha x piperita f. citrata* 'Chocolate' | Mint Chocolate Peppermint |
| | *Mentha x piperita f. citrata* 'Swiss Ricola' | Mint Swiss |

| Symbol | Herb | |
|---|---|---|
| | *Mertensia maritima* | Oyster Plant |
| | *Ocimum basilicum* 'Horpha Nanum' | Basil Thai |
| | *Ocimum x africanum* | Basil Lemon, Thai Lemon |
| | *Origanum vulgare* 'Nanum' | Oregano Dwarf |
| | *Origanum vulgare* 'Aureum' | Oregano Gold |
| | *Origanum vulgare* subps. *hirtum* 'Greek' | Oregano Greek |
| | *Persicaria odorata* | Vietnamese Coriander |
| | *Petroselinum crispum* | Parsley Curly |
| | *Petroselinum crispum* 'French' | Parsley French |
| | *Salvia lavandulifolia* | Sage, narrow leaf |
| | *Salvia Rosmarinus* (Prostrata Group) | Rosemary prostrate |
| | *Salvia viridis* | Sage Painted |
| | *Thymus* 'Culinary Lemon' | Thyme Lemon |
| | *Thymus* 'Fragrantissimus' | Thyme Orange Scented |
| | *Thymus* 'Jekka' | Thyme Jekka |
| | *Thymus* 'Silver Posie' | Thyme Silver Posie |
| | *Thymus vulgaris* 'Compactus' | Thyme Compact |
| | *Tropaeolum majus* 'Empress of India' | Nasturtium Empress of India |

Culinary herb garden

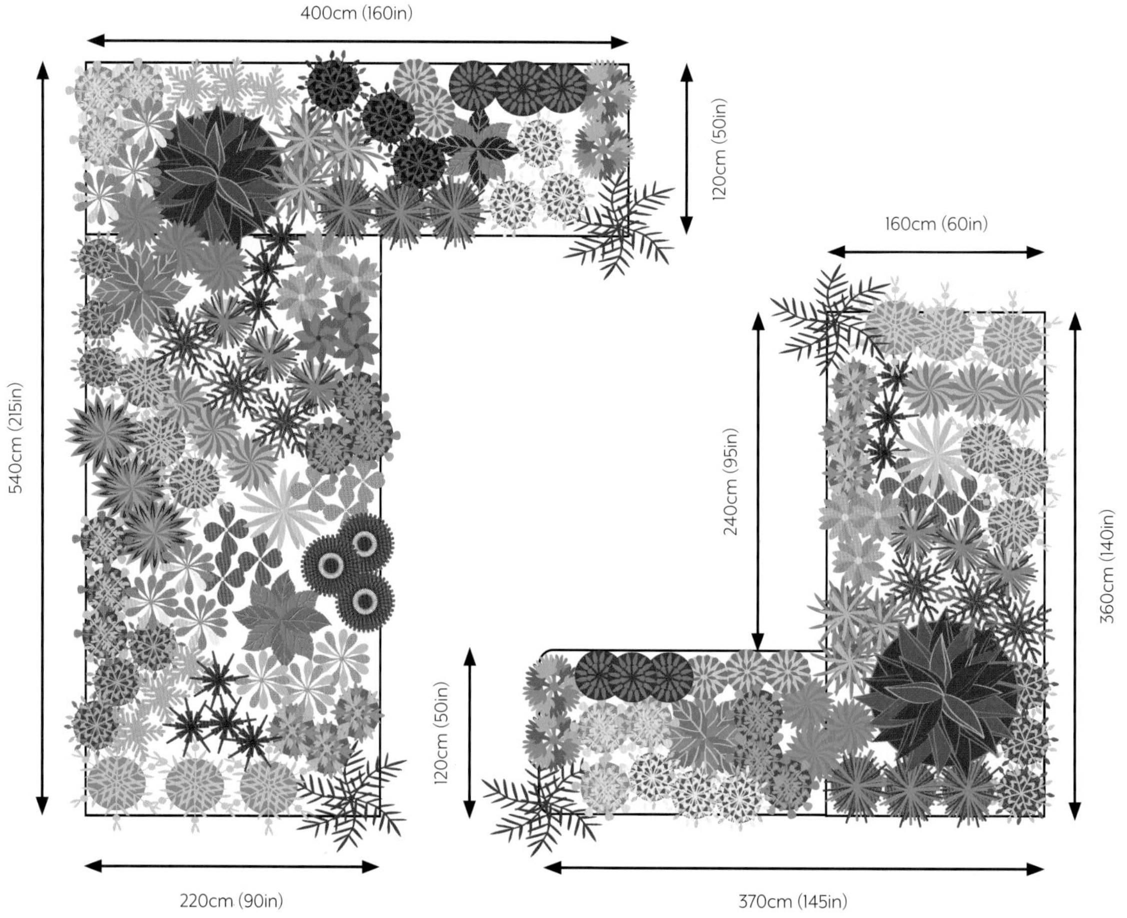

400cm (160in)

120cm (50in)

160cm (60in)

540cm (215in)

240cm (95in)

360cm (140in)

120cm (50in)

220cm (90in)

370cm (145in)

Rectangle culinary herb garden 250cm x 150cm (100in x 60in)

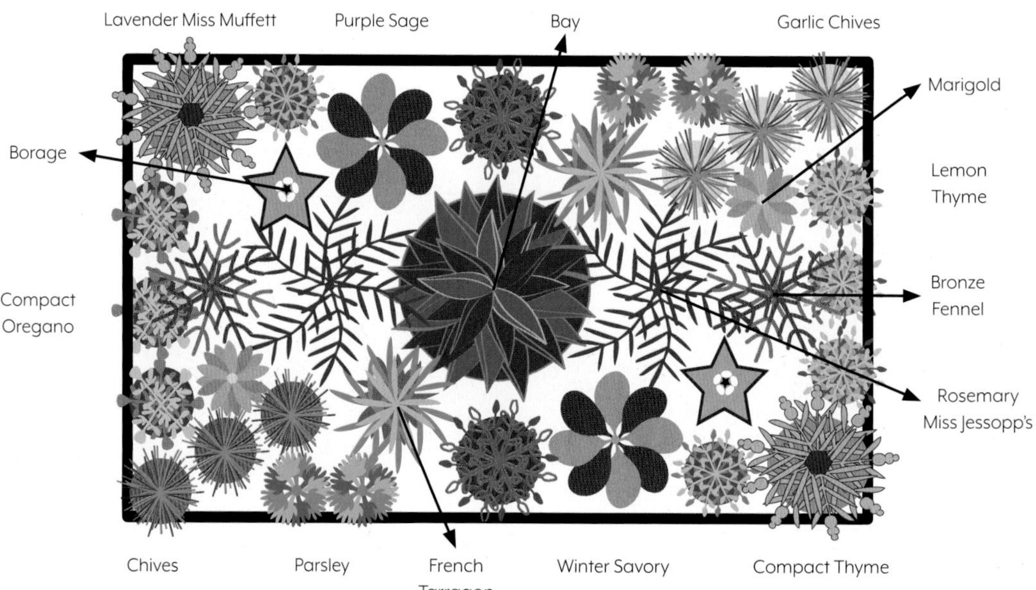

The square culinary herb garden
200cm x 200cm (80in x 80in)

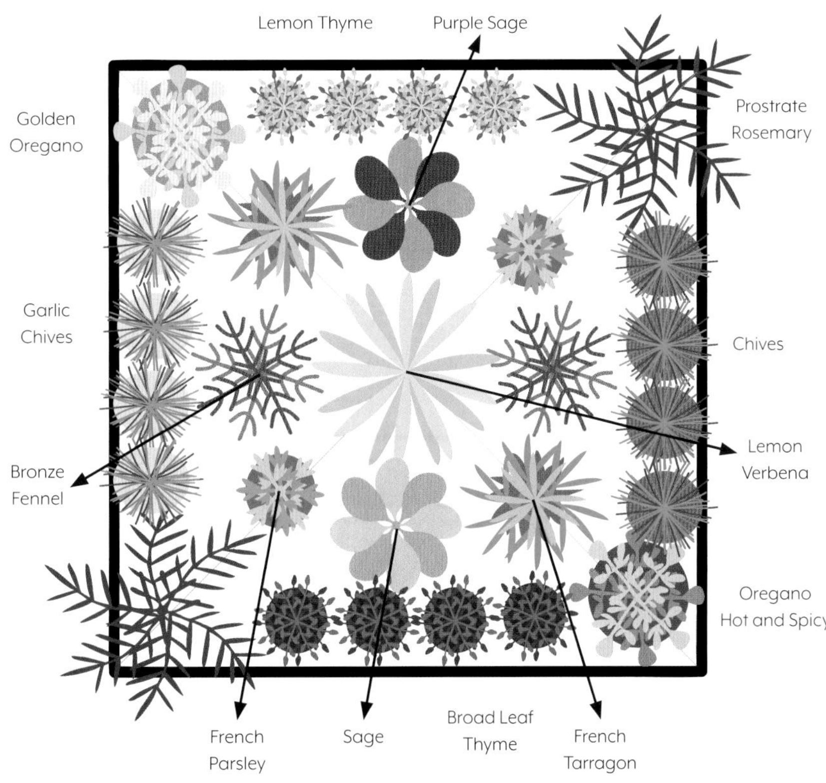


Balcony herb garden, pots and raised bed
120cm x 275cm
(50in x 110in)

## Growing in containers

For those of you who do not have a garden but can grow in containers, you have the freedom to control the soil and the herbs' position in your garden. Another major plus is you can put a few by the door to your house or flat so you do not need to rush down to the garden to pick your favourites for use in the kitchen. Most herbs adapt to being containerised. Check the relevant herb in the A–Z section of this book.

## Key points for growing herbs in containers

I know I am repeating myself but it is worth highlighting a few crucial points about growing herbs in containers.

**1 | Drainage**
Make sure that your chosen container has adequate drainage holes. It is well worth adding broken terracotta or large stones to the bottom of the container for extra drainage and to stop the root ball sitting in water. Also, some bricks or extra stones for the container to sit on in winter to increase the drainage.

**2 | Compost**
As the soil is the engine of the garden, the compost is the engine of the container so do not skimp on quality as the plant has to live in a restricted environment. You will note that in the majority of occasions I recommend a soil-based potting compost, often I will recommend adding horticultural sand or horticultural grit, especially if they need extra drainage.

**3 | Fertiliser**
We give all our container plants a good feed with a liquid fertiliser every Friday. I am particularly fond of a liquid seaweed fertiliser, or a comfrey fertiliser rather than a manufactured one as it is not the nitrogen the plant needs but the minerals.

Four pots of herbs, at the back *Punica granatum*, left *Chamaemelum nobile*, right *Thymus serpyllum* 'Elfin', front *Sempervirens*

**4 | Water**
This is the most difficult job on my farm. Everyone thinks that watering is easy – it is not. You must use your eyes and feel the weight of the plant, over- and under-watering will cause both stress and damage to your plant. How often a container plant needs water is dependent on the size and type of the plant and the size and type of the container. For example, a terracotta pot dries out more quickly than plastic, however it is better for the root ball as it has better aeration and drainage. Never let container plants totally dry out as once the compost is totally dry it is very difficult to get it to take up water again. Equally, do not mother the plant and over-water. Try not to water the foliage – water underneath directly onto the compost.

**Right** Mixed pot of herbs
**Overleaf** *Agastache rugosa*, Korean Mint

# The Herbs

# Achillea millefolium

**This invasive herb, which many consider a gardener's nightmare, is amazingly useful. Not only can it stop a cut bleeding, but also, when the leaves are added to the compost heap, it can also speed up decomposition. It is known as a 'plant doctor' because when planted near a poorly plant, the secretion from its roots will help to heal the plant as well as give it strength to fight off disease.**

*Achillea millefolium*, Yarrow

**WARNING**
Not to be used during pregnancy. Yarrow's leaves and flowers can cause minor skin irritation, which lasts for a few minutes.

## History

Yarrow is steeped in fame and fiction. The stems were used by the druids to divine seasonal weather, while the stalks were used in China to foretell the future. The Ancient Greeks used it to control haemorrhages and heal cuts, which led to it being known as the carpenter's herb.

## Species

*Achillea ageratum*, English Mace, Sweet Yarrow
Hardy, H4 (USDA 8,9), herbaceous perennial. Height: up to 45cm (18in) in flower; spread: up to 60cm (24in) in light soil. Flat clusters of small, creamy, daisy-like flowers in summer. Aromatic, mid-green, pinnately divided leaves, with toothed edges.

*Achillea millefolium*, Yarrow
Hardy, H6 (USDA 6,7), herbaceous perennial. Height 30–90cm (12–35in) in flower; spread: up to 60cm (24in). Small white to pale pink flowers grouped in flat clusters in midsummer. Green, aromatic, feathery foliage.

## Propagation

**Seeds:** sow yarrow seeds in the autumn into prepared seed trays or modules using a standard seed compost. Place the container in a cold frame or cold greenhouse for the winter. Germination is erratic. Plant young plants out in the spring 20–30cm (8–12in) apart. This plant can be invasive so I do not advise sowing seeds directly into the garden. If you do have yarrow growing in the garden and you wish for more plants, check in early autumn or spring for self-seeded seedlings which transplant easily and can be wintered in a cold frame or cold greenhouse. English mace does not set seed in the northern hemisphere.

**Division:** yarrow produces loads of creeping root stock. Divide mature plants in spring or early autumn which will enable you to keep yarrow in check and stop it running riot through the garden.

English mace produces controllable clumps which can be simply divided in the spring or early autumn by digging up the clump and dividing it into small clumps, which can then be replanted into prepared sites in the garden. Alternatively, you can break off small offsets and grow them on in small pots filled with a loam-based potting compost.

## Pests and diseases

The only pests that can be a nuisance are aphid, green and black fly. To be honest I do not spray these plants; if it is a bad infestation, I cut the plant back, the new growth comes through clean. For more information on these pests see page 267.

## How and where to grow

Yarrow, being a native herb, and often classed as a wild plant or weed, is far better as part of a wild, rewilding garden, where it blends in well with poppies. Both these herbs are very adaptable, they survive in most soils and are both drought tolerant. Top tip: to stop the yarrow self-seeding cut back as soon as the flowers start to turn brown.

English mace looks lovely when planted mid-border – the creamy flowers are most graceful. Leave access so you can harvest the leaves for use in the spring.

## Growing in containers

Both these herbs can be grown happily in containers; use a soil-based potting compost. As a native herb, yarrow looks lovely when combined with other UK natives, such as poppies, cornflowers and wood sage. English mace on the other hand looks great with bronze fennel and garlic chives. If you are using either of these herbs in the kitchen they will need to be fed with a seaweed liquid fertiliser weekly from spring until summer to keep the leaves soft and succulent.

## Yearly maintenance

**Spring:** divide established clumps.

**Summer:** cut back as soon as the flowers start to fade to prevent self-seeding.

**Autumn:** sow yarrow seeds; divide established plants.

**Winter:** no need to protect.

## Harvesting and storing

**Leaves:** harvest the young leaves of both herbs in spring. To preserve them, chop them finely, and freeze them in an ice-cube tray with no added water; this will give you good portion sizes for use later in the season. Harvest yarrow leaves to dry for medicinal use before flowering in spring.

**Flowers:** harvest yarrow flowers just as they open, use fresh sparingly and for drying. English mace flowers taste horrid!

## Culinary uses

**Leaves:** yarrow has recently had a resurgence due to foraging. Choose small, new growth leaves that have a good green colour – they have a light, warm, mild flavour that's great in salads and especially lovely with sorrel.

English mace leaves have a warm, light, spicy flavour. Pick new growth in the spring before flowering. Use the leaves with egg dishes, cheese, pasta and salads.

## Medicinal uses

Yarrow is renowned for its properties in staunching blood. Simple crush the leaves to release its tannins then apply to the wound which will stop the bleeding. English mace has no medicinal uses of which I am aware.

# Agastache foeniculum (Pursh) Kuntze

**This stunning member of the *Lamiaceae* family is a firm favourite of mine and of all forms of bumblebee. Not only does it look beautiful in summer with its spires of violet blue flowers, it is also a wonderful source of seed in the early autumn for the charms of gold finches. And as if that is not enough, the leaves are a culinary delight; their minty, anise flavour is delicious. This lovely herb is often confused with Hyssop, *Hyssopus officinalis* (see page 142).**

*Agastache foeniculum* (Pursh) Kuntze, Anise Hyssop

## History

Anise hyssop is a native of the North American great plains, where it was used by the Native Americans as both a pot herb and medicinal herb to treat coughs and fevers.

## Species

*Agastache foeniculum* (Pursh) Kuntze, Anise Hyssop
Hardy, H3 (USDA 9), herbaceous perennial, grown as an annual in cooler or damp climates. Height: up to 70cm (27in) when in flower; spread: 30cm (12in). Erect long spikes of violet/blue flowers in summer. Aromatic, oval, toothed, mid-green leaves. The leaves have a mild anise, minty flavour.

*Agastache rugosa*, Korean Mint, Huo Xiang
Hardy, H3 (USDA 9), herbaceous perennial. Height: up to 1m (3ft) when in flower; spread: 30cm (12in). Lovely mauve/purple flower spikes in summer. Distinctly mint-scented, mid-green, oval, pointed leaves that can be used in cooking. Makes a good tea for hangovers.

## Propagation

**Seeds:** both anise hyssop and Korean mint can be grown from seed sown in early spring in modules or seed trays filled with a standard seed compost. Place under protection at 20°C (68°F); germination will take place in 7–10 days. Alternatively sow seeds in late spring into prepared open ground, when the air temperature does not go below 10°C (50°F) at night; germination will occur in 2–3 weeks. They will flower in the first year.

**Cuttings:** softwood cuttings can be taken in early summer and put into small pots or modules filled with three parts seed compost and one part perlite. After they have rooted, pot up, and winter in a cold frame or cold greenhouse.

**Division:** established plants can be divided in the late spring of the second or third year established. This is a good method as not only does it keep the plant healthy, it also increases the stock for the garden or enables you to pot it up for a container display using a soil-based compost.

## Pests and diseases

As anise hyssop is an aromatic plant, pests keep their distance. It rarely suffers from disease, with the exception of seedlings which can 'damp off' when over-watered.

## How and where to grow

Both anise hyssop and Korean mint like to be planted in a warm sunny site in any well-drained soil. These herbs can withstand very dry conditions, however, they are not very tolerant of clay soils – if you have these you might find it best to grow them as an annual.

## Growing in containers

Both have long flowering spikes so choose a container that will not topple over when they are in flower. Use three parts soil-based compost mixed with one part horticultural grit, as this will prevent them sulking in a wet winter. Lift the pots off the ground in winter and place on bricks or stones to aid drainage. They both look lovely combined with bronze fennel and rosemary

## Yearly maintenance

**Spring:** sow seeds; divide second or third year plants.

**Summer:** take softwood or semi-ripe cuttings in late summer; cut back after flowering to encourage a second crop of leaves to use in the kitchen.

**Autumn:** protect young plants from frost; cut back as late as possible so the birds can feast on the seed.

**Winter:** lift pots on to bricks to aid drainage.

## Harvesting and storing

**Leaves:** harvest the leaves before the plant flowers to use fresh, conserve in vinegar or to make a delightful cordial.

**Flowers:** pick the flower spikes, just as the flowers open; gently remove the small individual florets before using. Both species taste delicious.

## Culinary uses

**Anise hyssop**: the leaves can be used to make refreshing tea. Like borage, they can be added to summer fruit cups. Equally they can be chopped and used as a seasoning to accompany pork dishes or savoury rice. Always add towards the end of cooking as the leaves do not like to be cooked for too long.

Flowers can be added to fruit and rice salads and cordials, giving a lovely splash of colour and flavour.

**Korean mint:** the leaves of this plant have a light peppermint flavour and make a very refreshing tea, which is said to be extremely good first thing in the morning after a night on the town. The leaves are also good chopped up in salads. Again, these leaves do not like to be cooked for any length of time so add them at the end of cooking. The flowers look very attractive and tasty scattered over a pasta salad.

## Medicinal uses

Anise hyssop is used for coughs, shortness of breath and wheezing. A tea made from the leaves is said to be good for easing morning sickness. Native Americans use an oil made from the leaves to kill lice; they also mix the green leaves with vinegar to heal cuts and wounds. In Traditional Chinese Medicine, Korean mint is included in the list of 50 fundamental herbs and is used to treat anxiety, nausea, infections, cholera and many other ailments.

# Allium

**The *Alliaceae* family is an essential part of any herb garden. Chives are one of the first herbs I grew in my own garden and they have featured in many of our gold medal RHS Chelsea Flower Show displays. Not only do they herald spring as they push their way through the soil with their bright green cylindrical leaves, they also flower in May. Over the years I have collected many different forms of chive from all around the world.**

*Allium fistulosum*, Welsh Onion

*Allium schoenoprasum*, Chives

## History

The generic name *Allium* is the Latin word for garlic, the species is *sativum*, so *Allium sativum* means cultivated garlic. One of my favourite bits of historic knowledge is that the Egyptians swore their oaths while invoking onion and garlic, which indicates that they considered these plants sacred, and they laid onions on graves in honour of the dead as onion skins symbolised eternity. Another delightful historic fact is that in medieval agricultural books, garlic was burnt in the garden to drive away caterpillars and hung in trees to keep away the birds.

## Species

*Allium fistulosum*, Welsh Onion, Japanese Leek
Hardy, H5 (USDA 7,8), perennial. Height and spread: 50cm (20in). Large, creamy-white, globe-shaped flowers in the second year. Hollow, cylindrical mid-green leaves. Whole plant is edible.

*Allium nutans*, Siberian Chives
Hardy, H6 (USDA 6,7), perennial. Height: 40cm (16in); spread: 15cm (6in). Blue/mauve star-shaped flowers. Flat, solid, narrow, lance-shaped green leaves that have a mild onion/garlic flavour.

*Allium sativum*, Garlic
Hardy, H5 (USDA 7,8), perennial, grown as an annual. Height: 40–60cm (16–24in); spread 10cm (4in). White or pink flowers in summer. Flat, lance-shaped green leaves. The bulb is made of several cloves that can vary in colour from white to pink. The strongest member of the onion family both medicinally and in the kitchen, where it is king.

*Allium schoenoprasum*, Chives
Hardy, H5 (USDA 7,8), herbaceous perennial. Height and spread: 30cm (12in). Purple globe-shaped flowers. Narrow, cylindrical mid-green leaves.

*Allium tuberosum*, Garlic Chives, Chinese Chives
Hardy, H5 (USDA 7,8), perennial. Height: up to 60cm (24in); spread: 30cm (12in). White star-shaped flowers. Flat, solid, narrow, lance-shaped green leaves with a mild garlic flavour.

*Allium ursinum*, Wild Garlic, Ramsons
Hardy, H6 (USDA 6,7), herbaceous perennial. Height: up to 45cm (18in); spread: 60cm (24in). Clusters of star-shaped flowers in late spring. Elliptical mid-green leaves. Plant in a moist, fertile soil in semi-shade. Sow seeds in autumn. Divide rhizomes in autumn. Eat leaves before flowering. Flowers are edible.

## Propagation

**Seeds:** *Alliums* are easily grown from seed. Seeds can be sown in early spring in prepared modules filled with a standard seed compost. Place under cover at 18° C (64°F). Germination takes 10–20 days. Alternatively, sow seeds in late spring into prepared open ground, when the air temperature at night remains above 7°C (45°F). Germination takes 2–3 weeks. Thin seedlings to 25cm (10in) apart. Wild garlic seeds are best sown in the autumn and the seeds wintered in a cold frame or cold greenhouse.

**Cloves:** it is quicker to grow garlic from saved cloves from the previous crop than from seed, the reason being that when grown from seed it takes two years to make a bulb. The ideal time to plant the cloves is in winter as garlic needs a cold, dormant period of 1–2 months to yield a decent-sized bulb. There is a very apt saying: 'plant on the shortest day, harvest on the longest day'.

**Division:** established clumps of chives and Welsh onion bulbs can be lifted in spring and divided. These clumps are made up of small bulbils. They should be split into groups of 6–10 bulbils or 3 bulbs in the case of the Welsh onion and replanted in the garden 15cm (6in) apart into soil that has had a generous feed of compost or well-rotted manure. Divide the rhizomes of wild garlic in the autumn, replanting in a prepared site.

## Pests and diseases

One of the most annoying pests is green fly and/or black fly depending on the season, because the flies attack the crown of small bulbs, especially chives. To get rid of aphids, spray with a horticultural soft soap weekly until they give up and move out.

*Allium* leaf miner can be a real nuisance as it loves onions, chives and garlic. You will notice a line of white dots on the stems which is where the fly has punctured the stem and laid its eggs. This develops into a headless maggot which tunnels through the stems. The pupae then embed themselves in the stems and bulbs, which causes rot in the autumn. Burn infected plants. The best control is an insect-proof mesh and crop rotation.

A cool, wet autumn may produce ideal conditions for downy mildew – the leaves will become velvety and die back from the tips. This is common in poorly ventilated polytunnels. Dig up the infected plants, cut off 90 per cent of the leaves, leaving about 2cm (¾in) of growth, split and re-pot.

Many *Alliums* suffer from 'rust'. You will notice orange/brown dots appearing on the green stems. As this is a virus it is essential to cut back the growth to 4cm (1 ½in) above the ground and burn it; do not compost. If it is very bad remove the plant and burn. For more information on pests and diseases, see pages 266–277.

## How and where to grow

Most of the *Allium* family are pretty tolerant regarding soil and position but produce the best growth in a rich, moist soil in a fairly sunny position. If the soil is poor and lacking nutrients, alliums will turn yellow followed by brown at the tips. Plant at a distance of 15cm (6in) from other plants.

In the spring, keep newly transplanted plants well watered and in the summer make sure that alliums do not dry out, because the leaves will quickly shrivel up. In the autumn, when chives die back, it is worth digging up a clump, potting them in a soil-based potting compost and placing the plant somewhere warm, with good light to force them for a winter cutting.

I always give the area I have chosen to plant the garlic crop a good feed of well-rotted compost in late autumn prior to planting in December. Save the healthiest plumpest bulb from your summer crop, divide into cloves and plant vertically with the flattened base at the bottom, twice the depth of the clove with at least 2.5cm (1in) of soil above the tip and 10cm (4in) apart. It is better to use a dibber rather than shove the clove into the soil as this can inhibit root growth and damage the clove. Lift the bulbs in the summer.

## Growing in containers

Garlic can be grown in a container and/or window boxes. Plant the same way as those planted in the ground (see previous page) using a good soil-based compost and do not allow the compost to totally dry out. Lift in the summer. I find that I cannot resist the garlic leaves, I use them in salads, stir-fry dishes, and on jacket potatoes.

All chives grow well in pots or on a windowsill. They flourish in a window box if it is partially shaded. The plant needs plenty of water and occasional liquid feed. Chives can easily be grown on a patio although their fragrance is not particularly attractive and as a pot plant, it needs an enormous quantity of water to stay green and succulent.

An important point to remember is that because they are bulbs, chives need some top growth for strengthening and regeneration so do not cut away all the leaves. They must also be allowed to die back in winter if you wish them to return the following season. Because chives die right back into the ground in winter, it is worth digging up a clump in the autumn, potting them into a rich mix of compost and placing the pot somewhere warm, with good light to force them for a winter cutting. They will need a good long rest after forcing so once finished put the pot into a cold frame or cold greenhouse until spring, then they can be planted out in the garden.

## Yearly maintenance

**Spring:** clear the soil around emerging established alliums, put a ring of bark and/or cinders around each clump to prevent onion fly from laying its eggs. Feed with liquid fertiliser if you have not given the soil a good mulch of well-rotted compost in winter. Sow seeds.

**Summer:** harvest the flowers of chives and Welsh onion. Once flowering has finished, cut the whole clump of chives back to 6cm (2 ½in) above the ground. Give the whole plant a generous liquid feed. You will have a new crop of fresh leaves within three weeks. Harvest and dry the garlic bulbs.

**Autumn:** prepare the site for garlic planting. Dig up a small clump of chives, pot into good potting compost and bring inside for forcing for use in the kitchen through the winter. Sow wild garlic seeds or divided established plants.

**Winter:** cut forced chives and feed regularly. Feed established clumps, which will have died back into the ground, with well-rotted manure. Plant garlic cloves.

## Harvesting and storing

**Leaves:** cut fresh leaves of garlic using scissors in early spring, and Welsh onion and chives from early spring to mid-autumn. You can cut the chives hard back to 5cm (2in) above the ground up to four times a year to maintain a supply of fresh succulent leaves. However, if you do this you will forego the flowers. The leaves can be refrigerated in a bag to retain crispness and will last for about 5 days. Alternatively, the chopped leaves can be frozen in ice-cube trays, which make ideal portion sizes, or they can be preserved and frozen as a herb butter. Wild garlic leaves are best in early spring.

**Flowers:** you can pick the flowers of all forms of chive, Welsh onion and wild garlic from mid-spring until midsummer, but they are best used in early summer.

## Bulbs/cloves

In summer, lift the garlic bulbs, leave them somewhere dry and warm to dry out (in good weather, you can dry them outside, or put them in crates and dry them in an airy room or garage). Once dry (in hot weather a matter of days, in damp weather a few weeks), they can be stored for use through the season. Keep the healthiest, plumpest bulbs for replanting in the winter.

## Culinary uses

**Chives:** all forms of chive are delicious freshly cut using scissors and included as a garnish or flavour in omelettes, scrambled eggs and salads or added to soured cream as a filling for jacket potatoes. They are good sprinkled on soup or over grilled meat. The leaves should be added towards the end of cooking, because if they are cooked for too long, they lose their delicious onion flavour and become bitter. The flowers have a sweet onion flavour, which is great with salads, rice and many other dishes. Divide the flower heads into individual bulbils and add at the end of cooking or else the sweet flavour will disappear.

**Garlic:** divide the bulb into individual cloves. To know if you should peel the clove or not: peel it if you are going to slice it, pound it, chop it or fry it; do not peel it if you are going to roast it as this will help to stop it burning, or when you add it to boiling water. When you have roasted or boiled, remove the garlic from the pan, then squish the clove to remove the soft pulp, which is no longer strong but creamy and sweet in flavour. Add it to sauces, soups, or simply mix with the cooked vegetables or roasted meat and enjoy.

## Medicinal uses

**Chives:** chives have similar properties to garlic but they are much milder and are therefore rarely used medicinally. However, they do increase the appetite and are very beneficial for the digestive system and blood circulation.

**Garlic:** modern science has confirmed many of garlic's reputed healing properties. It has been shown to reduce blood pressure in both animals and humans, it is evidently useful in guarding against strokes, which can occur when blood pressure is raised or blood clots in the cranial arteries. It has also been successful in controlling diarrhoea, dysentery, TB, whooping cough, typhoid and hepatitis. It is effective against many fungal infections and it can be used to expel worms. It has been shown to lower blood sugar levels, indicating its use in controlling diabetes.

*Allium nutans*, Siberian Chives

# Aloe vera

**At the mention of this herb I am transported back to my childhood. I used to suck the index and middle fingers of my right hand and my mother was paranoid that I would distort the shape of my mouth so used to cover them in bitter aloes, which was, as its name indicates, incredibly bitter. It did not work.**

*Aloe vera*, Aloe

## History

Aloe has been identified in the wall paintings of the Ancient Egyptians and aloe vera is said to have been one of Cleopatra's secret beauty ingredients. Today you find it in hand creams, suntan lotions and shampoos.

## Species

*Aloe Vera*, Aloe
Tender, HIC (USDA 11), evergreen perennial. Height and spread: up to 60cm (24in), only in warm climates. Yellow or orange bell-shaped flowers appear on mature plants. Grey/green, fleshy, spear-shaped leaves with spiny edges.

## Propagation

**Seeds:** to be honest, raising aloe from seed is a long process but if you are up for a challenge, sow the small seeds on to the surface of a prepared small pot or seed tray filled with three parts seed compost and one part sharp horticultural sand. Once sown, cover lightly with some sharp horticultural sand. Put into a propagator at 18°C (64°F). Germination is erratic, taking anything from 4–24 months.

**Offsets:** rather than struggle with seed, it is much easier to remove the offsets that appear at the base of the plant. The best time of year to do this in the UK climate is the summer. Remove the offset gently by hand and place in an empty seed tray and leave to slightly dry out for a day. Pot up in a compost made up of two parts potting compost and one part sharp horticultural sand. Water in and leave in a warm place to root. This is a very successful method and makes up for any failure with the seed.

## Pests and diseases

When grown in its natural habitat aloe is not attacked by pests, but in cold climates when aloe is grown as a house plant, mealybug and scale are prevalent. For information on how to control both these pests see page 270.

The disease that can occur is caused by overwatering, especially in autumn and winter. It will turn the stem black at the base and this will 'rot off'. The solution is to cut back watering to virtually dry. Sadly, if you do get the base turning black there isn't much that can rescue it, remove any offsets if there are any – these can be saved as above.

## How and where to grow

This herb can only be planted outside in the garden in tropical or sub-tropical climates. Plant in full to partial shade in a free-draining soil. In cooler climates it makes an ideal pot plant.

## Growing in containers

Aloe is a very good container plant, especially in cold climates. Use three parts soil-based compost mixed with one part horticultural grit. Although this plant looks like a succulent, aloe is more closely related to the lily family so it needs water in the growing season. The thing is not to over-water – be mean, especially in winter when it needs to be kept virtually dry but not completely dry. Keep it frost free in a light room – the kitchen windowsill is ideal; a bathroom windowsill is another good position. When grown as a pot plant feed monthly throughout the growing season with liquid seaweed fertiliser. In winter, keep watering to a minimum, but do not allow the compost to dry out. Protect plants from frost.

## Yearly maintenance

**Spring:** if you are growing the plant in a container, now is the time to give it a good dust! Spray the leaves with water and wash off any cobwebs etc. and give the compost, not the leaves, a good feed of liquid fertiliser – a seaweed feed is very beneficial.

**Summer:** remove the 'offsets' of a mature plant – by doing this you will keep the parent plant in good condition and the pot will not become overcrowded.

**Autumn:** start cutting back the watering.

**Winter:** if grown outside, in a frost-free climate, the plant will look after itself. Bring in pots if there is any danger of frost. Rest all pot-grown plants in a cool room (minimum temperature of 5°C (41°F)) and keep watering to an absolute minimum.

## Harvesting and storing

Fresh leaves can be used throughout the growing season. The best leaves are those from plants over 2 years old as they have stronger medicinal properties. The cut leaves can be kept in an airtight container in the refrigerator for up to 2 weeks.

## Culinary uses

None.

## Medicinal uses

The famous gel is the glutinous part which comes from the centre of the leaves when they are broken. This gel can be applied to wounds and minor burns, where it is immediately soothing. It forms a clear protective seal and encourages the skin to regenerate. The gel can also be used on eczema and can help with fungal infections, such as ringworm and thrush. The gel is used internally to soothe peptic ulcers and help irritable bowel syndrome.

**WARNING** | Do not take fresh aloe internally without seeking qualified advice. The leaves are a potent laxative and should not be taken by pregnant women or young children.

# Aloysia citrodora

**I have never found anyone with a bad thing to say about this herb: when you rub the rough leaves and release the sharp lemon sherbet scent, you are immediately relaxed. Personally, lemon verbena reminds me of my great aunt Ann, who had a large specimen growing against her back door so that as you entered the house from the garden you automatically brought the scent of lemon verbena with you. She was also the first person I knew who drank lemon verbena tea which she called a tisane de verveine.**

## History

This beautiful herb, native to South America, was introduced to Europe in the 17th century by either the Spanish or the Portuguese for its oils and perfume.

## Species

*Aloysia citrodora*, Lemon Verbena
Half-hardy H3 (USDA 9), deciduous shrub. Height: up to 3m (9ft 10in); spread: 2.5m (8ft 2in). Small, delicate white flowers tinged with lilac in summer; they have a light lemon flavour when eaten. Highly fragrant, lemon sherbet-scented, narrow, oval, rough textured mid-green leaves.

*Aloysia citrodora* 'Spilsbury Mint'
Half-hardy, H3 (USDA 9), deciduous shrub. Height: up to 3m (9ft); spread: 2.5m (8ft). Delicate small white flowers with a hint of lilac in summer. Fragrant, narrow, oval, rough textured mid-green leaves with a fruity, minty scent. Use the leaves in drinks, sorbets and with fruit.

*Aloysia polystachya*, White Brush
Half-hardy, H3 (USDA 9), deciduous shrub. Height: up to 3m (9ft); spread: 2.5m (8ft). Small, delicate, slightly vanilla-scented white or violet-tinged flowers in late summer. Small, lance-shaped, spearmint-scented grey–green leaves. Trailing branches that often root where they touch the ground. Use the leaves in drinks and with fruit.

*Aloysia virgata*, Sweet Almond Bush
Hardy H3 (USDA 9), deciduous (evergreen in mild climates) shrub. Height: up to 3m (9ft); spread: 2.5m (8ft). Lovely almond-scented terminal spikes of small white flowers in late summer and early autumn, which are loved by bees and butterflies for their late nectar. Slightly glossy, oval, mid-green leaves with serrated edges. Deer resistant!

## Propagation

**Seeds:** I have never grown this herb from seed as it does not set seed in cooler climates but I do know from other growers that it is possible. The seeds are very fine and can be sown in spring into a prepared seed or plug, with protection at 18° C (64°C). Germination takes 10–20 days. When seedlings are large enough to handle, pot up into small pots, using three parts soil-based compost mixed with one part sharp horticultural sand. Grow on in pots, under cover, for a minimum of 2 years before planting in the garden.

**Cuttings:** take softwood cuttings from the new growth in late spring and put into small pots or modules filled with three parts seed compost mixed with one part sharp horticultural sand. The cutting material can wilt very quickly so have your module tray prepared and well watered before you collect the material.

Take semi-ripe cuttings in late summer. Once rooted and potted into small pots using the same mix as seeds above, all cuttings will need protection throughout the winter. Grow on in a greenhouse, polytunnel or cold frame for at least 2 years before planting out. In winter, let the compost nearly dry out, reintroducing regular watering once the days start to draw out.

## Pests and diseases

When this plant is grown under cover, in a conservatory or in a cool greenhouse, it can suffer from either whitefly or red spider mite. Both can be controlled by spraying regularly, at the first sign of attack with horticultural soft soap. For more information see pages 270 and 272.

## How and where to grow

I have been growing this herb for over 40 years. When I started there was no way I would recommend growing it outside in climates that drop below 4°C (39°F). However, for the past few years I have been successfully growing it outside in the Herbetum, Admittedly this is in a raised bed but it has tolerated frosts as cold as -7°C (19°F). It is the persistent wet it really doesn't like, mixed with the cold. To help it survive, we did mulch the roots with straw mixed with leaf mould to give it warmth and protection from the wet.

Ideally plant in a light, free-draining soil in a warm, sunny site. Against a wall in the sun is the perfect position as it gets the warmth and protection from the wall. In spring the plant can look very dormant. Once all threat of frost has passed, and when you notice a leaf bud swelling, be brave and prune hard back to just above a leaf node. New growth can appear very late in spring so never discard a plant until the summer. In late summer to early autumn, harvest the leaves by cutting the stems, don't be greedy, make sure you leave enough leaves on the plant so that it can go through its ritual of dropping its leaves and going dormant. Also do this in early autumn as this will give the plant time to seal the branches where you have cut them, which will protect the plant in the winter.

## Growing in containers

All the *Aloysia* make ideal container plants. Use three parts soil-based compost mixed with one part horticultural grit. Place the container in a warm, sunny, light and airy spot and water well throughout the growing season. Don't be greedy, or for that matter lazy, only pot your plant up one size at a time, it likes being pot bound and hates – to use a good cooking analogy – a 'soggy bottom' caused by too much compost and over-enthusiastic watering. In winter either bring the plants inside or lift onto bricks to increase drainage.

## Yearly maintenance

**Spring:** in warm climates sow the seeds; trim plants once all threat of frost has passed; take softwood cuttings.

**Summer:** harvest the flowers; take semi-ripe cuttings.

**Autumn:** harvest the leaves, well before the frosts start.

**Winter:** protect; keep pot plants on the dry side.

## Harvesting and storing

**Leaves**: if stored in the refrigerator for any length of time the leaves will turn black, so it is far better to use them fresh or dry them. The best flavoured leaves for drying are those picked while they are bright green before they start to lose colour and curl in the autumn. Place them on a tray, in a light airy room and they will dry in a matter of days. Store in an airtight container. Alternatively, make syrups or cordials, which will keep in the refrigerator.

**Flowers:** pick the flowers as and when required; they do not store well.

*Aloysia citrodora*, Lemon Verbena

## Culinary uses

**Leaves:** fresh and dried leaves can be used to make teas, which can be served hot or cold. If any of the tea is left over, it can be frozen in ice cubes which can then be added to a fruit cup or a gin and tonic. The leaves can be used to flavour oils and vinegars, fruit puddings and jellies. You can transform cakes by simply laying whole leaves on to the bottom of a well-greased cake tin, before pouring in the cake mixture and baking.

**Flowers:** the flowers have an intense lemon sherbet flavour; scatter over fruit or salads and add to jellies.

## Medicinal uses

A tisane made from 3–5 leaves, either dried or fresh, is a wonderful relaxant, so is good at any time of the day for relieving stress, or last thing at night to help you unwind.

# Althaea officinalis

**You can see this majestic flower growing near the sea and on salt marshes. It is a survival herb and in times of famine in the UK and Ireland it became an essential food. I love the flowers with their large pink stamen that attracts both bees and butterflies. In the UK, this beautiful herb is sadly in decline as its natural habitats are reclaimed.**

## History

This herb is a true plant of the people. The name *Althaea* comes from the Greek *althos* meaning 'healing'. The Romans considered it as a delicious vegetable; they also used it in barley soup and for stuffing suckling pigs. It is the quintessential pot herb as it was used to thicken the broth and stews that were all cooked in the one pot over the open fire. The soft sweet marshmallow came from the roots, which were dug up from the marshes of the Thames estuary. In France, the dried roots are still sold in chemists as teethers for babies.

## Species

*Althaea officinalis*, Marsh Mallow
Hardy, H6 (USDA 6,7), Herbaceous perennial. Height: up to 1.5m (5ft) when in flower; spread: 60cm (24in). Pink/white flowers in summer until early autumn. The seeds are flat, button-shaped and often called cheese cakes due to their shape. The grey/green leaves are velvety and round to ovate. Long tap root that is edible.

## Propagation

**Seeds:** as a UK native it is best to sow fresh seeds in the autumn in a seed tray or in modules filled with a standard seed compost. Cover the seed with seed compost, then put in a cold frame or outside covered in glass. Alternatively, in early winter, mix some seed in damp – not wet – sand, put into a plastic bag with a label and date, then pop into the crisper drawer of a refrigerator. After a month, remove the seeds from the fridge and sow into a seed tray that has been half-filled with seed compost. Cover the sown seeds with the seed compost, put into a cold frame or a cold greenhouse. This method does speed up germination. Both methods germinate in the following spring.

**Division:** divide established plants either in spring or autumn. Replant into a prepared site in the garden.

## Pests and diseases

Rust is the only major disease this plant suffers from. You will notice orange/brown dots appearing on the underside of the leaves. As this is a virus it is essential to cut back the growth to 3cm (1in) above the ground and burn the offcuts – do not compost. If it is very bad, remove the plant and burn. Do not plant any rust-prone plants in that area, including alliums, mints, tarragon or grasses, as the virus stays in the soil for several years. For more information see page 276.

## How and where to grow

Marsh mallow is a beautiful plant to grow as a feature or in a clump at the back or centre of a border. It is highly attractive for butterflies. It is good plant for seaside gardens as it tolerates salt, wind and spray. It likes a site in full sun with a moist or wet moderately fertile soil. Cut back after flowering to encourage some new leaves, which can be used in salads.

## Growing in containers

Marsh mallow will adapt to growing in a container. Choose a large sturdy pot which will accommodate its height when in flower. Fill with a soil-based compost. Place the container in semi-shade to protect it from the midday sun; this will help prevent the soil drying out. Water regularly throughout the summer and liquid feed it monthly with a seaweed fertiliser until the autumn.

## Yearly maintenance

**Spring:** divide established plants.

**Summer:** harvest the seeds; cut back to encourage new growth.

**Autumn:** sow seeds and winter the tray outside.

**Winter:** sow seeds in damp sand, put in the refrigerator for a month prior to sowing in a seed tray. No need to protect plants in the garden.

## Harvesting and storing

**Leaves:** pick leaves as required to use fresh or dried for use through the winter.

**Flowers:** pick flowers throughout the summer to use fresh.

**Roots:** dig up the roots of a 2-year-old plant in the late autumn once the plant has died back. Can be used fresh or dried.

## Culinary uses

The leaves can be eaten raw or cooked. In my opinion they are best cooked in the traditional way – put in the pot to cook slowly with all the other ingredients. Do not use loads of leaf as it makes the dish all guppy, rather like wallpaper paste and your meal will be ruined. The root can be cooked as a vegetable, though again it is a bit glutinous. It is best boiled to soften it, then peeled and quickly fried in butter. It can also be dried and ground into a powder, then made into a paste, as the original marshmallows were made. The flowers can be used to make a tisane or added to salads.

## Medicinal uses

Due to its high mucilage content – 35% in the root and 10% in the leaf – marsh-mallow is a soothing healing plant useful in treating inflammation, ulceration of the stomach and small intestine, coughs and cystitis.

An infusion of the leaves or flowers serves as a soothing gargle, while an infusion of the root can be used for coughs, diarrhoea and insomnia. The pulverised roots may be used as a healing and drawing poultice which should be applied warm. A cold poultice can be used for irritations and burns.

*Althaea officinalis*, Marsh Mallow

# Anethum graveolens

**In my opinion, dill is a 'must-have' in the kitchen. My mother found a use for every part of it. She used the leaves with mashed potato and the seeds with courgettes, and the flowers were added to pickles. If we had the hiccups, she would steep a teaspoon of seed in hot water and give us teaspoons of the liquid until we stopped. Today it can be found in many dishes from gravlax (salmon marinated with dill leaf) to pickled gherkins.**

## History

The common word 'dill' is said to have been derived from the Anglo-Saxon *dylle* or the Norse *dilla*, which meant to soothe or lull. It has been in cultivation for thousands of years and is mentioned in the Ebers Papyrus around 1500BC. Dill was found among the names of the herbs used by the Egyptian doctors 5000 years ago and the remains of the plant have been found in the ruins of Roman buildings in Great Britain.

## Species

*Anethum graveolens*, Dill
Hardy annual, H4 (USDA 8,9). Height: up to 1.5m (4ft 11in) when in flower; spread: 20cm (8in). Umbels of small, yellow/green flowers in summer, followed by aromatic seeds. Fine, feathery, aromatic mid-green leaves.

There are many forms of dill seed available from seed merchants. Some have been bred for leaf crop and some especially for seed. Varieties worth looking out for are:

*Anethum sowa*, an Indian variety this has a rounded spicy flavour.

*Anethum graveolens* 'Bouquet', an American variety.

*Anethum graveolens* 'Dukat', a leaf production variety.

*Anethum graveolens* 'Mammoth', excellent for pickling.

*Anethum graveolens* 'Vierling', this variety has dark bluish green leaves that are great for salads and other vegetable dishes.

## Propagation

**Seeds:** sow seeds in early spring into prepared seed trays or modules using a standard seed compost. Place under cover at 15°C (59°F). Germination takes 5–20 days. Alternatively, sow seeds in late spring into prepared open ground, when the air temperature at night remains above 7°C (45°F). Germination takes 2–3 weeks. Thin seedlings to 15cm (6in) apart. In my opinion, sowing the seeds directly into open ground gives the best crop because dill hates being transplanted, which can cause the plant to bolt and run to seed. Sow in succession – every 3 weeks until midsummer – to give a constant supply of leaf.

## Pests and diseases

Aphid is the main pest. Only if it becomes badly infested should you spray the plant with soft, horticultural soap following the manufacturer's instructions.

## How and where to grow

When deciding where in the garden to plant you must make sure you keep dill well away from fennel, otherwise they will cross-pollinate and their individual flavours will become muddled. Plant in a well-drained soil in full sun. As the plants are rather fragile, if you live on a windy site, it may be necessary to provide some form of support. Twigs pushed into the ground around the plant and enclosed with string or raffia will give better results than attempting to stake each plant individually.

## Growing in containers

Dill can be grown in containers using a soil-based compost. Place the container in a sheltered corner with plenty of sun, however it will need staking. The art of growing dill successfully is to keep cutting the plant for use in the kitchen; that way you will promote new growth and keep the plant reasonably compact. The drawback is that it will be short-lived so you will have to do successive sowings in different pots to maintain a supply of leaves. As an annual, dill will bolt to flower if transplanted and/or the compost is allowed to dry out when grown in a container. This is great if you need flowers or seeds quickly but you would be missing out on the delicate flavour of the leaves.

## Yearly maintenance

**Spring:** sow the seeds, successively for a leaf crop; harvest seeds as required.

**Summer:** feed plants with a liquid fertiliser after cutting to promote new growth; harvest flowers.

**Early autumn:** harvest seeds.

**Autumn/early winter:** after the seeds have been harvested, dig up all the remaining plants. Make sure all the seed heads have been removed before you compost the stalks, otherwise you will have dill in your compost, which will spread to your garden because as mentioned earlier the seed is viable for 3 years. If you do not dig the plants up from the garden and let it self-seed, which it certainly will, it will live up to its other name, dillweed.

## Harvesting and storing

**Leaves:** for the best flavour, pick leaves before the plant starts to flower; the leaves freeze beautifully.

**Flowers:** pick flowers as soon as they start to form.

**Seed:** seeds can be harvested when green to use immediately or for use in pickling. Alternatively, harvest the seeds when they turn brown and start to drop.

## Culinary uses

**Leaves:** use the leaves either fresh, dried or frozen with fish, cream cheese, yogurt or crème fraîche, with eggs, potatoes or salads.

**Flowers:** the flowers and the pollen from the flowers have a lovely fresh flavour that is great with fish dishes, vegetables and salads made with couscous and bulgur wheat.

**Seeds:** the seeds are great fresh, dried or roasted with vegetables, soups, meats, in pickles and breads.

## Medicinal uses

Throughout the world dill seed is well known for its medicinal qualities. The seed contains volatile oils, the main one being carvone, which has antispasmodic, diuretic and carminative properties. Medicinally a tea made from a teaspoon of seeds is good for dyspepsia, flatulence and stomach ache. A teaspoon of this tea is a good cure for hiccups.

*Anethum graveolens*, Dill flower

*Anethum graveolens*, Dill leaf

# Angelica archangelica

**The first time I really noticed angelica flowers was one late spring morning when I was walking down to the Herb Farm and I was bewitched by a heavenly sweet honey scent on the breeze. It did not take me long to track it down to the angelica, which, standing at full height and magnificence, was in full flower and alive with bees and other pollinators.**

*Angelica archangelica*, Angelica

## History

Traditionally angelica has been used to flavour many drinks including absinthe, anisette, vermouth, chartreuse and gin, in which it is combined with juniper. Here in the UK, angelica used to grow wild all along the banks of the Thames. The root of this herb became one of the main botanicals in the original London gin and it is still used today. Very sadly the root is now imported, as it is very rare to find it growing wild in this country.

**WARNING** | ALL of the angelicas may cause skin photosensitivity or dermatitis. Medicinal use is not recommended for those suffering from diabetes.

## Species

All the varieties mentioned are monocarpic, which means that they are not annual, biennial or a short-lived perennial, but die after they have flowered and set seed.

*Angelica archangelica*, Angelica
Hardy, H5 (USDA 7,8), monocarpic. Height: up to 2.5m (8ft); spread: 1m (3ft) in the second year. Round umbels of sweetly-scented white/green flowers in late spring to early summer of the second season. Large, bright green, deeply divided leaves around the base of the plant that decrease in size as they progress up the stem.

*Angelica gigas*, Korean Angelica, Purple Angelica
Hardy, H6 (USDA 6,7), monocarpic. Height up to 1.4m (4ft); spread: 80cm (30in). Lovely spherical, crimson umbels with tiny white flowers from late summer until early autumn – they are immensely attractive to butterflies. Shiny, dark green, divided leaves.

*Angelica pachycarpa*, Portuguese Angelica, Spanish Angelica
Hardy, H5 (USDA 7,8), monocarpic. Height: up to 1.5m (5ft); spread: 1m (3ft). Lovely flat umbels; creamy white flowers from late summer until early autumn. Glossy, rich, pinnately divided green leaves, which have a light anise scent when crushed.

*Angelica sylvestris*, Wild Angelica, Ground Ash
Hardy, H5 (USDA 7,8), monocarpic. Height: up to 1.5; spread: 1m (3ft). Round umbels of white flowers, often tinged with pink, in summer; these are smaller than *Angelica archangelica*. The large mid-green leaves are sharply toothed. The stems often have a purple tinge.

## Propagation

**Seeds:** all forms of angelica can only be grown from seed. For quick and reliable germination, sow fresh seeds in the autumn either where you want it to grow next year directly into the ground, or in plug trays that are filled with a standard seed compost. Place outside once sown so that they can have a cold period. There is no need to protect the seedlings from frost. If you wish to sow in the spring, you will need to mix the seed with damp horticultural sand, put this into a plastic bag then into the crisper drawer of a refrigerator for a period of stratification, approximately 10 weeks. Check after week 5 to see if the seed has started to chitter (root). If so, pot into small pots using a soil-based compost.

## Pests and diseases

Susceptible to aphids and leaf miner. If you notice the latter, as soon as you see the light green tracks in a leaf, pick the leaf and bin it – see pages 267 and 269.

## How and where to grow

If you have a small garden and you really want to grow angelica, I recommend *Angelica gigas*, as it is not as large as *A. archangelica* and produces stunning flowers in late summer. All forms of angelica prefer a deep, moist soil with its roots in the shade and its flowers in the sun. Position at the back of a border. This is a good architectural plant that gives structure to a herb garden. If growing in an exposed windy site, you may need to stake the plant when it goes to flower to stop it breaking.

## Growing in containers

It is possible to grow angelica in containers. Because of its tap root, which hates being disturbed, choose a large container that has a good wide base so that it does not blow over once the plant goes to flower. Fill with a soil-based compost. Keep the plant in partial shade and water daily in summer. Do not let the plant dry out. Feed monthly in the first year, then weekly in the second year from spring until summer with a seaweed liquid fertiliser.

## Yearly maintenance

**Spring:** clear ground around existing plants; plant [illegible] autumn seedlings; sow seeds after a period of str[illegible]ion (see page 18) in the refrigerator.

**Summer:** cut stems of second year growth f[illegible]allising. Cut young leaves before flowering for use i[illegible]ds or dry them for medicine or culinary uses. Reme[illegible]o water the plants.

**Autumn:** sow seeds.

**First-year plant:** mark their spot a[illegible] plant will die back fully during the winter.

**Second-year plant:** if the plant has flowered and seeded, cut it back and dig up the roots. If you do not want thousands of angelicas, do not compost the flower head, discard it.

**Winter:** dig up the roots of a two-year-old plant that has not flowered for medicinal use or for making gin.

## Harvesting and storing

**Leaves:** pick young leaves to use fresh in late spring to early summer while still soft.

**Flowers:** harvest from late spring until early summer in the second season just as you see them opening.

**Stems:** cut the stems of second year growth, before the flower head forms, in late spring to use fresh or conserve by candying them.

**Seeds:** collect seeds when ripe in early autumn of the second season.

**Roots:** harvest the roots in the spring of the second year before flowering for eating fresh or drying.

## Culinary uses

*Angelica archangelica* is the only angelica that can be used in the kitchen.

**Young leaves:** young leaves are good chopped and added to salads, soups and stir-fry dishes.

**Stem:** the second year's stem growth can be candied or used with stewed fruit. Peel the stalks and stems before use.

**Flowers:** the flowers have an interesting, sweet, slight anise flavour; add them to fruit salads, cream cheese and cordials.

**Seeds:** the seeds have a sweet anise flavour that is good in soups, with eggs and in custards. They are often dried and used as a condiment and are also famous for being used in liqueurs, such as chartreuse.

**Roots:** traditionally cooked as a root vegetable, I fear these roots would not be pleasant to modern-day taste buds!

## Medicinal uses

Medicinally it is used to treat indigestion, anaemia, coughs and colds. It has antibacterial and anti-fungal properties. A tea made from the young leaves is good for reducing tension and nervous headaches.

# Anthriscus cerefolium

**This is a herb that I have known all my life – my mother always grew it and used it, especially in winter. In my opinion it is a very underrated herb, as its delicate flavour will permeate food subtly. It is also great in the garden, especially in the spring, with its bright green new growth that is very heartening on a dank grey day.**

## History

Chervil has been used for thousands of years throughout Europe and north Africa, though it is said to be a native of Siberia. It was almost certainly brought to Britain by the Romans in their wagon train. It is considered to be one of the Lenten herbs, thought to have blood cleansing and restorative properties. It was eaten in quantities during Lent, especially on Maundy Thursday. Gerard, the Elizabethan physician who superintended Lord Burleigh's gardens, wrote in his herbal of 1636: 'the leaves of sweet chervil are exceeding good, wholesome and pleasant among other salad herbs, giving the taste of anise seed unto the rest'.

## Species

*Anthriscus cerefolium*, Chervil
Hardy, H4 (USDA 8,9), biennial, often grown as an annual. Height: up to 60cm (24in) in flower; spread: 25cm (10in). Tiny white flowers that grow in umbelliferous clusters in the second year, or when the plant becomes stressed due to heat or lack of water. Light green, anise-flavoured leaves that often develop a purple tinge in drought or early autumn – this does not impair their flavour. One of the original *fines herbes*.

## Propagation

**Seeds:** This is an easy herb to grow as it is raised from seed that germinates rapidly in the warmth of spring as the air and soil temperatures rise. The seed must be fresh as it loses it viability after one year. Sow the seed in early spring, in small pots or modules filled with a standard seed compost. Place under cover at 15°C (59°F). Germination takes 5–10 days. Pot up or plant out as soon as you see the roots emerging. Alternatively, sow seeds in late spring into prepared open ground when the air temperature at night remains above 7°C (47°F). Germination takes 2–3 weeks. Thin seedlings to 25cm (10in) apart. Sow the seeds where you want to crop it, either into a large pot, or directly into the ground. The most useful crop is the one I grow at the end of summer, as this gives fresh leaves for the majority of the winter months.

## Pests and diseases

In spring, chervil can suffer from green fly on the lush new growth. Either wash off with water, or for a bad infestation treat with horticultural soap. See page 267 for more information.

## How and where to grow

Plant in the garden in a light soil that retains moisture in the summer but is not waterlogged in winter. A semi-shaded position is best because chervil will bolt to flower if the soil dries out or it gets too hot. For this reason some gardeners sow it between rows of other garden herbs or vegetables or under deciduous plants to ensure shade during the summer months.

Be warned, chervil is a prolific self-seeder. Removing some of the flower heads as they appear will prevent you from being overrun with seedlings. I always allow a few flowers to remain, so I can collect seed for the following year.

## Growing in containers

Chervil is not a good herb to grow inside unless one treats it as a cress herb. To do this, sow the seeds into a seed tray, using a seed compost, then cut as soon as the leaves start to appear. Add to sandwiches, or use as a garnish for fish.

For pots outside, sow into a large pot using a soil-based compost so that it does not dry out quickly. Place in partial shade and water regularly, plus feed weekly with a liquid seaweed feed.

## Yearly maintenance

**Spring:** sow seeds.

**Summer:** in late summer sow seeds for winter crop.

**Autumn:** if excessive rain is forecast, cover with a cloche.

**Winter:** cover with a cloche or agricultural fleece when the weather is excessively wet or the temperature dips below -2°C (28°F).

## Harvesting and storing

**Leaves:** leaves can be picked 6–8 weeks after sowing in spring. They are then available all year until the first hard frost.They are not damaged by frost, however they become limp and unusable until the temperature picks up.

**Stems:** the stems can be used from spring onwards.

## Culinary uses

This is a useful culinary herb; it is the fourth ingredient in *fines herbes* (the others are parsley, chives and tarragon). It is a very good substitute for parsley, especially in winter. The leaves can be used generously in salads, soups, sauces with vegetables, chicken, fish and egg dishes. Always add freshly chopped chervil towards the end of cooking to avoid flavour loss.

## Medicinal uses

Eaten raw, the leaves provide additional vitamin C, carotene, iron and magnesium. A tea can be made from the leaves to stimulate digestion and alleviate circulation disorders, liver complaints and chronic catarrh.

*Anthriscus cerefolium*, Chervil

# Apium graveolens

**I never cease to be amazed and fascinated by herbs – even after growing them for over four decades. I recently discovered that celery leaf has been grown in China for thousands of years. It is smaller and more pungent than the European form and all parts of the plant are used medicinally. The leaf and stem are used in Chinese cooking where the flavour is more peppery than its European cousin.**

*Apium graveolens*, Celery Leaf

## History

Wild celery has been used for thousands of years; there are records showing that the seeds were found in Pharoah Tutankhamen's tomb. In Greek and Roman times, celery was dedicated to Hades/Pluto, the ruler of the underworld – wreaths were made from the leaves to dress the dead and the leaves strewn on gravestones to placate the Gods. The use of Chinese celery dates back to the Han Dynasty (206 BC–220 AD) where it was used medicinally and also in the kitchen. The salad stem celery, *Apium graveolens* var. *dulce* was originally bred in the 17th century from this wild form.

**WARNING** | There are some people who are allergic to the seeds as they have been known to cause anaphylaxis, similar to a nut allergy. If the plant is infected with the fungus *Sclerotinia sclerotiorum*, contact with the sap can cause dermatitis in sensitive skin. Never take medicinally when pregnant.

## Species

*Apium graveolens*, Celery Leaf
Hardy, H5 (USDA 7,8), biennial. Often grown as an annual. Height: up to 1m (3ft) when in flower, 30cm (12in) when in leaf; spread: up to 30cm (12in). Umbels of tiny green/white flowers early in the second summer followed by ridged grey–brown seeds. Mid-green cut leaves have a strong celery flavour. The leaves are very similar to itscousin, French parsley, with which celery leaf is often confused when young.

**Other species worth looking out for are:**

*Apium graveolens* 'French Dinant', which is very flavoursome and excellent for drying.

*Apium graveolens* 'Amsterdam', which is aromatic and prolific, producing thin stems and loads of leaves.

*Apium graveolens*, Indian celery leaf, ajmoda; the seed is used both in the kitchen and medicinally where it is highly valued in Ayurveda.

*Apium graveolens* var. *secalinum Alef.* Chinese celery or Nan Ling celery, Khan choy, which has a slightly more peppery flavour than the wild celery leaf.

## Propagation

**Seeds:** sow the fresh seed in early spring into pots or plug modules using a standard seed compost. Do not cover the seed with compost as light is needed for germination. Place under protection at 15°C (59°F). Germination takes 2–3 weeks. Alternatively, sow seeds in late spring when the air temperature does not drop below 7°C (47°F) at night, into a well-prepared site that has been fed in the previous autumn with well-rotted manure. Germination takes 2–3 weeks.

If you are growing it just for leaf not for seed then sow it annually in the late spring into a prepared site in the garden when all threat of frost has passed.

## Pests and diseases

Often this herb can have a peaceful year with no problems, but sometimes it can be attacked by everything, including slugs and celery leaf miner or celery fly larvae, which cause brown tunnel marks through the leaf. As soon as you see affected leaves remove them and burn them. If you have a bad infestation, cut the plant back to 3cm (1in) above the ground and make sure you remove all debris.

Celery pale leaf spot (early blight) appears in spring as tiny yellow spots on the leaf surfaces accompanying grey mould in damp conditions. If I see this, I bin and burn the crop and give the soil a good feed, cover it with carboard and leave fallow until the autumn.

Carrot root fly can be a real nuisance in early summer as it attacks the roots and stem bases. To prevent this, cover the crop with agricultural fleece and only thin the seedlings in the early morning before the temperature rises. Cover immediately after thinning with agricultural fleece to prevent the fly laying its eggs. For more information on these pests and diseases see page 267.

## How and where to grow

Celery leaf is a hungry plant; it likes a good deep soil that does not dry out in summer. Always feed the chosen site well in the previous autumn with well-rotted manure. If you wish to harvest celery leaf all year round, have two different sites prepared. For summer supplies, a western or eastern border is ideal because the plant needs moisture and prefers a little shade. For winter supplies, a more sheltered spot will be needed in a sunny position, for example against a south-facing wall.

## Growing in containers

Celery leaf is an ideal herb for containers. It can adapt happily to any deep container as, like many of its cousins, such as parsley and coriander, it has a long tap root that likes room to develop. In summer, place in partial shade to prevent the leaves from becoming tough. Use a soil-based compost, feed with a liquid fertiliser and water regularly throughout the growing season.

## Yearly maintenance

**Spring:** sow seeds under protection.

**Summer:** sow seeds into a prepared site; remove flowers if seed is not needed to maintain growth; give plants liquid feed.

**Autumn:** harvest seeds; feed soil for next season's crop.

**Winter:** pick leaves; only protect if temperatures fall below -5°C (23°F).

## Harvesting and storing

**Leaves:** pick the new young shoots throughout the growing season.

**Stems:** pick young stems throughout the season.

**Flowers:** pick in the second year in early summer.

**Seed:** harvest in the second season in late summer/early autumn when they are fully ripe and start falling from the seed head. Dry them before storing in a dark jar.

**Roots:** dry the roots of the second year's growth for medicinal use.

## Culinary uses

**Leaves:** delicious in salads or mashed potato, the leaves are also great in soups or sweated down with onions. In my opinion the mature tough leaves are inedible and bitter.

**Stems:** these are lovely roasted when slightly mature or chopped into salads when young and tender.

**Flowers:** the flowers have a light celery flavour that is great in tomato salads, casseroles and soups.

**Seeds:** these have a very strong celery flavour, great when combined with salt for adding to soups and for rubbing into chicken; also lovely added to dough for flavoursome bread. In India the ground seeds are used as a spice.

**Roots:** traditionally grown as a root crop and as a cousin of the carrot, celery leaf produces good-sized tap roots.

## Medicinal uses

Traditionally celery leaf was used to treat low mood, stimulate the kidneys and as a remedy for dropsy (oedema). In Europe it is rarely used today, but it is still valued and used throughout the East where the whole plant is used medicinally: roots, stem, leaves and seeds. Because of the deep tap root the leaves are very beneficial – high in calcium iron, carotene and vitamins B1, B2, C and K. The seeds are also beneficial and can be crushed and used externally for fungal infections.

# Aralia racemosa

**When I first saw this plant growing in a friend's garden I had no idea it was a herb. I was captivated by its small, rather insignificant flowers, which were covered in pollinators. On returning home I did some research and found out – with much delight – that it was in fact a culinary, medicinal and homeopathic herb.**

*Aralia racemosa*, American Spikenard

## History

This Native American herb was adopted as a medicinal herb by the colonists, who learnt how to use this herb from the local Native Americans. They made a tea from it to ease childbirth and also used it to treat coughs.

## Species

*Aralia racemosa*, American Spikenard
Hardy, H7 (USDA 6), herbaceous perennial. Height and spread: up to 1.5m (5ft). Numerous umbels of small, greenish/white flowers, followed by tiny edible black/blue berries that ripen in the autumn. Large, pinnate, mid-green leaves, which have good autumn colour. The roots are very aromatic.

## Propagation

**Seeds:** sow the fresh seed in late autumn/early winter into pots or plugs modules using a standard seed compost. Do not cover with compost as light is needed for germination. Place under protection – a cold greenhouse or cold frame – for the winter. Germination will occur in the spring as the days get longer and the night temperatures increase.

**Cuttings:** take softwood cuttings from the new growth in late spring and transfer to prepared small pots or modules filled with three parts seed compost mixed with one part sharp horticultural sand. The cutting material can wilt very quickly, so have everything prepared before you start. The best time to collect the material is in the early morning.

**Division:** this is a great method especially if the plant is getting too large in its present position. Dig up the roots in early autumn, either replant directly into a prepared site or if you live in a cold climate, store the roots in sand in a frost-free environment, then replant or pot up in the following spring. Divide the suckers in the late winter, by digging up the root under the shoot then removing the shoot from the root either using a sharp knife or secateurs. These can be replanted in the garden or potted up for replanting in the spring.

## Pests and diseases

*Aralia* can suffer from green fly and/or black fly in the spring and most certainly blackbirds in the autumn when the fruit has set. For more information on green fly see page 267.

## How and where to grow

This herb's natural habitat is in the wooded mountains of North America along its highly fertile riverbanks. Plant in a moderately rich soil that drains well in sun to partial shade – it will tolerate full sun but it much prefers partial shade. A word of warning: do not be fooled by this herbaceous plant, which disappears to nothing in winter, it is a tremendous grower and can fill a space in the spring with exuberance and is known to swamp established plants.

## Growing in containers

This is not an ideal pot plant as it grows very large, but if you are prepared to repot each year it can look stunning, especially when it turns to orange and yellow in autumn. Pot it up using a soil-based compost. Position the container in partial shade, water regularly throughout the growing season. Feed monthly with a seaweed liquid fertiliser. In winter remove the root ball from the container, remove the bottom 3cm (1 ¼in) of the root ball and repot into a larger pot with fresh compost.

## Yearly maintenance

**Spring:** prick out seedlings and pot up; harvest new shoots.

**Summer:** plant out autumn sown seedlings.

**Autumn:** sow seeds; harvest berries.

**Winter:** harvest roots; divide mature plants.

## Harvesting and storing

**Leaves:** pick in spring; they can be dried but are better fresh in soups and stews.

**Fruit:** pick in autumn to make jelly or syrup.

**Seeds:** pick some berries – each fruit contains several light brown small seeds. Line a seed tray with paper; spread the berries out on the paper to dry prior to sowing.

**Roots:** lift the roots for drying once the plant has died back in late autumn/early winter.

## Culinary uses

This is a very useful culinary herb as the young leaf shoots, the fruit and the roots are all edible.

**Leaves:** pick the young shoot tops in spring as they appear. Add to soups and stews; they have a light woody, spicy flavour.

**Fruit:** the fleshy purple berries are edible. They have a very pleasant taste and can be eaten raw or cooked. They make a great fruit jelly, on their own or with other fruit, and a lovely syrup or shrub (a sweet drinking vinegar).

**Roots:** the root should always be cooked (never eaten raw). It has a unique flavour with both spice and liquorice with an undertone of bitter. Some say it is an acquired taste. It has been used as a substitute for *Smilax ornate* (sarsaparilla) to make a root beer.

## Medicinal uses

Being a deep-rooted herb it is high in vitamins A, C and E, selenium, manganese, magnesium, iron and zinc. A sweet, bitter, pungent tonic made from the roots is used internally for coughs and bronchial complaints, rheumatic disorders and blood poisoning. A poultice made from the root and/or fruit can be applied to sores, minor burns and itchy skin. In Ayurvedic medicine it is considered rejuvenating. It is important in homeopathy where it is used to treat coughs and chest complaints.

# Armoracia rusticana

**This was my father's favourite herb and the only dish he could cook was baked apples with horseradish cream. The horseradish cream was not from a supermarket – they did not exist. He made it by whipping double cream and adding a teaspoon of Mum's preserved horseradish root sugar, which he called crunch – that was a luxury in the 1950s. He served the cream with the baked apples which were stuffed with sultanas and drizzled with golden syrup – a feast.**

*Armoracia rusticana* 'Variegata' Variegated Horseradish

## History

Horseradish has been cultivated since classical times. It is thought that it was brought to British shores by the Romans when they invaded; they used it mainly for its medicinal properties. By the Middle Ages, in the UK, horseradish was used as a painkiller as well as a condiment.

## Species

*Armoracia rusticana*, Horseradish
Hardy, H6 (USDA 6,7), perennial. Height: up to 90cm (3ft); spread: infinite via the roots. Tiny white flowers in early spring; this does not occur every year. Large, crinkled, oblong mid-green leaves. Long, thick tap root which can reach 60cm (24in)in length.

*Armoracia rusticana* 'Variegata', Variegated Horseradish
Hardy, H6 (USDA 6,7), perennial. Height: up to 75cm (30in); infinite spread via the roots. Tiny white flowers in early spring. Mid-green, white variegated leaves in spring.

*Wasabia japonica*, Japanese Horseradish, Wasabi
Semi hardy, H3 (USDA 9), perennial. Height and spread: 60cm (24in) after 2 years. Small white flowers in spring. Mid-green, heart-shaped leaves. The root takes 2–3 years to be mature enough to harvest. Plant in semi-shade in damp soil that does not dry out. In the wild it grows under trees beside streams and rivers. The whole plant is edible: flowers, stems, leaves and root.

## Propagation

**Cuttings:** it is not worth raising this plant from seed as it can take 2 years to produce root. Instead take root cuttings in late autumn, once the plant has died back. If not lifting the whole crown you can store the roots (when they reach the thickness of a pencil and are about 20cm (8in) long) in damp sand, in a frost-free shed or garage. Plant in a prepared site in the spring 60cm (24in) apart. Alternatively, you can fill a 13cm (5in) diameter (1L/34fl oz) pot with good soil-based potting compost. Dib a hole longer than the root and push the root in, cover it with soil, water in well, then leave under the bench in the glasshouse or in the garage or shed for the winter months. Don't let the compost dry out, but only water if absolutely dry. Bring the pot back into a cold frame or glasshouse or windowsill in early spring and reintroduce water – the plant should start shooting in a matter of weeks.

## Pests and diseases

In spring, slugs can be a pest, and in summer the cabbage white butterfly caterpillars can strip the leaves, so keep an eye out for both and remove by hand. This should not be a problem with vigorous plants. Do not plant in soil affected by club root. See page 274 for more information.

## How and where to grow

Think seriously before planting horseradish in the garden – it is invasive and very difficult to eradicate or move if planted in the wrong place. It will tolerate all but the driest of soils. Plant in a light, well-dug, rich, moist soil in dappled shade to full sun.

## Growing in containers

I recommend growing horseradish in a dustbin that has good drainage holes, filled with rich soil and positioned in partial shade. This keeps the plant under control and makes it easy to harvest.

## Yearly maintenance

**Spring:** plant root cuttings that were taken in the winter in the garden.

**Summer:** feed with a liquid seaweed feed; water and keep the crop clear of weeds.

**Autumn/winter:** lift the whole crown once the plant has died back. Keep large roots for use in the kitchen. Take cuttings from the smaller roots.

**Winter:** prepare the site for replanting with well-rotted manure.

## Harvesting and storing

**Leaves:** leaves can be eaten in spring, added to salads, but they are not to everyone's taste (including mine).

**Roots:** harvest the roots once the plant has died back in late autumn. Preparing the root for preserving does take time, but once it is clean with all the little roots removed, use a food processor with a grater attachment to grate it – this will stop you crying, which you will do if you use a hand grater. Put the grated root into a plastic bag, then into the freezer. Alternatively preserve in white wine vinegar as the other vinegars discolour the root. Do not leave the root once lifted and cleaned for more than 48 hours as the root will turn green and lose its flavour.

## Culinary uses

In Europe the root is renowned as a condiment; it loses all flavour when cooked. When raw it stimulates digestion and can be used grated in coleslaw, dips, pickles, cream cheese, cream, mayonnaise, avocado fillings – and not forgetting baked apples.

## Medicinal uses

The fresh root is high in vitamins A, B and C, and is rich in calcium, sodium, potassium, iron and magnesium. Medicinally it is a powerful circulatory stimulant with antibiotic properties. A country remedy for hayfever is a sandwich filled with a small amount of freshly grated horseradish root.

**WARNING** | Do not use if your thyroid function is low or if taking thyroxin. Avoid continuous dosage when pregnant or suffering from kidney problems.

# Artemisia

**French tarragon played a huge role in my childhood and now at the Herb Farm. For my mother it was a must-have herb in the kitchen, so, of course, when I had my first herb garden, I grew French tarragon, which in turn became the first herb I grew commercially because over 40 years ago, you could only buy dried, and nothing beats the flavour of fresh.**

*Artemisia annua*, Sweet Wormwood

## History

Throughout history, *Artemisia* in many forms, including wormwood, southernwood and tarragon, has been used to heal the bites of snakes, serpents and other venomous creatures. The Greeks and Romans attributed exceptional powers to this plant: they considered it an erotic herb, and it was said, that if it were placed under the mattress, not only did it simulate sensuality, but it also did away with all inhibitions.

## Species

*Artemisia abrotanum*, Southernwood, Lad's Love, Old Man
Hardy, H5 (USDA 7,8), shrub, Height and spread: up to 1m (3ft). Rarely flowers in the UK; aromatic, feathery grey-green foliage. Cut back in spring not autumn to keep bushy.

*Artemisia absinthium*, Wormwood
Hardy, H5 (USDA 7,8), deciduous perennial. Height: up to 1m (3ft); spread: 1.2m (4ft). Tiny yellow flowers, silver/green aromatic foliage. The leaves and flowers are very bitter.

*Artemisia annua*, Sweet Wormwood, Sweet Annie
Half-hardy, H2 (USDA 10), annual. Height: up to 3m (9ft); spread: up to 1.5m (5ft). Tiny yellow flowers clustered in loose panicles. Aromatic, finely cut, bright green leaves. Medicinally it is very important, endorsed by the WHO (World Health Organization) for the treatment of malaria.

*Artemisia dracunculus*, French Tarragon
Hardy, H4 (USDA 8,9), herbaceous perennial. Height: up to 90cm (35in); spread: 45cm (18in). Rarely flowers in the UK. Long, narrow, smooth, aromatic green leaves that have an anise flavour. French tarragon does not set seed in the UK so can only be propagated from new growth or root cuttings.

*Artemisia dracunculus dracunculoides*, Russian Tarragon
Hardy, H6 (USDA 6,7), herbaceous perennial. Height: 1.2m (4ft); spread: 45cm (18in). Tiny, yellow flower heads are borne in sprays in summer. The long, narrow leaves are slightly coarser than those of French tarragon. The flavour is similar to upper-class grass. This plant originates from Siberia, which also explains why it is so hardy.

## Propagation

**Seeds:** Russian Tarragon, sweet wormwood and wormwood can be all grown from seed, and all prefer a compost that is free draining. Mix three parts seed compost with one part sharp horticultural sand. In spring, fill either seed trays or modules, sow the seed and cover with perlite not compost. Place under protection at 18°C (64°F). Germination takes 10–20 days. Once germinated, be very careful not to over-water the seedlings as this will cause damping off (see page 274).

**Cuttings:** French tarragon, southernwood and wormwood can all be grown from cuttings taken in spring until summer from the new growth. Fill either small pots or modules with three parts standard seed compost mixed with one part perlite.

**Root cuttings:** take tarragon root cuttings in late winter or early spring and transfer to prepared small pots or modules using three parts seed compost mixed with one part perlite.

**Division:** to keep tarragon's superior flavour, divide established plants every other year, replanting in a well-prepared site. For wormwood, divide established plants in spring every 3–4 years, replanting in a well-prepared site.

## Pests and diseases

Black fly is known to attack wormwood in summer. If there is a profusion of fly, use horticultural soft soap. Mildew is known to affect southernwood and wormwood. For more information on how to control this fungus, please visit page 275. Tarragon can also suffer from puccinia, which is a fungus related to mint rust (for more information about rust see page 276). Easily identified, the leaves will have round rust-coloured spots, which start on the underside of the leaf. It is best and simplest to dig up the plant and destroy it. Do not replant any of the following in that position: chives, mint or marsh mallow because the virus will continue to live in the soil for a couple of seasons.

## How and where to grow

All the *Artemisia* mentioned are predominately Mediterranean and prefer a light well-drained soil and full sun. They also all prefer shelter from strong, cold winter winds. With the exception of the Russian tarragon, they all hate being grown in a cold clay soil, especially in winter. If you do have a cold damp soil it is worth over-wintering French tarragon as either root cuttings or digging up some of the plants and potting them in a soil-based compost, then replanting them the following spring.

## Growing in containers

All the *Artemisia* mentioned will adapt to being grown in containers. Use a soil-based compost. If you are cropping the tarragon regularly it is worth using a liquid seaweed fertiliser weekly from spring until midsummer. Lift all the pots off the ground in winter, placing on bricks and place against a wall, which will provide a bit of shelter and warmth. Bring French tarragon into a cold greenhouse or cold frame for the winter and cut the watering to a minimum.

## Yearly maintenance

**Spring:** cut southernwood back to roughly 20cm (8 in) above the ground; sow Russian tarragon seeds and divide established plants of both varieties. Take root cuttings if you missed doing this in winter. Sow wormwood seeds; cut back established plants to roughly 15cm (6in) above the ground. Sow sweet wormwood seeds.

**Summer:** if not using regularly, trim tarragon in early summer to produce new growth for late summer cooking and inhibit flowering. Trim wormwood if getting unruly. Harvest sweet wormwood leaves.

**Autumn:** take French tarragon root cuttings. Cut wormwood back to a sensible shape, do not cut back hard until the spring.

**Winter:** protect French tarragon as the plant dies back into the ground in winter – it is an ideal candidate for either agricultural fleece, straw or a deep mulch. Russian tarragon is fully hardy.

## Harvesting and storing

**Tarragon:** pick the leaves for use throughout the growing season. The flavour of the leaves varies as the season progresses – the sweetest flavour is in early spring and this is ideal for making tarragon vinegar as the leaf and stalk can be employed. In summer, the leaves become coarser and have a more intense flavour; these are ideal for long cooking in stews and casseroles, for baking and for freezing.

**Southernwood:** pick leaves in summer and dry them to use as a moth repellent.

**Wormwood:** pick young leaves (they are very bitter) in early summer for use with cheese, or dry for medicinal use.

**Sweet wormwood:** pick the leaves in early summer to dry for medicinal use.

## Culinary uses

**French tarragon:** the Rolls-Royce of the Mediterranean kitchen – its anise flavour stimulates the appetite and complements chicken, fish, tomatoes, rice dishes, and is wonderful in Béarnaise sauce and salad dressings.

**Southernwood:** young leaves can be used sparingly in salads; they do have a very strong flavour. In my opinion the spring leaves make a very good herb vinegar.

**Wormwood:** wormwood is renowned for its use in many drinks, such as absinthe and vermouth.

## Medicinal uses

French tarragon is a very good digestive, antioxidant, diuretic and sedative. It contains vitamins A, B and C, as well as calcium, magnesium and potassium. It is also very beneficial for the liver, eases heartburn and gastric upsets. A tea made from tarragon leaves drunk before bedtime is said to overcome insomnia. Southernwood and wormwood have been used to expel worms, though please do not self-medicate. Sweet wormwood has been used in Traditional Chinese Medicine for over 2,000 years to treat fevers. Research began in the early 1970s in response to increasing resistance to established anti-malarial dugs. It has now been endorsed by the WHO (World Health Organization) for the treatment of malaria, and is currently under research at the Royal Botanic Gardens, Kew.

**Right** *Artemisia dracunculus*, French Tarragon

# Bergera koenigii (Murraya koeniggi)

**When I first started herb farming over 40 years ago, the only curry plant available in the UK was *Helichrysum italicum*, an evergreen shrub that perfumed the air with the scent of curry. With the advent of TV chefs, the new culinary delight on the market was the leaf from the curry tree. This was imported from Sri Lanka either dried or preserved in oil. My first plant was given to me over 25 years ago. I treasured this baby and only ate a few of its leaves each year. I was so excited when 10 years later I saw, for the first time, this herb growing in a herb garden in The Royal Botanic Garden in Sydney. It was prolific and I realised I would need loads more patience growing my small, now 10-year-old plant in the cool climate of the UK.**

*Bergera koenigii* (syn *Murraya koenigii*), Curry Leaf

## History

The use of curry leaves as a flavouring for vegetables is described in early Tamil literature dating back to the 1st century AD. These leaves are essential for the authentic flavour of Southern Indian and Sri Lankan cuisine.

## Species

*Bergera koenigii*, Curry Leaf
Tropical, H1C (USDA 11), evergreen shrub or small tree. Height: up to 4m (13ft); spread: up to 3m (9ft). Clusters of small, creamy-white, sweetly scented, star-shaped flowers from late summer, which are followed by small black edible fruit, the seed of which is poisonous if digested. Soft, oval-shaped, glossy, green pinnate leaves, which are very aromatic. Each leaf is divided into 11–21 leaflets which have a marvellous aroma when crushed and an even better flavour when eaten.

## Propagation

Propagating the curry leaf is one of the skills of which I am most proud. It has taken me over 20 years to crack it because I did not want to use extra light or heat the glasshouse to a high temperature as that would upset all my other herbs. The trick is fresh seed, harvested from my own plants which are acclimatised. I sow the seeds as soon as they are ripe and soft.

**Seeds:** sow fresh seeds in late autumn in prepared modules or seed trays using three parts standard seed compost with one part perlite. Place under protection at 18°C (64°F). Germination can be slow – 1–9 months.

**Cuttings:** take cuttings from the new strong growth in late spring/early summer, choosing non-flowering shoots. Use a module tray filled with equal parts potting compost and perlite. Place in a heated propagator at 18–20°C (64–68°F); do not let the cuttings dry out. Grow on in a small pot, using three parts soil-based compost with one part perlite, under protection for at least two seasons.

**Cuttings from suckers:** carefully remove the small suckers, which grow around the base of a mature shrub, trying to maintain some small roots. Grow on in a small pot, using the same mix as for rooted cuttings. Do not plant out for at least two seasons in warm climates, never in cold climates.

## Pests and diseases

Young plants are prone to aphid attack. Treat them with liquid horticultural soap following the manufacturer's instructions. When grown inside watch out for mealybugs and scale. To treat these please see page 270. Root rot may occur if the compost is kept too wet, especially in winter.

## How and where to grow

The curry leaf can only be grown in a garden in the tropics or sub tropics where it prefers a fertile light soil in partial shade. It will adapt to dry hot climates, however, it will not be so productive nor so tall. When growing it outside the tropics it will need protection when the night temperatures fall below 12°C (54°F).

## Growing in containers

The curry leaf makes a lovely container plant; it's great as a house plant (as long as it has a good light source) or a conservatory plant. Pot up using three parts soil-based compost mixed with one part standard perlite. Keep in a frost-free environment. Feed monthly through the growing season with a liquid seaweed fertiliser.

In winter, we keep our pots of curry leaf at a minimum of 8°C (46°F). Some years, if the temperature dips below that, the plants shed their leaves – do not panic. If you keep the plant virtually, but not totally dry, and keep the minimum temperature no lower than 8°C (46°F) the leaves will return in the spring as the days get longer and the temperature increases.

## Yearly maintenance

**Spring:** prick out and pot up germinated seedlings.

**Summer:** check for aphids on new growth.

**Autumn:** bring inside before the evening temperature dips below 12°C (54°F).

**Winter:** sow fresh seed.

## Harvesting and storing

**Leaves:** the best time for harvest is before flowering. When fresh, the leaves have a very short shelf life; they may be stored in the refrigerator for up to a week or they can be frozen. In the main they are usually dried, so if you have a tree and wish to dry them, pick them then divide into individual leaflets, place on a muslin frame on a tray in a light airy room. They take about 7 days to become crisp and dry. Store in a dark jar.

## Culinary uses

The pungent, aromatic leaves are a common ingredient in curries, chutneys and stews. Since South Indian cuisine is predominantly vegetarian, curry leaves seldom appear in non-vegetarian food; the main uses are in lentil or vegetable curries and stuffings for samosas. Because of their soft texture, they are not always removed before serving.
In some recipes the leaves are oven-dried and toasted immediately before use or quickly fried in butter or oil; this scented oil is then poured on top of dishes to add richness and flavour. Equally, the leaves can be dropped into hot oil before adding to the main ingredient.

## Medicinal uses

The leaves are a digestive, tonic, stimulant and rich in vitamin A and calcium. Fresh leaves, eaten raw, are reputedly a good cure for dysentery. They can be made into an infusion to stop vomiting, or drunk to lower blood pressure, so do not drink this infusion if you are on blood pressure pills. The traditional use of the curry leaf to treat diabetes has attracted a great deal of interest. Recent medicinal research has found special compounds that could make it an effective new medicine in the treatment of diabetes.

# Borago officinalis

**This wild herb, originating in the Mediterranean, has managed to naturalise in northern Europe and North America. It brings back very positive and happy memories of my childhood when I used to make necklaces by stringing borage flowers together. For my 21st birthday my mother put the flowers in ice cubes, then into an ice bucket with a bottle of champagne. Here in my vegetable garden I have it surrounding my French beans for this is the one herb that helps with the pollination of vegetables as all forms of bees love it, hence one of its common names 'bee-bread'.**

*Borago officinalis*, Borage

## History

It was the Romans' courage and comfort 'cuppa', often given to young soldiers before they marched off to war. It was for courage, too, that borage flowers were floated in stirrup cups given to the Crusaders. Interestingly in Roman times borage was considered a pot herb/ vegetable and the leaves were added to vegetable stews.

**WARNING** | The fresh leaves can cause contact dermatitis.

## Species

*Borago officinalis*, Borage
Hardy, H4 (USDA 8,9), annual. Height and spread: 60cm (24in). Loose racemes of blue star-shaped flowers with black stamens from early summer until the first frosts. Bristly, oval or oblong, succulent mid-green leaves.

*Borago officinalis* 'Alba', White Borage
Hardy, H4 (USDA 8,9), annual. Height: 45cm (18in); spread: 60cm (24in). Loose racemes of white star-shaped flowers with black stamens from early summer until the first frosts. Bristly, oval or oblong, succulent mid-green leaves.

*Borago pygmaea*, Prostrate Borage, Corsican Borage
Hardy, H4 (USDA 8,9), perennial. Height and spread: 45cm (18in). Bright blue, small, star-shaped flowers which fade to pink with age. Very bristly, oval-shaped, dark green leaves that grow in basal rosettes. Only the flowers are edible.

## Propagation

**Seeds:** sow the seeds of all forms of borage in early spring into prepared pots or modules using a standard seed compost. Place under 18°C (64°F). Germination takes 5–14 days. Alternatively, sow seeds in late spring into prepared open ground, when the air temperature does not drop below 7°C (45°F) at night. Germination takes 2–3 weeks. Thin seedlings to 60cm (24in) apart. Borage has a long tap root and hates being disturbed, so if started in a pot, once the seedlings are large enough to handle, plant in their final position and do not move again.

**Division:** Corsican borage is a perennial so established plants can be divided in the spring, then replanted into a prepared site in the garden.

## Pests and diseases

If you are growing borage as a companion plant, black fly will not worry you, however, if it is in the garden and becoming a nuisance, spray it with horticultural liquid soap. At the end of the season, borage can be susceptible to mildew. As it is an annual, it is far better to dig the plant up so that this disease does not spread to comfrey or your courgettes, if grown in the vegetable garden.

## How and where to grow

Plant in a well-drained, light, poor soil in a sunny position, although it will tolerate most soils, including clay. If the soil is too rich, borage can grow tall and weak and require staking.

## Growing in containers

All forms of borage adapt to being grown in a container using a soil-based compost. Because the annual borages can grow tall when in flower and because of its long tap root, choose a container that is deep enough and has a wide base. It looks lovely combined with other annuals, such as poppies and cornflowers, as when they flower they will all help to hold each other up.

## Yearly maintenance

**Spring:** sow seeds.

**Summer:** sow seeds for a later crop. Look out for flower heads turning into seeds – collect or destroy if you do not want hundreds of borage plants all over the garden.

**Autumn:** remove old plants – do not add to the compost if you do not want borage plants appearing all over your garden.

**Winter:** final removal of old plants.

## Harvesting and storing

**Leaves:** the young leaves are by far the best for use in cooking. As this is a bit of a thug of a herb there are always new shoots and new leaves appearing. Always pick the leaves before the flowers form.

**Flowers:** pick the flowers throughout the summer.

**Seeds:** collect seed for next season's crop in autumn.

## Culinary uses

**Leaves:** the fine bristles on the surface of a young leaf dissolve on the tongue when eaten. The leaf has a cool, cucumber flavour. They are great cut up and added to salads, cream cheese or yoghurt. The leaves are very high in mineral salts so are good for those on a salt-free diet. The best way to use them cooked is to make a lovely cold summer soup. Alternatively, the leaves combine well with spinach and make a great filling for pasta.

**Flowers:** the flowers look lovely added to salads – both vegetable and fruit, frozen in ice cubes or in ice bowls and added to summer drinks such as Pimm's. They look beautiful crystallised for cake decoration.

## Medicinal uses

The leaves and flowers are rich in potassium and calcium and are therefore a good blood purifier and a tonic. Because it is a tonic for the adrenal glands, borage provides an invaluable support for a stressful lifestyle.

One day when I was driving over the Downs in the late 1980s I saw this amazing blue crop. I had to stop to find out what it was, it was borage which was being grown as a crop for gamma linoleic acid (GLA), and it was considered an even more valuable medicinal substance than evening primrose oil. Subsequently, cultivation problems coincided with a dramatic slump in prices because a waste – blackcurrant pulp – provided a cheaper and richer source of GLA. Hopes for the future of borage as a commercial crop have diminished, but it is a plant that I believe deserves more medicinal research.

*Borago pygmaea*, Corsican Borage

# Brassica juncea

**I am totally fascinated by the origins of plants. I spend hours at the Herb Farm checking the seedlings that appear in our Herbetum, always looking out for a new species. This delicious, useful annual herb apparently originates from the natural hybridisation between *Brassica nigra* (black mustard) and *Brassica rapa* (turnip mustard), a fact that has only been discovered since the sequencing of plant DNA.**

*Brassica juncea* 'Rubra Crispa', Red Frills Mustard

## History

Mustard has been used for thousands of years both medicinally and for cooking. The Romans used *Brassica juncea*, brown mustard, as a pungent salad vegetable and the seeds of *Brassica nigra*, black mustard, as a spice. The English name 'mustard' is said to derive from the Latin *mustem ardens*, which translates as 'burning wine', a reference to the heat of mustard and the French practice of mixing unfermented grape juice with the ground seeds.

## Species

*Brassica juncea*, Brown Mustard
Hardy, H3 (USDA 9), annual. Height: up to 80cm (30in); spread: 30cm (12in). Clusters of pale yellow flowers in summer followed by long seed pods with brown seeds. Oval, lobed, olive-green leaves with pale green veins and crinkled edges.

*Brassica juncea* 'Rubra Crispa', Red Frills Mustard
Hardy, H3 (USDA 9), annual. Height: up to 30cm (12in); spread: 20cm (8in). Yellow flowers in summer. Oval, red-purple-tinted leaves with toothed edges and a pungent mustard flavour. Good in salads and sandwiches.

*Brassica nigra*, Black Mustard
Hardy, H3 (USDA 9), annual. Height: up to 90cm (35in); spread: 30cm (12in). Pale yellow flowers in summer followed by long seed pods with dark brown seeds. Rough, bristly, oval, lobed green leaves.

## Propagation

**Seeds:** sow seeds in the spring for seed and leaf production and in the autumn for leaf, into pots or plug modules using a standard seed compost. Cover with perlite, place under protection at 15°C (59°F). Germination takes 5–10 days. Plant out after hardening off at a distance of 20cm (8in) apart. Alternatively, sow seeds in late spring or early autumn into prepared open ground, when the air temperature does not go below 7°C (45°F) at night. Germination takes 2–3 weeks. Once the seedlings are large enough, thin to 20cm (8in) apart.

## Pests and diseases

All mustards can be attacked by flea beetle, which is a tiny, shiny, dark blue beetle that hops from plant to plant. A tell-tale sign that the plants are being attacked is small round holes on the leaves, which turn pale brown making the leaves look unattractive. The best organic method is to put a horticultural mesh over the plants in spring so that the beetles cannot attack the leaves.

## How and where to grow

All brassicas like to feed well and mustard is no exception. Give the site a good feed of well-rotted manure and/or compost in the winter prior to sowing in the spring. Don't make the soil too rich as this will create soft and flabby growth that is prone to attack from pests. When sowing in the autumn for leaf production, clear the soil of weeds a month before sowing, then cover the soil with compost. Make a shallow drill and sow direct. Keep the seedlings well watered, covering with horticultural fleece for the first few weeks.

When grown as a green manure in contaminated land, mustard helps clean the soil of heavy metals, a process called phytoremediation. Used as a green manure in the vegetable garden it can help reduce soil-borne root-rot diseases.

## Growing in containers

Mustard can successfully be grown in a container, using a standard potting compost. Place the container in partial shade. Water and feed with a liquid fertiliser regularly from spring until early autumn. Crop regularly to keep the leaves young and succulent.

## Yearly maintenance

**Spring:** sow seeds.

**Summer:** pick leaves and flowers.

**Autumn:** harvest seeds; sow autumn crop.

**Winter:** prepare ground for next season's crop.

## Harvesting and storing

**Leaves:** pick young leaves as required.

**Flowers:** pick flowers just as they open.

**Seeds:** harvest the seed pods as they change colour. Dry the pods in a light airy room until totally dried, remove the seeds from the pods and store in clean jars with a tight lid.

## Culinary uses

**Leaves:** the mustard leaves have a distinctive warm peppery taste and are very low in sodium so are excellent as part of a low-sodium diet. They can be eaten raw, sliced or added to stir-fry dishes.

**Flowers:** the flowers also have a mild mustard flavour. They are great in salads, stir-fry dishes and can transform a sandwich into a delight.

**Seeds:** mustard seeds are only pungent when crushed. The flavour of the crushed seeds increases when mixed with water and allowed to stand. If, on the other hand, you mix the crushed seed with vinegar or salt, you kill the flavour and if you boil the seed it will become bitter.

## Medicinal uses

Mustard has been and is still used to ease muscular pain and treat respiratory tract infections. It is a warming stimulant with antibiotic effects. In China, the leaves are eaten to ease bladder inflammation. In Korea, the seeds are used in the treatment of abscesses, colds, lumbago, rheumatism and stomach disorders. Since 2002, numerous medical papers have been written that have found mustard seeds inhibit the growth of cancerous cells in animals.

**WARNING** | Mustard seeds have been known to cause an allergic reaction. Prolonged contact with the skin can cause blistering.

# Bulbine frutescens

**I was lucky enough to see this attractive drought-resistant herb in South Africa, where it can be found growing naturally in clumps with their lovely yellow and/or orange flowers dancing in the sun. It grows in the desert grasslands of the Northern, Western and Eastern Capes.**

## History

As an indigenous plant of South Africa, bulbine has played a pivotal role in traditional healing and has been used by the Zulu for hundreds of years, not only to cure rashes, to stop bleeding and as an antidote to poison, but also to treat their sick livestock.

## Species

*Bulbine frutescens*, Bulbine
Tender, H3 (USDA 9), evergreen perennial. Height: up to 60cm (24in) when in flower; spread: up to 1m (3ft). Attractive, star-shaped, yellow/orange single flowers that grow in a linear cluster around the stem, appearing sequentially throughout the summer. The flower has a characteristic hairy stamen. The leaves are succulent, cylindrical and narrow, and vary in length. They are glutinous when broken.

*Bulbine latifolia* syn. *Bulbine natalensis*, Broad-leaved Bulbine
Tender, H3 (USDA 9), evergreen perennial. Height: up to 60cm (24in) when in flower; spread: up to 1m (3ft). Attractive, star-shaped, yellow flowers, which grow on 60cm (24in) flowering spikes throughout the summer. Triangular, aloe-like, succulent green leaves, which form a basal crown.

## Propagation

**Seeds:** sow fresh seeds in spring into prepared seed trays or module plugs, using a seed compost mixed in equal parts with perlite. Place under protection at 18°C (64°F). Germination takes 10–20 days, however it is erratic as, like many herbs, it will happily self-seed in a warm garden but in a controlled situation it will sometimes not perform. Once the seedling is well rooted, pot up using a seed compost mixed in equal parts with horticultural sand. Grow on until the plant has at least four well-developed leaves before either planting out – in warm climates – in a prepared site in the garden or potting up in cold climates to grow on as a container plant.

**Cuttings:** cuttings can be taken from early spring for plants raised under protection or late spring for plants grown outside. Using a sharp knife take a cutting with some roots attached. Put the cuttings into a small pot or large module plug, using a seed compost mixed in equal parts with propagating bark. Place the container in a warm position. It will root very quickly. Once the plant is established, either pot up using a loam-based compost mixed in equal parts with horticultural sand or, in warm climates, plant out into a prepared site in the garden.

**Division:** this plant grows rapidly in a container or garden and benefits from being divided. In spring or early summer, before dividing, remove all the flowering stems, this will make it easier to handle and also to see what one is doing. Divide established garden plants, replanting immediately into a prepared site.

## Pests and diseases

This herb is rarely troubled by pests or disease, except for vine weevil when grown in pots. To control this pest repot every spring removing the weevil by hand, alternatively use a natural predator (see page 272).

Mealybugs may also cause problems. These are small, oval, sap-sucking insects up to 4mm (⅛in) long. They look like tiny pinkish or grey woodlice close up, but are usually covered with a fluffy layer of protective wax. Colonies resemble blobs of sticky cotton wool and may be accompanied by sooty mould. They are particularly annoying when growing tender herbs in a conservatory or heat glasshouse. To learn how to control this pest see page 270.

## How and where to grow

This herb is a good drought-loving plant. Plant in a well-drained fertile soil in full sun or semi-shade and protected from cold winds. It is ideally suited for growing in cities where the night temperature does not fall below -5°C (23°F). Alternatively, in cold climates, lift the plant from the garden before the frosts start and then winter in a greenhouse.

## Growing in containers

This useful attractive herb, which can flower all year round, is ideal for growing in a warm conservatory as it requires good light. Pot up using a loam-based potting compost mixed in equal parts with horticultural sand. Water regularly and feed monthly, from spring until autumn, with a liquid fertiliser, following the manufacturer's instructions. It is advisable either to divide and repot, or simply repot each year.

## Yearly maintenance

**Spring:** in early spring remove flowering spikes; sow fresh seeds and divide established clumps.

**Summer:** remove flowering spikes that have finished flowering; take cuttings.

**Autumn:** remove flowering spikes.

**Winter:** do not over-water, however, do not allow the compost to become totally dry. Protect when temperatures drop below 0°C (32°F).

## Harvesting and storing

The leaves can be picked for use throughout the year.

## Culinary uses

None.

## Medicinal uses

The leaves are filled with a clear gel similar in appearance and consistency to aloe vera (see page 48). This gel can be used directly on minor burns, wounds, cuts, abrasions, stings and rashes. It can also be used to treat eczema, cracked lips and herpes. An infusion or tincture made from the roots of *Bulbine latifolia* is taken to quell sickness and diarrhoea; it is also used to treat urinary complaints and rheumatism. Currently the medicinal properties of this herb are under research, the leaf gel is being used to aid the healing of post-operative scars.

*Bulbine frutescens*, Bulbine

*Bulbine latifolia* syn. *Bulbine natalensis*, Broad-leaved Bulbine

# Calendula officinalis

**This cheerful herb is a native of the Mediterranean and Iran and is now grown worldwide, often as a garden plant rather than for its herbal properties. It has been said that simply looking at the colourful flowers lifts the spirits and encourages cheerfulness – and I agree. It is a very good barometer as the flowers are sensitive to temperature variation and dampness, so open flowers forecast a fine day.**

*Calendula officinalis* 'Indian Prince', Marigold Indian Prince

## History

This ancient herb has been used as a medicine, a colourant and cosmetic in Arabic and Indian cultures. Because the marigold flower follows the sun, it became a symbol of obedience. However, in the language of flowers, the pot marigold represents pain and grief. On a happier note, in medieval times, the flowers were considered an emblem of love; it was said that if they appeared in your dreams this was an omen of good things to come and to simply look at them drove away evil humours.

## Species

*Calendula officinalis*, Marigold
Hardy, H3 (USDA 9), annual. Height and spread: up to 60cm (24in). Large, orange/yellow, daisy-like single or double flowers that are in bloom from spring until the first frosts. Lance-shaped, slightly hairy, lightly aromatic, light green leaves.

*Calendula officinalis* Fiesta Gitana, Marigold Fiesta Gitana Group
Hardy, H3 (USDA 9), annual. Height and spread: up to 35cm (14in). Large, orange/yellow, daisy-like double flowers that are in bloom from spring until the first frosts. Lance-shaped, slightly hairy, light green leaves.

*Calendula officinalis* 'Indian Prince', Marigold Indian Prince
Hardy, H3 (USDA 9), annual. Height and spread: up to 48cm (19in). Large, deep orange flowers that have a dark crimson back to the petals – they flower from spring until the first frosts. Lance-shaped, slightly hairy, light green leaves.

## Propagation

**Seeds:** sow seeds in early spring into prepared small pots or modules using a standard seed compost. Place under protection at 18°C (64°F). Germination takes 5–14 days. Alternatively, sow seeds in late spring into prepared open ground, after all threat of frost has passed and when the air temperature does not go below 5°C (41°F) at night.

## Pests and diseases

Slugs love the leaves of young marigolds. Mount a night-time vigil with a torch and a bucket, or beer traps will be needed in late spring. Marigolds can become infested with black fly, which spreads very quickly. You can treat this in the early stages by brushing off the fly and cutting away the affected areas. If really uncontrollable, spray with a horticultural soft soap, as directed by the manufacturer's instructions. In early autumn, when the weather becomes damp, the leaves can sometimes become covered with powdery mildew. Cut these off and burn to stop mildew spreading to other plants, but as marigold is an annual it is sometimes safer to bin them. For more information on pests and diseases see pages 266–276.

## How and where to grow

Marigold is a very tolerant plant; it will grow in virtually any soil with the exception of waterlogged. It prefers and looks best in a sunny position. Sow directly into a prepared site, in the late spring or early summer; it will germinate easily. When the seedlings are large enough to handle, thin to 30–45cm (12–18in) apart.

Marigolds are a very good companion plant; however, do not confuse this marigold – *Calendula officinalis*, which deters asparagus beetle and tomato horn worms – with French or African marigold (*Tagetes*), which deters white fly and Mexican bean beetles.

## Growing in containers

Marigolds look very cheerful in containers and combine well with other plants. They are well suited to window boxes but are not so good in hanging baskets as they will become stretched and leggy. Use a soil-based compost, pinch out the growing tips to stop the plant from becoming too tall and leggy. Deadhead the flowers when flowering finishes, to encourage more throughout the season.

## Yearly maintenance

**Spring:** sow seeds in garden.

**Summer:** deadhead flowers to promote more flowering.

**Autumn:** sow seeds under protection for early spring flowering.

**Winter:** protect young plants.

## Harvesting and storing

**Leaves:** pick the leaves when young and use them when they are fresh; they're not much good preserved.

**Flowers:** pick just-opened flowers any time in the summer for using fresh and for drying. Dry at a low temperature to preserve the colour.

## Culinary uses

**Leaves:** traditionally the word 'pot' before the common name indicates that it was used as a pot herb and the leaves were added to the pot over the open fire. Today the young leaves can be added to salads, however this is an acquired taste!

**Flowers:** the flower petals are known as poor man's saffron; they are a very good natural culinary dye. They can be used to make cheese, butter, scones and omelettes more golden.

## Medicinal uses

Marigold is renowned as a remedy for the skin: it is effective for most minor skin problems, cuts, grazes, wounds, inflamed skin, including minor burns, sunburn, many rashes and fungal conditions, such as athlete's foot, thrush and ring worm. It is helpful for nappy rash. The sap from the stem has the reputation for removing warts, corns and calluses. If you infuse the flowers of marigold and use it as a skin lotion it reduces large pores, nourishes and clears the skin, and is good for spots and pimples.

# Capparis spinosa

**This trailing evergreen shrub is now native in the Mediterranean but most probably originated in the Middle East. It can be seen growing in the most unlikely places, from the ruins of ancient walls to the rubble of a newly built hotel, and also near the seashore. When I first saw the caper flower, I fell in love. It is stunning. It is also fascinating to realise that the capers you buy in the jars are made from the flower bud and the seed pods are known as caper berries.**

*Capparis spinosa* var. *inermis*, Caper

## History

The first recorded use of the caper was by the Sumerians in 2000 BC, for medicinal purposes. Since then it has not only been used for its medicinal properties but also as a very useful condiment in the kitchen.

## Species

*Capparis spinosa*, Caper
Half hardy, H3 (USDA 9), evergreen shrub. Height: up to 1m (3ft); spread: up to 1.5m (5ft). Masses of green buds (it is these that are pickled), followed by very pretty, solitary, white four-petalled flowers with long pink/purple stamen from early summer until autumn. Oval, mid-green, with a hint of brown, leaves with two stipular spines at the base of the leaf. These leaves grow on long stems which have been known to reach over 1.5m (5ft) in length.

*Capparis spinosa var. inermis*, Spineless Caper
Half hardy, H3 (USDA 9), semi-deciduous evergreen shrub. Height: up to 90cm (3ft); spread: up to 1.2m (4ft). Masses of edible green buds followed by solitary, pinkish-white four-petalled flowers with long pink/purple stamen from early summer until autumn. Oval, mid-green with a hint of brown, leaves. This caper lacks the stipular spines.

## Propagation

**Seeds:** if possible, sow fresh caper seeds, straight from a ripe pod, into prepared seed trays. Place in a heated propagator at 18°C (64°F). Germination is erratic: some seedlings come through very quickly, some take longer – anything up to 4 months. Once the seeds dry, they are dormant and are notably more difficult to germinate. Immerse the dried seed in hot water – 40°C (104°F) – and leave to soak for a day. Carefully remove the seeds and place them on some damp white kitchen towel. Put the kitchen towel with the seeds into a sealed container and keep in the refrigerator for 2–3 months. After refrigeration, soak the seeds again in warm water overnight and then sow into prepared modules or plug trays, filled with a seed compost mixed in equal parts with perlite. Sow the seeds on the surface of the compost and cover with perlite. Keep warm at a minimum of 10°C (50°F). Plants raised from seed will not flower until their fourth or fifth year.

**Cuttings:** the most consistent method is to raise plants from cuttings taken from the new growth in spring. Put them into prepared modules or plug trays filled with seed compost mixed in equal parts with propagating bark, or sharp horticultural sand for extra drainage. Put the tray on a heated propagator at 18°C (64°F), making sure the cuttings do not dry out. Once well rooted, pot up using a loam compost mixed in equal parts with propagating bark.

## Pests and diseases

This herb is rarely attacked by pests. Young cuttings and seedlings can keel over if the watering is either too much or too little.

## How and where to grow

A simple rule of thumb is that the caper bush can be planted where the olive tree grows. It will thrive when planted in lean, well-drained soil in a hot, sunny location with little or no water. It hates damp, cold wet winters so, if you live at cooler latitudes, it will need to be grown in a container. As an ornamental plant, caper bushes can be an attractive loose ground cover; a specimen small shrub can be used as an espalier, which presents the flower buds well for picking. The caper bush is salt-tolerant and will flourish along shores. As flowers are born on first-year branches, cut back plants back annually in the autumn.

## Growing in containers

Capers are ideal as a pot plant for those living in a damp cold climate. For ease and self preservation I advise growing the spineless variety *Capparis spinosa* var. *inermis*. My top tip is to prune to reshape in the autumn, repot in the spring using a loam potting compost mixed in equal parts with horticultural grit or standard perlite. Protect the plant in winter and keep watering to the absolute minimum.

## Yearly maintenance

**Spring:** take cuttings.

**Summer:** harvest flowering buds.

**Autumn:** sow fresh seed; prune established plants.

**Winter:** protect container plants from excessive wet in winter.

## Harvesting and storing

**Leaves:** harvest the leaves before flowering in late spring. Preserve in brine or pickle.

**Flower buds:** pick the flower buds early in the morning, in case they open, from early summer until early autumn. Use for pickling and salting.

**Berries:** harvest the berries (the seed pods), when they are still firm to the touch in early autumn and preserve in brine or pickle. Use with salads or charcuterie boards.

**Roots:** the roots are dug up in autumn, the bark is then stripped from the roots and dried prior to medicinal use.

## Culinary uses

**Leaves:** the leaves are edible, either boiled or pickled and stored in brine prior to being added to salads or used with fish and cheese dishes, especially cream cheese, which makes the combination of brine leaf and cheese magical.

**Flower buds:** the flower buds are bright green and tightly closed; the smallest have the best flavour. However, if eaten fresh they do not taste particularly good, the flavour comes only after they have been pickled. This is due to the development of an organic acid called capric acid, which is an important flavouring in the kitchen. Capers are used in many dishes, including fish and boiled meats.

**Berries:** the seed pods are green verging on olive, depending on the summer. The flavour is best once they have been pickled or preserved in brine.

## Medicinal uses

The parts used medicinally are the bark from the roots and the flower buds. The bark is used to treat diarrhoea and rheumatism. In South Africa the roots are used to treat insanity, snake bites, chest pains, jaundice and malaria and the flower buds are used to treat coughs.

# Cedronella canariensis

**As its botanical name indicates, this herb is a native of the Canary Islands, as well as the Azores and Madeira, but it has now naturalised in South Africa, New Zealand and California. Over three decades ago I was given my first plant by a neighbour who was a true plant collector. He used to arrive at the Herb Farm, shout my name from the gate in a booming voice, and say, 'I have brought you treasures'. Our deal was that he would give me plants as long as I gave him some of its babies the following spring.**

## History

Rather confusingly, this lovely aromatic herb shares the common name 'balm of Gilead' with three other plants that have similar musky eucalyptus, camphor-scented leaves and roots. Their botanical names are *Commiphora opobalsamum* which was given to Solomon by the Queen of Sheba and is a very rare aromatic desert shrub found in the holy lands, this is now endangered and has protected status; *Balsamodendron opobalsamum*, which is mentioned in the Bible though is now sadly thought to be extinct; and *Populus balsamifera*, a medicinal tree that grows in temperate countries. If you grow this plant, on an early summer's day, you will catch a waft of sweet balsam on the warm air.

## Species

*Cedronella canariensis* (syn. *triphylla*), Balm of Gilead Hardy, H3 (USDA 9), perennial. A subshrub that is short-lived in cold climates. Height: up to 1m (3ft) when in flower; spread 60cm (24in). Pink to pale mauve, two-lipped flowers in summer, which are followed by lovely black seeds that look like miniature teasel heads. Strongly eucalyptus-scented, three-lobed, tooth-edged leaves. Square stems.

## Propagation

**Seeds:** sow the seeds in spring into prepared modules or a seed tray filled with a standard compost. Water the container prior to sowing, then sow the seeds on the surface and cover with a thin layer of perlite. Place under protection at 18°C (64°F). Germination takes 14–20 days; it can be spasmodic, so be patient. Once germinated be careful not to overwater as the seedlings are prone to damping off (see page 274).

**Cuttings:** take cuttings from the new non-flowering growth in early summer. Fill a small pot or modules with three parts seed compost mixed with one part perlite. When the cuttings have rooted, pot in small pots using a soil-based compost, then winter under cover in a frost-free environment. Plant out in the following spring once all threat of frost has passed.

## Pests and diseases

When balm of Gilead is grown as a pot plant it can suffer from white fly, especially when grown in a conservatory. Spray with horticultural soft soap or one of the modern organic sprays, which contain a blend of surfactants and nutrients, following the manufacturer's instructions (see page 272 for more information). Seedlings are prone to damping off (see page 274).

## How and where to grow

Plant in a warm sunny site, ideally against a south-facing wall in a very well-drained soil. It will need protection in cool climates. If you are likely to have night temperatures that fall below -3°C (27°C) it would be advisable to dig up the plant in the garden in early autumn, pot it up and winter in a frost-free greenhouse or conservatory. If you are only likely to have the occasional light frost, then cover the plant in the garden with horticultural fleece. This herb has a bit of an unruly habit, so it is worth cutting back lightly after flowering and again in the spring to encourage new growth from the base of the plant. In a warm garden a mature plant can self-seed. In spring check the leaves of the seedlings are scented so that you don't confuse with young nettles as they look very similar.

## Growing in containers

Balm of Gilead makes a very attractive large container plant. Pot up annually until the plant reaches full size, using a soil-based compost. The flowers are very long-lasting and will hold their flower for most of the summer; they are followed by attractive seed heads. When you water the plant the scent of the leaves will fill a greenhouse or conservatory with a delightful perfume. Trim in the late summer after flowering and in the spring to maintain shape. Feed monthly with a liquid seaweed fertiliser. In winter lift the pots off the ground so that the plant can drain and cut back the watering so that the root ball is just damp and not sodden.

## Yearly maintenance

**Spring:** sow seeds under protection; plant out once all threat of frost has passed.

**Summer:** take cuttings in early summer from new shoots; trim in late summer to restore shape.

**Autumn:** collect seeds.

**Winter:** protect from frosts and excessive rain.

## Harvesting and storing

**Leaves:** pick leaves for drying before the plant starts to flower.

**Flowers:** pick flowers for drying just as they start to open.

**Seeds:** pick seed heads for drying any time after the flower petals have fully dropped.

## Culinary uses

None.

## Medicinal uses

Medicinally the leaves can be used in an infusion to clear the head or blocked nose, which is sometimes called 'thé de Canaries'. An infusion of the leaves can be added to bath water for an invigorating bath.

The leaves can be rubbed on to the skin as a mosquito repellent. The leaves also have the reputation of being an aphrodisiac – I could not possibly comment.

*Cedronella canariensis*, Balm of Gilead

**Common names:** Gotu Kola, Pennywort, Indian Pennywort, Tiger Grass, Brahmi

# Centella asiatica

**This is an important ancient medicinal herb, native to the subtropical and tropical climates of India, Pakistan, Sri Lanka and South Africa, where it can be found growing in swampy areas including paddy fields. The first time I saw it growing was in South Africa where it was being used for skin complaints and I was informed that it was also used to treat leprosy. A few years later I went to Malaysia where it was part of ulam, used as a culinary herb to stimulate the appetite and aid digestion. Today it is one of the key ingredients in South Korean face creams.**

*Centella asiatica*, Gotu Kola flower

## History

In China, gotu kola is described as one of the 'miracle elixirs of life'. This was attributed to a healer named Li Ching Yun who reputedly lived 256 years by drinking a tea brewed from gotu kola and other herbs. In areas of India it is known as tiger herb because it is said that wounded tigers roll in the leaves to help themselves heal. It has been an important Ayurvedic medicinal herb for thousands of years where it is called Brahmi, or knowledge. It was also reputed to prolong life. A Sinhalese proverb says, 'two leaves a day keep old age away'. It did not become important in Western medicine until the 1800s.

## Species

*Centella asiatica*, Gotu Kola
Tender, H3 (USDA 9), partial evergreen. Height: 8cm (3in) with an indefinite spread. In summer, the tiny magenta flowers are surrounded by green bracts which grow in small umbels near to the soil surface. Bright green, kidney-shaped leaves with indented margins.

## Propagation

**Seeds:** in warm climates this herb will happily self-seed, conversely in cool climates it rarely sets seed. As I grow this herb in a polytunnel I have found that after a hot summer, in early autumn, it has set seed. Collect the seed and sow under protection at 18°C (64°F). Use a seed compost mixed in equal parts with vermiculite to make sure the compost does not dry out. The seedlings will emerge the following spring.

**Cuttings:** as this plant tends to root where the stems touch the ground, it is prolific when growing in damp conditions. It is easy to propagate any time during the growing season from spring until early autumn. Separate the plantlet from the main plant by cutting the stem above the ground, and then gently tease the small roots from the ground. Depending on the size of the root, you can then either pot on into small pots or trim the roots and ease them into a plug tray using a seed compost mixed in equal parts with vermiculite. Once rooted, which happens very quickly in summer, pot up using a loam-based compost mixed in equal parts with vermiculite and winter the plants in a frost-free environment.

**Division:** divide established plants in summer either replanting into a prepared site in the garden or repotting using a loam-based compost mixed in equal parts with vermiculite.

## Pests and diseases

When grown as a container plant it can be prone to red spider mite. If this is the case introduce *Phytoseiulus persimilis*, its natural predator, or treat regularly with horticultural soap following the manufacturer's instructions. Do not use both.

## How and where to grow

This plant will only grow successfully outside all year round in tropical or subtropical climates. Its appearance changes, depending on growing conditions. In shallow water, the plant puts forth floating roots and the leaves rest on top of the water. In dry locations, it puts out numerous small roots and the leaves are small and thin.

## Growing in containers

It will adapt happily to being grown in containers and looks very interesting in a hanging basket where it will cascade. Plant in a loam-based compost mixed in equal parts with vermiculite. Place the container in partial shade, not full sun. Water and feed regularly from early spring until early autumn with a liquid seaweed fertiliser following the manufacturer's instructions; this is especially important if you are harvesting the leaves regularly. In warm summers the container can live outside; don't forget to water regularly and do not allow the compost to dry out. In winter, bring the container inside to protect from frost, snow and cold rain.

*Centella asiatica*, Gotu Kola leaf

## Yearly maintenance

**Spring:** take cuttings; repot container-raised plants.

**Summer:** take cuttings and do not allow the plants to dry out at this time of year.

**Autumn:** protect young plants and container-grown plants from frost.

**Winter:** cut off any damaged leaves to prevent the spread of disease.

## Harvesting and storing

**Leaves:** pick the leaves to use them fresh from spring until late summer. Pick leaves for drying in late spring.

## Culinary uses

When harvesting leaves for use in the kitchen choose the new tender leaves, the mature ones are dry and tough, especially if grown in dry conditions. Add the young leaves to salads, sandwiches and stir-fry dishes where the dry, slightly spicy flavour combines well with fish and vegetables.

## Medicinal uses

This is one of the most important medicinal herbs I grow. It is a rejuvenating, diuretic herb that clears toxins and reduces inflammation. It is being used in the treatment of rheumatism and rheumatoid arthritis. There have been many recent papers, but one of the most interesting was in 1987 when the Indian Council of Medical Research carried out a double-blind clinical test on 30 children with learning disabilities to study the effect on their general mental ability. After a 12-week period, results indicated a significant improvement in both general ability and behavioural patterns. Gotu kola is commonly used to treat depression, but be warned it has been reported to also cause depression in well-adjusted individuals.

**WARNING** | Excessive use of this herb taken internally or externally can cause itching, headaches and even unconsciousness. Avoid gotu kola if you are pregnant or nursing, or using tranquillisers or sedatives or have an overactive thyroid.

**Common names:** Chamomile, Roman Chamomile, Ground Apple, Garden Chamomile

# Chamaemelum nobile

**There seems to be a lot of confusion over which chamomile is which. *Chamaemelum nobile*, which before reclassification was *Anthemis nobilis*, is known as Roman chamomile or garden chamomile. It is tall when in flower, looks lovely with poppies and cornflowers and the flowers are bitter so do not make a good tisane. Then there is *Chamaemelum nobile* 'Flore Pleno', double-flowered chamomile, which is low-growing, great for lawns, living herb cushions and the flowers can be used in tisanes – they are slightly sweeter than the garden chamomile. *Chamaemelum nobile* 'Treneague' is the non-flowering chamomile renowned for its lawns. There are other herbs known as chamomile: *Matricaria recutita* – German chamomile, which grows wild, is the best medicinal chamomile and is grown as a crop throughout Europe, and *Anthemis tinctoria*, dyer's chamomile, which is a plant used for dyeing.**

## History

It is said that the bowling green in Plymouth, on which Sir Francis Drake was playing bowls when the first sightings of the Spanish Armada were announced in 1588, was chamomile.

## Species

*Chamaemelum nobile*, Roman Chamomile
Hardy, H5 (USDA 7,8), evergreen perennial. Height: up to 30cm (12in) in flower; spread: up to 45cm (18in). White flowers with yellow centres all summer. Sweet-smelling, finely divided green leaves.

*Chamaemelum nobile* `Flore Pleno', Double-flowered Chamomile
Hardy H5 (USDA 7,8), evergreen perennial. Height up to 8cm (3in); spread: up to 30cm (12in). Double white flowers all summer. Dense, aromatic, finely divided green leaves.

*Chamaemelum nobile* 'Treneague', Chamomile Treneague, Lawn Chamomile
Hardy, H5 (USDA 7,8), evergreen perennial. Height up to 6cm (2.5in); spread: up to 30cm (12in). Non-flowering. Dense, aromatic, finely divided green leaves.

*Cota tinctoria*, Dyer's Chamomile, Yellow Chamomile
Hardy, H6 (USDA 6,7), perennial. Height and spread: up to 1m (3ft). Yellow, daisy flowers in the summer. The leaves are mid-green with a grey underside, and fern-like in shape. This is principally a dye plant.

*Matricaria recutita*, German Chamomile, Scented Mayweed, Wild Chamomile
Hardy, H7 (USDA 6), annual. Height: up to 60cm (24in); spread: up to 40cm (16in). Sweet-scented white flowers with conical yellow centres from spring to early summer. Finely serrated, aromatic foliage. The main use of this chamomile is medicinal.

## Propagation

**Seeds:** the species that can be grown from seed are *Anthemis tinctoria*, *Chamaemelum nobile* and *Matricaria recutita*. All these forms of chamomile have very fine seed so are best started in early spring in prepared modules or seed trays filled with a standard seed compost. Place under protection at 18°C (64°F). Germination takes 14–20 days. Because the seed is very fine, I do not advise sowing directly into soil.

**Cuttings:** Both *Chamaemelum nobile* 'Flore Pleno' and *Chamaemelum nobile* 'Treneague' can only be raised from cuttings. These can be taken in spring and autumn from the 'offsets' or clusters of young shoots. Fill small pots or large modules with a standard seed compost. Place the container in a cold greenhouse or a cold frame. Do not let the compost dry out. The cuttings will root in 10 days in summer, up to 4 weeks in autumn.

**Division:** all the perennial chamomiles will benefit from being lifted in spring of the second or third year and divided. They can be either replanted in the garden in a prepared site or potted up for a container display using a soil-based compost.

## Pests and diseases

All the chamomiles are highly aromatic, and as such they are not troubled by pests. Disease is so minimal it is not worth mentioning.

## How and where to grow

All the chamomiles need a well-drained soil and a sunny situation, but they will adapt to most growing conditions.

I do not want to be a killjoy, especially if you have set your heart on having a chamomile lawn but perhaps the following might curb your enthusiasm. A chamomile lawn is grown from the cuttings of chamomile 'Treneague' and it is high maintenance. The chosen area must be weed and stone-free and very free-draining. Plant the plants 10cm (4in) apart. Once planted they should be rolled weekly for two months with an old-fashioned roller and the area will need to be weeded by hand. I suggest you plant just a small area, a living cushion or somewhere where you regularly walk so you can experience the delightful scent of the chamomile as you crush its leaves.

Wild chamomile (*Matricaria recutita*) is a true companion plant – when planted next to ailing plants it helps revive them, which is why it is known as the 'physician's plant'. When planted next to onions it is said to repel flying insects and improve the crop yield. A spray made from the leaves and flowers helps prevent the damping off (see page 274) of seedlings. The leaves can also be added to the compost heap as an activator.

## Growing in containers

All the chamomiles adapt happily to being grown in a container using a soil-based compost. The tall dyer's chamomile and the Roman chamomile look stunning combined with cornflowers and poppies. The double-flowered chamomile makes a lovely pot, especially when in flower, and a pot of summer bulbs with lawn chamomile planted in between them can look amazing.

*Chamaemelum nobile* 'Flore Pleno', Double-flowered Chamomile

## Yearly maintenance

**Spring:** sow seeds; take cuttings; divide established plants.

**Summer:** do not allow newly planted or pot plants to dry out.

**Autumn:** take cuttings; cut back to promote new growth.

**Winter:** protect pot plants from becoming waterlogged.

## Harvesting and storing

**Leaves:** you can gather the leaves at any time, but the verdant ones in the spring and early summer have the best flavour. Use them fresh or dry.

**Flowers:** pick the flowers when they are fully open, which is around midsummer; you can use them fresh or dried. Dyer's chamomile flowers should be harvested in summer for their yellow dye.

## Culinary uses

A syrup made from wild chamomile (*Matricaria recutita*) flowers is lovely drizzled over pancakes; it can also be used in cake-making and ice cream.

## Medicinal uses

The most potent medicinal chamomile is *Matricaria recutita* (German chamomile). *Chamaemelum nobile* can be used but it is not as strong and quite bitter. There has been much research into *Matricaria recutita*, which is renowned for its sedative properties. A tea made from the flowers relieves insomnia, stress, digestive disorders, travel sickness and hyperactivity in children. Also, it can be used as a gargle for mouth ulcers and as an eye wash. Chamomile oil is good added to the bath to help you relax. A hair rinse made with chamomile flowers makes fair hair brighter.

*Chamaemelum nobile*, Roman Chamomile

**Right** *Matricaria recutita*, German Chamomile

**Common names:** Good King Henry, Wild Spinach, Lincolnshire Spinach, Lincolnshire Asparagus

# Chenopodium bonus-henricus

**Over 45 years ago I was working at Tumblers Bottom Herb Farm as a potter. One day, while potting good King Henry, I decided I had to find out who Good King Henry was, and for that matter, who was Bad Henry? It turns out that good King Henry was named after King Henry IV of Navarre, a kingdom of Spain that was dissolved in 1620, and bad Henry was Dog Mercury, *Mercurialis perennis*, which is highly poisonous.**

*Chenopodiium bonus-henricus*, Good King Henry

## History

Good King Henry was popular in the UK for hundreds of years. Until the last century the leaves were traditionally boiled and pounded with butter, the young flowering tips were eaten with salad and the seeds were added to gruel and dried and ground into flour for bread-making. In Lincolnshire, good King Henry was cultivated and became known as Lincolnshire spinach; it was popular until the 16th century when the spinach we know today arrived in the UK from Asia and quickly replaced it and all other forms of the fat hen family. There was a slight uptick in its favour after the Second World War when it was cultivated and foraged for in the wild.

## Species

*Chenopodium bonus-henricus*, Good King Henry, Lincolnshire Spinach
Hardy, H5 (USDA 7,8), herbaceous perennial. Height: up to 60cm (24in); spread: 45cm (18in). Tiny greenish-yellow flowers in summer; large, arrow-shaped mid-green leaves.

*Chenopodium giganteum*, Tree Spinach, Giant Goosefoot
Hardy, H5 (USDA 7,8), annual. Height: up to 2m (6ft); spread: up to 45cm (18in). Tiny greenish flowers in summer and arrow- and goosefoot-shaped leaves with serrated edges. The new leaves have the most wonderful magenta colour that fades to green as it ages. The young leaves can be eaten raw in salads or cooked as you would cook spinach, which makes the colour revert to green.

*Chenopodium album*, Fat Hen, Lamb's Quarters, Common Pigweed, Bacon Weed
Hardy, H7 (USDA 6), annual. Height: up to 2m (6ft); spread: up to 1m (3ft). Small greenish-white flowers in summer and green lance- and goosefoot-shaped leaves. This herb can be found growing wild all over Europe; its fatty seeds have been identified at neolithic villages in Switzerland. The seeds can be ground into flour and used to make a gruel.

## Propagation

**Seeds:** sow fresh seeds in autumn into prepared seed modules or tray filled with a standard seed compost. Germination is rapid (it takes only a few days), winter seedlings in a cold greenhouse or cold frame. Alternatively sow seeds in early spring under cover at 18°C (64°F). Germination takes 14–20 days. Seeds can also be sown directly into the soil in a prepared site that has been well fed with rotted manure the autumn before. Sow when the air temperature at night remains above 7°C (45°F), in 1cm (½in) drills, allowing 45cm (18in) between rows. Germination takes 2–3 weeks. Thin seedlings to 30cm (12in) apart.

**Division:** divide established plants of perennial species of *Chenopodium* in spring, replanting into a well-prepared site that has been fed well with well-rotted compost or manure.

## Pests and diseases

I have never known this herb suffer from pests or disease.

## How and where to grow

For the best leaf supply, plant in a sunny position, in a well-drained soil that has been fed with well-rotted compost or manure in the autumn prior to sowing. It will tolerate any soil condition, with the exception of waterlogged, but will not be as prolific.

## Growing in containers

Good King Henry can be grown outside in a large container filled with a soil-based compost. You will need to feed it weekly from March until September with a liquid seaweed fertiliser to maintain leaf supply. Do not let the compost dry out in summer. Only the perennial good King Henry will need to be repotted in the spring.

## Yearly maintenance

**Spring:** sow seeds; lift and divide established plants.

**Summer:** water plants in the garden regularly when the weather is hot; feed container plants weekly; harvest the seeds.

**Autumn:** prepare the garden with well-rotted manure for planting the following season. Mulch established plants with rotted manure.

**Winter:** no need for protection.

## Harvesting and storing

**Leaves:** pick from early spring until late spring.

**Flowers:** pick the flowering spikes in early summer as they begin to open.

**Seeds:** harvest in late summer as the seeds turn light brown and collect by picking the whole branch, lay them on trays of newspaper and put in a dry room out of the sun. Within a few days you will notice that the seeds start falling off the branch. Lift the flowering branch carefully and all the seeds will drop onto the tray, these should be further dried for a week before storing in a clean, dark and labelled jar.

## Culinary uses

**Leaves:** the new early spring shoots are much prized by top restaurants. In mid-spring the young leaves, which are still tender, can be eaten raw in salads. From late spring the leaves become tougher and need to be cooked. They are ideal for adding to stuffings, soups, purées and pies. Because of the plant's long tap root the leaves are more nutritious than spinach or cabbage.

**Flowers:** these can be steamed and served hot tossed in butter or cold with a vinaigrette. Because of their high seed content they are very grainy so are not to everyone's taste.

**Seeds:** seeds can be added to soup or ground and used with flour to make pitta-type breads.

## Medicinal uses

The leaves of good King Henry and fat hen are rich in iron, calcium and vitamins B1 and C. It is recommended that they are included in the diet of anyone suffering from anaemia because of their high iron content. The seeds have a gentle laxative effect. When dried and ground they can be applied to stop itching. The whole plant is used to fatten poultry and as a remedy for coughs in sheep.

**Common names:** Chicory, Blue Endive, Bunks, Strip for Strip, Blue Sailors, Succory, Wild Chicory, Wild Succory

# Cichorium intybus

**This wildflower is a true stunner, worthy of a place in any border. The radiant blue flowers have dark blue anthers which make them look like jewels. It is a fascinating plant to watch as each individual flower head opens for only part of one day, while the whole plant opens new flower heads each day for many weeks.**

## History

The use of chicory can be traced back to the Egyptians who, like the Arabians, used to blanch the leaves for use as a salad, a custom continued to this day. Careful English wives grew chicory among their herbs. It was good for purging and for the bladder. Since the 17th century, dried, roasted and ground roots have been used as a coffee substitute. In fact, in *Household Words* Dickens described the extensive cultivation of chicory in England, which was generally grown for the root to be used as a coffee substitute.

## Species

*Cichorium intybus,* Chicory
Hardy, H5 (USDA 7,8), herbaceous perennial. Height: up to 1m (3ft); spread: 30cm (12in). Clear blue flowers in the second year, from summer until autumn. The mature leaves are mid-green, hairy underneath and coarsely toothed.

Different chicory varieties worth looking out for to plant in the vegetable garden:

**Magdeburg or Brunswick:** these are the best for producing roots that can be used as a coffee substitute.

**Witloof (Brussels chicory):** this is the one grown for the production of endives (chicons).

**Palla rossa precoce (radicchio):** this has lovely tight colourful heads. The leaves have a tangy slightly bitter flavour. It does not require blanching.

**Pain de sucre (sugar loaf):** this looks like lettuce and can be used in the same way. It does not require blanching

## Propagation

**Seeds:** Sow seeds under cover in spring into prepared seed trays or modules using a seed compost. If starting in very early spring put in a propagator at 15ºC (59ºF). Germination takes 5–10 days. Alternatively, sow seeds in summer into prepared open ground. Germination takes 2–3 weeks. Thin seedlings to 10–30cm (4–12in) apart depending on whether you want flower or leaf production. The seedlings are very hardy and will happily survive the cold weather, however watch out for pigeons – cover the row with fleece, or even better, a tunnel cloche.

## Pests and diseases

Slugs can be a problem, so dusk patrol is worthwhile (see page 272).

## How and where to grow

In a herb garden, chicory is a hardy perennial. It prefers a sunny, open site, ideally where it can get the early morning sun as the flowers start opening at sunrise. Plant in a light, preferably alkaline, soil. As a flowering plant in a herb garden chicory grows tall so it is ideal for the back of a border, or against a fence. In the autumn, cut the flowering stems down and collect the seeds for next year's sowing and then dig in well-rotted compost or manure.

You can force the plant to leaf in the winter by digging up some roots in late autumn. Cut off the tops to just above the ground and place in a box with soil-based compost with the crowns at soil level. Water well and cover so that the plants are in total darkness. Keep the temperature above 10ºC (50ºF). In 4–6 weeks chicons – blanched leaves – will have grown 15–20cm (6–8in) in length. They are great for Christmas salads or for roasting.

## Growing in containers

As a flowering plant chicory really does grow too tall for containers, but as a salad herb it is ideal. It is best to plant the seedlings you sowed earlier, 8cm (3in) apart in a large container, using a soil-based compost. Position in a sunny position, water regularly and feed weekly with a liquid seaweed fertiliser. If growing in a trough you can combine chicory with other salad plants.

## Yearly maintenance

**Spring:** sow seeds under protection for a herb garden.

**Summer:** harvest leaves and flowers.

**Autumn:** dig up the root for forcing, or dry it for coffee. Cut back the flowers of plants in a herb garden. Feed established plants with well-rotted farmyard manure.

**Winter:** dig in farmyard manure or compost in the spot where next year's salad crops are to grow.

## Harvesting and storing

**Leaves:** gather leaves from early spring until early autumn to use fresh.

**Flowers:** collect flowers in early summer until early autumn for use in the kitchen.

**Roots:** dig up the root from the second year onwards in late autumn for growing chicons or for drying.

## Culinary uses

We need to learn to appreciate bitter foods like chicory as they benefit the endocrine and digestive system. There is an old saying: 'bitter to the tongue is sweet to the tum'.

**Leaves:** these are best eaten fresh; they do not dry or freeze well. Young leaves can be added to summer salads. Forced leaves can be used as a winter salad. And endive (chicons) can be cooked and/or roasted.

**Flowers:** use the flowers in salads.

**Roots:** roasted chicory roots are still widely used as an excellent substitute or adulterant for coffee. The roots can be dug up when young and boiled like carrots. Serve with a white sauce, which makes a good contrast to the bitterness of the root.

## Medicinal uses

Chicory is a gentle but effective bitter tonic that increases the flow of bile. It is also a specific remedy for gall stones, like its cousin dandelion. It has diuretic properties and can be used for treating rheumatism and gout because it eliminates uric acid from the body. The roots in the form of syrup or succory make an excellent laxative.

*Cichorium intybus*, Chicory

**Common names:** Mountain Balm, Mountain Mint, Woodland Calamint, Nepitella

# Clinopodium menthifolia

***Clinopodium menthifolia* has recently been reclassified from *Calamintha menthifolia*. The only way I can tell the difference between *Clinopodium* and *Calamintha* is when they are in flower. At the moment, spots on the lower lips of the flowers seem to indicate *Clinopodium*, whereas splodges indicate *Calamintha*. Luckily, they both grow in the same conditions.**

*Clinopodium vulgare*, Wild Basil

## History

Traditionally calamint was known as a pot herb because it was included in the communal pot of food that was cooked over an open fire. It was also used as strewing herb, where it was scattered on the floors to release its lovely minty scent when walked on and to deter fleas.

## Species

*Clinopodium menthifolia* (*Calamintha menthifolia*), Mountain Balm, sometimes known as Nepitella
Hardy H5 (USDA 7,8), perennial. Height: up to 60cm (24in); spread: up to 45cm (18in). Small, tubular, pale white/pink flowers all summer. Oval, finely toothed, mint-scented mid-green leaves.

*Clinopodium menthifolium* subsp. *methifolium* (*Calamintha sylvatica*), Wood Calamint
Hardy H5 (USDA 7,8), perennial. Height: up to 60cm (24in); spread: up to 45cm (18in). Small pale pink tubular flowers with a white throat, pink spots and a pink lower lip. Oval, finely toothed, mint-scented mid-green leaves. UK native that grows in sandy light soil; can grow in semi-shade.

*Clinopodium menthifolium* subsp. *ascendens* (*Calamintha ascendens*), Common Calamint, sometimes known as Nepitella
Hardy, H5 (USDA 7,8), perennial. Height: up to 60cm (24in); spread: up to 45cm (18in). Small, tubular, pale pink /blue flowers all summer, with spots on the white lower lip. Mint-scented, mid-green, oval finely toothed leaves. Grows in grassland and on limestone.

*Clinopodium vulgare*, Wild Basil, Cushion Calamint
Hardy, H6 (USDA 6,7), perennial. Height: up to 60cm (24in); spread: up to 45cm (18in). Small, tubular pink/purple flowers from summer until early autumn. Small, hairy, lance-shaped mid-green leaves with serrated edges.

## Propagation

**Seeds:** all the *Clinopodiums* produce seeds that are best sown in the autumn into seed trays using a seed compost. Put the trays in a cold frame, a polytunnel, or cover with a sheet of glass and leave outside to experience the cold winter. The cold triggers germination the following spring – see page 18 for more information. When the seedlings are large enough to handle, prick out and plant into pots using a soil-based potting compost. Grow on until established before planting out in the garden into a prepared site. You can sow seeds directly into the garden in spring, once all threat of frost has passed but germination will be more erratic.

**Cuttings:** all the *Clinopodiums* mentioned here can be propagated with cuttings. Take softwood cuttings from established plants in late spring. Use three parts seed compost mixed with one part perlite. Keep in the shade until rooted. Once fully rooted they can be potted up prior to planting out.

**Division:** once the plants are established, they can be divided either in the spring or autumn. You can lift a whole plant and divide, or take a section off one side. Replant immediately, either into a prepared site or into pots using a soil-based potting compost. If this method is chosen in the autumn, the pots must be kept in a cold frame for the winter.

## Pests and diseases

Not known to be attacked by pests. If grown in a polytunnel it can suffer from mildew (see page 276 for tips on how to control this).

## How and where to grow

All the *Clinopodiums* like to be planted in sun to partial shade in a well-drained soil, low in nutrients. All apart from wild basil are well behaved in the garden. They do all self-seed a bit, but wild basil is a prolific self-seeder, so choose your site with care. All are excellent for attracting pollinators and in summer the flowers hum with the sound of bees.

## Growing in containers

All these *Clinopodiums* can be grown in containers using a soil-based compost. Mountain balm looks pretty when grown with thyme and oregano and wild basil combines well with rosemary and sage.

## Yearly maintenance

**Spring:** sow seeds; take softwood cuttings from new growth.

**Summer:** cut back after first flowering and keep the plant tidy; give a feed of liquid fertiliser – this can promote a second flowering.

**Autumn:** cut back new growth after a second flowering.

**Winter:** new growth will need protecting in frosts below -4°C (25°F) – use either agricultural fleece, bracken, straw or pine needles.

## Harvesting and storing

Pick the leaves for drying and freezing before flowering. Once dried, store in an airtight container in a dark cupboard. The leaves freeze well and can also be preserved in butter, oil or vinegar. They also make a very good savoury jelly that goes will with cheese and meat dishes, especially lamb. Pick the leaves for using fresh before and after flowering.

## Culinary uses

The leaves have an aromatic mint/spice/pepper flavour. Use freshly picked young shoots in early spring in salads, with vegetables and mushrooms or rubbed on meat to add a minty flavour – this is particularly good with lamb. The mature leaves in summer have a bitter mint flavour that can be used with mushrooms, in casseroles, stews, soups and sauces. There is one exception to this: wild basil, which tastes nothing like its namesake, as it has a slightly bitter, minty, oregano flavour; the leaves can be added to a foraged salad, but there has to be a shortage of other leaves to be included.

## Medicinal uses

A tea made from the leaves of mountain balm is a real tonic. It tastes minty, with undertones of its cousins, basil and oregano. It is said that this tisane eases weak digestion. Wild basil is used to treat skin irritation, wounds and warts; the leaves are also used to make a brown and yellow dye.

**Common names:** Coriander, Chinese Parsley, Yuen Sai, Pak Chee, Fragrant Green, Dhania (seed), Dhania Pattar, Dhania Sabz (leaves)

# Coriandrum sativum

**I vividly remember when coriander came to fame in the 1980s in the UK. The Herb Farm was wholesale at that time and Delia Smith's cookery television series was inspiring people to cook with coriander – we couldn't grow enough. Everyone thinks of coriander as a hot-weather plant but it is not. In summer it always runs to seed; it hates high temperatures, especially if the soil dries out.**

*Coriandrum sativum*, Coriander flower

## History

Coriander has been cultivated for over 3,000 years. There are records from the 21st Egyptian Dynasty (1085–945 BC), showing that seeds were found in tombs of the period. Coriander was brought to northern Europe by the Romans who, combining it with cumin and vinegar, rubbed it into meat as a preservative. I love the fact that the ancient Chinese believed it bestowed immorality and in the Middle Ages throughout Europe it was an ingredient in love potions. Coriander was introduced to the Americas by the Europeans in the 1600s where it is now known throughout the US by the Spanish name for the leaves, *cilantro*.

## Species

*Coriandrum sativum*, Coriander
Hardy, H3 (USDA 9), annual. Height: up to 60cm (24in); spread: 23cm (9in). White flowers in summer followed by round seeds. The first and lower leaves are broad and scalloped with strong scent and flavour, the upper leaves are finely cut with a pungent flavour.

Here are some varieties worth looking out for:

**Cruiser:** compact habit, good for cutting and re-growing, slow to bolt in dry or hot weather.

**Santo:** good leaf production, slow to bolt, great flavour.

**Topf:** this is the best one for growing in containers.

**Leafy leisure:** very vigorous, good for leaf production.

## Propagation

**Seeds:** Sow seeds in early spring under protection into prepared seed or module trays using three parts seed compost mixed with one part standard perlite. Put into a propagator at 18°C (64°F). Germination takes 5–10 days. Alternatively, sow seeds in late spring into prepared open ground when the air temperature at night remains above 7°C (45°F). Germination takes 2–3 weeks. Thin seedlings to 5cm (2in) apart for a leaf crop or 23cm (9in) apart for a seed crop. Sow in succession until late spring to give a constant supply of leaf. Stop for the summer months, then start again at the beginning of autumn for a winter crop. Plants will survive until the temperature goes below -5°C (23°F). If you regularly suffer from cold weather, cover the crop with a cloche, which will give you at least some crop to harvest until winter sets in.

## Pests and diseases

Green fly can be a pest. If the infestation is light, use a hand spray filled with water to wash them off. If it is out of control, use horticultural soft soap following the manufacturer's instructions. Pick off slugs by hand in the early evening.

## How and where to grow

When I first started growing, coriander liked being grown in a well-drained, light soil. Now I recommend a soil that has been fed with compost a month before sowing. For an early spring/summer crop, coriander needs to be grown in partial shade, in a soil that does not dry out in summer, but does not become waterlogged in heavy rain. If you are growing plants for a seed crop, stake the stems because as the seeds ripen they can become too heavy for the stem. Once the seeds have been collected (see Harvesting and Storing below), pull the plant up and give the soil a good mulch of compost. If you are doing an early autumn sowing, it is best to choose a sunny site, so that you get maximum light.

## Growing in containers

Coriander can be grown in containers inside with diligence, and outside on a windowsill or patio. Use a soil-based compost that does not dry out too quickly. Water in the morning, so that it does not go to bed with a 'soggy bottom'. Feed weekly with a liquid seaweed fertiliser. Keep picking the leaves, leaving the tiny new ones so that you get another crop. When growing in containers, it is a good idea to have three on the go: one just sown, the second on first harvest, the third on final harvest, for a constant supply of leaves. In summer, try and give plants some protection from the midday sun.

## Yearly maintenance

**Spring:** sow seeds.

**Summer:** harvest leaves, flowers and seeds.

**Autumn:** dig up old plants; sow a winter crop.

**Winter:** cover outside crops with a tunnel cloche to extend the season.

## Harvesting and storing

**Leaves:** pick young leaves any time. Cut them when about 10cm (4in) in height and bright green in colour. Alternatively dig up the whole plant, including the root (which you can also use in cooking), when the leaves reach 10cm (4in). They do not preserve well so keep in the fridge and use the same day or within a few days.

**Flowers:** pick flowers when the whole umbel is open.

**Seeds:** watch the seeds carefully as they ripen suddenly and will fall without warning. Cut the flower stems just as the seeds starts to smell pleasant. Cover bunches with a paper bag. Tie the top of the bag and hang upside down in a dry, warm, airy place. Leave for roughly 10 days. The seeds should come away from the husk quite easily. Store in an airtight container.

## Culinary uses

This is one herb you either like or dislike. The leaves and ripe seeds have two distinct flavours. The seeds are warmly aromatic, the leaves have an earthy pungency.

**Leaves:** the leaf has a pungent oily flavour with a hint of earthiness. Add lower leaves to curries, stews, salads, sauces and use as a garnish. Delicious in salads, vegetables and poultry dishes. A bunch of coriander leaves with a vinaigrette dressing is particularly good with hard-boiled eggs.

**Flowers:** the flowers have a warm aromatic and slightly scented flavour that is great in salads, with rice dishes and with fresh tomatoes.

**Seeds:** the seeds keep their flavour, which is warm and aromatic with a hint of orange. I use them ground in tomato chutney, ratatouille and curries, also in apple pies, cakes, biscuits and marmalade. Add whole seeds to soups, sauces and vegetable dishes.

## Medicinal uses

The main medicinal use is to treat the loss of appetite and dyspeptic complaints. It is good for the digestive system, reducing flatulence and stimulating the appetite, aiding the secretion of gastric juices.

*Coriandrum sativum*, Coriander leaf

# Crambe maritima

**Over the past few years this herb has come back into favour in the kitchen garden. You only have to visit formal vegetable gardens to see it in what looks like rhubarb forcing jars but the jars are wider and set out in neat rows. If you have never eaten it you are in for a treat, especially when it is served with béchamel sauce, which was the tradition in Victorian times.**

*Crambe maritima*, Sea Kale leaf and flower bud

## History

This herb is native to the western European coastline and has also been found along the shoreline of the Black Sea. The Romans used to preserve it in wooden barrels to eat on long journeys to prevent scurvy as it is naturally high in vitamin C. It was first cultivated in the 1600s and became widespread in Europe and North America in the 1800s. Thomas Jefferson planted sea kale in his Monticello garden in 1809, and it then became naturalised on the west coast of the United States.

## Species

*Crambe maritima*, Sea Kale
Hardy, H4 (USDA 8,9), herbaceous perennial. Height: up to 75cm (30in); spread: up to 60cm (24in). Clusters of honey-scented white flowers in summer. Attractive, fleshy grey–green leaves with crinkled edges.

## Propagation

**Seeds:** in autumn, sow fresh seeds into prepared small pots or modules using a seed compost mixed in equal parts with horticultural sand. If the seed has been collected from the wild, it will need scarification by putting a nick into the outer cork-like casing with a sharp knife to aid germination (see page 18). Place the container in a cold frame; germination will occur the following spring. Alternatively, in late spring, sow the cleaned, flat, dark brown seed directly into a well-prepared site. Germination takes 24–36 days.

**Cuttings:** this is the most usual method of propagation. In autumn, when the leaves have died back, take root cuttings from the side shoots; these are called 'thongs'. Either store in sand to prevent them drying out, prior to planting in the garden in the spring, or pot them up using a loam compost mixed in equal parts with horticultural sand. When buying 'thongs' from a nursery, make sure that the crown has been marked so you know which way to plant them.

## Pests and diseases

Cover crops with horticultural mesh in early summer to protect crops being attacked by flea beetle. Sea kale can catch club root, so never plant in infected beds. See page 274 for more information.

## How and where to grow

Sea kale is attractive grown in a flower border. It forms compact rosettes of large, wavy-edged glaucous leaves with large bunches of white honey-scented flowers towering above the foliage in summer. It prefers a well-drained light, preferably sandy, soil in a sun or dappled shade. Prior to planting, in the previous autumn, feed the soil well with well-rotted manure because this plant can happily remain in position for up to five years. As it is a halophyte, it tolerates salt, so is an ideal plant for a seaside garden. This herb is renowned for attracting bees, beneficial insects and other pollinators as its flowers are high in nectar and pollen.

**Forcing:** in autumn, cut back the old foliage of a two-year-old or older plant. Cover the crown with straw and add a generous dollop of well-rotted manure around the plant. From late autumn until early spring, place a bucket or a terracotta forcing jar over the crown. When the blanched sprouts are 7–20cm (3–8in) long, cut with a sharp knife. Stop harvesting in late spring, uncover the plant, cut back and feed well. Do not allow the plant to dry out in summer.

## Growing in containers

Sea kale adapts to being grown in large containers. Use a loam-based compost mixed in equal parts with horticultural sand. Do not allow the container to dry out in summer. It looks great planted with other seaside plants, such as *Armeria maritima*, sea thrift, and *Crithmum maritimum*, rock samphire (see page 100). Planting these plants that naturally grow by the sea together means that in the spring you can give them a dose of magnesium, in the form of Epsom salts, following the instructions on the pack.

## Yearly maintenance

**Spring:** sow cleaned seed; force crops outside.

**Summer:** water regularly – do not allow the plant to dry out; feed occasionally; collect seeds.

**Autumn:** take root cuttings; sow seeds; force plants; remove yellowing foliage.

**Winter:** lift crowns for forcing; protect the crowns of established plants with a thick covering of straw when temperatures fall below -1°C (30°F).

## Harvesting and storing

**Leaves:** harvest new young growth in late spring; pick forced growth from autumn until spring.

**Flowers:** pick the young flower heads before flowering from early summer onwards.

## Culinary uses

Sea kale is very versatile in the kitchen. The blanched stems are delicious and in summer the young flower heads, when in bud, can be cooked like sprouting broccoli or lightly steamed.

## Medicinal uses

Sea kale is rich in vitamin C and magnesium. Traditionally a broth was made from the tender new spring growth to help cure colds and served as a tonic.

*Crambe maritima*, Sea Kale flower

**Common names:** Rock Samphire, Sea Fennel, Samphire, Crest Marine, Kritamo

# Crithmum maritimum

**This is a seaside herb, growing in cliffs and rocks by the sea. It has been used as a vegetable for centuries but it falls in and out of favour. It is a native of the Atlantic, Mediterranean and Black Sea, where it has been dedicated to Saint Peter, the fisherman's saint. This herb is often confused with *Salicornia europaea*, marsh samphire, which grows on mud flats or salt marshes, though they look nothing like each other as marsh samphire has scale-like leaves and is bright green, while rock samphire looks like a succulent version of fennel, to which it is related.**

## History

Rock samphire was at one time cultivated in English gardens for its seed pods and sold in London, where it was called 'crest marine'. In Gerard's time it was considered a very good condiment. In 1597 he wrote:

'The leaves kept in pickle and eaten in salads with oil and vinegar, is a pleasant sauce for meat, wholesome for the stoppings of the liver, milt, kidneys and bladder... It is the pleasantest sauce, most familiar, and best agreeing with man's body.'

In the 19th century, rock samphire from Dover and the Isle of Wight was sent in casks of brine to London, where wholesalers would pay up to four shillings a bushel for it.

## Species

*Crithmum maritimum*, Rock Samphire
Hardy, H4 (USDA 8,9), herbaceous perennial. Height and spread: up to 30cm (12in). Tiny white/green flowers are produced in flat umbels in summer. Aromatic, succulent sea-grey/green leaves with long, linear lance-shaped segments.

## Propagation

**Seeds:** sow fresh seeds in autumn into prepared modules or a seed tray filled with a seed compost mixed in equal parts with sharp horticultural sand. Place under protection at 10°C (50°F). Germination takes 2–3 weeks. If there is no germination within that period, place the container in a refrigerator for 4 weeks (vegetable compartment) then return to 10°C (50°F). Germination should occur within 4–6 weeks. Winter seedlings in a frost-free environment; plant out the following spring.

**Cuttings:** take cuttings in late spring/early summer from non-flowering shoots. Use a seed compost mixed in equal parts with sharp horticultural sand.

**Division:** divide established plants in spring. Once divided, replant in a well-prepared site. Container-raised plants can be divided gently so as not to destroy the crown and re-potted into a loam-based compost mixed in equal parts with horticultural grit.

## Pests and diseases

Pests are not a problem but rock samphire can suffer from 'root rot', especially when grown in containers in a potting mix that does not drain well in winter.

## How and where to grow

As this is a seaside plant that grows literally in the crevices between rocks, it is essential to prepare your site well by making sure it is well drained, adding extra grit to the soil if necessary. Plant in a sunny position and protect from cold winds. It will need protection from hard frosts at temperatures below -5°C (23°F). Do not mulch and do not feed with manure or compost.

## Growing in containers

Rock samphire will adapt to growing in containers as long as you use a well-draining compost, either a soil-based compost mixed in equal parts with horticultural grit, or standard perlite. Lift the pot in winter and put it on bricks or stones so that it drains well. In spring, give the plant a feed of horticultural Epsom salts, to help it regain its magnesium level.

## Yearly maintenance

**Spring:** divide established plants; take cuttings.

**Summer:** pick leaves until it starts to flower.

**Autumn:** sow fresh seeds.

**Winter:** protect from hard frosts below -3°C (27°F). Lift container plants and put on bricks.

## Harvesting and storing

**Leaves:** the best time for harvesting is in late spring/early summer before the plant flowers. The leaves can be eaten fresh, blanched or pickled.

**Flowers:** pick the flowers just before they open in summer; they can be eaten fresh, cooked or pickled.

## Culinary uses

**Leaves:** prior to cooking, remove any leaves that have begun to turn slimy and any hard parts of the stalk. Soak in salt water for an hour prior to cooking. The leaves have an aromatic salty flavour, which combines well in salads or cooked in butter. They can also be used to make sauces and aromatic pickles.

**Flowers:** the buds taste very similar to fennel flowers but with slightly less anise – these can be added to salads, fish dishes or sauces.

## Medicinal uses

This herb is very high in vitamin C and the seeds contain a fragrant oil rich in eugenol and other aromatic substances that are widely used in modern perfumery and medicine. The plant also contains sulphates, iodine compounds and pectin. It relieves flatulence, eases digestion and is a diuretic.

*Crithmum maritimum*, Rock Samphire

**Common names:** Turmeric, Indian Saffron, Haldi, Haridra

# Curcuma longa

**Turmeric is a herb when it is living and turns into a spice when it is dried and ground. It is a powerhouse of goodness that should be incorporated into your diet as much as possible. It is regarded as one of the most valuable herbs to mankind because of its health-giving properties.**

*Curcuma longa*, Turmeric

## History

Turmeric has its origins in southeast Asia. It has been used traditionally since 600BC as a dye, in medicine, and to flavour and preserve food.

## Species

*Curcuma longa*, Turmeric
Tropical, sub tropical, H1c (USDA 11), herbaceous perennial. Height up to 1m (3ft); spread by underground fleshy rhizomes: indefinite. The yellow/white flowers, tinged with pink at the tips of the petals, appear in spring, surrounded by pale green bracts on a single stem. The flowers are sterile and do not produce viable seed. Aromatic, long – up to 60cm (24in) – mid-green, oval leaves.

## Propagation

**Cuttings:** a word of warning before you start taking root cuttings – wear gloves and an apron because once the root is cut it produces a yellow sap that will stain your fingers and can be indelible in cloth. Unless you live in the tropics the best source for fresh turmeric root is from Asian and Caribbean shops. However, be aware that the quality can be variable – often after it has been air-freighted, the cold temperatures can kill the growth. Alternatively it may have been treated with chemicals to inhibit sprouting. Choose a fresh, plump, juicy-looking root with a tooth bud growing on one side. Use a shallow container not much larger than the root and fill with a seed compost mixed in equal parts with horticultural grit. Place the root in the container with the tooth bud facing up, cover the roots with compost, making sure the tooth bud is peeping through the compost. Put the container into a plastic bag, seal and place in a warm place or in a propagator at 20°C (68°F). The shoots should emerge in 3–4 weeks, though it may take longer depending on the warmth. Once the shoots emerge, remove the plastic bag. Keep the container in a warm place (a minimum temperature of 18°C (64°F) but not direct sunlight until fully established) and do not allow the compost to dry out. Only pot up one size of pot at a time, when the plant looks as if it is bursting out of the container; it likes being pot bound. Use a potting compost mixed in equal parts with horticultural grit.

**Division:** if you live in the tropics, or have a plant raised in a container, it can be divided in the spring. Once divided replant into a prepared site in the garden. Pot-raised plants should be removed from the container; also remove excess compost so that you can see the rhizome. Choose a section of rhizome with a growing bud and slice the root using a sharp knife. Pot up the cutting into a small container that just fits the cutting using a seed compost mixed in equal parts with horticultural grit. Follow the instructions for taking cuttings.

## Pests and diseases

Red spider mite can be an occasional problem in older plants; regular misting and keeping the leaves well-washed will reduce this. If it gets out of hand, use a horticultural soft soap spray, following the manufacturer's instructions. Alternatively introduce the predator *Phytoseiulus persimilis* but please do not use both.

## How and where to grow

This herb can only be grown outside in the tropics. It requires a minimum temperature of 18°C (64°F) at night. It is an under-storey plant so plant in dappled shade in a soil that does not completely dry out in the heat of the day.

## Growing in containers

Turmeric is ideal for growing in a container in cool and cold climates. However, you will not be able to harvest much useful root from your plant. Pot up using a loam-based potting compost mixed in equal parts with horticultural grit. Be mean with the container size; do not over pot, as this can cause the rhizome to rot in cool climates. In summer, place the plant in partial shade, water and feed regularly with a liquid seaweed fertiliser. In dry weather plants will benefit from a daily light misting with rainwater. In the autumn, cut back on the watering, keeping the compost fairly dry. Keep the plant frost-free at a minimum of 18°C (64°F).

## Yearly maintenance

**Spring:** divide rhizomes.

**Summer:** pick leaves as required.

**Autumn:** cut back on watering of container plants.

**Winter:** grow at a minimum of 18°C (64F).

## Harvesting and storing

**Rhizomes:** harvest the rhizome when grown in the tropics in late summer/early autumn. Only the cured turmeric rhizome, which is grown commercially, has the aroma and colour necessary for cooking.

**Leaves:** the leaves can be used as a flavouring, pick as required throughout the growing season.

## Culinary uses

Turmeric is an essential ingredient in Indian cuisine; it is used in virtually every meat, vegetable and lentil dish, with the exception of greens because it turns them grey and bitter. Fresh turmeric root is eaten as a pickle and grated into stir-fries. In Malaysia, the young roots are eaten as ulam, they are sliced and beautifully arranged and served during the meal. The leaves have a warm, rich sweet aroma and can be used fresh to wrap fish or sweets before steaming. They are used in India to prepare a special medicinal herbal bread.

## Medicinal uses

Turmeric has been used medicinally for thousands of years. It is an important Ayurvedic herb used to treat inflammation, coughs and gastric disorders. It is also a very good first-aid remedy in the home; a paste can be used as a quick household antiseptic for cuts, grazes and minor burns. Turmeric can also be used as a decoction to calm the stomach, and applied externally to alleviate itching.

**WARNING** | If the roots are cut they produce an indelible yellow dye.

**Common names:** Lemon Grass, Fever Grass, Bhustrina, Takrai

# Cymbopogon citratus

**Over the years I have become a huge fan of this herb, especially since seeing it growing and flourishing in Malaysia where I could appreciate how classically elegant this plant is in true grass fashion, rather than the small plants I raise and the stumps of stem you can buy from the supermarkets.**

*Cymbopogon citratus*, Lemon Grass

## History

Lemon grass has been used for thousands of years in Southeast Asia and the West Indies, where it is not just considered an important culinary herb, it is also highly valued for its many medicinal properties. It has only come to the fore in European and Australian cooking during the past 20 years.

## Species

*Cymbopogon citratus*, Lemon Grass
Half hardy, H2 (USDA 10), evergreen perennial. Height: up to 1.5m (5ft); spread: up to 1m (3ft). Rarely flowers in cold climates. Lemon-scented, linear leaves, up to 90cm (3ft) in length. Robust, cane-like stems.

*Cymbopogon flexuosus*, East Indian Lemon Grass, Cochin Grass, Malabar Grass
Half hardy, H2 (USDA 10), evergreen perennial. Height and spread: 1.5m (5ft). Rarely flowers in cold climates. Lemon-scented, linear leaves up to 1m (3ft) in length. Robust, cane-like stems. This form has a good lemon flavour and can be used in the kitchen in the same way as *Cymbopogon citratus*.

*Cymbopogon martinii* var. *motia*, Palmarosa, Rosha, Indian Geranium
Half hardy, H2 (USDA 10), evergreen perennial. Height: up to 1.3m (4ft); spread: up to 1m (3ft). Small clusters of tiny grass flowers appear throughout the summer, though this is rare in cold climates. Rose-scented, pale green, linear leaves up to 50cm (20in) in length. These leaves have the most heavenly rose scent. Use the leaves to flavour cakes, puddings and syrups.

## Propagation

**Seeds:** sow seeds in spring into prepared seed trays or modules using a seed compost mixed in equal parts with horticultural sharp sand. Place under cover at 18°C (64°F). Germination takes 15–25 days. Once the seedlings are large enough, pot up using a loam-based potting compost and grow on until well established. Either plant out in the garden in warm climates, or grow on as a container plant in cooler climates.

**Cuttings:** take cuttings in spring, from a plant that is more than a year old and has an established crown. Gently remove the swollen lower stems from the crown. Remove any grass from the stem and cut the stem back to 10cm (4in). Place in a prepared module, plug or a very small pot using a seed compost mixed in equal parts with standard perlite; do not be tempted to over-pot the cutting as this will cause it to rot. Place under protection or in a warm position away from cold draughts. Once rooted, pot up in a small pot using a loam-based compost.

**Division:** in the garden, in warm climates, use two forks back to back and gently tease the plant apart, replanting immediately into a prepared site. Divide container plants either with your fingers, or two small forks, teasing the crown apart, then repotting into a pot which fits snugly around the roots. This plant is happiest when pot bound. Use three parts loam-based compost mixed with one part horticultural grit.

## Pests and diseases

Outside the tropics this herb can be prone to rot and mildew. To prevent this, in winter, keep container plants nearly dry and in a well-ventilated, frost-free room.

## How and where to grow

You can only grow lemon grass outside where the night temperature does not fall below 8°C (46°F), so at cooler latitudes this herb can be planted out in summer only. Plant in any soil, including a heavy soil, as long as the summers are hot and wet and the winters are warm and dry.

## Growing in containers

This herb makes an excellent container plant. Use a loam-based compost and do not allow it to dry out in summer. In winter bring the plant into a frost-free environment, 8°C (46°F) minimum. When the light levels and night temperatures drop, the plant will go 'dormant' – the grass will gradually turn brown and the outside leaves will shrivel. Keep the watering minimal. In early spring, as the days lengthen and the temperatures rise, you will notice the grass starting to grow. Cut it back to 10cm (4in) and repot into the next size pot or divide and repot. Start feeding weekly from early spring until late summer with a liquid seaweed fertiliser.

## Yearly maintenance

**Spring:** cut back garden plants and container grown plants. Divide or take root cuttings of established plants. Start feeding container plants weekly.

**Summer:** do not allow container plants to dry out. In cold climates, plant out for the summer.

**Autumn:** in cold climates, lift plants from the garden. Stop feeding the container plants.

**Winter:** keep container plant watering minimal and protect from frosts.

## Harvesting and storing

**Leaves:** the young leaves have a much fuller flavour than the older ones, which tend to have a slightly bitter undertone. The best flavour of the leaves comes from the lower 10cm (4in) of the plant. Pick to use fresh or to dry throughout the growing season.

**Stems:** this is only available from mature plants. To prepare the swollen stems, cut at the base just where the stem joins the soil, trim off the top leaves and save for later use. Peel off the outer green sheathes around the thick stem, which will reveal a white core. Slice finely or pound the white stem to release the flavoursome oils before adding them to your chosen dish.

## Culinary uses

The fresh leaves and stems have been traditionally used in southeast Asian and Caribbean cooking. The lemon flavour complements curries, seafood, garlic and chilli. Take a handful of leaves, tie them into a knot and add them to water to flavour rice or steamed vegetables. Remove before serving.

## Medicinal uses

The leaves and roots are high in iron, chromium magnesium, zinc, selenium, potassium and phosphorus; they also contain vitamins A, B and C. Lemon grass is carminative and diuretic. The essential oil is antiseptic, antibacterial and deodorising and is used in perfumery and in poultices to ease pain and arthritis. A tea made from fresh leaves is very refreshing as well as being a stomach and gut relaxant; it is also a good antidepressant and helps lift the spirits if one is in a bad mood.

# Cynara cardunculus

**You may think that cardoons and globe artichokes (*Cynara scolymus*) are the same, but they are in fact quite different. Cardoons are grown for their leaf rib, which tastes like a cross between an artichoke and asparagus and globe artichokes are grown for their flower bud. Both are structurally magnificent and a showstopper in any garden. Sadly cardoons are now classed as a weed in Australia, but hope is on hand as research is ongoing regarding its potential as a vegetable, winter fodder for livestock, a vegetable oil (extracted from the seed) and an environmentally friendly biofuel.**

## History

The cardoon has been in cultivation for thousands of years as a vegetable and as a gentle laxative. The Romans considered it a prized vegetable and they took it with them as part of their wagon train as they marched through Europe and North Africa. The name is derived from the Latin *carduus* meaning 'thistle'. It is thought that it was introduced to the UK in the 17th century by John Tradescant the Elder for his employer, the first Earl of Salisbury.

## Species

*Cynara cardunculus*, Cardoon
Hardy, H5 (USDA 7,8), evergreen (in warm climates) perennial. Height: up to 2.5m (8ft); spread: up to 1.2m (4ft). Lovely large thistle-like blue/violet flowers in summer. Thick fibrous stems. Downy, silver/grey/green, deeply cut, leathery leaves with a silver underside. Some forms of cardoon have very spiny leaves.

## Propagation

**Seeds:** the seeds are large and easy to handle. In early spring, sow under protection at 18°C (64°F) either individually into prepared plug modules or sow three seeds in an 8cm (3in) pot using a standard seed compost. Germination takes 5–10 days. Alternatively, sow seeds in late spring into prepared open ground, when the air temperature at night does not fall below 7°C (45°F). Germination takes 2–3 weeks.

**Division:** in spring or autumn, use a spade to remove the suckers (side shoots) from the main stem, then pot up using a soil-based compost and grow on in a cold frame or cold greenhouse. Plant out in the spring once all threat of frost has passed.

## Pests and diseases

In spring, slugs are a total nuisance – they hide in the folds of the leaf ribs and munch their way through them. Mounting a night patrol with a torch and hand picking the pests off the plant is the best method. Alternatively, use slug traps made from beer or milk. In late summer caterpillars can also strip the leaves, so as soon as you see damage remove the pests by hand. Powdery mildew can be a problem if the plant is in a container or growing against a wall. Remove damaged leaves and make sure that the ground or compost has not dried out, then water as necessary. If it is a bad infestation spray with baking powder (for information see page 276).

## How and where to grow

Plant in a sunny situation in a well-drained, deep, fertile soil that has been well fed the previous autumn with well-rotted manure. Space plants 90cm (2ft 11in) apart. Cardoons can become inedible when grown under hot conditions as the leaves and stalks become pithy and tough and the flower bud hard. Mulch well in early spring with either leaf mould, composted bark or well-rotted compost and maintain a constant, uniform supply of water throughout the growing season. In autumn, when the plant has died back, feed with well-rotted manure.

To blanch the leaves, which are a culinary delight, choose a sunny day in late summer/early autumn to prepare the plant for blanching. The plant needs to be totally dry, including the crown. Tie the outer mature leaves together near the top, wearing gloves and long sleeves for protection, especially if you have grown the spiny variety. Wrap the whole plant in sacking, straw or paper and build the earth up around the plant. Do not use polyethylene because it will make the plant sweat and rot the leaves and crown. Leave for 4–5 weeks, no longer because this can cause rot. When blanched, cut just below the crown, trimming excess loose leaves off, leaving the trimmed blanched heart. Use as soon as possible. Once the harvest is finished, protect the remaining trimmed blanched heart with straw until the new growth reappears.

## Growing in containers

Despite its size, this herb can be grown successfully in large containers and can look stunning. Use a soil-based compost; this will help prevent the soil from drying out in summer. Protect from the midday sun and once in flower protect from high winds. Water regularly throughout the year. Make sure, especially in summer, that the container does not dry out. Feed weekly with a liquid seaweed fertiliser from spring until late summer.

## Yearly maintenance

**Spring:** sow seeds under cover or in late spring in the ground; check for slugs.

**Summer:** feed and water regularly; remove any damaged leaves; check for caterpillars.

**Autumn:** in early autumn blanch the leaves; feed mature plants.

**Winter:** in excessive cold, protect the crown with straw or bracken.

## Harvesting and storing

**Flowers:** pick the flower buds before the bracts start to open. Pick flowers in summer just as they open for drying.

**Seeds:** collect seeds in early autumn as the flowers start to drop again, wear gloves and beware of the prickles on certain species.

**Stems:** harvest the blanched stems from early winter onwards.

## Culinary uses

The blanched leaf, ribs and stalks are used chiefly as a winter vegetable. To prepare, remove the tough outer ribs, cut the inner blanched ribs into 8cm (3in) slices and soak in water that has either the juice of a lemon squeezed into it or a couple of tablespoons of white wine vinegar – this prevents the lovely creamy white stems browning. After soaking for 20 minutes the prepared ribs can be eaten either raw, or boiled, braised or baked depending on your recipe. Personally, I love eating them raw with an olive oil, garlic and anchovy dip called bagna cauda. The flower buds are occasionally eaten but I consider them to be inferior to globe artichokes.

## Medicinal uses

Cardoons are a good source of potassium, calcium and iron. A decoction made from the leaves can be used as a detoxifier – it is said to help the liver regenerate and is a good stimulant for the gall bladder in exactly the same way as its cousin the dandelion (*Taraxacum officinale*).

*Cynara cardunculus*, Cardoon

# Digitalis purpurea

**One late spring I was walking in the woodlands on Exmoor in the west of England and came across an area where the trees had been felled. The whole hillside seemed to be dancing with the purple spires of foxgloves. Obviously because the trees had been felled the land had been exposed to light and rain, triggering germination the year before, which had produced this glorious sight.**

## History

This native wild plant of Europe and North America was given its name *Digitalis* by the Swedish botanist Carl Linnaeus in 1753 because he thought the flowers looked like fingertip gloves. An infusion of the leaves was once used in folk medicine to treat sore throats, catarrh and as a compress for swellings and bruises despite its known high toxicity. It was not until late into the 18th century that it became an important medicinal herb when William Withering prescribed foxglove tea for dropsy. From this he discovered its invaluable properties as a remedy for heart disease. There is evidence that foxgloves were among the commonplace herbs taken by the settlers on their voyage to America.

## Species

*Digitalis purpurea*, Foxglove
Hardy, H6 (USDA 6,7), biennial. Height: up to 1.8m (6ft); spread: up to 60cm (24in). Purple or white tubular flowers with purple spots on the throatn appear in early summer of the second season. Large,lance-shaped, textured green leaves. This is one of the most poisonous plants in British flora.

## Propagation

**Seeds:** for the quickest germination, sow the very fine seed while it's fresh in the autumn. As the seed is so fine it is worth mixing a very small amount with sharp horticultural sand, which will help prevent it being sown too thickly. Sow into prepared modules or seed trays using a standard seed compost. Don't cover the seed with compost or perlite as this inhibits germination. Place the container outside in a cold frame or simply outside on a flat surface. Germination takes 5–7 weeks. When sowing in spring, germination can be more erratic and the seedlings appear when they wish rather than together.

## Pests and diseases

You may need to protect young plants from slugs and snails. Either hand-pick them in the early evening, or put down a slug trap (see page 272 for more information). The caterpillars of some moths eat foxglove leaves and flowers, but these caterpillars are food for baby birds in spring, so it's best to leave them be.

## How and where to grow

Foxgloves will adapt to most conditions with the exception of very dry and exposed sites. The best situation is in partial shade in a moist but well-drained soil that has been enriched with leaf mould. In the autumn, it is a good idea to give the one-year-old plants a mulch of leaf mould too, so that it not only provides a source of food but also offers a bit of protection through the winter. In the second season, remove the centre spike of flowers after flowering. This will increase the size of the side flower spikes. Foxgloves are an important source of pollen for bees, especially long-tongued bees, such as the common carder bee. The brightly coloured flowers and dark spotted lip attracts the bee, while the lower lip of the flower allows the insect to land before climbing up the tube.

As foxgloves are renowned for self-seeding it is worth checking around second-year plants for seedlings – thin them out if overcrowded. Prick out and pot up a few for planting out in the following spring into a new site and as insurance against a hard winter.

A word of advice: foxgloves should not be planted next to edible plants. I once saw foxgloves underplanted with wild strawberries – the combination looked lovely but you could not eat the strawberries because the seeds of foxgloves are highly poisonous and they are so tiny that you cannot see them if they fall on the fruit.

## Growing in containers

Foxgloves can adapt happily to being grown in a container using a soil-based compost. Place the container in partial shade and shelter from high winds because in the second year, when it goes to flower, it will become tall. Water well in dry weather. They look lovely planted with *Centranthus* (valerian) – either the white or the pink form.

*Digitalis purpurea*, Foxglove

## Yearly maintenance

**Spring:** sow seeds; plant out first-year plants.

**Summer:** remove main flowering shoot after flowering.

**Autumn:** sow seeds for overwintering; check around second-year plants for self-sown seedlings.

**Winter:** in the majority of cases no protection needed.

## Harvesting and storing

This is not advised unless you are a herbalist or pharmacist. The leaves are picked in the summer. Wear gloves because even touching the plant has been known to cause rashes, headaches and nausea.

## Culinary uses

None.

## Medicinal uses

This is an important medicinal plant and it is still grown commercially for the extraction of glycosides from the second-year leaves. The raw herb is no longer used, but carefully prepared formulations in the form of pills and or drops are used to treat a weak heart. The typical expression of a weak heart is oedema, also known by the outdated term 'dropsy' when the legs become swollen due to an accumulation of fluid.

**WARNING** | The whole plant, including the seed, is highly poisonous. DO NOT USE without medical supervision.

**Common names:** Wild Rocket, Arugula, Ruccola, Rucola, Rocquette

# Diplotaxis muralis

**I love rocket; it is so versatile as it goes well with meat, fish and vegetables and it is the one herb I must have in my garden. When I ran a wholesale nursery growing for garden centres and shops I had a large crop of *Eruca vesicaria* (salad rocket) growing on the Herb Farm, the sun came out and it ran to flower so I could not sell it. As I stood next to it pondering what to do, I started eating the flowers. They are wonderful – so wonderful that they became the inspiration for my book *Good Enough to Eat*, published in 1997, which was all about growing and eating flowers.**

*Diplotaxis muralis*, Wild Rocket

## History

For hundreds of years rocket has been collected in the wild and sold in markets. Both the leaves and seed of rocket were used as flavouring by the Romans. In England the Elizabethans were extremely partial to it in salads.

## Species

*Diplotaxis muralis*, Wild Rocket
Hardy, H4 (USDA 8,9), perennial, often grown as an annual. Height: 30cm (12in); spread: 15cm (6in). Yellow, four-petalled flowers form in summer. Green, deeply divided, aromatic leaves, which form a rosette as the plant matures.

*Eruca vesicaria*, Salad Rocket, Arugula
Hardy, H3 (USDA 9), annual. Height up to 90cm (3ft) in flower; spread: 15cm (6in). The flowers start yellow, then fade to cream with purple veins. Oval, lance-shaped leaves with a nutty, spicy flavour.

## Propagation

**Seeds:** the following is appropriate for both species. Sow seeds in early spring into prepared seed trays or modules using a seed compost. Place in a propagator at 18°C (64°F). Germination takes 5–10 days. However, for the best results, because this plant dislikes being transplanted, sow seeds in late spring, into prepared open ground, when the air temperature at night does not fall below 7°C (45°F). Germination will take 2–3 weeks. Thin plants to 20cm (8in) apart. For a winter crop of wild rocket, either sow seeds in early autumn under protection and plant out into a prepared site 20cm (8in) apart, or sow directly into open ground. Cover with a cloche tunnel either covered with film or with horticultural fleece to extend the season before the hard frosts set in, plus to protect it from birds.

## Pests and diseases

This herb is very prone to flea beetle attack in the spring, so protect it with horticultural fleece from mid-spring or when the oilseed rape starts to flower. Either lay the fleece on the young plants or use a cloche tunnel covered with horticultural fleece. For more information on flea beetle please see page 269.

## How and where to grow

The best place to grow this herb is in light shade in a prepared site. If you want succulent tender leaves it is worth feeding the soil with well-rotted compost a month before sowing or in the autumn before if you have the space. If you are not digging up the wild rocket at the end of the season and over-wintering, it is a good idea to cover the plants with a cloche tunnel. This will extend the picking season until the temperature falls below -1°C (30°F). In spring, dig up the old plants and sow a new crop, on a different prepared site to maintain a good supply of leaf.

## Growing in containers

If you have a salad pot, then salad rocket is a great plant to add to it as you will have a delicious mix of leaves to add to your salads. The best container is a window box as you can sow a drill the whole length which will give you a good supply of leaf. Use a soil-based potting compost as this helps to retain moisture and position the container in partial shade. Do not allow the container to dry out in high summer and ideally feed weekly with a liquid seaweed fertiliser.

## Yearly maintenance

**Spring:** sow seeds; protect from flea beetle.

**Summer:** harvest the leaves and flowers; feed container plants.

**Autumn:** sow seeds; cover to prolong the picking season.

**Winter:** dig up two-year-old plants; prepare site for next year's crop.

## Harvesting and storing

**Leaves:** the best flavoured leaves are those that have reached full size but have not turned dark green – these are picked in the spring to early summer and the autumn. Summer leaves, especially if the weather is hot, tend to become very tough. A great way to preserve the leaves is to make a rocket pesto.

**Flowers:** the flowers of both species are edible, however the salad rocket ones are by far the best – pick as soon as the flower begins to open and use immediately.

## Culinary uses

This leafy salad green has become a very popular herb to add to salad mixes. The flavour of the salad rocket is nutty, spicy with a hint of bitterness. The flavour of wild rocket depends on the season: in spring it is spicy and hot; in the summer it is decidedly hot and the leaves tend to be a bit tough so it is a good idea to chop them up before adding to a salad. However, whatever the time of year, dress the leaves with salt, oil and vinegar, or simply serve them on their own with a little fresh Parmesan. The whole flower is edible, although any excessive green should be removed. The swelling behind the flower, where the seeds are formed, adds crunch, so you can use just the petals, the whole flowers, or the whole flowers plus the crunch depending on your taste or the recipe.

## Medicinal uses

Both wild and salad rocket stimulate the appetite and digestion. The leaves are high in sulphur, which is good for healthy skin, hair and nails. They also contain vitamins A, B, C and E.

*Diplotaxis muralis*, Wild Rocket flower

# Echinacea purpurea

**This marvellous American herb proves that folk medicine should be more highly regarded. The Native Americans have known for years that it increases resistance to infection. Only in the past decade has modern research confirmed its properties and now it is held in high regard and is in much demand. Because of this, *Echinacea angustifolia*, *Echinacea pallida* and *Echinacea purpurea*, which all have similar medicinal properties, are becoming increasingly rare in the wild due to over-collection, so only commercially grown herbs should be used.**

## History

The generic name *Echinacea* comes from the Greek *echinos*, meaning 'hedgehog', which refers to the central golden cone that becomes more pointed and prickly as the flower matures. It wasn't known in Europe until the end of the 19th century.

## Species

*Echinacea purpurea*, Echinacea
Hardy, H5 (USDA 7,8), herbaceous perennial. Height: up to 1.2m (4ft) when in flower; spread: 45cm (18in). Lovely large, daisy-like, purple/pink flowers with a central, golden-brown spiky cone, which become more pointed as the plant matures. Oval, deep-veined leaves. This is the easiest echinacea to grow and the one grown commercially.

*Echinacea pallida*, Echinacea, Coneflower
Hardy, H5 (USDA 7,8), herbaceous perennial. Height: up to 80cm (30in) when in flower; spread: 45cm (18in). The flower is single with long, narrow, drooping mauve/pink petals, with a spiky central cone in summer to early autumn. Oval, narrow, dark green, veined leaves. This species is not as strong medicinally as *Echinacea purpurea*, nevertheless it is a very graceful plant often seen in herbaceous borders.

*Echinacea angustifolia*, Narrow-leafed Echinacea, Black Sampson
Hardy, H5 (USDA 7,8), herbaceous perennial. Height: up to 60cm (24in) when in flower; spread: 30cm (12in). The flower is single with long purple, or occasionally white, petals, with a spiky central cone in summer to early autumn. Mid-green linear leaves. This herb has been become endangered in the wild from over-collection.

## Propagation

**Seeds:** sow seeds in early spring into prepared seed trays or modules using a standard seed compost. Place under cover at 18°C (64°F). If no germination has occurred after 28 days, place the container outside, or in the crisper drawer of the refrigerator for a further 21 days, then place back under cover, out of direct sunlight. Germination should then occur within the next 20 days. Plant out into a prepared site, when large enough to handle, 30cm (12in) apart.

**Division:** in winter, divide established plants while they are still dormant. You can either replant into a prepared site or pot up and place in a cold frame or cold greenhouse until spring.

**Root cuttings:** unless you require masses of plants, division is far more reliable. If you do want to do root cuttings take them in late autumn. Dig up an established plant, choose some vigorous pencil-thick roots cut each root into 5–8cm (2–3in) lengths, root in either a small pot or modules filled with three parts seed compost mixed with one part perlite. In the following spring, once rooted, pot up, grow on and plant out in the next spring.

## Pests and diseases

In general, echinacea is not prone to pests and diseases. In spring, young plants can be attacked by slugs and snails, so it is worth doing a couple of night patrols with a torch to remove any which you may find in the crown of the plant. In a damp, warm late summer it can suffer from powdery mildew; if this happens, cut back any affected parts, bin, do not compost (see page 276 for more information).

## How and where to grow

Echinacea grows wild on the fertile plans of North America, so to keep it thriving in the garden plant in a fertile loam soil which is free-draining and in plenty of sun. It will adapt to most soils with the exception of excessive wet conditions and cold wet clay soils, which can cause the roots to rot. *Echinacea purpurea* is not as sensitive to wet soils as the other two species. Deadhead the flowers as they fade to encourage more to form, but in the autumn leave the seed heads for the birds. It is lovely to watch charms of finches chattering with delight as they feast on the seeds. Lightly mulch established plants with well-rotted manure in the spring.

## Growing in containers

Echinacea adapts happily to being grown in containers. Use three parts loam-based potting compost mixed with one part horticultural grit. Divide pot-bound plants in the autumn. Alternatively, pot up one size of pot. Place the container in full sun for the growing season. Feed regularly with a liquid fertiliser following the manufacturer's instructions. In winter if you live in a wet cold climate, lift the container off the ground and place on bricks under the eaves of the house, or by a wall to give a bit of shelter.

## Yearly maintenance

**Spring:** sow seeds; feed established plants lightly with well-rotted manure.

**Summer:** cut back stems as the blooms fade, to encourage further flower production.

**Autumn:** divide established plants; take root cuttings.

**Winter:** no need for protection from the cold, only from excessive wet.

## Harvesting and storing

**Leaves:** harvest the leaves during flowering before the cone is fully formed and the petals have started to fall back.

**Seeds:** when the petals have died back, pick the seed heads and dry well.

**Roots:** dig up the roots and rhizomes of four-year-old plants in autumn for cutting material and/or for drying and making fresh tinctures.

## Culinary uses

None.

## Medicinal uses

Echinacea is a blood purifier and digestive stimulant for those regaining their health. It has the ability to raise the body's resistance to infection by stimulating the immune system. It is very effective in preventing colds and flu or reducing their severity. A decoction – the juice extracted from the flowers – can be used externally to treat minor wounds, burns and boils and also as a gargle for throat infections.

**WARNING** | If you are allergic to plants in the *Asteraceae* family, for example chrysanthemums, marigolds or daisies, then you could be allergic to echinacea. People who are suffering from progressive systemic auto-immune disorders should not take this herb without full consultation.

*Echinacea purpurea*, Echinacea

# Elettaria cardamomum

**There have been two incidents that made me sit up and realise how important this herb is. The first was on a visit to Goa, seeing it growing and realising that it had to be hand-picked in the rainforest; the second was during one of our HerbFests, when Simon Mills, one of the UK's leading practiitoners, had a bag full of spices and herbs that could be found in your kitchen cupboard and he extolled the medicinal merits of this herb.**

*Elettaria cardamomum*, Cardamom

## History

This tropical herb was originally found growing wild under the canopy of the rainforest in the Ghat Mountains on the Malabar coast of southwest India in an area known as the Cardamom Hills. It is cultivated commercially in India, Sri Lanka, Guatemala and Tanzania. It has been used for thousands of years in Ayurvedic and Traditional Chinese Medicine for digestive ailments. The Ancient Egyptians used it as a perfume and medicine and the Greeks and Romans used it as a culinary spice. Historically, the Arabs enjoyed cardamom seeds in their coffee, a practice which continues today, and which explains why cardamom is mentioned so often in Sir Richard Burton's translation of *The Arabian Nights*.

## Species

*Elettaria cardamomum*, Cardamom
Tropical, subtropical, H2 (USDA 10), evergreen perennial. Height: up to 3m (9ft); spread: indefinite. Orchid-like white flowers with a striped purple-pink lower lip, followed – in tropical climates only – by 15–20 aromatic seeds. Smooth, linear, lance-shaped, pointed, dark green leaves with a silky and paler underside, which is highly aromatic when crushed or heated.

## Propagation

**Seeds:** outside the tropics it is very difficult to get fresh seed, which only remains viable for 7–10 days once harvested. Sow the fresh seeds into prepared modules or plugs using a seed compost. Place in a warm place or propagator at 24°C (75°F). Germination takes 14–21 days. Plants raised from seed take 3–5 years to flower.

**Division:** divide established plants in late spring/early summer. Either replant in a prepared site in a tropical garden or tropical greenhouse. Alternatively, if dividing a pot plant, replant using a loam-based potting compost mixed equally with fine composted bark. In the tropics, plants that have been divided take three years to flower, however, it rarely flowers outside the tropics, even when raised in a tropical house, due to the light levels.

## Pests and diseases

Red spidermite can be an occasional problem in older plants, especially when grown in a glasshouse or conservatory; regular misting with soft rainwater and keeping the leaves well-washed will reduce this. If it gets out of hand use a horticultural soap spray following the manufacturer's instructions.

There are well over 150 species of thrip found in the UK; they cause mottling on the foliage. As they are incredibly hard to see with the naked eye, use a magnifying lens. If you have a bad infestation in a glasshouse you can use biological control (see page 266), blue sticky traps, or we often use a plant invigorator spray that combines nutrients and fatty acids (see page 272).

If plants are too cold their leaves turn brown. If the leaves develop brown tips at any time (even if the plant is kept warm) it is a sign of over-watering. If the leaf develops creamy patches, this can be caused by too much sun and is a form of scorch.

## How and where to grow

Cardamom will flower and fruit only under tropical conditions. In subtropical or cool regions it makes an attractive foliage container plant, ideal for a warm conservatory or warm greenhouse. However, if you do live in the tropics this herb can be invasive in the garden, so control its creeping rhizomes in spring by digging them up and replanting in a different area.

## Growing in containers

Cardamom likes to be pot bound so do not be greedy and pot it in a large pot as it will sulk. Use a loam-based potting compost mixed in equal parts with fine composted bark. It can be fussy and does not like draughts, sudden changes of temperature or direct sunlight. Grow in a warm, steamy, shady place, like a warm bathroom and mist the plant daily with rainwater. Alternatively, stand the pot on a big saucer of pebbles, which are kept moist, to encourage a humid atmosphere around the plant. In winter, keep the plant warm at a minimum of 20°C (68°F) and cut back on the watering, however do not allow the plant to dry out. Repot container-grown plants in the spring either by planting up one size larger than the previous one or by dividing the plant and replanting in the same-sized pot. Feed container plants regularly with a liquid seaweed fertiliser from spring until early autumn.

## Yearly maintenance

**Spring:** divide established plants or pot plants.

**Summer:** spray leaves with rainwater; check for thrip and/or spidermite.

**Autumn:** sow fresh seeds.

**Winter:** cut back the watering of container plants; protect from cold weather.

## Harvesting and storing

**Seeds:** in the tropics the seeds are harvested before they are fully ripe, in the dry season. They are picked individually by hand which makes this a very labour-intensive and expensive crop to produce.

**Leaves:** pick the leaves to use fresh as required.

## Culinary uses

**Seeds:** there are green and brown pods depending on the variety of cardamom. In each pod there are approximately 12–18 black seeds that are often stuck together – they have a warm, spicy, lemony flavour. The bright lime green pods are the best culinary variety; the brown pods are the best for medicinal use. They are both used to flavour food – sweet and savoury – and drinks, including coffee and wine. The white pods are simply those that have been bleached.

**Leaves:** the leaves don't smell the same as the seeds; they have a warm sweet aromatic scent and can be used to wrap around fish, rice or vegetables to add flavour during cooking. The long stalks are useful to tie the leaves together to make a neat parcel – when used with fish they keep it beautifully moist.

## Medicinal uses

Cardamom's medicinal properties can be found in the seeds, which have pain-relieving, anti-inflammatory, and antispasmodic properties. In Ayurvedic medicine cardamom is often used to improve the flavour and quality of medicine and as an expectorant. Seeds extracted from the pod and chewed after a meal freshen the breath and aid digestion.

**Common names:** Wild Rosemary, South African Wild Rosemary, Snowbush, Kapokbos, Cape Snowbush

# Eriocephalus africanus

**This remarkable drought-loving plant, which is well known in the Cape of South Africa, has a special place in my Herb Farm, not only because it is known as Eric, but also because while the majority of my herbs are becoming dormant in winter, it goes into full flower, which lifts everyone's spirits during the short grey days of the winter months. These flowers are followed by the most attractive seed heads that are covered in white tufts, hence its Afrikaans name *kapokbos* which is derived from *kapok*, meaning 'cotton', and *bos*, meaning 'bush'.**

*Eriocephalus africanus*, South African Wild Rosemary

## History

I had been growing this herb for a number of years when I was given a book on the medicinal plants of South Africa prior to my visit in 2007. You can imagine my excitement when I realised the full potential of Eric as a medicinal herb and that it had been used for many hundreds of years by the Khoekhoe as a diuretic.

## Species

*Eriocephalus africanus*, South African Wild Rosemary
Half-hardy, H3 (USDA 9), evergreen shrub. Height and spread: 1m (3ft). Clusters of small, white, daisy-like flowers with magenta centres through the winter are followed by seeds covered in masses of tiny white hairs that make them look fluffy. Small, needle-like, silver-haired, oval, slightly succulent, aromatic leaves that grow in tufts along the branch.

## Propagation

**Seeds:** in spring sow fresh seeds into prepared plug modules, or small containers using a seed compost mixed in equal parts with perlite. Position in a warm place or a propagator at 20°C (68°F). Germination takes 10–15 days. Once large enough to handle, pot up using three parts loam-based compost mixed with one part horticultural sand. In cool climates, winter young plants in a frost-free environment prior to planting out the following spring.

**Cuttings:** as the seeds rarely set in our winters, it is far easier to take cuttings in late spring from the growing tips and transfer them to prepared plug modules, using three parts seed compost mixed with one part standard perlite. In cool climates, grow under protection for the first year prior to planting out the following spring.

## Pests and diseases

Wild rosemary is rarely attacked by pests, but wet winters in the garden and over-watering container plants can cause this plant to die.

## How and where to grow

This herb can be found growing wild in South Africa on granite and clay slopes. It can also be found growing by the sea where it likes the sea spray and wind, which make it an ideal seaside plant. In the garden, it prefers full sun and a well-drained soil and as a drought-loving plant it looks really lovely growing in a gravel garden. The plant is well adapted to survive drought, the silver leaves reflect sunlight which reduces the leaf temperature. The minute, silvery hairs covering the leaves trap moisture thus reducing transpiration. In warm climates, it can be grown as a hedge or clipped into ball shapes. Because this herb flowers in winter it is most beneficial to pollinators as a late-nectar plant. In winters that consistently have temperatures below -3°C (27°F), either protect the plant with horticultural fleece or bring into a polytunnel or greenhouse, replanting in the spring once all threat of frost has passed.

## Growing in containers

Wild rosemary makes a spectacular container plant as it cascades beautifully over the pot; another advantage is that it does not mind a bit of neglect. Use three parts loam-based compost mixed with one part sharp horticultural sand. Repot every spring and give the plant a good haircut after flowering in early spring. Water regularly throughout the summer and feed monthly with a general-purpose liquid fertiliser from spring until the first flowering in early autumn. Cut back the watering during the winter months. If you live in damp, wet conditions, lift the pot off the ground and place it on bricks to aid drainage.

## Yearly maintenance

**Spring:** prune after flowering in late spring to encourage new growth; sow seeds.

**Summer:** feed container-grown plants regularly.

**Autumn:** in cold climates protect from heavy autumn rains.

**Winter:** protect from excessive wet and when temperatures fall consistently below 0°C (32°F) during the day.

## Harvesting and storing

Pick the leaves to use fresh or to dry after flowering from spring until early autumn. Harvest the seeds when they start to drop in early spring.

## Culinary uses

The leaves of this herb can be used in a very similar way to *Salvia rosmarinus* (rosemary), especially with lamb dishes and vegetable stews. It can be used dried or fresh. When finely chopped it is a good accompaniment to soups, salads, vegetables and used in a marinade.

## Medicinal uses

Wild rosemary has traditionally been used as a medicine for many ailments, such as coughs and colds, flatulence and colic, as a diuretic and a diaphoretic. It is said to have similar qualities to *Salvia rosmarinus* (rosemary). An infusion of the leaves can be used in the bath to help relaxation, as recommended by the wonderful South African herb grower Margaret Roberts – I learned so much from this amazing lady, not only at her herb farm but also when she took me on a private tour of Kirstenbosch National Botanic Garden.

*Eriocephalus africanus*, South African Wild Rosemary

# Ferula communis

**Giant fennel is – without exaggeration – a superb plant. After three to four years the vast flower-stalk rises from a huge mound of dark green, finely cut foliage, thick as a broomstick and reaching at least 4m (13ft) with huge umbellifer flowers made up of hundreds or even thousands of bright yellow flowers, which are stunning against a blue sky in summer. Giant fennel should not be confused with *Foeniculum vulgare*, common fennel, which you will find on page 122.**

*Ferula communis*, Giant Fennel

## History

The Romans ate the young stems and flower heads of the giant fennel, however that was very risky as some varieties of *Ferula* are poisonous. Nearly all the *Ferula* species have been used for medicinal purposes for thousands of years – the resin, in the form of a sticky latex, was extracted from the root and used medicinally and in the kitchen (as it is today). Also, it is said that rods and whips were made from giant fennel's stalks.

## Species

*Ferula communis*, Giant Fennel
Hardy, H3 (USDA 9), herbaceous perennial. Height: up to 4m (13ft) when in flower; spread: 1.5m (5ft). Striking round umbels of tiny yellow flowers. Large, feathery dark green leaves which die back in summer and reappear in the autumn. Very large, long tap root. May die after flowering.

*Ferula assa-foetida*, Assa-foetida, Asafoetida, Devil's Dung, 'Food of the Gods', Hing
Hardy, H4 (USDA 8,9), herbaceous perennial. Height: up to 4m (13ft) in flower; spread: 1.5m (5ft). Flowers from the fourth year in early spring, producing flat umbels of tiny yellow flowers, followed by small brown seeds. Large, finely divided, green–grey, garlic-scented leaves that die back in summer and reappear in the autumn. This plant often dies after flowering. Asafoetida gets its name from the Persian *aza*, meaning 'resin', and the Latin *foetidus*, 'stinking', which is highlighted by one of its common names 'devil's dung'. Ironically it is also called 'food of the gods' because minute quantities of the sulphur-smelling resin can enhance the flavour of many foods.

## Propagation

**Seeds:** This herb originates from the Middle East where it is dependent on the winter rainfall. When this herb is allowed to grow naturally the seeds drop in summer and are germinated by the first rains. So, following this natural rhythm, sow the fresh seeds in late summer into prepared plug modules or small pots using three parts seed compost mixed with one part sharp horticultural sand. Once the seedlings are large enough, pot up using three parts loam-based compost mixed with one part horticultural sharp sand into a deep pot, ideally a long tom. Winter the young plants in a cold frame or a cold greenhouse.

## Pests and diseases

Giant fennel rarely suffers from pests or disease. Container-raised plants can be attacked by aphids. Treat with a horticultural soap spray following the manufacturer's instructions.

## How and where to grow

When choosing where to plant this structurally magnificent plant in the garden, it is worth remembering that it does not like to be moved and that it will grow to at least 4m (13ft) when in flower. If your garden is exposed to the prevailing wind, it just might need to be staked. It prefers a well-drained soil and a sunny position. In winter, especially if you live in a cold dank climate, it is worth protecting the crown with straw, not bark, which will cause the crown to rot.

## Growing in containers

Long tom pots are ideal for all *Ferulas* as they have a very long tap root. These pots were much loved by the Victorian gardeners for deep-rooted plants. They have, I am grateful to say, come back into fashion and are readily available. It is best, if possible, to choose a terracotta pot as terracotta is porous which allows more air to flow through your plants – without that extra breathing space, the plants are most likely to wilt and/or become susceptible to root mould and/or disease. It is well worth investing in a few long toms as this is such a spectacular plant. Only pot up one size of pot at a time – this plant does not like being over-potted – use three parts loam-based compost mixed with one part horticultural sharp sand or grit. Place the container in full sun and give it liquid feed regularly throughout the growing season following the manufacturer's instructions.

## Yearly maintenance

**Spring:** stake flowering spikes when grown on an exposed site.

**Summer:** sow seeds; harvest root from fourth year onwards.

**Autumn:** mulch established plants with well-rotted manure.

**Winter:** protect from excessive wet.

## Harvesting and storing

Harvest the seed and resin from four-year-old plants in the summer. Cut off the stems and make successive slices through the roots. A milky, smelly liquid will exude from the cuts. As it is exposed to the air it forms a resin that turns from a creamy, greyish-white colour to reddish-brown when dry. After successive slicing one root can yield up to 1kg (2lb 2oz) of resin. Please be aware that this amount is produced in the Middle East – more northerly latitudes can expect a lesser yield.

## Culinary uses

The part of the asafoetida that is used is the dried sap or gum resin, which is extracted from the roots. Once dried, it is ground into a coarse, pungent yellow powder, which is used throughout southern India in the preparation of beans, peas and lentils. The easiest way to use asafoetida in the kitchen is to buy it already prepared in an airtight container so that the odour of the dried resin is kept contained. Add a minute pinch of resin to hot oil before adding the other ingredients – this calms the aroma and balances the flavour of the other ingredients.

## Medicinal uses

In Ayurvedic and Eastern herbal medicine, asafoetida gum resin is used to treat bloating, wind, indigestion and constipation. It also helps lower blood pressure and thins the blood. Owing to its foul taste and smell it is usually taken in pill form.

**WARNING** | None of the green parts or the roots of *Ferula* should be eaten raw and the resin from the roots should be dried and ground before use.

# Filipendula ulmaria

**Meadowsweet grows throughout the northern hemisphere, including in Scandinavia and the USA. It can be found in wet meadows, ditches, damp woods and down country lanes. The flowers have the most beautiful almond scent, which catches the summer air, and they taste amazingly like honey.**

## History

Historically this is a very famous plant. In the 19th century, salicylic acid was isolated from the sap of the plant and later synthesised as acetylsalicylic acid, which is known today as aspirin. The name aspirin is said to have derived from the plant's old botanical name, *Spirea ulmaria*. The common name, meadowsweet, is said to be derived from the Anglo-Saxon word 'medesweete', which is a reference to the fact that the plant was once used to flavour mead, a drink made from fermented honey.

## Species

*Filipendula ulmaria*, Meadowsweet
Hardy, H6 (USDA 6,7), herbaceous perennial. Height: up to 1.2m (4ft) in flower; spread: 75cm (30in). Clusters of frothy, almond/honey-scented, creamy white flowers in summer. Darkish green, pinnate, serrated, deeply veined leaves, which are aromatic when crushed.

*Filipendula ulmaria*, Aurea Golden Meadowsweet
Hardy, H6 (USDA 6,7), herbaceous perennial. Height: up to 1m (3ft) in flower; spread: 75cm (30in). Clusters of lightly scented creamy-white flowers in midsummer. Bright golden-yellow, divided leaves in spring, which turn a lime colour in summer and are prone to sun scorch if planted in full sun.

*Filipendula ulmaria*, 'Variegata', Variegated Meadowsweet
Hardy, H6 (USDA 6,7), herbaceous perennial. Height: up to 1m (3ft) in flower; spread: 75cm (30in). Clusters of lightly-scented creamy-white flowers in midsummer. The divided leaf is dramatically variegated green and yellow in spring which fades a bit as the season progresses.

*Filipendula vulgaris*, Dropwort, Italian May
Hardy, H6 (USDA 6,7), herbaceous perennial. Height: up to 90cm (3ft) in flower; spread: 50cm (20in) Foamy sprays of creamy-white flowers in summer. Dark green, fern-like, toothed leaves that grow in a rosette.

## Propagation

**Seeds:** for the best results, sow seeds in prepared seed or plug trays in the autumn, using a seed compost. As the seeds are small, cover them with a sprinkling of compost and winter in a cold greenhouse or cold frame or outside covered with a sheet of glass. Check from time to time that the compost has not become dry as this will inhibit germination. Stratification is helpful but not necessary (see page 18). Germination should take place in the spring. When the seedlings are large enough to handle, plant out in the garden into a prepared site at a distance of 30cm (12in) apart.

**Division:** the golden and variegated forms are best propagated by division. This is easily done in the autumn. Dig up established plants and tease the plantlets apart. They separate easily and can either be replanted in a prepared site 30cm (12in) apart, or if it is one of the decorative varieties, pot up using a soil-based potting compost.

## Pests and diseases

This plant is prone to mildew; if this occurs cut off the diseased leaves. If it is a bad infestation, cut the plant down to the ground, making sure that the contaminated leaves are destroyed, not composted.

## How and where to grow

Plant meadowsweet in a moisture-retentive soil in sun or partial shade. It is a good plant for growing in clay soils and ideal for growing around and in the shallows of ponds. Cut back after flowering.

## Growing in containers

Meadowsweet will grow in a container if grown in a soil-based compost and positioned in partial shade. Do not allow the compost to dry out. If going on holiday, place the container in a bucket of water. Golden and variegated meadowsweet look very attractive in containers. The plant dies back in winter so leave it outside, preferably in a place where the natural weathers can reach it. If you live in extremely cold winters and the container will get damaged, place it in an area that will protect it from continuous frosts but is not warm. Only feed with a liquid fertiliser twice during flowering, following the manufacturer's guidelines.

## Yearly maintenance

**Spring:** dig up any self-sown seedlings, either for potting up or replanting.

**Summer:** cut back after flowering.

**Autumn:** divide established plants; sow seeds for wintering outside.

**Winter:** no need for protection.

## Harvesting and storing

**Leaves:** pick the young leaves to use fresh or to dry before flowering.

**Flowers:** pick the flowers just as they open to use fresh or to dry.

**Roots:** dig up the roots of a third-year plant to dry, to make medicinal tinctures or a black textile dye.

## Culinary uses

**Leaves:** young leaves (early spring) can be added to salads or soups. The leaves can be very dry in the mouth and, in my opinion, have a medicinal flavour, so consider carefully before adding them to salads.

**Flowers:** the flowers can be added to stewed fruits, jellies and jams. They have a mild honey and almond flavour. A delicious tea can be made with the flowers and a few leaves, which is lovely hot or cold with a slice of lemon on a summer's day. They are also good for flavouring meads and beers and make an interesting wine.

## Medicinal uses

The whole plant is a traditional remedy for an acid stomach. The fresh root is used in homeopathic preparations and can also be used in the treatment of diarrhoea. A tea made from the flowers is ideal for those suffering from aches or pains.

*Filipendula vulgaris*, Dropwort

*Filipendula ulmaria*, Meadowsweet

**WARNING** | This herb is not recommended for children or adults who are sensitive to aspirin.

# Foeniculum vulgare

**Fennel is a herb that can be used in the kitchen and the home throughout the year. It looks good in any part of the garden, it tastes good and it does you good by easing indigestion. When left on the plant after harvest, the seeds are loved by the wild birds in winter.**

*Foeniculum vulgare*, Fennel

## History

Fennel is as ancient as the Egyptian papyrus documents in which it is mentioned. The Greeks thought very highly of fennel and used it for slimming and for treating more than 20 different illnesses; the Romans ate its leaf, root and seed in salads and baked it in bread and cakes. In Anglo-Saxon times, it was used on fasting days, presumably because, as the Greeks had already discovered, it stilled the pangs of hunger.

## Species

*Foeniculum vulgare*, Fennel
Hardy, H5 (USDA 7,8), herbaceous perennial. Height: up to 2m (7ft) in flower; spread: 45cm (18in). Large flat umbels of small yellow flowers in summer, followed by aromatic seeds. Soft, green, feathery, aromatic foliage.

*Foeniculum vulgare* var. *dulce*, Florence Fennel, Finocchio
Hardy, H5 (USDA 7,8), herbaceous perennial, often grown as an annual. Height: up to 1.5m (5ft); spread: 40cm (16in). The flowers form small yellow clusters in late summer; the leaf is feathery and green. The base of the plant develops to form a sweet, bulbous white vegetable.

*Foeniculum vulgare* 'Purpureum', Bronze Fennel
Hardy, H4 (USDA 8,9), herbaceous perennial. Height: up to 1.5m (5ft); spread: 45cm (18in) with flat umbels of flowers in summer and lovely soft, striking, feathery bronze leaves. These have a milder flavour than the green variety but can still be used in cooking.

## Propagation

**Seeds:** sow seeds of the green and bronze fennels in spring into prepared seed trays or pots. Place in a propagator at 18°C (64°F). Germination takes 7–10 days. Grow on under protection until all threat of frost has gone. Alternatively sow in late spring into prepared open ground when the air temperature at night remains above 5°C (41°F). Germination takes 14–20 days. If you have a heavy clay soil, line the drill with sharp horticultural sand to give added drainage and to give the young plants a chance to establish.

Florence fennel is only grown from seed. Sow into prepared shallow trenches during the early summer in a rich well-composted soil for the bulbous roots to reach maturity by the autumn. When seedlings are about 2.5cm (1in) in height, thin out to a distance of 20cm (8in) apart. During dry spells, be prepared to water well. Unless seed is required, the flower heads should be pinched out as they appear. When the swelling is about the size of a golf ball draw some soil around it. After 2–3 weeks the bulbs will have blanched and grown in size. The best size for harvesting is roughly the size of a tennis ball. Dig up as required.

**Division:** divide established plants in the autumn – this is only successful in light soils because of its long tap root. If you have a cold damp heavy soil, renew plants every three years.

## Pests and diseases

Fennel is not usually troubled by pests or diseases. One thing that may occur when the plants are very young is root rot from over-watering. Green fly may also occasionally infest the plant; this can be treated with a horticultural soft soap (see page 267).

## How and where to grow

Plant in a warm sunny site in well-drained fertile soil. If fennel is grown in poor soil or arid conditions it will taste bitter. Do not plant near dill or coriander, the former because of cross-pollination and the latter alters the flavour. Cut back after seed harvest to promote leaf growth. When grown as a culinary herb it is best to replace plants every 3-4 years to keep the plants 'sweet'. In autumn, when the plant has died back, mulch around the plant with well-rotted manure, not on top as this will cause the plant to rot.

## Growing in containers

As with giant fennel (see page 118), long tom pots really suit this herb as they are deep enough to accommodate the long tap roots. Use a soil-based compost. The bronze fennel looks particularly lovely, especially when combined with *Calendula officinalis*, pot marigold. Position the container in sun to partial shade; be prepared to protect it from high winds or torrential rain when in flower and/or seed.

## Yearly maintenance

**Spring:** sow green and bronze fennel seed.

**Summer:** sow Florence fennel seed.

**Autumn:** Florence fennel bulbs should be dug up when sufficiently mature and as required. Cut back green and bronze fennels after flowering to produce new growth for autumn/early winter picking.

**Winter:** leave some seed heads on to feed the birds. Mulch mature plants with well-rotted compost, do not cover the crown.

## Harvesting and storing

**Leaves:** the best flavour is in the new shoots as they appear.

**Flowers:** pick the flowers just as the plant comes into flower.

**Stems:** pick young stems in early spring.

**Seeds:** gather in early autumn, still attached to the stems. Hang the stems upside-down in a light airy room. Once the seeds have dried, strip them from the branches and put them into an airtight glass jar.

## Culinary uses

**Leaves:** these are lovely chopped over salads and cooked vegetables, added to soups, and used in stuffings for fish.

**Flowers:** the pollen of fennel flowers is coveted by Michelin-star chefs. It is lovely but the flowers are even better – add them to salads and pickles. They are also great with apple dishes.

**Stem:** young stems have a great flavour to add to stews. Mature stems are great cooked on the barbecue.

**Seeds:** can be used fresh or dried. They are excellent with fish, stews, sauces, breads, barbecues, preserving, gherkins, cucumbers and other pickles, and in bread.

## Medicinal uses

Fennel is a renowned digestive that is used to flavour many types of liquor. It also helps to ease dyspepsia and flatulence. The seeds chewed at the end of the meal not only clear the breath but also help ease indigestion, especially after a spicy meal.

**Common names:** Wild Strawberry, Woodland Strawberry, Fraises des Bois, European Strawberry

# Fragaria vesca

**There is something magical about this lovely wild fruit. The strawberries look charming in the garden and they taste delicious. My childhood memory, apart from eating the fresh fruit, was eating a jam we were given every Christmas called Little Scarlet strawberry conserve made by Wilkin & Sons – it was divine. Wild strawberries are classed as a herb as both the leaves and the fruit can be used in the kitchen and medicinally.**

## History

This native wild strawberry is not a direct ancestor of the modern commercial strawberry, it is a species in its own right. In *Flora Britannica* Richard Mabey says that he has seen a 16th-century recipe for a form of strawberry shortcake made with almond flour and cooked simply by leaving the paste in the hot sun for a couple of hours. In the 17th century, Culpeper said that the fruit was 'excellent good to cool the liver or a hot choleric stomach, and to quench thirst', among many other attributes.

## Species

*Fragaria vesca*, Wild Strawberry
Hardy, H6 (USDA 6,7), perennial. Height: up to 30cm (12in); spread: indefinite when you include the runners. Small white flowers with yellow centres followed by small, sweet, aromatic white fruit – the taste of ambrosia throughout the summer. Trifoliate mid-green toothed leaves.

*Fragaria vesca* 'White Delight', White Fruiting Wild Strawberry
Hardy, H6 (USDA 6,7), perennial. Height: up to 30cm (12in); spread: indefinite when you include the runners. Small white flowers with yellow centres followed by small, sweet, aromatic white fruit, that turn cream when ripe, throughout the summer. Trifoliate mid-green toothed leaves.

*Fragaria vesca* 'Semperflorens', Alpine Strawberry
Hardy, H6 (USDA 6,7), perennial. Height: up to 30cm (12in); spread: up to 50cm (20in). Small white flowers with yellow centres all summer followed by small, sweet, aromatic red fruit. Trifoliate, toothed, mid-green leaves. This alpine strawberry does not set runners so can only be raised from seed.

## Propagation

**Seeds:** in late summer, pick some fruit and leave them to dry. Rub the seeds off the dried fruit and sow fresh in early autumn into a prepared seed tray or modules using a seed compost. Sow on the surface, do not cover. Place in a cold frame or a cold greenhouse or cover with a sheet of glass and leave outside. Germination takes 6–10 weeks. Plant out in spring when large enough to handle and all threat of frost has passed.

**Division:** established plants producer runners. Remove these from the parent plant any time during the growing season up until early autumn as each runner has a small root system. Plant where required into a prepared site in the garden, or into pots using a soil-based compost.

## Pests and diseases

Slugs love strawberries, so keep a watchful eye out for them. Birds are drawn to the red fruit but they leave the white fruiting strawberries alone. I have had golden retrievers for over 30 years and all three have loved wild strawberries and seem to know when they are perfect, so be warned. Vine weevils are a pesky pest and love this herb as much as we love the fruit. You may not notice your plant has been attacked until you brush past it and the crown falls over or you move a pot and find that the plant falls out with no roots. For information on how to get rid of this weevil see page 272. If grown in containers, the plants can suffer from mildew; if this happens, remove the affected parts and make sure the plant gets plenty of light and air.

## How and where to grow

Wild strawberries prefer a good fertile soil that does not dry out in summer in either full sun or partial shade. They grow well in woods and hedgerows and make a marvellous ground cover plant as they spread quickly by means of runners. A top tip if you are looking for wild strawberry leaves in the early spring before the berries: do not be confused by the barren strawberry *Potentilla sterilis*, which has similar flowers and leaves but very dry hard fruits. The *Potentilla* leaves are much shinier than the wild strawberry and have no scent or flavour.

## Growing in containers

Being small plants, wild strawberries are marvellous in containers, window boxes and hanging baskets, where the runners take on a new dimension. If the plant is put on the side of the basket the runners will hang down over the edge and can look most attractive. Use a loam-based potting compost. Water and feed with a liquid fertiliser regularly, especially when the fruit begins to set.

## Yearly maintenance

**Spring:** sow seed; divide runners.

**Summer:** feed with liquid fertiliser.

**Autumn:** divide runners if they have become invasive.

**Winter:** no need for protection.

## Harvesting and storing

**Fruit:** pick the fruit when ripe to eat fresh or to preserve.

**Leaves:** the best flavoured leaves are the young bright green ones; pick in spring to eat them fresh.

**Seeds:** the seed of the strawberry is visible to all as it is embedded around the outside of the fruit. To collect your own seed, leave the fruit in the summer sun to dry. When fully dry and shrivelled, rub the seed off and keep in an airtight container until required for sowing.

## Culinary uses

**Fruit:** eat the fruit fresh in fruit salads, on its own with cream, or use in cakes, pies and syrups and to flavour cordials. If you have enough you can also make jam.

**Leaves:** these have a musky flavour and scent. You can make a tea from them, but on their own are a bit musky, but when combined with sweet woodruff (see page 126), the tea can taste delicious.

## Medicinal uses

The strawberry fruit is a mild diuretic and has a laxative effect, which improves the digestive function. The leaves are included in many blended herbal teas; they were traditionally used to treat stomach upsets. Please note this does not apply to the cultivated form of strawberry, which is why this is a herb and not just a fruit.

*Fragaria vesca*, Wild Strawberry

**Common names:** Sweet Woodruff, Woodward, Hay Plant

# Galium odoratum

**My favourite quote about this herb comes from Alan Paterson's book *Herbs in the Garden*. He says, 'sweet woodruff used to be used as a strewing herb, though today it is redundant being bound to clog the vacuum cleaner.' I have also, when reading the old herbals, found that there is a certain amount of confusion between woodruff and lady's bedstraw, which is because in Europe the common name for what we know as woodruff, *Galium odoratum*, is lady's bedstraw *Galium verum*.**

## History

Woodruff, or hay plant, was associated with magic and folklore. It was said that witches feared this small flower and it was included in the nine-herb posy to ward off evil, along with angelica which protected against evil spirits, and dill, which stopped the evil eye. It was also considered a magical charm for children and was hung on the bedstead or carried in a linen pouch on the body as a deterrent against poisonous animals and other bad influences.

## Species

*Galium odoratum*, Sweet Woodruff
Hardy, H6 (USDA 6,7), herbaceous perennial. Height: 15cm (6in); spread: indefinite due to its creeping rhizome roots. Small white star-shaped flowers from spring until early summer. Aromatic, narrow, lance-shaped green leaves; 6–8 of these leaves grow in complete circle around the stem.

*Galium verum*, Lady's Bedstraw, Yellow Bedstraw
Hardy, H7 (USDA 6), perennial. Height and spread: up to 50cm (20in). Terminal panicles of tiny, four-lobed yellow flowers in summer. Sprawling stems bearing whorled linear green leaves.

## Propagation

**Seeds:** this plant happily self-seeds, however, trying to grow it in controlled situation is a challenge because it can take two years to germinate. As the viability of the seeds is a matter of months, sow them fresh in autumn into prepared modules or seed trays filled with three parts seed compost mixed with one part sharp horticultural sand. Once sown, cover with the sharp horticultural sand, not compost. Place the container outside to endure all the weathers – frost, rain, snow, etc. Germination takes 1–6 months.

**Division:** this method and root cuttings are by far the easiest methods of propagating this plant. In spring dig up a section of an established garden plant. You can then divide this into small pieces which you can either replant in the garden into a prepared site, or pot up for planting later.

**Root cuttings:** the creeping rhizome roots are very brittle so take care when digging up the plant, every little piece will grow. The best time to take root cuttings is either in the early spring, before flowering, or in the early autumn. Cut off pieces of the root, about 2–4cm (¾–1 ½in) long. As the root is thin, fibrous and very fragile, it is better to use a seed tray filled with a standard seed compost rather than plug trays. Simply lay out the roots, evenly spaced, on the seed compost and cover with a thin layer of compost. Water and leave in a warm place. There is no extra heat needed and the woodruff will begin to sprout again. When large enough to handle, split up and plant out in the garden where required.

## Pests and diseases

This plant rarely suffers from pests or diseases. When pot-grown, for a number of years it can be attacked by vine weevil (see page 272 for information).

## How and where to grow

Woodruff will adapt to most soils, but it prefers a moist, fertile soil in partial shade. This plant is ideal for ground cover, good under deciduous trees, by hedges or on banks. It can be mildly invasive under optimum conditions. In hot, dry conditions this herb can die back, causing the leaves to turn yellow. Cut it back and it will revive with watering and the cooler temperatures of late summer. If the plant is becoming invasive, dig up before the flowers have set, to check the spread.

## Growing in containers

As this herb produces creeping rhizomes, you can pot it up into a fairly large pot. The rhizomes will eventually wrap themselves around the outside of the root ball. Once this happens either divide the plant or pot up into a larger pot. Use a soil-based compost. Only feed with a liquid fertiliser when the plant is flowering. Do not feed at other times because this will make the growth too lush and the plant weak. Position the container in semi-shade and do not over-water. Remember it normally grows under trees, so it has to fight for water and light.

## Yearly maintenance

**Spring:** take root cuttings before flowering.

**Summer:** make sure woodruff has not wandered into areas you do not want it. If it has, dig up now before the flowers have set.

**Autumn:** take root cuttings, sow seeds.

**Winter:** no need for protection.

## Harvesting and storing

In early summer, pick the flowers and the leaves for drying together – this will bring out the true aroma which is just like newly mown hay!

## Culinary uses

Fresh leaves are used as flavouring agents in non-alcoholic and alcoholic beverages. May wine is prepared by adding fresh sprigs of woodruff to Rhine wine.

## Medicinal uses

As a medicinal plant, woodruff has traditionally been considered an antispasmodic, diaphoretic and diuretic. A tea made from the leaves is diuretic and beneficial for those prone to gallstones. Dried leaves are used as an insect repellent.

**WARNING** | Consumption of large quantities can produce symptoms of poisoning, including dizziness and vomiting.

*Galium odratum*, Sweet Woodruff

# Ginkgo biloba

**This amazing stately tree is regarded as the ancestor of all conifers. The *Ginkgo biloba* is the only surviving member of the ancient ginkgo family. The tree's longevity is deemed to be due to its indestructible qualities, being able to resist attack from disease, pest and pollution which is why you can find it growing very happily and gracefully in the centre of many cities, including London and Beijing, which is where I saw it in fruit for the first time. One of the most amazing examples of the tenacity of this plant may be seen in Hiroshima, Japan. Six trees were growing approximately 2 kilometres (1.25 miles) from the site of the 1945 atom bomb explosion. Almost everything in that area was destroyed, but those ginkgos – although they were charred – survived and recovered and can still be seen today.**

*Gingko biloba*, Ginkgo

## History

This tree, a native of China, is considered to be a living fossil and thought to be one of the oldest trees on the planet, dating back to the dinosaur era. Chinese monks are credited with keeping the tree in existence, as a sacred herb. Ginkgo is derived from the Japanese word *ginkyo*, meaning 'silver apricot', referring to its fruit; while the Latin scientific name *biloba*, which translates as 'two-lobed', refers to the split in the middle of the fan-shaped leaf blades. It is one of the most well-researched herbs in the world.

## Species

*Ginkgo biloba* Ginkgo, Maidenhair Tree
Hardy, H6 (USDA 6,7), deciduous tree. Height: up to 40m (130ft); spread: up to 20m (65ft). It is dioecious, which means that it bears male and female flowers on different trees in early summer. These are followed by small, yellow, unpleasantly-scented fruit on the female tree. Fan-shaped green leaves are sometimes whole, but often they have a single central, vertical slit.

*Ginkgo biloba* 'Fastigiata Blagon'
Hardy, H6 (USDA 6,7), deciduous tree. Height up to 12m (39ft); spread: up to 4m (13ft). This is a sterile cultivar that has a columnar habit with bright, almost emerald-green leaves that turn butter-yellow in autumn. They are ieal for a medium-sized garden.

*Ginkgo biloba* 'Troll'
Hardy, H6 (USDA 6,7), deciduous tree. Height and spread: up to 1m (3ft). This is a sterile cultivar, which is extremely slow growing. It has dark green, ruffled, fan-shaped leaves that turn butter-yellow in autumn. Ideal for growing in containers or city courtyard gardens.

## Propagation

**Seeds:** in autumn, wearing gloves (because they are toxic), remove the pith from around the seed, then wash in a mild detergent to remove any germination inhibitors. Sow immediately into individual small pots using a seed compost mixed in equal parts with horticultural grit. Cover with coarse grit and place in a cold frame. Germination takes 4–6 months, however it can take longer. Plant into growing position 5 years after germination. You may not be able to tell the sex of the seed-raised plant for 20 years, i.e. until it flowers.

**Cuttings:** take cuttings from new growth in summer or semi-ripe growth in early autumn. Place in a seed compost, mixed in equal parts with horticultural grit. Keep frost-free until rooted. Grow as a container plant in exactly the same way as a seed-raised plant before planting in the garden.

## Pests and diseases

Rarely suffers from pests or diseases.

## How and where to grow

Plant ginkgo in full sun to partial sun in a light, deep, fertile soil, however it is very adaptable and will cope with winter salt sprays and air pollution so is ideal for town planting. To produce a fruit, in warm climates, a male and a female tree are needed and they need to be planted near each other. Over 35 years ago I sowed three seeds with my children, we have one of those plants, which is now a tree, growing in the Herbetum; it has yet to flower.

## Growing in containers

Young ginkgo plants grow happily in containers. Once the plant is over two years old, use a loam-based potting compost mixed in equal parts with horticultural grit. Water and liquid feed regularly throughout the growing season, repotting the following spring into the next size pot.

## Yearly maintenance

**Spring:** repot or topdress container-raised plants.

**Summer:** take cuttings from semi-ripe growth.

**Autumn:** sow fresh seeds.

**Winter:** no extra protection needed.

## Harvesting and storing

**Leaves:** harvest the leaves as they turn from green to yellow in autumn, then dry them.

**Fruit:** pick the small fruits when ripe – you will know when it is the correct time as they start to drop and they really do smell. The kernel (nut) is extracted and dried in autumn.

## Culinary uses

There is current debate regarding the toxicity of the fresh nut, and therefore whether it can be eaten raw or cooked. I would err on the side of caution as most recipes say cooked; it is used in soups, stir-fries and roasted. The nuts are available to buy tinned from Eastern supermarkets – they are often called 'white nuts'.

## Medicinal uses

Ginkgo is one of the bestselling western herbal medicines taken to improve the memory. In Chinese medicine, the ginkgo nuts are used in the treatment of asthma, bronchial congestion and coughs. In Western medicine, the leaves are taken to improve the circulation, memory, maintain brain function, and ease tinnitus and vertigo.

**WARNING** | Do not exceed the stated dosage. Can cause toxic reactions if taken in excess. Seeds harmful if eaten.

*Ginkgo biloba*, Ginkgo in autumn

# Glycyrrhiza glabra

**This herb, in its many forms, can be found worldwide, and is an important medicinal and culinary herb. I vividly remember chewing liquorice root as a child, extracting its amazingly sweet flavour. Now, when I teach how to take liquorice root cuttings, I give the students the fresh root to chew – it is wonderful to see their incredulity as they taste it.**

*Glycyrrhiza glabra*, Liquorice

## History

Liquorice has been used medicinally for over 3,000 years. The Ancient Egyptians and Greeks recognised the herb's benefits in treating coughs and lung disease. It was introduced to the UK by the Crusaders in the 11th century, returning from the Middle East campaigns. It was later grown in the 14th century by Spanish monks in Pontefract Friary in northern England. Today, commercial crops can be found in Turkey, Spain and Italy. It is one of the most popular and widely consumed herbs in the world.

## Species

*Glycyrrhiza glabra*, Liquorice
Hardy, H6 (USDA 6,7), herbaceous perennial. Height: 1.2m (3ft 11in); spread: 1m (3ft). Short spikes of pea-like mauve/purple-tinged white flowers in late summer followed by long pods. Large green leaves divided into oval leaflets. This is the main liquorice used medicinally and as a flavouring.

*Glycyrrhiza glandulifera*, Spanish Juice Plant
Hardy, H5 (USDA 7,8), herbaceous perennial. Height: up to 1.5m (5ft); spread: 1m (3ft). Pale blue to violet flowers grow on loose upright spikes in late summer. Upright stems bear sticky green leaves with numerous opposite pairs of leaflets. This liquorice is great for a wild or informal garden where it can flourish. The roots do not have the same intense flavour as *Glycyrrhiza glabra* but can still be used as a sweet flavouring.

*Glycyrrhiza echinata*, Wild Liquorice
Hardy, H6 (USDA 6,7), herbaceous perennial. Height: up to 1m (3ft); spread: 60cm (24in). Oval clusters of small, pale blue to violet flowers in late summer. Multiple stems of green leaves divided into numerous opposite pairs of leaflets. This liquorice is a hardy nitrogen-fixing plant. By fixing the nitrogen into the soil, you will need to feed the soil less and so it decreases the use of fertiliser. It also protects the soil from erosion by holding it in place with its strong root system. If growing the plant for its roots, inhibit flowering by cutting it back in early summer and keep the roots well-watered, lifting them in mid-autumn once the plant has died back. Very beneficial for attracting lacewings and parasitoid wasps.

*Glycyrrhiza lepidota*, American Licorice, Wild Liquorice
Hardy, H6 (USDA 6,7), herbaceous perennial. Height: up to 1.5m (5ft); spread: 75cm (30in). The creamy-white/yellow flowers grow in spike-like clusters in summer followed by long brown seed pods that are covered with long-hooked prickles. The mid-green leaves are alternate with 7–21 oblong leaflets. This herb is a good nitrogen fixer, and the leaves and stems make excellent mulch or compost as they are high in minerals and nutrients. The roots were traditionally used as a flavouring for root beer and chewing tobacco but

today it is mainly *Glycyrrhiza glabra* that is used medicinally and as a flavouring.

## Propagation

**Seeds:** seeds from cool climates tend not to be viable, unless we have had a long hot summer. Sow seeds in spring into prepared modules or seed trays filled with a seed compost. Place under protection at 20°C (68°F); germination takes 10–14 days though it can be erratic. Grow on for two years in a container before planting out in open ground.

**Division:** divide established plants in autumn after the plant has died back. Make sure there is a growing bud in each division, replanting into a well-prepared site.

**Root cuttings:** in late autumn/early winter, before the soil becomes frozen and hard, dig up some roots. You will notice that there are growing buds spaced along the root and often where one root splits off. Take a cutting that includes a growing bud. Put the cuttings into small pots that have been filled with a seed compost mixed in equal parts with horticultural grit. Put the pots in a frost-free, light place – a glasshouse or conservatory is ideal. These cuttings will start shooting in the spring once the day length increases.

## Pests and diseases

Mature plants are not bothered by pests or disease. Seedlings can be prone to damping off (see page 274 for more information).

## How and where to grow

Liquorice needs a deep, fertile, well-cultivated soil and a sunny position. To produce a good root crop it is essential to feed the soil well in autumn with a good mulch of well-rotted manure. In spring, cut back old growth. Do not be fooled by this ancient herb – it would not have survived for all this time if it weren't a bit of a thug. You will find that its deep rhizome roots can reappear in the garden where you least expect them.

## Growing in containers

Liquorice has a very long, deep root system, which does not make it ideal for growing in containers. I recommend that if you wish to harvest the roots that you choose a deep pot, or even a dustbin. Use a soil-based compost, position the container in partial shade or full sun. If in full sun do not allow the compost to become too dry.

## Yearly maintenance

**Spring:** replant autumn divided plants in the garden.

**Summer:** do nothing, enjoy the flowers.

**Autumn:** divide established plants; sow fresh seeds.

**Winter:** take root cuttings; in very cold winters protect first-year plants with a mulch or agricultural fleece.

## Harvesting and storing

Dig up the roots for drying in early winter from established three- or four-year-old plants. As this is a slow-growing plant, I suggest you only dig up a third, leaving the remaining two-thirds so that the plant can be harvested the following years. Fill the area from which the roots were removed with well-rotted manure.

## Culinary uses

Liquorice root is used to flavour black treacle, gingerbread, Guinness, stout and other beers. The root can be used to flavour sugar and is wonderful mixed with salt for a great marinade.

## Medicinal uses

Medicinally, liquorice is the second most prescribed herb in China following ginseng. It is prescribed for treatment of the spleen, liver and kidneys. The Japanese use a liquorice preparation to treat hepatitis. In Western medicine it is used to treat upper respiratory ailments, including coughs, hoarseness, sore throat and bronchitis.

**WARNING** | Liquorice should not be taken medicinally by anyone who is pregnant, has high blood pressure, kidney disease, or when taking digoxin-based medicines.

**Common names:** Sweet Vine, Sweet Tea Vine, Jiaogulan, Five-leaf Ginseng

# Gynostemma pentaphyllum

**This fascinating herb is native to China, originating in Guizhou, a mountainous province of southwest China. It can also be found growing in northern Vietnam, southern Korea and Japan. It is often called the immortality herb because the northern Chinese tribes who drank a tea made from this herb were said to have lived more than 100 years.**

## History

The first records of this herb date from 1406 by Zhu Xiao who, in the *Materia Medica* for famine, mentions it as a survival food rather than a medicinal herb. It was considered a herbal tonic until the 1970s when a team of researchers from the Chinese Academy of Medical Sciences started to research its properties. It is now used in Traditional Chinese Medicine and was rated one of the ten most important tonic herbs at the TCM 1991 conference. Today it is still rated as one of the top ten and is currently under research for its anti-cancer effects (2016) and is used in anti-obesity therapy (2019).

## Species

*Gynostemma pentaphyllum*, Sweet Vine
Hardy, H4 (USDA 8,9), herbaceous perennial vine, though can be grown as an annual in cold climates. Height: up to 8m (26ft); spread: up to 2m (6ft). This herb is dioecious therefore it needs both a male and a female plant to produce seed; it flowers in summer. The leaves are palmate, with five serrated, glossy green leaves, hence *pentaphyllum*.

## Propagation

**Seeds:** prior to sowing the seeds in spring, it is best to soak them the night before in warm water. Sow into prepared small pots using three parts seed compost mixed with one part horticultural sharp sand. Place in a propagator at 18°C (64°F). Germination is erratic, so be patient; it can take 4–6 weeks.

**Division:** divide pot-raised plants in late spring just as the new shoots appear, or in autumn when the plant has died back. Either replant into more pots using a soil-based potting compost, or plant out into a prepared site after all threat of frost has passed.

**Cuttings:** young shoots are easy to take as cuttings in early summer prior to flowering. There are two methods, either rooting them in a small glass of water, or in a coir compost that is kept moist at all times until the cutting has fully rooted. Then pot up into a soil-based compost.

**Root cuttings:** if you grow this herb in a container, you will notice when you come to repot it in the spring or autumn that around the outside of the root ball it has produced creeping rhizomes. These are easily taken as root cuttings using the same method as mint cuttings (see page 173).

## Pests and diseases

Sweet vine rarely suffers from pests. It can occasionally suffer from green fly so either wash it off with water, or the infestation is bad, spray it with horticultural soft soap (see page 267).

## How and where to grow

This herb can be found growing wild in thickets, open forest and in mountain regions of China and Japan, so it likes partial shade and a good fertile loam that does not get waterlogged in winter. It is a vine so does need support through the growing season – either a trellis or a frame is ideal.

## Growing in containers

Sweet tea vine adapts happily to being grown in containers. As it is a vine it will need a frame of a wigwam of sticks to grow up. Use a soil-based potting compost. Position the container in semi-shade. Feed weekly from spring until the end of summer as this will keep the leaves productive and tender. Pot up or divide in the spring, or, if you live in a cold climate, in the autumn as the extra compost will give protection to the roots in the winter. However, if you do pot up you must not over-water as this herb hates a 'soggy bottom'.

## Yearly maintenance

**Spring:** sow seeds; divide established plants.

**Summer:** take growing tip cuttings; harvest leaves.

**Autumn:** divide established plants.

**Winter:** take root cuttings.

## Harvesting and storing

**Leaves:** in late spring/early summer, harvest the leaves before the flowers open and the plant is at least 30–50cm (12–15in) tall. Cut the vines into 7–12cm (3–5in) pieces to give the stems a chance to dry at the same rate as the leaves. Place the leaves on a muslin frame or a cooling rack used for baking in a dry airy room. Once dry, store in an airtight jar in a cupboard.

## Culinary uses

The leaves have a bittersweet cucumber taste and when young can be added to salads or used with fruit dishes. In Japan, jiaogulan was discovered as an effective and healthy natural sweetener and you can find it in Japanese ice cream and bottled drinks.

## Medicinal uses

The list of jiaogulan's medicinal uses is very long, however many have yet to be scientifically proven. It is used in the treatment of high blood pressure, helps with nervous tension, diabetes and improving the memory.

*Gynostemma pentaphyllum*, Sweet Vine

**WARNING** | Jiaogulan may stimulate the immune system therefore it must not be taken with drugs that suppress the immune system as the herb can potentially make them less effective.

# Houttuynia cordata

**Rather like coriander, you either love this herb or hate it. I find the scent of the leaves too pungent, but quite enjoy the flavour when it is finely cut and added to salads as it combines well with many salad herbs, such as lettuce and chicory. We have many visitors to the Herb Farm and at one open day a lovely lady from Vietnam was delighted we grew this herb and told us how she used it in the kitchen with noodles and in stir-fry dishes. Apparently, her family also used it as a detoxifying tea.**

## History

This genus, a native to China, was originally described in 1783 by Carl Peter Thunberg; it was thought then that this was the only species. In 2001 it was discovered that there was a different species in China but this has still has to be scientifically confirmed. It has been noted that the Japanese form tastes slightly of oranges and the Chinese form tastes a bit like coriander. I will follow the outcome with interest.

## Species

*Houttuynia cordata*, Fish Mint
Hardy, H6 (USDA 6,7), herbaceous perennial. Height: up to 30cm (12in); spread: 1m (3ft) and more. Dense spikes of tiny flowers surrounded by 4–8 pretty white bracts that appear in conical heads in summer. Blue/green heart-shaped leaves.

*Houttuynia cordata* 'Chameleon', Variegated Fish Mint
Hardy, H6 (USDA 6,7), herbaceous perennial. Height: up to 30cm (12in); spread: 1m (3ft 3in) and more. Dense spikes of tiny flowers surrounded by 4–8 pretty white bracts appear in conical heads in summer. Heart-shaped leaves that are splashed and margined with cream and often heavily with pink to red. This species is neither culinary nor medicinal.

*Houttuynia cordata* 'Flore Pleno', Double-flowered Fish Mint
Hardy, H6 (USDA 6,7), herbaceous perennial. Height: up to 45cm (18in); spread: 1m (3ft) and more. Spikes of tiny flowers surrounded by numerous, very attractive white bracts in summer – when in full flower these look like dancing ladies in crinolines. Blue/green heart-shaped leaves. Both culinary and medicinal.

## Propagation

**Cuttings:** in late spring/early summer take semi-ripe cuttings and put them into modules or pots filled with three parts seed compost mixed with one part vermiculite – this will help to maintain the moisture in the compost. Once rooted, pot up into a soil-based compost.

**Division:** divide established garden plants either in the autumn when the plant is starting to go dormant, or in the early spring before it puts on too much new growth. Replant into a prepared site. If you have a light soil, add some well-rotted compost.

**Root cuttings:** this is a very rewarding way to produce new plants. Take root cuttings in late autumn once all the growth has died back. Fill small pots or large modules half full with a seed compost mixed three parts compost to one part vermiculite. Wear gloves if you do not want your hands to smell of this herb for the rest of the day. Put root pieces into the container, cover with the compost mix and water in well. The new shoots take a few weeks to reappear. Once fully rooted, pot up or plant out the following spring.

## Pests and diseases

Not known to suffer from pests or diseases.

## How and where to grow in the garden

*Houttuynia* is a very tolerant herb; it can cope with a range of soils from dry to wet and sun or shade, and one could justifiably say it is invasive. It will grow in shallow water and is renowned for spreading, especially in wet soils via its creeping rhizome. If you do choose to grow this plant in the garden please be warned – it effortlessly smothers other plants.

## Growing in containers

Because this herb can be invasive in the garden it is ideally suited for growing in containers. Use a soil-based compost and feed it weekly from spring to autumn if you are wishing to harvest the leaves for the kitchen. It will need to be repotted every year: either divide and pop back into the same-sized pot or pot up.

## Yearly maintenance

**Spring:** divide established plants; take semi-ripe cuttings.

**Summer:** harvest leaves for use in the kitchen; feed container plants; cut back after flowering so that you have a new crop of leaf.

**Autumn:** take root cutings; divide established plants.

**Winter:** established plants do not need protection.

## Harvesting and storing

**Leaves:** the leaves can be harvested in the spring and after flowering for using fresh or for drying.

**Roots:** the roots can be harvested in the autumn for preserving in chutney or for using medicinally.

## Culinary uses

This is rarely thought of as a culinary herb in the West, however, throughout the East, it is commonly grown as a leaf vegetable. It has a unique fishy flavour, hence its common name, fish mint. In northeast India, it is used in the making of salsa, and the rhizome's roots are used to make chutney. In China, it is used in many dishes, including fried rice, noodles and in dipping sauces.

## Medicinal uses

This herb is used medicinally throughout India, Korea, Vietnam, Japan and China. It is a pungent, cooling herb that is aromatic, diuretic, clears fevers and toxins and is used to treat many more aliments, from diabetes to coughs and dysentery. In South Korea *Houttuynia* is added to many of its famous skincare products to calm and soothe red, irritated or inflamed skin.

*Houttuynia cordata* 'Flore Pleno', Double-flowered Fish Mint

# Humulus lupulus

**The first garden in which I saw hops being grown in a spectacular way was at Barnsley House, a luxury hotel in the west of England. Rosemary Verey, OBE, VMH, had grown a golden hop over an old established yew tree and it looked stunning for it not only gave the old tree shape, it gave it bling.**

*Humulus lupulus* 'Aureus', Golden Hop

## History

There are Roman records from the 1st century which describe hops as a popular garden plant and vegetable – the young shoots were sold in markets to be eaten as you might asparagus. Hops have been used medicinally for hundreds of years as a sedative. A pillow stuffed with hops finally cured George III's insomnia and it is a remedy that is still used today. The cultivation of hops was most probably introduced to the UK at the end of the 15th century. Hops revolutionised brewing in the UK, enabling beer to be kept for longer by replacing traditional bitter herbs that were used to flavour ale, such as wormwood (see page 66) and alecost. By the 19th century, the hop industry was fully established throughout the country.

## Species

*Humulus lupulus*, Hops
Hardy, H6 (USDA 6,7), herbaceous perennial vine. Height: up to 9m (29ft). It is a dioecious plant (male and female flowers grow on separate plants). The female flower is cone-like, hidden by papery scales. Male flowers grow in clusters without sepals; both flower in summer. Green three- or five-lobed leaves with sharply toothed edges and small hooks on the underside. The stem is hollow and covered with tiny hooked prickles that enable it to climb and cling to trees, walls and trellises.

*Humulus lupulus* 'Aureus', Golden Hop
Hardy, H6 (USDA 6,7), herbaceous perennial vine. Height: up to 6m (20ft). The main difference between this plant and the common hop is that the leaves and flowers are much more golden, which makes it very attractive in the garden and in dried flower arrangements. It has the same properties as the common hop.

## Propagation

**Seed:** obtain seeds from a specialist seedsman to prevent hop wilt disease. Sow seeds in autumn into prepared modules or seed trays filled with three parts seed compost mixed with one part sharp horticultural sand. Once the seed is sown cover with sharp horticultural sand. Place the container outside, exposed to all weathers. Germination usually takes 4–6 months but can be erratic and take up to one season. If the seed is not fresh it is advisable to mix it with damp sharp horticultural sand, in either a bag or small container. Put the container into the crisper drawer of the refrigerator for at least 4 weeks, then sow as above. It is difficult to identify the gender of plants grown from seed until they are 2–3 years old .

**Cuttings:** take softwood cuttings in spring or early summer and put into prepared modules or a small pot filled with three parts seed compost mixed with one part perlite. Once rooted, pot up into small pots using a soil-based compost.

**Division:** spring is the ideal time to divide established plants. I have one that I have trained to cover an arch, but after four years I have noticed it has been producing offshoots, which are difficult to incorporate. These can be divided away from the main plant and either replanted in a prepared site, or potted up using a soil-based compost.

## Pests and diseases

Hops are notorious for suffering from hop wilt whereby the plant literally wilts. It is very contagious so dig up the plant and burn it, do not plant hops in that area again. It is also susceptible to leaf miner – remove infected leaves immediately and burn. Powdery mildew can be a problem: if minor, remove the infected leaves; if a bad infection, treat it with potassium bicarbonate (baking powder – see page 276 for more information).

Golden hops can suffer from scorching if planted in full sun. You can prune the plant back so it produces new growth and, if possible, dig it up in the following spring and replant in partial shade.

## How and where to grow

Plant in a sunny position in a soil that is rich in leaf mould and has been deeply dug. In autumn cut back any remaining growth to the ground, clear away any leaf or stem debris and feed with well-rotted manure or compost. Plant golden hops in partial shade to prevent sun scorch.

## Growing in containers

Hops can look fantastic when grown in a container. It will need support either to climb up or cascade over. Use a soil-based compost. If you are growing the golden variety in this way make sure it does not scorch in the sun by providing some form of shading during sunny periods. During the winter months when the plant has died back, make sure it has a rest by putting the pot in a cool place like a garage and keeping the compost on the dry side. It will need repotting each year.

## Yearly maintenance

**Spring:** divide roots and separate rooted stems and suckers. Repot container-grown plants.

**Summer:** sow fresh seeds in late summer.

**Autumn:** cut back all remaining growth to the ground. Give garden plants a good feed of well-rotted compost or manure. Bring containers into a cold greenhouse or polytunnel; cut back the watering.

**Winter:** no need for protection.

## Harvesting and storing

**Shoots:** the young side shoots can be picked to use fresh as required in spring.

**Leaves:** harvest in early spring.

**Flowers:** the female flowers can be picked in early autumn. Dry well and use within in a few months as the flavour deteriorates rapidly.

## Culinary uses

**Shoots:** the side shoots can be steamed or lightly boiled.

**Leaves:** the young leaves can be blanched to remove bitterness and used in soups and salads.

**Flowers:** the male flowers can be par-boiled and eaten in salads; dried female flowers are used in the making of beer.

## Medicinal uses

Medicinally the female flower is good for insomnia and intestinal cramps; a pillow stuffed with female flowers is a sedative. The leaf can be used to make a brown textile dye.

**WARNING** | Contact dermatitis can be caused by the pollen of the female flower.

# Hyoscyamus niger

**Henbane suddenly appeared on the grass outside my cottage but I have no idea where it came from. It was the flower that made me stop and look, with its sinister purple veins running through the cream petals. It is a member of the *Solanaceae* family, which includes tomatoes, potatoes, peppers, tobacco, chili, aubergine and mandrake (see page 168). The common name henbane literally translates as 'hen killer'. It is derived from the Anglo-Saxon: *hen* and *bana*, meaning murderer, because when hens eat the seed they become paralysed and die. Even those with no knowledge of plants might suspect this plant, because when it is in flower it does looks evil.**

## History

Henbane is one of the oldest recorded poisonous and magical plants. It was mentioned in the Ebers Papyrus (the most extensive record of Ancient Egyptian medicine) and in the 1st century the physicians Pliny and Dioscorides prescribed it as a painkiller and as a sleep remedy. The Greeks and Gauls poisoned their arrows and javelins with a decoction of henbane. In the Middle Ages, it was known as the witches' plant and was used by magicians and healers in ritual purifications where the smoke from the burnt plant produced the sensation of flying. Later, it was traditionally prescribed as a specific remedy for toothache, though it would have dulled the pain but not the sufferer's imagination! It is believed that Hamlet's father was killed by pouring a distillation of henbane in his ear, and in 1910 Dr Crippen used hyoscine, which he had extracted from the plant, to murder his wife just before flying to the United States with his mistress, Ethel Le Neve. Traditionally, in Europe, it was collected in the summer and hung in barns on St John's Day (24th June) as a deterrent against mice (apparently, mice are repelled by its unpleasant smell).

## Species

*Hyoscyamus niger*, Black Henbane
Hardy, H4 (USDA 7,8), biennial; sometimes an annual. Height: up to 90cm (3ft) in flower; spread: 30cm (12in). Flowers are yellow/brown or cream, funnel-shaped and usually marked with purple veins, particularly at the petal base, in the summer. The leaves are hairy, with large teeth; the upper leaves have no stalks. The whole plant has a foetid smell.

*Hyoscyamus alba*, White Henbane
Hardy, H3 (USDA 9), annual. Height: up to 80cm (30in) when in flower; spread: 30cm (12in). The funnel-shaped flowers are pale yellow with a deep purple centre in summer. The leaves are hairy with large teeth; the upper leaves have no stalks. The white henbane is native to the Mediterranean. The seed is much easier to germinate than black henbane.

## Propagation

**Seeds:** sow in autumn into prepared seed trays or modules using a seed compost. Cover the seeds with perlite and put in a frost-free environment. Germination takes 14–21 days; it can be erratic. Winter the young plants in a cold greenhouse or cold frame. Plant out in the spring; the plants will flower in the second season. If you sow in spring the plants will be annuals; germination takes 10–15 days.

## Pests and diseases

Very rarely suffers from pests or diseases.

## How and where to grow

Henbane is native to sandy soil and chalk soil disturbed by rabbit warrens, so when planted in the garden it likes a well-drained soil and a sunny site. Choose your site with care because the whole plant is toxic. It is a very interesting-looking plant and can look striking in a mixed border or a wildflower patch.

## Growing in containers

This herb will happily grow in a container. Plant in three parts soil-based compost mixed with one part horticultural grit and place the container in a sunny site. Please make sure that the container is not in reach of children or chickens.

## Yearly maintenance

**Spring:** sow seeds for annuals.

**Summer:** deadhead flowers to maintain flowering (wear gloves).

**Autumn:** sow seeds for second-year flowers.

**Winter:** protect young plants.

## Harvesting and storing

**(NB: please wear gloves when harvesting any part of this herb)**

**Seeds:** the seed head turns brown and opens at the end. Collect the seed into a paper bag and use for either autumn or spring sowing.

**Leaves:** the leaves should be harvested when the plant is in full flower, then dried for later use.

## Culinary uses

None.

## Medicinal uses

Henbane has a long and interesting history as a narcotic when used during surgery and as a hallucinogen when used in witchcraft. It was used up until the 16th century for a wide range of conditions that required sedation. Several South American and European pharmacopoeias contain henbane in many forms for use in various medicinal ways as an aid for painful spasms. It is also used externally in analgesic preparations to relieve rheumatism and arthritis. The syrup has a sedative effect in the case of Parkinson's Disease.

*Hyoscyamus niger*, Henbane

**WARNING** | All parts of the plant are very toxic. Children have been poisoned by eating the seeds or seed pods. Symptoms of poisoning include impaired vision, convulsions, coma and death.

**Common names:** St John's Wort, Aaron's Beard, Balm-of-warrior, Touch and Heal, Grace of God

# Hypericum perforatum

**I know I keep saying this or that herb is amazing; this one truly is. When you hold a leaf up to the light you can see the oil glands, which look like little holes. When they are crushed they release a balsamic odour similar to incense which was said to be strong enough to drive away evil spirits. When the yellow flowers are crushed, they turn red due to the release of a red fluorescent pigment called hypericin. This was an important factor in the development of the folklore which surrounds this herb as it was thought that the red signified the blood of St John after his beheading. Today you will find it in full flower on 24th June, St John's Day.**

## History

In Anglo-Saxon times, the word 'wort' attached to a plant's name signified that it was a 'medicinal herb'. Not only was it medicinal, it was also said to protect from thunderstorms and other works of the devil. In England, to preserve children from nightmares, a sprig of dried St John's wort was combined with dried thyme and then added to mattress stuffing to encourage sweet dreams. In Russia it was said to give protection against hydrophobia and the Brazilians knew it as an antidote to snake bite. There is a saying that whoever treads on St John's wort after sunset will be swept up on the back of a magic horse that will charge around the heavens until sunrise before depositing its exhausted rider on the ground. Back on earth, it has many good medicinal properties, historically it was a wound healer, and now it is used in the treatment of neuralgia and varicose veins. It is also famous for being 'nature's Prozac', used in the treatment of depression.

## Species

There are many species of *Hypericum*, however, the only one that has the medicinal and magical properties is the wild herb, *Hypericum perforatum*.

*Hypericum perforatum* St. John's Wort
Hardy, H6 (USDA 6,7), semi-evergreen perennial. Height: up to 90cm (3ft) when in flower; spread: 30cm (12in). Lightly scented yellow flowers with tiny black gland dots in summer. Small, stalkless, oval green leaves, covered with tiny translucent resin glands that look like small holes when held up to the light.

## Propagation

**Seeds:** sow fresh seeds in autumn into prepared seed trays or modules that have been filled with a standard seed compost. As the seed is very fine, mix a tiny bit with some fine horticultural sand prior to sowing – this will help you sow thinly. Do not cover the seed; place in a cold frame. Germination takes 15–30 days. Winter the young plants in a cold frame or cold greenhouse. You can sow in spring; place in a propagator at 18°C (64°F); germination takes 10–20 days.

**Division:** divide established plants in early autumn or in late spring, replanting into a site, or pot up using a soil-based compost.

## Pests and diseases

The herb rarely suffers from pests or disease.

## How and where to grow

The ideal position to plant St John's wort is in a sunny position in a well-drained chalky soil, however, it will happily adapt to partial shade and any soil, with the exception of waterlogged. Be warned that when grown in a light soil it can become invasive. It also can self-seed, so to prevent this cut back hard after flowering and harvest the seeds if you require them for resowing – this will allow the new leaves to form a semi-evergreen mat in winter. Please note that in some countries this herb is subject to statutory control as a weed, notably in Australia.

**WARNING** | Can poison livestock. High doses can cause photosensitivity. Do not mix with other drugs, especially some birth control pills. Always check with your doctor or herbalist before using medicinally.

## Growing in containers

This herb will happily grow in a container; use a soil-based potting compost. If you require the flowers of this herb for medicinal use, do not give it liquid feed during the growing season as you will produce lots of leaves and no flowers. It looks lovely when planted with other wild herbs, such as poppies and wood sage (see pages 196 and 242).

## Yearly maintenance

**Spring:** sow seeds; divide established plants.

**Summer:** cut back after flowering to prevent self-seeding.

**Autumn:** sow fresh seeds; divide established clumps.

**Winter:** no need for protection.

## Harvesting and storing

**Flowers:** harvest the flowers in summer just as they open, remove all green parts, then either dry or preserve in oil.

## Culinary uses

None.

## Medicinal uses

This is an important medicinal herb, not an edible plant. It acts as a tonic for the nervous system and is an antidepressant, though it should not be given to patients with chronic depression. It was traditionally used for any ailment involving nerves and nerve pain, such as sciatica, radiating spinal pain and neuralgia. In recent studies, St John's wort has been helpful with neuralgia resulting from chemotherapy. An oil infused with the flowers turns red – it is very good for stimulating tissue repair and is used with wounds, burns and shingles, it is also good for sciatic pain, sunburn, ulcers and varicose veins. It is used in homeopathy for pain and inflammation caused by nerve damage.

*Hypericum perforatum*, St John's Wort

# Hyssopus officinalis

**I love this Mediterranean herb: in summer it abounds with bees and butterflies that are drawn to its mass of blue flowers. It is one of my must-have herbs when I am designing a herb garden, especially if the herb and vegetable gardens are intertwined. This is because of hyssop's ability to attract bees, which increases the pollination of the vegetables and therefore their yield. In the kitchen it has been a great standby herb, adding another dimension to food.**

*Hyssopus officinalis*, Hyssop

## History

Hyssop is steeped in history. The Jews regarded hyssop as a holy herb that symbolised forgiveness; they used it as a purifier and as a guardian against the plague and leprosy. The hyssop mentioned in the Bible is thought to be an *Origanum*, because hyssop does not grow in Palestine but *Origanum* does. It was certainly used by Hippocrates (460–377 BC) who recommended it for chest complaints, for which it is still used today.

## Species

*Hyssopus officinalis*, Hyssop
Hardy, H5 (USDA 7,8), semi-evergreen perennial. Height: up to 80cm (30in) when in flower; spread: up to 90cm (3ft). Dense spikes of small, dark blue/violet, tubular, lightly-scented flowers with double lips characteristic of the *Lamiaceae* family. In flower from summer until early autumn. Small, narrow, lance-shaped, aromatic, slightly bitter green leaves.

*Hyssopus officinalis* f. *albus*, White Hyssop
Hardy, H5 (USDA 7,8), semi-evergreen perennial. Height: up to 80cm (30in) when in flower; spread: up to 90cm (3ft). Dense spikes of small white flowers from summer until early autumn. Small, narrow, lance-shaped, aromatic green leaves.

*Hyssopus officinalis* subsp. *aristatus*, Rock Hyssop
Hardy, H5 (USDA 7,8), semi-evergreen. Height: up to 30cm (12in) when in flower; spread: up to 60cm (24in). Dense spikes of small dark blue flowers from summer to early autumn. Small, narrow, lance-shaped, aromatic darkish-green leaves.

*Hyssopus officinalis* 'Roseus', Pink Hyssop
Hardy, H5 (USDA 7,8), semi-evergreen perennial. Height: up to 80cm (30in) when in flower; spread: up to 90cm (3ft). Dense spikes of small pink flowers from summer to early autumn. Small, narrow, lance-shaped, aromatic darkish-green leaves.

## Propagation

**Seeds:** sow seeds in spring into prepared seed trays or modules using a seed compost. Cover the sown seeds with perlite. Keep under protection at 18°C (64°F). Germination takes 5–10 days.

**WARNING** | Hyssop's essential oil can cause epileptic fits. This oil should not be used in aromatherapy for anxious patients. Do not take any form medicinally when pregnant.

**Cuttings:** take softwood cuttings in early summer from non-flowering shoots and transfer to prepared modules or small pots with three parts seed compost mixed with one part standard perlite. This is the only method of propagation for rock hyssop as it does not set seed.

## Pests and diseases

Hyssop can occasionally suffer from an attack of green fly in spring or early summer. Wash off with water or if the infestation is bad spray it with soft horticultural soap. Powdery mildew can be a problem in humid summers. If flowering has finished cut back the whole plant to 15cm (6in) and it will reshoot above the ground, which will give protection in winter. If it hasn't flowered, it is best to spray the whole plant with the baking powder mixture on page 276.

## How and where to grow

Plant in a sunny position in a well-drained neutral-to-alkaline soil. Good drainage is essential as hyssop will die if waterlogged. It makes a good short-term hedge. Hyssop is a good companion plant: planted near cabbages it lures away the cabbage white butterfly and planted near vines it increases the yield as the flowers attract bees so pollination of the vine is increased. This is a short-lived perennial lasting 4–5 years. Cut back to 15cm (6in) in late summer, early autumn in mild areas or early spring after all frosts have finished in cold areas.

## Growing in containers

Hyssop is ideal for growing in containers as it likes being grown on the dry side. Use a soil-based compost. In winter, lift the container on to stones or bricks to help drainage. It looks lovely in a pot with thyme and oregano as they all like the same conditions.

## Yearly maintenance

**Spring:** sow seeds; cut back mature plants in cold areas; trim hedges.

**Summer:** deadhead flowers to maintain supply; trim after flowering to maintain shape; trim hedges; take softwood cuttings.

**Autumn:** cut back only in mild areas or when grown under protection.

**Winter:** protect container-grown hyssop from really wet winters and when temperatures fall below -5°C (23°F).

## Harvesting and storing

**Leaves:** pick young leaves throughout the growing season to use fresh or, in summer, from non-flowering stems for drying.

**Flowers:** pick flowers just as they open to use fresh or to dry. The scent becomes more intense when dried.

## Culinary uses

Hyssop has a slightly bitter, aromatic, minty flavour. The leaves are quite strong in flavour, so do not be too lavish with them. Use them in salads, soups, with meat stews, in stuffings and also for making marinades and salad dressings. In the USA it they are added to apple pie. The flowers are delicious tossed in green salads.

## Medicinal uses

Medicinally an infusion made from the leaves helps relieve bronchial congestion and coughs. It is also a tonic for the digestive and nervous systems. Hyssop oil in the bath is good for nervous exhaustion.

*Hyssopus officinalis* 'Roseus', Pink Hyssop

**Common names:** Elecampane, Elfwort, Elfdock, Horse Heal

# Inula helenium

**This robust and hardy herbaceous perennial is beautiful in the garden. The lovely yellow flowers, which attract butterflies, are followed by small seed clocks that fly around the garden. They are not invasive like their cousin *Taraxacum officinale* agg. (dandelion) and are much loved by the birds.**

*Inula helenium*, Elecampane

## History

Helen of Troy was believed to be gathering this herb when she was abducted by Paris. The Romans used to candy the roots and dye them red with the cochineal insect. This idea persisted for centuries and in the Middle Ages apothecaries sold the candied root in flat pink sugary cakes, which were sucked to alleviate asthma, indigestion and to sweeten the breath. The Tudor herbalists also candied them for the treatment of coughs, catarrhs, bronchitis and chest ailments, which is still its main medicinal use today.

## Species

*Inula helenium*, Elecampane
Hardy, H6 (USDA 6,7), herbaceous perennial. Height: up to 2.4m (8ft); spread: up to 1m (3ft). Bright yellow, large, daisy-like flowers, whose petals are very fine, often giving the flower a ragged look; they are about 7cm (3in) in diameter when fully open in the summer. Large, green, oval, lightly toothed leaves that have a slight textured down on the underside. When in flower, if planted in an exposed garden, it might need a stake. Native to Europe and northern Asia, naturalised in North America

*Inula hookeri*, Hooker's Inula, Hooker's Fleabane
Hardy, H6 (USDA 6,7), herbaceous perennial. Height: up to 1m (3ft); spread: up to 75cm (30in). Light yellow, daisy-like ragged flowers, about 8cm (3in) in diameter and slightly scented in summer. Lance-shaped, hairy leaves that are smaller than *Inula magnifica*, and mid-green in colour. Dies back fully in winter. Native to the Himalayas where it is used medicinally.

*Inula magnifica*, Giant Fleabane
Hardy, H6 (USDA 6,7), herbaceous perennial. Height: up to 2m (6ft); spread: up to 1m (3ft). Large, yellow, daisy-like ragged flowers, which are about 15cm (6in) in diameter, in early summer. Lots of large, dark green, lance-shaped rough leaves. This variety may need staking in an exposed garden. It is often mistaken for *Inula helenium* but the leaf colour is the biggest difference, and on average *Inula magnifica* grows much larger. It dies back fully in winter. Native to the eastern Caucasus where it is used medicinally.

## Propagation

**Seeds:** sow seeds in spring, into prepared seed trays or modules filled with a seed compost. Place under protection at 18°C (64°F) or in a cold frame. Germination takes 1–3 weeks with heat, or 3–4 weeks cold. The cold method can give better results with home collected seeds although both methods can be erratic.

**Division:** in autumn, after the plant has fully died back, divide established plants. As the roots are very strong it can be easier to remove off-shoots that grow around the root of the parent plant. Remove carefully, maintaining its root system, replanting in a well-prepared site 1m (3ft 3in) apart or pot up, using a soil-based potting compost. Winter in a cold frame or cold greenhouse and replant in the spring.

## Pests and diseases

This plant rarely suffers from disease. If the autumn is excessively wet, the leaves, as they die back, may suffer from a form of mildew. Simply cut the plant back and destroy the leaves.

## How and where to grow

This herb is without doubt a focal point in the garden. Plant in moist, fertile soil in full sun – it looks very striking against a stone wall or in front of a screen of deciduous trees. In a windy or exposed site the flower heads may need staking. In hot, dry summers the plant will need extra water. In autumn, after the plant has died back, mulch well with well-rotted compost or leaf mould.

## Growing in containers

If you wish to grow this magnificent herb in a container, choose a container with a wide base so that it does not blow over once the plant goes to flower. Use a soil-based compost. In summer water regularly and feed with a liquid seaweed fertiliser monthly. In the autumn, once the plant has died back, either repot into a bigger pot, or remove the offshoots. Pot up the offshoots into a soil-based compost and winter in a cold greenhouse or cold frame.

## Yearly maintenance

**Spring:** sow seed, divide established plants.

**Summer:** remove flower heads as soon as flowering finishes.

**Autumn:** cut back growth to stop self-seeding and to prevent the plant becoming untidy. Remove offshoots for replanting.

**Winter:** no protection needed.

## Harvesting and storing

**Flowers:** the flower heads are picked either when fully open and dried whole for medicinal use, or for dried flower arrangements just as the seeds turn colour from green to beige but before they explode and fly away, like its cousin the dandelion.

**Roots:** the roots of a two- or three-year-old plant are dug up in the autumn to be used fresh in the kitchen or dried for medicinal use.

## Culinary uses

This herb was once a culinary delicacy: the roots were used to flavour desserts and sweets. I have noticed that with cooks becoming more adventurous, the roots are being included as a traditional sweetener. Interestingly the Council of Europe lists *Inula helenium* as a natural food flavouring.

## Medicinal uses

Used for irritating coughs and chronic chest complaints. The flowers are used in decoctions; the roots are used to make syrups, powders and tinctures. Recent research has shown that it is effective against bacterial and fungal infections and contains a substance that expels intestinal parasites. *Inula* is known as pushkaramula in Ayurvedic medicine and is highly regarded as a lung tonic.

**WARNING** | Do not take medicinally if you are being treated for diabetes or high blood pressure.

# Iris pseudacorus

**Iris is a very large family – there is said to be an iris for every position in the garden and for every season. There are four that stand out as having beneficial herbal qualities: *Iris pseudacorus*, *Iris germanica*, *Iris* 'Florentina' and *Iris versicolor*.**

*Iris* 'Florentina', Florentine Iris

## History

The Ancient Greek word *iris* means 'rainbow' and it was used to describe the variable colours of the plant. It is one of the oldest cultivated plants; there is a painting on the wall of an Egyptian temple dating from 1500 BC. The Ancient Egyptians thought the three leaves of its flower symbolised faith, wisdom and valour. During the Second World War, on the island of Jersey the seeds of the yellow iris were used as a substitute for coffee.

## Species

*Iris pseudacorus*, Yellow Iris
Hardy H7 (USDA 6), herbaceous perennial. Height: up to 1.5m (5ft); spread: up to 1.25m (4ft). Flowers are bright yellow with radiating brown veins and are very slightly scented. Flowers from early to midsummer. The root is a thick rhizome from which many rootlets descend. This iris is a native of the British Isles.

*Iris germanica*, Garden Iris, Common Iris, Flag Iris
Hardy H6 (USDA 6,7), evergreen perennial. Height: up to 1m (3ft); spread: up to 50cm (20in). The fragrant flowers are blue/violet, occasionally white in late spring. The leaves are greyish-green and sword-shaped. The root is a thickish rhizome. There are many cultivated varieties. It is grown commercially for the rhizomes and, like *Iris* 'Florentina', is used in perfumery and pharmaceutical preparations.

*Iris* 'Florentina', Florentine Iris, Orris Root
Hardy, H6 (USDA 6,7), semi-evergreen perennial. Height: up to 1m (3ft); spread: up to 1m (3ft). Large white flowers tinged with pale lavender and with a yellow beard, appearing early to midsummer. Green, sword-shaped leaves. The root of this iris has a violet scent and has been powdered and used in perfumes since the times of the Ancient Egyptians and Greeks. Today the dried root is used in the making of gin.

*Iris versicolor*, Blue Flag Iris, Boston Iris, Flag Lily, Fleur de Lys, Liver Lily, Poison Flag, Snake Lily
Hardy H7 (USDA 6), perennial. Height: up to 1m (3ft 3in); spread: up to 50cm (20in). Flowers are claret/purple/blue from early to midsummer. Large sword-shaped green leaves. This native herb of North America was employed by both the Native Americans and the early settlers as a remedy for gastric complaints.

**WARNING** | Large doses of the fresh root can cause nausea, vomiting and facial neuralgia. Small doses of the dried root are advised. Handling the plant may cause dermatitis.

## Propagation

**Seeds:** all the irises produce large seeds, which take some time to germinate and often benefit from a period of stratification (see page 18). As the seeds are easy to handle and a good size, in the autumn, sow the seeds directly into small pots using two parts seed compost mixed with one part horticultural grit and one part propagating bark. Water in well and cover the pots with glass to stop mice from eating the seed. Put the containers on a flat surface outside for the winter. Check that the compost remains damp – if there is any fear of it drying out, stand the container in water. This is especially important for blue and yellow flag irises.

**Division:** divide the rhizome roots in late spring or early autumn (this suits all varieties). Replant immediately in the garden in a prepared site, or if it is the autumn, pot up using a soil-based compost mixed with extra horticultural grit.

## Pests and diseases

The iris sawfly is the only real pest; it can occur during the summer months. The darkish grey larvae feed along the leaf margins, removing large chunks. Pupation takes place in the soil beneath or near the host plants, and the adult sawflies are on the wing during early to midsummer. Cut the infected leaves off if you find them unsightly, however, the plant will not be damaged and you can ignore the pest if you wish. As this is an annual pest there is not much one can do to prevent it.

## How and where to grow

Choosing a site for your iris is dependent on the variety: orris and common iris prefer a well-drained rich soil and sunny situations. When planting make sure that part of the rhizome is showing above the soil.

Yellow and blue flag irises are both marsh-loving plants and are ideal for those who have a pond or ditch or a piece of boggy ground. Although they grow happily in semi-shade, they need full sun in order to produce the maximum bloom. In deep shade, it will not flower at all but will spread quickly by stout underground rhizomes so a certain measure of control will be necessary.

## Growing in containers

Irises can be grown in containers because of their large rhizomes but make sure that the container is strong enough – terracotta is ideal because it breathes. Also make sure it is large and heavy enough, firstly to accommodate the plant, which grows quickly, and secondly to accommodate the plant's height when in flower. Use a soil-based potting compost. For the marsh-loving irises make sure the compost does not dry out; water regularly. For the dry-loving iris, even though they love the dry, do not let the compost totally dry out. Both types of iris will become pot-bound within a season, so repot and/or divide every autumn.

## Yearly maintenance

**Spring:** divide rhizomes of mature plants.

**Summer:** collect the seeds as soon as ripe.

**Autumn:** sow seeds and leave outside; divide rhizomes of mature plants.

**Winter:** no need for protection.

## Harvesting and storing

Harvest the rhizomes of all the irises in the autumn for drying; once dried and ground it can then be used in potpourri. Commercially, the dried orris root is used for perfume and for making gin.

## Culinary uses

Apart from the historical use of yellow flag iris seeds, which can make a coffee substitute, there are no culinary uses.

## Medicinal uses

Herbalists still use blue flag iris as a blood purifier – it acts on the liver and gall bladder to increase the flow of bile, as well as an effective cleanser of toxins. It is also said to relieve flatulence and heartburn, belching and nausea. It is used for headaches associated with digestive problems.

**Common names:** Woad, Dyer's Woad, Glastum, Glasto, Ash of Jerusalem

# Isatis tinctoria

**This ancient dye plant is undergoing a huge revival because of the interest in natural dyes. It is also now popular with gardeners and flower arrangers. I fell in love with it when I grew it with my children for a school project. I was on the farm when this rich honey scent came wafting through the air. I traced it back to the foamy clusters of small bright yellow, pollen-rich flowers of woad.**

## History

This herb has been used as a dye plant for thousands of years. It was the only source of blue dye available in Europe until the end of the 16th century when *Indigofera tinctoria* (indigo) arrived in this country via the spice trade from India. Woad was made virtually obsolete by the growing popularity of indigo. Glastonbury, in Somerset, derives its name from the Old Celtic 'glasto', which means 'a place where woad grows'. Now the word glasto is synonymous with the famous festival which is held in the village of Pilton, which is where I lived during my childhood.

## Species

*Isatis tinctoria*, Woad
Hardy, H4 (USDA 8,9), biennial, sometimes a short-lived perennial. Height: first year 45cm (18in), second year up to 1.5m (5ft) when in flower; spread: up to 75cm (30in). Clusters of numerous small, bright yellow flowers in the second summer, followed by pendulous black seeds. Lance-shaped, lightly toothed, blue/green leaves. The tap root in the second season can be up to 1.5m (5ft) long. Excellent pollinator plant, especially for all forms of bee.

## Propagation

**Seeds:** sow fresh seeds in autumn into prepared plug modules or small pots using a seed compost mixed in equal parts with perlite. Place the container in a cold greenhouse or cold frame. Germination takes 3–4 weeks. In the spring, plant out into a prepared site 30cm (12in) apart. Alternatively, sow in late spring, when the night-time temperature does not fall below 9°C (48°F), directly into a well-prepared site. Once the seedlings have emerged, thin to 30cm (12in) apart.

## Pests and diseases

Woad seedlings, like its other cousins in the brassica family, can be attacked by the flea beetle. To prevent this, in spring, cover with a fine horticultural mesh for the first season only (see page 269 for more information).

## How and where to grow

Plant in a sunny position in a well-drained, well-fed soil. Be aware that this herb has a very long tap root and hates being transplanted once the plant starts to become established. In the second year, you may need to stake the flowers to stop them being crushed by high winds or heavy rain. In late summer, collect the seeds before they fall as woad is renowned for self-seeding.

## Growing in containers

Woad is not ideal for growing in a container. Not only does it have a long tap root, it looks boring in the first year and grows very tall in the second. As it flowers in May in the UK, we have grown it for the Royal Horticultural Society's Chelsea Flower Show for the show gardens. To achieve this, in the autumn we sow a number of seeds directly into large pots, grow them on, then in the spring, pot them up into larger pots before the tap root is established.

## Yearly maintenance

**Spring:** protect new seedlings from flea beetle; mulch second-year plants.

**Summer:** harvest the leaves for drying.

**Autumn:** sow fresh seeds. Harvest the seeds and roots of second-year plants.

**Winter:** no need for protection.

## Harvesting and storing

**Leaves:** in late summer pick the leaves, either to dry for medicinal use or to ferment, then dry for use as a dye.

**Roots:** dig up the roots of the second year's growth in autumn, then dry for medicinal use.

**Seeds:** harvest the seeds in autumn as they turn dark brown and before they drop.

## Culinary uses

Woad is a brassica so one feels that it should be edible, however, after trying to make the leaves edible I have given up. The recipe said harvest the leaves of the first year's growth, then soak them in cold water for 48 hours to remove the bitterness. To be honest 48 hours was not enough as they were far too bitter for my palate. Woad is unpalatable but not toxic – cattle refuse to graze it but sheep readily consume the leaves until the plant starts flowering.

## Medicinal uses

In Traditional Chinese Medicine, the root of this herb is known as ban lang gen; it is used to treat meningitis and mumps. However, be aware that woad root is very astringent and poisonous and should only be taken internally under supervision. In 2006, the *New Scientist* reported that Italian biochemists have discovered that its leaves contain more than 60 times the amount of glucobrassicin, a type of glucosinolate, than broccoli, which might help in the prevention of cancer.

*Isatis tinctoria*, Woad

**WARNING** | Do not take internally unless under supervision. Woad is classed as a noxious weed in Australia and the USA.

**Common names:** Bay, Sweet Bay, Bay Tree, Bay Laurel

# Laurus nobilis

**This magnificent evergreen tree has grown in all the gardens where I have lived. I can picture my mother wearing an apron, with what looked like branches of bay, the leaves of which she used when making baked egg custards in her trusty Rayburn cooker which was forever needing more coal.**

## History

The Latin *laureatus* means 'crowned with a wreath of laurel leaves', but the idea of being crowned or wreathed with laurel originally came from the Ancient Greeks. The bay tree was considered to be sacred and was associated with showing dedication to Apollo, the Greek god of prophecy, poetry and healing and his son Aesculapius, the Greek god of medicine, who reputedly loved the trees. A wreath of bay leaves later became a prize, linking it with victory, and it is still a mark of excellence for poets and athletes – laureates were adorned with wreaths to show they had achieved something. In the 17th century, Culpeper wrote that 'neither witch nor devil, thunder nor lightening, will hurt a man in the place where a bay tree is'. Historically the leaves were not only used fresh, usually added to a long cooking pot over the fire, they were also dried then ground over the fresh vegetables as we would grind salt and pepper.

## Species

*Laurus nobilis*, Bay
Hardy, H4 (USDA 8,9), evergreen shrub. Height: up to 8m (26ft); spread: 3m (9ft). Dense clusters of small, pale yellow flowers in spring, followed by oval berries that are black when ripe. Oval, dark green leaves with a shiny upper surface. When held to the light, the leaves are translucent revealing all the veins. Culinary and medicinal.

*Laurus nobilis* 'Aurea', Golden Bay, Yellow-leaved Bay Tree
Hardy, H4 (USDA 8,9), evergreen shrub. Height: up to 8m (26ft); spread: up to 4m (13ft). Small, pale yellow flowers in spring, followed by oval berries that are black when ripe. Golden, oval, pointed leaves, which are aromatic when crushed. Needs protection from wind, frosts and full sun to stop leaf scorch. Trim in spring to maintain leaf colour. It can be used in the kitchen and has a mild flavour.

*Laurus nobilis* f. *angustifolia*, Willow Leaf Bay, Willow-leaved Laurel
Hardy, H4 (USDA 8,9), evergreen shrub or small tree. Height: up to 8m (26ft); spread: up to 6m (20ft). Small, pale yellow flowers in spring, followed by oval berries that are black when ripe. Aromatic, oval, narrow (much narrower than *Laurus nobilis*), pointed, dark, shiny upper surface, green leaves. Useful in the kitchen and a flavour similar to *Laurus nobilis*.

## Propagation

**Seeds:** before sowing the fresh seed in autumn they need to be scarified (see page 18). Place in a small pot that has been filled with three parts seed compost mixed with one part coarse horticultural sand. Once the seed is sown, cover with coarse horticultural sand, place under protection 18°C (64°F) for one month, then move to an area under protection with a minimum night temperature of 13°C (55°F). Germination takes 5–12 months. Once germinated and fully rooted, pot up one size of pot, and pot on in a container, filled with a soil-based compost under protection for 2–3 years before planting out.

**Cuttings:** if you have patience, take cuttings in late summer from the new growth into modules or a very small pot filled with three parts seed compost mixed with one part coarse horticultural sand. High humidity is essential. Rooting takes 3 weeks to 6 months. Protect from drying out and direct sun.

**Division:** sometimes mature trees, especially standards, produce offshoots around their base; these can be removed from the parent plant in spring or autumn, pot up using a soil-based compost and grow on under protection until well established.

## Pests and diseases

Bay is susceptible to sooty black spots, which are caused by the scale insect which sticks both to the underside of leaves and to the stems, sucking the sap. The only way to get rid of them is either by hand or by spraying them with a soft horticultural soap (see page 266 for more information).

## How and where to grow

The bay tree is a shallow-rooted plant, which means that it can, in cold climates, be prone to frost damage. Choose your site carefully: for warm and hot, but not humid climates, plant in a well-drained soil in partial shade. In cold climates, where night-time temperatures fall below -5°C (23°C), plant in a sheltered position in full sun. If your site is prone to cold winds, you may find that the leaves become scorched in winter. This is not a problem with mature established plants as you can prune the damaged leaves the following spring. Young plants under 5 years old will need extra protection. Prune into shape – in spring for cold climates, in autumn for warm climates.

## Growing in containers

Bay is ideal for growing in a container. Pot into a soil-based compost. Because you know that eventually bay will grow into a beautiful tree, don't be in a hurry to plant it into a large pot thinking you will save time, because if you plant a young bay into a large pot, then overwater it, you will lose it. Bay prefers to be pot-bound. Bring into a cold greenhouse or cold shed for the winter if your temperature falls below -2°C (28°F) at night. Cut back the watering to minimal.

*Laurus nobilis*, Bay

## Yearly maintenance

**Spring:** sow seeds. Cut back standard bay trees to maintain shape and to promote new growth. Cut back garden bay trees to keep them under control and to give them a good shape. Cut back golden bay trees to maintain colour. Check for scale insect and eradicate at the first sign (see page 270). Start feeding container-grown plants weekly with a liquid seaweed feed.

**Summer:** check that young plants are not drying out too much. In very hot weather it is a good idea to spray container-grown plants with water, especially if you live in a city; it will remove the dust from the leaves. Propagate by taking stem cuttings in late summer. Remove small side shoots from the base of mature plants and either use as cutting material or potting material.

**Autumn:** take cuttings of mature plants in early autumn. Protect and/or bring in container-grown plants and young garden plants. Protect garden plants with horticultural fleece.

**Winter:** in severe winters the leaves will turn brown and you will think the plant is dead. Don't despair – sometimes in the spring the plant will shoot new growth from the base. To encourage this, cut the plant nearly down to the base.

## Harvesting and storing

**Leaves:** as this is an evergreen tree that can be picked all year round there is no need to have an abundance that one urgently needs to preserve. However, if a friend gives you a branch and you wish to preserve the leaves for future use then I recommend drying them or alternatively putting them in salt, oil or vinegar to impart flavour.

**Seeds:** harvest the seeds once fully ripe and slightly soft to the touch. In the Mediterranean region a cooking oil is extracted from the seed.

## Culinary uses

This herb has been used as a flavouring herb for many thousands of years. The evergreen leaves have a wonderful spicy scent and flavour with a hint of nutmeg and citrus; they add depth to all forms of food. To get the best flavour, add at the beginning of cooking so that it can slowly permeate the food. The Bedouin of North Africa traditionally used the leaves to flavour their coffee. Bay leaves are not just for savoury dishes, they are delicious with custards and rice pudding. A firm family favourite is bay ice cream.

## Medicinal uses

Bay leaves used in cooking promote digestion and absorption of food. They assist in the breakdown of heavy food, i.e. meat. They also stimulate the digestive tract, help to settle the stomach and are said to relieve flatulence. Added to the bath they relieve aching limbs.

*Laurus nobilis* f. *angustifolia*, Willow Leaf Bay

# Lavandula angustifolia syn L. officinalis

**Lavender is the quintessential herb: it smells good, looks good and does you good. This very popular herb can be a hardy evergreen shrub with highly aromatic grey leaves or a tender evergreen shrub with eucalyptus- rather than lavender-scented leaves. As there so many different types of lavender – all eminently collectable – I have decided to restrict myself to the ones I use the most in the garden, the kitchen and my home.**

*Lavandula angustifolia* 'Hidcote', Lavender Hidcote

## History

The Romans were the first to introduce *Lavandula stoechas* – French lavender – to Britain. They brought the flower heads over dried, which they then ground and used as a condiment. The use of lavender as a condiment was very common in medieval times: meat was difficult to keep so condiments were used to hide the disagreeable flavours and tastes of semi-cooked or half-rotten flesh. The Romans also used it as an antiseptic and toiletry herb; the common and botanical name are derived from the Latin lavare – to wash.

## Species

These are my top seven in botanical order.

*Lavandula* 'Bee Happy', Lavender 'Bee Happy'
Hardy, H3 (USDA 9), evergreen shrub. Height: up to 45cm (18in); spread: up to 50cm (20in). Oblong flower heads covered in small blue flowers topped with white bracts in early summer. Narrow, short, green/grey aromatic leaves. Add flowers and bracts to salads. This *Lavandula* certainly does make bees happy and if you cut it back after the first flowering you will get a second flowering in late summer.

*Lavandula* x *chaytoriae* 'Sawyers', Lavender Sawyers
Hardy, H4 (USDA 8,9), evergreen shrub. Height: up to 60cm (24in) in flower; spread: 45cm (18in). Richly scented, long conical spikes of deep purple flowers in summer. Soft, linear silvery-grey aromatic leaves. This lavender is a hybrid of *Lavandula lanata* and *Lavandula angustifolia* and it can only be grown from cuttings. The flowers can be added to drinks, pastries and puddings.

*Lavandula* x *christiana*, Lavender Christiana
Tender, H1C (USDA 11), evergreen shrub. Height: up to 75cm (30in) in flower; spread: 50cm (20in). Blue trident flowers all year round. Serrated, aromatic silver foilage. A very attractive lavender which is ideal for growing in a pot. Protect from frosts and excessive wet weather in winter. Add the flowers to ice cubes.

*Lavandula* x *intermedia* 'Seal', Lavender Seal
Hardy, H5 (USDA 7,8), evergreen shrub. Height and spread: up to 1m (3ft). Aromatic, long pointed spikes of pale purple flowers in summer. Long narrow aromatic silver/grey/green leaves. *Lavandula* x *intermedia* is a hybrid of *Lavandula latifolia* and *Lavandula angustifolia*; it has a higher yield of essential oil and is often known as lavandin.

*Lavandula angustifolia* Hidcote, Hidcote Lavender
Hardy, H5 (USDA 7,8), evergreen perennial. Height: up to 55cm (22in); spread: up to 45cm (18in). Richly scented, short, rounded spikes of deep purple/blue flowers in summer. Short, narrow, aromatic grey leaves. This lavender is ideal for hedges. Plant at a distance of 30cm (12in) apart.

*Lavandula dentata*, Fringed Lavender, French Lavender
Hardy, H3 (USDA 9), evergreen shrub. Height and spread: up to 50cm (20in). Oblong flower heads covered in small pale mauve flowers, topped with short pale mauve bracts all year round. Deeply serrated, highly aromatic, green leaves that smell strongly of eucalyptus. This is such a generous lavender – it never stops flowering, especially if you remember to keep deadheading it. This herb will only tolerate a light frost, so in winter transfer to the conservatory or greenhouse. If you live by the sea or in a town that rarely gets frost, you can grow it outside all year round.

*Lavandula pedunculata* subsp. *pedunculata*, Spanish Lavender, Papillon
Hardy, H3 (USDA 9), evergreen shrub. Height and spread: up to 60cm (24in). Oblong flower heads covered in small purple flowers, topped with long, wavery, mauve bracts in summer. Narrow, short, grey/green aromatic leaves. When this lavender is in flower and there is a light breeze the bracts look like butterflies dancing. It is a beautiful, elegant lavender.

## Propagation

**Seeds:** it is possible to grow lavenders from seed, however they hardly ever produce plants that look identical. So, if you do not mind what turns up, sow the fresh seed in autumn. Fill your seed tray or module tray with three parts seed compost mixed with one part perlite. Cover the sown seeds with perlite and put under cover at 18°C (64°F). Germination takes 18–28 days.

**Cuttings:** if you are wanting to grow a hedge, or it is important to have plants looking identical, then it is advisable to grow plants from cuttings. In late spring, take softwood cuttings or semi-hardwood cuttings taken in summer or early autumn from non-flowering stems. Fill modules or small pots with three parts seed compost mixed with one part horticultural sharp sand. Once the cuttings have fully rooted pot up using a loam-based potting mix. Winter the young lavenders in a cold greenhouse or cold frame, keeping watering to a minimum.

**Layering:** mature, woody, hardy lavenders respond well to this form of propagation. This is a good method for creating a new plant from a much-loved old one. Choose a low-growing branch that can be easily pinned into the soil. Gently remove the bark at an old growing point, lay the branch on the soil, pin into place, then cover with soil. Leave undisturbed until the following spring. Once rooted, remove carefully from the parent plant, making sure you gently dig up all the roots. Either replant in a prepared site in the garden, or pot up using a soil-based compost to grow on and re-shape prior to planting out. Then you can make the decision on what you are going to do with your old woody faithful lavender.

## Pests and diseases

Froghopper and cuckoo spit can be a problem; to control see page 269.

Quite a few moths love lavender, so the plants may attract caterpillars (see page 267). If you do see caterpillars, pick them off by hand.

You may notice small white marks on the grey leaves; it will most probably be leaf hopper. Outside there really isn't any need to do anything unless the infestation gets out of hand (see page 269 for more information as this is a common pest of the *Lamiaceae* family).

In wet seasons the flowers may be attacked by downy mildew. This can occur all too readily after a wet winter. Cut the infected parts back as far as possible but again remember not to cut into the old wood if you want it to shoot again. For more information see page 275.

Lavender can be prone to shab, a fungus that attacks the stems and branches, causing wilting followed by the death of the affected branches. If this occurs, dig up the plant immediately and destroy it – do not compost, keeping it well away from any other lavender bushes and do not replant a lavender in that area for at least two seasons.

## How and where to grow

Lavenders are more than often killed by the wet and/or high humidity, rather than the cold. Plant in a sunny position, in a fertile well-draining soil. Lavender will adapt to semi-shade as long as the soil is well drained otherwise it will be killed in winter. If you consistently have temperatures below -12°C (10°F), it is worth growing even hardy varieties in containers (see right).

When I first started herb farming we trimmed in the autumn and pruned in the spring. Now with climate change, we prune hard in the summer as soon as flowering has finished, then trim any damaged branches in the spring. Do not cut into the old wood, always stay where there is growth. By trimming this way you will keep the bush neat and encourage it to make new growth, thereby stopping it becoming too woody. If you have inherited a straggly mature plant, then give it a good cut back in the autumn, followed by a second cut in the spring and then adopt the above routine. If the plant is aged I would advise layering, if possible, and taking cuttings so you can preserve the plant if all else fails.

## Growing in containers

Lavenders are ideal for growing in containers. Use a soil-based potting compost mixed with one part horticultural grit. Choose containers which show off the colour of the flowers and foliage; they all suit terracotta pots. The ideal position is sun, but all lavenders will cope with partial shade, however the aroma can be impaired. Feed regularly through the flowering season with liquid seaweed fertiliser. Allow the compost to dry out in winter (not totally but nearly), and slowly re-introduce watering in the spring. If wintering pots outside, lift them and put them on bricks or stones to increase the drainage of the pots.

*Lavandula x intermedia* 'Seal', Lavender Seal

## Yearly maintenance

**Spring:** give a remedial spring trim if needed.

**Summer:** take cuttings; cut back after flowering.

**Autumn:** sow seed; take cuttings; protect half-hardy plants and bring containers into a cold greenhouse.

**Winter:** keep the watering of seedlings and containers to a minimum.

## Harvesting and storing

**Leaves:** these can be used fresh; for drying, harvest before flowering.

**Flowers:** cut the flowers in summer, just as they open to use fresh and for drying. Dry on open trays or by hanging in small bunches.

## Culinary uses

The best part of lavender to use in the kitchen is the flowers. They are great infused in sugar, in cakes, puddings and paired with strong-flavoured fruit. Lavender is a strong flavour so start off sparingly.

## Medicinal uses

Throughout history, lavender has been used medicinally to soothe, sedate and suppress. Nowadays it is the essential oil that is in great demand. It is an excellent remedy for burns, stings and helps to heal cuts with its strong antibacterial action. Lavender water made from the flowers is lovely added to the bath water to relieve aching muscles.

*Lavandula pedunculata* subsp. *pedunculata*, Spanish Lavender

**Right** Assorted *Lavandula angustifolia*

# Leonotis leonurus

**I was lucky enough to see this herb growing naturally in South Africa. We now grow it here in one of our cold tunnels. It is a showstopper: the glowing orange flowers are magnificent and they bring the joy of sun to all of us every year on a cold, dank, grey, early winter's day. The name *Leonotis* is derived from the Greek words *leon* meaning lion and -*otis* meaning ear.**

## History

Early South African dwellers, especially the Hottentot tribe, used to dry the flowers and leaves, which they smoked during spiritual ceremonies. They also used the herb for pain management. It was one of the many Cape plants taken to Europe in the 1600s.

## Species

*Leonotis leonurus*, Lion's Ears
Tender, H2 (USDA 10), semi-evergreen shrub. Height: up to 2.5m (8ft); spread: up to 1.5m (5ft). Bright orange, tubular flowers are borne in characteristic rounded groups that are neatly arranged along the branch ends. The leaves are long, narrow and toothed in the upper half, and distinctly hairy. They are also highly aromatic when crushed.

*Leonotis nepetifolia*, Christmas Candlestick, Bird Honey
Tender, H2 (USDA 10), either annual or short-lived perennial. Height up to 2m (6ft), occasionally 3m (9ft); spread: up to 1.5m (5ft). Reddish-orange, tubular flowers are borne in dense rounded clusters in the upper leaf forks. The flowers are smaller than *Leonotis leonorus* and not as showy. The leaves are long, broad at the base, toothed and distinctly hairy. This herb is considered invasive in many countries.

## Propagation

**Seeds:** sow the seeds in spring, into prepared seed trays or modules using three parts seed compost mixed with one part sharp horticultural sand. Sow on the surface, gently press the seed into the compost, then cover with perlite. Put into a propagator at 18°C (64°F). Germination takes 10–21 days; it can sometimes be a bit erratic depending on the harvest.

**Cuttings:** with its lovely square stems this herb takes easily from cuttings. Take in summer from the new growth, use three parts seed compost mixed with one part horticultural sharp sand. Once rooted, pot up using a soil-based compost. Winter the young plants in a greenhouse or conservatory that is frost-free. Plant out or pot up in the late spring once all threat of frost has passed.

**Division:** after flowering in midwinter, cut back to 10cm (4in) for pots or 20cm (8in) in the garden. At the end of winter, divide established plants, either repotting or replanting into the garden where the soil has been given a good feed prior to planting.

## Pests and diseases

Leaf hopper is renowned for attacking all the *Lamiaceae* family; it leaves tiny marks on the leaf. In the garden there is no control other than cutting back, but then you will stop the plant flowering. In pots you can, if you must, spray it with soft horticultural soap (see page 266 for more information). White fly only really occurs when the plant is grown undercover all year round (see page 272 for how to control this pest). Downy mildew can occur, especially if you live in an area where it is damp and cold in winter. To save spraying, we cut the plants back, especially as it is often the dying flowers that get infected first.

## How and where to grow

This herb can tolerate moderate to severe frost, but extreme cold will force the plants into complete dormancy. Cover the roots with a thick organic mulch in winter to protect the roots from freezing. When planting it in the garden, plant in full sun in a rich, well-drained, loamy soil that has been fed prior to planting with some well-rotted compost. In the height of summer make sure it has extra water. At the end of winter, cut hard back to 20cm (8in) above the ground, topdress with well-rotted manure or compost.

## Growing in containers

Lion's ears looks fabulous grown in large containers. Being a member of the mint family, it is very robust and a fast grower so you can be more generous with your container than, for example, if you were growing a Mediterranean herb that hates having wet roots. Use a soil-based compost and feed weekly from early spring to early winter. In midwinter, cut back to 10cm (4in) above the soil and either pot up or divide. If you do this yearly, you will have a wonderful display. It is a tall grower so make sure the pot is near a wall so that the flowers are supported.

## Yearly maintenance

**Spring:** sow seeds; divide pot plants and garden plants.

**Summer:** take cuttings.

**Autumn:** enjoy the flowers.

**Winter:** cut back after flowering to a height of 20cm (8in) for plants in the garden, 10cm (4in) for pot plants.

## Harvesting and storing

**Leaves:** harvest the leaves to use fresh or to dry in summer before flowering.

**Flowers:** harvest the flowers to dry just as they start opening.

## Culinary uses

None.

## Medicinal uses

The leaves and stems and roots are all widely used to treat bites and stings, including snake bites. Externally, decoctions have been applied to treat eczema, skin diseases, itching and muscle cramps. Internally, decoctions are used for coughs and colds. Leaf infusions have been used to treat asthma and viral hepatitis.

*Leonotis leonurus*, Lion's Ears

**WARNING** | This herb is banned in Poland and illegal in Latvia due to its mildly psychoactive properties.

# Levisticum officinale

**If someone asked you to close your eyes then gave you some crushed lovage leaves to smell you would most probably say it was celery. Yet it has a much more intense flavour with a hint of yeast, some would say umami. Adding just a few leaves to potato soup turns it into a feast, or a few crushed seeds added to dough makes delicious bread that is gorgeous served with unsalted butter and cheese.**

*Levisticum officinale*, Lovage in spring

## History

This herb has been cultivated for thousands of years. The Romans preserved the leaves in vinegar for year-round flavouring. The Ancient Greeks chewed the seed to aid digestion and relieve flatulence. The medieval monks grew it in cloister gardens for many medicinal uses, including making a tea to treat nausea, while travellers in the Middle Ages used it as a latter-day 'odour eater' by lining their boots with the leaves. In Europe a decoction of lovage was reputedly a good aphrodisiac, which no worthy witch was without.

## Species

*Levisticum officinale*, Lovage
Hardy, H5 (USDA 7,8), herbaceous perennial. Height: up to 2m (6ft) when in flower; spread: 1m (3ft). Flat clusters of tiny, pale, greenish-yellow flowers in summer followed by brown seeds that ripen to light brown and have a warm, umami, celery flavour. Deeply divided green-toothed leaves, celery-scented when crushed. As the leaves age, they darken in colour and toughen, losing their lovely celery flavour and becoming bitter.

## Propagation

**Seeds:** sow fresh seeds in early autumn, into prepared seed trays or modules using a standard seed compost. Put into a propagator at 18°C (64°F). Germination takes 6–10 days. Once the seedlings are fully rooted, pot up in small pots, winter in a cold greenhouse or cold polytunnel. If you miss sowing in autumn, sow in spring; you may simply find they take longer to germinate. Alternatively, you can sow fresh seeds in early autumn into a prepared site in the garden, when the air temperature at night does not fall below 10°C (50°F). It is worth covering the sown seeds with some horticultural fleece until they are established.

**Division:** divide established plants in spring, replanting either into a well-prepared site in the garden or repotting using a soil-based compost.

## Pests and diseases

Leaf miner is sometimes a problem. Watch out for the first tunnels, which will appear like silver trails in the leaves, pick off the affected leaves and destroy them, otherwise the tunnels will extend, broad dry patches will develop and the leaves will start to wither away. A good way of controlling this pest is to cut the plant right down to the ground, burning the affected shoots. Give the plant a feed and the plant will shoot with new growth, which is just what one wants in the kitchen.

## How and where to grow

Lovage is a large plant, so choose its position in the garden carefully. It will be fully mature in 3–5 years. Plant in a rich, well-fed and well-draining soil in full sun or partial shade. To keep the leaves young and producing new shoots, and to stop the plant taking over the garden, cut back hard either all the way around, or choose one half, leaving the other half to run to seed. Once the flowering stem starts to grow and runs to flower you may need to stake the plant, especially if you live in an exposed site and suffer from high winds.

## Growing in containers

Lovage can be grown in containers using a soil-based potting compost. Choose a container with a wide base, which will help to stop it blowing over when it's in flower. Do not allow the compost to dry out in summer. Feed regularly with a liquid seaweed fertiliser throughout the growing season to help keep the leaves tender and productive.

## Yearly maintenance

**Spring:** sow seeds; divide established plants.

**Summer:** harvest young leaves; harvest flowers.

**Autumn:** harvest seeds.

**Winter:** no need to protect established plants.

## Harvesting and storing

**Leaves:** pick the main crop of leaves before flowering to use fresh, or to preserve in vinegar.

**Seeds:** harvest the seeds as they turn brown, dry well and store.

## Culinary uses

**Leaves:** lovage leaves have a very strong flavour so they need to be added to dishes sparingly. The best flavoured leaves are the new spring shoots; the mature leaves are bitter. To maintain a supply of young leaves throughout the season, cut sections of the plant down to the ground and new shoots will reappear. These can be added to stocks, stews and served with cheese and salads. Alternatively, crushed leaves can be rubbed over a chicken prior to roasting or around a salad bowl before adding the salad and then discarded.

**Flowers:** pick flowers when they are just open, divide into individual little flowers and scatter over tomatoes. They also have a strong flavour so use sparingly.

**Seeds:** the seed heads should be harvested when the seeds start to turn brown. On a dry day, pick them, tie a paper bag over the heads, and hang upside down in a dry airy place – the seeds will fall out of the head into the bag. The seed can be crushed and used in winter soups, in bread and pastries and sprinkled on salads, rice and mashed potatoes.

## Medicinal uses

Lovage is a good carminative and digestive, it contains vitamins A, B and C and the minerals iron, sodium and magnesium. It is considered to be one of nature's antibiotics with the ability to deal with bacteria and viruses. It has a cleansing effect on the body.

**WARNING** | Do not take medicinally when pregnant or if you suffer from kidney disease.

# Linum usitatissimum

**The first time I saw acres of this herb growing in the south of the UK, I had to stop the car to find out what the beautiful, elegant sky-blue flower dancing on the breeze was. On close inspection I saw it was flax. Cultivars of this herb have been developed firstly for fibre production (this is a tall version with fewer branches and flowers) and secondly for its seed (this plant is more floriferous and therefore produces more seed, which can also be used to make linseed oil and as an animal fodder).**

## History

Flax has been in cultivation for at least 7,000 years; it was one of the first crops domesticated by man. In the Stone Age, it was grown to produce fibres and for its seeds. In the early Egyptian tombs, linen cloth made from flax was used to wrap the mummies; the Greeks used it to make sails for their boats. In the 8th century, the Emperor Charlemagne decreed that flax seed should be consumed in order to maintain good health. The Latin *linum* was the source of the old English *lin*, meaning flax, and also linen, linseed and line, which are all made from this plant.

## Species

*Linum usitatissimum*, Flax, Linseed, Common Flax
Hardy, H3 (USDA 9), annual. Height: up to 80cm–1.2m (30in–4ft) in flower; spread: 30cm (12in). Sky-blue flowers that face upwards towards the sky in summer – they only last one day and are followed by round capsules filled with shiny brown seeds. Pointed linear green leaves on long thin stems.

*Linum perenne*, Perennial Flax
Hardy, H4 (USDA 8,9), semi-evergreen perennial. Height up to 60cm (24in) in flower; spread: 30cm (12in). Sky-blue saucer-shaped flowers in summer followed by capsules that contain the seeds. Pointed, linear, blue-green leaves on long thin stems.

## Propagation

**Seeds:** as neither form of flax likes being transplanted it is best to sow directly into a prepared site in the garden in spring or on the surface of a large pot filled with three parts soil-based potting compost mixed with one part horticultural grit. If sowing directly into the garden, wait until the temperature at night does not fall below 9°C (48°F). Germination can take 3–4 weeks; it is dependent on the temperature of the soil. Once the seedlings have germinated, keep the site well weeded until the plants get established.

**Cuttings:** the perennial flax can be propagated using stem tip cuttings taken from non-flowering stems from established plants in late spring/early summer. Fill small pots or modules with three parts seed compost mixed with one part perlite. Once fully rooted, plant out into a prepared site in full sun.

## Pests and diseases

The young plants of this herb are loved by slugs, snails and, if growing in too rich a soil, aphids. In early spring, an evening patrol is a great way to control slugs and snails by simply hand-picking them off the plants. Aphids will only need control if they become invasive, see page 267 on how to control them.

## How and where to grow

This herb is so beautiful in the garden: the lovely arching stems with their glorious flowers are a magnet for bees and other pollinating insects. Plant in full sun, in a very well-drained fertile soil. This herb looks lovely in many forms of garden – a gravel garden, a Mediterranean garden and an informal garden. It is well worth planting in generous clumps so that you can see the flowers dancing on the breeze.

## Growing in containers

The best way to grow any form of *Linum* in containers is to actually sow the seed into a pot filled with compost. Choose a good pot that has enough room to hold several plants. Use two parts soil-based compost mixed with one part horticultural sand and one part horticultural grit; this will provide enough drainage and enough water retention. Water the container prior to sowing, then sow the seeds on the surface and cover with a light covering of soil compost. Put the container in a warm sunny position. Germination in spring takes 21–28 days.

## Yearly maintenance

**Spring:** sow seeds.

**Summer:** take cuttings.

**Autumn:** harvest seeds.

**Winter:** the perennial *Linum* does not need protection from the cold. Lift container plants on to bricks to aid drainage.

## Harvesting and storing

**Seeds:** linseed is ripe when the stems turn yellow and the seed capsules turn brown. During wet summers, the stems may remain green and the plants continue to flower long after the early seed capsules ripen. In this case, harvest when the majority are ripe. Dry thoroughly before extracting the seed. Store the seed in an airtight container. Both forms of flax have edible seeds.

**Fibre:** to harvest the stems as they turn yellow, dry thoroughly before use.

## Culinary uses

The seeds can be added to smoothies, soups, yogurt, granola and bread; they add texture and are excellent for the health of one's gut. They can also be roasted and used as a coffee substitute. An edible oil is obtained from the seed, though it needs to be refined before use.

## Medicinal uses

Medicinally the oil from this herb is high in essential fatty acids, making it valuable in helping to maintain a healthy heart and circulation. The plant has a long history of use in the treatment of cancer and has been found to contain various anticancer agents. The seeds are used to treat constipation; they are often mixed with breakfast cereals. The seeds have also been used in poultices to treat boils and draw splinters.

**WARNING** | The plant has caused poisoning in livestock.

*Linum perenne*, Perennial Flax

**Common names:** Aztec Sweet Herb, Honeyherb

# Lippia dulcis (syn. Phyla dulcis)

**This delightful herb is a native of Mexico, Central America and the Caribbean. It was used as a natural sweetener by the Aztecs and indigenous people of Central America and is said to be 1,500 times sweeter than sugar, so should be used sparingly. Some prefer this as a sweetener to stevia (see page 234). It also is far more attractive and looks stunning grown in a container because as the plant matures, it will cascade over the rim.**

*Lippia dulcis*, Aztec Sweet Herb

## History

The recorded use of this herb dates back for hundreds of years in Mexico, where it was used to cause miscarriage. It is a source of hernandulcin, which is the first known intensely sweet compound. In the 16th century, the Spanish physician Francisco Hernandez wrote about *Lippia dulcis* saying that it was a medicinal plant used by the Aztec people, known to them for centuries by the Nahuatl name, *tzonpelic xihuitl*, meaning 'sweet herb'. Until the 19th century it was used to treat coughs and bronchitis.

## Species

*Lippia dulcis*, Aztec Sweet Herb
Tender, H2 (USDA 10), evergreen subshrub. Height: up to 30cm (12in); spread: indefinite. Beautiful clusters of cone-shaped white flowers. Small, oval, veined, green, toothed leaves that grow in opposite pairs. They can have a purple tinge if the night temperature dips below 3°C (37°F) or if they are in strong sunshine.

*Lippia graveolens*, Mexican Oregano
Tender, H2 (USDA 10), evergreen subshrub. Height and spread: up to 2m (6ft). Clusters of small white flowers with yellow centres. Small, lance-shaped, veined green leaves. The leaves have an intense aroma and flavour that is similar to oregano.

## Propagation

**Seeds:** sow the seed in late spring, into prepared seed trays using three parts seed compost mixed with one part sharp horticultural sand. Cover the seed with perlite not compost. Place in a propagator at 20°C (68°F). Germination takes 3–4 weeks. This seed rarely sets in cold climates.

**Cuttings:** as this herb roots wherever the stem touches the soil it is very easy to take cuttings. Look for a leaf join, and you will notice a swelling on the underside of the stem – these two points are where it will produce root. Fill either small pots or modules with the same mix as for sowing seeds above. Once rooted, pot up into small pots using three parts loam-based compost mixed with one part horticultural grit. Water in well and position in a frost-free environment. Do not water again until the compost is virtually but not quite dry.

## Pests and diseases

This aromatic herb rarely suffers from pests or diseases. However, in humid conditions, it can suffer from mildew and fungal conditions (see page 275).

## How and where to grow

In warm climates, plant in a well-drained soil in a sunny position or partial shade. It makes very good ground cover and spreads quickly. In cold, wet climates this herb can only be planted out in the summer and lifted in the autumn. Choose a sunny site and a well-drained soil. The benefit from planting it in the garden is that when you lift it you will find that as it has spread it has rooted – these stems can either be potted into small pots or put into modules using three parts seed compost mixed with one part sharp horticultural sand and then wintered in a frost-free environment.

## Growing in containers

This sweet herb looks beautiful in a container where the spreading branches hang over the edge attractively, or in a hanging basket. Use three parts soil-based compost mixed with one part horticultural grit. In cold climates, bring the container into a frost-free environment for the winter and place on bricks or stones to maintain drainage.

## Yearly maintenance

**Spring:** sow seeds; take cuttings.

**Summer:** plant out in the garden in cold climates.

**Autumn:** bring plants into a frost-free environment; take cuttings as insurance.

**Winter:** protect from frost.

## Harvesting and storing

**Leaves:** in warm climates, the leaves of this herb can be harvested most of the year. In cold climates, harvest in early summer. The leaves can be used fresh or dried for use in the winter.

**Flowers:** pick the flowers to use fresh throughout the summer; alternatively, they can be dried. Once dried the flower does crumble but this is equally delicious.

## Culinary uses

**Leaves:** the leaves have a curious and intensely sweet flavour and have been eaten in salads both savoury and fruit, as well as used to sweeten tea and other drinks.

**Flowers:** the flower buds are edible; they taste amazing – a mixture of sweet bubblegum with just a hint of liquorice. A few added to a fruit salad not only tastes good but looks lovely. They are also used to decorate cakes, especially banana cake.

**Roots:** the roots have a liquorice flavour and are used to flavour drinks, such as beer.

## Medicinal uses

Medicinally this herb is under research with regards to its antioxidant and anti-inflammatory properties. It is still used as a traditional herbal remedy in Central America to treat diarrhoea, coughs and colds, and tinctures are used to treat sinus congestion, asthma and bronchitis.

**WARNING** | This herb should not be taken medicinally while pregnant or while breastfeeding. It is not recommended to take this herb medicinally for any length of time. Some of the active constituents have shown carcinogenic activity when taken medicinally.

# Malva sylvestris

**Mallow is a wonderful all-round herb that originally was not just a vegetable, it was also reputed to 'cure all'. Pliny the Elder (AD23–79), is reputed to have said, 'whosoever shall take a spoonful of the juice of the mallows shall that day be free from all diseases that may come to him'. The flowers make it a very worthy plant for any form of garden, especially the less formal, and they are extremely beneficial for pollinating insects, including bees, butterflies and hoverflies, which feed on its nectar.**

## History

In the Middle Ages, common mallow was thought to be a calming antidote to aphrodisiacs and love potions. Prior to that, the Romans ate the young shoots as a vegetable delicacy. The Ancient Celts believed that placing the disc-shaped fruit over a dead man's eyes would keep evil spirits from entering the body in an attempt to get into heaven. According to the *Doctrine of Signatures* (see glossary on page 278) the hairs on the plant meant that it would help to grow hair. The root was also used as a toothbrush or peeled and given to teething children to chew. It was the shape of the seed rather than the flowers which led to the folk name 'Billy buttons'. The seeds are edible – they have a bland, slightly nutty taste. They are known as cheeses, or pick-cheeses, again because of their shape.

## Species

*Malva sylvestris*, Common Mallow
Hardy, H5 (USDA 7,8), herbaceous, short lived, perennial. Height: up to 90cm (3ft); spread: 60cm (24in). Pretty, pale purple/pink flowers with five petals and dark-coloured veins. Flowers throughout the summer until the first frosts. The leaves are mid-green, lobed and downy with prominent veins on the underside.

*Malva moschata*, Musk Mallow
Hardy, H5 (USDA 7,8), herbaceous perennial. Height up to 80cm (30in); spread: 60cm (24in). Rose/pink flowers (sometimes white) in late summer to early autumn. The leaves are kidney-shaped at the base and the stem leaves are deeply divided and mid-green in colour. Leaves omit a musky aroma in warm weather or when gently pressed.

## Propagation

**Seeds:** sow seeds in autumn. Place the container outside, it will survive all weathers, including snow and frost. Germination is erratic. Plant out into a prepared site 60cm (24in) apart when well established in early summer.

**Cuttings:** take cuttings from firm basal shoots in late spring or summer.

## Pests and diseases

Mallows can catch hollyhock rust but not usually to a serious degree. There is a fungus that also can attack the plants, which produces spots on the leaves and a serious black canker on the stems. If this occurs, dig up the plants and destroy them. It is a seed-borne fungus and may be carried into the soil, therefore it is a good idea to change the plants' site in the following season. Equally, do not plant mint, chives or French tarragon in that position as they are all susceptible to rust (see page 276).

## How and where to grow

Mallows are very tolerant plants that grow in most soils but they prefer a sunny site. They will survive in semi-shade, in a well-drained fertile soil. If the soil is too damp they may well need staking in summer. Cut back stems after flowering; not only will this promote new growth, it will also keep it under control and encourage a second flowering. In autumn, cut the stems down to the basal leaves.

## Growing in containers

Musk mallow is the best variety to grow in a container. Use a soil-based potting compost so that it retains moisture in summer. Position in a sunny spot and keep it well watered throughout the growing season, only giving it a feed of liquid fertiliser twice in a growing season. Cut back after the first flowering to encourage a second, and also to keep it under control. Give a final cutback in the autumn. Put the container on bricks in winter to aid drainage; pot up the following spring.

## Yearly maintenance

**Spring:** in late spring take softwood cuttings from the young shoots.

**Summer:** cut back after flowering.

**Autumn:** sow fresh seed.

**Winter:** no need for protection.

## Harvesting and storing

**Leaves:** pick the new growth to use fresh throughout the season.

**Flowers:** harvest during the summer to use fresh.

**Roots:** dig up the roots of the second year's growth to dry for medicinal use.

## Culinary uses

**Leaves:** the tender young leaves taste like a mixture of lettuce and spinach. Their tips can be used in salads or steamed and used like a vegetable.

**Flowers:** the flower and petals are edible; they have little to no flavour but look lovely scattered over salads.

**Seeds:** the seeds are edible; they have a bland, slightly nutty flavour. Add to salads.

## Medicinal uses

A decoction made from the roots and leaves can be added to bath water to ease skin rashes, boils and ulcers. Medicinally this herb is thought to be inferior to *Althea officinalis* (marsh mallow; see page 52), however, there is current research into its properties for urinary complaints. The root can be cut into slices and used to draw out splinters and thorns.

*Malva moschata*, Musk Mallow

# Mandragora officinarum

**A true herb farmer or herb nursery cannot be without this magical mystical herb. It looks both evil and beautiful at the same time, with its flowers clustered on very short stems just above the leaves. It is said that the long tap root looks like the human form, which is why it is called mandrake. It was thought to be fatal for anyone to dig the plant up as the screams would drive one to death! Having grown it with moderate success over the past three decades I can honestly say I have not heard it scream. But I have seen Harry Potter fans stare in awe.**

*Mandragora officinarum*, Mandrake

## History

In 200 BC the Carthaginians created a bait for the Romans who were invading their city made from wine spiked with mandrake juice. This rendered the Romans insensible and the city was saved. In the Odyssey, the Greek enchantress Circe used mandrake in a brew to turn Odysseus's men into swine. It has been used in witchcraft to make barren women fertile and this is also referenced in the Bible, Genesis 30, where Rachel, the second wife of Jacob, becomes fertile after her sister found mandrake growing in a field. It has been used as an anaesthetic – a piece of the root being given to the patient to chew before an operation.

In ancient times, wine was made from the mandrake fruit and in his book *Gerrard's Herbal,* John Gerrard said that the apples were edible: 'the apples are milder, and are reported that they may be eaten, being boyled with pepper and hot spices.'

## Species

There are six species of mandrake; the two that are best know are those below.

*Mandragora officinarum*, Mandrake, Satan's Apple
Hardy, H4 (USDA 8,9), perennial. Height: 5cm (2in); spread: 50cm (20in). Small, bell-shaped white/blue flowers with white lines running through them grow on very short stems in spring. The flowers can also be a greenish-white with a hint of beige. Whatever the colour, the flowers are followed by aromatic round yellow fruits in late summer, though only in warm climates. Large, rough, oval-green leaves that become darker and rougher as they mature. Native to northern Italy, the Balkan Peninsula, Lebanon and Syria.

*Mandragora autumnalis*, Mandrake
Hardy, H4 (USDA 8,9), herbaceous, perennial. Height: 25cm (10in); spread: 30cm (12in). Small, bell-shaped pale blue/violet flowers in autumn, followed by aromatic, round, yellow, fruits in late summer, which are toxic. Large, oblong, hairy dark green leaves. Native to Lebanon, Syria, Morocco, Tunisia, Turkey, Spain and Portugal.

The American mandrake, *Podophyllum peltatum*, is an entirely different plant belonging to the barberry family and should therefore not be confused with the toxic European mandrake, which is a member of the *Solanaceae* family.

## Propagation

**Seeds:** sow the seeds of *Mandragora officinarum* in autumn or *Mandragora autumnalis* in spring into prepared seed tray or modules, using three parts seed compost mixed with one part sharp horticultural sand. Once sown, cover the seeds with sand and place in a cold frame. Mandrake does need stratification (see page 18) to trigger germination. Germination can take anything from 4 months to 2 years.

**Cuttings:** you can see the new shoots appearing in the early spring for *Mandragora officinarum* or autumn for *Mandragora autumnalis*. Clear around the plant to expose the crown and the top of the roots. Choose a side that has new shoots appearing and using a sharp knife, slice the root, including a new shoot. Place the cutting in a small pot filled with a loam-based potting compost mixed in equal parts with sharp horticultural sand. Place the container in a warm position until rooted. Grow on in a container, under protection, for two years prior to planting into a prepared site.

## Pests and diseases

In spring, the plant looks wonderful in flower but you admire it, turn around and it has vanished. Do not panic, it is 'bonne bouche' for slugs. Mark the spot, check it from time to time and by late summer the leaves will reappear.

## How and where to grow

Plant in full sun or partial shade in a well-drained, fertile, deep soil to allow the tap root to grow. This herb dislikes chalk and gravel soils and is prone to rot in clay or cold, wet soils.

## Growing in containers

This plant has a very long root system – up to 1.2m (4ft), which makes it is not particularly suitable for growing in containers, however it is possible. Choose a long tom, deep pot, so that the tap root can develop. Fill the container with three parts soil-based compost mixed with one part horticultural grit. The plant will be smaller than when grown in the ground and it will not set fruit. Repot every spring or autumn into the next size of pot. Lift the pots in winter, stand on bricks or stones to aid drainage.

## Yearly maintenance

**Spring:** sow seeds; take root cuttings.

**Summer:** check watering.

**Autumn:** sow seeds; take cuttings.

**Winter:** protect from excessive wet; lift containers off the ground.

## Harvesting and storing

Only a qualified medicinal herbalist should harvest this herb.

## Culinary uses

None.

## Medicinal uses

Mandrake contains the powerful tropane alkaloids, which have an intense effect on the central nervous system. It was used as a soporific and pain-killing plant for many hundreds of years. It is a powerful narcotic, sedative and hallucinogen. It is rarely used in herbal medicine today, however, tinctures made from the root are still widely used in homeopathy as a treatment for asthma and coughs.

**WARNING** | The whole plant is toxic: only take under professional supervision. Not to be taken in any form during pregnancy.

**Common names:** Lemon Balm, Sweet Balm, Bee Balm, Cure All

# Melissa officinalis

**Over the years I have heard many a gardener cuss this herb because like its cousin mint (see page 172) it is invasive. However, for cooks it is incredibly useful and underused, and as any good beekeeper knows, when planted around a beehive, which is a very traditional thing to do, not only are the flowers high in nectar, it was also said that rubbing a new hive with the leaves encouraged the bees to settle and the scent of the herb stopped bees swarming. The Latin *melissa* is said to be derived from the Greek *melisso* meaning 'bee'.**

*Melissa officinalis*, Lemon Balm

## Species

*Melissa officinalis*, Lemon Balm
Hardy, H7 (USDA 6), herbaceous perennial. Height: up to 90cm (3ft); spread: 45cm (18in) or more. Clusters of small, pale, creamy flowers in summer. Highly lemon-scented, oval, toothed, textured green leaves.

*Melissa officinalis* 'All Gold', Golden Lemon Balm
Hardy, H5 (USDA 7,8), herbaceous perennial. Height: 30cm (12in); spread: 40cm (16in) or more. Clusters of small white flowers with a lilac tint in summer. Lemon-scented, oval, toothed, textured golden-yellow leaves. These leaves are very prone to scorch, so plant in partial shade. To maintain good leaf colour cut back in summer. It can only be propagated by cuttings or division.

*Melissa officinalis* 'Aurea', Variegated Lemon Balm
Hardy, H5 (USDA 7,8), herbaceous perennial. Height: 45cm (18in); spread: 40cm (16in) or more. Clusters of small, pale, creamy flowers in summer. Lemon-scented, oval, toothed, textured, variegated green and gold leaves. The leaves often revert to green in summer, and the gold parts can suffer from scorch. To maintain variegation, cut back in summer before flowering. It can only be propagated by cuttings or division.

## History

This herb is steeped in history: records show that over 2,000 years ago the Ancient Greeks and Romans prescribed lemon balm for indigestion and overindulgence and to chase away melancholy. It was very popular in Elizabethan times for use in salads, as a tea and to flavour wine. At that time, in 1696, the London Dispensary reported that 'balm in wine, taken every morning, would renew youth, strengthen the brain, relieve languishing nature and prevent baldness'. Interestingly, current research has shown that it sharpens the memory and relieves anxiety.

## Propagation

**Seeds:** in spring, sow the seeds into prepared seed trays or modules using a seed compost. Place under cover at 18°C (64°F), germination takes 1–2 weeks. Be careful not to overwater the seedlings once they emerge as they are very prone to damping off (see page 274). Pot up when large enough, using a soil-based compost. Once all threat of frost has passed, plant in the garden into a prepared site.

**Cuttings:** take cuttings from the new growth in early summer from non-flowering shoots and transfer to prepared modules or small pots filled with a seed compost. Once rooted, pot up or plant out.

**Division:** division is the best way to control this herb in the garden. Divide established plants in early autumn or early spring, replanting into a well-prepared site or potting up using a soil-based compost.

## Pests and diseases

Like its cousin mint, this herb is prone to the rust virus (see page 276) for more information. If affected, dig the plant up – do not compost it, destroy it.

## How and where to grow

Lemon balm is a very tolerant herb that will grow in all soils, with the exception of waterlogged. A word of warning: it will be invasive in light fertile soils. Ideally the best situation is a well-drained soil in a sunny site with a bit of shade at the height of the day. To maintain a good supply of leaf and to stop the plant being woody and straggly, cut back just before flowering finishes. This will promote new growth and – a major plus – inhibit self-seeding. As this plant can be invasive dig up encroaching roots as necessary. This herb is great planted in an orchard, as it can be allowed to spread and the flowers will attract pollinating insects, which will help increase the fruit harvest.

## Growing in containers

All forms of lemon balm adapt to being grown in a container. This is the best method if you have a small garden as it is much easier to keep it under control. Use a soil-based potting compost. Repot either into a larger pot or divide and make two pot plants. Lift the pots in winter and put on to bricks to aid drainage.

## Yearly maintenance

**Spring:** sow seeds; divide established plants.

**Summer:** cut back just before flowering finishes to prevent self-seeding.

**Autumn:** divide established plants.

**Winter:** prevent from becoming waterlogged.

## Harvesting and storing

**Leaves:** the best flavoured leaves are those before it flowers or from non-flowering stems.

**Flowers:** when using these flowers, remove all the green parts as they do not have flavour.

## Culinary uses

**Leaves:** the leaves have a lovely lemon scent which is lost in cooking, however, when added to stewing fruit they cut down the sugar needed and also remove the tartness. Fresh leaves can also be added to cream cheese, vinegars, wine cups, tea, and chopped with vegetables.

**Flowers:** add the flowers to salads – both fruit and leaf – use in jellies and flavoured butters.

## Medicinal uses

Lemon balm is high in vitamins A, B and C. It is a natural carminative, is antispasmodic and a great digestive. A tea made from the leaves is not only a digestive it is also calming and relaxing and helps to sharpen the memory! Currently recent research shows that it can be beneficial in the treatment of cold sores, on average halving the healing time. It also reduces the chance of further outbreaks. It is a very good insect repellent as well as for rubbing on insect bites to help reduce the itching.

# Mentha

**How many products can you name that has mint, spearmint or peppermint among its ingredients? It is one of the best-known herbs, not only is it a classic kitchen essential, but it is also used for its medicinal properties and to disguise the horrid flavour of some medicines. It is used in confectionery, cakes, cosmetics, toothpaste, shampoo and scent... the list is endless. And to top it all, it is great to grow and amazingly beneficial for attracting all forms of pollinating insects.**

## History

Mint has been cultivated for medicinal properties since ancient times and was found in Egyptian tombs dating back to 1000 BC. The Japanese have been growing it to obtain menthol for at least 2,000 years. The story that I am particularly fond of illustrates its long association with hospitality. Two strangers were walking in Asia Minor; no one had offered them food or drink for many days. When finally, an elderly couple invited them in, and before laying the food on the table, the couple rubbed mint leaves over the table and plates and scattered it over the food. The strangers were so pleased with the hospitality shown to them that, on parting, they expressed their gratitude by transforming the couple's humble home into a mansion, for the strangers were none other than the two gods Zeus and Hermes.

## Species

There are now over 120 species, cultivars and hybrids of mint, so I have limited this list to my top 12, which are classics, culinary must-haves, great for pollinators, useful, and/or just beautiful.

*Mentha* 'Berries and Cream', Berries and Cream Mint
Hardy, H5 (USDA 7,8), herbaceous perennial. Height: up to 45cm (18in) in flower; spread: indefinite. Attractive tight terminal clusters of mauve flowers. Dark green, with mulberry veins, peppermint- and fruity-scented leaves. Use the leaves and flowers in summer drinks.

*Mentha arvensis* var. *piperascens*, Japanese Mint
Hardy, H5 (USDA 7,8), herbaceous perennial. Height: up to 60cm (24in) in flower; spread: indefinite. Tight terminal clusters of lilac flowers. Bright green, round, peppermint-scented leaves. Medicinal and culinary.

*Mentha longifolia*, Buddleia Mint group
Hardy, H6 (USDA 6,7), herbaceous perennial. Height: up to 90cm (3ft) in flower; spread: indefinite. Long, terminal cones of mauve flowers. Long, oval, grey-green, hairy-toothed leaves. This mint attracts many forms of pollinator: tiny flies, all forms of bee and beautiful butterflies. It is great for a pollinator garden.

*Mentha pulegium* 'Upright', Upright Pennyroyal
Hardy, H6 (USDA 6,7), semi-evergreen perennial. Height: up to 15cm (6in) in flower; spread: up to 60cm (24in). Small mauve flowers in terminal, globular clusters around the stem in summer. Highly peppermint-scented, small oval leaves. Rub crushed leaves on mosquito bites to remove the swelling and irritation. Edible flowers.

*Mentha requienii*, Corsican Mint
Hardy, H5 (USDA 7,8), semi-evergreen perennial. Height: up to 1–2cm (½–¾in) in flower; spread: up to 60cm (24in). Tiny purple flowers. Tiny peppermint-scented leaves that look just like its cousin thyme (see page 244), until you rub the leaves. The flowers are edible.

*Mentha spicata* 'Tashkent', Tashkent Mint
Hardy, H6 (USDA 6,7), herbaceous perennial. Height: up to 60cm (24in) in flower; spread: indefinite. Purple/mauve, small flowers in terminal, cylindrical spikes in summer. Mid-green, oval, lance-shaped, wrinkled, spearmint-scented and flavoured leaves. This is the mint I grow in my garden just outside my kitchen door. I use it for all of my basic mint uses in the kitchen. It has a clean mint flavour and scent, and is lovely with yoghurt, cucumber, strawberries and summer cocktails.

*Mentha spicata* var. *crispa* 'Moroccan', Moroccan Mint
Hardy, H6 (USDA 6,7), herbaceous perennial. Height: up to 50cm (20in) in flower; spread: indefinite. White flowers in the summer. Bright green leaves that have got texture. Excellent mint scent. Great flavour.

*Mentha suaveolens*, Apple Mint
Hardy, H5 (USDA 7,8), herbaceous perennial. Height: up to 60cm (24in) in flower; spread: indefinite. Mauve flowers in summer. Roundish hairy leaves. Tall vigorous grower. It gets its name because the scent of the leaves is a combination of mint and apples. It is more subtle than some mints and for this reason is good to use in cooking.

*Mentha x gracilis*, Ginger Mint, Scotch Mint
Hardy, H5 (USDA 7,8), herbaceous perennial. Height: up to 45cm (18in) in flower; spread: 60cm (24in). The stem has whorls of small, two-lipped mauve flowers in summer. The leaf is variegated gold/green with serrated edges. The flavour is a delicate warm mint that combines well in salads, especially tomato dishes. This is not a vigorous mint. Plant it in a well drained soil.

*Mentha x piperita* 'Black Mitcham', Peppermint, Black Peppermint
Hardy, H5 (USDA 7,8), herbaceous perennial. Height: up to 60cm (24in) in flower; spread: indefinite. Pale purple, small flowers in terminal, cylindrical, spikes in summer. Dark brown, tinged with green, pointed, oval, toothed peppermint-scented and flavoured leaves. This mint makes an excellent peppermint tea and a mean chocolate mousse.

*Mentha x piperita f. citrata* 'Basil', Basil Mint
Hardy, H5 (USDA 7,8), herbaceous perennial. Height: up to 60cm (24in) in flower; spread: indefinite. Tight clusters of purple flowers both terminal and as a whorl around the stem. Mid-green leaves that have a slight shine on the upper surface, maroon stems. A great substitute for its cousin basil in early spring – it is great with tomatoes and pasta.

*Mentha x villosa* var. *alopecuroides* Bowles's Mint, Bowles Mint
Hardy, H5 (USDA 7,8), herbaceous perennial. Height: 1m (3ft) in flower; spread: indefinite. Pale mauve, small flowers in terminal, cylindrical, spikes in summer. Large, round, hairy, soft green leaves, which have a unique flavour – a mixture of peppermint and spearmint. A very good culinary mint – excellent for mint sauce. This mint is prone to mildew so plant where it gets a good breeze.

## Propagation

**Seeds:** there are many forms of mint seed for sale. However, there is only one that grows true from seed, which is pennyroyal. If you want to experiment and see if you can find a new flavour then great, but if you want a definitive flavour start from cuttings or division. Sow the seed in spring into prepared modules or a seed tray using a standard seed compost; do not cover the seeds. Place under protection at 18°C (64°F). Germination takes 10–20 days.

**Cuttings:** softwood cuttings can be taken in late spring from the new non-flowering growth and transferred to prepared modules or a small pot filled with three parts seed compost mixed with one part standard perlite. Once rooted, either pot up using a soil-based compost, or plant out into a prepared site.

**Root cuttings:** this is the easiest way to increase your stock; simply dig up a piece of root or get one from a friend. Cut it where you can see a little growing node and place the cuttings either into a module or you may find it easier to lay it out in a seed tray filled with the same mix as above. Make sure the roots are under the compost. Water in. Keep under protection in a cold greenhouse or in a polytunnel. In spring, new shoots will emerge in about 2 weeks depending on light levels.

**Division:** mature plants can be divided either in spring or in autumn. As mint produces root runners all over the place, it is a good idea to dig it up every few years and divide the plant. As with cuttings, each bit of root will grow, so if you are moving the plant and not wishing to replant in the same

*Mentha spicata* var. *crispa* 'Moroccan', Moroccan Mint

position, do take care. Corsican mint is slightly different and does not set root runners, therefore, it is better to dig up a section in spring and divide by easing the plant apart and replanting in the garden in a chosen site.

## Pests and diseases

A fungus called *Puccinia menthae* is a common problem. It is known as 'mint rust', which is easily identified, as small rusty spots which cover the leaf, starting on the underside. The only organic way to get rid of this disease is to dig the plant up, bin – do not compost – the contaminated leaves, then sterilise the roots (see below). Be warned: mint rust can spread in the wind, and it does remain in the soil for at least three years, so do not plant any mint, tarragon, mallow or chives in that area.

To sterilise the roots, start by washing all the compost off the rhizomes. Once clean, immerse them in hot water at 44°C (111°F), not hotter, for exactly 10 minutes, then plunge them into cold water. These roots can then be used to take cuttings in the mix given under Propagation (see previous page).

## How and where to grow

Mint is invasive, so choose the area in which you wish to plant with care. The best flavour and healthiest plants are those that are grown so the plant can spread naturally. Plant in rich, well-drained soil in a sunny position. To maintain healthy plants, divide established plants every few years. Cut back after flowering to encourage new leaf growth, feed a liquid fertiliser – either seaweed or comfrey – and the tender new growth will be ready for picking in about 6–8 weeks. In winter, when the plant has died back, feed with well-rotted manure.

## Growing in containers

Mint is ideal for growing in containers. Use a soil-based compost and repot every autumn, this will give you lush new growth in spring and prevent root rot. Please do not be tempted to pot two different mints in the same pot to save space because within 9 months, if you had planted a spearmint and a peppermint they would end up tasting the same and not have their own unique lovely flavours.

*Mentha arvensis* var. *piperascens*, Japanese Mint

## Yearly maintenance

**Spring:** dig up root if cuttings are required; split established plants if required.

**Summer:** after flowering, cut back to 6cm (2in) above the ground to promote new growth and to control the spread of unruly plants.

**Autumn:** dig up roots for forcing; bring in containers.

**Winter:** sterilise roots if rust has been present during the growing season and take root cuttings.

## Harvesting and storing

**Leaves:** leaves taste best before flowering but if you remember to cut back hard after flowering, those late-summer/early autumn new leaves are equally delicious. The leaves can be used fresh, preserved in vinegar, turned into a syrup or frozen.

**Flowers:** pick the flowers throughout the summer to use fresh.

## Culinary uses

**Leaves:** fresh leaves are lovely in salads, with yoghurt, with fruit and scattered over vegetables. They can also be used in marinades, sauces, ice cream and cocktails. The leaves are incredibly versatile and, at the end of the day, they make a lovely cup of tea.

**Flowers:** in the main, fresh flowers have a light mint flavour or a light peppermint flavour. They can be scattered over sweet and savoury dishes and pastries and cakes.

*Mentha pulegium* 'Upright', Upright Pennyroyal

## Medicinal uses

Mint's beneficial properties as a digestive, antispasmodic and carminative, when used in cooking, are well known. It also has antioxidant and antiviral properties. Medicinally spearmint and peppermint are used to promote digestion, relieve indigestion, nausea, wind, diarrhoea, and colic. The tea is good for colds and it can be used as a cooling wash to bring down a fever. A cooled mint tea is also a good gargle to freshen the breath.

**Common names:** Oysterleaf, Oyster Plant, Gromwell, Sea Bluebells, Sea Lungwort, Northern Shorewort

# Mertensia maritima

**This is a quintessential herb: it looks good, tastes amazing, does you good and is fabulous for pollinators. The leaves taste of the sea; I'm not sure about oysters but many firmly say they do. For me it is the beauty of this plant that is totally captivating. And it is one of our UK native herbs. It is sadly now threatened with extinction due to climate change. It features on the UK red list which is a critical indicator of the health of our biodiversity and is listed on the International Union for Conservation of Nature's red list (IUCN) of threatened species. Oysterleaf is now also becoming rare throughout the northern hemisphere and is on the IUCN red list in North America. This gives us even more reason to grow and nurture it for future generations.**

## History

This herb is eaten in Alaska and by the Inuits.

## Species

*Mertensia maritima*, Oysterleaf
Hardy, H6 (USDA 6,7), herbaceous perennial. Height: up to 15cm (6in) in flower; spread: 25cm (10in) and in the right conditions, more. Lovely pink buds followed by stunning bell-shaped bright blue flowers in summer. Fleshy, blue/grey/green leaves that bruise when you touch them and grow on long sprawling stems that can reach 50cm (20in) in length. The plant has a large taproot, which, in the wild, reaches down through the shingle and sand to find water and also to anchor the plant.

## Propagation

**Seeds:** the seeds need a period of cold stratification, to germinate well (see page 18). In the autumn, we have found it best to mix the seed with damp sand and put it in the crisper drawer of the refrigerator for 2 weeks, then sow the seeds into prepared seed trays or modules with three parts seed compost mixed with one part horticultural grit that has been well watered prior to sowing. Once sown, cover lightly with the horticultural grit. Place the container outside for the remainder of the winter. Bring into a cold greenhouse in early spring. Once the seedlings are large enough to handle, pot up using a soil-based compost mixed in equal parts with horticultural grit.

**Cuttings:** due to such a high demand for this plant by chefs, I once – out of desperation – took some cuttings. We now raise all our stock from cuttings as this is a more reliable method than raising the plant from seed. Take cuttings of new shoots in late spring into modules or small pots filled with a seed compost mixed in equal parts with perlite. Rooting takes 10–14 days at 18°C (64°F).

**Division:** mature, established plants can be divided very gently. This herb has a long tap root and does not like being disturbed. In early spring, remove any old winter growth, clear around the crown, then using a sharp knife, remove half leaving the other half with the tap root in situ. The half you have removed will have a small amount of root. Prepare a pot to fit the crown, fill with the cutting mix, place the crown on the compost, ease in any roots using a dibber, water in well and keep in a cold greenhouse or cold frame until fully rooted. It can then be planted into a prepared site in the garden.

## Pests and diseases

Slugs, slugs, slugs. Pick off and remove as soon as you see them – they love this plant.

## How and where to grow

As this herb naturally grows on exposed beaches where it occurs among shingle or on shingle mixed with sand, one needs to bear this in mind when planting it in the garden. Ideally a rock garden or a gravel garden would suit this herb. It likes a well-drained soil in full sun but at the same time it does like water. So, in the summer months water regularly, especially when it is very hot.

## Growing in containers

Oysterleaf happily adapts to being grown in a container. Choose a deep container, a long tom would be ideal, as it has a long tap root. Fill with soil-based potting compost mixed in equal parts with horticultural grit. Top dress around the crown with horticultural grit. Water regularly throughout the summer and feed monthly with a liquid seaweed fertiliser.

## Yearly maintenance

**Spring:** take cuttings; divide established plants.

**Summer:** water regularly.

**Autumn:** sow seed.

**Winter:** lift pots off the ground so that they can drain.

## Harvesting and storing

**Leaves:** fresh leaves can be harvested from the spring onwards and, if you remove the flowers, after flowering.

**Flowers:** only harvest the flowers in summer off established cultivated plants – never from the wild – to eat fresh.

## Culinary uses

**Leaves:** the leaves can be added to salads or served with fish dishes; they are best eaten raw.

**Flowers:** the flowers look fabulous scattered over fish dishes or in salads.

**Root:** the root is edible, however, as it is now such an endangered plant, I do not recommend it.

## Medicinal uses

There is current research into how to reproduce this plant via micropropagation, not only for its culinary properties but also for its digestive and anti-cancer properties.

*Mertensia maritima*, Oysterleaf

# Meum athamanticum

**In 1993, at my first Royal Horticultural Society Chelsea Flower show, I created a herb display divided into four sections: medicinal, culinary, historic and UK native herbs. I had been informed that the royal party would not be coming to see my plants but was asked to stay near at hand. To my total delight and honour, Her Majesty Queen Elizabeth II and Prince Philip stopped at the stand and the then RHS President asked me to come and explain my display. Not only were they both interested, they loved the fact that I had included *Meum*, which is one of the wild herbs of Scotland. They were fascinated by its traditional uses and had never thought of it as a vegetable. On returning to the Herb Farm, I sent two plants to Balmoral. A few weeks later I had a letter from the head gardener thanking me for sending them one of their weeds!**

## History

This ancient wild medicinal herb was used throughout the Middle Ages for complaints and illnesses of the stomach and as an appetite stimulant. The root was traditionally eaten by the Scottish Highlanders as a vegetable. One of its local names is Baldmoney or Bald-money, which is said to be a corruption of Blader who was the Norse god of light, a son of the gods Odin and Frigg. It has a reputation for being able to spice up one's love life. In the UK, many of the pre-1970 sites for Meu were lost before 1930 as a result of agricultural improvement of grassland and probably also through deliberate destruction because it can taint cow's milk. Since the birth of the rewilding movement in the UK, new sites have been found in north Wales and Cumbria.

## Species

*Meum athamanticum*, Meu
Hardy, H6 (USDA 6,7), herbaceous perennial. Height 30cm (12in); spread: 20cm (8in). Umbels of small white flowers with a hint of pink around the edges of the cluster in early summer. Feathery, soft, spice-scented bright green leaves. The long tap root is fibrous with a strong spicy flavour.

## Propagation

**Seeds:** the best time to sow this seed is in the autumn, using fresh seed, into prepared small pots or small seed trays. The seeds need stratification to germinate (see page 18). Place the container outside so that it is exposed to all weather. Alternatively, place the seed pot or tray in the crisper drawer of the refrigerator for four weeks, followed by a period outside. Germination will take place the following spring, though it can be erratic.

**Division:** divide established plants in the early autumn, replanting into well-prepared open ground, or pot up using a soil-based potting compost. This is not an invasive plant.

## Pests and diseases

The only time I have ever known this plant suffer was when it was potted up in a potting compost with loads of fertiliser. The leaf growth was so lush that it got attacked by aphids, which got right into the crown. If this happens treat with soft horticultural soap following the manufacturer's instructions.

## How and where to grow

Meu is happiest growing in grassland. Plant in full sun in fertile soil that retains moisture in summer. It will adapt to most soils, with the exception of waterlogged or totally arid. If you wish to grow this plant as an alternative root vegetable, it must be mulched with well-rotted manure in the autumn. If you are growing it for its leaf crop, then feed with a liquid fertiliser – either comfrey or seaweed – in the early spring. Only feed it once, otherwise it will grow too soft and lose flavour.

## Growing in containers

Meu will adapt to being grown in a container. Fill a long tom pot or a deep pot with a soil-based compost – the pot has to be deep enough to accommodate its long tap root. Repot every autumn. It looks lovely when combined with *Malva moschata*, musk mallow (see page 166) or *Galium odoratum*, sweet woodruff (see page 126).

## Yearly maintenance

**Spring:** harvest young leaves.

**Summer:** harvest the seeds after flowering.

**Autumn:** sow fresh seeds; divide established plants.

**Winter:** no need for protection.

## Harvesting and storing

**Leaves:** harvest the leaves to use fresh either before or after flowering but not during.

**Roots:** harvest the root of three-year-old plants in early autumn; these can be used fresh, dried or turned into wine.

## Culinary uses

**Leaves:** since the resurgence of foraging, this herb has seen much demand from chefs. The leaves can be added to omelettes, cheese, salads, soups. They have a spicy, slightly anise flavour.

**Roots:** this plant is a member of the carrot family. The roots have a strong spicy flavour and are good in stews, casseroles and soups. The roots can be used to make a spicy wine.

## Medicinal uses

Medicinally it was traditionally used for everything from curing viper bites to coughs, flatulence and expulsion of the afterbirth. Nowadays it is little used, however the root is good for digestive problems.

*Meum athamanticum*, Meu flower

*Meum athamanticum*, Meu leaf

**Common names:** Bergamot, Oswego Tea, Bee Balm, Blue Balm, High Balm, Low Balm, Mountain Balm, Mountain Mint, Wild Bergamot, Horsemin

# Monarda fistulosa

**I have a very soft spot for this herb, with its magnificent flamboyant flowers that look like a hat that could be worn to a 1960s society wedding or the RHS Chelsea Flower Show. It is a native of North America where it was introduced to the settlers by the Oswego Native Americans.**

## History

The common name bergamot is said to have originated from the scent of the crushed leaf, which resembles *Citrus bergamia*, the small bitter Italian bergamot orange. In the 18th century, bergamot became known as 'Oswego tea' when a Quaker botanist sampled a tea made from the leaves at Fort Oswego, New York. It became such a popular tea during the colonial period that in 1745 the settlers sent bergamot seeds back to the UK.

## Species

There are many species, cultivars and hybrids of bergamot that look beautiful in the herb garden or a herbaceous border. I have chosen my favourite three, all of which are spectacular in the garden and useful in the kitchen.

*Monarda fistulosa*, Wild Bergamot
Hardy, H5 (USDA 7,8), herbaceous perennial. Height: up to 1.2m (4ft); spread: 45cm (18in). Lovely lilac flowers with mauve bracts in summer until early autumn. Aromatic, green-toothed, slightly hairy green leaves. Culinary and medicinal.

*Monarda didyma*, Bee Balm Bergamot, Red Bergamot
Hardy, H5 (USDA 7,8), herbaceous perennial. Height: up to 80cm (30in); spread: 45cm (18in). Large red flowers in dense terminal whorls with dark red bracts. Mid-green aromatic green-toothed slightly hairy green leaves. The leaves of this variety can be used with pork, fish and salad dishes. They also make a good cup of tea.

*Monarda citriodora*, Lemon Bergamot
Hardy H3 (USDA 9), annual. Height: up to 1.2m (4ft); spread: 45cm (18in). Beautiful lilac flowers with mauve bracts that have a pink tinge in summer. Bright green, toothed, slightly hairy, lemon-scented leaves. The leaves are great in puddings, savoury dishes and for making cordials. The flowers are also lemon-flavoured.

## Propagation

**Seeds:** only the species, which includes the three listed (so not hybrids or cultivars), will grow true from seed. Sow in early spring into prepared seed trays or modules using a seed compost, place under protection at 18°C (64°F). Germination takes 1–2 weeks. Do not overwater once the seedlings emerge as they are prone to damping off (see page 274).

**Cuttings:** in cool climates, root cuttings from the creeping rhizomes are best taken in the spring and transferred to small pots or modules filled with seed compost. Cuttings from non-flowering stems can be taken in early summer and transferred to prepared small pots or modules using a seed compost.

**Division:** established plants can be divided in the autumn. Either pot up using a soil-based compost or replant into a prepared site in the garden.

*Monarda didyma*, Bee Balm

## Pests and diseases

Slugs love young plants, so it's worth checking early evening and removing them before they have their feast. Mildew is renowned in this species. At the first sight of the mould appearing on the leaves, pick them off and bin them. See page 275 for more information.

## How and where to grow

There is a certain amount of confusion regarding where to position *Monarda fistulosa* in the garden. It likes a well-drained soil and a sunny position. *Monarda didyma* likes a rich fertile soil that retains moisture in the summer and partial shade. Neither like a cold, wet soil. It is worth digging up plants over three years old, removing the dead centre and replanting into a prepared site. Keep your *Monarda* species apart by planting them in different areas of the garden so they do not cross-pollinate, which would make the seed not true to species.

## Growing in containers

Bergamot looks very attractive when grown in a large pot using a soil-based compost. Position the container so that it gets some shade from the midday sun. Feed regularly from spring until autumn with a liquid seaweed fertiliser. Lift the pots in winter, putting them on bricks or stones to aid drainage. Repot each spring.

## Yearly maintenance

**Spring:** sow seeds; divide established plants.

**Summer:** take stem cuttings of cultivars and hybrids.

**Autumn:** after the seeds have set, which are a good bird food, cut back; feed established plants with well-rotted compost; divide established plants.

**Winter:** in very cold hard winters mulch the crowns of the plant with straw or fine bark to provide a bit of protection.

## Harvesting and storing

**Leaves:** collect fresh leaves as desired for use in the kitchen. For the best flavour, use the ones before the plant flowers. The leaves do dry well.

**Flowers:** pick the flowers to use fresh as they open. Cut the flowers for drying when they are just fully opened. They will dry beautifully and keep their colour.

**Seeds:** it is only worth collecting seed if you have planted your species well-spaced apart in the garden. If they are planted near each other, they will be cross-pollinated so the seed will be very variable, which, on a positive point, can create a lovely display of various colours. Collect the flower heads on a dry sunny day when they have changed to a brown colour.

## Culinary uses

**Leaves:** use before the plant flowers as they become bitter as they age. They have a warm, minty, spicy flavour. Use the leaves with cheeses, pork, vegetables, such as cauliflower, and with fish, where the spicy flavour is especially good.

**Flowers:** these can be picked throughout the summer. Remove the flowerets individually from the flower head and scatter over salads, both sweet and savoury.

## Medicinal uses

Medicinally this herb is a stimulant; it is good for colds, catarrh, headaches, fevers and relieves flatulence and nausea. A decoction made from the leaves is a good steam inhalant that soothes bronchial complaints and eases colds. A tea made from the leaves is said to help insomnia, nausea and flatulence. The essential oil is used in aromatherapy to treat depression and fight infections.

*Monarda fistulosa*, Wild Bergamot

# Myrrhis odorata

**Over 40 years ago when I was restoring a beautiful herb garden for a client, I found a herb labelled sweet cicely. I became fascinated by its history and the fact that it was little used these days. With the culinary trend for foraging, this herb will become better known. Everything about this herb smells and tastes of sweet anise, so do not confuse it with its cousin, *Anthriscus sylvestris*, cow parsley, or the infamous and highly poisonous *Oenanthe crocata*, hemlock.**

*Myrrhis odorata*, Sweet Cicely

## History

This is a very ancient herb and can be found growing wild throughout the northern UK. The Greeks called it *seselis* or *seseli*, so it is logical to presume that cicely was derived from this, and the 'sweet' came from its flavour. There are records of the herbalist John Gerard enjoying the roots boiled like parsnips in the 16th century. In the countryside the seeds are known as a wayside nibble. The leaves were used to polish oak panels. On the Isle of Man, sweet cicely is believed to bloom on the Twelfth Night (6 January) or on 'Old Christmas' eve (5 January) and there was a tradition to pick the frothy creamy blooms to take to the church as a herald of the new season.

## Species

*Myrrhis odorata*, Sweet Cicely
Hardy, H5 (USDA 7,8), herbaceous perennial. Height: up to 90cm (3ft); spread: 60cm (24in). Flat umbels of sweetly scented white flowers in early spring until early summer, followed by long angular green seeds that ripen to black. The leaves are fern-like, very divided, and they smell and taste of sweet aniseed when crushed.

## Propagation

**Seeds:** these large seeds need stratification to germinate (see page 18). In cold climates, sow the fresh seed in autumn into prepared seed trays, small pots or modules using three parts soil-based compost mixed with one part perlite and place the container outside to expose it to all weathers. Germination takes place the following spring.

**Cuttings:** take root cuttings in the spring. The easiest way to check the root for new shoots is to look for swellings on the root as this is the sign new shoots will develop at that point. Using a sharp knife, include the new shoot and a chunk of root. Pot up in a small pot using three parts soil-based compost mixed with one part perlite. Do not let the compost dry out and keep the pot frost free until fully rooted.

**Division:** divide established plants in the autumn, but beware, any small roots left will root so make sure you really do want to divide the plant before you start.

## Pests and diseases

Sweet cicely does not often get attacked by pests and only suffers from mildew when grown in a polytunnel, which is often due to restricted air flow.

## How and where to grow

This plant can be invasive, especially in fertile light soil so choose where you plant it carefully. Ideally plant in a soil rich in humus, in light shade. If you do not want this plant to invade your garden, collect the seeds when green to use in salads, then cut back hard and new leaf growth will appear. If you wish to move or remove the plant from the garden, any piece of root left behind will in time produce another plant.

This plant will not grow in humid or hot climates because it needs a good dormant period in winter so that it can produce root followed by lush foliage in early spring.

## Growing in containers

It is not an ideal plant for a container as it has a long tap root. However, if you have a light fertile soil, you will need to contain it, so grow it in a large container, something as large as a dustbin is ideal. Use a soil-based compost and place the container in partial shade. Water regularly through the summer months.

## Yearly maintenance

**Spring:** take root cuttings.

**Summer:** to prevent the seeds self-seeding all round your garden, harvest the seeds in the green before they run into the black and cut the plant back hard to 8cm (3in) above the ground. However, if you want ripe seeds, harvest in late summer for use in the kitchen.

**Autumn:** sow ripe seeds; divided established plants.

**Winter:** no need for protection.

## Harvesting and storing

**Leaves:** pick leaves to use fresh either side of flowering.

**Flowers:** pick flowers when the cluster has nearly fully flowered.

**Seeds:** harvest seeds in the green when required to use fresh. Harvest the seeds when brown and just starting to drop for resowing in the autumn.

## Culinary uses

**Leaves:** the flavour of the leaf is sweet aniseed. Chop finely and stir into salads, dressings and omelettes. Add to soups, stews and to boiling water when cooking cabbage. Add to cream for a sweeter, less fatty taste.

**Flowers:** the whole flower is edible. Remove each individual flower from the cluster making sure all green bits are removed. The sweet anise flavour is lovely with tart fruit dishes. Try it mixed with apple purée, plum fool or rhubarb tarts.

**Seeds:** toss unripe green seeds, which have a sweet anise flavour and a nutty texture, into fruit salads. Chop into ice cream. Use ripe seeds whole in cooked dishes, such as apple pie, otherwise use crushed to flavour soups and sauces.

**Roots:** this can be cooked as a vegetable and served with butter or a white sauce, or allowed to cool, then chopped up and added to salads. Alternatively, it can be eaten raw, peeled and grated and used in a French salad dressing. The best description of the flavour is parsnip with a hint of aniseed.

## Medicinal uses

Medicinally it is used for digestive complaints, coughs and as a pick-me-up tonic. It is the sweet anise flavour of the leaves and seeds which aid digestion of acid, as well as spicy and fatty foods.

**Common names:** Myrtle, Common Myrtle, Mirto

# Myrtus communis

**Myrtle is one of my top must-haves. It looks wonderful growing in the garden or in containers, and is, in my opinion, a very underrated and underused culinary herb. It can transform a summer's barbecue into a Mediterranean feast.**

*Myrtus communis*, Myrtle

## History

Myrtle has been used for over 2,000 years as a flavouring, a perfume and as a medicine. It was sacred to the goddess of love, Venus – her head was crowned with a wreath of myrtle leaves and she was sometimes call Murtia. The plant was reputed to make love grow and also to preserve it, hence today's fashion for brides carrying a sprig of myrtle in their bouquets as a symbol of love and consistency. The Ancient Romans made myrtle wine by immersing the ripe fruit in mosto – grape juice. According to Pliny the Elder (77 AD), the savoury berries were used to prepare a dish called myrtle sausages, and also for seasoning wild boar.

## Species

*Myrtus communis*, Myrtle
Hardy H4 (USDA 8,9), evergreen shrub. Height and spread: up to 3m (9ft). Very attractive fragrant white flowers with dense clusters of golden stamens in summer, followed by blue–black berries. Oval dark green leaves that are very aromatic when crushed and a great substitute for bay leaves.

*Myrtus communis* subsp. *tarentina* , Tarentum Myrtle
Hardy, H4 (USDA 8,9), evergreen shrub. Height and spread: up to 2m (6ft). Small white flowers with golden stamens, followed by blue–black berries. Small, oval with a point, shiny, dark green, aromatic leaves. The berries and leaves can be used in cooking. This makes a beautiful hedge; I was so excited when I saw it in Granada, Spain, at the Alhambra, either side of the rill.

*Myrtus communis* 'Variegata', Variegated Myrtle
Hardy, H4 (USDA 8,9), evergreen shrub. Height and spread: up to 2m (6ft). White flowers with a hint of pink, followed by blue–black berries. Oval, light green and cream variegated, aromatic leaves. The berries and leaves can be used in cooking.

*Myrtus communis* 'Jekka's All Gold'
Hardy, H3 (USDA 9), evergreen shrub. Height and spread: up to 2m (6ft). White flowers with a hint of pink, followed by blue–black berries. Oval, light green and yellow variegated, aromatic leaves. The berries and leaves can be used in cooking.

## Propagation

**Seeds:** remove the pulp of the ripe berry from around the seed in spring. Sow into a prepared seed tray or modules using three parts seed compost and one part coarse horticultural sand. Water the compost prior to sowing, sow thinly, cover with coarse horticultural sand and place under protection at 18°C (64°F). Germination takes 1–2 months, though it can be shorter or longer. Once rooted, pot up into small pots using three parts soil-based compost mixed with one part coarse horticultural sand. Grow on in containers for a least 2 years before planting out. It will take 5–7 years for seed-raised plants to flower.

**Cuttings:** take softwood cuttings in summer from non-flowering shoots into small pots or modules filled with three parts seed compost mixed with one part perlite. When well-rooted, pot up and grow on in a container for two seasons before planting into a prepared site in the garden.

## Pests and diseases

Myrtle suffers from two pests – scale insect and myrtle thrip, especially if you are growing it in a container and bringing it in for the winter months. For more information on both, see pages 270 and 272.

## How and where to grow

Myrtle is much hardier than some would think. *Myrtus communis* can withstand -8°C (18°F) and variegated forms down to -5°C (23°F). It is the wet that will kill it quicker than the cold. Plant in a well-drained soil in full sun. Where the site is exposed to cold winds plant against a south- or west-facing wall. This is an extremely tolerant plant, in the garden only feed it once in spring with well-rotted compost. Overfed plants will not flower. Myrtle can be clipped in the autumn in Mediterranean climates or spring in colder climates.

## Growing in containers

All varieties of myrtle look lovely growing in containers. Use three parts soil-based compost mixed with one part coarse horticultural sand. Do not over-pot, it prefers being pot-bound. Liquid feed with a seaweed fertiliser throughout the growing season. Lift pots off the ground in winter and place on bricks or stones to increase drainage.

## Yearly maintenance

**Spring:** sow seeds; in cold climates, trim back growth to regain shape; take softwood cuttings.

**Summer:** take semi-ripe cuttings.

**Autumn:** bring containers inside or lift on to bricks.

**Winter:** protect from hard frosts and/or excessively wet weather.

## Harvesting and storing

**Leaves:** the best flavoured leaves are in midsummer from the new shoots that have started to change colour from light bright green to dark green – these are the ones to preserve in oil or dry. The mature leaves, which can be harvested all year round, can be used in roasts and in stews.

**Flowers:** pick the flowers in the summer to use fresh as required.

**Berries:** pick the berries in late autumn when they turn a beautiful blue black and are slightly soft to the touch – use fresh or conserve.

## Culinary uses

**Leaves:** the leaves have a slightly bitter, aromatic taste so use carefully. They can be added to soups, casseroles, stews, vegetable or poultry and meat dishes. Remove before serving – like bay leaves, they are not eaten but used to flavour. The straight branches of *Myrtus tarentina* are great to use as natural barbecue skewers, ideal for grilling, kebabs – both meat and vegetable – sausages, fish and peppers. Foods flavoured with myrtle smoke are common in rural areas of Italy and Sardinia.

**Flowers:** the flowers have a warm and spicy flavour when dried.

**Berries:** the ripe berries have a very dry spicy flavour that goes well with strong meat dishes, such as boar, duck and quail. The dried berries can be ground like pepper – they are known as 'mursins' in the Middle East and used as a spice. In Sardinia they make a delicious liqueur from the berries called mirto. I have made a South Gloucestershire version and it was tasty!

## Medicinal uses

Myrtle leaves and berries have antiseptic properties. The flower buds and flowers contain vitamin C and citric acid.

# Ocimum basilicum

**I think that basil might merit a complete book on its own. It is one of the herbs that never ceases to amaze me, thanks to its culinary delights and its astounding medicinal properties. When I started herb farming over four decades ago, I was told to use it sparingly. Now I use it with panache in many dishes from pasta to custards, teas, salads and sauces. It is one of the must-have culinary delights, which can transform a meal into a feast. It is also nature's fly deterrent.**

*Ocimum basilicum* 'Horapha Nanum', Thai Basil

## History

Before becoming king of the kitchen this herb was steeped in history and folklore. It is said that it was found growing around Christ's tomb after the resurrection. Some Greek Orthodox churches use basil to prepare their holy water and put pots of it below their altars. In the 16th century sweet basil was used as a snuff for colds and to clear the brain and cure headaches. You can find different forms of basil growing throughout the world and each culture uses it differently. In the Democratic Republic of Congo the leaves are still used to ward off fate and to protect oneself from evil spirits.

## Species

There are many cultivars of basil and each year I have had the pleasure of growing a new one. Here are a few that are great in the kitchen, including the wonderful *Ocimum tenuiflorum* which not only has a wonderful history, it is also an important medicinal herb.

*Ocimum basilicum*, Sweet Basil, Genovese Basil
Tender, H1C (USDA 11), annual. Height: 45cm (18in); spread: 30cm (12in). Clusters of small white tubular flowers in summer that have a lovely sweet basil flavour. Green, oval, pointed leaves that smell wonderful when crushed. This is the basil most commonly found in the supermarkets and is the main one used for making pesto.

*Ocimum basilicum* 'Cinnamon', Cinnamon Basil
Tender, H1C (USDA 11), annual. Height: 45cm (18in); spread: 30cm (12in). Clusters of small pink/mauve tubular flowers in summer. Dark purple/brown stems. Olive green/brown, oval, pointed, slightly serrated leaves that have a very spicy flavour. Lovely in stir-fry dishes.

*Ocimum minimum* 'Greek', Greek Basil
Tender, H1C (USDA 11), annual. Height: 23cm (9in); spread: 15cm (6in). Clusters of small white tubular flowers in summer. Small green, oval, pointed leaves. In Greece pots of basil are placed on gate posts as a sign of welcome, or on tables to keep flies away.

*Ocimum basilicum* 'Dark Opal', Dark Opal Basil, Purple Basil
Tender, H1C (USDA 11), annual. Height: 45cm (18in); spread: 30cm (12in). Clusters of small pink/mauve tubular flowers in summer. Light purple stems. Dark purple, oval, pointed leaves that have a very spicy warm flavour. Great added to rice and pastas as a stunning colour contrast.

*Ocimum basilicum* 'Horapha Nanum', Thai Basil, Dwarf Anise
Tender, H1C (USDA 11), annual. Height: 30cm (12in); spread: 20cm (8in). Clusters of small mulberry/purple tubular flowers in summer. Dark purple/brown stem. Olive green/purple oval, pointed, hairy and slightly serrated leaves that have a very pungent scent and flavour. Used prolifically in Thai and Vietnamese cooking.

*Ocimum basilicum* var. *purpurascens* x *kilimandscharicum*, African Blue Basil
Tender, H1C (USDA 11), short-lived evergreen perennial. Height: up to 70cm (28in); spread: 40cm (16in). Clusters of small pink/mauve tubular flowers in summer. Dark purple, hairy, oval, pointed leaves with a camphor scent. The leaves are used in cooking with vegetable dishes.

*Ocimum tenuiflorum*, Holy Basil, Tulsi, Purple Tulsi
Tender, H1C (USDA 11), annual. Height: 40cm (16in); spread: 30cm (12in). Clusters of small pink/mauve tubular flowers in summer. Olive green/brown/purple oval, pointed, hairy and slightly serrated leaves that have a very pungent scent and flavour. Tulsi is considered one of the sacred plants of India – it forms an integral part of Hindu ceremonies and sacraments associated with the goddess Lakshmi, wife of the Hindu god Vishnu. In a Hindu wedding, the parents of the bride present the groom with a tulsi leaf as they give their daughter away. As a show of wealth this leaf is often made of solid gold and covered in precious gems. Current research has shown that this basil has the ability to reduce blood sugar levels and is used in the treatment of some types of diabetes.

*Ocimum* x *africanum*, Lemon Basil, Thai Lemon Basil
Tender, H1C (USDA 11), annual. Height: 40cm (16in); spread: 30cm (12in). Clusters of small white tubular flowers in summer that have a lovely sweet, fruity basil flavour. Bright green, oval, pointed leaves that smell of lemon when crushed.

## Propagation

**Seeds:** sow seeds in early spring into prepared modules or a seed tray using a seed compost that has been watered well before sowing. Cover with perlite and place under protection at 18°C (64°F). Keep watering to the absolute minimum until germination has taken place, after 5–10 days. Once germination starts, water only when necessary in the morning and before midday, this will prevent the seedlings from damping off (see page 274). As the seedlings emerge, remove them from the extra heat, place in a warm, light position and grow on. Plant out in the garden when all threat of frost has gone, in a very sheltered position or pot up. Alternatively, in warm climates with a minimum night temperature of 13°C (55°F), sow directly into a prepared site in the garden.

**Cuttings:** over the past two decades I have been taking cuttings from my spring-sown plants in early summer because cuttings grow twice as fast as seed-raised basil. Transfer the cutting into either modules or small pots filled with three parts seed compost mixed with one part perlite. Place under protection at 18°C (64°F). Rooting takes 7–10 days. Once rooted, pot up or plant out depending on night temperatures.

## Pests and diseases

Because basil originated from a tropical climate, it dislikes fluctuating temperatures. For this reason, water before midday, which will help prevent mildew and/or damping off (see page 274). It is prone to attack from slugs, white fly, red spider mite and leaf hopper. For more information please see pages 267–272.

*Ocimum basilicum* 'Dark Opal', Purple Basil

## How and where to grow

Plant in a well-drained fertile soil in a sunny warm situation, with a bit of shelter from the midday sun. If you live in a cool, damp climate or have a cold soil, for example a clay soil, then, if you want a good crop and to save disappointment, it is far better to grow basil either in a greenhouse or in containers.

## Growing in containers

Basil is ideal for growing in containers. Use three parts soil-based compost mixed with one part horticultural grit. Topdress with horticultural grit once planted. Basil is a good companion plant; it repels white fly, aphids, fruit fly, also flies from the kitchen. Pinch out the growing tips of shoots regularly to prevent flowering. The reason for this is that as soon as it flowers the stems can become woody and the flavour in the leaves changes and becomes bitter. Feed weekly with a liquid seaweed fertiliser from spring until autumn. Basil's excellence in the kitchen more than compensates for the trouble needed to grow it.

## Yearly maintenance

**Spring:** sow seeds.

**Summer:** take cuttings; keep pinching out to inhibit flowering.

**Autumn:** collect seeds; bring in pot plants before the frosts start.

**Winter:** clean seeds ready for sowing in the spring.

*Ocimum basilicum* var. *purpurascens* x *kilimandscharicum*, African Blue Basil

## Harvesting and storing

**Leaves:** the leaves can be picked for preserving from early to midsummer. They do not freeze well as they become slimy when thawed so the best preserving methods for use in the home are either in oils, vinegars or butters.

**Flowers:** the flowers are best used fresh. Gently pull each one away from the flowering spikes before adding to the dish.

**Seeds:** harvest the seeds in late summer/early autumn, once they turn beige/brown and are crispy dry. Remove the seeds from the chaff, store in a dry container for sowing the following spring.

*Ocimum minimum* 'Greek', Greek Basil

## Culinary uses

**Leaves:** basil in any form is a culinary delight. Tear the fresh leaves and add them to salads, tomato dishes and pasta dishes. A word of warning: the flavour can be ruined if cooked for too long – basil is best added to warm dishes at the end of cooking and the heat will release the flavour and aroma. The leaves are rarely used in Indian cooking, more often they are used to make herbal teas, combined with other herb seeds or simply with Indian tea leaves to make a refreshing drink. In Thailand, Vietnam and Malaysia they are added to soups and fish dishes.

**Flowers:** the flowers are very good in salads – both savoury and sweet – and jellies, especially with fruits, such as pears or strawberries. They taste like a sweet version of the leaf, slightly spicy with a hint of mint.

## Medicinal uses

Medicinally, it is used to treat bronchitis, colds, fevers and stress. The juice of the leaves is used for skin complaints, the essential oil is used to treat ear infections and as an insect repellent. Current research has shown that basil has the ability to reduce blood sugar levels and is used in the treatment of some types of diabetes. Rubbing basil juice on to exposed skin repels mosquitoes, which is great on a summer's evening.

*Ocimum tenuiflorum*, Purple Tulsi

# Olea europaea

**Nine years ago I planted an olive tree in the Herbetum. One winter it got hit by some very cold nights, then snow followed by a bitter spring. I thought I had lost it – nearly all the leaves had turned black. I checked the branches and they were alive, so rather than dig the tree up, I cut it hard back in mid-spring. By early summer the branches had masses of new growth sprouting and the tree is now looking beautiful. The lesson that olive tree taught me was to never to give up on a plant; look, check, read and believe.**

## History

With its beautiful gnarled bark and twisted trunk, the olive tree is one of the oldest domesticated plants in the Mediterranean. In the Old Testament, the dove returned to Noah's Ark with a sprig of olive in its beak, which showed that the flood waters were abating. It has been the symbol of peace for many centuries. The olive tree is steeped in the history and the culture of the Mediterranean. The Greeks and Romans valued the oil; the winners of the Olympic Games were initially crowned with the leaves, though later the bay became the wreath. According to Homer, green olives were brought to Greece by Cecrops, the founder of Athens and by 571 BC the olive had reached Italy.

## Species

*Olea europea*, Olive
Hardy, H4 (USDA 8,9), evergreen tree. Height: up to 10m (32ft); spread: up to 5m (16ft). Numerous clusters of small, creamy-white, fragrant flowers in early summer followed by green fruit which ripens to black. Oval green/grey, leathery leaves with silvery undersides.

There are many olive cultivars available, and many are self-sterile, which is why they are often planted in pairs or in alternating rows. Some European cultivars include: 'Arbequina', a small brown olive from Catalonia, Spain; 'Kalamata', a large black olive from Greece; 'Picholine', a long medium green olive from France; 'Queen Manzanillas' from Spain, which are the biggest of the green pickling olive varieties.

## Propagation

**Seeds:** before sowing the seeds they will need to be scarified by cutting a small nick in the rounded end of the seed (see page 18). Sow the fresh prepared seeds in early autumn into seed trays or modules filled with three parts seed compost mixed with one part coarse horticultural sand. Press the prepared seeds into the compost, cover with the coarse sand and place under protection at 18°C (64°F). Germination can happen in 3–4 weeks. If it doesn't, remove the trays from the heat, but keep in a greenhouse. Germination can take anything up to a year. Please note when growing from seed the plant may not grow true to type.

**Cuttings:** take cuttings from new growth in summer. Use three parts seed compost mixed with one part coarse horticultural sand. Do not allow the cutting to dry out. It takes anything from 4–8 weeks to root. Once rooted, pot up into small pots using three parts seed compost mixed with one part coarse horticultural sand. Grow all young plants on in a container for at least two years before planting out; four years in cool climates.

## Pests and diseases

Olive rarely suffers from pests or diseases when grown outside, however when grown as a container plant and wintered in a polytunnel or cold greenhouse, it can be attacked by the scale insect. Either rub them off by hand, or use a horticultural soap spray following the manufacturer's instructions (see page 270).

## How and where to grow

Olives prefer a well-drained, light soil that is lime-based. Due to climate change, they do now bear fruit outside of the Mediterranean region and there is a productive grove in Essex in the UK. It is the wet combined with cold that kills the plant quicker than just cold, dry weather. As olives are produced on the previous year's growth, only do a remedial prune to remove dead, diseased or crossing branches if you require a good crop. If, however, you have a young plant that has become leggy then prune much harder as it produces new growth off old wood. An olive tree rarely produces a good crop of olives until it is over eight years old. In summer, do not let the tree dry out. Feed every autumn with well-rotted manure or compost.

## Growing in containers

Olives make a very attractive container plant; they are very tolerant. Use a soil-based compost. Feed container-grown plants weekly from spring until autumn with a seaweed liquid fertiliser. Lift the container in winter on to bricks or stones to increase drainage. If the night temperatures consistently fall below -8°C (18°F) you will need to wrap the tree in horticultural fleece

## Yearly maintenance

**Spring:** lightly prune, remove dead or diseased branches.

**Summer:** take cuttings from new growth.

**Autumn:** sow fresh seeds.

**Winter:** feed established trees with well-rotted manure or compost; lift container plants on to bricks, or bring into a dry greenhouse, polytunnel or cold frame.

## Harvesting and storing

**Leaves:** pick leaves to use fresh as required.

**Fruit:** harvest the fruit in the autumn until early winter depending on the climate and cultivar. The fruit is either green (unripe) or black (ripe) and all must be treated before they are stored or eaten (see culinary uses).

## Culinary uses

**Fruit:** the raw green or black fresh fruit is unpalatable and very bitter. The easiest way to make it palatable is to soak it in a brine solution (10g (0.5oz) salt per 100ml (3.5fl oz) water) for a couple of months. There are nearly as many methods of preserving olives as there are cultivars so choose one that suits your palate. The oil extracted from the fruit is used in a multitude of Mediterranean dishes.

## Medicinal uses

Medicinally the leaves can be infused and used as an antiseptic wash for cuts and grazes or made into a tea to lower the blood pressure and relieve nervous tension (it's not very pleasant-tasting). The oil is good for circulatory diseases and helps improve digestion, especially if one suffers from indigestion. Olive oil is one of the safest laxatives.

*Olea europaea*, Olive

**Common names:** Oregano, Wild Marjoram, Winter Marjoram, Mountain Mint

# Origanum vulgare

**I am often asked what the difference is between oregano and marjoram and the answer is that they are from the same family *Origanum*, it is the use of the common name that causes the confusion. It also depends on where you live in the world as to which common name is used – for *Origanum vulgare* is known as wild marjoram, oregano and winter marjoram; the only species to mention the word marjoram is *Origanum majorana*, therefore it would follow that only this is true marjoram. When in doubt return to the botanical name. If you have ever been lucky enough to go to Crete and wander through the hills you will agree with the origins of the word 'oregano'. It is said to have been derived from the Greek *oros* meaning mountain and *ganos* meaning joy and beauty, hence 'joy of the mountain', which it certainly is.**

## History

Aristotle reported that tortoises that swallowed a snake would immediately eat oregano to prevent death; this gave rise to the belief that it could be taken as an antidote to poisoning. In medieval times marjoram was combined with alecost to flavour ale. This was before hops were introduced to this country in the reign of Henry the VIII. Geoffrey Grigson's *The Englishman's Flora*, first published in 1958, is illustrated with woodcuts from the 16th century, one of which shows an Italian lady watering marjoram. Under the woodcut are the following words: 'confortat cerebrum et omnia viscera' meaning 'comforts the head and all internal organs'.

## Species

I have a rather greedy passion for the *Lamiaceae* family. *Origanum* is no exception as I grow over 25 different species, cultivars and hybrids. Some are great for attracting pollinators and some transform a meal into a feast. I have chosen just seven of my favourites. They illustrate that whichever name you choose, *Origanum* is a quintessential herb: it looks good, smells wonderful, tastes amazing and does you good.

*Origanum vulgare*, Oregano, Wild Marjoram
Hardy, H5 (USDA 7,8), evergreen sub shrub. Height and spread: 45cm (18in). Clusters of tiny, tubular mauve flowers in summer. Dark green, aromatic, hairy leaves, which form a mat in winter. The vigour and flavour of this plant can vary greatly; it is dependent on the country, planting situation and amount and strength of the sun.

*Origanum vulgare* 'Compactum', Compact Oregano, Compact Marjoram
Hardy, H4 (USDA 8,9), evergreen sub shrub. Height and spread: 30cm (12in). Lovely large clusters of small, tubular pink flowers. Oval, green, aromatic leaves, which form a mat in winter. Neat compact habit. In the kitchen it's good with meat and vegetable dishes.

*Origanum majorana (Majorana hortensis)*, Sweet Marjoram
Hardy, H3 (USDA 9), perennial, often grown as an annual in cool climates. Height and spread: 30cm (12in). Tiny, tubular white flowers that grow around a green centre in a knot shape. Very aromatic, pale green, soft, oval leaves. Great culinary flavour, lovely with tomatoes and on pizza.

*Origanum* x *majoricum*, Italian Marjoram
Hardy, H3 (USDA 9), evergreen sub shrub. Height and spread: 45cm (18in). Tiny, tubular white flowers covered in pale green bracts. Small, very aromatic, pale green, soft oval leaves. In the kitchen it's wonderful with tomato, pasta, pizza and breads. Medicinal. Native of Italy.

*Origanum Dictamnus*, Dittany of Crete, Cretan Oregano
Hardy, H4 (USDA 8,9), evergreen sub shrub. Height: up to 15cm (6in); spread: 40cm (15in). The tiny, tubular pink flowers are surrounded by grey/green bracts that turn to pink/purple/rust colour with maturity. Highly aromatic, round, grey/green leaves are covered in soft white woolly down. Culinary and medicinal. Native of Crete.

*Origanum* 'Jekka's Beauty'
Hardy, H4 (USDA 8,9), evergreen sub shrub. Height: up to 20cm (8in); spread: 30cm (12in). Tiny, pretty pink flowers surrounded by grey/green bracts that turn deep pink/purple as they mature. Aromatic, round, slightly hairy grey/green leaves. Edible flowers. Lovely grown in containers. Great for pollinators.

*Origanum syriacum*, Middle East Oregano, Za'atar
Hardy, H4 (USDA 8,9), evergreen sub shrub. Height: up to 60cm (24in); spread: 45cm (18in). Clusters of white knotted flowers. Oval, grey/green, slightly hairy leaves that have a strong flavour. For cooking, they have a very spicy flavour that works with meat and vegetables. Traditional medicinal herb. Native of Syria.

## Propagation

**Seeds:** oregano rarely grows true from seed, so if you want identical plants it is better to grow it from cuttings. The seeds are very fine. Ideally mix them with fine horticultural sand prior to sowing into prepared seed trays or modules using a seed compost. This will help to disperse the seed on the surface of the compost and will also help to stop overcrowding of seedlings. Once sown, do not cover with compost or perlite. Place under protection at 18°C (64°F). Germination takes 10–20 days. Do not overwater once the seedlings emerge as they are prone to damping off (see page 274).

**Cuttings:** all *Origanum* can be raised from cuttings taken from the new non-flowering growth from early summer until early autumn, then either transferred to small pots or modules with three parts seed compost mixed with one part perlite. Once rooted, pot up into small pots using three parts soil-based potting compost with one part horticultural grit or horticultural sharp sand.

**Division:** in warm climates, divide established plants in spring or after flowering in late summer. Replant either into pots using a soil-based compost or into a prepared site in the garden.

## Pests and diseases

Just occasionally, if the new growth is very lush due to the soil or compost being too rich, oregano will suffer from green fly and leaf hopper. For more information on both pests see pages 267 and 269. Powdery mildew can be a problem if growing oregano inside in a polytunnel or greenhouse. If possible move the plants outside, as this is caused by lack of air movement, or treat with bicarbonate of soda as per page 276.

*Origanum dictamnus*, Cretan Oregano

## How and where to grow

The wet will kill even hardy oreganos so make sure that the soil is well drained, or rocky, especially if you live in areas where there is high rainfall in the cold winter months. Choose a sunny position – this is especially good for the culinary oreganos as the sun brings the oils to the surface, which give a wonderful flavour when used in cooking. Sweet marjoram is a very good companion plant; it deters aphids and is said to improve the flavour of vegetables when planted between rows. Cut back all oreganos after flowering to encourage them to put on new growth and give added protection for the winter.

## Growing in containers

All oreganos can be grown successfully in containers. Use three parts soil-based compost mixed with one part horticultural grit. When growing *Origanum dictamnus* in containers, topdress with horticultural grit to stop the beautiful soft leaves being damaged by rain and watering. Liquid feed the containers once a month from spring until autumn with a seaweed fertiliser. In winter, if you are not bringing in the containers, lift them on to bricks or stones to increase drainage.

*Origanum x majoricum*, Italian Marjoram

## Yearly maintenance

**Spring:** sow seeds; divide established plants.

**Summer:** in early summer take softwood cuttings; cut back after flowering; divide established plants in late summer.

**Autumn:** cut back all the year's growth to 5cm (2in) to help the plants produce new growth for winter protection.

**Winter:** lift container plants; bring in tender varieties in a wet, cold climate and winter in a cold greenhouse.

## Harvesting and storing

**Leaves:** the best flavoured leaves come from the new growth in the spring or, after flowering, the new growth in the early autumn. They can be used fresh or dried. The winter mat-forming leaves are much milder but can be still harvested when required.

**Flowers:** pick just as they open throughout the summer.

## Culinary uses

**Leaves:** the leaves are a favourite in the kitchen. Oregano combines well with tomato dishes, is renowned with pasta, good with meat, especially lamb, is great with fish and also lovely in marinades. Sweet marjoram and Italian marjoram are the most likely to be found on pizzas and added to dried herb mixtures; it is also an ingredient in a bouquet garni.

**Flowers:** scatter the flowers over salads, soups and roast vegetables.

## Medicinal uses

Marjoram and oregano have a very soothing effect on the digestive system; they stimulate digestive juices, which help to break down rich and heavy foods. They are also highly valued for treating dyspepsia, loss of appetite and colic nausea. Sweet marjoram tea is a general tonic, helping to ease bad colds, headaches and insomnia; it also has tranquillising effect on the nerves. Chewing the leaf will give temporary relief to toothache. It is also said to lower one's sexual drive. Oregano is one of the best antiseptics owing to its high content of thymol oil. It is used in the treatment of respiratory conditions, such as coughs, bronchitis and asthma.

**Right** Assorted *Origanum*

# Papaver rhoeas

**This beautiful herb, with its glorious crêpe-paper-like blooms, adds colour and charm to any garden. I particularly like the fact that it generously self-seeds itself and offers a different display each year. Sadly, I have recently learnt that growing your own opium poppy (*Papaver somniferum*) in the USA is illegal so there the seed is imported for use in the kitchen.**

*Papaver rhoeas*, Field Poppy

## History

Cultivation of poppies dates back to 3,000 BC, according to clay tablets found in the Sumerian city of Nippur. And in Europe, poppy seeds were found next to dried corpses in the Murciélagos cave in southern Spain that date from between 4,000 and 3,500 BC. According to the *Doctrine of Signatures* (see page 278), opium poppy belongs to the moon, which is fitting as it induces sleep and turbulent dreams (*somniferum* means sleep-bringing). There is a legend about how the opium poppy was created. Apparently Buddha, not wanting to fall asleep, cut off his eyelids and where they fell upon the earth, a plant sprang up bearing beautiful mauve petals.

## Species

*Papaver rhoeas*, Field Poppy
Hardy, H5 (USDA 7,8), annual. Height: up to 60cm (24in) when in flower; spread: 45cm (18in). Brilliant scarlet flowers with black basal blotch from summer to early autumn. The mid-green leaf has three lobes and is irregularly toothed.

*Papaver somniferum*, Opium Poppy
Hardy, H5 (USDA 7,8), annual. Height: up to 90cm (36in) when in flower; spread: 45cm (18in). Large, pale lilac, white, purple or variegated flowers in summer. The blue/green leaf is long with toothed margins. There are double-flowered varieties known as *Papaver somniferum* 'Paeoniiflorum Group'.

## Propagation

**Seeds:** sow fresh seeds in the autumn. Be aware the seed is very fine so mix it with fine horticultural sand to prevent over-sowing. Prepare seed or plug trays with seed compost, water in, sow on the surface , do not cover with compost. Cover with a sheet of glass or Perspex and put the containers outside to experience the winter frosts. If you live in an area that does not get frost, after Christmas or in very early spring place the container in the refrigerator for a month, then place the container in a cold greenhouse. When the seedlings are large enough, plant out in the garden in a prepared site. Alternatively, sow the seeds, mixed with fine horticultural sand, directly into a prepared site in autumn. Mark the spot to remind yourself where you sowed. Check them once the days start to get longer and the temperature becomes more clement. Thin the seedlings if required, but a good group is very attractive in summer.

## Pests and diseases

In the majority of cases the annual poppies are free from pests and diseases.

## How and where to grow

Poppies are one of the most colourful flowers to grow in the garden and when allowed to self-seed, a kaleidoscopic combination of colours will result with other plants in the garden and themselves. The opium poppy can not only vary in colour, it can vary from single to double flowered. They all prefer a sunny site and a well-drained fertile soil.

## Growing in containers

All the annual poppies look lovely growing in containers. It is best to combine them with other plants with which they look great, such as oxeye daisy, Roman chamomile and cornflowers – you will have your own mini wildflower pot. The opium poppy also looks good growing with a white trailing geranium or even bronze bugle. In both cases make sure the container is large enough and use a soil-based compost. Place the container in full sun out of the wind and water well during the summer months. Refrain from feeding with liquid fertiliser as this will inhibit flowering and produce far too much leaf.

## Yearly maintenance

**Spring:** plant the wintered seedlings in the garden.

**Summer:** deadhead flowers to prolong flowering and prevent self-seeding; collect seed.

**Autumn:** sow fresh seed; dig up dead plants.

**Winter:** protect young plants from hard frosts.

## Harvesting and storing

Harvest both the field poppy and the opium poppy seed – the latter is not narcotic – in late summer when the seed pods turn brown. Collect on a dry day. The seed must be ripe if it is to be stored otherwise it will become mouldy. The best way to store seeds for use in the kitchen is to put them into a container and pop them into the freezer.

## Culinary uses

The ripe seeds of annual poppies can be used on bread, cakes and biscuits and have a good nutty flavour. They can also be added to curries for texture and flavour and are great in salad dressings. They are transformed in flavour when toasted.

## Medicinal uses

The flowers of the field poppy have long been used as a painkiller for soothing mild aches and pains (e.g. toothache, earache and sore throat), as a mild sedative/relaxant, an expectorant for treating catarrh and coughs, as a digestive, and even for reducing the appearance of wrinkles and in lipstick. The opium poppy is renowned for inducing sleep.

*Papaver somniferum*, Opium Poppy

# Perilla frutescens

**Until recently, this Far Eastern herb was relatively unknown as a culinary delight in western countries. Even in the early 1980s purple perilla was being used in the UK as a spectacular spot bedding plant rather than in the kitchen. I discovered its culinary prowess about 30 years ago at the same time as I was exhibiting it at one of the RHS's London flower shows; it very quickly became my signature plant at the Chelsea Flower Show. I particularly love the dark purple shiso which, when planted next to green-leafed herbs, really showed them off. Interestingly, it is now a chef's designer herb, often served as a cress herb in which the flavours of the leaves are intensified.**

*Perilla frutescens* var. *purpurascens*, Purple Shiso

## History

The leaves and seeds of shiso have been widely used in China since 500 AD, both in the kitchen and medicinally to treat morning sickness. It was introduced to Japan from China where it has been used in Japanese cuisine for hundreds of years, The name 'beefsteak plant' refers to the purple shiso leaves looking like a large slice of raw beef. The name originated in the USA, where it has become a naturalised wild plant in many southern and eastern states.

## Species

*Perilla frutescens*, Perilla
Hardy, H2 (USDA 10), annual. Height: up to 1.2m (4ft); spread: 60cm (24in). Small mauve flowers in summer and large, aromatic green leaves that have a brown tinge on the underside and a serrated edge. In the USA this herb has become a toxic weed to livestock; it is not the same as the Chinese or Japanese shiso.

*Perilla frutescens* var. *frutescens*, Zi Su, Egoma
Hardy, H2 (USDA 10), annual. Height: up to 1.2m (4ft); spread: 60cm (24in). Small mauve flowers in summer and large, aromatic green leaves with a hint of brown and a deep purple underside. This is an important culinary and medicinal herb from Korea.

*Perilla frutescens* var. *crispa*, Green Shiso, Green Cumin, Aoshiso
Hardy, H2 (USDA 10), annual. Height: up to 1.2m (4ft); spread: 60cm (24in). Small white flowers in summer. Deeply cut green leaf with crinkled edges. Aromatic when crushed or eaten. There can be considerable variation in seed-raised plants, the flowers can be cream in colour or even pink and the leaves smooth. Green leaf shiso is the variety most commonly seen in Japanese markets; it is used as a vegetable.

*Perilla frutescens var. purpurascens*, Purple Shiso, Beefsteak Plant
Hardy, H3 (USDA 9), annual. Height and spread: 50cm (20in). Pink flowers in summer. Deeply cut dark purple leaf with crinkled bronzed edges. Aromatic when crushed or eaten. There can be considerable variation in seed-raised plants; the flowers can be red and the leaves smoother.

## Propagation

**Seeds:** sow seeds in spring, into prepared seed or module trays using a seed compost. Place under protection at 18°C (64°F). Germination takes 1–2 weeks. Top tip: do not overwater once the seedlings start emerging as they can be prone to damping off (see page 274), especially if the nights are cold. Alternatively, sow in late spring into prepared open ground, when the air temperature does not fall below 8°C (46°F) at night. Germination takes 14–20 days.

**Cuttings:** take cuttings from non-flowering shoots in early summer and transfer either to small pots or modules filled with three parts seed compost mixed with one part perlite. Once fully rooted, either pot up using a soil-based compost or plant out into a prepared site in the garden.

## Pests and diseases

Beware of caterpillars, especially in late summer. Hand-pick them off as soon as you spot them.

## How and where to grow

Shiso prefers a fertile, well-drained soil that has been prepared with well-rotted compost or leaf mould the previous autumn. In hot dry summers, water regularly, especially if you are cropping for use in the kitchen.

## Growing in containers

This herb looks lovely growing in containers, especially the purple-leafed varieties. Plant in a soil-based compost. Place the container in a sunny position. Water regularly and liquid feed weekly either with seaweed or comfrey following the manufacturer's instructions. Keep pinching out the growing tips to maintain shape and to produce a bushy plant.

## Yearly maintenance

**Spring:** sow seeds.

**Summer:** take cuttings from non-flowering shoots; keep pinching out the growing tips to maintain shape and produce a bushy productive plant.

**Autumn:** harvest the seeds; prepare the garden with a good feed.

**Winter:** clean the seeds for next year.

## Harvesting and storing

**Leaves:** the leaves can be picked fresh as required. Picking the growing tips will keep the plant more productive than picking the side leaves.

**Flowers:** harvest the sweet flowers just as they open.

**Seeds:** harvest the seeds when they are beige/brown in colour in late summer; they have a very interesting, rather sweet, flavour. Shiso is grown as a seed crop in Japan and northern India, it is then crushed and the oil is extracted; it is similar to linseed oil (see page 162).

## Culinary uses

**Leaves:** shiso is sometimes confused with its cousin basil (*Ocimum*), however, the flavour is very different. In my opinion, it is a mixture of cumin and nutmeg with a hint of plum for the purple variety and anise for the green variety. Purple shiso is used as a dye for pickling fruit and vegetables, as a side dish with rice in the form of a dried powder, as an ingredient in cake mixes and as a flavouring in beverages. Green shiso is used as a vegetable, while its leaves are used as a wrapping for rice cakes, in salads and tempura. The three- to six-week-old seedlings or sprouts are used as a garnish.

**Flowers:** the flower heads are used as a condiment with sushi.

**Seeds:** the seed from green shiso is used as a condiment and in pickles. The essential oil extracted from the leaf and flowering parts contains a substance that is a thousand times sweeter than sugar, which is used in confectionery.

## Medicinal uses

Shiso is used in both traditional Chinese medicine and in the Japanese pharmacy. It is one of the strongest natural antioxidants. It has been under research at Osaka University in Japan where they have found that it is more powerful than vitamin C. It is also a good first aid herb – the leaves, stems and seeds have many therapeutic uses, including easing hiccups, coughs and colds.

# Persicaria odorata

**The first time I ate the leaves of this herb I was completely taken by surprise. To begin with the taste is mild with a hint of lime and spice, then as the flavour developed it became hot and peppery. I was given this herb by a friend, who was an extremely good plant collector who specialised in water plants. He was given this herb by a nursery in Australia, which in turn received it from some Vietnamese boat people. In Australia it is called Vietnamese mint, which is a misnomer as it is not a member of the mint family; it is a member of the knotweed family.**

## History

There is a long history of this herb being grown under cultivation throughout Southeast Asia and used as a culinary herb. Medicinally, it also has been, and still is, used to treat indigestion, flatulence and stomach aches. It is reputedly eaten by Buddhist monks to suppress sexual urges. There is now interesting research into the essential oil from Vietnamese coriander, called 'kesom oil' for use in food flavouring.

## Species

*Persicaria odorata*, Vietnamese Coriander, Rau Ram
Tender, H2 (USDA 10), perennial. Height and spread: 45cm (18in), however it can spread much further because where a stem touches the ground it will root. Small, attractive, creamy-white flowers in summer, rarely produced under cultivation and in cold climates. Narrow, pointed green leaves with a brown/maroon V-shaped marking near the base, which are highly aromatic when crushed.

*Persicaria hydropiper* var. *rubra*, Red Water Pepper
Tender, H1C (USDA 11), perennial. Height: up to 70cm (28in); spread: 45cm (18in), however it can spread much further because where a stem touches the ground it will root. Attractive pink flowers in summer. Dark red, lance-shaped aromatic foliage. The pungent, highly-flavoured leaves are used in Japanese and Vietnamese cooking; add raw before serving, do not cook them because they turn bitter and lose their flavour.

*Persicaria bistorta*, Common Bistort, Dragonwort
Hardy, H7 (USDA 6), perennial. Height and spread: up to 1m (3ft). Dense spikes of small pink flowers in summer until early autumn. Hairless, triangular, prominently-veined mid-green leaves. This is a UK native wild herb. This herb is not edible; it is medicinal. The root is used to staunch blood flow and contract tissues. It is one of the most astringent of all medicinal plants.

## Propagation

**Seeds:** It is very rare for the tropical *Persicaria odorata* and *hydropiper* to set seed outside of the tropics. If you can get hold of the seed, sow it in the autumn, winter the young plants under cover before planting out the following spring. We have found that the seeds of *Persicaria hydropiper* var. *rubra* needs a few weeks of stratification (see page 18); this certainly helped with germination. Sow fresh seeds of *Persicaria bistorta* in the autumn into prepared modules or seed trays using a seed compost.

**Cuttings:** cuttings can be taken from spring until late summer. Take the cutting just below the stem joint, place into prepared modules or a small pot filled with a seed compost. Once the cuttings are fully rooted, in warm climates plant out into the garden into a prepared site; in cool and cold climates pot up and grow on as a container plant. Alternatively, place in water and it will root very quickly. If using this method, as soon as you see the roots, remove from the water, and pot up into a small pot using a seed compost.

**Division:** divide established plants from the garden or pot grown any time from spring until late summer. This will stop them invading the garden and outgrowing the pot.

## Pests and diseases

This highly aromatic plant rarely suffers from pests or disease.

## How and where to grow

This plant is related to the knotweed family and as any gardener knows, that can be invasive. As it is a tropical plant it will need protection when temperatures fall below 7°C (45°F) at night. In warm climates, plant in a rich fertile soil in partial shade. Because this plant is invasive be prepared to dominate it by digging up and removing surplus roots. In cool climates, it is worth taking cuttings in the summer as insurance against a hard winter or if you are thinking of reorganising the garden.

## Growing in containers

This herb grows very happily in containers, especially in cold climates. Use a soil-based compost. As this is a vigorous plant it will need repotting twice a year to maintain good-quality leaves. Feed weekly during the growing season from spring until autumn. Do not let the pot dry out as this will make the leaves tough and rather inedible. Place the container in semi-shade in the summer months.

## Yearly maintenance

**Spring:** re-introduce watering to container grown plants; take cuttings. In warm climates, divide established plants.

**Summer:** cut back to produce new growth.

**Autumn:** in cold climates bring into a frost-free environment. Sow seeds

**Winter:** in cool and cold climates cut back on the watering of container plants.

## Harvesting and storing

Pick the leaves to use fresh as required throughout the growing season. They do not dry.

## Culinary uses

This herb is used as a fresh leaf herb, always added at the end of cooking rather than cooked. In Asia, it is usually eaten raw as a salad or herb accompaniment. It combines well with meat, vegetables and fruit. It is important in Vietnamese cooking, used copiously with noodle soups. It is an ingredient in a Vietnamese pickled dish resembling sauerkraut. The leaves are also good for making chilli oil or vinegar to use in marinades, dressings and sauces.

## Medicinal uses

The leaves aid digestion and are anti-diarrhoeal; they are also anti-inflammatory. The juice prepared from the crushed leaves is taken as an antidote against poisonous snake bites. Externally, the crushed leaves are applied on ringworm.

*Persicaria hydropiper* var *rubra*, Red Water Pepper

# Petroselinum crispum

**This brilliant herb has been misunderstood and misused in the UK. It is not just a garnish; it is one of the most widely used herbs throughout the world. It can be used as a vegetable – both leaf and root – and can make bland food into a feast.**

*Petroselinum crispum*, Parsley

## History

Parsley has been popular since records began. The Romans ate it as a deodoriser, the ancient Greeks believed that the plants grew from the blood of their heroes so it was fed in abundance to their athletes. During the Middle Ages, in the UK, monks grew parsley in order to treat the sick.

## Species

*Petroselinum crispum*, Parsley, Curly Parsley
Hardy, H4 (USDA 8,9), biennial. Height: up to 40cm (16in); spread: 30cm (12in). Small creamy-white flowers in flat umbels in the summer of the second season. The leaves are bright green, serrated, with variable curly-toothed edges and a clean, fresh, mild flavour. They have a higher vitamin C content than an orange and the high chlorophyll content in the leaves and stem makes them a natural breath freshener when eaten.

*Petroselinum crispum* 'French', French parsley, Flat-leaf Parsley
Hardy, H4 (USDA 8.9), biennial. Height: up to 60cm (24in); spread: 30cm (12in). Small creamy-white flowers in flat umbels in the summer of the second season. Flat, dark green, divided leaves with serrated edges. In my opinion this parsley has a stronger flavour than the curly. It is lovely used in sauces, soups or torn up and added to salads.

*Petroselinum crispum* var. *tuberosum*, Hamburg Parsley, Parsnip-rooted Parsley, Turnip-rooted Parsley
Hardy, H6 (USDA 6,7), perennial, grown as an annual. Height: up to 60cm (24in); spread: 30cm (12in). Small creamy-white flowers in flat umbels in the summer of the second season. Once it has flowered, collect the seeds. Flat, dark green, divided leaves with serrated edges, very similar to French parsley. In the second year, when the plant runs to flower, the leaves become bitter and inedible. Root length: up to 15cm (6in). The roots are harvested in the late autumn/early winter. They taste of a mixture of parsley, parsnips and celery; the largest roots taste best.

## Propagation

The trick for growing parsley successfully is to keep the temperature consistent during germination and not allow the compost or soil to dry out. Sow the seeds in early spring, into prepared modules or a seed tray using a seed compost. Place under protection at 18°C (64°F). Germination takes 2–4 weeks. Pot up or plant out as soon as the roots develop and before the tap root starts to grow. Alternatively, sow the seeds in late spring, into prepared open ground. Do not be impatient: wait until the air temperature does not consistently go below 7°C (45°F) at night. A second sowing in late summer will give a great winter crop. Water the site well prior to sowing. Germination takes 2–4 weeks. Hamburg parsley is better grown directly into the soil, so that it can produce good roots. From early to mid-spring, if you live in a cold climate, cover with a cloche. This will protect the young plants from the cold, stop the birds from getting to them and also help protect the plants from carrot fly. Once the seedlings are established, thin to 20cm (8in) apart.

## Pests and diseases

Slugs love young parsley plants. Put a thick line of bran around the plant or both sides of the row – this acts as a good barrier. The other major pest is carrot root fly. As with all members of the *Apiaceae* this pest is attracted to the smell of the roots, therefore, the plant is most vulnerable when the plants are lifted, or planted out or the seedlings are thinned. The fly lays its eggs in the soil adjacent to the plant and the grub then feeds off the roots. Prevent it by companion-planting chives or garlic next to the parsley – their scent will discourage the fly. Alternatively, use a barrier in the form of horticultural fleece, a cloche or, for a small clump, cut off the bottom of a plastic bottle and use that to cover it. Whichever barrier you use, do not leave any gaps between the barrier and the soil for the fly to get through. Do not allow plants to dry out in summer. Feed weekly with liquid comfrey or a seaweed liquid fertiliser.

## How and where to grow

Parsley is a hungry plant; it likes a good deep soil, not too light and not acid. Always feed the chosen site well in the previous autumn with well-rotted manure. If you wish to harvest parsley all year round, the ideal situation is to have two different sites prepared. For summer supplies, a western or eastern border is perfect because the plant needs moisture and prefers a little shade. For winter supplies a more sheltered spot will be needed in a sunny position, like under a south-facing wall. Remember to water well during hot weather.

Hamburg or turnip parsley differs only in that it is a root not a leaf crop. The soil should be prepared in exactly the same way and the seed should be sown in shallow drills in mid-spring. Water well all summer. The root tends to grow more at this time of year, and unlike a lot of root crops the largest roots taste the best. Lift the roots from the ground in late autumn until early winter.

## Growing in containers

Curly and French parsley happily adapt to being grown in a container as long as you keep potting up a pot size until you get to a size large enough to supply you with leaves, ideally a 2–3 litre (3–5 pint) pot, using a soil-based compost. Alternatively, sow the seeds into the chosen pot in late spring and again in another pot in the autumn so you have a winter crop. Place the container in semi-shade, water regularly and feed weekly with a liquid feed.

## Yearly maintenance

**Spring:** sow seeds for harvesting through the summer.

**Summer:** harvest leaves; sow seeds in late summer for a winter crop.

**Autumn:** feed the soil with well-rotted manure.

**Winter:** harvest leaves.

## Harvesting and storing

**Leaves:** pick leaves as required throughout the growing season to use fresh or to freeze or dry.

**Seeds:** harvest in summer

**Roots:** in late autumn, dig up the roots of the Hamburg parsley; they can be stored in a cold shed in sand or bark until required.

## Culinary uses

**Leaves:** parsley is a widely used culinary herb, valued for its taste as well as its rich nutritional content. When cooking with parsley it enhances the flavour of other foods and herbs. It is always best to add it just before the end of cooking to get the best flavour.

**Seeds:** this is hardly used in cooking but like its cousin caraway, it is delicious ground and used to flavour soups, stews or casseroles.

**Roots:** the roots of Hamburg parsley make a great alternative to carrots or celeriac – lovely cooked on their own, roasted or added to soups, stews or casseroles. They are good grated raw into salads.

## Medicinal uses

Parsley is a very beneficial herb: it helps clear the toxins from the body and is well known for its digestive properties. It is also a diuretic, carminative, antispasmodic and a good antioxidant. It is renowned for its high vitamin and mineral content due to its long tap root; the leaves are high in beta-carotene and vitamins A, B, B2, B3, C and E, plus calcium, iron, sodium phosphorus and magnesium. All in all, this is a must-have herb that should be eaten regularly.

**Common names:** Poke Root, Pork Berry, Virginian Poke Weed, Ink Berry, Indian Poke, Pigeon Berry

# Phytolacca americana

**This herb has many facets: it is classed as a weed in the USA but in Europe it is valued as a structural and ornamental garden plant. Currently it is under research in controlling the disease bilharzia (an infection caused by a parasitic worm that lives in fresh water in subtropical and tropical regions), for it has been discovered that the roots can destroy snails. Traditionally, the Native Americans used it as a pot herb and the young shoots were considered a wonderful delicacy. However, do be warned that this plant is toxic and poisonous if handled incorrectly. To put that into perspective, so is a potato – its leaves are highly toxic if eaten and if eaten raw the tuber has a toxic compound that can even cause death in extreme cases.**

## History

This herb was introduced to American settlers by the Native Americans to whom it was known as *pocan* or *coccum* and from which the name 'pokeweed' originates. They used it for a number of medicinal remedies, including as an emetic. From there it arrived in England in the late 18th century where it got the name American poke. It obtained a reputation as a remedy for internal cancers, hence its early name, cancer root.

## Species

*Phytolacca americana* (syn. *Phytolacca decandra*), Poke Root DA 6), herbaceous perennial. Height: up to 2m (6ft); spread: up to 1.5m (5ft). Long clusters of small, shallow, cup-shaped flowers with a hint of pink, white and green in summer, followed by black juicy berries on magenta stems. Oval, lance-shaped mid-green leaves that turn pink and orange around the edges in autumn.

*Phytolacca clavigera*, Pokeweed
Hardy, H7 (USDA 6), herbaceous perennial. Height and spread: 1.2m (4ft). Clusters of shallow, cup-shaped pink flowers in summer followed by rounded blackish berries with poisonous seeds. Oval- to lance-shaped mid-green leaves that turn yellow in autumn. The main difference between this species and *Phytolacca americana* is that its flower racemes are more compact and the berries are black and remain sticking up. This plant is a native of China.

*Phytolacca polyandra*, Indian Paint, Chinese Poke
Hardy, H5 (USDA 7,8), herbaceous perennial. Height: up to 2m (6ft); spread: up to 1.5m (5ft). Tight clusters of shallow, cup-shaped pink flowers in summer followed by closely-packed clusters of rounded purple/black berries with poisonous seeds. The new shoots in spring are bronze; they grow into green oval leaves that turn golden-yellow in autumn.

## Propagation

**Seeds:** extract the seed from the berry, wearing gloves if the seeds are fresh, unless you want pink hands for the next week, and sow into prepared seed trays or modules filled with three parts seed compost mixed with one part coarse horticultural sand, either in the autumn or spring. Cover with coarse horticultural sand, not compost, and place in a cold frame. Germination takes 3–4 weeks. Autumn-sown seedlings should be wintered in the cold frame.

**Division:** divide established garden plants in the spring or autumn using a sharp knife or when growing in the garden, use a spade. Make sure you have a new shoot visible in the section you are removing; replant it into a well-prepared site. If by mistake you end up with a small piece of root with a new shoot, then pot up using three parts soil-based compost mixed with one part coarse horticultural grit and grow on until fully rooted before planting back in the garden.

## Pests and diseases

In the majority of cases this plant is free from pests and diseases.

## How and where to grow

As this plant can leave its mark in the form of seedlings and/or coloured splodges from the berries, choose your site with care. On the plus side, it looks wonderful in autumn and the berries are great for attracting birds into the garden. Plant in a fertile moist soil, in sun or partial shade. Clear all the debris away in late autumn, especially if there are still berries on the ground – this will save digging up the excess seedlings in the spring.

## Growing in containers

*Phytolacca* looks stunning in a large container filled with three parts soil-based compost mixed with one part coarse horticultural grit. Make sure the container has a wide base so it will not blow over when the plant goes into flower followed by fruit.

## Yearly maintenance

**Spring:** sow seeds; divide established plants.

**Summer:** cut flowers off if you do not want the berries.

**Autumn:** sow seeds; divide established plants; clear any berries from the ground.

**Winter:** it is hardy and it dies back into the ground, therefore no protection is needed.

## Harvesting and storing

**Leaves:** harvest young leaves in late spring, however, please be warned that if wrongly handled they are toxic.

**Berries:** harvest the berries for use medicinally or as a natural dye in early autumn as they start to fall. They are not to be eaten.

**Roots:** harvest the root of a two-year-old plant in autumn for medicinal use.

## Culinary uses

**Leaves:** the young leaves can be eaten like spinach; however, they need to be boiled for 30 minutes with two changes of water before they are safe. Eating them is rather like picking mushrooms in the wild, do be cautious. Mature leaves are toxic so if unsure do not pick.

## Medicinal uses

Medicinally, poke root is an important herb but should only be taken under professional supervision. It is used for respiratory tract infections and chronic infections. It is also used as a poultice or ointment for fungal infections and scabies.

**WARNING** | All parts of the plant are toxic.

*Phytolacca americana*, Poke Root

**Common names:** Cuban Oregano, Jamaican Broad Leaf Thyme, Indian Borage, Spanish Thyme, Mexican Mint

# Plectranthus amboinicus (syn. Coleus amboinicus)

**This fascinating plant, which I seem to have followed around the world, has taught me so much about herbs and why botanical names are very important. The first time I met this herb I was working on a cruise liner as a horticultural expert. We were visiting the West Indies and on the first island we stopped, this herb was called Jamaican broad leaf thyme, on the next it was called Cuban oregano, and on the final island, Spanish thyme. I then went to Malaysia, to do some work for the Malay government and in the Melaka Botanical Garden it was called bangun bangun. This made me realise that using and understanding the botanical name was essential, especially if you were going to eat the herb, or more importantly, take it medicinally.**

*Plectranthus amboinicus*, Cuban Oregano

## History

This herb originated from the Indonesian spice Island, Amboina, hence its botanical name, and because of its medicinal and herbal use it was soon taken to India and the Far East by early voyagers. It is still widely used by the indigenous people of the tropical rain forest, either to treat colds, asthma, constipation or headaches, or as a culinary herb where it is eaten raw or cooked and used as a stuffing for fish or meat.

## Species

*Plectranthus amboinicus*, Cuban Oregano
Tender, H1c (USDA 11), evergreen, trailing, perennial. Height: 30–70cm (12– 28in); spread: in the tropics over 1.5m (5ft); in cold climates: 40cm (16in). Pale, purplish two-lipped flowers grow in dense whorls throughout the year. Fleshy, velvety leaves with finely scalloped margins; the foliage is strongly aromatic, especially when crushed.

## Propagation

As this herb rarely sets seed, and certainly not outside the tropics, it is raised by cuttings.

**Cuttings:** these can be taken from non-flowering shoots when required, but in cold climates it is best done in summer. Fill small pots or large modules with three parts seed compost mixed with one part perlite. Rooting is quick, just 1–2 weeks. Pot up into a small pot using three parts soil-based potting compost mixed with one part horticultural grit. Winter the cuttings in a frost-free environment, which can be the house, conservatory or heated greenhouse.

## Pests and diseases

I have grown this herb for over 25 years and during that time I have had no pest problems and the only disease has been caused by overwatering in the winter months.

## How and where to grow

In warm tropical climates plant in sun to partial shade and in a fertile loam soil that does hold moisture. As this herb cannot withstand temperatures lower than 0°C (32°F) and becomes stressed when colder than 10°C (50°F), in the temperate zones, it can only be planted in the garden for the summer, then lifted for the winter. The easiest way to do this is to sink the pot in which it is growing into the garden for the summer. When you lift it, the roots will be coming out of the bottom of the pot. Repot into only one size larger, then bring in for the winter months.

## Growing in containers

The great thing about growing this herb in a cold climate is that it does make a great house plant. The compost must be fertile; it also must be well drained. Mix three parts soil-based potting compost with one part horticultural grit. The soil will retain moisture in the summer and the grit will aid drainage in winter. My top tip for keeping this plant happy and productive is the watering. In the spring and summer you can water and feed it monthly with a liquid fertiliser, but as soon as the day length shortens and winter sets in the plant must be kept virtually dry. It will survive drought, but it will not survive if the compost in the container is over-watered and cold.

## Yearly maintenance

**Spring:** reintroduce regular watering; pot up container plants.

**Summer:** take cuttings; plant in the garden in cold climates.

**Autumn:** lift garden plants and bring in container plants once the night temperature drops to 12°C (54°F).

**Winter:** protect in cold weather; cut back the watering to virtually dry.

## Harvesting and storing

Pick the leaves as required; they are best used fresh as this plant does not dry well.

## Culinary uses

**Leaves:** the leaves are infused to make a tea, added to beans, salads and strong-flavoured meat and fish dishes. They work well when combined with garlic and lemon for making marinades. They also make a great syrup which then can be used to make cocktails or added to fruit dishes. In India, the leaves are dipped in a spicy Indian batter and fried as pakora; they also can be added to Indian chutneys, which is great with rice, breads and rice dumplings. The leaves are often used to flavour salsas.

## Medicinal uses

*Plectranthus amboinicus* is an important medicinal herb. It has been under research and has been found to have a huge future in meeting the global demand for natural, cost-effective bioactive molecules in the pharmaceutical and nutraceutical industries. Externally, the leaves are used for headaches, sores, burns and scorpion stings; internally, for bronchitis. In Ayurvedic medicine it is used for its antimicrobial, antioxidant and antiepileptic properties. Over the years of growing this herb, families from all over the UK have come to the Herb Farm to collect plants so that they can make a juice from the leaves, which they mix with honey to give to their children when they have a cough.

**Common names:** Primrose, First Rose, Easter Rose

# Primula vulgaris

**Being lucky enough to have been brought up in the countryside, both primroses and cowslips were part of my childhood. We used cowslips to make a 'tisty-tosty', which was a fragrant ball of flowers. To find out who we were going to marry we would throw it around the circle saying, 'rich man, poor man, beggar man, thief; tinker, tailor, farmer, sailor'. This would be repeated until the ball fell in front of someone, and that was the person they were going to marry.**

## History

The generic name *Primula* is from the Latin *primus* meaning 'first'; so named after its early flowering in spring. One legend of northern Europe is that St Peter let his keys drop when he was told that a duplicate key to heaven had been made. If one removes the corolla of a *Primula* the remaining calyx resembles an old keyhole. According to early German superstition the plant was a gift from the gods to show people the way to hidden treasure, hence the English, French and German common names keys of heaven, clé de saint Pierre and schlüsselblume.

## Species

*Primula vulgaris*, Primrose
Hardy, H5 (USDA 7,8), herbaceous perennial. Height and spread: 15cm (6in). Sweetly-scented flowers in spring: single, pale yellow with a dark yellow centre. Finely haired stems. Mid-green, oval, textured leaves. This plant has become increasingly rare in the UK countryside and it is now illegal to dig up plants growing in the wild.

*Primula veris*, Cowslip, Keys of Heaven
Hardy, H5 (USDA 7,8), herbaceous perennial. Height and spread: 20cm (8in). Tight clusters of up to 30 fragrant, tubular, drooping yellow flowers are produced on stout stems in spring. Oval, mid-green, textured, finely haired leaves. Cowslips are often mistaken for oxlip (*Primula elatior*), which is a hybrid between cowslip and primrose, (*Primula vulgaris*). The difference between the two is that oxlip has large pale yellow flowers in a one-sided cluster, whereas cowslip flowers are much deeper yellow, smaller and there are more in the cluster.

## Propagation

**Seeds:** it is important to use fresh seed. Sow in late summer/ early autumn into small pots, seed trays or modules filled with a seed compost and place in a cold frame or unheated greenhouse. Germination takes 2–3 weeks. Winter the young plants in the cold frame or cold greenhouse. Plant out into a prepared site the following spring. The plant may not flower in the first season. Bought or old seed will need a period of stratification (see page 18) before germination, then you can either mix the seed with damp horticultural sand and put it in the refrigerator for a couple of months, or you can sow as above, putting the containers outside to experience all weathers. Germination can be erratic – it can take as long as two years.

**Division:** all primulas benefit from being divided. Lift established plants in the autumn, either replant into a prepared site in the garden, or pot up ready for the spring using a soil-based compost.

## Pests and diseases

The scourge of all Primula plants is the vine weevil (see page 272 for how to control this pest). Pollinated primrose flowers produce sticky seeds that attract ants, who then disperse them around the garden, which is why you can find primroses where you least expect them.

## How and where to grow

Both primroses and cowslips prefer moist soil. Primroses like semi-shade, such as the lee of a hedge or under a deciduous tree, whereas cowslips prefer sun to partial shade which is why you will sometimes find them growing in the middle of fields. Plant in clumps or drifts so that they can lift your spirits on a gloomy spring day.

## Growing in containers

Both primroses and cowslips look lovely growing in containers. Use a soil-based compost and position the container out of the midday sun. They make a lovely combination with sweet violets, giving you spring in a pot. You could bring your pots into the home for colourful cheer. Position them on a cold windowsill so that they last longer.

## Yearly maintenance

**Spring:** early in the year clear all the winter debris from established plants. Stratify any seed not previously sown (see page 18). Plant out young plants.

**Summer:** only deadhead if you do not want to save the seed. At the end of summer, sow fresh seed.

**Autumn:** divide established plants.

**Winter:** hardy, do not need protection.

## Harvesting and storing

**Flowers:** pick the flowers as required in the spring to use fresh or to dry.

**Leaves:** pick the leaves for use fresh or to dry in the spring for medicinal use.

**Roots:** dig up the roots of a three- to our-year-old plant in autumn to dry for medicinal use.

## Culinary uses

**Flowers:** both primrose and cowslip flowers are edible and taste like they smell. They can be added to salads, cakes and puddings. Primrose flowers can be used to make primrose jam while cowslip flowers make a delicious shrub, a sweet vinegar which can be used as a drink when diluted with fizzy water, or as a syrup used on puddings. They are also still used to make a country wine.

**Leaves:** the young leaves of primrose can be added to salads; they are preferable to cowslip leaves, which should really be stir-fried or cooked before eating as they are quite tough.

*Primula vulgaris*, Primrose

## Medicinal uses

Medicinally cowslip has lots of uses in traditional remedies. Today the roots are used in the treatment of respiratory tract infections, insomnia and anxiety. Primroses are considered a substitute for cowslips, however they are reputedly less strong. The flowers of both are used in infusions, ointments and tinctures.

**WARNING** | Do not take medicinally when pregnant or on anticoagulant drugs. All Primulas can cause skin allergies or irritation.

# Punica granatum

**Amazingly there are more than 500 named cultivars of this beautiful shrub. When I visited China to see the scholastic gardens, we also went to Xi'an to see the Terracotta Army and passed acres and acres of pomegranates. In a nearby town, one of the streets was lined with very small stalls, each selling their own crop. It was fascinating to learn that the pomegranate is valued just as much for its fruit as for its medicinal properties.**

*Punica granatum*, Pomegranate

## Species

Most pomegranate shrubs are self-pollinating so you only need one plant to produce fruit.

*Punica granatum*, Pomegranate
Hardy, H3 (USDA 9), deciduous shrub. Height and spread: up to 2.5m (8ft). Beautiful red flowers followed by leathery red/orange fruit. Green, glossy, narrow oblong leaves. The new growth is bronze in colour and in autumn the leaves turn yellow.

*Punica granatum* 'Provence'
Hardy, H5 (USDA 7,8), deciduous shrub. Height: up to 3m (9ft); spread: up to 1.5m (5ft). Beautiful orange/red flowers followed by leathery red/orange fruit in late autumn. Green, glossy, narrow oblong leaves. The new growth is bronze in colour and in autumn the leaves turn yellow. This ancient French variety is very hardy and the fruit will normally ripen outdoors in the south of the UK.

*Punica granatum* var. *nana*, Dwarf Pomegranate
Hardy, H3 (USDA 9), deciduous shrub. Height and spread: up to 1m (3ft). Beautiful red flowers followed by leathery red/orange fruit. Green, glossy, narrow oblong leaves. The new growth is bronze in colour and in autumn the leaves turn yellow. Ideal for growing in a container.

## History

This herb is steeped in ancient history. It is mentioned in the Bible; it has been the symbol of fertility throughout the centuries in Chinese, Persian, Semitic, Greek and Roman lore. Over 4,000 years ago the Egyptians knew about the medicinal properties of the pomegranate root for eradicating internal worms. From 150 BC the Hebrew coin, the shekel, carried the image of a pomegranate but over time it was replaced. Then in 1986 the coinage was reorganised and once again the pomegranate replaced the former pound as the symbol on the shekel.

## Propagation

**Seeds:** over 30 years ago, my children and I sowed some pomegranate seeds from a fruit I had bought from a large supermarket; three germinated. The best time to sow the seed is in winter. Wash all the pulp off the seeds, leave them to dry for a day, then sow in a seed compost which has been pre-watered. Push the seed into the compost and cover with horticultural sand. Put in a propagator at 18°C (64°F). Germination takes anything from 2–8 weeks. Do not let the compost dry out. Once fully rooted, pot up using a soil-based potting compost. These young plants will need to be grown on as a container plant under protection for two more years before planting in the garden.

**Cuttings:** take semi-ripe cuttings in summer, from non-flowering shoots and transfer to prepared modules or a small pot filled with three parts seed compost and one part standard perlite. Once rooted, pot up into small pots using a soil-based compost. Grow under protection for the first two years.

## Pests and diseases

When grown inside, either in a greenhouse, conservatory or polytunnel, pomegranate can be prone to white fly and thrips (see page 272 for information on how to control them). In warm humid summers when the plant is flowering, the flowers can be susceptible to mildew – remove damaged flowers, especially when grown inside. Spray with potassium bicarbonate (see page 276).

## How and where to grow

Grow pomegranates in a sunny, sheltered spot in well-drained soil, so that the plant does not sit in dank wet ground in winter. If you live in a cold climate, look out for the French variety 'Provence', which fruits at much colder temperatures than the standard pomegranate. If you really do want fruit and cannot source this variety, then grow in a large greenhouse, conservatory or polytunnel.

In early spring, give established plants a good mulch of well-rotted manure or compost. Lightly prune your established plants after all threat of frost has passed in late spring, remove any damaged branches or diseased shoots. Pomegranate trees typically bloom off last year's wood, so be cautious when pruning. When in doubt, only remove this year's growth from the tree. Even though this is a drought-loving plant, to encourage fruiting, water regularly, especially in very hot weather. Harvest the fruit in the autumn when the crown of the fruit has started to turn brown and curl, either using a sharp knife or, even better, secateurs. After harvest, and after all the leaves have fallen, give the shrub a good feed of well-rotted manure or compost.

## Growing in containers

The dwarf pomegranate, of which there are many cultivars, is ideal for the small garden and it makes an excellent, attractive and productive container plant. Plant in a soil-based compost, bring into a cold greenhouse or cold polytunnel for winter and place it on bricks to aid drainage. Feed weekly with liquid fertliser from spring until autumn. Pot up established plants in the spring, give the plant a very light prune, removing any dead branches or damaged stems.

## Yearly maintenance

**Spring:** mulch established plants; lightly prune off damage branches; repot container plants.

**Summer:** water in hot weather.

**Autumn:** harvest.

**Winter:** sow seeds.

## Harvesting and storing

In the autumn, when the fruit is ready to harvest, don't pull it off the shrub, cut the fruit as close as possible to the branch taking the stem with the fruit. They can be stored in the refrigerator for up to two months, alternatively you can store them in the freezer for up to a year.

## Culinary uses

Add the fruit to salads, rice, couscous and grain dishes. It's wonderful with aubergine and cheese, and lovely in ice cream, cakes, with apples and for juicing.

## Medicinal uses

The pomegranate is an antioxidant, good for heart and urinary health. It is high in magnesium, phosphorus, potassium and vitamins C and D. Pomegranates are under research as they have shown to have anticancer effects and reduce inflammation. All parts of the pomegranate are used in traditional medicine and the rind is used to treat diarrhoea, dysentery and other stomach ailments. The leaves were used as a mouthwash and the bark of the pomegranate tree is used as an astringent and as a decoction to treat tape worm.

**Common names:** Apothecary's Rose, Red Rose of Lancaster, Crimson Damask Rose, The Official Rose

# Rosa gallica var. officinalis

**This beautiful genus, which consists of about 100 species, has been in cultivation for thousands of years. I could write a book about this single herb and how historically it has been entwined with our health and wellbeing, but I have decided to focus on just one, which is both culinary and medicinal and a joy to grow in the garden.**

## History

Roses have been used for thousands of years. The first records come from China in AD470, where they were using *Rosa laevigata*. Pliny in AD77 recorded using *Rosa gallica* and *Rosa damascena* to treat 32 different disorders. Several thousand years ago the *Rosa damascena* gave its name to the town of Damascus and to the silk material made there in the colour of the flower. Syria means 'land of the rose'.

## Species

*Rosa gallica* var. *officinalis*,Crimson Damask Rose
Hardy, H7 (USDA 6), bushy small shrub. Height and spread: up to 1m (3ft). Lovely fragrant semi-double light crimson flowers in early summer. Dull greyish-green foliage on thorny stems. The flowers are used to make rose water, syrups and jams plus the northern African spice mixture ras-el-hanout.

**Some other culinary and medicinal roses**

*Rosa canina*, Dog Rose, Bird Briar
Hardy, H7 (USDA 6), deciduous shrub. Height: up to 4m (13ft); spread: up to 2.5m (8ft). Solitary, or small clusters of, pale pink or white single flowers in summer followed by oval red fruits. Mid-green foliage on thorny stems. The rosehips are famous for making syrups and cough mixtures; they are also used in the making of wine, vinegar and preserves.

*Rosa laevigata*, Cherokee Rose, Three-leaved Rose, also the state flower of Georgia USA
Hardy, H4 (USDA 8,9), large rambling rose. Height and spread: up to 1m (3ft). Lovely large single, slightly fragrant white flowers in summer. Bright green, semi-evergreen leaves with three leaflets. Used medicinally internally for urinary dysfunction and chronic diarrhoea.

*Rosa rubiginosa* (syn *R.eglanteria*) Eglantine, Sweet Briar
Hardy, H7 (USDA 6), deciduous shrub. Height and spread: up to 2.5m (8ft). Single, light pink flowers in summer followed by oval red fruits. Mid-green, slightly apple-scented foliage on very prickly stems. Used medicinally externally to treat burns, scars and wrinkles. Wonderful herb for pollinators, especially butterflies and moths. It is a caterpillar food plant, has nectar/pollen-rich flowers, provides shelter and habitat, has seeds for birds and makes a good wildlife hedge.

*Rosa rugosa*, Japanese Rose, Ramanas Rose
Hardy, H7 (USDA 6), deciduous shrub. Height and spread: up to 1.5m (5ft). Pink to deep magenta, single, scented flowers in summer and autumn followed by large scarlet fruits, which are much loved by blackbirds. Glossy, strongly veined leaves that turn yellow in the autumn on very prickly stems. Used medicinally to treat poor appetites and digestion.

## Propagation

**Seeds:** it is possible to grow some species of rose from seed and *Rosa gallica* is one which you can. However, germination is erratic and it can take 3–4 years before you see your first bloom. In autumn, choose fruit that are red and firm to the touch, gently cut them with a knife, then with your fingers ease the fruit in half to expose the seed. Wash the seeds, then put them in a plastic bag with damp horticultural sand, label and put in the crisper drawer of the refrigerator to stratify for 4 months (see page 18). Sow the seeds into small pots filled with seed compost. If you have a propagator, put them in the propagator at 18°C (64°F) for 2 weeks, then put them in a cold greenhouse to germinate slowly.

**Cuttings:** the easiest and more reliable method of propagating *Rosa gallica* is from cuttings. In late summer, once flowering has finished, take cuttings from semi-ripe stems, put the cuttings into large modules filled with three parts seed compost mixed with one part perlite. You can use small pots if you prefer. Place in a warm draught-free place. In around 3–4 weeks the cuttings will root. If you have taken them in the large modules, they can happily winter in these if you keep them in a cold greenhouse or cold frame prior to planting out the following spring.

## Pests and diseases

All roses suffer from a number of pests – aphids and leaf cutter are the most common. For more information on how to control these, see page 267. The most common disease is powdery mildew (see page 276).

## How and where to grow

Plant *Rosa gallica* in full sun, in fertile, humus-rich, moist, well-drained soil. For best flowering, apply a balanced fertiliser and mulch in late winter or early spring. Prune after flowering in late summer; in early autumn, cut back long shoots by a third and side shoots by two thirds.

## Growing in containers

Roses will grow in containers and this one looks lovely in a large terracotta pot filled with a good soil-based potting compost. With established pot plants they are well worth feeding with a balanced fertiliser in the spring, then weekly with a good liquid fertiliser.

## Yearly maintenance

**Spring:** apply fertiliser.

**Summer:** harvest flowers.

**Autumn:** sow seeds; take cuttings; prune.

**Winter:** mulch around established plants. No need for protection as it is fully hardy.

## Harvesting and storing

**Flowers:** pick the flowers for drying just as they start to open. The easiest way is to cover a tray with kitchen towel, place the flowers individually on the tray and put the tray into a light cool room. Turn the flowers daily until the petals start to fall off. Put the petals on a frame covered in muslin. Leave them for a few days until they are crispy dry, then keep them in an airtight container.

## Culinary uses

Rose water and rose syrup made from petals are used in numerous Middle Eastern and Indian pastries and confections. They are also used to make jams, jelly, butter, vinegar, syrup, tea cakes and desserts. They are ideal for crystallising and are good macerated with wine and fruit. They are also used to garnish desserts and salads. Rose water gives flavour to Turkish delight, sorbets and mousses. I have a long-lasting memory of having a table with my fresh herbs at Fortnum & Mason in London; next door to me was a wonderful lady who specialised in rose petal jam – it was total nectar.

## Medicinal uses

*Rosa gallica* has been used internally to treat colds, bronchial infections, depression and lethargy. Externally it has been used to treat minor injuries and skin problems. In Ayurvedic medicine it is used to treat inflammation and aid circulation. It is also used in aromatherapy to counter depression, anxiety and negative feelings. You will find that rose oil and rose water are used in bath preparations and skin products.

*Rosa gallica* var. *officinalis*, Crimson Damask Rose

**Common names:** Sorrel, Broad-leaved Sorrel, Bread and Cheese, Sour Leaves, Tom Thumbs, A Thousand Fingers, Sour Sauce

# Rumex acetosa

**When my children were at the local infant school, I employed a lovely guy from New Zealand and the two of us enacted the Romans, introducing the children to the herbs that the Romans brought as medicine and food when they invaded this country. I had been talking about how the Romans used to eat a leaf of sorrel to stop themselves feeling thirsty as they marched, as they did not have bottles of water. One little boy asked if he could eat a leaf, I gave him one, he ate it and proclaimed, 'it's a Granny Smith', which is a sharp green apple. Ever since we have known it as the Granny Smith's herb.**

*Rumex scutatus*, Buckler Leaf Sorrel

## History

The historical use of sorrel as a food dates back to 3,000 BC. It is said that eating sorrel leaves cured Julius Caesar's soldiers of scurvy. The Ancient Egyptians and Romans ate sorrel to offset their rich food, and the Tudors considered it to be one of the best vegetables. The traditional countryside name for this plant was 'cuckoo's meate' from an old belief that the bird cleared its voice by eating it. In Lapland, sorrel juice has been used instead of rennet to curdle milk.

## Species

*Rumex acetosa*, Sorrel, Broad-leafed Sorrel, Common Sorrel, Garden Sorrel, Meadow Sorrel
Hardy, H7 (USDA 6), herbaceous perennial. Height: up to 50cm (20in) in leaf and 1m (3ft) when in flower; spread: up to 50cm (20in). The flowers are small, dull and inconspicuous. They are greenish, turning reddish-brown as the fruit ripens. The mid-green leaves are lance-shaped with two basal lobes pointing backwards.

*Rumex acetosella*, Sheep's Sorrel
Hardy, H3 (USDA 9), perennial. Height: 15cm (6in) in leaf, up to 50cm (20in) in flower. The individual plant spreads up to 50cm (20in) but it self-seeds so the spread can become indefinite. This herb grows wild on acid soil, on heaths and grassy places, so if your soil is acidic, it can become invasive. If this is the case, simply add some lime to the soil to eradicate it. It may need a few applications if you want to remove the whole plant.

*Rumex scutatus,* Buckler Leaf Sorrel, French Sorrel
Hardy, H6 (USDA 6,7), perennial. Height: 15cm (6in) in leaf; 45cm (18in) in flower; spread: up to 1.5m (5ft). It does self-seed so the patch can become much larger. The flowers are small, dull and inconspicuous, as they are greenish, turning brown as the fruit ripens. The mid-green leaves are shaped like squat shields. Use the young leaves in salads and sauces; they can be eaten raw or cooked.

## Propagation

**Seeds:** for an early crop, sow in spring into prepared seed trays or modules using a seed compost. Place under protection at 15°C (60°F). Germination takes 5–10 days. Alternatively, sow seeds thinly in late spring into prepared open ground, when the air temperature does not go below 7°C (45°F) at night. Germination takes 2–3 weeks. Thin seedlings to 30cm (12in) apart.

**Division:** it is a really good idea to divide both buckler and broad-leaved sorrel every other year – this not only helps to keep the plant under control but it also keeps the leaves young and succulent. Cut the plant back prior to division, divide and replant into a prepared site that has been well fed with well-rotted compost prior to planting.

## Pests and diseases

Wood pigeons, slugs and occasionally leaf miners attack sorrel but should cause no problem with established plants. Remove the affected leaves and put out traps for the slugs (see page 272 for more information).

## How and where to grow

Plant in a rich fertile, well-drained soil that has been well fed with well-rotted manure in the autumn prior to planting. Position it in the garden so that it gets shade from the midday sun. In summer and warm climates sorrel leaves will become bitter as the season progresses. A leaf or bark mulch – not the huge pieces, the medium-sized propagating bark that has been composted – will keep the soil cooler and once the season gets colder the flavour will improve. Do not allow the soil to dry out as this will also impair the flavour of the leaves. Keep cutting back the flowers on both the buckler and broad-leaved sorrels, which will help to keep the leaves productive and you can often have an autumn flush before the winter sets in. In winter, if you are not dividing, feed around established plants with well-rotted farmyard manure.

## Growing in containers

Buckler leaf sorrel is ideal for growing in a large pot. Use a soil-based compost, as it does not dry out as fast as coir or other peat-free composts. Position the container out of the heat of the midday sun. Feed containers regularly throughout the growing season with liquid seaweed fertiliser or comfrey.

## Yearly maintenance

**Spring:** sow seeds under protection, in early spring, and in the garden from mid-spring.

**Summer:** cut off flowers to maintain leaf production and prevent self-seeding. If it is a hot summer, water regularly to keep the leaves succulent.

**Autumn:** divide established plants.

**Winter:** feed established plants. No need for protection.

## Harvesting and storing

**Leaves:** the young leaves are tender and not as sour or tough as the mature leaves, so they are the best for adding to salads or eating in sandwiches. The mature leaves are great cooked as they are tough.

## Culinary uses

A few young leaves added to salads gives a refreshing sharp flavour; they make great sauces, which can be served with fish or meat. The leaves can be used as a natural meat tenderiser when wrapped around tough meat while it is cooking. The leaves can also be added to stews and casseroles or combined with eggs and cheese.

## Medicinal uses

Sorrel is high in oxalic, tannic and tartaric acid as well as vitamins A, B1 and C, calcium, potassium, iron and sulphur. Sorrel leaves stimulate the salivary gland which means that eating a small leaf is very beneficial to digestion. Medicinally it is considered to have blood-cleansing qualities that improve haemoglobin content. The leaves can be used as a poultice to treat boils and acne.

**WARNING** | Avoid over-eating a lot of fresh leaves while breastfeeding. Do not take medicinally if you suffer from gall stones.

# Ruta graveolens

**I understand why rue has had a very bad press – it can cause phytophotodermatitis, or skin burn – but as with all plants respect should be shown; even the humble potato is toxic if the wrong part is eaten. This herb is a very beneficial medicinal herb, looks very attractive in the correct position in the garden and is considered the herb of grace – all brides at the wedding should have a piece in their wedding bouquet. It is regarded as a protector against the devil, witchcraft and magic, was an antidote for poisonous snakes and toadstools and it was famous for preserving eyesight. So, with all those attributes, no good herb garden should be without it.**

## History

Rue made its way across northern Europe to Britain on the Roman wagons. In the Middle Ages it was one of the herbs carried in nosegays by the rich when they went out of doors as protection from evil and the plague, and, like rosemary, it was placed near the judge before prisoners were brought out as protection from the pestilence-ridden gaols and gaol fever. It was famous for preserving eyesight and it was said to promote second sight, perhaps acting on the third eye or mind's eye. Rue was said to have inspired grand masters, such as Leonardo da Vinci and Michelangelo, who are both believed to have said that their inner vision had been enhanced by this herb.

## Species

*Ruta graveolens*, Rue
Hardy, H5 (USDA 7,8), evergreen shrub. Height and spread: up to 80cm (30in). Small, waxy yellow flowers with four or five petals in summer. Green/blue leaves that are very prettily divided into small rounded oval lobes and have an odd scent, which is hard to describe. The leaf is only dangerous in full sun, when the sun shines on the plant, when it is wet after rain or watering.

*Ruta graveolens* 'Jackman's Blue', Rue Jackman's Blue
Hardy, H5 (USDA 7,8), evergreen shrub. Height and spread: up to 80cm (30in). Waxy yellow flowers with four or five petals in summer. Small, rounded lobed leaves of a distinctive blue colour.

*Ruta graveolens* 'Variegata', Variegated Rue
Hardy, H5 (USDA 7,8), evergreen shrub. Height and spread: 80cm (30in). Waxy yellow flowers with four or five petals in summer. Small, rounded lobed leaves with a distinctive cream/white variegation, which is particularly marked in spring, fading in the summer unless the plant is kept well clipped.

## Propagation

**Seeds:** sow seeds in early spring, into prepared modules or seed trays using three parts seed compost mixed with one part sharp horticultural sand. Place under protection at 18°C (64°F). Germination takes 1–2 weeks. Watch the watering after germination, the seedlings are prone to damping off (see page 274).

**Cuttings:** take cuttings from new growth in late spring/early summer and transfer to prepared modules or a small pot filled with three parts seed compost and one part standard perlite. Do not overwater as the cuttings are prone to rot. Once fully rooted, pot up into a small pot using a soil-based compost.

## Pests and diseases

Rue is very prone to white fly, which is followed by black sooty mould. Use a soft horticultural soap spray following the manufacturer's instructions as soon as you see the pest; this will also control the mould. See page 272 for more information.

## How and where to grow

Plant rue somewhere in the garden where you or your family will not accidentally brush against it while wearing shorts or a skirt on a sunny day or after rain, which is when the plant is most likely to burn. Plant in a well-drained, poor soil in a sunny position, in the middle or back of the border. Despite all my warnings, it is a most attractive and easy plant to grow in the garden. In the spring, cut back to new shoots which will help to keep the plant bushy. Ideally do this on a cloudy day or early in the morning or evening when the plant is dry. Also cut back after flowering in late summer. Wear gloves.

## Growing in containers

Rue does grow happily in a container, using a soil-based compost. Position the pot in a sunny position, where you can enjoy its attractive habit, especially the variegated form, and out of the way of anyone walking by, who could brush against it by mistake. Lift containers in winter, putting them on bricks or stones to increase drainage.

## Yearly maintenance

**Spring:** cut back established plants to regain shape; sow seed; take softwood cuttings.

**Summer:** cut back after flowering to maintain shape.

**Autumn:** lift containers off the ground and put on bricks to aid drainage.

**Winter:** in the majority of cases rue is hardy and requires protection only in extreme conditions.

## Harvesting and storing

Pick leaves to use fresh or to dry for medicinal use as required.

## Culinary uses

Traditionally this herb was used in the kitchen, but as our taste has changed over the ages and bitter is not common in our daily food, it has fallen out of favour. In my time running the Herb Farm there was one chef that raved about this herb and immediately saw how it could balance sweet, sour, salty and hot flavours – his name was Heston Blumenthal. Today it is still used in some Italian dishes and is used in Ethiopia in the making of coffee where they use both the leaf and the seed.

*Ruta graveolens*, Rue

## Medicinal uses

Rue is still used medicinally in the Mediterranean region to treat pain, dermatitis, rheumatism and other inflammatory diseases. In homeopathy it is used for back pain, sciatica, strained muscles, tennis elbow and eyestrain. Excitingly medicinal research is ongoing as rue has been found to be very beneficial in treating certain types of cancer. The medicinal properties of this herb are certainly one for the future.

**WARNING** | Handling the plant can cause allergic reactions or phytophotodermatitis. This herb should not be self-administered.

# Salvia officinalis

**Sage is an archetypal herb for the herb garden and cottage garden, especially when it is in full flower and a magnet to bees and butterflies. It is a herb that is very well known and while you think you can imagine the flavour, until you have had fresh pasta tossed in sage butter you have not known its true delight.**

## History

The Romans regarded sage as a sacred plant; they called leaves *folia salviae*, meaning 'healing leaves'. People were not allowed to pick the sage unless they had washed and purified themselves according to certain rules, wore a white tunic, were barefoot and had made an offering to the gods. Historically it was combined with salt and used to preserve meat and before it became a culinary delight it was dried, powdered and scattered over food in a similar fashion to the way we use pepper today. In the 1940s, travellers used to chop sage and salt together then, using a piece of linen, rub it onto their teeth as a latter-day toothpaste.

## Species

There are now well over 900 species of *Salvia* so I have chosen a few of my favourites. I have given *Salvia rosmarinus* – rosemary – its own chapter (see page 222), because to be honest I still have difficulty classing it as a sage.

*Salvia officinalis*, Common Sage, Garden Sage, Sawge
Hardy, H4 (USDA 8,9), evergreen shrub. Height and spread: 60cm (24in). Mauve/blue flowers in summer. Highly aromatic, oval, green/grey textured leaves. This is the standard culinary and medicinal sage.

*Salvia officinalis* 'Purpurascens', Purple Sage, Red Sage
Hardy, H5 (USDA 7,8), semi-evergreen dwarf shrub. Height and spread: 85cm (33in). Grown from cuttings only. Mauve/blue flowers in summer. Aromatic, oval, purple/red/grey textured leaves. The leaves have a milder flavour and are good with vegetable dishes, such as stuffed peppers and courgettes and for use as an antiseptic gargle for sore throats.

*Salvia lavandulifolia*, Narrow-leaved Sage, Spanish Sage
Hardy H4 (USDA 7,8), Evergreen shrub. Height and spread: 45cm (18in). Grown from cuttings only. Attractive blue flowers in summer. Small, narrow, oval, textured, highly aromatic leaves, which have an excellent, very strong culinary flavour. The leaves make a stimulating infusion. This sage is ideal for container growing.

*Salvia elegans* 'Scarlet Pineapple', Pineapple Sage
Half-hardy, H2 (USDA 10), sub shrub. Height: 90cm (3ft); spread: 60cm (24in). Stunning long thin trumpet-shaped red flowers from mid-summer until early autumn, although with climate change I am now noticing that it does not flower until mid-autumn in my garden. Oval, pointed green leaves that have a slight red/brown tinge to the edges and a wonderful pineapple scent when crushed or rubbed.

*Salvia microphylla* var. *microphylla*, Blackcurrant-scented sage
Hardy, H4 (USDA 8,9), evergreen perennial. Height and spread: up to 1.2m (4ft). Lovely raspberry-coloured flowers, with the distinctive lower lip of the *Lamiaceae* family, in late summer until early autumn. Oval, mid-green aromatic leaves which smell of blackcurrant when rubbed.

*Salvia sclarea*, Clary Sage, Muscatel Sage
Hardy, H5 (USDA 7,8), biennial or short-lived perennial. Height: 60–90cm (2–3ft); spread: 45cm (18in). Colourful flower bracts, blue/purple/lilac with a whitish base in summer. The leaves are often 20–23cm (8-9in) long, soft green in colour and slightly wrinkly. Easily grown from seed. There is another variety *Salvia sclarea* var. *turkestanica* with white flowers tinged with pink.

*Salvia viridis* syn. *horminum*, Painted Sage, Red-topped Sage
Hardy, H5 (USDA 7,8), annual. Height: 45cm (18in); spread: 20cm (8in). Small purple and white or white flowers, which are overshadowed by wonderful, colourful, sterile bracts of purple, pink, blue and white often with green veins all summer. Downy, rough-textured, aromatic green leaves. The bracts are lovely in salads and summer drinks and great for flower arrangements.

## Propagation

**Seeds:** common sage, painted sage and clary sage can all be grown from seed. Sow in early spring into prepared modules or seed trays using a standard seed compost. Place under cover at 18°C (64°F). Germination takes 1–2 weeks. Alternatively sow seeds in late spring into prepared open ground, when the air temperature remains above 7°C (45°F) at night. Germination takes 2–3 weeks. Thin to 45cm (18in) apart. Protect young common sage plants in their first winter.

**Cuttings:** take cuttings from the shrub and perennial salvias in late spring to early summer and transfer either to modules or a small pot filled with three parts seed compost and one part standard perlite.

**Layering:** established plants of common or purple sage can be layered in spring or autumn. Prepare the chosen woody plant by removing any leaves or old branches, pin the branch into the soil, cover the pinned part with soil and give it a label with a date so you can see how long it has been layered. After 8–10 weeks in spring, check the layering to see if it is rooting, if it is, cut the branch away from the parent plant, lift carefully, including all the lovely new roots, pot up into a pot using a soil-based compost, grow on for the rest of the year in a cold frame, cold greenhouse or polytunnel. If layering in the autumn, leave until the spring to check for rooting.

## Pests and diseases

The main rather annoying pest is leaf hopper, which discolours the leaves. Only spray with soft horticultural soap if it really gets out of hand (see page 269 for more information). In dank springs and autumns, when young plants are being grown on under protection, watch out for powdery mildew. The first and easiest way to control this is to remove any infected leaves. If it gets out of hand, spray it with baking powder mixed with soft horticultural soap (see page 276 for more information).

*Salvia officinalis*, Sage

## How and where to grow

Plant all varieties of sage in a warm sunny site in well-drained, acid-free soil. Tender *Salvias* will only tolerate night temperatures in the garden above 10°C (50°F). Prune lightly in spring to encourage young shoots for a strong leaf flavour and again after flowering in late summer. This will help to keep common and purple sage from getting woody. Clear away dead leaves from under the plant in spring to prevent mildew in damp weather.

## Growing in containers

This herb is ideal for growing in containers. Use a soil-based compost. In the winter, it is the wet that will kill the tender *Salvia* quicker than the cold, so cut the watering down to minimal and lift the pots on to bricks or stones to increase drainage.

*Salvia sclarea*, Clary Sage

## Yearly maintenance

**Spring:** sow seeds; trim if needed; take softwood cuttings.

**Summer:** trim back after flowering; deadhead annual *Salvia*.

**Autumn:** protect all half-hardy sages, and first-year plants. Check for self-sown seedlings of annual and biennial *Salvia*. Dig up them up, winter in a cold greenhouse or cold frame for early flowering.

**Winter:** protect plants if they are needed for fresh leaves.

## Harvesting and storing

**Leaves:** pick fresh leaves from this evergreen herb throughout the year. In spring (before the plant flowers), the leaves have a mild, warm flavour. After flowering, the leaves have a stronger, tannin flavour.

**Flowers:** the flavour of the flower is similar to the leaf with a slight hint of sweetness, which makes them an ideal accompaniment for rice, meat, duck and stir-fry dishes where one wants an extra zing.

## Culinary uses

Over the years, sage has fallen out of favour in the UK kitchen, whereas in Europe it is used fresh and is wonderful with pasta, tomatoes and potatoes. It also goes well with pork. It aids digestion of fatty food and is a natural antiseptic. It has long been used in sausages because of its preservative qualities. It makes a delicious herb jelly, or oil and vinegar.

## Medicinal uses

Sage is a digestive; it also eases flatulence. A tea made from 3–4 leaves can be used to alleviate upset stomachs, diarrhoea and as a gargle for sore throats. Sage is known to be antiseptic, carminative and systemically antibiotic.

**Right** *Salvia viridis*, Painted Sage in the foreground

# Salvia rosmarinus

**With the advance of research and scientists sequencing plant DNA, reading the genetic code of a plant is regarded to be the most reliable way to identify its species. This had led to many plants being reclassified and therefore long-established names are being changed. *Rosmarinus officinalis* has been reclassified as part of the *Salvia* genus, so the botanical name is now *Salvia rosmarinus*. In this book, I have used the latest information available, but I am very aware that the plant world is evolving.**

**If I had to choose one culinary herb to take with me to a desert island it would be rosemary. No herb garden should be without this plant; it is one of the most versatile and useful herbs in the kitchen, the home and medicinally. It is associated with remembrance and for hundreds of years it has been used to improve and strengthen the memory; currently it is being trialed in the treatment of senility.**

*Salvia rosmarinus* 'Sissinghurst Blue', Rosemary Sissinghurst Blue

## History

There are many lovely stories associated with rosemary – it is said that the Virgin Mary threw her blue cloak over a rosemary bush during her flight into Egypt, transforming its formerly white flowers to blue. In medieval times, rosemary was used at banquets as an edible table decoration – large branches were dipped in egg white and sprinkled with grated tree resin to make it glisten, then set in bread or lard and placed on the table. In Elizabethan times, the wedding couple wore or carried a sprig of rosemary as a sign of fidelity and bunches of rosemary were tied with coloured ribbon tipped with gold and given to guests at weddings to symbolise love and faithfulness.

## Species

*Salvia rosmarinus*, Rosemary
Hardy, H4 (USDA 8,9), evergreen shrub. Upright habit, height and spread: 1m (3ft). Small, pale blue flowers in early spring to early summer, occasionally a second flush in early autumn. Short, needle-shaped, dark green, highly aromatic leaves.

All forms of *Salvia rosmarinus* are edible; they can vary in flavour, from the standard form to eucalyptus and to pine. They grow in three different habits: upright, prostrate and arching. These are just a few of my favourites.

### Upright

*Salvia rosmarinus* 'Green Ginger', Rosemary 'Green Ginger'
Hardy, H4 (USDA 8,9), evergreen shrub. Upright habit. Height and spread: 90cm (3ft). Small blue flowers. Short, dark green, ginger-scented, needle-shaped aromatic leaves. Great culinary flavour.

*Salvia rosmarinus* 'Jekka's Green Dragon', Rosemary 'Jekka's Green Dragon'
Hardy, H4 (USDA 8,9), evergreen shrub. Upright habit. Height and spread: 80cm (30in). Small, bright blue flowers in early spring. Mid-green, needle-shaped aromatic leaves. Great culinary flavour.

*Salvia rosmarinus* 'Sissinghurst Blue', Rosemary 'Sissinghurst Blue'
Hardy, H5 (USDA 7,8), evergreen shrub. Upright habit. Height and spread: 80cm (30in). Small, dark blue flowers. Short, fine, dark green, needle-shaped aromatic leaves.

**Prostrate**

*Salvia rosmarinus* (Prostrata Group) 'Capri'
Hardy, H3 (USDA 9), evergreen shrub. Prostrate habit. Height: 15cm (6in); spread: 60cm (24in). Small pale blue flowers. Short, bright green, needle-shaped aromatic leaves.

*Salvia rosmarinus* (Prostrata Group) 'Rampant Boule'
Hardy, H4 (USDA 8,9), evergreen shrub. Prostrate habit. Height: 40cm (16in); spread: 60cm (24in). Small blue flowers. Short, dark green, narrow, needle-shaped leaves with light silver underside.

*Salvia rosmarinus* 'Severn Sea'
Hardy, H4 (USDA 8,9), evergreen shrub. Prostrate habit. Height: 40cm (16in); spread: 90cm (3ft). Striking small blue flowers. Short, dark green, needle-shaped aromatic leaves.

**Arching**

*Salvia rosmarinus* f. *albiflorus* 'Lady in White'
Hardy, H4 (USDA 8,9), evergreen shrub. Arching habit. Height and spread: 60cm (24in). Exquisite small white flowers. Short, dark green, needle-shaped aromatic leaves.

*Salvia rosmarinus* 'Jekka's Blue'
Hardy, H4 (USDA 8,9), evergreen shrub. Arching habit. Height and spread: 70cm (27in). Small, dark blue flowers from mid-winter until mid-spring. Short, dark green, needle-shaped aromatic leaves. Good culinary flavour.

*Salvia rosmarinus* 'Majorca Pink'
Hardy, H4 (USDA 8,9), evergreen shrub. Arching habit. Height and spread: 90cm (3ft). Small, pale pink flowers with dark line in the lower lip. Short, mid-green, needle-shaped aromatic leaves.

## Propagation

**Seeds:** only the standard *Salvia rosmarinus* can be raised from seed. None of the other seeds run true to form, they are better taken as cuttings. Sow the seeds in early spring into prepared modules or seed trays using a seed compost. Place under protection at 18°C (64°F). Germination takes 1–2 weeks. It is critical to watch your watering after germination, as the seedlings are prone to damping off (see page 274). Prick out or pot up once fully rooted using a soil-based compost. Grow on in a cold frame or cold greenhouse, it is the wet that will kill the young plants not the cold. Plant out the following spring.

**Cuttings:** take cuttings of new growth in summer, after flowering, and transfer to prepared modules or small pots using three parts seed compost mixed with one part perlite. Pot up when well rooted using a soil-based potting compost. Grow on under cold protection for one season before planting out.

**Layering:** rosemary lends itself to being layered, especially with lower branches that hang down. Layer in summer by pegging a branch into the soil. In the following year, check that it is rooted, then cut the branch, removing it from the parent. Dig up the layered bit of branch and replant where required in the garden.

## Pests and diseases

The main pest to attack rosemary is the leaf hopper (see page 269). If it is on a plant growing outside it is best to tolerate it; if it is growing inside, then if you must, you can spray with a horticultural soft soap following the manufacturer's instructions. Rosemary beetle, a tiny shiny beetle about the size of my little fingernail, eats the leaves of rosemary and the flower buds on lavender. When you see them in spring through to summer remove them by hand and dispose of them. The other method is to get someone to tap the bush while you hold a sticky yellow trap underneath so the beetles fall on to it.

Rosemary dieback is becoming a problem in the UK. It is a form of phytophthora, which is noticeable when a branch suddenly goes dark brown and brittle. Immediately cut the infected branch right off to the main stem and burn the branch (do not compost). If you do not act quickly the whole bush will die. It is more prevalent in plants over five years old. If, however, you live in Europe it could be *Xylella fastidiosa*, which is a bacteria. If you do have this, remove the plant and burn it.

## How and where to grow

Rosemary requires a well-drained soil in a sheltered sunny position. It is frost-hardy, but in cold, wet areas, it is preferable to grow it against a south- or south-west facing wall. If the plant is young, it is worth giving it some added protection in winter. Sometimes the rosemary looks a bit scorched after frosts, in this case, it is best to cut it back to healthy green growth in late spring. Always prune after flowering, which will stop the plant becoming woody and maintain the shape. Remember to stay within the green as rosemary does not shoot off old wood. It is best in cold damp climates not to prune hard in the autumn, but you can cut it for use in the kitchen.

## Growing in containers

This herb looks lovely growing in containers. It is the ideal method for those living in winter temperatures below -8°C (18°F), as the plant can be brought into a cold greenhouse or shed for the winter months. Use a soil-based compost. The prostrate and less hardy varieties look very attractive and benefit from the extra protection offered by being in a container. Use three parts soil-based compost mixed with one part horticultural grit for extra drainage. Do not overwater, and feed only after flowering. Lift the pots in winter on to bricks or stones to increase drainage.

*Salvia rosmarinus* f. *albiflorus* 'Lady in White', Rosemary Lady in White

## Yearly maintenance

**Spring:** trim after flowering; sow seeds of *Salvia rosmarinus*; take softwood cuttings.

**Summer:** feed container plants; take semi-hardwood cuttings; layer plants.

**Autumn:** protect young tender plants.

**Winter:** lift container plants and put them on bricks to aid drainage.

## Harvesting and storing

**Leaves:** this is a very useful herb, as it can be picked all year round for use in the kitchen or for making a herbal tisane.

**Flowers:** harvest from early spring until early summer for use in the kitchen.

## Culinary uses

**Leaves:** the flavour of the leaves is very versatile as they go well with many forms of food from roast vegetables, meat, soups, fish and eggs, and in all forms of bread.

**Flowers:** the small flowers taste of sweet rosemary; they are lovely added to salads and scattered over cooked vegetables.

## Medicinal uses

Rosemary tea alleviates hangovers and is also helpful for clearing the head and restoring the memory. It also aids recovery from long-term stress and chronic illness. It is useful for mild to moderate depression. The oil is a good insect repellent and can be rubbed into the temples to alleviate headaches or added to the bathwater for a reviving soak. When used in cooking, it helps to stimulate the appetite. The leaves have antioxidant and antibacterial properties.

**Right** *Salvia rosmarinus* 'Majorca Pink', Rosemary Majorca Pink

# Sambucus nigra

**This herb was once regarded as one of the most magically powerful of plants in both good and evil ways. It was said that if you put the wood on the fire you would see the devil, but planted outside the back door it protected the household from evil. It is also a truly useful herb; all parts of the plant have been used at one time or another to make everything from wine to flutes. It was also considered a 'cure-all' for everything from toothache to the plague. Current research has shown that it is very good in helping people recover from colds and the flu.**

*Sambucus nigra*, Elder fruit

## History

Stone age sites from Europe reveal that elder has been valued by mankind for thousands of years for its flowers and fruit. They have been used in the kitchen and in herbal medicine, both in medieval monasteries and by the Native Americans who also ate the fruit and used it to make medicinal compounds.

## Species

*Sambucus nigra*, elder, Common Elder, Black Elder
Hardy, H6 (USDA 6,7), deciduous shrub. Height: up to 6m (20ft); spread: up to 3m (9ft). Attractive flat heads of lightly-scented, creamy-white, star-shaped flowers, which are followed by masses of small, round, black fruits. Large leaves made up of green saw-edged leaflets, which turn yellow in autumn. The leaves have an unpleasant smell when crushed and are poisonous, but they can be used to make a potent caterpillar or fly repellent.

There are over 20 species of *Sambucus*, which are rarely grown in gardens or in containers. There are however many very attractive cultivars which can look beautiful in a garden and in containers. One of my favourites is:

*Sambucus nigra* f. *porphyrophylla* 'Black Lace'
Hardy, H6 (USDA 6,7), deciduous shrub. Height: up to 4m (13ft); spread: up to 2.5m (8ft). Attractive flat heads of lightly-scented, tiny pinkish flowers, which are followed by masses of small, round, blue–black fruits. Large, deeply dissected, purplish black foliage, which looks like lace, from spring to autumn.

## Propagation

**Seeds:** in late summer collect the fruit, wash off the pulp and sow immediately. Cover with coarse horticultural sand. The seeds need stratification (see page 18). In cold climates, place outside to experience all weathers. Alternatively mix with sand and place in the crisper drawer of the refrigerator for 4 weeks, then sow. Germination takes 4–6 months, but may not occur until the following spring, so do not give up. Unlike many plants, elder will flower within three years when grown from seed. Once fully rooted, prick out and pot up using a soil-based compost. Winter the pot seedlings in a cold frame or cold greenhouse. Plant out the following spring.

**Cuttings**: take new-growth cuttings in late summer into modules or small pots, using three parts seed compost mixed with one part perlite. When fully rooted, pot up into a small pot using a soil compost and winter in a cold frame or cold greenhouse prior to planting out the following spring. Take hardwood cuttings in late autumn/early winter; they will eventually root the following spring. Use the same compost mix as for new-growth cuttings.

## Pests and diseases

In the majority of cases this herb is pest and disease free, however, I have an elder growing outside my cottage and the pest I experience is a blackbird named Denise, who usually beats me to the fruit.

## How and where to grow

Plant in a fertile moist soil in sun or dappled shade. Elder grows very rapidly – it can grow 1.2m (4ft) in one season. To maintain shape, it is worth pruning the plant back hard in autumn every three years. By doing this you will most probably sacrifice the flowers and fruit, but you will have a wonderful show of leaves and also keep the plant under control.

## Growing in containers

The standard *Sambucus nigra* does not happily grow in a container because it grows too fast. However, the 'Black Lace' variety looks very attractive. Use a soil-based compost and place in partial shade. Feed weekly with a liquid fertiliser following the manufacturer's instructions. Pot up every spring into the next size of pot. Prune every autumn to maintain shape.

## Yearly maintenance

**Spring:** check for any winter damage.

**Summer:** take semi-ripe cuttings; in late summer sow seeds.

**Autumn:** take hardwood cuttings; prune all elders back.

**Winter:** established plants do not need protection.

## Harvesting and storing

**Flowers:** pick just before they are fully open.

**Berries:** pick when they are dark-purple/blue.

## Culinary uses

**Flowers:** the flowers are lovely in the kitchen not only for making the famous elderflower cordial but also for mousses, sorbets, jellies and in stewed fruit.

**Berrles:** elderberries should not be eaten raw as they are slightly toxic; they should be cooked, which removes the toxicity. Once cooked they are great in sauces, syrups and pies.

## Medicinal uses

Medicinally the flowers are used to treat coughs, colds, allergies and arthritis. The berries are mildly laxative. The berries are high in vitamins A, B, and C, as well as calcium, potassium and iron. They are also high in the antioxidant anthocyanin.

**WARNING** | The leaves and stems are poisonous.

# Sanguisorba minor

**At the primary school that I attended in the village of Chew Magna there was only one teacher, Miss Woods. She was formidable. In those days, I was left-handed and she did not like that as it made her class room untidy (I am now right-handed). There is one thing, however, for which I am incredibly grateful: her nature walks. She taught us the names of the trees and the birds and showed us what we could eat as we walked along. One of those herbs was salad burnet. The young leaves have a dry, cool cucumber flavour, great in cheese sandwiches.**

*Sanguisorba minor*, Salad Burnet leaf

## History

The name *Sanguisorba* comes from *sanguis*, meaning 'blood', and *sorbere*, meaning 'to soak up', which is very apt because in ancient times this herb was used to staunch wounds. Salad burnet was taken by the Pilgrim Fathers to the New World. In 1865, in *The New Family Herbal*, Matthew Robinson wrote: 'the continual use of it preserves the body in health and the mind in vigour. Pick two or three of the stalks, with leaves put into a cup of wine, especially claret, are known to quicken the spirits and drive away melancholy'.

## Species

*Sanguisorba minor*, Salad Burnet
Hardy, H6 (USDA 6,7), evergreen perennial. Height: up to 60cm (24in) in flower; spread: 30cm (12in). Tiny magenta flowers are borne in summer in compact thimble-shaped heads on flowering stalks that stand 30cm (12in) or so above the leaves. Soft, grey/green leaves are divided into neat ovals with toothed edges.

*Sanguisorba officinalis*, Great Burnet, Bloodwort, Drumsticks, Maiden's Hairs, Red Knobs
Hardy, H7 (USDA 6), herbaceous perennial. Height: up to 1.2m (4ft) in flower; spread: 50cm (20in). Produces small spikes of dark crimson flowers in summer that are excellent for pollinators. Mid-green leaves divided into oval leaflets. Medicinally, this is used in Traditional Chinese Medicine to stop bleeding. This wild plant is becoming increasingly rare in the UK due to modern farming practices.

There are now many ornamental species of this herb: a good example is *Sanguisorba officinalis* 'Red Thunder'.

## Propagation

**Seeds:** sow the small flattish seed in spring or autumn into prepared seed or plug trays using a seed compost. Cover the seeds with perlite. If sown in the autumn, winter the seedlings under protection and plant out the following spring to a prepared site 30cm (12in) apart. If sown in spring, allow a period of hardening off and plant out in the same way.

**Division:** this herb is easy to divide. Dig up an established plant in the early autumn, cut back any excessive leaves, divide the plant and replant in a prepared site in the garden, or pot up using a soil-based compost. Winter in a cold frame or cold greenhouse prior to replanting in the garden in the spring.

## Pests and diseases

In the majority of cases this herb is free from pests and diseases.

## How and where to grow

The soft green leaves of salad burnet belie their strength; they are evergreen, surviving most winters in the UK and in hard ones will only die back for a short time before reappearing in early spring. This makes them very useful in the kitchen, especially in winter when all other salad herbs have finished. Plant in a well-drained soil in sun or partial shade. They are renowned for growing in chalk and in hot summers for being the only plant surviving. Traditionally, in the 16th and 17th centuries, in herb gardens, salad burnet was planted alongside the pathways mixed with thyme. This is a lovely way to incorporate it into today's herb garden, as paths give easy access to the plant, especially in winter when all other salad herbs have died back.

## Growing in containers

Salad burnet looks good and is very useful grown in a container because it comes into its own in winter. Use a soil-based compost. Once hot weather arrives, the leaves will become bitter. Trim the plant back to keep its compact form and to inhibit flowering; this will also promote new, tender growth. Maintain watering throughout the growing season. Feed weekly with comfrey or a liquid seaweed fertiliser.

## Yearly maintenance

**Spring:** sow seeds; divide established plants.

**Summer:** keep cutting the plant to stop it flowering if being used for culinary purposes.

**Autumn:** sow seeds; divide established plants.

**Winter:** no need for protection, it is fully hardy.

## Harvesting and storing

**Leaves:** pick young new-growth leaves when required – they can be harvested all year round. They can also be preserved in a white wine vinegar if required.

## Culinary uses

**Leaves:** the best season for harvest is spring from the new growth and early autumn once you have cut back to encourage the plant to produce new growth. Mature leaves are very bitter and very drying to the mouth and are really not of much culinary merit. Use young leaves in salads, with egg dishes, with cream or cottage cheese and in drinks.

## Medicinal uses

Salad burnet reputedly gives relief from indigestion if a few leaves are eaten. It is known to be a carminative, digestive and antioxidant. It contains, vitamin A, B and C and is rich in calcium, potassium, iron and magnesium.

*Sanguisorba minor*, Salad Burnet flower

**Common names:** Winter Savory, Mountain Savory, Timo, Sajolida, Throumbi, Sarriette de Garrigues

# Satureja montana

**It was not until I started the Herb Farm that I found out that were lots of different savorys other than the summer savory that my mother grew every year to use liberally on her broad beans. They are all delicious with food and for making preserves and vinegars.**

*Saturjea montana* subsp. *illyrica*, Illyrica Savory

## History

This ancient herb has been used as food flavouring for over 2,000 years. The Romans used it to flavour sauces and vinegar and the Ancient Egyptians used it in love potions. In southern Italy, where it grows wild, it has been used not only with grilled fish and lamb but also to swill out the wine barrels before refilling them with the new season's crop. Bunches of winter savory, which is known as mountain savory, were attached to each barrel to deter fruit flies from entering the barrels while the grapes fermented.

## Species

*Satureja montana*, Winter Savory
Hardy, H4 (USDA 8,9), partial evergreen shrub. Height and spread: up to 45cm (18in). Small mauve flowers tinged with white and pink in summer. Dark green, linear, pungent, aromatic leaves.

*Satureja hortensis,* Summer Savory, Bean Herb, St Julian's Herb
Hardy, H2 (USDA 10), annual. Height and spread: 25cm (10in). Small, white-tinged mauve flowers in summer and small, linear, pungent, mid-green/olive leaves. This is a favourite in Europe and America, where it is widely used with bean dishes. In Germany it is known as *bohnenkraut*, bean herb.

*Satureja montana* subsp. *Illyrica*, Illyrica Savory, Dwarf Winter Savory
Hardy, H4 (USDA 8,9), partial evergreen shrub. Height and spread: up to 40cm (16in). Attractive small purple flowers in summer and dark green, linear, pungent leaves. Like winter savory, this has a strong flavour which is excellent for marinades, grilled meat, vegetables and pulses.

*Satureja spicigera*, Creeping Savory
Hardy, H4 (USDA 8,9), herbaceous perennial. Height: 8cm (3in); spread: 60cm (24in). Small white flowers in late summer until early autumn and bright green, linear, highly pungent leaves. This can be found growing wild in Sardinia where it is one of the ingredients in salami. In cold, damp climates only prune hard in late spring, removing all last year's growth, which will expose the new growth.

*Satureja biflora*, African Savory, Lemon Savory
Hardy, H3 (USDA 9), partial evergreen shrub. Height and spread: 30cm (12in), Small, white/pink flowers that have a lemon flavour. Narrow, mid-green, linear leaves that have a spicy lemon flavour. This savory goes well with pulses and vegetable dishes.

## Propagation

**Seeds:** only winter and summer savory can be raised from seed. Sow seeds in early spring into prepared modules or seed trays using three parts seed compost mixed with one part perlite. Place under protection at 18ºC (64ºF). Germination takes 1–2 weeks. Once germinated do not overwater as the seedlings are prone to damping off (see page 274). Once the seedlings are large enough to handle pot up into small pots using three parts soil-based compost mixed with one part horticultural grit. Grow under protection for a few weeks, then harden off before planting out into a prepared site when all threat of frost has passed.

**Cuttings:** all savorys can be grown from cuttings, including summer savory. Take the cuttings in late spring/early summer before flowering. Use three parts seed compost mixed with one part perlite. Once fully rooted, pot up into small pots using three parts soil-based compost mixed with one part horticultural grit. Grow on in containers in a cold greenhouse prior to planting out the following late spring into a prepared site.

**Division:** only creeping savory can be divided; you will find that each section has its own root system similar to its cousin, creeping thyme (see page 246). Dig up an established plant in the spring after the frosts have finished and divide into as many segments as you require. The minimum size of a new plant is only dependent on each having a root system and the time you are prepared to wait until the plant is re-established. Replant into the garden into a prepared site.

## Pests and diseases

These herbs rarely suffer from pests or disease. Summer savory may get green fly if grown in too rich a soil or potting compost.

## How and where to grow

All types of savory prefer to be planted in a well-drained poor soil in a sunny position that has not been fed with well-rotted manure or compost the previous autumn. Winter savory can be used as a low edging plant; it is very pretty in the summer, especially when in flower. Cut back perennial savorys after flowering, with the exception of creeping savory, which flowers in the autumn. Keep picking summer savory from the top to maintain leaf supply for as long as possible. Do not feed garden plants with compost or liquid fertiliser, this will make the plant too lush, prone to pests and lose flavour.

## Growing in containers

Because savory grows naturally in hot climates in rocky conditions, in cold or damp climates they work well as container plants. Pot up using three parts soil-based compost mixed with one part horticultural grit. Place in a sunny, dry, sheltered position for the growing season. Place on bricks in the winter to aid drainage.

## Yearly maintenance

**Spring:** sow seedsof winter or summer savory; divide creeping savory; take cuttings in late spring.

**Summer:** keep picking and do not allow summer savory to flower if you wish to maintain the leaf production. After flowering of the shrub varieties, prune to maintain shape.

**Autumn:** do not prune creeping savory.

**Winter:** protect in hard frosts.

## Harvesting and storing

**Leaves:** the best leaves are from the new tip growth; these are the most pungent and succulent.

**Flowers:** pick the flowers just as they open.

## Culinary uses

**Leaves:** savory is known as 'the bean herb'; it combines well with all forms of bean, from broad beans to dried pulses, and it also aids digestion and prevents flatulence from the beans. Savory has a sweet aroma and pungent flavour; it has been used as a substitute for black pepper but the flavour is lost when the herb is boiled.

**Flowers:** the small flowers pack a powerful flavour; they go well with cheese, salads and with plums and pears.

## Medicinal uses

The leaves aid and stimulate digestion; they also ease colic, flatulence and feelings of fullness. Savory is anti-bacterial, antifungal and antiseptic which is similar to its cousins thyme, rosemary and oregano.

**WARNING** | Do not take the essential oil internally without professional supervision. Do not take medicinally during pregnancy.

# Silybum marianum

**The botanical name of this herb always gives delight to children. It is a wonderful way to introduce them to the world of herbs and plants. I have grown this herb for years and despite its knack of appearing where it is not wanted, it is saved by the fact that the seedlings are edible, as well as the joy of watching the bees, especially the bumblebees, feasting in the sweetly scented flowers. For these reasons, it is worth accepting its annual invasion.**

## History

The botanical name *Silybum* is from the Greek *silybon*, a term used by Dioscorides for thistle-like plants. It was most probably introduced to the UK before the 16th century as a medicinal herb. In the Mediterranean, which is where this herb originated, it was not only used medicinally it was also traditionally cultivated as a vegetable. When boiled, the roots are rather like salsify, while the flavour of the cooked young leaves, with their spines removed, is said to resemble spinach.

## Species

*Silybum marianum*, Milk Thistle
Hardy, H4 (USDA 8,9), biennial, often grown as an annual. Height: up to 1.2m (4ft) when in flower; spread: up to 60cm (24in). The sweetly scented purple flower heads with spiny bracts flower in the second year. These are followed in summer by black seeds, each bearing a tuft of white hairs. Rosettes of large, dark green leaves with prominent white veins that are lobed or pinnately cut, with spiny margins.

## Propagation

Sow fresh seeds either in the autumn as a biennial, or in the spring as an annual, into prepared module trays or small pots, using a standard seed compost. If you sow in a standard seed tray you can find that the seedlings do not thrive so well when transplanted. If sown in autumn, the seeds often germinate within days; winter the seedlings in a cold frame or unheated greenhouse. When sown in spring no extra heat is required. Once the seedlings are large enough, either plant out in the garden in a prepared site or pot up using a soil-based potting compost.

## Pests and diseases

This herb rarely, if ever, suffers from disease. With regards to pests, young plants are 'bonne bouche' for slugs and snails.

## How and where to grow

This is a stunning herb but as each seed has its own mini parachute, if they set seed when there is a breeze be prepared for an invasion of seedlings; it is very lucky they are edible. When choosing where to plant this herb take this point into consideration. There are, despite this, many reasons for growing this herb, it is wonderful for attracting pollinators and the flowers smell delightful. It will tolerate most soils, but grow in sun or partial shade as it does not like shade.

## Growing in containers

Milk thistle happily grows in containers. It is best to actually sow the seeds into a large container using a soil-based compost. The reason to sow directly into them is that you get a far better and stronger display. Once the seeds have germinated, and depending on the size of the container, thin the seedlings to either one or two seedlings per 2-litre (4USpt) pot. Once the leaves fill the size of the pot, pot up to a 5-litre (10USpt) pot and let it run to flower.

## Yearly maintenance

**Spring:** sow seeds; harvest young leaves.

**Summer:** harvest flowers and seeds.

**Autumn:** sow seeds.

**Winter:** winter seedlings in a cold frame or cold greenhouse.

## Harvesting and storing

**Seedlings:** harvest the seedlings in spring.

**Leaves:** harvest the leaves from plants sown in the spring in that same summer.

**Flower heads:** harvest the flower heads just before they open.

**Seeds:** harvest the plant when it is flowering; collect the seeds when ripe.

**Roots:** harvest the roots in the late spring from seeds sown the previous summer.

All parts can be dried for use in infusions and tinctures or for extraction of silymarin.

*Silybum marianum*, Milk Thistle

## Culinary uses

Every part of the milk thistle may be eaten and is nutritious.

**Seedlings:** the young seedlings before they develop prickles are eaten raw in salads.

**Leaves:** steamed, the leaves have a flavour similar to spinach. The sharp spines need to be cut off the leaves before cutting or shredding prior to steaming or cooking.

**Flower heads:** flower heads can be prepared in the same way as the globe artichoke, but they are very small and it is a bit fiddly – to put it mildly.

**Seeds:** the seeds can be eaten raw, they have a nutty flavour and can be ground in a food processor and then sprinkled over breakfast cereal. However, toasting the seeds helps to break down a mildly irritating substance in the seed coat (if you eat the seeds raw and they have the coating on them they can make you cough). The toasted and ground seed can be sprinkled over cereals or combined with other herbs as a seasoning.

**Roots:** the roots are best steamed or roasted and have a similar flavour to parsnips or salsify.

## Medicinal uses

Milk thistle contains a unique substance that is collectively referred to as 'silymarin'. It protects the liver against toxins. It is used medicinally to treat liver and gall bladder diseases, jaundice, cirrhosis, hepatitis and poisoning by alcohol, drugs and other chemicals.

**Common names:** Stevia, Aztec Herb, Sweet Leaf, Honey Leaf, Yerba Dulce, Caa-ehe

# Stevia rebaudiana

**This is a truly amazing herb: you only have to take the smallest piece of leaf and put it on the end of your tongue to realise that all the claims that it is 100–300 times sweeter than table sugar are true; and it has no carbohydrates, calories or artificial ingredients. Sadly, here in the UK, the Food Standards Agency class this herb as a 'novel food', which is a food that has not been widely consumed by people in the UK or EU before May 1997. Equally, the US Food and Drug Administration (FDA) says that it doesn't have enough information about the fresh herb and therefore potential impact on your health. But its use in any processed drink, food or dried product is totally safe.**

*Stevia rebaudiana*, Stevia

## History

The leaves of this herb have been used as a sweetener for hundreds of years by the indigenous peoples of Brazil and the Guarani Indians of Paraguay who called it kaa jheé and have used it to sweeten their yerba mate tea. Commercial cultivation is now worldwide from Japan to the USA and the hilly areas of Nepal.

## Species

*Stevia rebaudiana*, Stevia
Half hardy, H3 (USDA 9), sub-tropical perennial, often grown as an annual. Height: up to 60cm (24in) in flower; spread: up to 50cm (20in), in warm climates the height and spread can reach 1m (3ft). Loose clusters of tubular white flowers in late summer/early autumn. Lance-shaped bright green leaves.

## Propagation

**Seeds:** in spring, sow fresh seeds into prepared seed or module trays using a standard seed compost mixed in equal parts with standard perlite. Water the trays before sowing, sow on the surface, cover with perlite and place under protection at 18°C (64°F). Germination is erratic – be patient. Once the seedlings are large enough, pot up using three parts soil-based potting compost mixed with one part standard perlite.

**Cuttings:** this is a far more reliable method. Take semi-ripe cuttings from established plants from non-flowering shoots in late spring/early summer. Place in prepared modules using the same mix as for seed sowing. Place in a propagator at 18°C (64°F); rooting takes 14 days dependent on light levels. Once rooted pot up using three parts soil-based potting compost mixed with one part standard perlite.

## Pests and diseases

If you are growing stevia in a glasshouse or conservatory you will find it is very prone to white fly and thrips (see page 272). To control these if they get out of hand, use a soft horticultural soap (see page 266 for more information). If it is early autumn, cut the plant back hard and it will shoot new growth from the base. It is also prone to die back if overwatered, especially in the winter months when the light level is low. The solution, if the stem has not gone black, is to keep the plants virtually dry, introducing water in the spring as the light levels increase. If the stem has gone black, bin the plants.

Mildew can be a problem, again this occurs if you are growing stevia in a glasshouse with little air movement in winter. Remove all infected leaves, spray with potassium bicarbonate (see page 276 for more information). If you cannot open the doors or vents, use a fan set to cold air – this is very beneficial for the whole greenhouse.

## How and where to grow

It is worth bearing in mind that stevia's natural climate is semi-humid, subtropical with temperature extremes from 21–43°C (70–109°F), averaging 24°C (75°F). The plants are not frost-hardy. In cold climates you can plant out just for the summer months. The easiest way is to sink the plant in the pot into the soil in a sunny position so that you can lift it in early autumn when the night temperature drops below 10°C (50°F).

## Growing in containers

In cool climates, this makes a great container plant: use three parts soil-based compost mixed with one part perlite. Throughout the season, water and feed regularly with a liquid fertiliser following the manufacturer's instructions. In the autumn, move the container into a frost-free environment, such as a conservatory, greenhouse or windowsill. Cut the plant back to between 10–15cm (4–6in) and reduce the water to minimal, but do not leave it totally dry. Reintroduce watering in the spring as the day length increases and pot up one size of pot. Place outside once all threat of frost has passed and the night temperature does not drop below 10°C (50°F). Moving the plant outside will help prevent it from getting attacked by pests.

## Yearly maintenance

**Spring:** sow seeds.

**Summer:** take cuttings; harvest leaves for drying.

**Autumn:** in cold climates bring plants inside to protect from frosts.

**Winter:** cut back the watering of container plants and keep frost free.

## Harvesting and storing

**Leaves:** outside the tropics you can harvest the leaves from late spring to mid-autumn. The best time to harvest for drying is in early summer.

## Culinary uses

This herb truly does mean that you can cook many dishes without the use of sugar. The most important point to remember is not to use too much because you will ruin your dish. Stevia is excellent with any recipe using fruit, juices or dairy. It can withstand high temperatures and they will not destroy its sweetness but it is not good for home baking (with a few exceptions) because it lacks sugar's abilities to add texture, caramelise or feed the fermentation of yeast.

## Medicinal uses

In today's society this herb really does have potential in the treatment of obesity, it is also used medicinally as a cardiotonic, for hypertension and heartburn and to help lower uric acid levels.

# Symphytum officinale

**My very first large order – in the 1980s – was for *Symphytum officinale*. I was contacted by one of the racing stables in Lambourn in the North Wessex Downs, who required 100 plants as they wished to use the leaves as a poultice on horses' cuts and strains and they were going to add the leaves to the feed to help prevent laminitis. At that time I only knew of comfrey as one of the best liquid fertilisers. It was this order that made me begin to realise the varied potential of herbs.**

## History

Comfrey has been used for thousands of years as a poultice and as a plaster. One of my favourite historic stories is from Yorkshire in the north of England. At the Yorkshire coal fields, comfrey poultices were used to treat what was called a 'beet knee'. This was caused by crawling in the low seams of the mine – it turned the knees purple and made it incredibly painful to walk. The cure was so simple. The comfrey leaves were boiled, drained and placed as hot as the patient could stand directly on the offending knee and a bandage was put tightly over the leaves to hold them in place. In the morning the swelling had gone down, nearly normal colour had returned to the knee and the patient was able to return to work.

## Species

Identifying *Symphytum* can be difficult as it can vary from plant to plant of the same species and is prone to hybridisation. The three most common species are identified here. All are interchangeable both as a culinary and medicinal herb.

*Symphytum officinale*, Comfrey, Wild Comfrey
Hardy, H7 (USDA 6), perennial. Height and spread: up to 1m (3ft). Clusters of white/purple/pink tubular flowers in summer. Green, lance-shaped, hairy leaves. This is the best medicinal comfrey and can also be used as a liquid feed. It makes a first-class composting plant as it helps the rapid breakdown of other compost materials.

*Symphytum x uplandicum*, Russian Comfrey
Hardy, H7 (USDA 6), perennial. Height and spread: up to 1m (3ft). Clusters of pink/purple tubular flowers in summer. Green, lance-shaped, hairy leaves. This is a natural hybrid that occurred in Upland, Sweden and is a cross between *Symphytum officinale*, the herbalist's comfrey, and *Symphytum asperum*, rough comfrey from Russia, which has blue flowers.

*Symphytum orientale*, White Comfrey
Hardy, H6 (USDA 6,7), deciduous to semi-evergreen perennial. Height and spread: up to 50cm (20in). Clusters of tubular white flowers in early summer. Lance-shaped, wrinkled, hairy dark green leaves. This comfrey is a native of Turkey and the Ukraine and is now naturalised in the UK.

## Propagation

**Seeds:** I do not recommend this as germination is slow and erratic. However, if it is impossible to get a plant, you can sow the seeds in autumn into a prepared seed or module tray using a standard seed compost. Place the container outside to experience all weathers. Germination should occur in the spring.

**Division:** established plants can be divided in the garden, however, be aware that by dividing you will always have the original plant as it is virtually impossible to remove all the roots.

**Root cuttings:** this is the most reliable method of propagation. Dig up an established plant; any root left in the garden will regrow. Slice the washed root into 2cm (1in) sections. Place the sections – there is no right or wrong way up – either in small pots or large modules using a standard seed compost. Water in well, then leave in a warm, frost-free place until you see new shoots appearing. Do not let the compost dry out.

## Pests and diseases

All comfrey plants sometimes suffer from rust and powdery mildew in late autumn. In both cases, cut the plant down and burn or bin the contaminated leaves. For more information see page 276.

## How and where to grow

All comfreys prefer sun or semi-shade and a moist soil but will tolerate most conditions. The large tap root is a problem in some gardens, so choose your site carefully before planting. Perhaps the best place is in an unwanted corner where you can let it grow undisturbed and where you can see the attractive flowers that are loved by many pollinators.

## Growing in containers

If you have a small garden and wish to grow comfrey so that you can harvest the leaves to make a liquid fertiliser then a large container, even a dustbin, is ideal. Use soil from the garden, or a soil-based compost as this will help retain water in the summer. Place the container in semi-shade.

## Yearly maintenance

**Spring:** divide plants.

**Summer:** cut back leaves for composting, or as a good mulch to put around other herbs in the growing season.

**Autumn:** take root cuttings; sow seed.

**Winter:** does not need protection.

## Harvesting and storing

**Leaves:** harvest very young leaves in spring for use in the kitchen. Harvest the leaves for drying before flowering in the spring. Harvest the leaves for making a liquid feed from spring until early autumn. Each plant is able to give four cuts a year.

**Flowers:** harvest the flowers from early summer until early autumn.

**Roots:** dig roots up in autumn for drying.

## Culinary uses

History shows that the fresh leaves and shoots were eaten as a vegetable and/or salad, however the leaves are hairy, and if you are tempted to eat them only pick young leaves and slice them very finely – they are not to everyone's taste and it is still questionable whether they are safe to eat. The flowers are edible and look great added to summer salads.

## Medicinal uses

Comfrey is a rich source of protein, minerals and vitamins. The root contains allotone, a jelly-like substance used in country medicine to help fractured bones. A cream made from the leaves is very healing for cuts, bruises, sores and varicose veins.

**WARNING** | The plant contains small quantities of a toxic alkaloid, which, when used internally, can have a cumulative effect on the liver.

*Symphytum officinale*, Comfrey

**Common names:** Winter Tarragon, Sweet Mace, Four-seasons Tarragon, Mexican Tarragon

# Tagetes lucida

**There are about 50 species of annual and perennial *Tagetes* found mainly in the tropical and subtropical Americas. I have chosen three Mexican marigolds, which I find invaluable in an organic herb garden. The first, which is the feature herb *Tagetes lucida*, was used by the Aztecs as a medicinal herb and is now a culinary delight. It is also incredibly useful because burning the leaves makes a good insect repellent and, if you have a pet, the juice from the crushed leaves dropped onto a tick makes them easy to remove. The other two, *Tagetes patula* and *Tagetes lemmonii*, are both good for pest control and great companion plants.**

*Tagetes lemmonii*, Lemmon's Marigold

## History

*Tagetes lucida* is indigenous to southern and central Mexico. It is said that the Aztecs used it to flavour chocólatl, a cocoa-based drink and today it is still popular with the Tarahumara Indians of Chihuahua and revered by the modern Huichol Indians as a shamanic trance – 'tobacco' – which is used in their religious rituals. Sadly, today it is on the International Union for Conservation of Nature (IUCN)'s red list of threatened plants.

## Species

*Tagetes lucida*, Winter Tarragon, Mexican Tarragon
Half-hardy, H3 (USDA 9), herbaceous perennial. Height: up to 80cm (30in) in warm climates only; spread: 45cm (18in). Sweetly-scented yellow flowers in late summer; it rarely flowers in cold temperatures. Narrow, lance-shaped, aromatic, toothed mid-green leaves, which have a strong aniseed scent and flavour. This herb, in cool climates, dies back in late winter, reappearing in late spring.

**Tagetes to control pests and to act as a companion plant**

*Tagetes patula*, Wild Mexican Marigold, French Marigold
Half hardy, H2 (USDA 10), annual. Height: 1.2 m (4ft); spread: 45cm (18 in). Clusters of single yellow flowers in midsummer until the first frosts. Aromatic, deeply divided, lightly toothed mid-green leaves. Deters nematodes in the soil and repels white fly from tomatoes. The leaves have been used to flavour food. Medicinally it is a diuretic and improves the digestion. Externally it has been used to treat sore eyes and rheumatism. The flowers have been used to feed poultry and to colour dairy products and textiles.

*Tagetes lemmonii*, Lemmon's Marigold
Half hardy, H3 (USDA 9), evergreen perennial. Height: up to 1.5m (5ft); spread: up to 3m (9ft). Pretty, bright golden daisy-like flowers about 5cm (2in) in diameter with darker yellow discs. Highly fragrant lemon- and musky-scented green divided leaves. The scent discourages deer and is attractive to bees and butterflies. It is also drought tolerant. Great as a low hedge in a Mediterranean garden.

## Propagation

**Seeds:** sow the seeds of all three mentioned above in spring into prepared seed or module trays using a seed compost mixed in equal parts with standard perlite. Place under protection at 18°C (64°F). Germination takes 14–21 days. Once the seedlings are large enough to handle, pot up using a soil-based potting compost mixed in equal parts with horticultural sand. Alternatively, if you live in a warm climate you can sow directly into a prepared site when the night temperature does not fall below 12°C (54°F). Germination takes 2–4 weeks.

**Cuttings:** both the perennial species mentioned here can be grown from cuttings taken in early summer. Place the cuttings into modules that have been filled with a seed compost mixed in equal parts with perlite. Grow on in a sheltered warm place – a windowsill or glasshouse – until rooted, which takes approximately 2–3 weeks. Once fully rooted, pot up into a loam-based compost mixed in equal parts with horticultural sand.

## Pests and diseases

Pests are not a problem but cold, damp climates are; mildew can occur. If it does, especially on the winter tarragon, either remove the infected leaves or cut the plant back. Make sure you place the plant in a well-ventilated position, so that there is good air circulation because if the old leaves become too damp they can rot the crown. If you feel as if you are losing the plants, spray with baking powder (see page 276).

## How and where to grow

All these *Tagetes* can be planted outside once all threat of frost has passed. Plant in a well-drained fertile soil in a sunny position; they will withstand partial shade. Alternatively, sink the plant in its pot into the ground for the summer; this way you will not stress the plant when you lift it when the nighttime temperatures fall below 12°C (54°F) and bring it into a frost-free environment.

## Growing in containers

All these *Tagetes* are ideal for growing in containers. Pot up using a soil-based potting compost mixed in equal parts with horticultural sand. Once the night temperature falls below 12°C (54°F) bring the container into a frost-free environment and cut back the watering to minimal but not totally dry. If you are living in a warm climate, lift the pots for the winter on to bricks or stones to aid drainage. Repot each spring, after removing any winter dieback. Only pot up one size of pot at a time as this herb likes being pot-bound.

## Yearly maintenance

**Spring:** sow seeds; cut back any winter growth.

**Summer:** take cuttings.

**Autumn:** lift garden plants and bring in containers once the night temperature falls below 12°C (54°F).

**Winter:** cut the watering back to minimal.

## Harvesting and storing

**Leaves:** The leaves of winter tarragon can be picked as required throughout the growing season for using fresh. Alternatively pick in midsummer for drying.

## Culinary uses

Winter tarragon not only makes a good substitute for *Artemisia dracunculus,* French tarragon, (see page 66) in winter when it has died back into the ground, it is also useful in places where it is difficult to grow French tarragon, i.e. in humid climates. The leaves of this tarragon are much stronger and more anise than the French variety so use with discretion until you get used to it.

## Medicinal uses

The leaves of winter tarragon are used as a relaxant and to treat diarrhoea, indigestion, malaria and feverishness. It also has the reputation of being a very good hangover cure.

**WARNING** | Not to be taken medicinally when pregnant or breast feeding.

# Tanacetum parthenium

**On all the old ordnance survey maps showing my farm, the land around us is called 'clay fields', which is not the ideal situation one might think of for growing herbs. However, there are many herbs that will adapt and flourish in these conditions. Feverfew and its fellow *Tanacetum*, tansy, give wonderful displays throughout the summer and because the soil is heavy, they do not romp away as they would do in a light soil, making them much more controllable.**

## History

The old herbalists called feverfew a febrifuge, which was a medicine used to reduce fevers. However, strange as it may seem, the herb was hardly ever employed in folk medicines to treat fevers. Gerard, the Elizabethan herbalist, advised use of the dried plant for those that were 'giddied in the head or have the turning called vertigo'. In the 17th century, Culpeper also advised it be used for pains in the head and colds. Tansy, on the other hand, was used by the ancients in the preparation of embalming sheets and was also rubbed on corpses to save them from earthworms or corpse worm, which is how it got the nickname 'the immortal herb'.

## Species

*Tanacetum parthenium*, Feverfew
Hardy, H6 (USDA 6,7), herbaceous perennial. Height: up to 1.2m (4ft); spread: 45cm (18in). Clusters of small, white, yellow-eyed daisy flowers from early summer until the first frosts. The leaf is mid-green, lobed and divided with lightly serrated edges.

*Tanacetum parthenium* 'Aureum', Golden Feverfew, Golden Feather
Hardy, H6 (USDA 6,7), perennial. Height: up to 45cm (18in) in flower; spread: 50cm (20in). Small, white, daisy-like flowers from early summer to early autumn. The leaf is a typical chrysanthemum shape – oblong with chunks cut out. The gold/green leaves remain colourful all year round.

*Tanacetum vulgare*, Tansy, Bachelor's Buttons, Bitter Buttons, Golden Buttons, Stinking Willy, Hind Heel, Parsley Fern
Hardy, H7 (USDA 6), herbaceous perennial. Height: up to 75cm (30in) in flower; spread: easily 1m (3ft) in light soil. Clusters of yellow, button-like flowers from summer until late autumn. Aromatic, feathery-looking dark green leaves, which are very divided, with toothed edges.

## Propagation

**Seeds:** both tansy and feverfew have small seeds that are oblong and often stick together, making them difficult to sow. Put a small amount of dry fine horticultural sand in a paper bag, add a small amount of seed, close the bag, then shake, so diluting the seed with the sand, making it easier to sow thinly. In autumn or spring, sow into a prepared seed tray (easier than modules), that has been watered prior to sowing. Sow on the surface, do not cover. Place in a cold frame or cold greenhouse. Germination takes 2–4 weeks in autumn or 7–10 days in spring. Winter seedlings in a cold frame. As soon as the seedlings are large enough to handle, either pot up or, if in spring, plant out after all threat of frost has passed.

**Division:** divide established plants of both feverfew and tansy in autumn or spring, replanting them into a prepared site. However, please be aware that tansy spreads on creeping rhizomes so every bit of tansy root left in the garden will grow, hence the description 'immortal herb'.

## Pests and diseases

This plant is unaffected by the majority of pests and diseases. The golden feverfew can suffer from sun scorch; if this occurs, cut back and the new growth will be unaffected.

## How and where to grow

Plant in a well-drained soil in a sunny position. Both species are drought tolerant and will adapt to most soils and conditions, however, if planted in shade they are unlikely to flower. You must consider carefully before planting *Tanacetum vulgare* in a small garden as it is very invasive. There is no need to feed the soil prior to planting as this will make the plants weak and prone to disease.

## Growing in containers

Both tansy and feverfew, especially golden feverfew, grow happily in containers. Use a soil-based potting compost. Only feed monthly through the growing season with liquid seaweed feed. Cut back plants after flowering as this will help maintain their shape and stop the feverfew self-seeding.

## Yearly maintenance

**Spring:** sow seeds; divide established plants.

**Summer:** cut back after flowering – this will encourage new leaf growth and minimise self-seeding.

**Autumn:** divide established plants. This is the best time for sowing if edging plants are required. The young plants will need to be wintered in a cold frame.

**Winter:** no need for protection – fully frost-hardy.

## Harvesting and storing

**Leaves:** pick the leaves before flowering to use fresh or to dry.

**Flowers:** pick the flower heads just as they open for drying.

## Culinary uses

The young leaves of feverfew can be added to salads, but they are bitter, so use sparingly. It is worth remembering that before reclassification feverfew was a chrysanthemum.

Tansy was used as a flavouring and colouring in tansy cakes, which were popular in England from medieval times until the mid-18th century. Tansy leaf is very bitter so use sparingly and only use very young spring leaves. I have noticed it is back in fashion due to foraging.

## Medicinal uses

Feverfew is a renowned remedy for certain types of migraines. Eat 2–3 fresh leaves in between slices of bread, adding a sprig of mint or parsley to make it more palatable. Do not be tempted to eat more. A decoction made from the leaves is a good basic household disinfectant. Tansy can only be used medicinally by a qualified herbalist. However, by rubbing the leaves into the coat of a dog or cat it is good for deterring fleas. A scattering of dried leaves and flowers over the floor or in a cupboard also helps to deter ants and mice.

**WARNING** | One side effect associated with taking feverfew is mouth ulcers.

*Tanecetum vulgare*, Tansy

**Common names:** Wood Sage, Gypsy Sage, Mountain Sage, Garlic Sage, Woodland Germander

# Teucrium scorodonia

**I have a soft spot for wood sage, it is ideally suited for my heavy-clay, slightly shady garden, giving a lovely subtle display in summer. The cultivated form, with its crinkled leaves, always causes a comment – it is either loved or disliked; to me it is delightful. It is wonderful that it is coming back into vogue, and is being used by many landscape architects and has featured in a number of RHS Chelsea Flower Show gardens recently.**

## History

Historically, it had the common name 'hind heal', which came from the theory that the hind (female deer) will eat it when sick or wounded. It is thought that it is probably the same herb as *Elaphoboscum*, which is eaten by the red deer on Crete. It grows wild in Jersey where it was known as 'ambroise' and was used as a substitute for hops.

## Species

*Teucrium scorodonia*, Wood Sage
Hardy H6 (USDA 6,7), herbaceous perennial. Height: up to 60cm (24in) when in flower; spread: 30cm (12in). Pale greenish-white flowers in summer. Soft green heart-shaped leaves, which have a mild smell of garlic when crushed. Traditionally, the leaves and flowers were used as a flavouring for ale, before hops were introduced. It was said that it cleared the ale from the sediment and solids because a clear or bright brew tended to be of higher quality, however it did give the ale a darker colour.

*Teucrium scorodonia* 'Crispum', Curly Wood Sage
Hardy, H5 (USDA 7,8), semi-evergreen perennial. Height and spread: 50cm (20in). Pale greenish-yellow flowers, which often have a red tint in summer. The leaves are soft oval, olive green with a reddish tinge to the crinkled edge. This herb was much used by Gertrude Jekyll (a British horticulturist and garden designer in the 19th century) who recognised its value within the garden.

## Propagation

**Seeds:** sow fresh seeds in autumn, using three parts seed compost mixed with one part perlite. Place outside for the winter. The seeds need stratification to germinate (see page 18). In warm climates, place the seed mixed with a small amount of damp horticultural sand in the crisper drawer of the refrigerator for 1 month prior to sowing. Germination after sowing will take 4–6 months. When large enough to handle, plant out into a prepared site 20cm (8in) apart.

**Cuttings:** both varieties can be grown from soft wood cuttings taken from the new growth in spring, or semi-hard wood cuttings in summer. Use the same compost mix as for seed. Once fully rooted, pot up into small pots and winter in a cold greenhouse or cold frame.

**Division:** both wood sages produce creeping root stock, just like their cousin mint. In the spring they are easy to divide. Dig up the plants, split in half and replant in your chosen site. Alternatively, if you have a free-draining soil you can divide established garden plants in the autumn, replanting into a prepared site.

## Pests and diseases

In the majority of cases, wood sage is free from pests and disease.

## How and where to grow

Planted in the right position in the garden, this plant can look most attractive. The plant grows well in semi-shaded situations but also thrives in full sun on sandy and gravelly soils. It will adapt quite happily to clay and heavy soils, but it does not produce such prolific growth. There is no need for extra watering during the summer months, nor for extra protection in winter as the plants die back and are fully hardy.

## Growing in containers

Curly wood sage looks most attractive grown in terracotta pots. Use a soil-based compost mixed one part horticultural grit to three parts compost. Plant in a large container as it does produce creeping root stock and can easily become pot-bound. Do not overfeed – it is better to be mean and only feed it twice in a growing season otherwise the leaves become large, soft and floppy. As the plant dies back in winter, put the container somewhere cool, lift it on to bricks or stones and keep it bordering on dry.

## Yearly maintenance

**Spring:** sow seeds; divide established plants; take soft wood cuttings.

**Summer:** take semi-hard wood cuttings; cut back after flowering.

**Autumn:** sow seeds if required; divide established plants if you have a well-drained soil.

**Winter:** no need for protection as the plants die back for the winter.

## Harvesting and storing

**Leaves:** for culinary use, pick the leaves in spring. For medicinal use, pick the leaves either side of flowering to use fresh or to dry.

## Culinary uses

It is said that the leaves and flower resemble the flavour of hops. Personally, I get a very light garlic flavour with extremely bitter notes. In spring, the very young leaves are good in salads. As the leaves mature, but before they become tough, they are interesting in stir-fry dishes. With the trend for home-brewed ales, there has been a resurgence in interest in this herb.

## Medicinal uses

Traditionally it was used to treat fevers, colds, sore throats, kidneys and urinary problems, however it is little used today.

*Teucrium scorodonia* 'Crispum', Curly Wood Sage

# Thymus vulgaris

**I am a little obsessed with thyme plants; I can be found at plant fairs hunting them out, as others hunt truffles. They come in all shapes and sizes and can vary in scent from wonderful spicy orange and herby lemon to pungent pine. The leaves can vary from large and round to long and thin, or even woolly. I defy anyone not to want thyme in the garden, especially when it is in flower.**

*Thymus pulegioides*, Broad-leaved thyme

## History

It is said that *Thymus* was derived from the Greek *thumos*, which stems from *thuos*, meaning 'a wood that gives off a pleasant smell when burned'. The Ancient Greeks burned thyme as an incense, not only for its lovely aroma but also for its cleansing, disinfectant and antiseptic properties. In the 16th and 17th centuries it was one of the many herbs used in nosegays to purify the odours from disease, and judges used it along with sage to prevent gaol fever.

## Species

We grow over 70 different varieties of thymes at the Herb Farm so I have chosen just a few of my favourites which I have divided into six growing types.

### 1. Common thyme

These varieties of thymes all have the botanical name *vulgaris*, which translates as common. They can be found in many forms all around the world. As a rule, these are the thymes of the people and have been used for thousands of years. They have the best culinary flavour and can also be used medicinally to make a beneficial herbal tisane.

*Thymus vulgaris*, Common Thyme
Hardy, H4 (USDA 8,9), evergreen shrub. Height: 25–30cm (10–12in); spread: 25–45cm (10–18in). Terminal clusters of small flowers that can vary in colour from white to pink to mauve. Small, highly aromatic, oval grey/green leaves. Great in the kitchen and for making a bouquet garni.

*Thymus vulgaris* 'French', French Thyme
Hardy, H4 (USDA 8,9), evergreen shrub. Height and spread: 30cm (12in). Terminal clusters of small, very pale pink flowers in summer. Small, highly aromatic, oval grey/green leaves. A lovely flavoured thyme that is great with roast vegetables.

*Thymus vulgaris* 'Italian', Italian Thyme
Hardy, H4 (USDA 8,9), evergreen shrub. Height and spread: 30cm (12in). Terminal clusters of small, pale pink/white flowers in summer. Very small, highly aromatic, oval grey/green leaves that grow very close together. Delicious flavour; lovely with tomatoes.

### 2. Upright thymes

There are many forms of upright thyme; many are hybrids. They grow with an open habit but can be easily clipped into a dome shape. They make a good edge to a herb garden and grow well in groups. Their leaves are highly aromatic and great in the kitchen.

*Thymus* 'Culinary Lemon', Lemon Thyme
Hardy, H4 (USDA 8,9) evergreen shrub. Height and spread: 30cm (12in). Terminal clusters of small, light mauve flowers in summer. Small, oval green leaves that have a strong lemon scent when rubbed and a great citrus flavour when cooked. Good with chicken, fish and vegetable dishes.

*Thymus* 'Fragrantissimus', Orange-scented Thyme
Hardy, H4 (USDA 8,9), evergreen shrub. Height: 30cm (12in); spread: 45cm (18in). Terminal clusters of very pale pink, bordering on white, flowers in summer. Small, highly aromatic, narrow oval grey/green leaves. This thyme has a delightful warm flavour that is not only good with meat and vegetables, but wonderful with treacle tart.

*Thymus* 'Porlock', Porlock Thyme
Hardy, H4 (USDA 8,9), evergreen shrub. Height and spread: 30cm (12in). Terminal clusters of small magenta/pink flowers in summer. Small, oval dark green leaves that have a good, strong thyme scent and flavour. This thyme has a pretty open habit; it flowers in early summer so is beneficial for bees and butterflies.

**3. Mound-forming thymes**

These thymes grow in a neat low mound. They look lovely when combined with the mat-forming thymes, either in a carpet, in a thyme lawn or as a garden edging plant.

*Thymus caespititius*, Cretan Thyme
Hardy, H4 (USDA 8,9), evergreen shrub. Height: 8cm (3in); spread: 45cm (18in). Small clusters of pale pink flowers in summer. Small, narrow, bright green, pine resin-scented leaves. The rounded shape of the plant acts to keep water loss to a minimum, allowing it to survive long periods of drought undamaged.

*Thymus* 'Jekka', Jekka's Thyme
Hardy, H4 (USDA 8,9), evergreen shrub. Height: 10cm (4in); spread: 60cm (24in). Small clusters of pink flowers with a dark purple line on the lower lip in late spring/early summer. Small, oval, bright green leaves that have a good culinary flavour. As one of the early flowering thymes, it is greatly loved by all forms of pollinator, especially bees.

*Thymus* 'Redstart', Redstart Thyme

*Thymus* 'Redstart', Redstart Thyme,
Hardy, H4 (USDA 8,9), evergreen shrub, Height: 4cm (2in); spread: 45cm (17 in). Terminal clusters of small dark crimson flowers. Small, lightly lemon-scented, dark green oval leaves. Both flowers and leaves are edible. This thyme makes a very pretty low-growing mound.

**4. Broad-leaved thymes**

These thymes can vary in habit from loose mound forming to flat creeping. The one thing they all have in common is the large leaves that make them very easy to pick and use in the kitchen.

*Thymus pulegioides*, Broad-leaved Thyme, Mother of Thyme
Hardy, H4 (USDA 8,9), evergreen shrub. Height: 25cm (10in); spread: 45cm (18in). Small terminal clusters of mauve flowers in summer. Small, aromatic, dark green rounded leaves. This is a very useful thyme that produces a lot of leaf with an excellent culinary flavour. It looks good cascading over a wall or at the edge of the garden.

*Thymus pulegioides* 'Bertram Anderson', Bertram Anderson Thyme
Hardy, H4 (USDA 8,9), evergreen shrub. Height: 20cm (8in); spread: 45cm (18in). Rounded terminal clusters of pink flowers in summer. Small, rounded golden leaves that have a good thyme scent and flavour. It's very good with marrow and tomato dishes.

*Thymus pulegioides* 'Kurt', Creeping Lemon Thyme
Hardy, H4 (USDA 8,9), evergreen shrub. Height: 6cm (2.5in); spread: 60cm (24in). Rounded terminal clusters of pink/purple flowers in summer. Rounded, dark green, lemon-scented and flavoured leaves. Great with chicken, fish and cheese dishes.

*Thymus* 'Jekka', Jekka's Thyme

**5. Creeping Thymes**

These lovely low-growing creeping thymes are ideal for growing in gravel or as a thyme walk in very free draining soil. The leaves are edible but fiddly to pick. The flowers look great in salads.

*Thymus serpyllum*, Creeping Thyme, Wild Thyme
Hardy, H4 (USDA 8,9), evergreen shrub. Height: 3cm (1 ½in); spread: 80cm (31in). Terminal clusters of small pink, mauve or purple flowers in summer. Small, aromatic, mid-green, hairy oval leaves. This thyme has strong medicinal properties and is highly antiseptic.

*Thymus serpyllum* 'Snowdrift', Snowdrift Thyme
Hardy, H4 (USDA 8,9), evergreen shrub. Height: 3cm (1 ½in); spread: 80cm (31in). Terminal clusters of lovely white flowers in summer. Small, aromatic, mid-green oval leaves. This thyme looks lovely growing in gravel.

*Thymus serpyllum* 'Russetings', Russetings Thyme
Hardy, H4 (USDA 8,9), evergreen shrub. Height: 3cm (1 ½in); spread: 80cm (31in). Terminal clusters of small pink, mauve or purple flowers in summer. Small, aromatic, dark green oval leaves. Loved by butterflies.

**6. Mat-forming thymes**

These differ to creeping in that they not only grow flat to the ground, but also make a perfect mat with the leaves very close together.

*Thymus* Coccineus Group, Creeping Red Thyme
Hardy, H4 (USDA 8,9), evergreen shrub. Height: 3cm (1 ½in); spread: 45cm (18in). Terminal clusters of small stunning magenta flowers in summer. Small, aromatic, dark green, hairy oval leaves.This is a must for any thyme garden or gravel path.

*Thymus* 'Lilac Time', Lilac Thyme
Hardy, H4 (USDA 8,9), evergreen shrub. Height: 3cm (1.5in); spread: 60cm (24in). Terminal clusters of small lilac flowers. Small, aromatic, dark green oval leaves. The leaves of this thyme make a very neat mat, ideal for a thyme carpet, cushion or lawn.

*Thymus* 'Dartmoor', Dartmoor Thyme
Hardy, H4 (USDA 8,9), evergreen shrub. Height: 3cm (1 ½in); spread: 45cm (18in). Terminal clusters of small purple pink flowers. Small, aromatic, grey/green, hairy oval leaves. Lovely growing in gravel.

## Propagation

Only the wild creeping thyme and common thyme are easily and reliably raised from seed. All the named varieties tend to be sterile, however as I well know, happy accidents do happen with this very promiscuous family. When growing lots of thymes together in the garden, look out for a seedling that is completely different to its parent and you just might have found a new cultivar.

**Seeds:** sow the very fine seed mixed with fine horticultural sand in spring, into either seed trays or modules using a seed compost. Cover the seeds lightly with standard perlite and place under protection at 18°C (64°F). Germination takes 5–10 days. Keep watering to the absolute minimum, as the seedlings are prone to damping off (see page 274).

**Cuttings:** take cuttings from new growth before flowering in late spring or in early autumn after flowering. Winter cuttings that have been taken late in a cold greenhouse or cold frame, putting the cutting either into modules or a very small pot filled with three parts seed compost and one part coarse horticultural sand. Plant or pot up in the spring.

**Division:** creeping thymes can be divided. In a cold damp climate, divide established plants in spring after the frosts have finished. In a hot dry climate, divide in the autumn and replant into a prepared site.

**Layering:** for mature upright thymes that are getting a bit woody, this is an ideal method of propagation In early spring. Choose a strong branch that is very close to the ground, pin it with wire so the stem touches the ground, then cover with soil. After 8–10 weeks check it has rooted. If yes, cut the stem and remove the rooted branch from its parent. Either pot up or replant into a prepared site in the garden.

## Pests and diseases

As a very aromatic plant, thyme does not suffer from pests. But if the soil or compost is too rich, it will produce soft growth that is often attacked by aphids. Either wash these off with water or if it is a bad infestation, spray with a liquid horticultural soft soap following the manufacturer's instructions. All varieties, if they become too wet in a cold winter, can be prone to rot.

## How and where to grow

All thymes prefer a well-drained soil in a sunny position. They hate being wet in winter and even more, they hate sitting in water. Make sure the soil has adequate drainage and if necessary dig in extra horticultural grit prior to planting. Cut back after flowering – this is important as it prevents the plants becoming woody and produces new growth for light picking in autumn and winter. Creeping thymes look lovely planted in gravel; this will also protect the crown in wet winters.

## Growing in containers

All varieties of thyme suit being grown in containers, especially if you live in an area with cold and/or wet winters. Use three parts soil-based compost mixed with one part horticultural grit. During the growing season, keep the container watered but bordering on dry and defiantly dry in winter. Feed with a liquid fertiliser occasionally in the summer months. Put the container into a sunny spot – this will help the aromatic oils come to the surface of the leaf, which produces a stronger flavour. Trim back after flowering to maintain shape and promote new growth.

*Thymus serpyllum* 'Snowdrift', Snowdrift Thyme

## Yearly maintenance

**Spring:** sow seeds; trim old plants; layer old plants.

**Summer:** take cuttings of non-flowering shoots, then trim back after flowering.

**Autumn:** protect tender thymes.

**Winter:** check containers – make sure they are protected and only water if absolutely necessary, stand containers on bricks to aid drainage.

## Harvesting and storing

**Leaves:** the best flavour for preserving and drying is in early summer from non-flowering shoots. The new growth has developed and the sun will have brought the oils to the surface of the leaf. For general use in the kitchen, the leaves can be picked all year round.

**Flowers:** pick from early spring until autumn, depending on the species.

## Culinary uses

Thyme is one of the great European culinary herbs. When used in cooking its wonderful smell fills the kitchen with a mouth-watering aroma. It is one of the main ingredients of a bouquet garni and is also good in stocks, marinades and stews; a sprig or two added to the inside of a chicken with half an onion makes a great herb stuffing. The alternative flavours, like lemon and caraway thymes, are great in salad dressings as well as in cooking.

## Medicinal uses

One of thyme's valuable properties is its oil, which is extracted from the leaves. This oil contains a constituent called thymol which is a strong antiseptic and muscle relaxant. A tea made from the leaves makes a good gargle or mouthwash.

**Right** *Thymus vulgaris* 'French', French Thyme

# Tropaeolum majus

**With its wonderfully brazen flowers, the common nasturtium will add joy and colour to any garden or container. It is rarely recognised as the useful culinary and medicinal herb that it is. For me it brings back many childhood memories, from using the flowers when creating miniature gardens, to astonishing school friends with the flavour of the leaves.**

*Tropaeolum majus*, Nasturtium

## History

This herb was introduced to Europe from Peru in the 16th century. It was first known as *Nasturtium indicum* (Indian cress), on account of its pungent watercress-like flavour. The custom for eating its petals and using them for tea originated in the Orient. From the early 17th century onwards, there are references to this herb being used in salads. In the mid-1800s even the famous Mrs Beeton suggested that they should be used to dress a summer salad.

## Species

There are many varieties of this colourful half-hardy annual: climbers, semi-trailers; spreading and compact dwarfs. I have only mentioned a few, as well as my favourite perennial.

*Tropaeolum majus*, Nasturtium
Half-hardy, H2 (USDA 10), annual. Height and spread: 30cm (12in). Red to orange helmet-shaped flowers with a long nectar spur all summer until the first frosts. Round mid-green leaves with the veins running into a centre point.

*Tropaeolum majus* 'Alaska Series', Alaska Nasturtium
Red/orange flowers with variegated cream/white and green leaves.

*Tropaeolum majus* 'Empress of India', Empress of India Nasturtium
Dark red flowers with dark green leaves.

*Tropaeolum majus* 'Whirlybird Cream', Whirlybird Cream Nasturtium
Creamy yellow flowers with bright green leaves.

*Tropaeolum majus* 'Peaches and Cream', Nasturtium 'Peaches and Cream'
Multicoloured pale pink/orange/cream flowers with mid-green leaves.

*Tropaeolum speciosum*, Flame Nasturtium, Scottish Flame Flower
Hardy, H5 (USDA 7,8), perennial climber. Height: up to 3m (9ft); spread: indefinite. Scarlet flowers in summer, followed by bright blue fruits. Green lobed leaves. Plant the roots in the shade so that they do not dry out in hot summers. Unlike the annual *Tropaeolum*, sow the seed in autumn and place in a cold frame. Germination takes 3–4 weeks. If no germination occurs, place the container outside for the winter. Germination usually takes 5–7 months but can take as long as 2 years. If using old seed, soak for 24 hours in warm water prior to sowing. Nasturtium flowers after 3–5 years.

## Propagation

**Seeds:** sow annual varieties in early spring into small pots filled with a seed compost. Place under protection in a frost-free environment; no extra heat is needed. Germination takes 10–20 days. Alternatively, sow the seeds in late spring into prepared ground 20cm (8in) apart, when the air temperature does not go below 9°C (48°F). Germination takes 14–21 days.

**Cuttings:** take cuttings of the perennial variety in late spring from the new growth and transfer to modules or a small pot using three parts seed compost with one part standard perlite. Once rooted, pot up into a small pot filled with three parts soil-based potting compost with one part horticultural grit. Grow on in a pot until the following spring before planting out.

## Pests and diseases

Nasturtium is renowned for attracting aphids and the caterpillars of the cabbage white butterfly. If the infestation is light, wash off with a hand spray filled with water. If severe, either cut back, removing all damaged leaves and the pest, or treat with horticultural soft soap following the manufacturer's instructions. For more information see page 267.

## How and where to grow

Plant in a well-drained soil in sun or partial shade. If the soil is too rich, there will be an abundance of leaf and little flower. In Claude Monet's garden at Giverny in France there is a border of nasturtiums that sprawls all over the path – it looks most effective. Deadhead regularly to maintain flowering. Pick off seeds as they form to eat or save and inhibit self-seeding. Maintain watering throughout the summer months.

## Growing in containers

Nasturtiums look great growing in containers, troughs, window boxes or hanging baskets. Pot up using three parts loam-based potting compost mixed with one part propagating bark. This will open the compost and dilute the potting compost which in turn reduces the amount of feed/fertiliser in the compost. Do not feed the pots with any extra feed as you will inhibit flowering. Deadhead and remove seed pods to keep the plants flowering.

## Yearly maintenance

**Spring:** sow seedsearly under protection, or after frosts in the garden.

**Summer:** deadhead flowers to promote longer flowering.

**Autumn:** dig up annual plants when dead; sow *Tropaeolum speciosum* seeds.

**Winter:** After *Tropaeolum speciosum* dies back in winter, clear the year's growth.

## Harvesting and storing

**Leaves:** harvest from late spring until the first frosts or late autumn.

**Flowers:** harvest from early summer until the first frosts or late autumn

**Seeds:** harvest from midsummer until early autumn.

## Culinary uses

**Leaves:** pick the young leaves throughout the growing season. Their peppery flavour works well in salads, especially when served with a vinaigrette dressing, with potatoes, crème fraîche or cream cheese.

**Flowers:** pick throughout the summer months. These have a light peppery taste that is ideal in all forms of salad, with lettuce, mustard leaves and fruit, especially strawberries.

**Seeds:** the best flavoured seed pods, from annual nasturtiums only, are those that are small and green, not the ones turning brown – save these for drying and sowing the following spring. The small green seed pods can be pickled or added fresh to salads; they are quite strong in flavour so use sparingly.

## Medicinal uses

Medicinally all parts of the plant appear to be antibiotic; it also contains large amounts of sulphur, and the leaves contain vitamin C and iron as well as an antiseptic substance, which is best before the plant flowers. Nasturtiums are reputedly good for the skin.

# Ugni molinae

**This herb originates from South America and different species can be found in China, yet now also goes by the common name 'New Zealand cranberry' which is totally confusing and a misnomer. Over the years I have had three golden retrievers and they all, without exception, adored this herb. They knew, before me, when the berries were ripe and if I wasn't prepared they could strip the whole bush.**

## History

This lovely herb was introduced to the UK in 1844. It is said to have been a great favourite of Queen Victoria, who demanded that a jam be made from the fruit.

## Species

*Ugni molinae*, Chilean Guava
Hardy, H4 (USDA 8,9), evergreen shrub. Height: up to 2.5m (8ft); spread 1.5m (5ft). Pretty, pale pink, cup-shaped, hanging flowers in summer, followed by round fruit, which ripen to very dark red. Aromatic dark green, small, oval, leathery leaves with a shiny upper surface and a matt underside; in autumn they can have copper tinges.

*Ugni molinae* 'Orange', Orange Chilean Guava
Hardy, H4 (USDA 8,9), evergreen shrub. Height: up to 1.5m (5ft); spread: 75cm (30in). Pretty pale pink cup-shaped hanging flowers in summer, followed by round fruit, which ripen to very dark red. Aromatic dark green, small, oval, leathery leaves with a shiny upper surface and a matt underside that have a profound orange tip.

*Ugni molinae* 'Variegata', Variegated Chilean Guava
Hardy, H4 (USDA 8,9), evergreen shrub. Height: up to 2.5m (8ft); spread: 1.5m (5ft). Pretty pale pink cup-shaped, hanging flowers in summer, followed by round fruit, which ripen to very dark red. Aromatic, variegated green/cream/ yellow, small, oval, leathery leaves with a shiny upper surface and a matt underside.

## Propagation

**Seed:** remove the remaining pulp of the ripe berry from around the seed in spring and sow immediately into prepared modules or a seed tray filled with three parts seed compost and one part coarse horticultural sand. Place under protection at 15°C (60°F). Germination takes 1–2 months but can take longer.

**Cuttings:** take softwood cuttings in summer from non-flowering shoots and transfer to modules or a small pot filled with the same mix as for seeds. When well rooted, pot up using three parts soil-based potting compost mixed with one part horticultural grit and grow on in a container for two seasons before planting into a prepared site in the garden.

## Pests and diseases

Rarely prone to pests. Container plants grown inside can suffer from myrtle thrip. See page 272 for more on how to control this pest.

## How and where to grow

Plant in a well-drained soil that has been fed with well-rotted compost or manure, in partial shade, which replicates where it naturally grows in the shady understorey of the Valdivian rainforest. In the UK climate *Ugni* will tolerate full sun, but the fruit will be smaller. It is wet heavy soil that will kill the plant quicker than the cold. Where the site is exposed to cold winds, plant against a south- or west-facing wall. In warm climates it can be grown as a low hedge. There is no need to feed again unless the soil is very weak as overfed plants will not flower. *Ugni* should be clipped to maintain shape in the autumn in warm climates or in spring for colder climates.

## Growing in containers

All varieties of *Ugni* look lovely growing in containers. Thirty years ago I used to pot it up into an ericaceous potting compost. Today we grow it in three parts soil-based potting compost mixed with one part horticultural grit and it flourishes. Do not over-pot, it prefers being pot bound, especially in autumn. From spring until the start of autumn feed weekly with a liquid seaweed fertiliser. Place on bricks in winter to aid drainage. Bring into a cold greenhouse if you live in a very wet climate.

## Yearly maintenance

**Spring:** sow seeds; take cuttings; prune if required and if not done in the autumn.

**Summer:** enjoy the flowers; take softwood cuttings.

**Autumn:** harvest fruit; prune into shape in warm climates only.

**Winter:** lift pots off the ground and place on bricks to increase drainage.

## Harvesting and storing

**Leaves:** harvest the leaves to use fresh throughout the year but they are best in the spring.

**Flowers:** pick the flowers to use fresh as required in the summer.

**Berries:** harvest the berries to use fresh or to make jam in late autumn, also to dry so that the seeds can be extracted in the spring.

## Culinary uses

The leaves can be used to make an interesting tea, or added to stews and casseroles – they have a warm spicy flavour. In Chile, the seeds of the berries are roasted and used as a coffee substitute. The fruit has an absolutely delicious flavour – they taste of spicy wild strawberries – and can be eaten raw or cooked, though they become bitter when cooked. In southern Chile, the fruit is used to make the traditional liqueur murtado.

## Medicinal uses

It is exciting to note that there is a great demand for foods that contain functional properties and/or bioactive compounds. One of the fruits that has been widely studied is *Ugni molinae*, which appears to contain various beneficial health properties, such as being antimicrobial, antioxidant and anti-inflammatory. It is definitely a herb for the future.

*Ugni molinae*, Chilean Guava

# Valeriana officinalis

**The sweet scent of valerian flowers, as it wafts on a summer's evening breeze, is delightful. The root, which is the medicinal part, smells strong and sweet with a hint of violets when first dug – cats find this sheer elixir, even more so than *Nepeta cateria,* catmint. However, when it is washed, peeled and dried the aroma changes, to stale sweet and old leather with a hint of cheese. It is said that both cats and rats are attracted to the scent of fresh root and the Pied Piper carried the root to entice the rats out of Hamelin. Today the root is often used as a bait for catching rats.**

## History

Valerian has been used to ease insomnia, anxiety and nervous restlessness since the 2nd century AD. It became a popular medicinal herb in Europe in the 17th century. A tincture of valerian was employed in the First and Second World Wars to treat shell shock and nervous stress. The rhizomes and roots are retained in several national pharmacopoeias.

## Species

*Valeriana officinalis*, Valerian
Hardy, H4 (USDA 8,9), herbaceous perennial. Height: up to 1.2m (4ft); spread: 1m (3ft). Clusters of small, tubular, sweetly scented white flowers that are often tinged with pink in summer and grow in flat clusters. Mid-green leaves, deeply divided and toothed around the edges; the underside of the leaf is covered in fine hairs. In spring the new growth has an attractive bronze tinge.

*Valeriana jatamansi*, Indian Valerian, Nard, Tagar-ganthoda
Hardy H6 (USDA 6,7), herbaceous perennial. Height: up to 60cm (24in); spread: 90cm (3ft). Clusters of small, tubular, sweetly scented snow-white flowers that are often tinged with pink in early summer. Mid-green divided leaves that turn in autumn. This valerian is used in Ayurvedic medicine and to treat snake poisoning and skin diseases. It is often used as a substitute for *Valeriana officinalis*.

## Propagation

**Seeds:** sow seeds in spring into prepared modules or seed tray with a seed compost, water in, then sow on the surface and cover very lightly with seed compost. Place the container in a cold frame or cold greenhouse. Do not let the container dry out. Germination takes 3–4 weeks. Pot up using a soil-based compost or plant out when large enough to handle, 60cm (24in) apart. Alternatively sow into prepared open ground in late spring, uncovered, when the air temperature is above 9°C (48°F). The seed is small so mark where you have sown by lightly covering it with sharp horticultural sand and a label.

**Division:** divide established plants in the autumn, cut off all the summer growth, divide and replant into a well-prepared site. Alternatively, pot up into a soil-based compost, winter the plant in a cold greenhouse or polytunnel, then plant out in the spring.

## Pests and diseases

Valerian rarely suffers from pests or diseases. Occasionally the Indian valerian can develop mildew, if this occurs, remove all damaged growth and spray with baking powder (see page 276 for more information).

## How and where to grow

Choose the position in your garden with care. Remember if you have to move this herb the scent of broken roots will attract all the neighbourhood cats. The roots like to be kept cool and damp in summer, so ideally plant in a soil that does not dry out in summer. It is happy in sun or partial shade and can be grown near a pond but not in it. Valerian makes a good companion plant when planted near vegetables – the roots stimulate phosphorus and earthworm activity – an infusion of the root sprayed on to the soil attracts the earthworms. Cut back after flowering to prevent self-seeding. Add the leaves to the compost heap as they are very high in minerals.

## Growing in containers

The best medicinal valerian to grow in a container is the Indian valerian as it has a much more compact habit than the European valerian and, when in flower, is much shorter. Use a soil-based potting compost, position the container in partial shade so the roots do not dry out and maintain watering in summer. Then in winter put the container on bricks or stones so that the pot does not become waterlogged.

## Yearly maintenance

**Spring:** sow seeds; divide roots.

**Summer:** cut back flowers after flowering to prevent self-seeding.

**Autumn:** divide established plants if needed.

**Winter:** no need for protection.

## Harvesting and storing

Dig up the roots of a second- or third-year plant for use either fresh as a medicinal herb or for drying.

## Culinary uses

This would not be my culinary herb of choice, especially if the dried root is used. That being said, extracts are used in the flavouring of ice cream, bread, soft drinks and beer and is especially important in enhancing apple flavours.

## Medicinal uses

This is one of the most important herbal sedatives and is incorporated into numerous products. It is a non-addictive tranquilliser that is specifically recommended for restlessness, sleeplessness and minor nervous conditions.

*Valeriana officinalis*, Valerian

# Verbena officinalis

**The only time you truly notice this herb is when it is in flower and even then, you may pass it by. Do not be fooled by the fact that it looks insignificant – it hides its potential. You will find it growing on waste ground and roadsides. This is a herb that has been used for centuries all around the world. Today it is used in the treatment of nervous tension and anxiety.**

## History

The Greeks and Romans named this herb vervain, *hiera botane,* which translates as the 'sacred herb'. Possibly my favourite historical story is that vervain symbolised peace. This is why the Roman peace envoys always had this herb with them; they were known as *verbenarii* because they approached the opponent carrying sprigs of vervain in their hands. It was credited with magical properties and was used by the Ancient Greeks who wore amulets made from it to protect themselves against demons and disease. In the Middle Ages, it was also an ingredient in a holy salve used as a powerful protector against demons of disease.

## Species

As this genus has about 250 species of annuals, perennials and subshrubs, to avoid any confusion I am only going to feature the medicinal *Verbena.*

*Verbena officinalis*, Vervain, Common Verbena, Herb of Grace, Holy Wort, Juno's Tears
Hardy, H5 (USDA 7,8), perennial. Height: up to 90cm (2ft 11in) when in flower; spread: 30cm (12in). Tiny terminal clusters of very pale lilac flowers in summer. Green leaves that are often deeply divided into lobes with curved teeth. The plant has no scent and is very bitter in taste.

## Propagation

**Seeds:** the seeds of this herb needs stratification (see page 18 for more information). In cold climates in autumn, fill a seed tray or small pot with seed compost, sow on the surface, cover the seed with sharp horticultural grit. Place the container outside for the winter so that the seed experiences cold, frosts and snow. Germination takes 4–6 months. In warm climates, prior to sowing, place the seeds in a container mixed with sharp horticultural grit. Put into the crisper drawer of the refrigerator for 8 weeks, then sow on to the surface of a container, cover with sharp sand and put outside until it germinates. Germination is erratic, so be patient and do not discard the container. Once the seedlings are large enough to handle, either pot up or plant out into a prepared site.

**Cuttings:** take cuttings in spring from the new growth. Fill small pots or modules with three parts seed compost and one part standard perlite. Once rooted, either plant out in the autumn, or pot up and winter in a cold frame or cold greenhouse, planting out the following spring.

**Division:** divide established plants every third year to maintain healthy leaves.

## Pests and diseases

This plant rarely suffers from pests or diseases. However, if its soil is too rich or high in nitrates, its growth will be soft and prone to attack by aphids. Fill a hand spray with water and wash them off.

## How and where to grow

As vervain is a wild herb it prefers a well-drained soil in a sunny position, however it will adapt to clay and partial shade. As this is a rather insignificant plant it is a good idea to plant it in clumps. It looks most effective planted against a dark background, wall, hedge or evergreen shrub. This will help to show off its flowers, which are iridescent in the early evening. Cut back after flowering to inhibit self-seeding, which, if left alone, will certainly happen as this herb is a true survivor. It is a great source of food for butterflies and moths.

## Growing in containers

Although this herb is not spectacular it can be grown in containers. Use a soil-based compost and repot each year to keep the plant healthy. There is no need for extra feed during the growing season. It looks lovely combined with dark-leaved herbs, such as bronze fennel (see page 122).

## Yearly maintenance

**Spring:** sow seeds; divide established plants if necessary; take cuttings.

**Summer:** cut back after flowering to stop it self-seeding everywhere.

**Autumn:** sow seeds; split established plants.

**Winter:** no need for protection.

## Harvesting and storing

If you are superstitious, you must bless the plant before picking or harvesting. Vervain can be harvested throughout the growing season for use fresh. For drying, pick when the plant is in bloom in summer.

## Culinary uses

Verbena officinalis is often mistaken for *Aloysia citriodora*, lemon verbena (see page 50). They are two totally different plants from different families. I know some say this herb is edible, but I can't believe they are serious, it is incredibly bitter to the extent that it is unpleasant.

## Medicinal uses

Vervain is an important medicinal herb used by Western and Chinese herbalists to treat nervous exhaustion, headaches and liver and urinary tract infections. It is occasionally made into a tea, however, do use with caution as it is very bitter. Chinese herbalists use a decoction to treat suppressed menstruation. Currently this herb is undergoing research and clinical trials in connection with treatment of certain types of tumours.

*Verbena officinalis*, Vervain

**WARNING** | Avoid in pregnancy.

# Viola odorata

**This herald of spring can be found flowering in late winter; you can catch the perfume of the flower wafting on the cold air of a crisp morning. Violets transport me back to my childhood – my mother would bribe me to go to dancing classes by taking me to Carwardines for a cake and I would always choose the one with the crystallised violet, which I would pick off and save until the end.**

## History

This charming herb has been much loved throughout the ages, and having been around for over 2,000 years, there are many stories surrounding it. The one that I am particularly fond of is based on a Greek legend that Zeus fell in love with a beautiful maiden called Io. He turned her into a cow to protect her from his jealous wife Juno. The earth grew violets to be Io's food and the flower was named after her. Historically the crystallising of the flowers dates back to the 13th century at which time they were boiled in sugar and sold by French apothecaries.

## Species

*Viola odorata*, Sweet Violet
Hardy, H6 (USDA 6,7), rhizomatous perennial. Height: up to 15cm (6in); spread: 30cm (12in) and further if you include its creeping stolons. White, dark purple and occasionally yellow, sweetly scented flowers from late winter until mid-spring. Broad, pointed, heart-shaped green leaves that grow in a loose mat.

Below are some species worth looking out for; they all have edible flowers:

*Viola arvensis*, Field Pansy – has predominately white or creamy flowers in early summer. The green leaves are oval with shallow blunt teeth.

*Viola reichenbachiana*, Wood Violet, Early Dog Violet – has pale lilac/blue flowers in early spring, heart-shaped green leaves. The flowers have little scent.

*Viola riviniana*, Common Dog Violet, also known as Blue Mice, Hedging Violet, Horse Violet – has blue/lilac flowers in early summer, heart-shaped green leaves.

*Viola sororia* 'albiflora', White Violet – has lovely white flowers, with a light scent in early summer and heart-shaped green leaves.

*Viola tricolor*, heartsease, also known as Johnny jump up and herb trinity, has attractive small tricolour flowers which can vary in many different combinations including, yellow, violet, blue, purple, white. The green leaves are deeply lobed. This is a short-lived perennial that is more often grown as an annual.

## Propagation

The following is how to grow *Viola odorata*, but it is applicable for all the perennial varieties.

**Seeds:** in autumn, prepare a seed tray or a small pot using a seed compost, or a small pot. These are better than modules as the containers will be wintering outside. The seed needs to be scarified before sowing. Divide a small piece of fine sandpaper in half, place a small amount of seed on one half, cover with the other half and gently scratch the surface of the seed. For more information on scarification see page 18. Sow thinly onto the surface of the compost, cover with coarse horticultural sand, label, place the tray or pot outside, on a level surface, so it is accessible to all weathers, including frosts. Do not worry if you live in a snow area and the containers get immersed in snow – melting snow will aid germination. Alternatively, in the autumn, if you live in a frost-free country, mix some seed with some sharp horticultural damp sand, pop it into the crisper drawer of the refrigerator for 6 weeks, after which sow as above. Germination will occur in the following spring and flowering the year after that.

**Cuttings:** in late summer remove creeping stolons (runners). You will notice that they are producing mini plants with roots, these can then be grown on either in small pots or in modules filled with a standard seed compost.

**Division:** divide established plants in autumn, replanting into a prepared site.

## Pests and diseases

Occasionally, if grown in a greenhouse, *Viola* can be attacked by red spider mite. See page 270 for how to control this pest.

## How and where to grow

In spring, I have an area in my garden that is a mass of sweet violets and primroses. It is a sight to lift the spirits after the dark days of winter. Sweet violets like to be planted in a moist but well-drained soil. Incorporate plenty of leaf mould into your soil, and if drainage is a problem, add some grit to the planting hole.

## Growing in containers

Sweet violets look lovely in containers. Use three parts soil-based compost mixed with one part horticultural grit. Pot up and/or divide each autumn to keep the plant happy and refreshed. They make a delightful spring pot when planted with wild primroses.

## Yearly maintenance

**Spring:** enjoy the flowers, harvest as required.

**Summer:** dig up runners and pot or replant.

**Autumn:** sow seed; divide established plants; repot containers.

**Winter:** no need for protection.

## Harvesting and storing

**Leaves:** harvest new leaves in spring.

**Flowers:** pick in the late morning when the dew has dried and the flower is fully open.

**Roots:** harvest the root for medicinal uses in early autumn.

## Culinary uses

**Leaves:** in spring the young leaves have a mild flavour that is good in salads.

**Flowers:** sweet violets have without doubt the best flavour and scent of all the violets. The flowers can be eaten fresh, crystallised, or infused in vinegar; they make a delectable shrub.

## Medicinal uses

The root of this herb has the strongest medicinal properties. The flowers traditionally were used in cough medicine and as a breath freshener. A syrup made from this herb is used in the treatment of coughs, insomnia and migraines.

*Viola tricolor*, Heartsease

**Common names:** Vitex, Chaste Tree, Monk's Pepper, Lygos, Hemp Tree, Agnus-castus, Abraham's Tree, Chaste Berry

# Vitex agnus-castus

**Throughout the world, there are 250 species of *Vitex* – they are predominately tropical and subtropical. In China, *Vitex negundo* is used to treat malaria and poisonous bite. Here in the UK, I have the lovely *Vitex agnus-castus*, which flowers late in the summer and is much loved by the pollinators who can be heard humming with delight across the Herbetum.**

*Vitex agnus-castus*, Vitex

## History

This aromatic shrub, indigenous to the Mediterranean and central Asia, has been used medicinally for thousands of years. The first known records of its medical use were recorded in the 4th century BC by Hippocrates, he used it to treat female disorders, particularly the diseases of the uterus. In Germany in the 20th century, Dr Gerhard Madaus conducted scientific research into the plant's effects on the female hormonal system. He subsequently developed a medicine made from the dried berries called 'Agnolyt' which is still available today. *Agnus-castus* translates as 'chaste lamb' which is the Christian symbol of purity. Historically the medieval monks used to chew the leaves and grind the dried berries over their food to help them keep their vow of celibacy.

## Species

*Vitex agnus-castus*, Chaste Tree
Hardy, H4 (USDA 8,9), deciduous shrub. Height and spread: up to 2.5m (8ft). Upright panicles of fragrant, tubular violet-blue flowers in late summer until mid-autumn, which are followed by small round orange/red fruit which holds four seeds, though rarely in cold climates. Dark green, aromatic leaves that are divided into five or seven lance-shaped leaflets.

## Propagation

**Seeds:** using fresh seed, sow in the autumn into prepared seed or module trays using three parts seed compost mixed with one part standard perlite. Place in a frost-free greenhouse or on a windowsill. Germination is erratic, about 4 weeks. Leave the seedlings in the seed tray over winter, the seedlings will drop their leaves, they are not dead. Just watch the watering, keep it minimal so the soil does not dry. New shoots will appear in the spring – prick out and pot up using three parts soil-based compost mixed with one part horticultural grit. It will flower in the fourth or fifth summer.

**Cuttings:** the easiest and the most reliable method of propagation is to take soft wood cuttings in the late spring/early summer from non-flowering shoots. Fill a small pot or modules using a seed compost mixed in equal parts with perlite. Place the cuttings in a sheltered, warm environment, they do not need bottom heat. Once rooted, pot up in exactly the same way as the seedlings and again winter in a frost-free environment. Flowering will occur in the second or third summer.

## Pests and diseases

As the whole plant is aromatic it is rarely attacked by pests. Over-watering of young container plants can cause rotting in winter, especially in cold and cool climates.

## How and where to grow

The best thing about this herb is that it is one of the last to flower, so when all the thymes and mints have finished this beauty is still going. Plant in a fertile soil; it will tolerate dry and moist soils but not cold, heavy clay soil. When living in cold areas, plant against a south- or west-facing wall, the wall will help cut down the amount of rain by about 25% which helps to keep the roots drier in winter and gives added protection and warmth in winter. Alternatively plant in full sun in a sheltered position. It will not tolerate shade.

## Growing in containers

From experience I know that this plant adapts happily to being grown in a container. Use three parts soil-based compost mixed with one part horticultural grit. Feed the container throughout the growing season with a liquid seaweed fertiliser. In winter allow the plant to drop its leaves, clear away any fallen debris to prevent disease. Place the container in a sheltered spot. In wet conditions raise the pot on bricks or stones so that it does not become waterlogged.

## Yearly maintenance

**Spring:** prune back last year's growth to 5cm (2in).

**Summer:** take cuttings in early summer.

**Autumn:** sow seeds.

**Winter:** protect from excessive wet.

## Harvesting and storing

**Leaves**: pick the leaves in early summer for use fresh or for drying.

**Stems:** cut the stems in late summer or autumn and dry them for medicinal use.

**Roots:** lift the roots from plants over 5 years old in late summer and autumn and dry them for medicinal use.

**Seeds:** the seed is ready in autumn for use fresh or for drying. However, this plant rarely sets seed in cold climates.

## Culinary uses

When dried, the small aromatic seeds are often used as a pepper substitute, though the flavour is milder and spicier. Today, it is rare to find vitex berries in recipes, but they can appear in a Moroccan spice mixture called ras-el-hanout, which translates as 'top (or head) of the shop', referring to the best combination of spices the seller can provide.

## Medicinal uses

*Agnus-castus* is one of the most important herbs for treating menstrual and menopausal problems and infertility. The key part of the plant used is berries which is take in tablet or tincture form. It is used to regulate the hormones, for increasing female fertility, for regulating irregular periods and during the menopause to balance the hormones. It is also used to relieve spasms of pain, especially PMS, and to treat migraines and acne associated with the menstrual cycle.

**WARNING** | Do not take excessive doses. Do not take agnus-castus during pregnancy. Do not take when taking any other product or drug that affects the female hormone system, such as HRT or the contraceptive pill.

# Zanthoxylum piperitum

**This shrub is worthy of a spot in the garden as it is a herald of each season. The leaves emerge in early to mid-spring, followed quickly by the flowers. The bees pollinate the flowers all on one day, which is an amazing sight and sound. As the months get warmer, the Szechuan flowers turn into berries that ripen from green to red as the summer progresses. Once ripe at the end of summer they open to expose the seed. Then in autumn you get the wonderful colour as the leaves turn to gold before they fall from the branches, and you are left with the beautiful structural spiny branches.**

*Zanthoxylum simulans*, Szechuan Pepper

## History

The *Zanthoxylum* species have a long history of being used as food sources and medicine by indigenous tribes throughout the world. Both *Zanthoxylum piperitum* and *simulans* have long been used as an anaesthetic; in China the Szechuan fruit was used as a remedy to relieve toothache. A few of the red outer casings were put on the offending tooth, then the sufferer bit it to hold it in position, thereby numbing the tooth so the toothache went away.

## Species

*Zanthoxylum piperitum*, Szechuan Pepper
Hardy, H6 (USDA 6,7), deciduous shrub. Height and spread: up to 2.5m (8ft). Clusters of small yellow/green flowers, which are followed by aromatic small red fruit. When ripe, the fruit open to reveal the black shiny seeds. Dark green aromatic leaves with tiny spines on the underside. This species has dark spines along the stems and branches.

*Zanthoxylum simulans* Chinese Szechuan, Flower Pepper
Hardy, H6 (USDA 6,7), deciduous shrub. Height and spread: up to 4m (13ft). Clusters of small yellow/green flowers, which are followed by aromatic small red fruit. When ripe, the fruit open to reveal the black shiny seeds. Mid-green aromatic leaves. This species has stunningly large spines on the stems and branches that look positively Jurassic.

## Propagation

**Seeds:** the best time to sow the seeds is in the autumn. First mix them with a little damp horticultural sand, put them into a container or plastic bag, with a label and a date. Leave them in the crisper drawer of a refrigerator for at least 4 months. In spring, sow the chilled seeds into a seed tray that has been filled with four parts seed compost mixed with one part horticultural sand. Cover the seeds very lightly with the compost. Place on a windowsill, in a greenhouse or somewhere where it can get good light. Germination is spasmodic so don't give up: it takes 4–8 weeks. Grow on until large enough to handle, then prick out into small pots filled with a soil-based compost.

**Cuttings:** take semi-ripe cuttings in late spring from non-flowering shoots and transfer to prepared modules or small pots using three parts seed compost mixed with one part horticultural sand.

## Pests and diseases

This herb rarely suffers from pests or disease when grown outside. Like citrus plants, to which the Szechuan pepper is closely related, when grown under glass or in a polytunnel, they can suffer from an attack of scale and red spider mite (see page 270 for more information on how to control these pests).

## How and where to grow

The Szechuan is a very attractive garden plant. Plant in a well-drained fertile soil, in sun or partial shade. If you live in a hot climate, it will benefit from some shade in the afternoon. Go steady with the pruning as next year's crop develops on the previous year's new growth. However, because of the spines that grow along the branches, sometimes pruning is necessary so that the plant does not become a hazard. Prune just after harvest before the leaves fall.

## Growing in containers

This herb looks lovely grown in containers; it can make quite a feature on a patio or balcony. Use a soil-based compost. Water throughout the growing season and feed weekly with a liquid fertiliser. In winter, lift the containers and place them on bricks to increase drainage and stand them against a wall for residual warmth and a bit of extra protection.

## Yearly maintenance

**Spring:** sow seedsthat has been stratified, take semi-ripe cuttings.

**Summer:** harvest leaves.

**Autumn:** harvest fruit; put fresh seed into the refrigerator.

**Winter:** no need for protection from the cold; lift containers off the ground so that they can drain.

## Harvesting

**Leaves:** harvest the new young leaves in spring and early summer to use fresh. They can be dried or infused in oil.

**Fruit/seeds:** harvesting usually starts any time from midsummer onwards. Start as soon as the pink/red outer casing of the fruit splits open to expose the black shiny seed. Pick whole florets and leave them to dry somewhere warm for a day or two, then separate the casing from the seed and store in airtight jars. If the peppercorns are still closed in mid-autumn, harvest them from the shrub, lay them out in single layers on trays lined with paper. Within a couple of days the heat from the room will dry the outer skins and they'll split to reveal the seed.

## Culinary uses

**Leaves:** the leaves of the Japanese pepper are used to flavour soups and meat dishes.

**Fruit/seeds:** once the seed has been removed, dry-roast the casing, then crush using a pestle and mortar, then sieve. You will be left with a fine power that is one of the ingredients of Chinese five spice, which is very much at the heart of Szechuan cooking. Most dishes only need a small amount as the flavour can be overpowering. The flavour of the dried fruit lasts a year if stored carefully.

## Medicinal uses

Szechuan has been used for thousands of years in Traditional Chinese Medicine for healing indigestion, arthritis, diarrhoea and many other complaints.

**Overleaf** *Origanum vulgare*, Oregano

# Pests and diseases

It is well known that when grown in their correct environment herbs rarely suffer from pests and diseases. However, at the Herb Farm we are growing a very diverse range of herbs, including some from the Mediterranean and the tropics, as well as native UK herbs, in the same conditions, which can give rise to a varied range of pests and diseases. Interestingly, when I wrote my first book on herbs in 1993 there were only 9 pests; today there are 17, indicating that the increase in warm weather, the strong winds and torrential rain caused by climate change does increase the spread of pests and disease.

## General methods of control

### Biological control

When I started the Herb Farm, you could not buy any biological control, so I paid my children and their friends five pence for every live ladybird they each put into the greenhouse. As you can imagine, the farm became a great place to come and play. Now many biological control methods are available commercially from garden centres and online. Always check that it is a bona fide source before you buy, i.e. a garden centre or well-known company online. This form of pest control is really only suited to a closed environment, ie. either a greenhouse or a conservatory, where the natural balance can break down and the pests can get out of control. By simply introducing predators you will help nature to regain its balance. All biological control methods are relatively expensive, and nearly all are dependent on warm temperatures, especially at night, to work efficiently. If you need more information, gardening clubs, local organic groups and the Royal Horticultural Society are all good sources.

### Organic sprays

Just as there were no commercial predators available when I first started growing in the 1980s there were also no organic sprays. We used to make our own sprays out of *Sambucus*, elder, leaves, chamomile and garlic; however, since the Control of Pesticides Regulations 1986 I can no longer use homemade sprays on commercial crops. You, on the other hand, can for home use. I only recommend those that are made from herbs that we eat or drink, for example garlic and chamomile.

You can buy ready-made organic sprays from garden centres and online. Personally I am a huge fan of horticultural soft soap. This comes under many commercial names and is a highly refined soap made from natural oils, which acts as a contact insecticide with no residual effects once it has dried. It is harmless to ladybirds, bees and other insects. There are also plant invigorators that combine a wide range of nutrients with surfectants or fatty acids – these can contain some synthetic ingredients, and some are not considered organic, but they are also harmless to bees and ladybirds.

### Chemicals for control of pests

I appreciate that some people need to use chemicals, however most herbs can be grown very successfully without, and if the herbs are being used as a food crop or medicinally it is worth taking that little bit of extra care. When choosing chemicals, read the labels on the back of the bottles carefully and choose the one relevant to the problem concerned. Follow the manufacturer's instructions carefully. Store the bottle after use in a secure cupboard away from animals and children.

# Pests

Here are some that are worth watching out for in the northern hemisphere. I am sure if you are growing your herbs in another part of the world you will have others which are equally destructive.

1

## *Allium* leaf miner

The *Allium* leaf miner feeds on leeks, onions, chives, shallots and garlic. The greyish-brown fly punctures the leaves and/or foliage, then sucks up the sap before laying its eggs in the foliage. You will notice distinctive lines of white dots on the foliage. The larvae are headless maggots; they tunnel in the foliage, stems and bulbs and the pupae embed themselves in the stems and bulbs. This causes the *Allium* to rot in autumn. The best control is an insect-proof mesh and crop rotation.

2

## Aphids, green fly, black fly

Keep a watch for green and black fly from early spring in the greenhouse and later outside. As soon as you see them, you can remove them by hand if there are few. If there is an infestation (I have seen clouds of them suddenly appear then alight on a crop), spray them with horticultural soft soap following the manufacturer's instructions in the early morning or early evening (not in the full sun). Sometimes there is a dense infestation of aphid on a single plant; you can gently wash these off with a hand spray filled with water – do not use a high pressure hose as you will damage the plant and mostly likely be left with the stalk. If it is a pot plant, like nasturtium, the leaves can be held under a tap and the aphids gently washed off. If this does not work use the horticultural soft soap as above.

3

## Carrot fly

The grub of this fly tunnels into the roots of plants during early summer, so herbs such as those from the *Apiaceae* (umbellifer) family which have a long tap root are at risk. The first sign of attack will be when you notice the yellowing or whittling of the leaves and any stunted growth. Parsley in the vegetable garden may be particularly vulnerable and here the plant should be pulled up and destroyed to get rid of the pests. However, large herbs like angelica should overcome attack, just pick off dead leaves and give the plant a boost by feeding it with a liquid seaweed fertiliser. A preventative method is to put a 75cm (30in) polythene barrier around the crop during mid-spring, or cover with horticultural fleece while the plants are young. Sowings after midsummer should miss the first batch of flies. If you wish to use biological control, the best method is to water the soil with nematodes, which are available online.

4

## Caterpillars: cabbage white and tortrix moth

These are attracted to herbs with large leaves, such as horseradish, in late spring through to early autumn. The best method of control is to check your plants weekly and simply pick them off by hand and destroy. Early in the season, when the plants are small, agricultural fleece is a good barrier.

Black fly

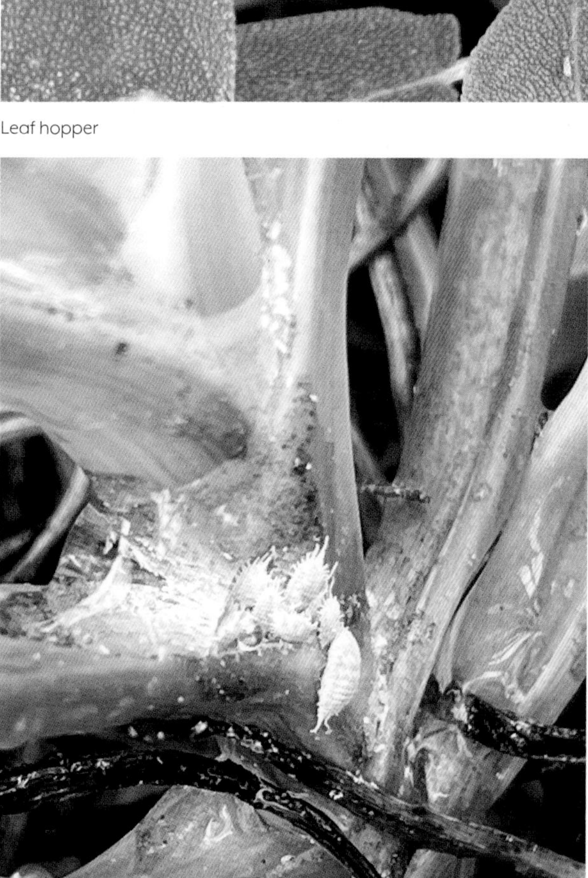

Leaf hopper

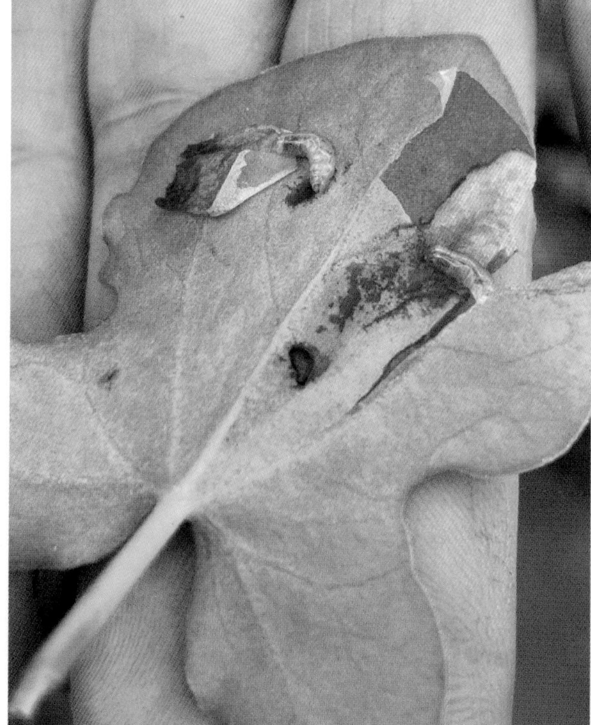

Leaf minor

Mealybug

5

## Flea beetle

There are 100 types of flea beetle but the best known is the one that attacks the *Brassica* family, which in the herb world means rocket, radish and nasturtiums. They riddle the leaves with tiny holes and jump – hence flea – when disturbed. There are no non-chemical ways to prevent this happening in the garden apart from creating a barrier. You can use an insect-proof mesh or horticultural fleece. Cover the plants as soon as possible, especially seedlings as they are very vulnerable. This pest is most prevalent from spring until the end of summer so crops sown at the beginning of autumn are usually clear. Flea beetles overwinter in leaf litter, so make sure that the area where you are growing brassicas is as clean as possible. Natural predators are birds, frogs and ground beetle, all of which will happily eat this pest.

## Froghopper, cuckoo spit

You will notice the spit created by the nymph of the froghopper in spring and summer. Reassuringly it's not spit at all but foam made by the young nymph to protect it from attack from parasitic wasps. This bug won't harm the plant, it just doesn't look good. Froghoppers are an important part of the garden. They are also an important food source for swifts and other birds, so I would recommend leaving them alone.

7

## Leaf hopper

This sap-sucking pesky pest creates coarse pale spotting on the upper leaves of sage, rosemary, oregano, bergamot and lavender to name a few. It is called the sage and ligurian leaf hopper from the *Cicadellidae* (leaf hopper) family. It jumps and flies short distances and lives outside from spring until early autumn, then overwinters in egg form. Outside there really is no need to take any action apart from attracting natural predators in the form of ladybirds, wasps and ground beetles. Inside, if you only grow under cover, then you can spray with a horticultural soft soap, but it is very difficult to eradicate them so spray weekly.

## Leaf miner

Leaf miners are the minute caterpillars of tiny moths. There are many different species, and the larvae vary in colour depending on the species. You can notice damaged leaves on lovage, angelica, wild celery and broad-leaf sorrel. The larvae feed by chewing the leaf's chlorophyll, leaving trails or patches of damaged leaves that are silver or brown in colour. Watch for the first tunnels and pick off the affected leaves and destroy them. If left, the tunnels will extend into broad dry patches and complete leaves will wither away. This pest is difficult to get rid of because it lives inside of the leaf, so the easiest method when you first notice the damage is to pick and bin it. Do not compost, unless you have a very hot compost pile. You can also grow herbs that attract the parasitoid wasps – they lay eggs in the leaf miner and when the eggs hatch the larvae start eating the leaf miner from inside out. These tiny wasps are attracted to dill, fennel and yarrow.

There is one home remedy that works by suffocating the leaf miner within the leaf. Use a soft horticultural soap and mix with water as per the manufacturer's instruction, then add one tablespoon of vegetable oil or rapeseed oil per 1 litre (34fl. oz) of water. Shake the container well, spray both sides of the leaf. It does take time so check after 3–4 days. Top tip: do not spray in full sun just in case the oil burns the leaves. Spray early morning, on a grey day or in the evening.

## Mealybug

Mealybugs are small, oval, sap-sucking insects up to 4mm (⅙in) long. They look like tiny pinkish or grey woodlice close up, but are usually covered with a fluffy layer of protective wax. Colonies resemble blobs of sticky cotton wool and may be accompanied by sooty mould. They are particularly annoying when growing tender herbs in a conservatory or heated glasshouse. They love aloe, bulbine and curry leaf. Natural predators can be introduced in the summer – *Leptomastix dactylopii,* a parasitic wasp certainly works. If you have to use physical methods, spray with horticultural soft soap following the manufacturer's instructions. Or, if it is really bad and you do not want to destroy the plant, dip a tiny paint brush in white spirit and paint it on to the pests. This method works well when they have crawled between the leaves or tucked themselves in between the branches. Not to be confused with woolly aphids, which look very similar but are usually found outdoors on apple trees or pyracantha.

10

## Onion fly

Onion fly can be a real nuisance. The adult flies, which look like grey house flies, lay their eggs in batches at the neck of young leaves or in the soil adjacent to the *Allium* bulbs. The eggs hatch and the maggots move from one plant to another through the soil. They pupate in the soil, then in about three weeks the next generation of flies emerge. To prevent the flies from laying eggs next to the plants, put a ring of bark or cinders around each plant. Ground beetles, birds and hedgehogs are all great predators and eat the maggots. If you know you already have onion fly, agricultural fleece or an insect-proof mesh does help. Bin really damaged plants at the end of the summer or burn to prevent the maggots from completing their cycle.

11

## Red spider mite

The spider mites like hot dry conditions and can become prolific in a glasshouse. Look out for early signs of the pests – you may notice signs of speckling on the upper surfaces of the leaves, and if you look under the leaf with a magnifying glass you will see these minute red spiders; another telltale sign are the cobwebs. At first sign of the pests, either use horticultural soft soap in the form of a spray, or the natural predator *Phytoseiulus persimilis* following the instructions that will come with them. Do not use both.

12

## Scale insects

This insect is often noticeable as immobile, waxy, brown/yellow, flat, oval lumps gathered on the backs of leaves or on the stems of bay trees. These leaves also become covered with sticky black sooty mould. Rub the scales off gently before the infestation builds up. Or use a horticultural liquid soft soap following the manufacturer's instructions.

13

## Scarid (Fungus gnats) and shore flies

Some people call scarid fungus gnats,and they are the little tiny flies that often can be seen where you propagate your plants, or where you have spilt compost that has got wet. Fungus gnats are dark brown or black, whereas shore flies are like miniature house flies. But they do look alike when they are flying around. Both love a damp location, and standing water, so scarid is common in greenhouses. To monitor if we have an infestation of scarid and shore flies, we use the carnivorous plant *Pinguicula guatemala*, Mexican Butterwort. Their leaves are covered in small mucilage-producing tentacles, which attract the scarid, shore flies and white fly in exactly the same way as the bright yellow sticky traps, but so much more convenient and ecological. If these plants do not keep them under control than you can use biological control – either nematodes or a predatory beetle.

Scale insects

Scarid flies on *Pinguicula guatemala*, Mexican Butterwort

Vine weevil beetle

Vine weevil grubs

# 14

## Slugs and snails

Slugs and snails are both true mega pests. You can only get rid of them by hand or by setting out some beer traps. Even better a size 10 wellie boot. At last there is a microscopic worm that can be used as a form of biological control. These worms infect the slugs with a bacterium which stops them feeding within a week and actually kills them in two weeks. It is an expensive way of getting rid of them, but worth it to protect your specimen plants.

# 15

## Thrips

The adult thrip is tiny, it is a dark narrow-bodied insect about 2mm (1/12)in length – you do need a magnifying glass to see it clearly. It likes all the *Myrtaceac* family and *Cardamom* mainly because they are grown under cover. You will notice the leaves that have been fed on by thrip because they become dull green and later develop silvery white discolouration on the upper surface and you may notice tiny black excrement spots on the under surface of the leaves. We control this pest by hanging blue sticky traps in the glasshouse. The adults are attracted to blue, so stick to the trap, and we also shake plants over the sticky traps. Finally, if the infestation is looking bad, we will spray with horticultural soft soap twice, three days apart.

# 16

## Vine weevils

These can be a major pest. Look out for them in the spring and early autumn. In the ground or pots you may see white horrid grubs with an orange head. The parent is a nocturnal small beetle with a weevil's nose. The grubs eat the roots of plants, the beetles eat leaves, especially vines. There are two methods of getting rid of vine weevil organically. Either repot all the containers checking each one for vine weevil grubs or, alternatively, water with a natural predator called *Heterorhabditis megidis* in late August/early September, when the night temperatures do not fall below 10°C (50°F). This natural predator is a nematode, which is a microscopic worm, that infects the weevil grubs with a fatal bacterial disease. Prior to using this nematode, make sure the compost in the containers is moist all the way down; so water well a few hours before you intend to add the biological control.

# 17

## White fly

Under protection in the glasshouse white fly can be a problem, less so outside. This is one pest where it is essential to act immediately. As soon as you see them, either introduce the natural predator *Encarsia formosa,* a minute parasitic wasp which lays its eggs in the white fly larvae usually found attached to the underside of the leaves. Unfortunately, these parasites need warm temperatures to multiply so they cannot be successfully used in early spring or autumn. Alternatively, spray with a soft horticultural soap and repeat 7 days later.

**Right** Snail

# Diseases

## 1

### Celery leaf spot

Pinprick spots develop on the leaf surface, followed by smaller black fungal fruiting bodies. The infection can spread to the leaf stalks. This fungus *Septoria apiicola* can infect lovage as well as celery leaf. It can be spread during harvest, by insects and by overhead watering. Equally dull, damp weather and especially misty nights are ideal conditions for this fungus to spread. Remove any damaged leaves, do not collect the seed from infected plants as the spores of this fungi can infect them. Remove any leaves that may have fallen on to the soil. Grow another crop in that area. Remember to disinfect your tools after you have removed, pruned or cleared the soil.

## 2

### Club root

This is a fungal infection of the roots of *Brassica*, it stunts and distorts the roots which in turn stunts the growth of the plant. It can be spread via tools, wheelbarrows and wellies. It can be reduced but not eliminated by raising the soil pH by adding lime and improving the drainage. However the best way is to remove the infected stock, add some lime, cover with cardboard, then mulch with well-rotted compost, leave until the autumn or spring and plant anything other than a *Brassica* in that area.

## 3

### Damping off

This can be caused by a number of things, e.g. dirty trays, pots and water collected in a water butt. I used to always collect water for the glasshouse until one day I lost a complete bench of cuttings and seedlings caused by a water-borne fungus, most probably *phytophthora*. I now only use mains water in the glasshouse. Another reason damping off occurs is sowing the seeds too thickly, and over-watering. The best tip is to water your seedlings in the morning so they do not go to bed wet, especially in northern Europe where we can have daytime temperatures of 21°C (70°F) with lows at night of 7°C (44°F) – this fluctuation is very difficult for seedlings so the drier they are at night, the better.

4

## Dieback

This is caused by various fungi, some which invade healthy stems while others enter the plant through wounds. Dieback, especially from stem tips downwards, may be caused by weak young plants, drought or waterlogging. To control this, as soon as you see any signs of a stem wilting or blotches and/or leaves wilting, prune the affected stems well below any sign of damage. If it is a container plant, move it away from any of the other plants into a sick area so that it does not spread to healthy plants.

5

## Downy mildew

Downy mildew gets its name from the grey fuzzy appearance of the spores formed on the undersides of the infected leaves. It causes yellowing and mottling of the leaf and can spread, causing the leaf to die. This fungal infection is spread in warm and moist conditions and is spread by wind and breeze. Remove infected leaves promptly and improve air circulation around the plants. increase ventilation if in a glasshouse, avoid overhead watering and watering the leaves. If possible, move container-grown plants outside. For those in the garden, cut back, clear around the plant to increase air flow. Afterwards, make sure you disinfect your tools and wash your hands.

## Grey mould

Grey mould is a very common fungus, the spores are almost always present in the air. It may attack through wounds or points of damage or flowers at the end of the season. Its spores are spread by rain, water splash and on air currents. It is difficult to control. Remove all dead and injured plants promptly, cut right back to healthy growth. Do not leave plant debris lying around. Clean your snips or secateurs with disinfectant so you do not spread it onto the next plant you prune.

# 7

## Powdery mildew

This common fungal disease can occur when the conditions are hot, dry and the plants are overcrowded. You will notice, white, powdery fungal growth developing on the upper leaf surface, but it might spread underneath. Sometimes the leaves distort and sometimes they turn yellow. A way of preventing this is to water well during the dry spells but not overhead as the splashes will spread the fungi. Follow the recommended planting distances and clear away any fallen leaves in the autumn. Adding a mulch in the autumn or early spring also helps. If your plant does suffer, destroy all the infected leaves, before spraying the whole plant with baking powder, either potassium bicarbonate or potassium phosphate. We use baking powder mixed with a horticultural soft soap at the following ratio: 1 litre (34fl.oz) soft water + 2ml (⅓ teaspoon) soft soap + 5g (1 teaspoon) baking powder. Spray on a dull dry day so you do not scorch the leaves.

# 8

## Mint rust and rusts

There are various fungi that cause rust and a number of herbs are infected by it. The spores need a moist environment to infect plants, so rust infections are generally most severe in damp conditions. You will notice brown to orange spores and spots on the underside of the leaves, which travel through to the upper surface. Mint is renowned for having mint rust but I have found over the years that if we sterilise the creeping rhizomes yearly, we keep it under control. But living in the countryside where grass can get rust, we can never eradicate it. As soon as you see any infected leaves on *Malva* or *Allium*, remove and bin or burn and do not compost the infected leaves; make sure you clear any leaves off the soil, as this fungi lives in the soil. Rotate crops in the ground, and with seriously infected plants bin them.

Powdery mildew

**Right** Mint rust

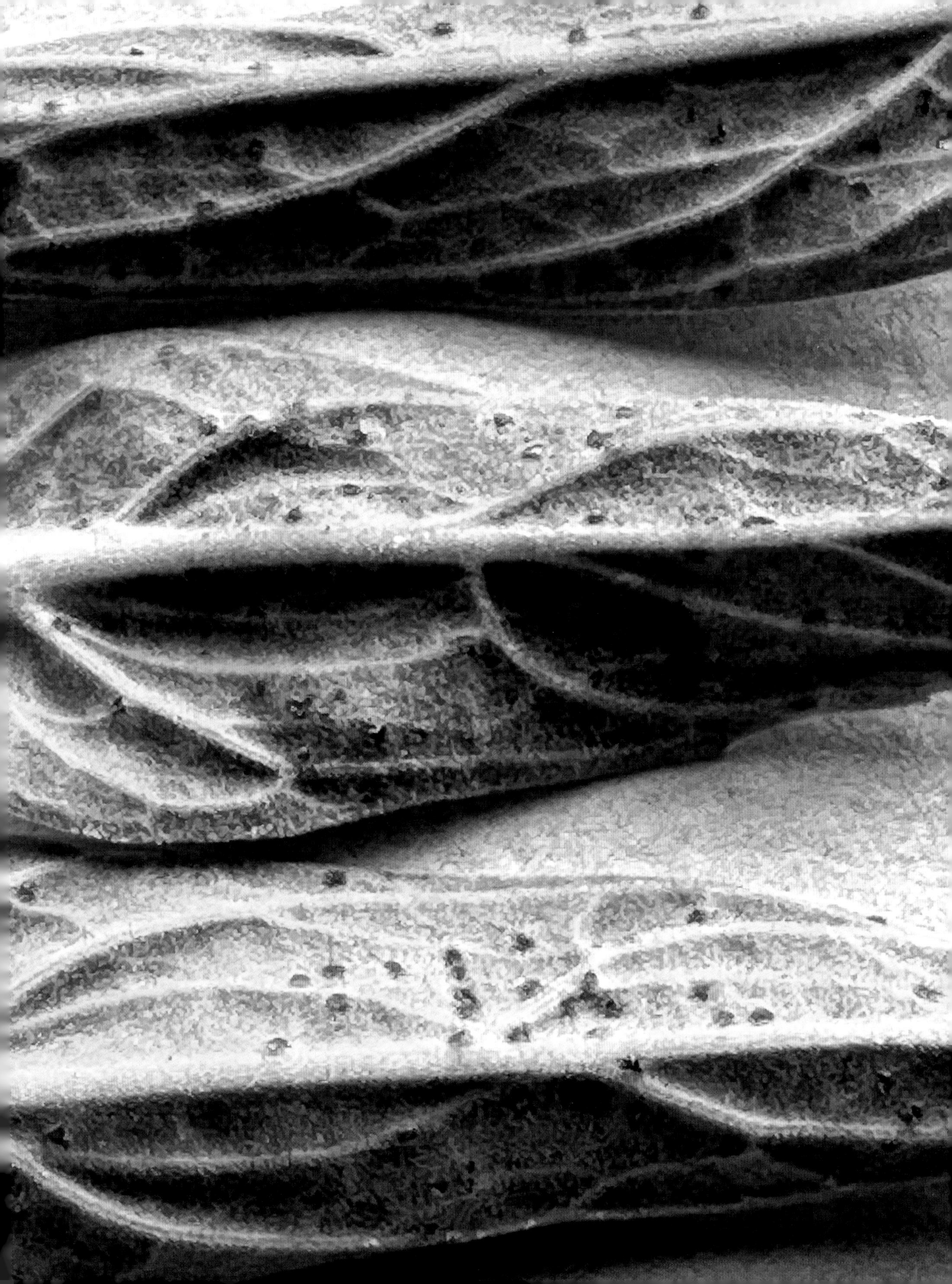

# Glossary

### Annual
A plant that completes its lifecycle – from germination to flowering and then death – in one growing season.

### Arboretum
A collection of trees.

### Basal crown
The growing point where the stems emerge from the roots.

### Biennial
A plant that produces roots and leaf in the first growing season. Flowers and seed followed by death in the second growing season.

### Bolt
When a plant produces flowers and seed prematurely.

### Botrytis
A genus of fungi containing plant pathogens.

### Bulbils
A small bulb rising above the ground in the axel of a leaf or bract.

### Chaff
The dry seed covering that is removed while cleaning the seed.

### Chitter
This is when the first root breaks through the outer protective coat of the seed (testa).

### Crown
The growing point of a plant from which new shoots emerge, usually at soil level.

### Cultivar
A cultivated or horticultural variety of a plant species which may have originated either in the wild or in cultivation.

### Damping off
The death of a seedling which can be caused by a fungal infection, inadequate light, poor ventilation and in most instances, by overwatering.

### Deciduous
A plant that loses its leaves annually at the end of the growing season.

### Doctrine of Signatures
In the 15th century it was thought that how the plant looked indicated what it cured, for example, eyebright was used for eye infections.

### Dormant
The plant and/or seed is alive but in a state of suspended animation until all the conditions are right for growth.

### Earth up
To draw the soil up around a plant to exclude light, protect it from frost, encourage roots to develop from the stems and in hot summers to conserve moisture.

### Floret/floweret
The small flowers that are part of a large group of flowers, which make up the flower head.

### Genus
The botanical name for a group of species with common structural characteristics.

### Gerard
John Gerard (1545–1612), English herbalist.

### Glaucous
With a blue-green, blue-grey or white bloom to either the stems or leaves or both.

### Glucosinolate
The natural components of many pungent plants, such as horseradish and mustard. These components are released when the plant is chewed or cut, therefore contributing to its strong flavour.

### Halophyte
A salt-tolerant plant, which will grow happily by the sea.

### Hard wood cutting
Cuttings taking from mature wood from early autumn to early winter once the leaves have fallen.

### Herbetum
A collection of herbs.

### Horticultural fleece
There are many different manufactured forms of this light woven fleece. When used to cover crops it protects them from frost, wind, hail, birds, rabbits and other pests that eat or chew the leaves. It allows light transmission of on average 85% and it allows rain to permeate.

### 'Jekka' variations
They all were 'sports' I found in the Herbetum, as seedlings; I grew them on, then raised them via propagation to check they ran true. It takes me between 5–8 years to grow a plant for sale.

### Long tom pot
A deep pot ideal for deep-rooting plants of the *Apiaceae* family.

### Monocarpic
A plant that does not die until it flowers, it could be 2–4 years. Angelica is a typical example.

### Offsets
A small plant that arises naturally at the side of the parent plant; aloe vera is a good example.

### Overpot
Repotting a plant from a small pot into a much larger pot rather than doing this in stages.

### Panicles
A branched flower cluster in which each branch from the main stem has one or more flowers.

### Pinching out
To remove the soft new growing points to encourage the plant to produce new growth and therefore become bushy.

### Pinnate leaf
A leaf made up of leaflets.

### Plantlet
A mature seedling or a young small plant.

### Pot out
To remove the plant from the pot and plant into a prepared site in the garden.

### Pot up
Place the seedling and/or cutting into small containers to grow on.

### Raceme
A flower cluster with separate flowers attached by short equal stalks at equal distances along a central stem.

### Rhizomes
A horizontal fleshy stem that grows either below the surface of the soil or deep in the soil. These rhizomes are often next year's growth.

### Scarification
To weaken the outer casing of a seed either by rubbing with sandpaper or making a small nick, which allows the water in.

### Self-seed
When a plant drops its seeds in the garden and they germinate with no human intervention.

### Soft wood cutting
Cuttings taken in the spring and/or early summer from new non-woody growth.

### Stipular
Plants that have thorns, spines and or prickles.

### Stratification
Putting the seed into the crisper drawer of the refrigerator for a period, so mimicking cold weather.

### Subshrub
A small shrub especially one that is woody only at the base, for example, oregano.

### Substrate
Substrate is the technically correct name for a potting compost, which is made up of components such as bark, loam, vermiculite, which have not been composted together.

### Topdress
Spread a layer of well-rotted compost or composted bark or grit over the soil

### Umbel
A cluster of flowers on stalks of nearly equal length; fennel and dill are good examples.

## MEDICINAL GLOSSARY

### Analgesic
A substance that allays pain.

### Antispasmodic
A herb used to relieve spasms of involuntary muscles.

### Astringent
Contracts the tissues of the body, checking discharges of blood and mucus.

### Ayurvedic medicine
An ancient Indian system of medicine that originated about 5,000 years ago . 'Ayur' means life and 'Veda' means knowledge.

### Calminative
A substance that allays pain and relieves flatulence and colic.

### Carminative
A herb that relieves flatulence.

### Decoction
An extract of a herb (when the material is hard and woody, i.e. root, wood, bark, nuts) obtained by boiling a set weight of plant matter in a set volume of water for a set time. An average decoction would be 25g (1oz) of herb to 570ml (1 pint) water. Bring to the boil and simmer for 10–15 minutes. Strain the decoction while still hot.

### Diuretic
A substance that increases frequency of urination.

### Dyspepsia
A pain or an uncomfortable feeling in the upper middle part of the stomach.

### Emetic
Induces vomiting.

### Essential oil
A volatile oil obtained from a plant by distillation, with a similar aroma to the plant itself.

### Expectorant
Herbs used to clear mucus, phlegm and to relieve congestion when you have a cold.

### Flatulence
Wind, gas in the alimentary canal.

### Mucilage
Viscous or gelatinous solution.

## CULINARY GLOSSARY

### Shrub
A syrup made from herbs, fruits, sugar and vinegar, which is often diluted with soda water to make a refreshing drink or used to make cocktails.

### Ulam
Ulam is a group of Southeast Asian herbs that are eaten raw or blanched in hot water. These herbs are added to salads or dipped into sauces to enhance their flavour.

# Index

# About the author

Jekka McVicar has worked with herbs since 1985, for which she is internationally recognised and was awarded the Victoria Medal of Honour in Horticulture, the VMH, by the Royal Horticultural Society and the Gardeners Media Guild Life Time Achievement Award. Keen to share the knowledge and her passion for herbs she has been awarded 62 RHS Gold Medals, appears frequently on national radio and advises governments, chefs and members of the public on the use of herbs. At Jekka's Herb Farm in South Gloucestershire she displays her collection of over 400 culinary and medicinal herbs in Jekka's Herbetum and Jekka's Herb Garden.

To date Jekka has published eight books and Jekka's bestselling herb book, *Jekka's Complete Herb Book* reached 1 million sales in 2014. Jekka's books include: *A Pocketful of Herbs: An A-Z* (Bloomsbury Publishing, 2019); *Jekka's Herb Cook Book* (Ebury Press, 2010); *Jekka's Complete Herb Book*: In association with the RHS (Kyle Cathie, 2007); *Jekka McVicar New Book of Herbs* (Dorling Kindersley, 2002); *Seeds: The Ultimate Guide to Growing Successfully from Seed* (Kyle Cathie, 2001); *Good Enough to Eat* (Kyle Cathie, 1997); and *Jekka's Complete Herb Book* (Kyle Cathie, 1994).

Jekka has appeared in many television programs including: ITV: Love Your Weekend with Alan Titchmarsh, BBC: Marcus Wareing's tales from a kitchen garden, Channel 4: Sunday Brunch, BBC: Escape to the country, BBC: Countryfile, BBC: Mary Berry Cooks and BBC: The Great British Garden Revival. Jekka contributes to a number of national publications, including: BBC Gardener's World Magazine; BBC Good Food; Gardens Illustrated; and the Guardian Newspaper and is often featured in the Telegraph.

She regularly broadcasts on BBC Radio 4 including for the *The Food Programme*, *Woman's Hour* and a series on BBC Radio 4 called *Herbs Pure and Simple* as well as *Farming Today*. She is regularly on BBC Radio Bristol and she has a weekly slot on BBC Radio Ulster.

Her roles include: Vice President of the RHS (2016 – present); President of the Friends of Bristol Botanic Garden (2014 – present); President of the West of England Herb Group (2006 – present); Vice President of the Herb Society (2015 – present); RHS Ambassador (2016 – present); a founder member of the RHS Herb advisory group (2011 – present). She was an RHS Judge (1999–2018), chairing the judging of the Great Pavilion at the Chelsea Flower Show (2012–15, 2018); President of the Herb Society (2013–2014); the RHS Nominations Appointments and Governance Committee (2009–2014); and the RHS Fruit, Vegetable and Herb Committee (1998–2014).

# Acknowledgements

I incredibly grateful to Quadrille for making this book come alive. With special thanks to:

**Sophie Allen**, Senior Commissioning Editor, whose immense patience and delicate tact has guided me and this book all the way through to publication.

**Katherine Case**, Design Manager, who has put up with me bombarding her with photographs and questions and has produced such a beautiful book.

**Imogen Fortes**, Copy Editor, who was meticulous at going through my text asking questions especially when I used horticultural jargon, which she translated into text that the reader could understand.

To **Monty Don** for his extremely kind words in the foreword and friendship over the past three decades.

To **Jamie Oliver** for his endorsement, friendship and wise words over the past two decades.

To **Jason Ingram** for taking my photograph over the past two decades – the only person I know who makes me relax in front of a camera.

To **Nathan Outlaw**, who fully understands how to use herbs in the kitchen and has given me such support and wonderful meals over the past decades.

To **the team at Jekka's** who kept everything going while I wrote this book and kept stopping to take photographs.

To my long-suffering agent **Martine Carter** at Sauce Management, who has given me valuable support and friendship.

Thank you all; without you this book would not have been possible.

*Papaver rhoeas*, Field Poppy

## *Picture Credits

**Jekka McVicar,** front and back cover; pages 2, 4, 7, 9, 11, 14, 17, 19, 20, 21, 22, 23, 25, 26, 29, 30, 36, 37, 40, 42, 44, 48, 51, 53, 55, 56, 59, 62, 64, 66, 69, 70, 72, 73, 74, 77, 78, 80, 83, 84, 85, 88, 89, 90, 93, 94, 96, 97, 98, 99, 101, 102, 104, 107, 110, 111, 113, 114, 116, 117, 118, 121, 122, 125, 127, 128, 129, 130, 133, 135, 136, 139, 142, 143, 144, 146, 149, 151, 152, 153, 156, 157, 159, 160, 163, 164, 168, 170, 173, 175, 177, 179, 180, 181, 182, 184, 186, 187, 189, 191, 193, 194, 195, 196, 197, 198, 202, 206, 209, 210, 213, 217, 220, 221, 222, 224, 225, 226, 228, 229, 230, 233, 234, 237, 238, 241, 244, 245, 246, 248, 249, 250, 253, 255, 257, 259, 260, 262, 264-265, 268, 271, 276, 277, 287, 288

**Hannah McVicar,** pages 12, 38-39, 47, 60, 87, 109, 121, 141, 155, 167, 174, 188, 201, 205, 214, 219

**Lucia Mencarelli,** page 273

**Torie Clarke,** page 243

**Jason Ingram,** page 286

## Disclaimer

This book contains information on a wide range of herbs that can be used medicinally. It is not a replacement for professional medical advice. Do not take any herbal remedies if you are pregnant or undergoing any other course of medicinal treatment without seeking professional advice. The Author and Publishers have made every effort to present accurate information. However, they shall be neither responsible nor liable for any adverse reactions to the recommendations ontained herein, and the use of any herb or derivation is entirely at the reader's own risk.


**Publishing Director**
Sarah Lavelle

**Senior Commissioning Editor**
Sophie Allen

**Copy Editor**
Imogen Fortes

**Designer Manager**
Katherine Case

**Photographer**
see Picture Credits (left)

**Head of Production**
Stephen Lang

**Senior Production Controller**
Sabeena Atchia

Published in 2024 by Quadrille,
an imprint of Hardie Grant Publishing

Quadrille
52–54 Southwark Street
London SE1 1UN
quadrille.com





Cataloguing in Publication Data: a catalogue record for this book is available from the British Library.





ISBN 978 1 83783 044 2

Printed in China